12th International Conference on Nanomaterials - Research and Application (NANOCON 2020)

Brno, Czech Republic
21-23 October 2020

ISBN: 978-1-7138-2695-8

Printed from e-media with permission by:

Curran Associates, Inc.
57 Morehouse Lane
Red Hook, NY 12571

Some format issues inherent in the e-media version may also appear in this print version.

Tanger Ltd
Keltickova 62
710 00 Slezka Ostrava
Czech Republic

www.tanger.cz

Additional copies of this publication are available from:

Curran Associates, Inc.
57 Morehouse Lane
Red Hook, NY 12571 USA
Phone: 845-758-0400
Fax: 845-758-2633
Email: curran@proceedings.com
Web: www.proceedings.com

2020

NANOCON®

CONFERENCE PROCEEDINGS

12th International Conference
on Nanomaterials - Research & Application

October 21 - 23, 2020

Brno, Czech Republic, EU

Tanger RCPTM CSNMT

NANOCON

TANGER Ltd.

The Czech Society for New Materials and Technologies

Regional Centre of Advanced Technologies and Materials

2020 NANOCON®

12th International Conference on Nanomaterials - Research & Application

CONFERENCE PROCEEDINGS

October 21 - 23, 2020

Brno, Czech Republic, EU

SESSION A - NANOMATERIALS FOR ELECTRONIC, MAGNETIC AND OPTIC APPLICATIONS. CARBON NANOSTRUCTURES, QUANTUM DOTS 11

NANOSTRUCTURED LAYER ENHANCING LIGHT EXTRACTION FROM GAN-BASED SCINTILLATOR USING MOVPE 12
Tomáš VANĚK, Tomáš HUBÁČEK, František HÁJEK, Filip DOMINEC, Jiří PANGRÁC, Karla KULDOVÁ, Jiří OSWALD, Alice HOSPODKOVÁ

POLYSTYRENE THIN FILMS WITH INCORPORATED BORANE CLUSTERS FOR ELECTRONIC APPLICATIONS INVESTIGATED BY INFRARED REFLECTION-ABSORPTION SPECTROSCOPY 18
Barbora HANULIKOVA, Tereza CAPKOVA, Jan ANTOS, Jakub SEVCIK, Pavel URBANEK, Michal URBANEK, Ivo KURITKA

STRUCTURAL AND MAGNETIC PROPERTIES OF Fe-OXIDE LAYERS PREPARED BY INKJET PRINTING ON Si-SUBSTRATE 24
Frantisek ZAZIMAL, Tomas SVOBODA, Petr DZIK, Tomas HOMOLA, Yvonna JIRASKOVA

THE TEMPERATURE DEPENDENCE OF THE PHOTOLUMINESCENCE STABILITY OF OCTADECABORANE IN POLYSTYRENE MATRIX THIN FILMS 30
Pavel URBÁNEK, Jakub ŠEVČÍK, Barbora HANULÍKOVÁ, Tereza ČAPKOVÁ, Jan ANTOŠ, Michal URBÁNEK, Ivo KUŘITKA

POLYMER CHAIN ORDERING MANIFESTATION IN PHOTOLUMINESCENCE OF THIN F8BT FILMS 34
Bita GHASEMI, Jakub SEVCIK, Pavel URBANEK, Ivo KURITKA

THE UV PHOTODEGRADABILITY STUDY OF OCTADECABORANE IN POLYSTYRENE MATRIX THIN FILMS 39
Jakub SEVCIK, Pavel URBANEK, Barbora HANULIKOVA, Tereza CAPKOVA, Jan ANTOS, Michal URBANEK, Ivo KURITKA

DIELECTRIC PROPERTIES OF NANOSTRUCTURED MIXED-OXIDE FILMS FORMED BY ANODIZING Al/Zr BILAYERS 44
Marcela SEPÚLVEDA, Kirill KAMNEV, Alexander MOZALEV

IMPOSING BIAXIAL STRAIN ON 2D LAYERED MATERIALS BY LIQUID-INDUCED SWELLING OF SUPPORTING POLYMER 50
Krishna SAMPATHKUMAR, Jan PEKAREK, Otakar FRANK

SIMULATION AND DIAGNOSTICS OF PLASMACHEMICAL PROCESSES DURING MICROWAVE PLASMA SYNTHESIS OF GRAPHENE NANOSHEETS FROM ETHANOL 57
Vít KUDRLE, Miroslav SNIRER, Jozef TOMAN, Martin KUBEČKA, Jana JURMANOVÁ, Ondřej JAŠEK, František KRČMA

THE SENSING PROPERTIES OF CARBON NANOTUBE FILLED COPOLYMERS FOR VOC VAPORS DETECTION 63
Rostislav SLOBODIAN, Robert OLEJNÍK, Jiří MATYÁŠ, Petr SLOBODIAN

DIELECTRICAL ANALYSIS OF COMPOSITE MATERIALS WITH RECYCLED CARBON FIBERS 68
Jana NOVOTNÁ, Blanka TOMKOVÁ, Jana MÜLLEROVÁ

FACILE MICROWAVE -ASSISTED SYNTHESIS OF CASEIN DERIVED CARBON NANODOTS 75
R. Blessy PRICILLA, David ŠKODA, Pavel URBÁNEK, Michal URBÁNEK, Ivo KUŘITKA*

POLYVINYLPYRROLIDONE COATING FOR NANODIAMOND STABILIZATION IN SALINE SOLUTION AND SILVER NANOPARTICLE DECORATION 80
Katerina KOLAROVA, Daria MILIAIEVA, Stepan STEHLIK

GROWTH AND PROPERTIES OF DIAMOND FILMS PREPARED ON 4-INCH SUBSTRATES BY CAVITY PLASMA SYSTEMS 86
Oleg BABČENKO, Štěpán POTOCKÝ, Kateřina AUBRECHTOVÁ DRAGOUNOVÁ, Ondrej SZABÓ, Philippe BERGONZO, Bohuslav REZEK, Alexander KROMKA

TCO WORK FUNCTION TUNING BY NANODIAMONDS 93
Jan ČERMÁK, Daria MILIAIEVA, Aurelien SOKENG DJOUMESSI, Harald HOPPE, Štěpán STEHLÍK

EFFECT OF THE SUBSTRATE CRYSTALLINE ORIENTATION ON THE SURFACE MORPHOLOGY AND BORON INCORPORATION INTO EPITAXIAL DIAMOND LAYERS 98
Jan VOVES, Alexandr POŠTA, Marina DAVYDOVA, Alexandr LAPOSA, Vojtěch POVOLNÝ, Pavel HAZDRA, Nicolas LAMBERT, Silvia SEDLAKOVÁ, Vincent MORTET

RAMAN MICROSPECTROSCOPY STUDY OF CALCINED ELECTRICALLY CONDUCTIVE NANOCOMPOSITE POLYPYRROLE/GHASSOUL 103
Pavlína PEIKERTOVÁ, Jonáš TOKARSKÝ, Lenka KULHÁNKOVÁ, Kateřina MAMULOVÁ KUTLÁKOVÁ

EXPANSION OF OPTICAL PROPERTIES IN TiO_x NANOPARTICLES BY THEIR LASER-MEDIATED ALLOYING WITH Ag 109
David ETTEL, Ondrej HAVELKA, Selingul ISIK, Fatma YALCINKAYA, Rafael TORRES-MENDIETA

PRODUCTION AND ANALYSIS OF ELECTROSPUN MATERIALS CONTAINING OXIDIC NANOPARTICLES 116
Alexandra BENEDIKOVÁ, Jan GRÉGR, Martin STUCHLÍK, Pavel KEJZLAR, Michaela KOZLOVSKÁ, Eva KUŽELOVÁ KOŠŤÁKOVÁ

ANODIC FORMATION OF HfO_2 NANOSTRUCTURE ARRAYS FOR RESISTIVE SWITCHING APPLICATION 122
Kirill KAMNEV, Zdeněk PYTLÍČEK, Jan PRÁŠEK, Alexander MOZALEV

EFFECT OF EXTRUSION PROCESS AND VARIOUS ELONGATION RATIOS ON THE STRUCTURAL AND DIELECTRIC PROPERTIES OF PVDF-BASED COPOLYMER CONTAINING MICRO AND NANO-SIZED CRYSTALLITES 127
Miroslav MRLÍK, Martin CVEK, Josef OSIČKA, Marcin MASLOWSKI, Pavel TOFEL

EMBEDDED SEMICONDUCTOR QUANTUM DOTS - CURRENT OVERVIEW 133
Eduard HULICIUS, Alice HOSPODKOVÁ, Markéta ZÍKOVÁ

SESSION B - INDUSTRIAL AND ENVIRONMENTAL APPLICATIONS OF NANOMATERIALS 139

ELIMINATION OF FIBERS CREATED FROM THE ELECTRODE ROD AND INFLUENCE ON ELECTROSPINNING 140
Ondřej BAŤKA, Josef SKŘIVÁNEK

RESEARCH OF ELECTRODES ENABLING THE PRODUCTION OF NANOFIBRES WITH DEFINED FINENESS 145
Josef SKŘIVÁNEK, Jiří KOMÁREK, Ondřej BAŤKA

PRODUCTION OF FIBROUS COMPOSITE MATERIAL WITH INCORPORATED ACTIVATED CARBON 151
Pavel HOLEC, Ivan ULMAN, Radek JIRKOVEC, Jakub VANĚK

THE NEW METHOD OF SURFACE-ASSISTED COF SYNTHESIS FOR OPTICAL SENSOR MODIFICATION 157
Elena MILIUTINA, Polina BAINOVA, Vasilii BURTSEV, Anna ZABELINA, Vaclav ŠVORČÍK, Oleksiy LYUTAKOV

HYDROPHILIC NANOFIBER MEMBRANES FOR OILY WASTEWATER TREATMENT 162
Evren BOYRAZ, Fatma YALCINKAYA, Jakub HRUZA

THE EFFECT OF NANOVOID ELONGATION ON ELECTRON MULTIPLICATION DURING (SUB)NANOSECOND ELECTRICAL BREAKDOWN 167
Ján TUNGLI, Petr BÍLEK, Zdeněk BONAVENTURA

ON ELECTRON ACCELERATION IN LIQUID RUPTURES CAUSED BY ELECTROSTRICTIVE FORCES............................ 173
Petr BÍLEK, Ján TUNGLI, Zdeněk BONAVENTURA

ELECTROCHEMICAL STUDY OF CuSCN INORGANIC HOLE-TRANSPORT MATERIAL FOR SOLAR CELLS PREPARED BY ELECTRODEPOSITION FROM AQUEOUS SOLUTION 177
Zuzana VLČKOVÁ ŽIVCOVÁ, Věra MANSFELDOVÁ, Milan BOUŠA, Ladislav KAVAN

THE CREATION OF Au@TiO_2 PLASMON-ACTIVE STRUCTURE FOR HYDROGEN PRODUCTION 183
D. ZABELIN, A. ZABELINA, R. ELASHNIKOV, V. SVORCIK, D. NAZAROV, M. MAXIMOV, O. LYUTAKOV

THE EFFECT OF ATMOSPHERIC COLD PLASMA CLEANING OF FTO SUBSTRATES ON THE QUALITY OF TiO2 ELECTRON TRANSPORT LAYERS FOR PRINTED CARBON-BASED PEROVSKITE SOLAR CELLS 189
Matej HVOJNIK, Július VIDA, Tomáš HOMOLA, Michaela PAVLIČKOVÁ, Michal HATALA, Milan MIKULA, Katarína TOMANOVÁ, Pavol GEMEINER

NICKEL-COBALT OXIDE THIN-FILMS ANODES FOR LITHIUM-ION BATTERIES 196
Ilya MITROFANOV, Denis NAZAROV, Yury KOSHTYAL, Ilya EZHOV, Pavel FEDOROV, Aleksander RUMYANTSEV, Anatoliy POPOVICH, Maxim MAXIMOV*

ELECTROCHEMICAL ACTIVITY OF LITHIUM NICKEL OXIDE THIN-FILM CATHODES OBTAINED BY ALD 202
Ilya MITROFANOV, Yury KOSHTYAL, Denis NAZAROV, Ilya EZHOV, Artem KIM, Aleksander RUMYANTSEV, Oleg MEDVEDEV, Oleksiy LYUTAKOV, Anatoliy POPOVICH, Maxim MAXIMOV*

SPINEL FERRITES NANOPARTICLES FOR ALLOY STEEL PROTECTIVE LAYERS.. 208
Martin OCHMANN, Fredericus M. A. LINDERHOF, Libor MACHALA

AB-INITIO STUDY OF SURFACE ENERGIES AND STRUCTURAL INFLUECE OF VACANCIES IN TITANIUM NITRIDE NANOLAYER.. 214
Miroslav LEBEDA, Petr VLČÁK, Petr VEŘTÁT, Jan DRAHOKOUPIL

PATTERNING OF CONDUCTIVE NANO-LAYERS ON GARNET... 221
Jana CHLUMSKÁ, Ondřej LALINSKÝ, Milan MATĚJKA, Stanislav KRÁTKÝ, Vladimír KOLAŘÍK

CONDUCTIVE SILVER FILMS ON PAPER PREPARED BY ATMOSPHERIC PRESSURE ARGON PLASMA CONVERSION OF SILVER NITRATE 225
Július VIDA, Aleš STÝSKALÍK, Masoud SHEKARGOFTAR, Juho Antti SIRVIÖ, Tomáš HOMOLA

APPLICATION OF MANGANESE OXIDE THIN-FILMS OBTAINED BY ALD FOR Li-ION BATTERIES ANODE 231
Ilya EZHOV, Paul VISHNIAKOV, Ilya MITROFANOV, Yury KOSHTYAL, Denis NAZAROV, Aleksander RUMYANTSEV, Anatoliy POPOVICH, Maxim MAXIMOV

ACTIVATION OF AIR-STABLE ZERO-VALENT IRON NANOPARTICLES: COMPARISION OF DIFFERENT APPROACHES 237
Viktorie VÍCHOVÁ, Jana OBORNÁ, Petr JAKUBEC, Jan FILIP

HYDROTHERMAL AND MICROWAVE SYNTHESIS OF ZnS NANOPARTICLES 243
Julie SMIJOVÁ, Pavlína PEIKERTOVÁ, Kateřina MAMULOVÁ KUTLÁKOVÁ, Jonáš TOKARSKÝ

THE EFFECTS OF MOLECULAR AND PROCESSING PARAMETERS ON ENERGY HARVESTING CAPABILITY OF PVDF-BASED NANOGENERATORS 249
Martin CVEK, Josef OSIČKA, Peter SRNEC, Miroslav MRLÍK, Pavel TOFEL

CATALYTIC ACTIVITY OF THE NOBLE METAL NANOPARTICLES 255
Libor KVÍTEK, Tomáš STRYŠOVSKÝ, Martina KUBÍKOVÁ, Miroslav ORSÁG, Aleš PANÁČEK, Robert PRUCEK

EFFECT OF ANNEALING ON LUMINESCENCE AND PHOTOCATALYTIC ACTIVITY OF ZNS NANOCRYSTALS UNDER UV LIGHT IRRADIATION 261
Hassan ALI, Milan MASAR, Michal URBANEK, Ali Can GULER, Pavel URBANEK, Michal MACHOVSKY, Ivo KURITKA

THERMO-CATALYTIC DEGRADATION OF POLYSTYRENE OVER A-Fe_2O_3 267
Kateřina KLEMENCOVÁ, Barbora GRYCOVÁ, Amer INAYAT, Pavel LEŠTINSKÝ

FACILE HPLC TECHNIQUE FOR SIMULTANEOUS DETECTION OF ESTROGENTIC HORMONES IN WASTEWATER 272
Muhammad YASIR, Tomáš ŠOPÍK, Dušan KIMMER, Vladimír SEDLAŘÍK

THE DEVELOPMENT OF OPTICAL SENSOR FOR INORGANIC SALTS DETECTION IN WATER 277
Polina BAINOVA, Elena MILIUTINA, Vaclav ŠVORČÍK, Pavel POSTNIKOV, Oleksiy LYUTAKOV

NANOPARTICLE-BASED WORLD - ORIGIN OF LIFE THEORY 282
Lukas NEJDL, Kristyna ZEMANKOVA, Kristyna PAVELICOVA, Eliska SEDLACKOVA, Marketa LUKLOVA, Vojtech ADAM, Marketa VACULOVICOVA

EXTRACTION AND mICRONIZATION OF EDESTIN FROM HEMP SEED 288
Milos BERAN, Ondrej VLTAVSKY, Josef DRAHORAD

CARBON MATERIALS PREPARED FROM CIGARETTE FILTERS APPLIED FOR CLOFIBRIC ACID ADORPTION 294
Susana C. R. MARQUES, Jan FILIP

COLORIMETRIC HYDROGEN SENSORS 300
Anna ZABELINA, Elena MILIUTINA, Olga GUSELNIKOVA, Denis ZABELIN, Vaclav ŠVORČÍK, Oleksiy LYUTAKOV

LARGE AREA CLEANING AND ACTIVATION OF FLEXIBLE ULTRA-THIN GLASS BY NON-THERMAL ATMOSPHERIC-PRESSURE PLASMA 305
Slavomír SIHELNÍK, Richard KRUMPOLEC, Monika STUPAVSKÁ, Jianyu FENG, Eva KOSOVÁ, Jakub KELAR, Miroslav ZEMÁNEK, Dušan KOVÁČIK, Mirko ČERNÁK

LABORATORY EXPERIMENT OF IRON NANOPARTICLE TRANSPORT IN A ROCK FRACTURE WITH ONLINE CONCENTRATION DETECTION PROBES 311
Milan HOKR, Petr PARMA, Filip JANKOVSKÝ, Milan ZUNA, Miloslav MRAZÍK

SESSION C - BIONANOTECHNOLOGY, NANOMATERIALS IN MEDICINE 317

STUDY OF THE EFFECT OF PARACETAMOL BINDED IN POLYMERic NANOPARTICLES ON DAFNIA MAGNA 318
Barbora HAVELKOVA, Karel SEHNAL, Dominik BANAS, Marta KEPINSKA, Branislav RUTTKAY-NEDECKY, Martina STANKOVA, Carlos FERNANDEZ, Miroslava BEKLOVA, Rene KIZEK

OPTIMIZATION OF NUCLEIC ACID BINDING TO MAGNETIC PARTICLES WITH THE AIM OF DETECTION OF DANGEROUS VIRUSES 324
Dominik BANÁŠ, Ondřej RYCHLÝ, Stefano SALMISTRARO, Ahmet Davut AKSU, Miroslava KRZYŽÁNKOVÁ, Rene KIZEK

MOLECULARLY IMPRINTED POLYMER NANOPARTICLES AS POTENTIAL TOOL FOR IMMUNOHISTOCHEMISTRY 330
Jaroslava BEZDEKOVA, Kristyna TOMECKOVA, Kristyna PAVELICOVA, Kristyna ZEMANKOVA, Marketa VACULOVICOVA

SPECIAL NANOFIBER SCAFFOLD DESIGNED FOR CELLULAR PRODUCTS IN THE TREATMENT OF CHRONIC WOUNDS 335
Petr BRAŤKA, Matej BUZGO, Hana WALASKÁ, Josef ROSINA, Martin ČERVEŇÁK, Matěj LOUDA

TEST OF COMPLEX NANOSTRUCTURES AS GENE DELIVERY SYSTEM TO CARDIAC CELLS 342
Josef SKOPALIK, Jaroslav PRUCHA, Jiri SEKORA, Vratislav CMIEL, Tomas PARAK, Josef MASEK

BIO-APPLICABLE METAL NANOPARTICLES 347
Vít VYKOUKAL, Radka DOPITOVÁ, Martin POLÁK, Jiří NOVÁČEK

ANTIBACTERIAL ELECTROSPUN MEMBRANE PREPARED FROM POLY (VINYLIDENE FLUORIDE)-CO-HEXAFLUOROPROPYLENE WITH LAURIC ACID MONOACYLGLYCEROL 355
Jana ZELENKOVA, Petra PEER, Pavel PLEVA, Magda JANALIKOVA, Jana SEDLARIKOVA, Petr FILIP

COMBINATION OF LABEL-FREE SURFACE-ENHACED RAMAN SPECTROSCOPY WITH CONVOLUTIONAL NEURAL NETWORK FOR DNA RECOGNITION 361
Anastasia SKVORTSOVA, Andrei TRELIN, Vaclav SVORCIK, Olga GUSELNIKOVA, Oleksyi LYUTAKOV

COVALENTLY CROSS-LINKED HYALURONIC ACID/BSA/GELATINE HYDROGELS AS BETTER SURFACE FOR CELL CULTURE 366
Simon KLIMOVIC, Jan PRIBYL, Vladimir ROTREKL, Šárka JELINKOVA, Hana VICAROVA

THE INTERACTION BETWEEN SELECTED ANTIDEPRESSANTS AND ZINC OXIDE NANOPARTICLES 373
Roman MARŠÁLEK, Martin ŠVIDRNOCH

DIFFUSION OF DYES IN BIOPOLYMERIC HYDROGELS 379
David VYROUBAL, Martina KLUČÁKOVÁ

METTALOTHIONEIN SENSING USING MOLECULARLY IMPRINTED POLYMERS COUPLED LASER ABLATION INDUCTIVELY COUPLED PLASMA-MASS SPECTROMETRY 385
Kristyna ZEMANKOVA, Kristyna PAVELICOVA, Jaroslava BEZDEKOVA, Lukas NEJDL, Marketa VEJVODOVA, Tomas VACULOVIC, Marketa VACULOVICOVA

USING QD-FRET BASED METHOD TO INVESTIGATE PROTEIN-PROTEIN INTERACTIONS 390
Kristyna PAVELICOVA, Kristyna ZEMANKOVA, Jaroslava BEZDEKOVA, Marketa VACULOVICOVA

ELEGANT, RAPID AND SIMPLE PROCEDURE FOR LABELING OF ANTIBODIES WITH FLUORESCENT ZnCd/S QUANTUM DOTS FOR LASER ABLATION ICP-MS DETECTION 395
Navid ASSI, Kristyna PAVELICOVA, Marketa VACULOVICOVA, Tomas VACULOVIC

HIGHLY SENSITIVE MICROFLUIDIC SENSOR ARCHITECTURE FOR SERS MEASUREMENTS OF HORMONES 399
Vasilii BURTSEV, Elena MILIUTINA, Mariia ERZINA, Vaclav ŠVORČÍK, Oleksiy LYUTAKOV

CELL BASED AFM BIOSENSENSING FOR SCREENING OF PULMONARY-DRUG RELATED ARRHYTMIC EFFECTS 404
Martin PESL, Jan PRIBYL, Simon KLIMOVIC, Martin SCUREK, Deborah BECKEROVÁ, Kristian BRAT, Petr SKLADAL, Vladimir ROTREKL

THE USE OF GOLD NANOPARTICLE-ANTIBODY CONJUGATES IN IMMUNE TEST FOR MICROCYSTIN-LR DETECTION 410
Elena A. ZVEREVA, Olga D. HENDRICKSON, Anatoly V. ZHERDEV, Boris B. DZANTIEV, Sergey A. EREMIN

TIME-LAPSE MONITORING OF CELL MECHANICAL PROPERTIES 416
Jan PŘIBYL, Vladimir ROTREKL, Martin PEŠL, Šárka JELÍNKOVÁ, Irena KRATOCHVÍLOVÁ

PREPARATION OF SILVER NANOPARTICLES BY GREEN SYNTHESIS OF VINE SEEDS - ANTIBACTERIAL EFFECT 422
Branislav RUTTKAY-NEDECKÝ, Karel SEHNAL, Dominik BANAS, Martina STANKOVA, Marta KEPINSKA, Duong Ngonc BACH, Jiri SOCHOR, Mojmir BARON, Awais FARID, Hoai Viet NGUYEN, René KIZEK

SILVER NANOPARTICLES SYNTHESIZED USING CANNABIS SATIVA EXTRACT AND THEIR ANTIBACTERIAL ACTIVITY 428
Jana MICHAILIDU, Alena ČEJKOVÁ

GREEN SYNTHESIS AND THE STABILIZATION OF SELENIUM NANOPARTICLES USING CARBOXYMETHYL STARCH 433
Vishakha VISHAKHA, A. M. ABDEL-MOHSEN, J. JANCAR

THE STUDY OF THE HYDROGEL SYSTEMS WITH MICELLAR NANODOMAINS AND THE EFFECT OF THE PH CHANGES ON THEIR PROPERTIES 440
Richard HEGER, Filip MRAVEC, Miloslav PEKAŘ

SULPHUR PARTICLES IMMOBILIZED ON ACTIVATED POLYSTYRENE SURFACE 446
Simona LUPÍNKOVÁ, Jaroslava JAROLÍMKOVÁ, Martin KORMUNDA, Zdeňka KOLSKÁ

SESSION D - MONITORING AND TOXICITY OF NANOMATERIALS 452

TOXIC RESPONSES IN HUMAN LUNG EPITHELIAL CELLS (BEAS-2B) EXPOSED TO PARTICULATE MATTER EXHAUST EMISSIONS FROM GASOLINE AND BIOGASOLINE 453
Táňa ZÁVODNÁ, Helena LÍBALOVÁ, Kristýna VRBOVÁ, Jitka SIKOROVÁ, Michal VOJTÍŠEK-LOM, Vít BERÁNEK, Martin PECHOUT, Jiří KLÉMA, Miroslav CIGANEK, Miroslav MACHALA, Jiří NEČA, Pavel RÖSSNER Jr., Jan TOPINKA

FINE AND ULTRAFINE PARTICULATE MATTER IN THE WORK ENVIRONMENT AND THEIR POTENTIAL IMPACT ON MENTAL STATE OF WORKERS ... 459
Michal URBÁNEK, Klaudia KÖBÖLOVÁ, Vladimír ADAMEC, Kateřina WOLFOVÁ, Kristina ČABANOVÁ, Jana Victoria MARTINCOVÁ

SCENTED CANDLES AS A SOURCE OF NANOPARTICLES IN THE WORKSPACE ... 465
Petra ROUPCOVÁ, Hana KUBÁTOVÁ, Karel KLOUDA, Ondřej CHROMEČKA

IMMOBILIZATION OF PHARMACEUTICALS IN SOILS ... 471
Martina KLUČÁKOVÁ

RNA EXTRACTION FROM SOIL BACTERIUM PSEUDOMONAS PUTIDA AND GREEN ALGA RAPHIDOCELIS SUBCAPITATA AFTER EXPOSURE TO NANOSCALE ZERO VALENT IRON ... 477
Cheryl S.Y. YEAP, Nhung H.A. NGUYEN, Olga Blifernez-KLASSEN, Jan H. MUSSGNUG, Tobias BUSCHE, Olaf KRUSE, Alena SEVCU

SENSITIVE LATERAL FLOW IMMUNOASSAY OF UNDECLARED CHICKEN INGREDIENT IN MEAT PRODUCTS ... 483
Olga D. HENDRICKSON, Elena A. ZVEREVA, Anatoly V. ZHERDEV, Boris B. DZANTIEV

INFLUENCE OF THE APPLICATION OF LIGNITE ON THE DISTRIBUTION OF ORGANIC CARBON IN SOIL ... 489
David ŠIRŮČEK, Michal KALINA, Martina KLUČÁKOVÁ

THE RELATION OF BIOCHAR TEXTURE TO ITS PHYSICOCHEMICAL AND MORPHOLOGICAL CHARACTERISTICS ... 495
Michal KALINA, Šárka SOVOVÁ, Monika TRUDIČOVÁ, Jan HAJZLER, Jiří SMILEK, Vojtěch ENEV, Ludmila MRAVCOVÁ

SESSION E - ADVANCED METHODS OF PREPARATION AND CHARACTERIZATION OF NANOMATERIALS ... 501

INTRODUCING FORCE TRACEABILITY TO NANOINDENTATION MEASUREMENTS ... 502
Radek ŠLESINGER, Anna CHARVÁTOVÁ CAMPBELL, Vilma BURŠÍKOVÁ

AFM CHARACTERIZATION OF NANOCOMPOSITE SAMPLES ... 506
Anna CHARVÁTOVÁ CAMPBELL, Marek HAVLÍČEK, Petr KLAPETEK, Vilma BURŠÍKOVÁ

PLASMA HYDROGENATION OF HYDROTHERMALLY GROWN ZnO MICROPODS ... 512
Zdeněk REMEŠ, Kateřina AUBRECHTOVÁ DRAGOUNOVÁ, Julia MIČOVÁ

THERMAL STABILITY OF Ti/Ni MULTILAYER THIN FILMS ... 518
Richard VÁCLAVIK, Lukáš ZÁBRANSKÝ, Pavel SOUČEK, Pavel SŤAHEL, Jiří BURŠÍK, Tomáš FOŘT, Vilma BURŠÍKOVÁ

NANOSPRAY PROCESSING OF SILVER NANOPARTICLES FOR FORMATION OF DRIED DEPOSITS ... 524
Anna TYCOVA, Vladimir JONAS, Jan PRIKRYL, Adela KOTZIANOVA, Vladimir VELEBNY, Frantisek FORET

CHARACTERIZATION OF EDGE STRUCTURE AND MISORIENTATION BETWEEN LAYERS OF MICROWAVE PLASMA SYNTHESIZED FEW-LAYER GRAPHENE NANOSHEETS ... 529
Jana JURMANOVÁ, Ondřej JAŠEK, Jozef TOMAN, Dalibor VŠIANSKÝ, Pavel SŤAHEL

ORGANOSILICON PLASMA POLYMERS DEPOSITED IN TRIMETHYLSILYL ACETATE/CH_4 PLASMA OF CAPACITIVELY COUPLED RF GLOW DISCHARGE 535
Štěpánka KELAROVÁ, Monika STUPAVSKÁ, Roman PŘIBYL, Vilma BURŠÍKOVÁ

COMPARISON OF HMDSO AND HMDSZ THIN FILMS GROWTH UNDER DUSTY PLASMA CONDITIONS 541
Roman PŘIBYL, Štěpánka KELAROVÁ, Lukáš ZÁBRANSKÝ, Vilma BURŠÍKOVÁ

CONTROLLING THE INTERNAL MICROSTRUCTURE AND PROPERTIES OF PHYSICALLY CROSS-LINKED PVA HYDROGELS BY THE RATE OF FREEZING 547
Monika TRUDICOVA, Jan ZAHRADKA, Petr SEDLACEK, Miloslav PEKAR

RADICAL-BASED TUNING THE SURFACE FUNCTIONALITY OF MXENE 553
Anastasiia OLSHTREM, Sergii CHERTOPALOV, Olga GUSELNIKOVA, Vaclav SVORCÍK, Oleksiy LYUTAKOV

ZnO NANOPARTICLES: SYNTHESIS AND EVOLUTION 558
Vojtěch PŘIKRYL, Zuzana BYTEŠNÍKOVÁ, Pavel ŠVEC, Lukáš RICHTERA, Vojtěch ADAM

MOLECULAR MODELING OF INTERACTIONS BETWEEN CATALYTIC NANOPARTICLES AND POLYMER CARRIERS 564
Adam VERNER, Jonáš TOKARSKÝ

SESSION A
NANOMATERIALS FOR ELECTRONIC, MAGNETIC AND OPTIC APPLICATIONS. CARBON NANOSTRUCTURES, QUANTUM DOTS

Chairmen

Prof. Dr. Eduard HULICIUS	Institute of Physics of the CAS, Prague, Czech Republic, EU
Assoc. Prof. Dr. Martin KALBAC	J. Heyrovsky Institute of Physical Chemistry of the CAS, Prague, Czech Republic, EU
Dr. Oldrich SCHNEEWEISS	Institute of the Physics of Materials of the CAS, Brno, Czech Republic, EU
Prof. Dr. Bohuslav REZEK	Czech Technical University in Prague, Czech Republic, EU
Prof. Dr. Zdenek SOFER	University of Chemistry and Technology, Prague, Czech Republic, EU

NANOSTRUCTURED LAYER ENHANCING LIGHT EXTRACTION FROM GAN-BASED SCINTILLATOR USING MOVPE

[1,2]Tomáš VANĚK*, [2]Tomáš HUBÁČEK, [2]František HÁJEK, [2]Filip DOMINEC, [2]Jiří PANGRÁC, [2]Karla KULDOVÁ, [2]Jiří OSWALD, [2]Alice HOSPODKOVÁ

[1]*Technical University of Liberec, Liberec, Czech Republic, EU,* *vanekt@fzu.cz*

[2]*Institute of Physics CAS v.v.i., Prague, Czech Republic, EU*

https://doi.org/10.37904/nanocon.2020.3698

Abstract

Light extraction (LE) efficiency of GaN buffer layer was studied by angle-resolved photoluminescence. We measured enhancement of light extraction efficiency (LEE) up to 154% by introducing the SiN_x layer atop the GaN buffer and subsequent GaN light extraction layer (LEL) overgrowth. Morphological properties of GaN "islands" forming the LEL, such as size and density, have been tuned by various growth parameters. Subsequently, the influence of different growth parameters, such as coalescence time, time of SiN_x growth or type of nucleation carrier gas (H_2 or N_2), on LE was discussed. We also experimentally showed that LE of this layer is more efficient for higher extraction angles. Finally, we present the change in the GaN surface morphology by Si etching in H_2 atmosphere during SiN_x growth (measured by the atomic force microscopy).

Keywords: GaN, light extraction, SiN_x, scintillator, MOVPE

1. INTRODUCTION

GaN-based heterostructures have been widely studied for more than 30 years since the first blue LEDs were discovered [1]. Nowadays, they are already spread to many LED, LD, and scintillator applications. They are still promising for new applications, thanks to their high luminescence efficiency, high radiation resistance and high exciton binding energy. On the other hand, they have a problem with light extraction due to their high refractive index (approx. 2.38 for green light). A vast scientific effort has been made during the last decade to find the best and commercially reasonable solution. Many different surface treatment techniques like electron beam lithography, laser interface lithography, nanoimprint lithography or anodic aluminum oxide were successfully established [2-9]. Unfortunately, these methods are expensive, time-consuming or unsuitable for large-scale wafer manufacturing and their LEE varies from tens to hundreds of percent, depending on the layer parameters and LEE measuring conditions [10].

The natural light extractors in InGaN/GaN multi-quantum well (MQW) scintillators are V-pits [11]. They form on the top of threading dislocations and their size increases with the thickness of the scintillator active region. In the scintillator case, an enormously thicker active region compared to LEDs is usually necessary due to sufficient radiation stopping power of the scintillator. Consequently, the dimension of V-pits in order of hundreds of nanometres is suitable for LE. Furthermore, their surface density is usually around 10^8 cm^{-2} for samples grown on the commonly used sapphire substrate. In fact, they cover most of the surface and the light extraction is very efficient. However, threading dislocations are generally a source of nonradiative recombination and the large empty space occupied by V-pits reduces the detection volume of the scintillator. Thus, there is an effort to decrease the number of threading dislocations, which can be realized by using a GaN substrate. The decrease of V-pits surface density about at least two orders of magnitude is achieved, but it causes a substantial reduction in LEE due to the almost flat surface of the scintillator.

In this work, we will show a GaN nanostructured layer grown using a SiN_x layer on the GaN buffer layer within a single MOVPE run. The dependency of the surface density of GaN "islands" and their size on the growth conditions will be discussed. A significant increase of LEE, thanks to the GaN overgrowth on the SiN_x layer and its interesting surface morphology, will be presented as well.

2. EXPERIMENTAL

Nine samples of GaN scintillators were prepared by the MOVPE technology in the Aixtron 3x2" CCS MOVPE apparatus equipped with Laytec EpiCurveTT in situ measurement. All samples were grown on the sapphire substrate with the same growth conditions of the first nucleation, coalescence and undoped GaN (uGaN) buffer layer.

The c-oriented sapphire substrate was firstly baked out at 1050°C and nitrified by NH_3. The 25 nm thick nucleation layer was grown at 540 °C and then overgrown by approximately 1.6 μm thick undoped GaN layer. Samples A1-A3 were just overgrown by 2.5 μm thick uGaN and n-doped GaN (nGaN) layer with temperatures ranging from 1070 to 1080°C, usually used for subsequent MQW growth, but the influence of these layers on the LE should be negligible in this work. Finally, the SiN_x layers were grown at 1080 °C with a growth time ranging from 200 to 400 s. Growth parameters such as nucleation time after SiNx, second coalescence time (CT) and annealing time that have been tuned are listed in **Table 1.** In situ measurement of reflectance and surface temperature with marked growth steps is shown in **Figure 1a**.

The scanning electron microscopy (SEM) images were obtained by Philips XL30 ESEM. The atomic force microscope (AFM) Solver P47H-PRO was used for detailed characterization of the surface.

Table 1 List of investigated samples grown with different parameters during and after the SiN_x layer growth

Sample	Buffer	SiN_x time [s]	Coalescence time [s]	Nucleation carrier gas	Nucleation time [s]	Annealing time [s]	Comments
DSP reference (DR)	uGaN + nGaN	-	-	-	-	-	stop growth before SiN_x on double-side polished Al_2O_3
SSP reference (SR)	uGaN + nGaN	-	-	-	-	-	stop growth before SiN_x on single-side polished Al_2O_3
A1	uGaN + nGaN	300	900	H_2	180	90	-
A2	uGaN + nGaN	300	200	H_2	180	90	-
A3	uGaN + nGaN	300	50	H_2	180	90	-
B1	uGaN	200	40	N_2	90	45	-
B2	uGaN	300	40	N_2	90	45	-
B3	uGaN	400	40	N_2	90	45	-
C	uGaN	600	-	-	-	-	stop growth after SiN_x

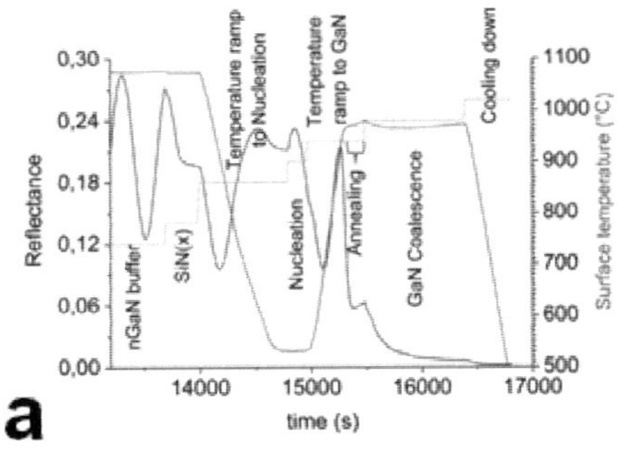

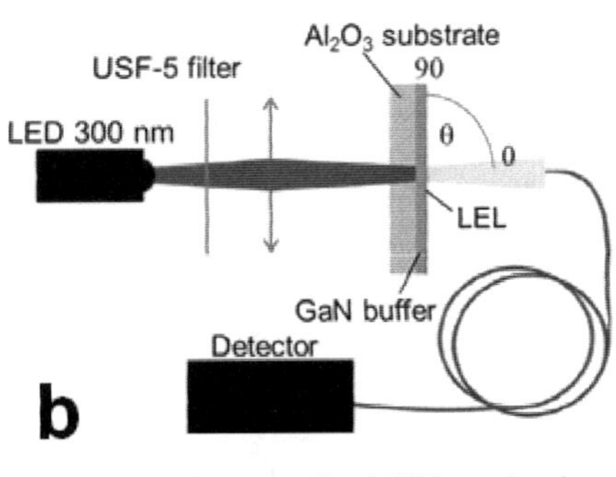

Figure 1 Evolution of reflectance and surface temperature during the growth of SiN_x and subsequent layers with marked growth steps **(a)**, the scheme of angular dependence PL measurement **(b)**.

The PL experimental setup is in **Figure 1b**. Samples were excited through the sapphire substrate with a focused 300 nm LED filtered by bandpass filter UFS-5 to suppress parasitic LED luminescence in the visible range. This excitation energy is above the GaN bandgap (3.4 eV ~ 365 nm). Thus, the light is absorbed approximately in the first 150 nm of the uGaN buffer. The luminescence light was collected to the optical fiber, which rotated around the sample from 0 to 75°. We didn't measure up to 90° due to the sample holder suppressing the luminescence from the edge of the scintillators. Light was detected by Thorlabs CCS200 spectrometer with spectral accuracy < 2 nm.

3. RESULTS AND DISCUSSION

It has been already published and confirmed by transmission electron microscopy that Ga etches Si from the SiN_x layer during GaN overgrowth, which creates a highly Si-doped GaN layer instead of two split layers. Consequently, the highly Si-doped GaN grows in 3D morphology with typical GaN "islands" [12-14]. SEM images in **Figures 2a,b** show a comparison of sample A1 (with LEL) with the technologically same sample without the LEL (SR). A significant increase of LEE (154%) was detected by PL measurement, see **Figure 2c**. Surprisingly, we didn't get the maximum intensity of luminescence in the 0° for samples with LEL nor SR sample without the LEL, see **Figure 2d**. We assume it is because of the light scattering on all rough surfaces in the scintillator. In **Figure 2e** is shown a comparison of the theoretical transmittance curve, which can be obtained from Snell's law and Fresnel equations, with curves measured by reference samples SR and DR. Equations, used for the calculation, can be written as:

$$T = \left[\frac{n_t \cos(\theta_t)}{n_i \cos(\theta_i)}\right] t^2 \qquad \text{where } t^2 = \frac{|E_{0t}|^2}{|E_{0i}|^2} \tag{1}$$

where:

T - the transmittance

n_t, n_i - the refractive indexes of the external and internal medium

θ_t, θ_i - the transmittance and incident angles

t - the ratio between the electrical intensity of transmitted E_{0t} and incidence beam E_{0i}

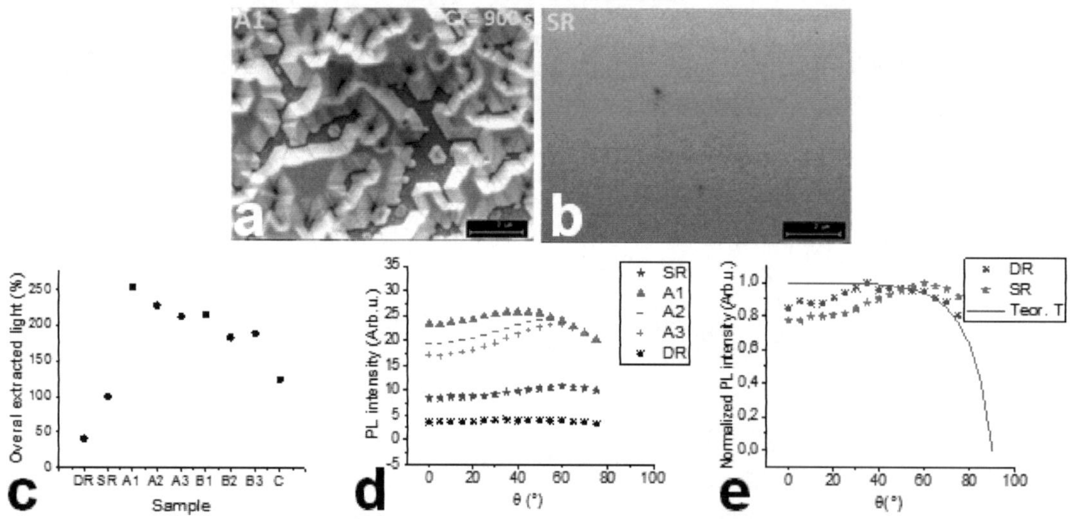

Figure 2 SEM images of sample A1 with the LEL **(a)** and SR without the LEL **(b)**, a relative comparison of overall light extracted from all angles for all samples **(c)**, angle dependence of PL intensity for individual samples **(d)**, the comparison of the normalized PL intensity of reference samples with theoretical values of transmittance **(e)**.

It's clearly seen that the intensity of transmitted light fits very well with theoretical expectations for high extraction angles in the case of the DR sample. The deviation in low angles could be explained by the scattering of light on the interface between the Al_2O_3 substrate and GaN, which is a known phenomenon because the crystal quality is very poor there [15].

Generally, it's necessary to approach the dimension of the LEL islands close to luminescence wavelength (λ_{em} = 564 nm) for the most efficient LE. Furthermore, the luminescence inhomogeneity on this scale produced by the LEL could also be unwanted. Thus, we reduced the coalescence time to create "islands" like the structure shown in **Figure 3**.

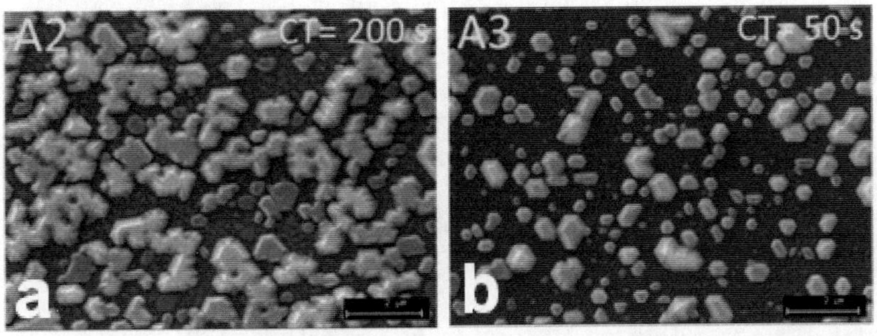

Figure 3 SEM images of samples grown with different coalescence time 200 s **(a)**, 50 s **(b)**

The low density of the GaN islands on the surface causes a decrease in LEE for small angles of extracted light, see **Figure 2d** for A3. We changed the nucleation carrier gas from H_2 to N_2 to decrease the surface mobility of atoms and we also dropped nucleation time and annealing time by a factor of two. The result was a slightly higher density of the GaN islands, see sample B2 in **Figure 4b**. A significant increase in the density occurred with a decreasing time of the SiN_x layer growth (SiT) to 200 s, **Figure 4a**. It can be attributed to lower Si doping concentration in the GaN and also a change in surface morphology of the buffer layer, which will be discussed later. An increase of LEE for small extraction angles, due to the higher density of the islands, is clearly observable on the graph in **Figure 4d**.

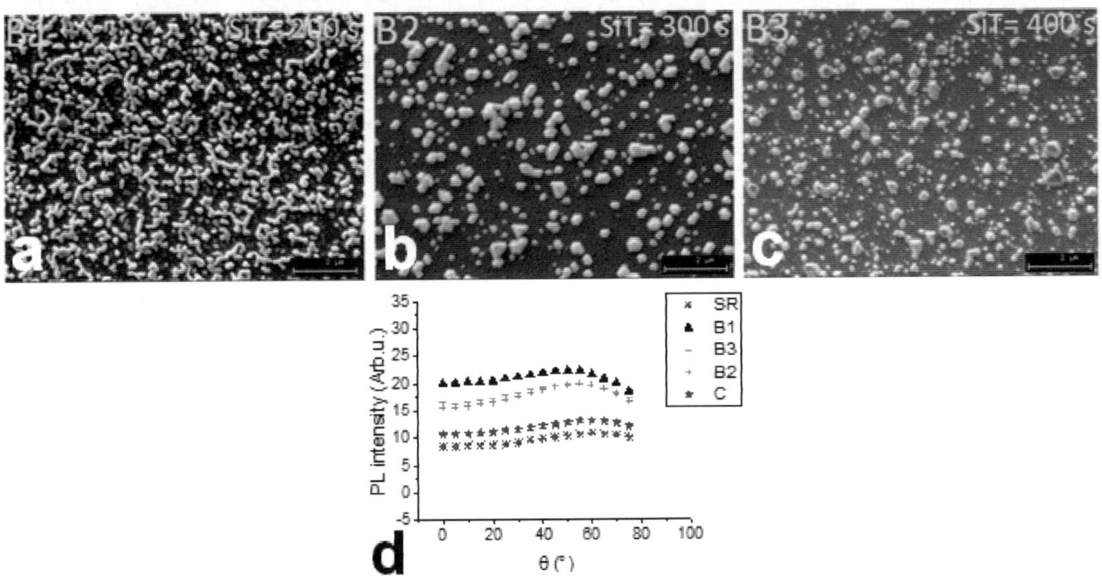

Figure 4 SEM images of samples grown with different times of SiNx growth 200 s **(a)**, 300 s **(b)** and 400 s **(c)**. Their comparison of PL intensity extracted from individual angles with the SR and C samples **(d)**

The ambiguous trend in the decreasing density of the GaN islands with the increasing growth time of the SiN_x layer, observable on the sample B3, induces some next mechanism except the higher doping concentration of Si in GaN. If we zoom in on the surface of the sample B3 (**Figure 5a)**, we can see small black holes indicating a porous morphology of the surface. It is better observable in the AFM image of sample C in **Figure 5b** ("stop growth" sample after 600 s of SiN_x). This trenched structure is probably created by the etching of GaN surface by Si in the H_2 atmosphere and its morphology could influence the subsequent GaN growth but this hypothesis needs further investigations. The crater's dimensions are in the order of tens of nanometers in depth and width up to approximately 150 nm (**Figure 5c)**. These pits, together with trenches, create a partially ordered surface corrugation with a lattice parameter comparable to emission wavelength, similar to photonic structures [10]. We can see, from **Figures 4d** and **2c**, that enhancement of LEE by this morphology is around 24% (compare sample C with SR).

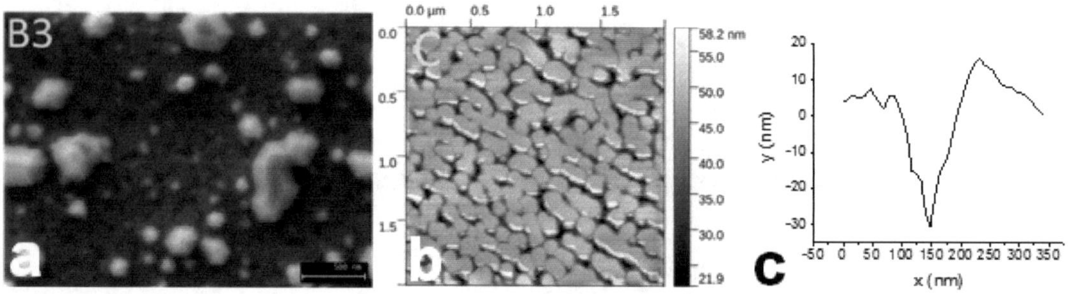

Figure 5 SEM image of the surface of sample B3 **(a)**, AFM image of the SiN_x layer morphology **(b)** and AFM profile of the surface's crater **(c)**.

4. CONCLUSION

We have prepared a GaN LEL suitable for LE from GaN-based scintillators. The advantage of this method using the SiN_x technology is its simplicity and possibility to grow this layer within the single MOVPE run upon the whole two inches wafer surface. Our maximal reached LEE was 154% for sample A1 compared to the reference sample on a single side polished sapphire substrate, which is comparable with other LEL prepared by different methods. The morphological properties of this layer can be tuned by changing the growth parameters. Concretely, the surface density of the GaN islands is very sensitive to the growth time of the SiN_x layer and their size can be easily controlled by coalescence time. At the same time, the results confirm the theory that with increasing concentration of Si doping, GaN tends to 3D growth and creates individual islands. Simultaneously, the GaN etching by Si in the H_2 atmosphere makes trenches surface morphology, which contributes to LE, too.

ACKNOWLEDGEMENTS

The authors acknowledge the support of MSMT project no. NPU LO1603 - ASTRANIT.

REFERENCES

[1] NAKAMURA, S. Growth of $In_xGa_{(1-x)}N$ compound semiconductors and high-power InGaN/AlGaN double heterostructure violet-light-emitting diodes. *Microel. J.* 1994, vol. 25, p. 651.

[2] JIN, Y. et al. Enhanced light extraction from a GaN-based green light-emitting diode with hemicylindrical linear grating structure. *Opt. Exp.* 2012, vol. 20, pp. 15818-15825.

[3] STARK, C. J. M., DETCHPROHM, T. & WETZEL, C. The Role of Mesa Size in Nano-Structured Green AlGaInN Light-Emitting Diodes. *Phys. Stat. Sol. C.* 2011, vol. 8, pp. 2311-2314.

[4] KUO, H. C., YEN, H. H., LEE, C. E. & CHAO, C. H. Far-field of GaN film-transferred green light-emitting diodes with two-dimensional photonic crystals. *Opt. Exp.* 2009, vol. 17, pp. 8795-8804.

[5] DONG HYUK, J., HEE KWAN, L. & JAE SU, Y. Light Output Extraction Enhancement in GaN-Based Green LEDs With Periodic AZO Subwavelength Nanostructure Arrays. *Phot. Tech. Lett.* IEEE, 2012, vol. 24, pp. 1381-1383.

[6] SANG, H., LEE, K. D., KIM, J. Y., KWON, M. K. & PARK, S. J. Fabrication of photonic crystal structures on light emitting diodes by nanoimprint lithography. *Nanotechnology.* 2007, vol. 18, p. 55306.

[7] HUANG, H. W. et al. Enhanced light output from a nitride-based power chip of green light-emitting diodes with nano-rough surface using nanoimprint lithography. *Nanotechnology.* 2008, vol. 19, p. 185301.

[8] YU, Z. G. et al. Obvious improvement of light extraction obtained by anodic aluminum oxide coverage on GaN surface. *App. Phys. A.* 2013, vol. 110, pp. 35-39.

[9] YU, Z. G. et al. Optimization of the nanopore depth to improve the electroluminescence for GaN-based nanoporous green LEDs. *Mat. Sci. in Sem. Process.* 2015, vol. 33, pp. 76-80.

[10] JIANG, S., FENG, Y., CHEN, Z. et al. Study on Light Extraction from GaN-based Green Light-Emitting Diodes Using Anodic Aluminum Oxide Pattern and Nanoimprint Lithography. *Scient. Rep.* 2016, vol. 6, p. 21573.

[11] HANGLEITERL, A. et al. Suppression of Nonradiative Recombination by V-Shaped Pits in GaInN/GaN Quantum Wells Produces a Large Increase in the Light Emission Efficiency. *Phys. Rev. Lett.* 2005, vol. 95, p. 127402.

[12] HOSPODKOVA, A. et al. Improvement of GaN Crystalline Quality by SiNx Layer Grown by MOVPE. *Lithuanian J. Phys.* 2019, vol. 59, no. 4, pp. 185-192.

[13] LAHRECHE, H. et al. Growth of high-quality GaN by low-pressure metal-organic vapor phase epitaxy (LP-MOVPE) from 3D islands and lateral overgrowth. *J. Cryst. Growth.* 1999, vol. 205, no. 3, pp. 245-252.

[14] TANAKA, S. et al. Self-assembling GaN quantum dots on AlxGa1−xN surfaces using a surfactant. *Appl. Phys. Lett.* 1996, vol. 69, p. 4096.

[15] LIAU, Z. L. et al. Light scattering in high-dislocation-density GaN. *Appl. Phys. Lett.* 1996, vol. 69, p. 1665.

POLYSTYRENE THIN FILMS WITH INCORPORATED BORANE CLUSTERS FOR ELECTRONIC APPLICATIONS INVESTIGATED BY INFRARED REFLECTION-ABSORPTION SPECTROSCOPY

Barbora HANULIKOVA, Tereza CAPKOVA, Jan ANTOS, Jakub SEVCIK, Pavel URBANEK, Michal URBANEK, Ivo KURITKA

Tomas Bata University in Zlín, University Institute, Centre of Polymer Systems, Zlín, Czech Republic, EU, hanulikova@utb.cz

https://doi.org/10.37904/nanocon.2020.3699

Abstract

The paper is focused on the investigation of thin polystyrene (PS) films and PS films with incorporated *anti*-octadecaborane(22) (*anti*-$B_{18}H_{22}$) clusters (PS+$B_{18}H_{22}$) with a thickness of 450 nm and 290 nm, respectively. The main aim is to describe the vibrational behavior of thin films in dependence on temperature and determine the changes connected with the glass transition of PS. Infrared reflection-absorption spectra were measured and from the plot of spectral region area (A_{range}) vs. temperature, glass transition temperature (T_g) of PS was extracted. The abrupt change in the course of *A* of C_{ar}-H stretching vs. temperature was assigned to the glass transition. T_g of PS and PS+$B_{18}H_{22}$ thin film was determined to be 74 °C and 77 °C, respectively. On the other hand, only a continuous decrease of *A* of C-H stretching vs. temperature was found for both samples indicating that each vibrational motion reacts uniquely on temperature increase. It was further found that *anti*-$B_{18}H_{22}$ is not fixed firmly in the thin layer at higher temperatures, because no B-H spectral response was detected above 91 °C. This result was also supported with TGA and DSC analysis showing a particular mass decrease at temperature 75 °C.

Keywords: Octadecaborane, polymer blend, thin film, glass transition, infrared reflection-absorption spectroscopy

1. INTRODUCTION

Polymer thin films have attracted attention due to their specific properties related to the thin layer arrangement of macromolecules. Semi-conductive polymer layers (e.g. MEH-PPV, poly[2-methoxy-5-(2-ethylhexyloxy)-1,4-phenylenevinylene]) have found their use in light-emitting diodes preparation [1] and insulating polymer layers (PS, polystyrene or PMMA, poly[(methyl) methacrylate] etc.) have been used as matrices for the incorporation of low molecular species. For example, blue-emitting borane clusters, especially *anti*-octadecaborane(22) (*anti*-$B_{18}H_{22}$) and its derivatives [2], are one of the highly investigated low molecular species nowadays, even though octadecaborane was synthesized already in the 1960s by Hawthorne and his co-workers [3]. *Anti*-$B_{18}H_{22}$ absorption and the emission maximum is located at 330 nm and 430 nm, respectively, and it also provides fluorescence that could be used in LED applications. However, some of its properties are not viable and several derivatives were investigated to improve solubility and to tune fluorescence, e.g. iodine- [4], pyridine- [5], sulfur- [6] derivative.

Properties of substrate-supported thin polymer films (the glass transition temperature, T_g) are influenced by chain confinement near the substrate surface, interactions between substrate and film (such as hydrogen bonding) [7], or surface roughness [8]. The T_g of a thin film can thus be lower or reach to higher values than the T_g of the bulk polymer. However, it cannot be investigated by routine measurement (DSC). Glass transition is related with the unlocking of polymer segments motion, which can cause conformational changes of chains observable by spectroscopic methods [9,10]. Infrared Reflection-Absorption Spectroscopy (IRRAS) has been used for the investigation of thin films on reflective substrates. Besides routine measurements related with confirmation of film structure or composition [11], it can be used for monitoring of the phase separation of thin films made from polymer blends, e.g. PMMA/poly(4-vinyl phenol) [12], or other important structure- and thickness-dependent properties, such as T_g [13,14] of thin films. For instance, the strong dependence of the T_g of poly(ethylene terephthalate) was observed below 100 nm thin layers, and T_g reduction up to 25 °C in comparison with bulk was found for film thickness below 65 nm [15].

In the contribution, we focus on the behaviour of *anti*-$B_{18}H_{22}$ incorporated in the PS thin film. Our preliminary study deals mainly with the effect of temperature on the IR spectra of PS films and PS+$B_{18}H_{22}$ films on the gold substrate. The experiments were performed with the advanced technique IRRAS that provide high spectral quality. We investigated vibrational motions of PS and PS+$B_{18}H_{22}$ films and the effect of temperature on the change in IR spectra and the glass transition process. The purpose of all our studies in this field is to unlock the potential of borane clusters in electronics as they represent a new class of materials based neither on π- nor on σ- electron delocalization.

2. MATERIALS AND METHODS

Thin films were prepared from PS (M_w 350000, M_n 170000) purchased from Sigma-Aldrich and *anti*-$B_{18}H_{22}$ obtained from the Institute of Inorganic Chemistry of the Academy of Sciences of the Czech Republic by spin-coating from solution. Chloroform (HPLC) from J. T. Baker was used as a solvent. The concentration of the PS solution was 30 mg/mL, and the concentration of $B_{18}H_{22}$ solution was 0.4 mg/mL. Solutions were mixed and stirred until full dissolution to achieve the ratio of PS:$B_{18}H_{22}$ equal 75:1 in the final thin film.

Thin films were deposited on gold substrates with spin coater Laurell WS-650Mz-23NPPd. The spin rate was set to 1000 rpm and the substrate was spun for 30 s. After, substrates with deposited solutions were removed and placed to vacuum oven at 40 °C to enable solvent evaporation.

The thickness of the prepared PS and PS+$B_{18}H_{22}$ films was measured with profilometer Dektak XT-E (Bruker).

IRRAS spectra were collected with spectrometer Nicolet iN10/iZ10 (Thermo Scientific) with a heated chamber Refractor-Reactor (Harrick) that enables reflection-absorption measurement of thin layers. The chamber is equipped with ZnSe windows and provides the angle of incidence of 75°. The spectra were recorded with a polarizer set to maximize p-polarized radiation. Thin films were heated from room temperature to 140 °C with a rate of 2.6 °C/min and spectra were recorded with resolution 4 cm^{-1} and 16 scans. This setting enabled measurement of one spectrum per 1 °C of film heating, which eliminated adverse effects connected with spectrum measurement and simultaneous sample heating.

TGA and DSC analysis of PS pellet and *anti*-$B_{18}H_{22}$ powder was performed with Labsys Evo DTA/DSC instrument from Setaram. Measurement was set in the air with heating from 30 °C to 500 °C with a rate of 10 °C/min.

3. RESULTS AND DISCUSSION

Thin films of PS and PS+$B_{18}H_{22}$ were prepared in two series for (i) analyses of film thickness and (ii) IRRAS measurement. Thickness determination, as well as a surface visual check of thin films, was done with a mechanical profilometer and its digital camera with 100x zoom. Three repeated measurements were performed on different positions of the film surface. It was found that PS+$B_{18}H_{22}$ has a lower thickness of 290 nm if compared with the 450 nm PS thin film. This is probably caused by the presence of $B_{18}H_{22}$, which may act as a surfactant and change the properties of the spin-coated liquid layer. The surface of both films was smooth without significant differences between PS and PS+$B_{18}H_{22}$ samples. Both films surface evinced radial inhomogeneities which origin from the spin-coating process.

Further, IRRAS analysis was performed with both thin films. IR spectra were collected during film heating and after that spectral regions 3120 - 2985 cm^{-1}, 2975 - 2800 cm^{-1} and 2660 - 2500 cm^{-1} of C_{ar}-H stretching vibrations of phenyl rings, C-H stretching vibrations of aliphatic PS part and B-H stretching vibrations of *anti*-$B_{18}H_{22}$, respectively, were examined. Spectra were baseline corrected, and area (A_{range}) was calculated. **Figure 1** depicts the dependence of $A_{3120-2985}$ and $A_{2975-2800}$ on temperature. As can be seen from the graph on the left side of **Figure 1**, the area of C_{ar}-H stretching decreases with increasing temperature until the minimum is reached, then the trend is reversed and $A_{3120-2985}$ begins to grow. The temperature, which can be extracted at the minimum of this dependence, is assigned to the T_g of the thin film. The drop of region area can be explained by the fact that the density of thin films can decrease at a higher temperature and thus IR intensity of the region declines. On the other hand, the intensity of IR vibration increases as the free volume increases and segmental motion is enabled. The latter effect becomes to prevail at a temperature close to the T_g, which corresponds with the area minimum in the given plot. The T_g of PS thin film was therefore extracted to be 74 °C, while the T_g of PS+$B_{18}H_{22}$ was determined to be 77 °C. *Anti*-$B_{18}H_{22}$ does not influence the PS glass transition at a significant extent. However, both of these values are 31 - 34 °C lower than the T_g of bulk PS 108 °C that was determined with a standard DSC method. This result indicates that no strong interaction between the gold substrate surface and PS are present and that high M_w of PS does not increase the thin layer T_g above the bulk T_g [16,17].

The right part of **Figure 1** is dedicated to the temperature dependence of the aliphatic C-H stretching area. The clear difference between aromatic and aliphatic C-H stretching vibrations behaviour was found. The $A_{2975-2800}$ does not evince any abrupt changes with increasing temperature, and it decreases linearly in the whole temperature range. This spectral region is thus not affected by the glass transition of PS, and no transition temperature can be determined. The reason for this different course of the plot probably originates in the structure of PS. C_{ar}-H vibrations are definitely influenced with mutual positions of phenyl rings and related non-bonding interactions, while aliphatic CH_2 on PS backbone are not. Moreover, CH_2 cannot rotate. Glass transition process influences C_{ar}-H vibrations to a great extent, which gives the opportunity of the T_g detection.

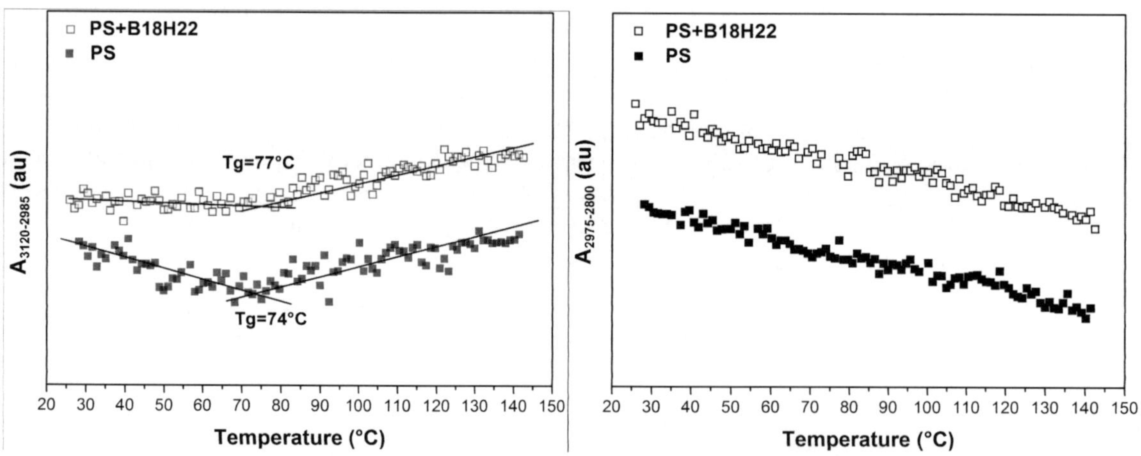

Figure 1 Area of C_{ar}-H (left) and C-H (right) stretching region plotted against temperature for PS and PS+$B_{18}H_{22}$ films

A surprising result was obtained from the detailed analysis of B-H stretching region that belongs to *anti*-$B_{18}H_{22}$ incorporated in PS+$B_{18}H_{22}$ thin film. It has been observed during the measurement that the intensity of the absorption band at 2585 cm^{-1} decreases at higher temperatures until it is undetectable. The area of this region vs. temperature is given in **Figure 2**. The region of temperature, in which the area decrease occurs is 77 - 91 °C. It is probably related to the T_g of PS thin film. As was stated above, the T_g was determined to 77 °C. Above this temperature, the *anti*-$B_{18}H_{22}$ molecules are not trapped in PS matrix anymore due to the release of segmental motions, and they start to migrate. This process might be joined with the sublimation of *anti*-$B_{18}H_{22}$ above 77 °C until it is fully released from the thin film.

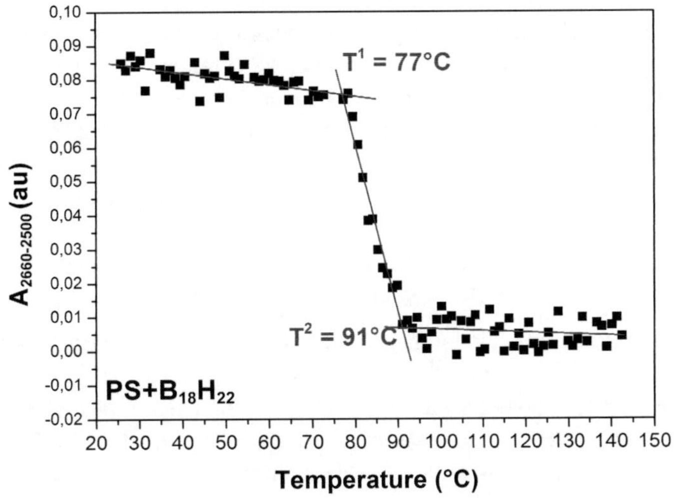

Figure 2 Area of B-H stretching region plotted against temperature for film PS+$B_{18}H_{22}$

To reveal the reason of the described release of *anti*-$B_{18}H_{22}$ from the thin film, TGA and DSC analysis of pure *anti*-$B_{18}H_{22}$ powder was performed in the air atmosphere to simulate similar conditions as in the case of IRRAS analysis. The curves are shown in **Figure 3**. A small weight loss of 2 % was detected at 75 °C on TGA curve and also heat flow decrease at 105 °C. This decrease in the TGA curve can be connected with sample moisture and its evaporation. It is a general fact that boranes are very sensitive to humidity, and thus thin films measured in the air atmosphere can suffer the same problem. However, there is observable a gradual decrease of the sample mass starting at about 120 °C while the main peak of *anti*-$B_{18}H_{22}$ melting is found at 180 °C in the DSC curve. It indicates the sublimation of the material. The mass loss step in the TGA curve smoothly continues with no disrupt change correlated with the *anti*-$B_{18}H_{22}$ melting, so the sublimation verges into evaporation and possible thermal degradation unnoticeably. Nevertheless, the effect of *anti*-$B_{18}H_{22}$ release from thin PS film needs to be explained yet, and the work on this issue continues.

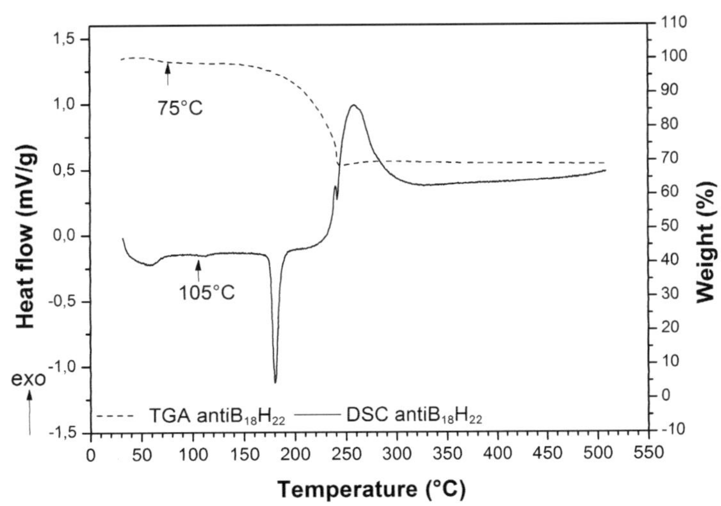

Figure 3 TGA and DSC curve of *anti*-$B_{18}H_{22}$ powder measured in the air

4. CONCLUSION

Thin films of PS and PS+$B_{18}H_{22}$ deposited on gold substrates were investigated with IRRAS analysis. IR spectra were used for the description of temperature influence on particular vibrational motions. We have focused on C_{ar}-H, C-H and B-H characteristic spectral regions and development of their area in dependence on temperature. It was found that vibrational motions respond to temperature increase differently. Whereas a clear turning point in the plot of area vs. temperature was detected for C_{ar}-H, only a slight continuous decrease of the C-H area was observed. This is probably caused by the effect of non-bonding interactions between phenyl rings that also influence vibrational motions and are more sensitive to temperature change. As a result, the determination of the T_g of PS thin film is enabled. An influence of *anti*-$B_{18}H_{22}$ presence on T_g of PS thin film was only marginal because the T_g of PS film was found to be 74 °C and T_g of PS+$B_{18}H_{22}$ 77 °C, which is 31 - 34 °C lower than T_g of bulk PS. As a result, different thin film T_g should always be considered if temperature demanding applications of polymer thin films are required.

During experiments, we also found that the intensity of the *anti*-$B_{18}H_{22}$ characteristic vibration decreases with increasing temperature (77 - 91 °C). *Anti*-$B_{18}H_{22}$ is not fixed firmly in the thin film structure and at higher temperatures, is not stable in the case of PS+$B_{18}H_{22}$ films. TGA and DSC analysis of pure *anti*-$B_{18}H_{22}$ powder revealed partial weight loss at 75 °C and heat flow decrease at 105 °C. This can be connected with the evaporation of humidity trapped in powder and a similar effect could act on the thin film. Another finding is that the T_g of PS+$B_{18}H_{22}$ thin film is identical with temperature, at which the B-H intensity decrease starts. It is possible that the glass transition triggers the migration and evolution of *anti*-$B_{18}H_{22}$ molecules from the film. However, the mechanism of *anti*-$B_{18}H_{22}$ release from thin PS film needs further investigation.

ACKNOWLEDGEMENTS

This work was supported by the grant from the Czech Science Foundation (Project No. 19-23513S).

The work was also supported by the Operational Program Research and Development for Innovations cofounded by the European Regional Development Fund (ERDF) and the national budget of the Czech Republic, within the framework of the project CPS - strengthening research capacity (reg. number: CZ.1.05/2.1.00/19.0409).

Michael Londesborough and Jonathan Bould from the Institute of Inorganic Chemistry of the Academy of Sciences of the Czech Republic are greatly acknowledged for synthesis and providing of anti-B18H22.

REFERENCES

[1] SKODA, D., URBANEK, P., SEVCIK, J. et al. Colloidal cobalt-doped ZnO nanoparticles by microwave-assisted synthesis and their utilization in thin composite layers with MEH-PPV as an electroluminescent material for polymer light emitting diodes. *Organic Electronics.* 2018, vol. 59, pp. 337-348.

[2] LONDESBOROUGH, M.G.S., HNYK, D., BOULD, J. et al. Distinct Photophysics of the Isomers of B18H22 Explained. *Inorganic Chemistry.* 2012, vol. 51, no. 3, pp. 1471-1479.

[3] PITOCHELLI, A.R. & HAWTHORNE, M.F. Preparation of a New Boron Hydride B18h22. *Journal of the American Chemical Society.* 1962, vol. 84, no. 16, p. 3218.

[4] LONDESBOROUGH, M.G.S., DOLANSKY, J., BOULD, J. et al. Effect of Iodination on the Photophysics of the Laser Borane anti-B18H22: Generation of Efficient Photosensitizers of Oxygen. *Inorganic Chemistry.* 2019, vol. 58, no. 15, pp. 10248-10259.

[5] LONDESBOROUGH, M.G.S., DOLANSKY, J., JELINEK, T. et al. Substitution of the laser borane anti-B18H22 with pyridine: a structural and photophysical study of some unusually structured macropolyhedral boron hydrides. *Dalton Transactions.* 2018, vol. 47, no. 5, pp. 1709-1725.

[6] SAURI, V., OLIVA, J.M., HNYK, D. et al. Tuning the Photophysical Properties of anti-B18H22: Efficient Intersystem Crossing between Excited Singlet and Triplet States in New 4,4 '-(HS)(2)-anti-B18H20. *Inorganic Chemistry.* 2013, vol. 52, no. 16, pp. 9266-9274.

[7] KEDDIE, J.L., JONES, R., & CORY, R.A. Interface and Surface Effects on the Glass-Transition Temperature in Thin Polymer-Films. *Faraday Discussions.* 1994, vol. 98, pp. 219-230.

[8] HANAKATA, P.Z., DOUGLAS, J.F., & STARR, F.W. Interfacial mobility scale determines the scale of collective motion and relaxation rate in polymer films. *Nature Communications.* 2014, vol. 5, pp. 4163.

[9] OLMOS, D., MARTIN, E.V., & GONZALEZ-BENITO, J. New molecular-scale information on polystyrene dynamics in PS and PS-BaTiO3 composites from FTIR spectroscopy. *Physical Chemistry Chemical Physics.* 2014, vol. 16, no. 44, pp. 24339-24349.

[10] SHIN, H.S., LEE, H., JUN, C.H. et al. Transition temperatures and molecular structures of poly(methyl methacrylate) thin films by principal component analysis: comparison of isotactic and syndiotactic poly(methyl methacrylate). *Vibrational Spectroscopy.* 2005, vol. 37, no. 1, pp. 69-76.

[11] DA SILVA, E.A., CASELI, L., & OLIVATI, C.d.A. Organization of polythiophenes at ultrathin films mixed with stearic acid investigated with polarization-modulation infrared reflection-absorption spectroscopy. *Colloids and Surfaces A-Physicochemical and Engineering Aspects.* 2017, vol. 529, pp. 628-633.

[12] TERASAKI, M., Khasanah, OZAKI, Y. et al. Study on phase separation in an ultra-thin poly(methyl methacrylate)/poly(4-vinyl phenol) film by infrared reflection absorption spectroscopy. *Polymer.* 2018, vol. 135, pp. 69-75.

[13] PENG, Y., LIU, Y., WU, Q. et al. Study on the Glass Transition Process of Polymer System Using Differential Scanning Calorimetry and Fourier Transform Infrared Spectroscopy. *Analytical Sciences.* 2017, *vol. 33,* no. 9, pp. 1071-1076.

[14] TRETINNIKOV, O.N. & OHTA, K. Conformation-sensitive infrared bands and conformational characteristics of stereoregular poly(methyl methacrylate)s by variable-temperature FTIR spectroscopy. *Macromolecules.* 2002, *vol. 35,* no. 19, pp. 7343-7353.

[15] ZHANG, Y., ZHANG, J.M., LU, Y.L. et al. Glass transition temperature determination of poly(ethylene terephthalate) thin films using reflection-absorption FTIR. *Macromolecules.* 2004, vol. 37, no. 7, pp. 2532-2537.

[16] MATTSSON, J., FORREST, J.A., & BORJESSON, L. Quantifying glass transition behavior in ultrathin free-standing polymer films. *Physical Review E.* 2000, vol. 62, no. 4, pp. 5187-5200.

[17] FORREST, J.A., DALNOKIVERESS, K., & DUTCHER, J.R. Interface and chain confinement effects on the glass transition temperature of thin polymer films. *Physical Review E.* 1997, vol. 56, no. 5, pp. 5705-5716.

STRUCTURAL AND MAGNETIC PROPERTIES OF FE-OXIDE LAYERS PREPARED BY INKJET PRINTING ON SI-SUBSTRATE

[1,2]Frantisek ZAZIMAL, [3]Tomas SVOBODA, [3]Petr DZIK, [1]Tomas HOMOLA, [2]Yvonna JIRASKOVA

[1]*Department of Physical Electronics, Faculty of Science, Masaryk University, Brno, Czech Republic, EU,* *zazimal@ipm.cz*

[2]*Institute of Physics of Materials, AS CR, Brno, Czech Republic, EU, jirasko@ipm.cz*

[3]*Brno University of Technology, Faculty of Chemistry, Brno, Czech Republic, EU*

https://doi.org/10.37904/nanocon.2020.3682

Abstract

Magnetic films with two, four, six, and eight layers were prepared using 2D inkjet printing on the 333 K heated Si-substrates at ambient conditions. The microstructure, phase composition of layers, and magnetic studies were investigated using wide spectrum of experimental methods with the aim to find the optimal conditions for producing magnetic sensors by digital printing technology in the near future. As the magnetic compound, the hematite powder was chosen and its milling with Si-binder dissolved in dowanol using glass balls and vial to prevent contamination was done to prepared suspension appropriate for printing. It is shown that hematite transformed markedly into maghemite, thus the layers consisted of small amount hematite and dominant maghemite phases determining the magnetic properties. From the viewpoint of magnetic behavior, the highest saturation magnetization and the lowest coercivity was obtained at the sample with 8 layers.

Keywords: Inkjet printing, hematite, physical properties, testing methods

1. INTRODUCTION

The reduction of materials scale leads to profound changes in their inner and surface microstructure and accompanying modification of their physical properties, e.g., electronic, optical, magnetic. In the case of magnetic nanoparticles, the miniaturization often means a deviation from the established laws governing the magnetic phenomena observed in bulk magnetic materials. The current research is oriented to preparation of magnetic nanoparticles using various technological procedures, to their microstructure at the nanometric scale, and to correlations between the microscopic and macroscopic properties. The usual and/or innovative experimental methods allow determination of anomalous or enhanced properties as giant magnetoresistance, coercivity, remanence and magnetocaloric effect enhancements and quantum tunneling of the magnetization, etc. This gives rise to enormous technological usage in, e.g., next generation of very high-density magnetic information storage devices, magnetic sensors, permanent magnets, biocompatible products, etc.

Development of 2D inkjet printing technology enabled to deposit thin layers of materials onto rigid and flexible surfaces. It presently attracts great interest predominantly in the prohexanolduction of low-cost and large-area electronic devices [1]. On the other hand, its usage in the production of magnetic devices is at the very beginning. Among pioneering works, the studies of the magnetic film prepared by a digital printing have to be mentioned. The magnetic film was prepared from the magnetite nanoparticles covered with oleic acid and investigated with the aim to realize magnetic cores for Radio Frequency Identification Resonators [2].

Present work concentrates on the possibility for the production of thin magnetic layer on Si-plate using 2D inkjet printing technology at the temperature slightly above room temperature under ambient atmosphere. The main aim is to produce films of different thickness and to characterize their structure and magnetic properties, and to predict the optimal conditions of production in relation to physical properties for future application in magnetic sensors.

2. EXPERIMENTAL DETAILS

As an input magnetic material, the commercial hematite nanoparticles of dimension < 50 nm (Sigma-Aldrich, Steinheim, Germany) was used. The hematite nanoparticles dispersed in dowanol were initially milled with polysiloxane binder dissolved in absolute ethanol [3] using balls in vial; both made of glass to prevent contamination. The aim was to decrease the particle size and to obtain the acceptable suspension. Prior printing on the 333 K heated Si-substrate at ambient conditions the suspension was in addition dilluted with hexanol. The Si-wafers of different size, corresponding to demands of the subsequently applied experimental methods, were prepared by cutting Si-wafers (100) using spark erosion. The smallest dimension 2.5 mm x 2.5 mm was used for magnetic measurements, the larger ones, 10 mm x 10 mm, for scanning electron microscopic observations (SEM), X-ray diffraction (XRD), and Mössbauer (MS) measurements.

2D inkjet printing equipment Dimatix Materials Printer DMP-2850 was used for the formation of iron-oxide layers of different thickness; two, four, six, and eight layers (L) were chosen and in conformity with it the samples were denoted 2L, 4L, 6L, and 8L. The approximate thickness of layers was determined using profilometer Dektak XT, Bruker.

The morphology of samples was followed by scanning electron microscope MIRA3 (Tescan, Brno) at accelerating voltage of 30 kV.

X-ray diffraction patterns were measured at room temperature (RT) using an EMPYREAN diffractometer (Panalytical) with Co Kα radiation (λ = 0.17902 nm) in the 2θ range from 15° to 130° in steps of 0.026° and time per step ≈400 s. The evaluation of powder patterns was realized by the Rietveld structure refinement method [4] by semi-automatic mode using the HighScore Plus program and the ICSD database of inorganic and related structures [5]. The phase composition and the lattice parameters were obtained from the pattern analysis.

^{57}Fe Mössbauer spectra at room temperature were taken in the transmission geometry using γ-rays and scattering geometry by detecting 7.3 keV conversion electrons (CEMS, [6]) with penetration depth of about 200 nm. Obtained spectra were analyzed using CONFIT program package [7] and calibration of velocity scale was done by a standard thin *α*-iron foil at RT. The transmission geometry was used for measurement of the hematite-suspension soaked in cellulose. Scattering geometry was applied for measurements of the final 2L and 8L samples.

The magnetic measurements were performed using a Physical Property Measurement System (PPMS) Quantum design, Inc. The hysteresis curves were taken at 300 K and 2 K in magnetic field of ± 800 kA/m. The zero field-cooled (ZFC) and field-cooled (FC) curves were measured between 2 K and 300 K in magnetic field of 8 kA/m.

3. RESULTS AND DISCUSSION

3.1. Sample characterization

The scanning electron microscope images from all studied samples appear very similarly without any dependence on the layer thickness, as shown in **Figure 1** representing the 8L (a) and 2L (b) samples. The thickness obtained from profilometry scans (not shown here) linearly increased from approximately 2.2 µm for the 2L sample to 7.5 µm for the 8L sample. The surfaces of all samples yield small agglomerated nanoparticles of size below 50 nm. The top layers are not fully homogeneous and, in some spots, the pores of dimensions between 50 nm and 300 nm can be observed. While in a case of the 8L sample the sub-layers are visible, the similar small pores observed at the 2L sample often detect the Si-substrate.

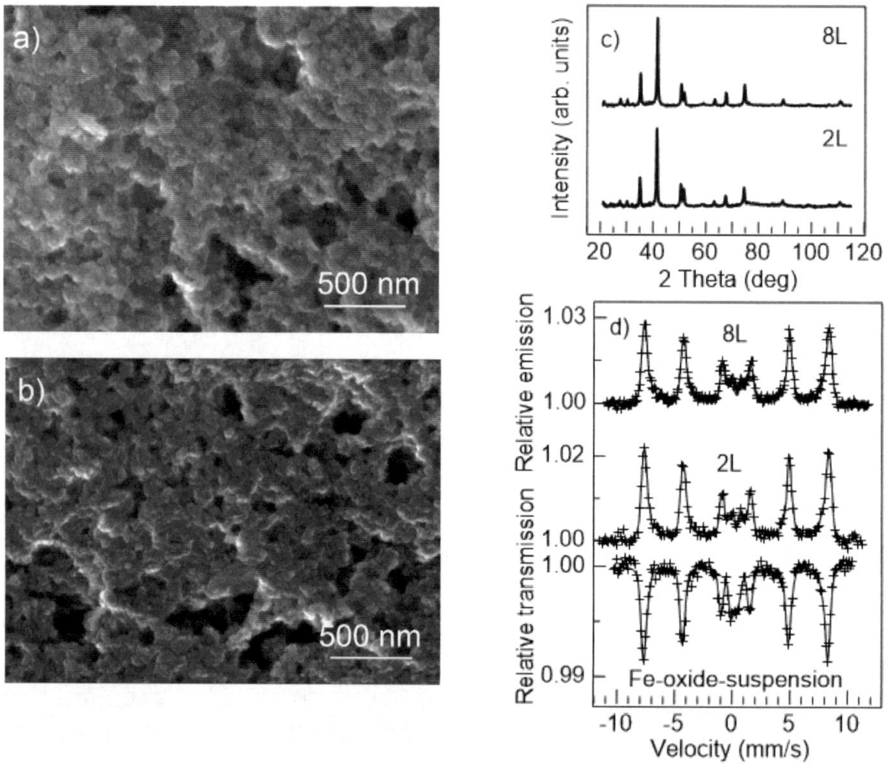

Figure 1 Scanning electron microscope images of the 8L (a) and 2L (b) samples, powder X-ray diffractograms (c) and Mössbauer spectra (d) of the selected samples

The X-ray diffraction measurements of all samples resulted in very similar patterns and therefore only those for the 2L and 8L are depicted in **Figure 1 (c)** as representatives. The diffractograms analysis resulted in a presence of dominant magnetite/maghemite and only minor content of hematite. This stimulated the Mössbauer measurements of the hematite suspension using transmission geometry and of the 2L and 8L samples using scattering geometry. The spectra are depicted in **Figure 1 (d)** and the results followed from experimental data analysis of both methods are summarized in **Tables 1** and **2,** respectively.

Table 1 Phase analysis of X-ray diffractograms; *A* - phase content, *a*, *b*, *c* - lattice parameters

	hematite		**maghemite**	
	***A* (wt%)**	***a* = *b*, *c* (nm)**	***A* (wt%)**	***a* (nm)**
2L	2.5	0.5033(6), 1.3689(20)	97.5	0.8346(6)
4L	5.7	0.5037(9), 1.3926(38)	94.3	0.8336(4)
6L	6.0	0.5038(6), 1.3669(22)	94.0	0.8336(6)
8L	4.4	0.5036(6), 1.3709(23)	95.6	0.8350(9)

Hematite is a common iron oxide with a formula of α-Fe_2O_3. It was supposed to be the initial iron-oxide for the present studies; however, the XRD measurements have shown dominant maghemite phase. It is well known that hematite is highly sensitive to various effects; e.g., pressure, external magnetic field, structural defects, impurities, and grain size, influencing its physical properties. For its determination in measured diffractograms the ICSD 15840 sheet with input values of the lattice parameter, $a = b = 0.5038$ nm and $c = 1.3772$ nm, was used. As it follows from **Table 1** its content in all samples is low, which reflects its partial transformation into dominant magnetite/maghemite phase. It could be very probably caused by induced stresses during milling in a process of the iron-oxide suspension preparation. The magnetite, Fe_3O_4, is crystallographically isomorphous with maghemite, γ-Fe_2O_3, and both these iron-oxides have cubic structure of similar lattice parameters. Therefore, their determination from diffractogram is not straightforward. For the Rietveld analysis the ICSD data sheets 26410 for magnetite (a = 0.83941 nm) and 172905 for maghemite (a = 0.84058 nm) were used. The resulted values of lattice parameters of both phases did not allow to distinguish between magnetite and maghemite unambiguously. Therefore, the values in **Table 1** correspond to weighted mean average.

Table 2 Mössbauer characteristics deduced from the transmission spectrum of the input iron-oxide-suspension and conversion scattering spectra of the 2L and 8L samples; A - phase content, B - hyperfine induction, δ - isomer shift, and Δ - quadrupole shift

Sample	hematite				maghemite				superparamagnetic		
	A (%)	**B (T)**	**δ (mm/s)**	**Δ (mm/s)**	**A (%)**	**B (T)**	**δ (mm/s)**	**Δ (mm/s)**	**A (%)**	**δ (mm/s)**	**Δ (mm/s)**
Iron-oxide suspension	10.3	50.5	0.359	-0.183	75.9	49.1	0.257	0.027	13.8	0.179	0.553
2L	7.6	51.5	0.396	-0.143	87.3	43.9	0.335	0.008	5.1	0.384	0.813
8L	10.1	51.3	0.412	-0.164	79.8	48.1	0.331	0.011	10.1	0.372	1.162

^{57}Fe Mössbauer spectra recorded at RT were analysed using a conventional least-square refinement method with combination of sextets and doublets of Lorentzian lines. The results shown in **Table 2** reflect about 10 % of hematite in the input iron-oxide-suspension represented by sextet of hyperfine parameters, isomer shift and quadrupole splitting, in good agreement with Ref. [9]. The rest is ascribed to magnetically ordered maghemite which documents hematite transformation owing to milling. This confirms the XRD observations and it is supported by Randrianantoandro and co-workers [10] reporting direct phase transformation from hematite to maghemite during high energy ball milling. The doublets in the middle of spectrum can be ascribed to superparamagnetic (SP) portion of iron-oxides in a form of very small nano-grains (<10 nm). Slightly lower content of this component was detected also in scattering spectra taken from the 2L and 8L samples in which dominant component was again maghemite. The values of hyperfine induction of hematite correspond to literature but those of maghemite, mainly at the 2L sample, are lower. It could be due to slight distortion of crystallographic sites mainly at the particle surfaces and insufficient energy needed for the lattice formation and vacancies reordering. For more detailed analysis, the Mössbauer measurements at low-temperature and, eventually, in an external magnetic field should be helpful.

3.2. Magnetic results

The nearly square hysteresis loops of all samples measured at room and low temperatures are shown in **Figure 2.** The changes of magnetic characteristic, saturation and remnant mass magnetizations M_s and M_r and coercivity H_c, in dependence on number of layers are presented in **Figure 3.** The mean values of the coercivity H_c and remnant magnetization M_r were obtained from the polynomial fitting of hysteresis loops between -60 and 60 kA/m and M_s was calculated from both branches in saturation (above ≈ 700 kA/m). The experimental points were fitted by linear functions (dashed lines) better to see tendency of parameter changes. The dependences (**Figure 3**) reveal that increasing number of layers (film thickness) leads to an increase of the saturation and remnant magnetizations at both measuring temperatures while the H_c embodies an opposite tendency. Such behaviour is not general. For example, in Permalloy film study is the behaviour of magnetic characteristics different bellow and above estimated critical thickness [8]. For the 8L sample the saturation mass magnetization is slightly lower compared to values (60-80 Am^2/kg) presented for maghemite in literature (e.g. [9]) probably due to influence of the low RT saturation magnetization of weakly ferromagnetic hematite (≈ 0.3 Am^2/kg, [9]) and reasons mentioned above in discussion of Mössbauer results.

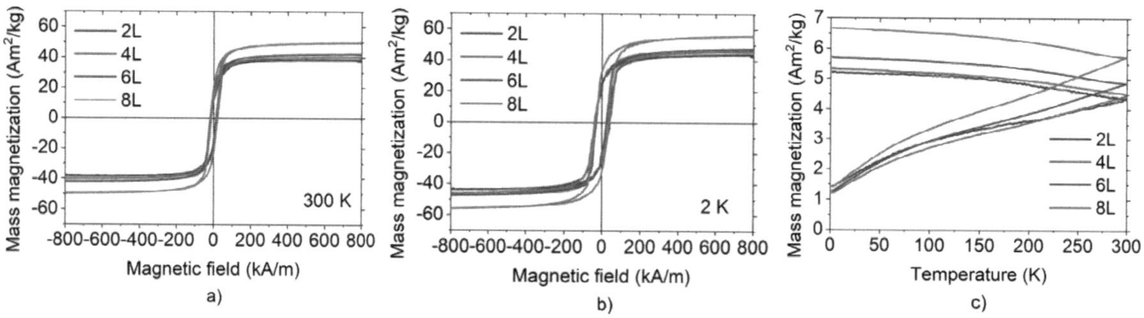

Figure 2 Hysteresis loops of 2L, 4L, 6L and 8L samples measured at 300 K (a) and 2 K (b); zFC-FC curves (c)

The H_c and M_r dependences on number of layers are not so unique compared to M_s due to their high structural sensitivity. The ZFC and FC curves for all samples in **Figure 3c** are similar. In agreement with XRD and MS observations they do not provide any sign of Morin temperature being for hematite 260 K or lower in dependence on particle size.

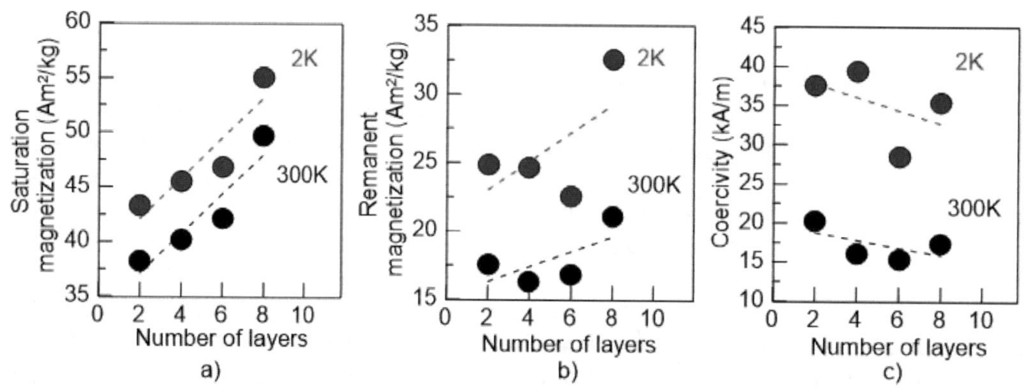

Figure 3 Dependences of saturation magnetization (a), remnant magnetization (b) and coercivity (c) on number of layers taken from hysteresis loops measured at 2 K and 300 K

4. CONCLUSION

The present investigations were devoted to application of the 2D inkjet printing procedure in preparation of magnetic film on the Si-substrate. The hematite powder dispersed in dowanol and mixed with siloxane binder dissolved in absolute ethanol was milled using glass balls and vial with the aim to form suspension applicable for digital printing. The samples with two, four, six, and eight laeyrs of magnetic film were produced and investigated with numerous experimental methods. The scanning electron microscope observations yielded very similar microstructure formed by particles of size below 50 nm and their agglomerations among them sometimes the pores were visible. These pores detected the Si substrate at the two-layers sample while at the eight-layers sample the bellow laying particles were seen in the pores. It means that cross-sectional homogeneity was not quite satisfactory. The analysis of the X-ray diffraction patterns suppored by Mössbauer phase analysis has found dominant magnetite/maghemite phase and only small amount of the initial hematite in layers of all sample. This transformation of hematite into magnetite/maghemite was found to be initiated during milling in procedure of the suspension preparation. This was subsequently confirmed by high values of saturation magnetization and the measurements of the ZFC-FC curves at which no Morin transition, characteristic for hematite, was observed. From the magnetic viewpoint, the highest saturation magnetization and the lowest coercivity was at the sample with 8 layers.

ACKNOWLEDGEMENTS

This research has been supported by GACR project 19-14770Y and by CEITEC 2020-National Sustainability Programme II, No. LQ1601. The authors thank M. Hapla from IPM Brno for his help with magnetic measurements and M. Filipska from BUT Brno for the profilometry measurements.

REFERENCES

[1] CHIOLERIO, A., MACCIONI, G., MARTINO, P., COTTO, M., PANDOLFI, P., RIVOLO, P., FERRERO, S., SCALTRITO, L. Inkjet printing and low power laser annealing of silver nanoparticle traces for the realization of low resistivity lines for flexible electronics. *Microelectronic Engineering.* 2011, vol. 88, pp.2481-2483.

[2] MARJANOVIĆ, M. N., CHIOLERIO, A., KUS, M., OZEL, F., TILKI, S., IVANOVIĆ, N., RAKOČEVIĆ, Z., ANDRIĆ, V., BARUDŽIJA, T., BAUMANN, R.R. Magnetite nanoparticles: Synthesis, thin film properties and inkjet printing of magnetic cores for inductor applications. *Thin Solid Films.* 2014, vol. 570, pp. 38-44.

[3] HOMOLA, T., ĎURAŠOVÁ, Z., SHEKARGOFTAR, M., SOUČEK, P., DZIK, P. Optimization of TiO2 Mesoporous Photoanodes Prepared by Inkjet Printing and Low-Temperature Plasma Processing. *Plasma Chemistry and Plasma Processing.* 2020, vol. 40, pp. 1311-1330.

[4] YOUNG, R. A. (ed.). *The Rietveld Method.* International Union of Crystallography Oxford University Press Oxford, 1993.

[5] ICSD Database, Version 1.9.4., 2014--1, NIST/FIZ.

[6] GRUVERMANN, I.J. (ed.). *Mössbauer effect Methodology.* In: SPIJKERMANN, J.J., *Conversion Electron Spectroscopy*, 1978, Vol. 7, p. 85.

[7] ZAK, T., JIRASKOVA, Y. CONFIT : Mössbauer spectra fitting program. *Surface and Interface Analysis.* 2006, vol. 38, pp. 710-714.

[8] YOUSSEF, J. B., VUKADINOVIC, N. Thickness-dependent magnetic excitations in Permalloy films with nonuniform magnetization. *Physical Review.* 2004, vol. B69, no. 17, p. 174402.

[9] CORNELL, R.M., SCHWERTMANN, U. *The iron oxides.* Weinheim, 1996.

[10] RANDRIANANTOANDRO, N., MERCIER, A.M., HERVEU, M., GRENECHE, J.M. Direct phase transformation from hematite to maghemite during high energy ball milling. *Materials Letters.* 2001, vol. 47, pp. 150-158.

THE TEMPERATURE DEPENDENCE OF THE PHOTOLUMINESCENCE STABILITY OF OCTADECABORANE IN POLYSTYRENE MATRIX THIN FILMS

[1]Pavel URBÁNEK, [1]Jakub ŠEVČÍK, [1]Barbora HANULÍKOVÁ, [1]Tereza ČAPKOVÁ, [1]Jan ANTOŠ, [1]Michal URBÁNEK, [1]Ivo KUŘITKA

[1]Tomas Bata University in Zlín, University Institute, Centre of Polymer Systems, Zlín, Czech Republic, EU, urbanek@utb.cz

https://doi.org/10.37904/nanocon.2020.3686

Abstract

The novel boron-hydride cluster compound (*anti*-$B_{18}H_{22}$) has been recently introduced as potential laser dye and interesting molecule for organic electronics. Blue light-emitting devices or photoluminescence (PL) sensors will be highly desirable. Nevertheless, the issue of their temperature stability may be critical for the use of this compound family as active molecules or at least fluorescence labels for any application. This contribution deals with the preparation and characterization of borane-polystyrene blend thin films. The influence of thermal history on the emission properties of prepared films was investigated. Based on the performed study, a set of critical limits and implications for the future molecular design was defined.

Keywords: Boron-hydride, polymer blend, thin film, temperature, stability

1. INTRODUCTION

Organic light-emitting device (OLED) technology passed through a huge development rapidly over the last decade after overcoming some technical problems with material stability, low brightness, and bad processability. Nowadays, there exists a wide group of new materials, such as novel organic emitters, conductive polymers that combine good workability and good physical properties resulting in good stability, good external quantum efficiency, and high brightness. Thus, OLED technology is currently widely used in various displays such as laptops, Smartphones, TV, and wearable devices [1], [2]. Despite the great progress that has been made in this field, some challenges still remain. The broad and asymmetric emission spectrum of OLEDs is a serious general issue that can play a negative role in the color rendering index. Another issue is the relatively low stability of available blue emitters, which can limit the long-term use of prepared devices [3]. Synthesis of novel material based on boron clusters [4] opens new possibilities on how to achieve blue emission with high brightness. This kind of material brings good solubility in common solvents and thus good workability. It is possible to also prepare thin film structures and furthermore, thin-film devices. Moreover, this material has also a relatively sharp emission band in comparison to e.g. emitting polymers. Up to the present time, achieved results provide further evidence of the potential of macropolyhedral borane systems as a useful alternative molecular components in the fabrication of luminescent devices [5,6]. On the other hand, the thermal and luminescence stability are key properties for the utilization of this novel material but still, they have not been studied.

In this contribution, we present the study of photoluminescence stability of novel boron-hydride clusters *anti*-$B_{18}H_{22}$ incorporated in a polymer matrix on the temperature. And here, the key question comes: Can the borane *anti*-$B_{18}H_{22}$ be a suitable material for light emitting devices? We believe that this study can at least partly contribute to the solution of the critical limits of novel material and can imply the future molecular design of this material group in practical use.

2. EXPERIMENTAL

2.1. Sample preparation

A series of spin-coated thin films were prepared from solutions of polystyrene (PS, Sigma Aldrich average M_w - 350 000, M_n - 170 00) in toluene, HPLC quality, purchased from J.T. Baker with incorporated borohydride molecules, *anti*-$B_{18}H_{22}$ - (M_w = 216,58 g.mol^{-1}) was synthesized at the Institute of Inorganic Chemistry of the AS CR. All solvents were stored over molecular sieves in the glovebox. The polymer/borane blend solutions were cast onto quartz glass substrates using spin coater Laurell WS-650-MZ-23NPP at a rotation speed of 1000 rpm. The whole sample preparation was performed in an inert atmosphere in the glove box.

2.2. Instrumentation and sample thermal stability test

The PL spectra and PL decays were taken by fluorimeter FLS920 in the air and a vacuum atmosphere (pressure 1 Pa) ensured by the cryostat Optistat DN-V (LN2), Oxford Instruments at room temperature. The thickness of films, measured by a mechanical profilometry Dektak XT-E and (Bruker) with a 1 nm resolution. Variable-angle spectroscopic ellipsometry UVISEL 2 (Horiba) with a spectral range from 180 nm to 2200 nm and a resolution higher than 0.5 nm was used to determine optical constants and changes in polarization angles and their wavelength dependence. The data was then used to calculate the film thickness using Delta Psi V2 software. The UV-VIS-NIR spectra were carried out by double-beam spectrophotometer Lambda 1050, Perkin Elmer. The instrument is equipped with double-monochromator and detectors with photometric range 8 A in all UV, VIS and NIR regions. The samples were individually heated in a vacuum oven up to the temperature 50, 60, 70, 80, and 90 °C with a temperature growth rate 2.6 °C/min. After the achievement of the maximum temperature, the sample was annealed for 10 min and then left to cool freely in the vacuum chamber.

3. RESULTS AND DISCUSSION

UV-VIS spectroscopy was used for the evaluation of absorbance characteristics of the prepared thin films. In **Figure 1** - left, the ultraviolet-visible absorption spectra of prepared thin films are depicted. The absorption spectrum of *anti*-$B_{18}H_{22}$ is characterized by two broad bands at 285 and 340 nm. Polystyrene is a suitable matrix for the preparation of thin films with borane additives because of its absorption edge, which is situated at about 275 nm and does not interfere the spectral features of borane molecules providing thus a sufficient spectral window. In the right part of **Figure 1**, the picture of real samples under UV illumination is presented.

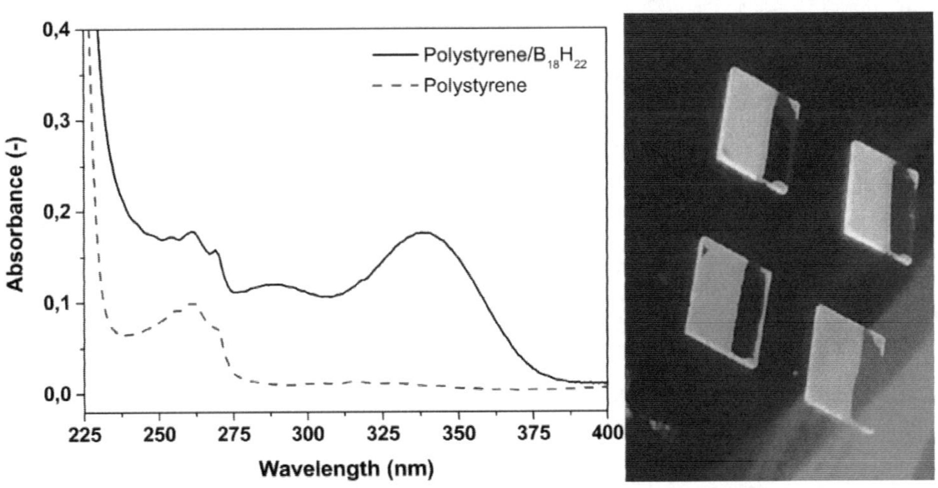

Figure 1 Absorption spectra films made of neat polymers and polymer/borane blend - left and luminescence of polymer/borane blend samples under UV lamp irradiation - right

Excitation (left) and emission (right) photoluminescence (PL) spectra of prepared thin films are depicted in **Figure 2**. The excitation spectra reveal that the maximum PL intensity emitted at 408 nm is achieved if the excitation wavelength of 340 nm is selected. In the graphs in **Figure 2**, we can observe the PL intensity decay with increasing temperature. The sample prepared at 25 °C serves as the first reference point without any temperature load history. From the data obtained, it is clear that the PL of the borane material is relatively stable until the samples have been exposed to temperatures higher than 60 °C.

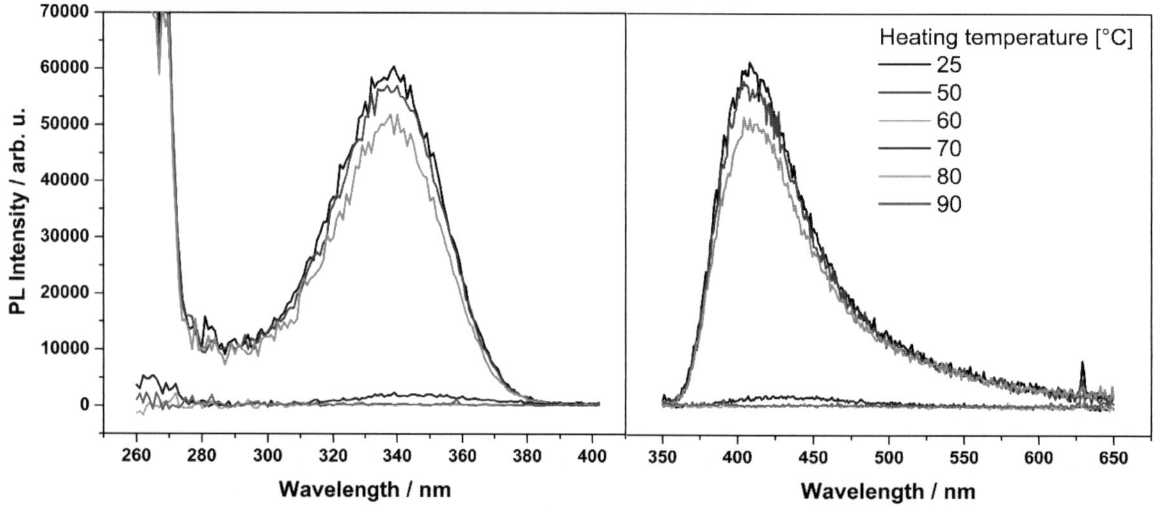

Figure 2 Excitation (left), λ_{em} = 408 nm, and emission (right), λ_{ex} = 340 nm, photoluminescence spectra of prepared thin films

The dependence of PL intensity on the heating temperature is depicted in **Figure 3**, left. The PL intensity decays slowly down to about 85 % of its initial value with increasing temperature up to 60 °C. Then, the PL intensity steeply decreases to approximately 2 % of its initial value at higher temperature.

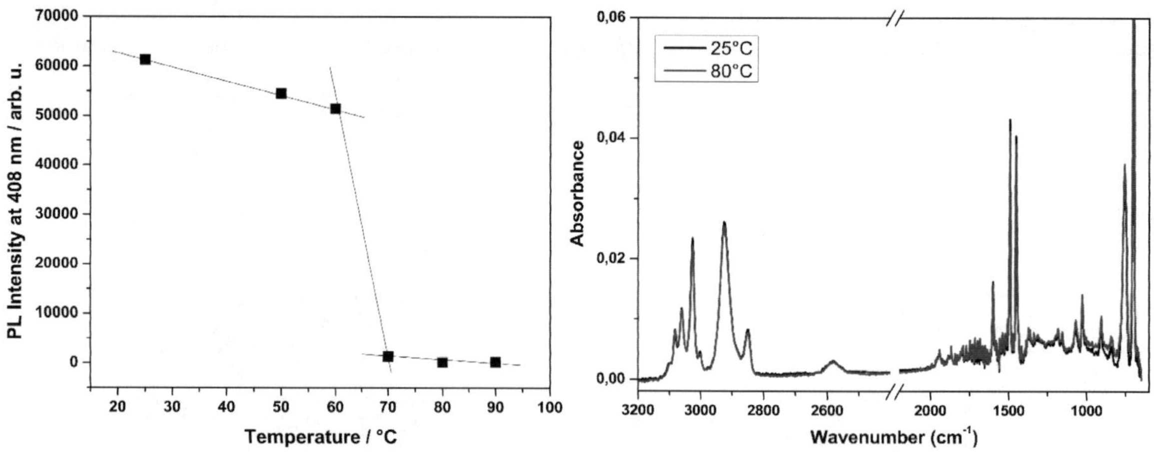

Figure 3 PL intensity dependence on the heating temperature of samples (left) and representative FTIR spectra of samples

Based on such a steep decrease of PL intensity, one could adumbrate that the borane molecules disappeared from the films. Nevertheless, the borane stayed in the polymer matrix as verified by FTIR spectra shown in **Figure 3** right. The presence of a typical borane absorption band situated below 2600 cm^{-1} in spectra of films heated at 80 °C confirmed the presence of borane. Then, observed PL decay shall be discussed in terms of temperature quenching. From the utilization of borane as an emitting material point of view, such behavior is undesired because the operating temperature of PLED devices may attain temperature higher than 60 °C. Under such operation conditions, no luminescence from borane could be expected. On the other hand, such behaviour is suitable for polymer labeling when the thermal history of the material needs to be indicated [7]. If the boranes should be still considered as active materials for blue-emitting diodes, a stabilization strategy must be developed. Among others, the anchoring of stabilizing side substituents on the borane cage skeleton seems to be a suitable way. For example, the recently published extensive methylation increases the stability of these compounds significantly [8].

4. CONCLUSION

To summarize, we investigated the photoluminescence stability of the borane cluster incorporated in the polymer matrix. We studied the dependence of its photoluminescence on the temperature. We revealed that the PL of *anti*-$B_{18}H_{22}$ is relatively stable in the polystyrene matrix heated until 60 °C. For temperatures below this value, the PL intensity decays only by about 15 %. For temperatures higher than 60 °C, the PL intensity rapidly decreases. The change in PL is irreversible. It seems to be more favorable to use substituted borane if it is intended as active material in light-emitting diodes. Nevertheless, the reported PL instability may be considered for application in polymer labeling.

ACKNOWLEDGEMENTS

The work was supported by the grant from the Czech Science Foundation (Project No. 19-23513S).

This work was also supported by the Operational Program Research and Development for Innovations cofounded by the European Regional Development Fund (ERDF) and the national budget of the Czech Republic, within the framework of the project CPS - strengthening research capacity (reg. number: CZ.1.05/2.1.00/19.0409).

The authors acknowledge to Michael Londesborough and Jonathan Bould from the Institute of Inorganic Chemistry of the Academy of Sciences of the Czech Republic for providing of the borane material.

REFERENCES

[1] BRÜTTING, W., FRISCHEISEN, J. ö, et al. Device efficiency of organic light-emitting diodes: Progress by improved light outcoupling. *Physica Status Solidi*. 2013, vol. 210, pp. 44-65.

[2] YANG, Z., GAO, M., et al. Recent advances in quantum dot-based light-emitting devices: Challenges and possible solutions. *Materials Today*. 2019, vol. 24, pp. 69-93.

[3] LEE, H., MAENG, M., et al. Highly efficient green, blue, and white phosphorescent inverted organic light-emitting diodes by improving charge injection and balance. *Journal of Materials Chemistry C*. 2017, vol. 5, pp. 9911-9919.

[4] COOKE, P. A., O'DOWD, C., et al. B-frame supported bimetallics. 'composite cluster' compounds and the structures of [2,7-(eta(5)-C5Me5)(2)-nido-2,7,8,6-Ir2CSB6H8] and its 9-chloro derivative. synchrotron and conventional X-ray studies. *Journal of Organometallic Chemistry*. 2000, vol. 614, pp. 57-60.

[5] CERDAN, L., BRABOREC, J., et al. A borane laser. *Nature Communications*. 2015, vol. 6, no. 5958.

[6] AXTELL, J. C., SALEH, L. M. A., et al. Synthesis and applications of perfunctionalized boron clusters. *Inorganic Chemistry*. 2018, vol. 57, pp. 2333-2350.

[7] KUŘITKA, I., SEDLAŘÍK, V., et al. Polymer labelling with a conjugated polymer-based luminescence probe for recycling in the circular economy. 2020, vol. 12, pp. 1226.

[8] LONDESBOROUGH, M. G. S., LANG, K., et al. Swollen polyhedral volume of the anti-$B_{18}H_{22}$ cluster via extensive methylation: Anti-$B_{18}H_8cl_2me_{12}$. *Inorganic Chemistry*. 2020, vol. 59, pp. 2651-2654.

POLYMER CHAIN ORDERING MANIFESTATION IN PHOTOLUMINESCENCE OF THIN F8BT FILMS

Bita GHASEMI, Jakub SEVCIK, Pavel URBANEK, Ivo KURITKA

Tomas Bata University in Zlín, University Institute, Centre of Polymer Systems, Zlín, Czech Republic, EU, ghasemi@utb.cz

https://doi.org/10.37904/nanocon.2020.3687

Abstract

Poly(9,9-dioctyfluorene-alt-benzothiadiazole), F8BT, thin films were successfully deposited using spin coating and drop-casting methods on glass and silicon substrates. Films with thicknesses varying from tens to hundreds of nanometers were obtained as a result of variation in the deposition conditions, such as concentration or coating methods. The trends in manifestations of 0-0 and 0-1 vibronic transitions in UV-VIS absorption and photoluminescence (PL) spectra correlate with the thickness of the thin films. A threshold in the intensity ratio of the two transitions was observed at the thin film thickness about 250 nm. The observed spectral features are interpreted in terms of the competitive effects of J- and H- aggregation of the macromolecular chains.

Keywords: F8BT, thin films, chain ordering, J- and H-aggregates, photoluminescence

1. INTRODUCTION

The possibility of processing the conjugated polymers to form useful and potent structure is the main advantage of polymeric organic semiconductors over non-polymeric organic semiconductors [1,2]. Conjugated polymers with various structures have been used in light-emitting diodes, photovoltaic cells, laser, and field-effect transistors mainly due to their absorption and electroluminescence feature. An important class of conjugated polymers are polyfluorenes that have attracted noticeable attention on the basis of their ease of spin coating or drop casting, and their ability to tune a wide range of optical and electronic properties. Poly(9,9-di-noctylfluorene-alt-benzothiadiazole) (F8BT) is a yellowish-green light emitting copolymer with a high luminescence quantum yield (60-80%), relatively high electron affinity, and large ionization potential which plays an important role as a host with electron transport [3-5]. According to previous reports on charge carrier mobilities and the time-of-flight studies on F8BT; however, the electron transport is dispersive, it is still the fastest charge carriers with mobility (10^{-3} cm^2 V^{-1} s^{-1}). Charge and energy transport in soft organic assemblies can be understood properly by considering the intermolecular (excitonic) coupling and electron-vibrational coupling using the concepts of H-and J-aggregation. Electronic interactions that occur either within a given chain or between chains stem from the aggregates of the conjugated polymer. J-aggregates (H-aggregates) occur when "head-to-tail" (side-by-side) orientations dominate. According to Kasha's work on the effect of molecular aggregation on the optical response, in J-aggregates (H-aggregates) the couplings are negative (positive), resulting in a spectral red shift (blue shift). But distinguishing these two aggregate types using the usual spectral shifts can be misleading. In case of poly(3-hexylthiophene) (P3HT), despite its H-aggregate nature, there is a considerable red shift which is attributed to improvement in intrachain planarization. The obtained information about the exciton bandwidth, the nature of disorder, and the exciton coherence length from the changes in the vibronic line strengths as a result of interaction are more distinguishing traits between these two types of aggregates [6-8]. Film thickness can impact on the microstructure of the thin conjugated polymer film and photoluminescence because of the various levels of manifestation of nonlocalized (aggregate states) and localized(intrachain) transitions. With increase of the thickness to some extent more ordered structure can be achieved and there is a thickness threshold in which the mesoscale (between nano-and micro-dimensions) effects such as self-healing mechanism will be revealed [10,11]. The effect of film thickness on optoelectrical properties and the correlation between the thickness and vibronic transition manifestations are presented in this study.

2. EXPERIMENTAL PROCEDURES AND DETAILS

Poly(9,9-dioctyfluorene-alt-benzothiadiazole), F8BT materials and toluene (p.a.) were purchased from Sigma-Aldrich and PENTA Czech Republic respectively and used without further purification. F8BT films were spin cast from toluene solutions with concentration ranging from 0.5%-3.0% to provide films with thicknesses varying from tens to hundreds of nanometers. To obtain films with thickness higher than 200 nm, F8BT solutions with 1.5% and 3.0% concentrations were drop cast onto the prepared substrates. All substrates were cleaned by successive 12 min sonication in distilled water plus hellmanex, acetone and isopropyl alcohol, followed by UV ozone treatment for 10 min. After deposition, the films were dried in vacuum furnace in 150 °C for 1 hour. The UV-Vis absorption spectra were recorded on a Perkin-Elmer Lambda 1050 Spectrometer. Fluorimeter FSL 920 from Edinburgh Instruments was used for the measuring of PL spectra. The thickness was measured by mechanical profilometer with 1 nm resolution (Bruker). The thickness of the F8BT films are shown in **Table 1.**

Table 1 Thickness of prepared F8BT films

	Concentration (%W)				
	0.5 %	**1.0 %**	**1.5 %**	**2.0 %**	**3.0 %**
Spin speed	**Thickness (nm)**				
1000 rpm	25	45	75	120	165
2000 rpm	20	27	47	75	118
3000 rpm	13	30	45	55	85
4000 rpm	10	30	45	60	105
5000 rpm	10	23	45	60	95

3. RESULTS AND DISCUSSION

3.1. UV-Vis spectroscopy

The UV-Vis spectra of F8BT films with different thicknesses are depicted in **Figure 1**. It can be noted from the graph the main absorption peak is observed at 460 nm. With an increase of thickness the absorption spectra show a tiny blue shift of maxima approximately 5 nm and the bands are broadened with increasing thickness. This may indicate the formation of a new energy state due to interchain aggregate states between polymer chains resulting in broadening of the absorption band [4]. On the other hand, one can expect that the formation of H-aggregates, which are more favored in thicker films, broadens the absorption spectra toward longer wavelengths. This contradiction can be

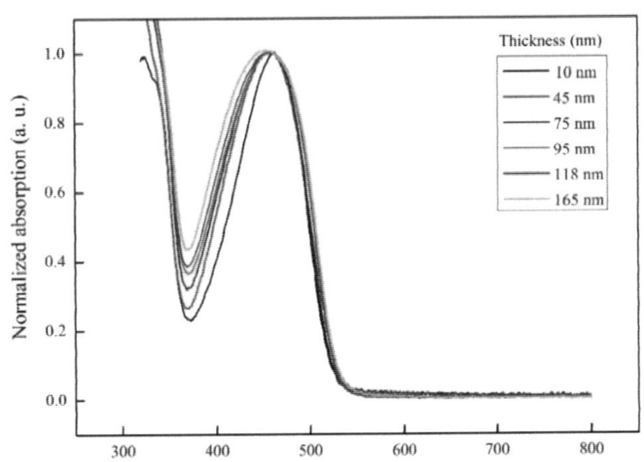

Figure 1 UV-Vis spectra of F8BT with different thicknesses on glass substrates

explained by JH-aggregates creation, where the interplay of these two aggregation modes results in the broadening toward higher energies. Similar explanation is introduced in [4], where it is described as alternating π-stacking of polymer chains.

3.2. Photoluminescence (PL) spectroscopy

The representative room temperature photoluminescence (PL) spectra of F8BT films are illustrated in **Figure 2.** From the graph, it can be seen that 0-0 peak is slightly red-shifted with increasing thickness. The spectral intensity for the second peak 0-1 relatively increases with increasing thickness. The 0-0 PL transition of the thinnest film is situated at 537 nm. For the thicker films up to 200 nm, the emission maxima of 0-0 transition are shifted towards 545 nm. For the films with a thickness higher than 200 nm, the 0-0 transitions are disappeared from the spectrum, and the 0-1 transition is prevailing. The shift of 0-0 transition can be attributed to a change of polymer chain packing [4], where the J-aggregation of chains supports this transition. Nevertheless, with increasing thickness, the polymer chains can form a film with a more organized structure, and thus the H-aggregation with alternating π-stacking of polymer chains is more favorable and changes the spectral features of the material. For the thickest films, the structural ordering of chains causes prevailing 0-1 with longer conjugation length resulting in low energy radiative states [4,10].

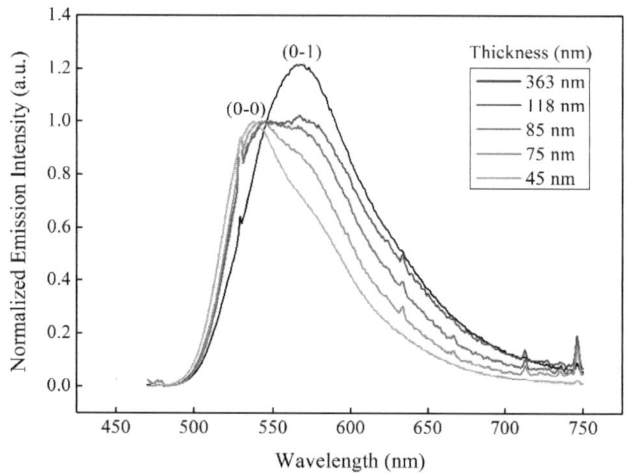

Figure 2 Emission spectra of F8BT with different thicknesses on silicon substrates λ_{ex}= 460 nm.

As emission spectra, excitation spectra can be analyzed in the same framework. The positions of excitation maxima and the shape of excitation spectra are influenced by the thickness of the films as illustrated in **Figure 3.** A slight blue shift and considerable broadening of these peaks are obvious with increasing thickness varying from 45 nm to 120 nm. In the case of the thickest film, significant change of spectrum shape and redshift of excitation maxima were observed. These phenomena can be plausibly explained by extension of conjugation length whereas the longer is the length of conjugated segments the higher delocalization of exciton and higher lowering of energy of transiting vibrational levels in excited states [11].

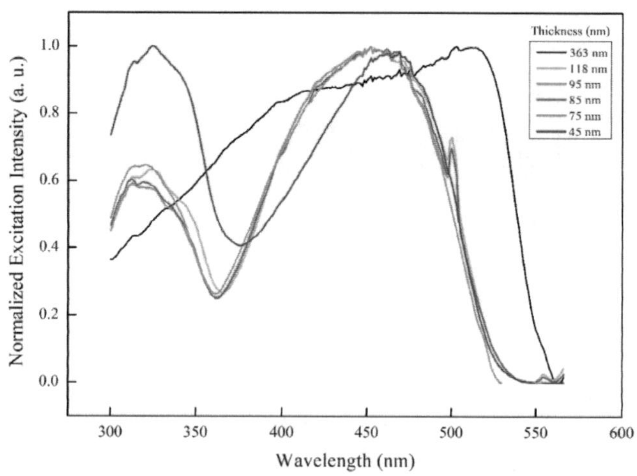

Figure 3 Excitation spectra of F8BT with different thicknesses on silicon substrates λ_{em}= 576 nm.

The PL emission spectra were analyzed in more detail. We introduced the ratio of spectral intensities of 0-0 and 0-1 transitions, $I_{0\text{-}0\,PL}/I_{0\text{-}1\,PL}$. The dependence of this ratio is shown in **Figure 4**. It is clearly seen that the ratio is steeply decreasing with increasing thickness to the thickness about 120 nm. For the samples with higher thickness, the ratio is close to value 1, for extra thick sample (360 nm), the ratio decreases below value 1.

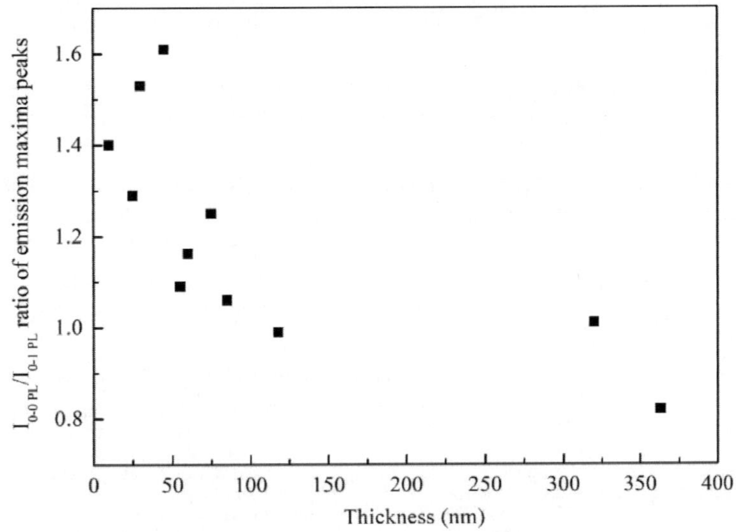

Figure 4 The ratio (0-0)/(0-1) transitions dependence on thickness

This behaviour can reveal that the structure in thinner films (below 120 nm) is prevailing organization of polymer chains in J-aggregation because of this structural ordering is related to radiative transition from the lowest exciton state to the vibrationless ground state. On the other hand, in case of thicker films (over 120 nm), the 0-1 transition starts predominate. This can indicate the structural ordering in more favorable H-aggregation and lowering of potential energy [13,14].

4. CONCLUSION

In our contribution, we investigated the optical and optoelectrical properties of F8BT films depending on the films thickness. We analyzed the absorption and photoluminescence spectra. There is a correlation between the thickness of the films and manifestation of 0-0, 0-1 vibronic transitions that can stem from the intrachain (J-aggregates) and interchain (H-aggregates) structure of the films. We have argued that the structural ordering of the thin conjugated polymer film may vary with the film thickness in a non-trivial way and that it is allied to different levels of manifestation of nonlocalized (aggregate states) and localized (intrachain) transitions. Such findings can contribute to the utilization of conjugated polymers in polymer electronic, concretely in light emitting diodes, where the optical and optoelectrical properties play a most important role.

ACKNOWLEDGEMENTS

The authors are thankful for the financial support from the internal grant IGA/CPS/2020/003 from TBU in Zlin, the Czech Republic.

This work was also supported by the Operational Program Research and Development for Innovations cofounded by the European Regional Development Fund (ERDF) and the national budget of the Czech Republic, within the framework of the project CPS - strengthening research capacity (reg. number: CZ.1.05/2.1.00/19.0409).

REFERENCES

[1] FARIA, G.C., FARIA, R.M., R DEZEVEDO, E., VON SEGGERN, H. Molecular structure and dynamics of F8BT-correlation with Opto-Electronic properties. In: *IEEE 2011: 14th International Symposium on Electrets.* Montpellier, France: 2011, pp. 101-102.

[2] BURROUGHES, J. H., BRADLEY, D. D. C., BROWN, A. R., MARKS, R. N., MACKAY, K., FRIEND, R. H., BRUNS, P. L., HOLMES, A. B. Light-emitting diodes based on conjugated polymers. *Letters to nature.* 1990, vol. 347, pp. 539-541.

[3] YAN, X., JUN-BIAO, P., HONG-BIN, W., JIAN, W. Improved performance of polymer light-emitting diodes with an electron transport emitter by post-annealing. *Journal of Chinese Physics Letters.* 2009, vol. 26, no. 9, pp.097801-4

[4] DONLEY, C. L., ZAUMSEIL, J., ANDREASEN, J. W., NIELSEN, M. M., SIRRINGHAUS. H., FRIEND, R. H., KIM, J. Effects of packing structure on the optoelectronic and charge transport properties in poly (9,9-di-n-octylfluorene-alt-benzothiazole). *Journal of the American Chemical Society.* 2005, vol. 127, no. 37, pp. 12890-12899.

[5] PETROZZA, A., FAZZI, D., AVILOV, I., BELJONNE, D., FRIEND, R. H., KIM, J. Effects of polymer packing structure on photoinduced triplet generation and dynamics. *Journal of Physical Chemistry C.* 2012, vol. 116, no. 20, pp. 11298-11305.

[6] BERNARDO, G., FERREIRA, Q., BROTAS, G., DI PAOLO, R. E., CHARAS, A., MORGADO, J. Synergistic effect on the efficiency of polymer light-emitting diodes upon blending of two green-emitting polymers. *Jornal of applied physics.* 2010, vol. 108, pp. 0145031-8.

[7] SPANO, F. C., SILVA, C. H-and J-aggregate behavior in polymeric semiconductors. *Jornal of Annual Review of Physical Chemistry.* 2014, vol. 65, pp. 477-500.

[8] SPANO, F. C. The spectral signatures of frenkel polarons in H- and J-aggregates. *Journal of Accounts of chemical research.* 2010, vol. 43, no. 3, pp. 429-439.

[9] URBANEK, P., KURITKA, I., DANIS, S., TOUSKOVA, J., TOUSEK, J. Thickness threshold of structural ordering in thin MEH-PPV films. *Journal of Polymer.* 2014, vol. 55, no. 16, pp. 4050-4056.

[10] URBANEK, P., KURITKA, I., SEVCIK, J., TOUSKOVA, J., TOUSEK, J., NADAZDY, V., NADAZDY, P., VEGSO, K., SIFFALOVIC, P., RUTSCH, R, URBANEK, M. An experimental study of the structural ordering of the PTB7 polymer at a mespscopic scale. *Journal of Polymer.* 2019, vol. 169, pp. 243-254.

[11] URBANEK, P., KURITKA, I. Thickness dependent structural ordering, degradation and metastability in polysilane thin films: A photoluminescence study on representative σ-conjugated polymers. *Journal of Luminescence.* 2015, vol. 168, pp. 261-268.

[12] WANG, R., YANG, X., HU, S., ZHANG, Y., YAN, X., WANG, Y., ZHANG, C., SHENG, C. Effect of thermal annealing on aggregations on MEH-PPV films. *The Journal of Physical Chemistry C.* 2019, vol. 123, no. 17, pp. 11055-11062.

[13] SPANO, F. C., YAMAGATA, H. Vibronic Coupling in J-Aggregates and Beyond: A Direct Means of Determining the Exciton Coherence Length from the Photoluminescence Spectrum. *The Journal of Physical Chemistry B.* 2011, vol. 115, pp. 5133-5143.

[14] SPANO, F. C.,CLARK, J., SILVA, C., FRIEND, R. H. Determining exciton coherence from the photoluminescence spectral line shape in poly(3-hexylthiophene) thin films. *The Journal of chemical physics.* 2009, vol. 130, p. 074904.

THE UV PHOTODEGRADABILITY STUDY OF OCTADECABORANE IN POLYSTYRENE MATRIX THIN FILMS

[1]Jakub SEVCIK, [1]Pavel URBANEK, [1]Barbora HANULIKOVA, [1]Tereza CAPKOVA, [1]Jan ANTOS, [1]Michal URBANEK, [1]Ivo KURITKA

[1]*Tomas Bata University in Zlín, University Institute, Centre of Polymer Systems, Zlín, Czech Republic, EU, j4sevcik@utb.cz*

https://doi.org/10.37904/nanocon.2020.3689

Abstract

Octadecaborane was announced in the literature as a new laser dye delivering blue luminescence with high quantum yield. To unlock the potential of this class of compounds in electronics, a representative of octadecaboranes, *anti*-$B_{18}H_{22}$, was preliminarily investigated as a dopant to polystyrene matrix. Polymer/borane thin films with thickness varying in the range of hundreds of nanometres were deposited onto quartz substrates by spin coating technique from solutions in organic solvents. The UV degradability of prepared samples was studied by fluorimetric observation. Effects of the surrounding atmosphere, the dopant concentrations and the molecular structure were observed, which has implications towards the reliability of studied materials in prospective applications in optoelectronic devices.

Keywords: Octadecaborane, polymer blend, thin film, UV degradation, fluorescence

1. INTRODUCTION

Polymer LEDs have the advantage of being easily assembled in comparison with traditional inorganic LEDs. An inorganic semiconductor must be processed in a vacuum, and maximum care has to be taken especially in the preparation process of materials for LEDs with emission in the blue region. In different circumstances, polymer materials have very good process-ability, because they can be formed at ambient conditions (temperature, pressure, etc.) through wet coating techniques, such as spin coating, dip coating, rolling, and inkjet fabrication methods that simply allow for printing of the active material onto the substrate [1-3].

Despite the noticeable advantages of organic and polymer LEDs, it is still a new technology that has many issues to work out, primarily the lifetime, thermal-stability as well as photo-stability [4]. For instance, there is still a color shift, particularly for blue emitters, which degrade faster. The active areas themselves also have to be protected from air by encapsulation to prevent degradation by oxygen. The encapsulation may affect the flexibility of the prepared devices adversely. [5,6]

The synthesis of novel materials based on boron-hydride clusters with a unique molecular architecture opens new possibilities for achieving the durability of the blue emission. The first announcement of a cage borane as a laser dye was published in [7]. This kind of material brings good solubility in common organic solvents and thus good workability. It is also possible to prepare blended material based on a suitable polymer matrix and boranes. The promises need to be tested to verify the practical potential of these compounds. Besides molecules and polymers with π- or σ-electron delocalisation, borane clusters may become a new class of electronic materials based on electron delocalisation due to electron-deficient multicentre bonds. The primary attention is paid to cage boron-hydride derivatives with blue luminescence emission located near 400 nm, in particular *anti*-$B_{18}H_{22}$, whose emission was reported as stable [8].

In this contribution, we introduce two embodiments of such polymer blends with blue emission due to the addition of the borane compound with a particular focus on film-formation-ability and photo-stability.

2. EXPERIMENTAL

2.1. Sample preparation

A series of spin-coated thin films were prepared from solutions of Polystyrene (PS, Sigma Aldrich average M_w - 350 000, M_n - 170 000) and polymethylmethacrylate (PMMA, Sigma Aldrich average M_w - 350 000) in toluene, HPLC quality, purchased from J.T. Baker with incorporated borohydride molecules, the *anti*-$B_{18}H_{22}$ - (Mw = 216,58 g mol^{-1}), which was synthesised at the Institute of Inorganic Chemistry of the AS CR. All solvents were stored in the glovebox in flasks with molecular sieves. The polymer/borane blend solution was cast onto quartz glass substrates using spin coater Laurell WS-650-MZ-23NPP with a rotation speed of 1000 rpm. The whole process of the sample preparation was performed in an inert atmosphere in a glove box.

2.2. Instrumentation

The thickness of films was measured by a mechanical profilometer Dektak XT-E and (Bruker) with the 1 nm resolution and by an optical profilometer CONTOUR GT-K with the vertical resolution < 0.01 nm (as indicated by Bruker) and lateral resolution < 0.5 µm.

Variable-angle spectroscopic ellipsometry UVISEL 2 (Horiba) with a spectral range from 180 nm to 2200 nm and a resolution higher than 0.5 nm was used to determine optical constants and changes in polarisation angles and their wavelength dependence. The data was then used to calculate the film thickness using Delta Psi V2 software.

The UV-VIS-NIR spectra were recorded by a double-beam spectrophotometer Lambda 1050, Perkin Elmer. The instrument is equipped by a double-monochromator and detectors all UV, VIS and NIR regions.

The PL spectra and PL decays were taken by fluorimeter FLS920 in the air and a vacuum atmosphere (pressure ≤1 Pa) ensured by the cryostat Optistat DN-V (LN2, Oxford Instruments) at room temperature. Excitation beam served simultaneously as the degradation light beam in the photo-stability studies. The wavelength of the degrading beam was set to the maximum in excitation spectra of the respective polymer/borane blend. A fresh sample spot was irradiated for 30 min in each experiment. Three different light intensities of the degradation beam were used. Radiometer RM22 with UVA sensor from Opsytec Dr. Gröbel was used for irradiance measurement. The PL intensity response was recorded at the PL emission maximum and then normalised and plotted against dose.

3. RESULTS AND DISCUSSION

3.1. Ultraviolet-visible spectroscopy

Ultraviolet-visible spectroscopy was used for the evaluation of absorbance characteristics of the prepared thin films, see in **Figure 1a**. Both polymers were confirmed as suitable matrices for the preparation of thin films with borane additives because of their absorption edge wavelengths. The spectral window of PMMA is larger than that of PS which already absorbs below 275 nm. Nevertheless, PMMA and PS provide transparent spectral windows in the UV region where boranes absorb light.

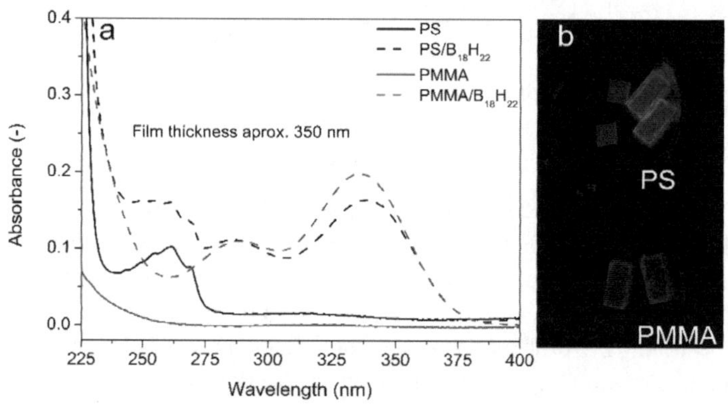

Figure 1 a) Absorption spectra of ca 350 nm thick films made of neat polymers and polymer/borane blends, b) luminescence of polymer/borane blend samples under UV lamp irradiation.

Indeed, the prepared polymer/(anti-$B_{18}H_{22}$) blend thin films show two typical absorption maxima related to borane at 290 nm and 340 nm. **Figure 1b** documents the luminescence of the prepared samples under UV irradiation. It was clearly observable by the naked eye that the luminescence of *anti*-$B_{18}H_{22}$ is quenched in the PMMA matrix in comparison with the PS blend samples.

3.2. Fluorimetry

Excitation (a) and emission (b) photoluminescence (PL) spectra of prepared thin films are depicted in **Figure 2**. The films consisting of PS/borane have PL intensity higher by two orders of magnitude than the films based on PMMA. From this point of view, the PMMA matrix does not seem to be an appropriate environment for borane molecules despite its good optical properties. A plausible explanation of this observation can be deprotonation of one of the borane's highly acidic bridging hydrogen atoms. The methyl ester side group of PMMA may accept the proton leaving a non-luminescent borane anion [9]. Moreover, PMMA is more prone to humidity adsorption than PS. Eventual traces of water may kill the luminescence of the boranes by the same mechanism. Based on this experience, further work was carried out with samples utilising the PS matrix only.

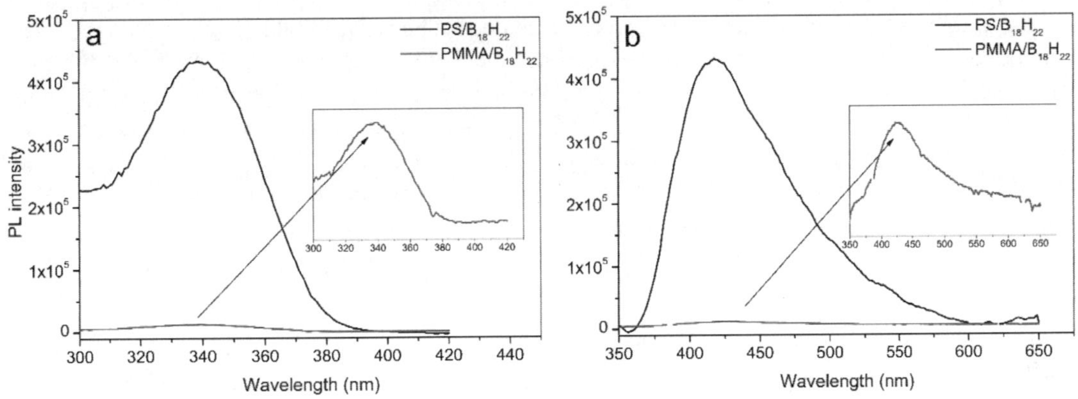

Figure 2 Photoluminescence spectra of approx. 350 nm thick PS/anti-$B_{18}H_{22}$ and PMMA/ PS/anti-$B_{18}H_{22}$ films in ratio 4:1 a) excitation spectra captured concerning the maximum of emission, b) emission spectra captured concerning the maximum of excitation.

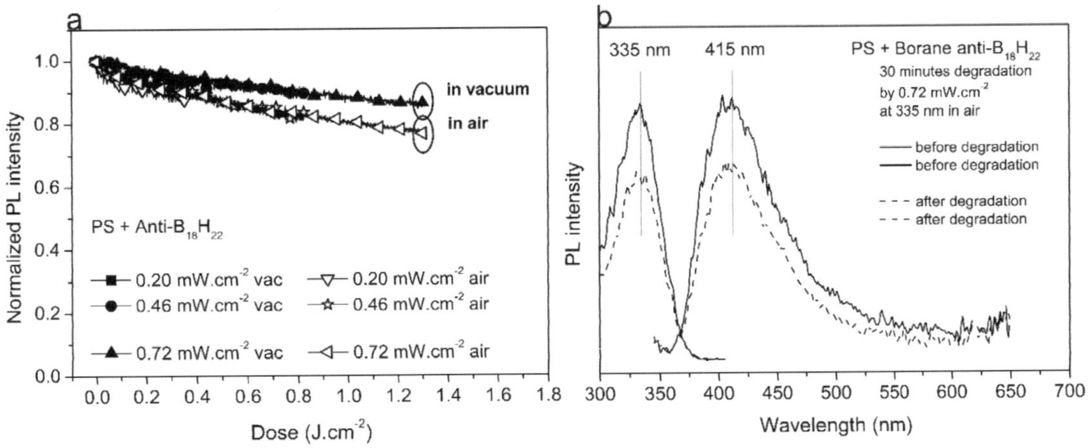

Figure 3 Photo-degradation study of 100 nm thick film of PS/anti-$B_{18}H_{22}$ in ratio approx. 30:1 a) Evolution of normalised PL intensity of emission maxima in both vacuum and air environment, b) The excitation and emission spectra measured before and after 30 minutes of degradation.

In the following part, the first attempts to address the photo-stability of blended PS/borane thin films are presented. The stability of the material is a crucial point for any of its potential applications. The study was performed in two different environments, i.e. in a vacuum and the air atmosphere, representing thus encapsulation or other protection of the device and open exposure to the ambient atmosphere, respectively. The PL decay curves are plotted in **Figure 3a** for PS/anti-$B_{18}H_{22}$ blend. The sample degrading irradiances are introduced in the graph windows. The coincidence of all triplets of the decay curves testifies for the fulfillment of the reciprocity laws. In **Figure 3b**, the emission and excitation spectra before and after degradation are shown.

It is clearly seen, the total PL intensity decay for the highest degradation dose is 10 per cent in a vacuum and 25 per cent in the air, respectively in comparison to the initial value. Concerning emission and excitation spectra, no change was observed, but an overall decrease of PL intensity. This fact is in direct contrast to published work [7], where the photo-stability was presented as a superior one, even comparable with Exalite 404 laser dye. Nevertheless, the authors [7] declared good photo-stability in solution while mentioned low efficiency of borane lasing in solid-state. Our observation indicated borane degradation in PS matrix although it was pumped by a much weaker and non-coherent source (Xe lamp) in a vacuum. The degradation was accelerated when humidity and air were allowed to be present. To improve stability of the borane molecule, anchoring of alkyl substituents seems to be a viable method. For example, extensive methylation increases the usefulness of these compounds significantly, as published recently [10]. Nevertheless, the photo-stability of methylated borane was measured only in the form of a solution again, and further research is necessary. Another stabilisation strategy was demonstrated recently. A borane cluster can be included as a guest in the cavity of a protective host, e.g. cyclodextrins [11,12]. This method seems to allow the preparation of waterborne dispersions or solutions by protection the borane molecule against hydrolysis.

4. CONCLUSION

To summarise, we investigated the photo-stability of *anti*-$B_{18}H_{22}$ borane incorporated in polymer matrices for the first time. The study was performed by direct on-line measurement of the PL decay using the excitation beam as the degradation stress simultaneously. The elimination of air and humidity can suppress the photo-degradation of *anti*-$B_{18}H_{22}$ to a reasonable extent. Nevertheless, the borane-polystyrene blend still suffers from photo-degradation to a certain extent, even in an inert environment (vacuum). The few photo-stability tests performed in solutions available in literature give reason to hope for further improvement of the stability of the borane molecules in polymer blends. A stabilisation method must be discovered to introduce these borane based alternative molecular components in the fabrication of light-emitting devices.

ACKNOWLEDGEMENTS

This work was supported by the grant from the Czech Science Foundation (Project No. 19-23513S).

The work was also supported by the Operational Program Research and Development for Innovations cofounded by the European Regional Development Fund (ERDF) and the national budget of the Czech Republic, within the framework of the project CPS - strengthening research capacity (reg. number: CZ.1.05/2.1.00/19.0409).

Michael Londesborough and Jonathan Bould are greatly acknowledged for synthesis and providing of anti-$B_{18}H_{22}$.

REFERENCES

[1] GATHER, M. C., KÖHNEN, A., et al. White organic light-emitting diodes. *Advanced Materials*. 2011, vol. 23, pp. 233-248.

[2] YEE LOW, J., MERICAN ALJUNID MERICAN, Z., et al. Polymer light emitting diodes (PLEDs): An update review on current innovation and performance of material properties. *Elsevier Ltd.* 2019, vol. 16, pp. 1909-1918.

[3] SKODA, D., URBANEK, P., et al. Colloidal cobalt-doped ZnO nanoparticles by microwave-assisted synthesis and their utilisation in thin composite layers with MEH-PPV as an electroluminescent material for polymer light emitting diodes. *Organic Electronic.* 2018, vol. 59, pp. 337-348.

[4] EMBAYE, N., RAMINI, S., et al. Mechanisms of reversible photo-degradation in disperse orange 11 dye doped in PMMA polymer. *The Journal of Chemical Physics.* 2008, vol. 129, pp. 054504-9.

[5] PALLARES, R. M., NGUYÊN, T. K. Thanh, XIAODI, S., SUO, H. L. Fine-tuning of gold nanorod dimensions and plasmonic properties using the Hofmeister effects. *Materials Chemistry C.* 2016, vol. 4, p. 53.

[6] DWIVEDI, V. K. and PRAKASH, G. V. Fabrication and room-temperature exciton photoluminescence stability studies of inorganic-organic hybrid (C12H25NH3)2SnI4 thin films. *Solid State Sciences.* 2014, vol. 27, pp. 60-64.

[7] CERDAN, L., BRABOREC, J., et al. A borane laser. *Nature Communications.* 2015, vol. 6, no. 5958.

[8] LONDESBOROUGH, M. G. S., DOLANSKÝ, J., et al. Effect of iodination on the photophysics of the laser borane anti-$B_{18}H_{22}$: Generation of efficient photosensitisers of oxygen. *Inorganic Chemistry.* 2019, vol. 58, no. 15, pp. 10248-10259.

[9] OLSEN, F. P., VASAVADA, R. C., et al. The chemistry of n-$B_{18}H_{22}$ and i-$B_{18}H_{22}$. *American Chemical Society.* 1968, vol. 90, pp. 3946-3951.

[10] LONDESBOROUGH, M. G. S., LANG, K., et al. Swollen polyhedral volume of the anti-$B_{18}H_{22}$ cluster via extensive methylation: Anti-$B_{18}H_8cl_2me_{12}$. *American Chemical Society (ACS).* 2020, vol. 59, p. 2651.

[11] TAN, C., CHEN, J., et al. The preparation and characterisation of n-$B_{18}H_{22}$-beta cyclodextrin inclusion complex. *IOP Conf. Ser.: Earth Environ. Sci.* 2019, vol. 233, p. 022005.

[12] TAN, C., ZHANG, B., ZHANG, L., CHEN, J. Preparation method of inclusion complex of n-$B_{18}H_{22}$ with cyclodextrin and application thereof. 2019, CN Patent 109336996.

DIELECTRIC PROPERTIES OF NANOSTRUCTURED MIXED-OXIDE FILMS FORMED BY ANODIZING AL/ZR BILAYERS

Marcela SEPÚLVEDA, Kirill KAMNEV, Alexander MOZALEV

CEITEC - Central European Institute of Technology, Brno University of Technology, Brno, Czech Republic, EU
lina.sepulveda@ceitec.vutbr.cz, alexander.mozalev@ceitec.vutbr.cz

https://doi.org/10.37904/nanocon.2020.3693

Abstract

ZrO_2 is a ceramic material suitable for high-temperature coatings, fuel cells as a solid proton-conducting electrolyte, and metal-oxide-semiconductor devices due to its recently explored promising dielectric properties. In this work, anodic nanostructured ZrO_2-Al_2O_3 mixed films were synthesized on substrates via anodizing/re-anodizing of a thin Zr layer through a porous anodic alumina (PAA) film at 40/240 V in 0.6 M $(COOH)_2$ and characterized by scanning electron microscopy and electrochemical impedance spectroscopy (EIS) including the measurements under various bias potentials. The films are composed of ZrO_2 nanofingers penetrating the alumina pores, partially mixing with Al_2O_3. Nanofingers are anchored to a ZrO_2 bottom-oxide nanofilm that forms under the PAA during anodization. The EIS reveals a nearly ideal dielectric behavior of the ZrO_2-Al_2O_3 mixed-oxide nanostructured films. After dissolution of the PAA layer, the dielectric properties of the remaining zirconium oxide film become slightly worse, due to the specific structure and deviation from perfect stoichiometry. The ZrO_2-Al_2O_3 mixed-oxide nanostructured film permittivity is calculated to be 11, which is higher than that of alumina (9.8) due to the contribution of ZrO_2 nanofingers grown in the alumina nanopores. After the PAA dissolution, the film permittivity increases substantially, up to 46, which is twice the permittivity of ZrO_2 (22) grown anodically on zirconium metal in a classical way. The ZrO_2-Al_2O_3 mixed-oxide nanostructured films prepared via the PAA-assisted anodization are of high interest for potential application to various types of capacitors due to their near-ideal dielectric properties. The unique dielectric behavior of the PAA-dissolved ZrO_2 film deserves detailed investigation in a future work.

Keywords: Anodizing, zirconium oxide, porous anodic alumina, dielectric

1. INTRODUCTION

Zirconium-oxide (ZrO_2) films have been extensively explored, mainly due to corrosion and hydrogen embrittlement resistance, which makes them suitable for selective CO sensors [1] and solid-electrolyte for fuel cells [2]. ZrO_2 is also viewed as one of the promising high-k dielectric materials to replace Ta_2O_5. Thin ZrO_2 films are also suitable dielectrics for volatile dynamic random access memory and for complementary metal-oxide-semiconductor devices [3,4]. Commonly, thin ZrO_2 films are synthesized using electron beam physical vapor deposition [5], chemical vapor deposition [6], atomic layer deposition [7], and chemical solution deposition [8]. Alternatively to the aforementioned techniques, the anodization method may be viewed as a simple and versatile approach for the synthesis of thin ZrO_2 films since it does not require high-budget equipment, ultra-high vacuum conditions, or elevated temperatures [9]. Additionally, anodic ZrO_2 films can be made nanostructured by so-called PAA-assisted anodization approach. When an Al layer is superimposed on a metal of interest, oxide nanostructures may form penetrating the initially grown porous anodic alumina (PAA) film during anodization [10]. In our previous works, we have reported that mixed aluminum-tantalum and aluminum-hafnium oxide films prepared by PAA-assisted anodization technique exhibit good dielectric performance, close to that of an ideal capacitor [11,12]. However, the electronic properties of mixed aluminum-zirconium films prepared by anodization of Al/Zr bilayers have never been studied.

Here we report on the formation of nanostructured ZrO_2-Al_2O_3 mixed films via PAA-assisted anodization of Al/Zr bilayers sputter-deposited on Si wafers. The films were analyzed by scanning electron microscopy (SEM) and electrically characterized by electrochemical impedance spectroscopy (EIS), followed by the measurements under various bias potentials, before and after selectively dissolving the PAA overlayer. The results obtained provide insights into the electrical and electronic properties of the ZrO_2-Al_2O_3 mixed films, assessing their applicability as dielectrics for electrolytic and thin-film capacitors.

2. EXPERIMENTAL

2.1. Sample preparation

One-side polished Si wafer covered with a 300 nm layer of SiO_2 was used as a starting substrate. A layer of Zr, 200 nm thick, followed by a layer of Al, 1000 nm thick, were deposited on the substrate via magnetron sputtering of Zr and Al targets of respectively 99.95% and 99.999% purity. Anodizing of Al/Zr bilayer films was carried out in 0.6M $(COOH)_2$ aqueous solution at room temperature in potentiodynamic mode by sweeping voltage from 0 to 40 V at a rate of 0.5 V s^{-1}. Subsequently, re-anodizing was performed in the same electrolyte by sweeping the voltage from 40 to 240 V at a rate of 10 V s^{-1}. Both processes were immediately followed by 3 min of current decay. After the anodizing and re-anodizing, the samples were thoroughly rinsed with deionized water and dried in an oven at 150 °C for 1 h in air at atmospheric pressure. For the ZrO_2-in-Al_2O_3 samples, a 30 s pore widening procedure was carried out to allow better permeation of buffer solution inside the pores (the 'PAA-in-built' samples). For selected samples, the PAA overlayer was fully dissolved in 1 wt% NaOH solution at room temperature (the 'PAA-free' samples).

2.2. Sample characterization

The surface morphology of the PAA-inbuilt and PAA-free samples was examined in a TESCAN MIRA II field-emission scanning electron microscope. Cross-sections of experimental samples were observed in a FEI Verios 460L High-Resolution Scanning Electron Microscope.

2.3. Electrochemical measurements

EIS measurements were carried out in borate buffer (0.5 M H_3BO_3; 0.05 M $Na_7B_4O_7$) aqueous solution, pH 7.5, using an Autolab PGSTAT204 Potentiostat/ Galvanostat with a FRA32M module (Metrohm). The electrochemical measurements were performed in a Teflon cell within an area of 0.27 cm^2. After measuring the PAA-inbuilt samples, the PAA layer was etched away in the NaOH solution at 23 °C without taking the sample out from the cell, then the sample was EIS measured again in the same cell. A two-electrode setup was employed for electrochemical measurements: a high-purity Au sheet was used as a counter electrode and positioned over the surface of the investigated sample; the Zr layer remaining after the anodization process underneath the oxide film was used the working electrode. EIS characterization was performed by applying a sinusoidal perturbation of 100 mV in a frequency range from 1 MHz to 0.01 Hz. The bias was applied in a cathodic direction, from -0.5 to -2.5 V with a step of -0.5 V. Experimental EIS data were analyzed by simulation and fitting software Autolab NOVA. All the EIS measurements were recorded from the open-circuit potential (OCP).

3. RESULTS AND DISCUSSION

3.1. Structure of the anodized Al/Zr bilayers

Figure 1 shows the top, cross-sectional, and 3-D view SEM images of the oxide films obtained after the PAA-assisted anodization of Al/Zr bilayer films. It is seen that the film is complex comprises a self-ordered PAA layer (**Figure 1a**). Glimpsing inside the PAA layer with help of a cross-section SEM image (**Figure 1 b**), the

PAA pores at the Al_2O_3/ZrO_2 interface are filled with ZrO_2 nanofingers. The top and 3-D SEM views after a complete PAA dissolution (**Figures 1 c,d**) reveal an array of free-standing vertically aligned ZrO_2 nanostructures. The location of these nanostructures corresponds to positions of pores in the PAA layer. The nanostructure bases are well distanced from each other, being anchored to a continuous ZrO_2 bottom-layer film (darker areas on the top view). The structure of the films formed is outlined in the schematic image in **Figure 2**.

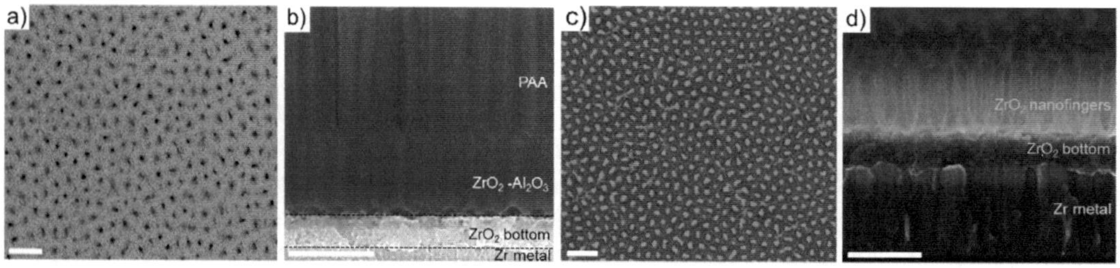

Figure 1 Top and cross-fractional SEM views of the (a, b) PAA-inbuilt and (c, d) PAA-free films, the scale bar in the SEM image corresponds to 300 nm

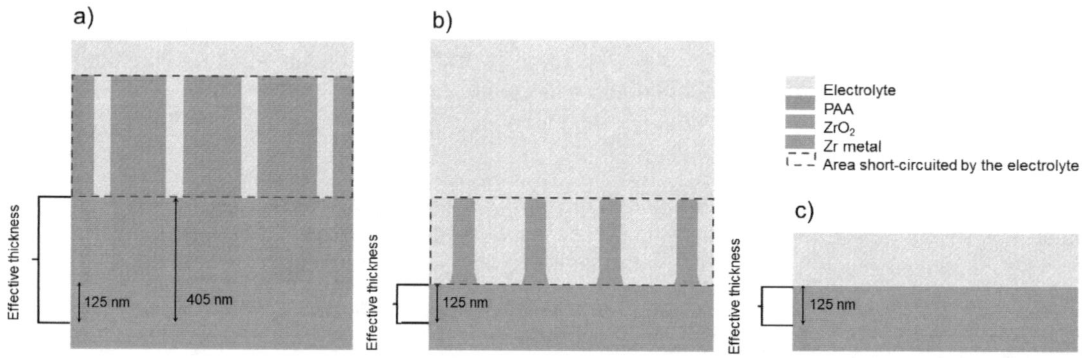

Figure 2 Schematic showing the development of the ZrO_2-Al_2O_3 mixed films: a) the PAA-inbuilt film, b) the PAA-free film, and (c) a barrier-type anodic ZrO_2 film

3.2. Electrical measurements

Electrical and electronic properties the PAA-inbuilt (**Figures 1 a,b**), and PAA-free (**Figures 1 c,d**) films were characterized by EIS sweep at OCP (**Figure 3**). The bode diagrams suggest a simple equivalent circuit for the PAA-inbuilt and PAA-free films. In the circuit, R_s is the solution resistance, R_1 is the film resistance, and Q_1 is the constant phase element (**Figure 3** inset). Both the mixed ZrO_2-Al_2O_3 nanostructured layer and the ZrO_2 flat bottom-oxide layer are expected to contribute to the film impedance. During electrical measurements, the layer of PAA residing above the level of protruding ZrO_2 nanofingers is short-circuited by the electrolyte (**Figure 2 a**) [12]. The phase shift of the PAA-inbuilt film is close to -90 degrees, which reflects a nearly ideal dielectric behavior of the film. However, after the complete dissolution of the PAA overlayer and thus excluding the ZrO_2 nanofingers from the measurements, the film exhibits slightly different electrical behavior. The phase shift starts to deviate from -90 degrees, highlighting a slightly worse dielectric behavior. A worsened dielectric behavior can be explained by the differences in structure and crystallinity between the nanostructured and bottom-oxide ZrO_2 layers. Due to the complex mechanism of oxide growth via the PAA-assisted anodizing, the bottom-oxide layer might possess more crystalline inclusions and less ZrO_{2-x} suboxides, which may alter its properties and worsen the dielectric behavior, or even introduce semiconducting properties to the oxide [12].

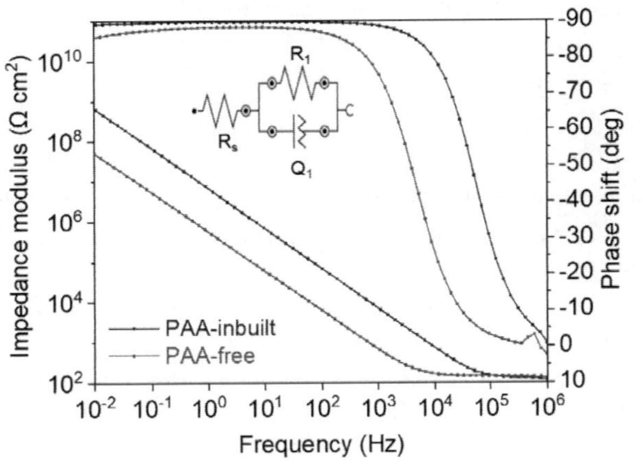

Figure 3 EIS characterization of the PAA-inbuilt ZrO_2-Al_2O_3 films and PAA-free zirconium-oxide films: experimental (symbols) and fitted (solid lines) Bode plots at OCP

From the EIS measurements, the capacitance of the oxide films was calculated (**Table 1**). The capacitance of the ZrO_2-Al_2O_3 mixed film is 24.0 nF cm^{-2}. However, PAA-free film shows a much higher capacitance of 326.8 nF cm^{-2}. This is because the solution short circuits the free-standing ZrO_2 nanostructures and only a bottom ZrO_2 layer contributes to the measurement, thus drastically reducing the film thickness [12]. Due to the exclusion of the nanostructured ZrO_2 upper layer from the measurement, one may expect that the capacitance and dielectric properties of the ZrO_2 bottom oxide should be similar to those of anodically grown ZrO_2 barrier-type film of the same thickness. However, the capacitance for the barrier-type ZrO_2 film is 152.4 nF cm^{-2}, which is roughly half the capacitance of the PAA-free ZrO_2 nanofilm.

Table 1 Quantitative results of EIS of the PAA-inbuilt, PAA-free, and a barrier-type ZrO_2 anodic films

Film	Thickness (nm)	Capacitance (nF cm^{-2})	Relative permittivity (ε_r)
PAA-Inbuilt	405	24.0	11
PAA-free	125	326.8	46
Barrier-type ZrO_2	125	152.4	22

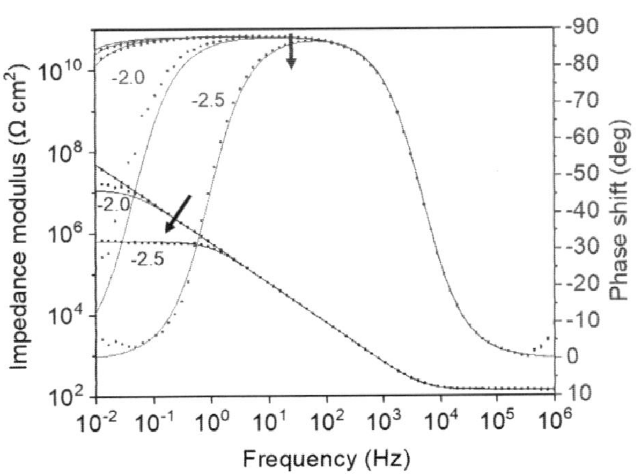

Figure 4 Bode plots of the PAA-free film under bias potentials ranging from -0.4 to -2.5 V with -0.5 steps, experimental (symbols) and fitted (solid lines)

To understand the abnormal behavior of the PAA-free ZrO_2 film, EIS measurements under the bias potentials were carried out (**Figure 4**). This analysis reveals a potential-independent impedance behavior under a negative applied potential changing from -0.5 up to -2.5 V, confirming that the ZrO_2 bottom oxide is a dielectric, not a semiconductor.

For each film type, dielectric constant (relative permittivity) was calculated from the capacitances and the thicknesses of the films measured by SEM (**Table 1**). The permittivity of the PAA-inbuilt sample ε_r appears to be equal to 11, which is smaller than ε_r of a pure ZrO_2 known from the literature (22-24). As was seen in the SEM images, the PAA-inbuilt film consists of ZrO_2 nanofingers intermittent by Al_2O_3 and anchored to a ZrO_2 bottom oxide. The ZrO_2 nanofingers surrounded by Al_2O_3 may be viewed as a set of parallel-connected capacitors while the ZrO_2 bottom oxide lying underneath contributes as a capacitor connected in series. Thus, the biggest impact on the resultant capacitance is given by the parallel-connected ZrO_2 nanofingers and the Al_2O_3 around them. As the volume of Al_2O_3 substantially exceeds that of the ZrO_2 nanofingers in the mixed-oxide film, it can be assumed that the capacitance of the Al_2O_3 portion dominates the resultant capacitance, making the resultant permittivity slightly higher than that of a pure Al_2O_3 (9.8) due to the ZrO_2 nanofingers inclusions. After the PAA layer is completely dissolved, the permittivity rises drastically, up to 46, neither corresponding to typical values reported for ZrO_2 (22-24). One can assume that, after the PAA dissolution, the ZrO_2 nanofingers would be short-circuited by the electrolyte and excluded from the measurement, leaving only the ZrO_2 bottom-oxide film alone, which should have electric properties comparable with those of the ZrO_2 film prepared by the convenient anodization of Zr metal. However, the normally prepared ZrO_2 film of the same thickness exhibit more than twice as smaller capacitance and therefore, permittivity (22). It is clear that the ZrO_2 bottom-oxide film derived from the PAA-assisted anodization exhibits unique electrical behavior in comparison with the ZrO_2 films prepared by the convenient anodization of Zr metal. Since the bias assisted EIS analysis showed the purely dielectric behavior of the PAA-free ZrO_2 film, the abnormal dielectric characteristics can be explained by unusual structural features of the oxide bottom layer. For example, having a high surface area, the nanofingers bases might not be completely excluded from the measurement and might influence film dielectric behavior after denudation of the ZrO_2 nanostructures following PAA dissolution. It is of high interest to further investigate the unique dielectric properties of the alumina-zirconia mixed oxide films prepared by the PAA-assisted anodization of Al/Zr bilayers as they show an ideal dielectric behavior and can be potentially employed in various microelectronic devices, as well as to uncover the paradoxes behind the abnormal behavior of the ZrO_2 bottom-oxide film in a future work.

4. SUMMARY AND CONCLUSION

Thin Al/Zr layers anodically processed in 0.6 M $(COOH)_2$ at room temperature revealed the following two stages in their growth: (1) the formation of a PAA film at 40 V followed by the pore-assisted oxidation of the Zr underlayer at the same voltage and (2) the growth of ZrO_2 nanostructures inside the PAA layer via re-anodizing to 240 V. The ZrO_2-Al_2O_3 mixed-oxide film consists of upward growing ZrO_2 nanostructures protruding inside the pores and anchored to a ZrO_2 bottom layer. The EIS characterization showed that the ZrO_2-Al_2O_3 film behaves like an ideal dielectric. After the dissolution of the PAA overlayer, the film exhibits worsened dielectric behavior. The EIS examination under the bias confirms that the film is still dielectric. Surprisingly, the measured capacitance and calculated apparent permittivity of the PAA-free film are twice those of a barrier-type anodic ZrO_2 film of the same thickness. The promising dielectric properties of the mixed ZrO_2-in-Al_2O_3 films will be explored more thoroughly in a future work in pursuit of better understanding and explaining the abnormal behavior of the ZrO_2 bottom oxide.

ACKNOWLEDGEMENTS

The work was supported by a GACR grant no. 20-25486S. We acknowledge CzechNanoLab Research Infrastructure supported by MEYS CR (LM2018110).

REFERENCES

[1] RAJABBEIGI, N., ELYASSI, B., KHODADADI, A. A., MOHAJERZADEH, S., MORTAZAVI, Y. and SAHIMI, M. Oxygen sensor with solid-state CeO2-ZrO2-TiO2 reference. *Sensors and Actuators B: Chemical*. 2005, vol.108, no. 1-2, pp. 341-345.

[2] MIURA, N., NAKATOU, M. and ZHUIYKOV, S. Impedancemetric gas sensor based on zirconia solid electrolyte and oxide sensing electrode for detecting total NOx at high temperature. *Sensors and Actuators B: Chemical*. 2003, vol. 93, no. 1-3, pp. 221-228.

[3] PANDA, D. and TSENG, T. Y. Growth, dielectric properties, and memory device applications of ZrO2 thin films. *Thin Solid Films*. 2013, vol. 531, pp. 1-20.

[4] FIORENTINI, V. and GULLERI, G. Theoretical evaluation of zirconia and hafnia as gate oxides for Si microelectronics. *Physical review letters*. 2002, vol. 89, no. 26, p. 266101.

[5] SCHULZ, U. and SCHMÜCKER, M. Microstructure of ZrO2 thermal barrier coatings applied by EB-PVD. *Materials Science and Engineering: A*. 2000, vol. 276, no. 1-3, pp.1-8.

[6] CHANG, J. P., LIN, Y. S. and CHU, K. Rapid thermal chemical vapor deposition of zirconium oxide for metal-oxide-semiconductor field effect transistor application. *Journal of Vacuum Science & Technology B: Microelectronics and Nanometer Structures Processing, Measurement, and Phenomena*. 2001, vol. 19, no. 5, pp.1782-1787.

[7] PERKINS, C. M., TRIPLETT, B. B., MCINTYRE, P. C., SARASWAT, K. C., HAUKKA, S. and TUOMINEN, M. Electrical and materials properties of ZrO2 gate dielectrics grown by atomic layer chemical vapor deposition. *Applied Physics Letters*. 2001, vol. 78, no. 16, pp. 2357-2359.

[8] HARDY, A., VAN ELSHOCHT, S., ADELMANN, C., CONARD, T., FRANQUET, A., DOUHÉRET, O. and HEYNS, M. Aqueous solution-gel preparation of ultrathin ZrO_2 films for gate dielectric application. *Thin Solid Films*. 2008, vol. 516, no. 23, pp. 8343-8351.

[9] GRUBBS, C. A. Anodizing of aluminum. *Metal Finishing*. 1999, vol 97, no.1, pp.476-493.

[10] MOZALEV, A., SAKAIRI, M., SAEKI, I. and TAKAHASHI, H. Nucleation and growth of the nanostructured anodic oxides on tantalum and niobium under the porous alumina film. *Electrochimica Acta*. 2003, vol. 48, no.20-22, pp.3155-3170.

[11] MOZALEV, A., SAKAIRI, M. and TAKAHASHI, H. Structure, morphology, and dielectric properties of nanocomposite oxide films formed by anodizing of sputter-deposited Ta-Al bilayers. *Journal of The Electrochemical Society*. 2004, vol 151, no. 11, p. F257.

[12] BENDOVA, M., PYTLICEK, Z., PRASEK, J. and MOZALEV, A. The growth and unique electronic properties of the porous-alumina-assisted hafnium-oxide nanostructured films. *Electrochimica Acta*. 2019, vol. 327, p. 135029.

IMPOSING BIAXIAL STRAIN ON 2D LAYERED MATERIALS BY LIQUID-INDUCED SWELLING OF SUPPORTING POLYMER

[1,2]Krishna SAMPATHKUMAR, [1]Jan PEKAREK, [2]Otakar FRANK

[1]*CEITEC - Brno University of Technology, Brno, Czech Republic, EU,*
krishna.sampathkumar@ceitec.vutbr.cz

[2]*J.Heyrovsky Institute of Physical Chemistry of the CAS, Prague, Czech Republic, EU,*
otakar.frank@jh-inst.cas.cz

https://doi.org/10.37904/nanocon.2020.3685

Abstract

2D layered materials promise to revolutionize the field of electronics, photonics, optoelectronics, energy storage, and sensing, etc. 2D materials have exceptional mechanical properties, with critical elongation >10%. Employing the strain to manipulate the electronic structure of these 2D materials could lead to further improvement of their implementation in many aspects. The ease of manipulation of their electronic structure can be one of the critical factors for their utilization in photonic devices. Apart from the strain, which decreases (increases) the bandgap energy at the rate of ~100 meV under 1% of biaxial tension (compression), also the layer number causes bandgap energy change of, e.g., 0.5 eV between bulk (1.3 eV) and monolayer MoS_2 (1.8 eV). In our work, we focus on using the swelling behavior of PMMA/SU8 polymer in methanol to impose the strain on 2D layered materials. In the first trials, we have shown that it is possible to reach a strain gradient from 0 to ~0.5% of biaxial strain via simple swelling of polymer substrates, both for graphene [1] and transition metal di-chalcogenides (TMDC) like MoS_2. Raman spectroscopy was used to probe the lattice strain in the materials through measuring changes of vibrational frequencies, and photoluminescence was used to probe the strain-induced bandgap character and energy in TMDC at room temperature. The surface corrugation of the 2D material after the soaking was recorded with the help of atomic force microscope (AFM).

Keywords: 2D material, graphene, TMDC, strain engineering, biaxial strain

1. INTRODUCTION

Most of the material's physical properties can be tuned via strain engineering by mechanically modifying its structure. Two-dimensional nanomaterials' unique mechanical properties are particularly promising candidates for strain engineering and related applications because they can withstand considerable strain before structural failure. The atomically thin monolayer graphene exhibits unique chemical and electronic properties. The strain in graphene can change its electronic structure, chemical potential, or induce pseudo magnetic gauge fields. Other than graphene, strain engineering offers great potential to control and modify the optoelectronic structure of transition metal dichalcogenides [1-3].

The fast-growing field of flexible devices requires more fundamental research to keep the material science to help the future application. For example, the recent growth of graphene usage in the near field communication (NFC) tags and antennae is the perfect illustration. However, the 2D materials often exhibit a change in their fundamental electrical, optical, and structural properties, requiring further studies and classifications based on their modulation in a real situation under strain/stress. The in-plane stress imposed on a 2D material can be either purely planar or can be manifested by out-of-plane buckling. The buckling patterns can have periodical tensile and compressive strains across the 2D material. Externally imposed deformation such as pressure-induced, tip-induced, blister formation, or substrate bending are the preferential methods in the case of 2D materials [4,5].

A polymer substrate swelled with diffusing fluids can also impose strain on the material. In the present work, we show polymethylmethacrylate (PMMA) swelled by methanol [6-8] inducing large deformation in selected 2D material resting on top of it. The strain-dependent change in electronic band structure were detected through the respective characteristic peak shifts in the Raman and photoluminescence spectra (PL) graphene and TMDC flakes [9,10].

2. EXPERIMENTAL METHODS

Polymethylmethacrylate (PMMA) slabs were coated with ~500nm thick SU8 2000.5 (MicroChem) negative photoresist. The SU8-covered PMMA substrates were annealed at 60°C for 5 minutes to evaporate the solvent present in the SU8. Graphene and MoS_2 flakes were mechanically cleaved using scotch tape and directly exfoliated on the SU8-coated PMMA substrates. The exfoliated samples were prebaked at 65°C for 30 minutes to get a conformal adhesion with the SU8 surface on the PMMA slab. The exfoliated graphene and MoS_2 sample thickness were identified using optical contrast measurement in an optical microscope. Raman and PL spectroscopy were used to quantify the evolution of the biaxial strain in graphene and MoS_2.

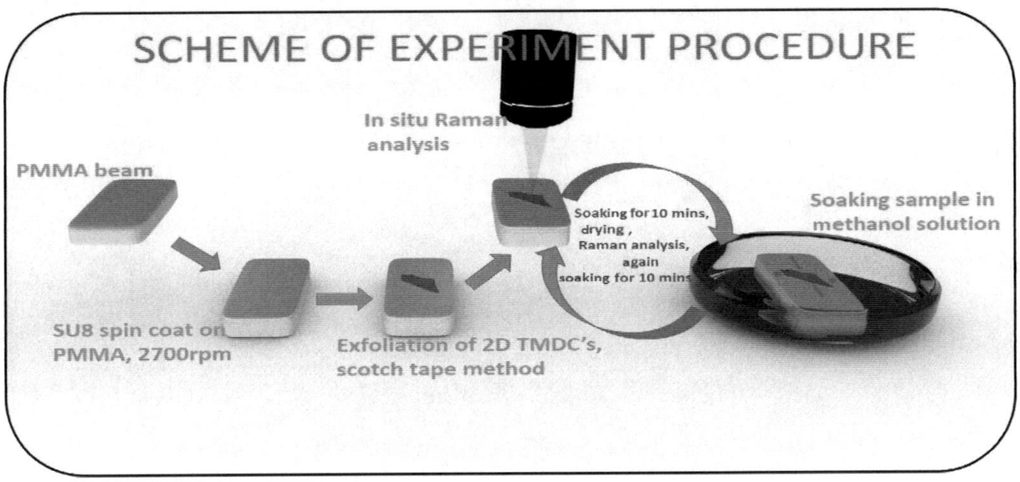

Figure 1 Schematic representation of the experiment

The biaxial strain was imposed on the 2D materials (graphene or MoS_2) by soaking in methanol in repeated ten-minute intervals [11-13]. After every soaking period (10 minutes), the samples were dried in air at room temperature before doing the Raman or PL spectral mapping. **Figure 1** represents the experimental scheme. For the graphene samples, the Raman spectral mapping, and for the MoS_2 sample, both Raman and PL spectral mapping were performed with LabRAM HR (Horiba). The Raman spectra were measured using a 633nm laser excitation, and PL was measured using 532nm laser excitation, both with 600 l/mm grating. Both Raman and PL maps were recorded with a 2-micrometer (µm) step size. The atomic force microscopy (AFM) images were obtained with the Dimension Icon microscope (Bruker).

3. RESULTS AND DISCUSSION

Topographically two different graphene samples, named G1 and G2, were considered for the initial swelling experiment. The swollen SU8 imposed strain on the graphene samples, which can be quantified using the in-situ Raman spectroscopy, showing a phonon softening (blue shift) of the characteristic Raman peaks [14] [15]. The Raman 2D band, with frequency ω_{2D} ~2680cm^{-1}, was used to quantify the strain in the graphene samples instead of the G band ω_G ~1580cm^{-1}, because the 2D band is much more sensitive than the G band to biaxial strain effects [10,16,17]. The AFM topography (**Figure 2e**) shows a large flake with a high level of structural uniformity. The color-coded ω_{2D} map in **Figures 2 a-e** shows the evolution of the imposed strain for the soaking intervals of 10 minutes. The localized tensile strain in the graphene flake's center region received the maximum interfacial stress transfer from the polymer swelling (to ~2510 cm^{-1}, corresponding to 0.5 % of biaxial strain) after 40 minutes of soaking time. After that, the stress transfer between the polymer and graphene G1 failed.

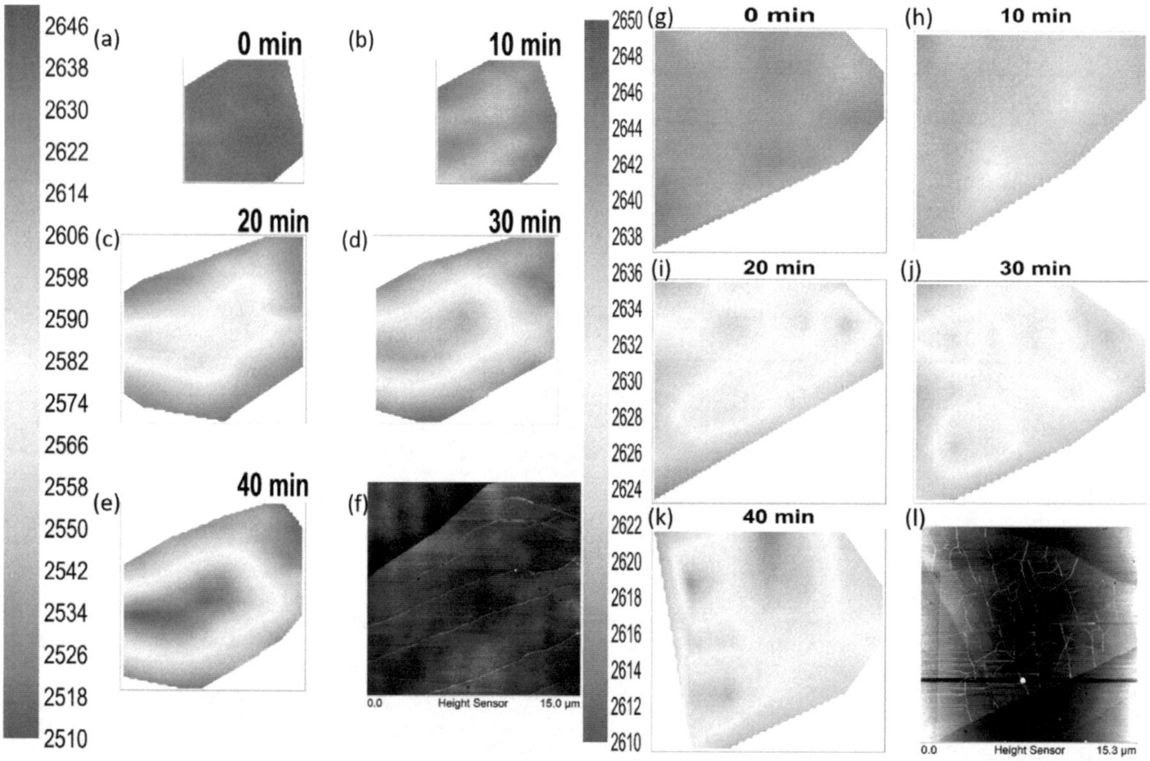

Figure 2 Evolution of Raman spectral features of monolayer graphene samples G1 and G2. (a-e), (g-k) show the Raman 2D band shift for different soaking times, in G1, and G2, respectively. (f), (l) the AFM topography images of G1 and G2, respectively, before soaking

In the same fashion, the topography of sample G2 was recorded before the soaking experiment. Sample G2 has more cracks, which separate the graphene into fragments of lateral dimension between 1-3 µm. **Figures 2 g-k** shows the color-coded Raman spectral maps of the 2D peak for the time intervals of 10 minutes. The imposed strain is not homogenous across the sample. The interfacial stress is very low in the small graphene domains, which results in the small and random strain in the sample G2. Although SU8 and graphene have an excellent interfacial stress transfer, the graphene grain boundaries restrict reaching such high strain levels as in the sample G1. The ω_{2D} and soaking time correlation plot, **Figure 3**, statistically compares the results from the two samples. **Figure 3** proves that smaller strain was imposed on the sample G2 compared to the sample G1. The median of the ω_{2D} shift reached in sample G1 corresponded to ~0.5%, and the maximum to more than 1% [18,19].

In the sample G2, less than 0.1% strain was achieved by the swelling experiment, evidencing the vital role of the grain boundaries present in an otherwise continuous flake. This because of the interfacial stress transfer

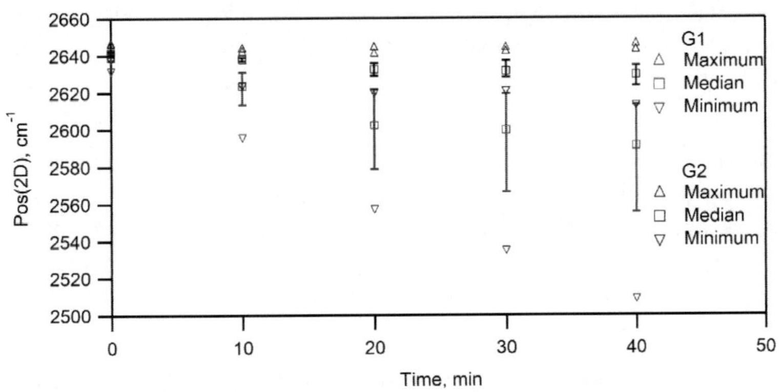

Figure 3 2D band shift of the G1 and G2 graphene samples for different soaking periods

failure at the edges of the graphene domains, i.e. boundaries [20]. The high stress-transfer in the sample G1 took place due to the absence of such boundaries.

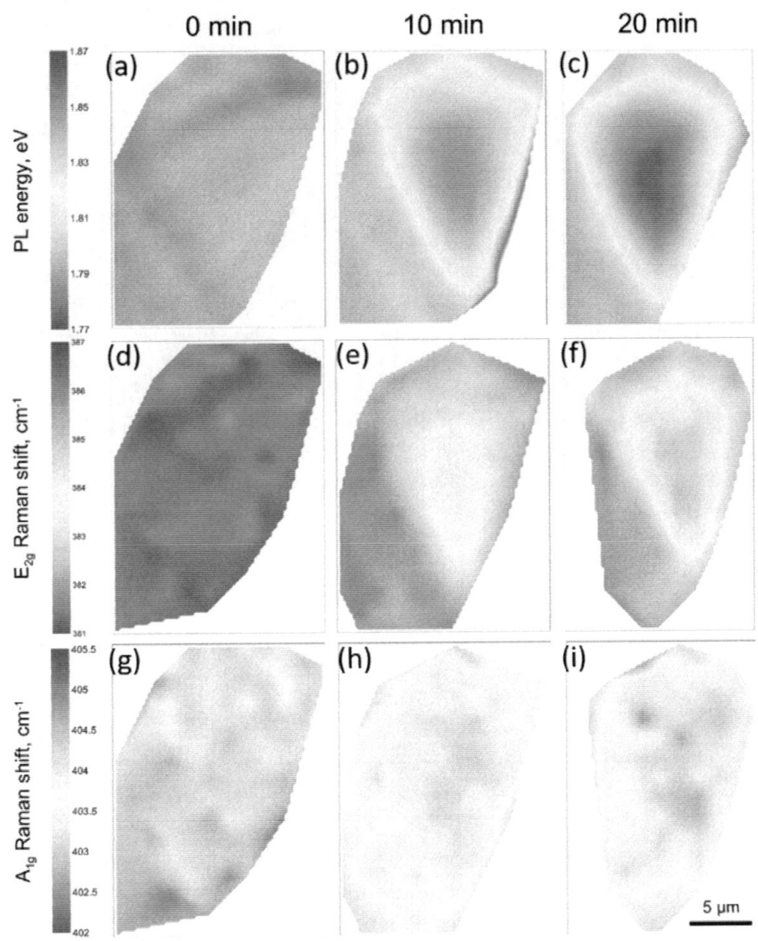

Figure 4 Evolution of PL and Raman spectral features of a monolayer MoS_2 sample. The shift in the color-coded (a-c) PL spectral map and Raman spectral map of E_{2g} (d-f) and A_1' (g-i) peaks for the different soaking period.

With the increasing soaking time, the extending size of the error bars in **Figure 3** for both G1 and G2 samples confirms the evolution of a strain gradient across the flakes. This evolution of the strain with the soaking time is evident as is the continuous strain gradient in the achieved biaxial strain on these atomically thin graphene layers [15,21].

We employ the same swelling technique to impose the biaxial strain on another 2D material, namely monolayer MoS_2. Since the MoS_2 has a different Raman signature than graphene, we considered the frequencies of the in-plane vibrational peak (E' or E_{2g}) at 386cm^{-1} and the out-of-plane vibrational peak (A_1') at 406 cm^{-1} to quantify the strain evolution in MoS_2. Besides the Raman modes, we employed the PL signal of the A exciton at ~1.88eV. The PL redshift as well as the Raman peaks' blue shift correspond to the tensile strain in the MoS2 sample [22,23].

The color-coded maps in **Figures 4 a-c** show the PL map of the MoS_2 flake as a response to the soaking times. To simplify the analysis, we treated both the A neutral exciton and trion as a single PL peak. **Figures 4 d-f** and g-i show the E' and A_1' peak shifts, respectively, as a result of the different soaking times [9]. As expected, the shift of the E' peak is larger than the shift of the A_1' peak for the given soaking time, due to the in-plane character of the E' mode and thus an increased sensitivity to an in-plane deformation. The stress transfer from the polymer to the MoS_2 flake failed after 20 minutes of soaking due to small size of the MoS_2 flake.

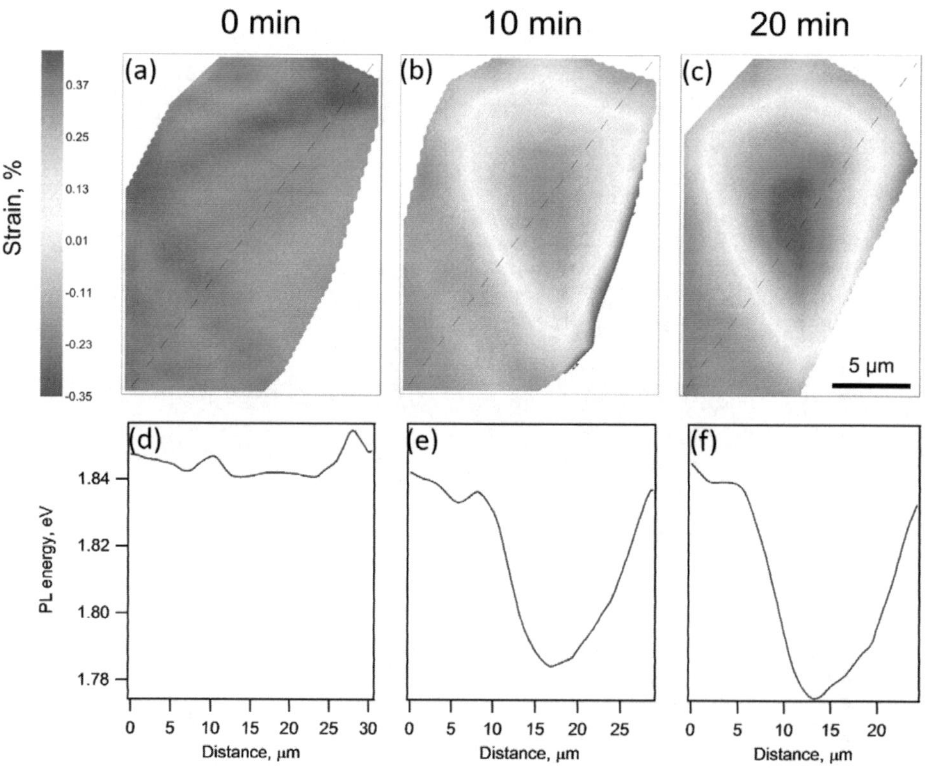

Figure 5 Evolution of biaxial strain quantified from the PL shift in MoS_2 for the different soaking times. (a-c) Maps of lattice deformation and (d-f) the corresponding PL shift from the profiles extracted diagonally, along the dashed lines in a-c.

Due to a relatively smaller strain-sensitivity of either of the Raman modes to small strains, PL A exciton peak was considered to quantify the imposed strain on the MoS_2 flake. Approximately maximum of 0.6% of biaxial strain was imposed on the center of the MoS_2 flake after 20 minutes of soaking time [23]. According to the

Raman shifts, a potential change in charge-transfer doping during the experiment was negligible, as the ratio of the E' and A_1' shifts corresponds to a pure effect of strain [24,25]. The profile across the color-coded PL spectral map in **Figure 5** shows the redshift in PL at different soaking times localized at the centre of the continuous MoS_2 flake where the highest strain was achieved. The profile extracted from **Figure 5 c** (i.e. **Figure 5 f**) shows the PL energy gradient forming a potential energy funnel imposed by the biaxial strain. Such an energy funneling, if even higher strain could be achieved as maxima, could be used in applications to power future devices [26-29].

4. CONCLUSION

We evidence that biaxial strain can be imposed on atomically thin monolayers of graphene and MoS_2 using the swelling of their polymer substrates by methanol. The Raman spectral shift of the 2D band was used to quantify the strain evolution in graphene, while in the case of MoS_2 also photoluminescence was employed. The stress transfer failed after 40 minutes of soaking time for graphene and after 20 minutes of soaking time for MoS_2. The different soaking time is due to the different sizes of the flakes or domains within. The large flake size can bear the more considerable biaxial deformation in the swelling experiment. The smaller flake size or more abundant sample boundaries fail to transfer the strain at an earlier soaking time. In both graphene and MoS_2, the biaxial strain is tensile corresponding to the volume swelling of the substrate. Hence, the MoS_2 band gap energy was decreased as the effect of the imposed biaxial strain, and the median strain level achieved was 0.5% in both graphene and MoS_2.

ACKNOWLEDGEMENTS

We acknowledge the support of the Grant Agency of the Czech Republic under the contract GJ18-06498Y and the support of internal grant of CEITEC VUT/FEKT-J-20-6541.The support of the European Regional Development Fund; OP RDE; Project: "Carbon allotropes with rationalized nano interfaces and nano links for environmental and biomedical applications" (No. CZ.02.1.01/0.0/0.0/16_026/0008382) is also acknowledged.

REFERENCES

[1] GUINEA, F. Strain engineering in graphene. *Solid State Communications*. 2012; vol. 152, no. 15, pp. 1437-41.

[2] DENG, S., SUMANT, A.V., BERRY, V. Strain engineering in two-dimensional nanomaterials beyond graphene. *Nano Today*. 2018; vol. 22, pp. 14-35.

[3] SI C., SUN Z., LIU F. Strain engineering of graphene: a review. *Nanoscale*. 2016; vol. 8, no. 6, pp. 3207-17.

[4] SCIDÀ, A., HAQUE, S., TREOSSI, E., ROBINSON, A., SMERZI, S., RAVESI, S. et al. Application of graphene-based flexible antennas in consumer electronic devices. *Materials Today*. 2018, vol. 21, no. 3, pp. 223-30.

[5] ANDROULIDAKIS, C., KOUKARAS, E.N., SAMPATHKUMAR, K., PARTHENIOS, J., PAPAGELIS, K., FRANK, O. et al. Wrinkled Few-Layer Graphene as Highly Efficient Load Bearer. *ACS Applied Materials & Interfaces*. 2017; vol. 9, no. 31, pp. 26593-601.

[6] SHUNDO, A., HORI, K., PENALOZA, D.P., YOSHIHIRO, K., ANNAKA, M., TANAKA, K. Nonsolvents-induced swelling of poly(methyl methacrylate) nanoparticles. *Physical Chemistry Chemical Physics*. 2013, vol. 15, no. 39, p.16574.

[7] SAUNDERS, J.E., CHEN, H., BRAUER, C., CLAYTON, M., CHEN, W., BARNES, J.A., et al. Quantitative diffusion and swelling kinetic measurements using large-angle interferometric refractometry. *Soft Matter*. 2015, vol. 11, no. 45, pp. 8746-57.

[8] KIM, H-N, KANG, J-H, JIN, W-M, MOON, J.H. Surface modification of 2D/3D SU-8 patterns with a swelling-deswelling method. *Soft Matter*. 2011, vol. 7, no. 6, pp.2989-93.

[9] HE, X., LI, H., ZHU, Z., DAI, Z., YANG, Y., YANG, P. et al. Strain engineering in monolayer WS2, MoS2, and the WS2/MoS2 heterostructure. *Applied Physics Letters*. 2016, vol. 109, no. 17, p. 173105.

[10] MUELLER, N.S., HEEG, S., ALVAREZ, M.P., KUSCH, P., WASSERROTH, S., CLARK, N. et al. Evaluating arbitrary strain configurations and doping in graphene with Raman spectroscopy. *2D Materials*. 2017, vol. 5, no. 1, p. 015016.

[11] WOUTERS, K., PUERS, R. Diffusing and swelling in SU-8: insight in material properties and processing. *Journal of Micromechanics and Microengineering*. 2010, vol. 20, no. 9, p. 095013.

[12] PAPANU, J.S., HESS, D.W., SOANE, (SOONG) D.S., BELL, A.T. Swelling of poly(methyl methacrylate) thin films in low molecular weight alcohols. *Journal of Applied Polymer Science*. 1990, vol. 39, no. 4, pp. 803-23.

[13] YI, L., XIAODONG, W., CHONG, L., ZHIFENG, L., DENAN, C., DEHUI, Y. Swelling of SU-8 structure in Ni mold fabrication by UV-LIGA technique. *Microsystem Technologies*. 2005, vol. 11, no. 12, pp.1272-5.

[14] JIE, W., YU HUI Y., ZHANG, Y., PING, LAU S, HAO, J. Effects of controllable biaxial strain on the Raman spectra of monolayer graphene prepared by chemical vapor deposition. *Applied Physics Letters*. 2013, vol. 102, no. 22, p. 223112.

[15] ZABEL, J, NAIR, R.R., OTT, A., GEORGIOU, T., GEIM, A.K., NOVOSELOV, K.S. et al. Raman Spectroscopy of Graphene and Bilayer under Biaxial Strain: Bubbles and Balloons. *Nano Letters*. 2012, vol.12, no. 2, pp. 617-21.

[16] BOUSIGE, C., BALIMA, F., MACHON, D., PINHEIRO, G.S., TORRES-DIAS, A., NICOLLE, J. et al. Biaxial Strain Transfer in Supported Graphene. *Nano Letters*. 2017, vol. 17, no. 1, pp. 21-7.

[17] TSOUKLERI, G., PARTHENIOS, J., PAPAGELIS, K., JALIL, R., FERRARI, A.C., GEIM, A.K. et al. Subjecting a Graphene Monolayer to Tension and Compression. *Small*. 2009, vol. 5, no. 21, pp. 2397-402.

[18] ANDROULIDAKIS, C., KOUKARAS, E.N., PARTHENIOS, J., KALOSAKAS, G., PAPAGELIS, K., GALIOTIS, C. Graphene flakes under controlled biaxial deformation. *Scientific Reports*. 2016, vol. 5, no. 1, p. 18219.

[19] SAMPATHKUMAR, K., DIEZ-CABANES, V., KOVARICEK, P., DEL CORRO, E., BOUŠA, M., HOŠEK, J. et al. On the Suitability of Raman Spectroscopy to Monitor the Degree of Graphene Functionalization by Diazonium Salts. *The Journal of Physical Chemistry C*. 2019, vol. 123, no. 36, pp. 22397-402.

[20] ANAGNOSTOPOULOS, G., ANDROULIDAKIS, C., KOUKARAS, E.N., TSOUKLERI, G., POLYZOS, I., PARTHENIOS, J. et al. Stress Transfer Mechanisms at the Submicron Level for Graphene/Polymer Systems. *ACS Applied Materials & Interfaces*. 2015, vol. 7, no. 7, pp. 4216-23.

[21] FU, X., SU, C., FU, Q., ZHU, X., ZHU, R., LIU, C. et al. Tailoring Exciton Dynamics by Elastic Strain-Gradient in Semiconductors. *Advanced Materials*. 2014, vol. 26, no. 16, pp. 2572-9.

[22] PAN, H., ZHANG, Y-W. Tuning the electronic and magnetic properties of MoS2 nanoribbons by strain engineering. *The Journal of Physical Chemistry C*. 2012, vol. 116, no. 21, pp. 11752-7.

[23] LLOYD, D., LIU, X., CHRISTOPHER, J.W., CANTLEY, L., WADEHRA, A., KIM, B.L., et al. Band Gap Engineering with Ultralarge Biaxial Strains in Suspended Monolayer MoS2. *Nano Letters*. 2016, vol. 16, no. 9, pp. 5836-41.

[24] KOU, L., DU, A., CHEN, C., FRAUENHEIM, T. Strain engineering of selective chemical adsorption on monolayer MoS 2. *Nanoscale*. 2014, vol. 6, no. 10, pp. 5156-61.

[25] MICHAIL, A., DELIKOUKOS, N., PARTHENIOS, J., GALIOTIS, C., PAPAGELIS, K. Optical detection of strain and doping inhomogeneities in single layer MoS2. *Applied Physics Letters*. 2016, vol. 108, no. 17, p.173102.

[26] CASTELLANOS-GOMEZ, A., ROLDÁN, R., CAPPELLUTI, E., BUSCEMA, M., GUINEA, F., VAN DER ZANT, H.S.J., et al. Local strain engineering in atomically thin MoS2. *Nano letters*. 2013, vol. 13, no. 11, pp. 5361-6.

[27] DING, Z., PEI, Q-X, JIANG, J-W, ZHANG, Y-W. Manipulating the thermal conductivity of monolayer MoS2 via lattice defect and strain engineering. *The Journal of Physical Chemistry C*. 2015, vol. 119, no. 28, pp. 16358-65.

[28] TYURNINA, A.V., BANDURIN, D.A., KHESTANOVA, E., KRAVETS, V.G., KOPERSKI, M., GUINEA, F. et al. Strained Bubbles in van der Waals Heterostructures as Local Emitters of Photoluminescence with Adjustable Wavelength. *ACS Photonics*. 2019, vol. 6, no. 2, pp.516-24.

[29] MOON, H., BERSIN, E., CHAKRABORTY, C., LU, A-Y, GROSSO, G., KONG, J. et al. Strain-Correlated Localized Exciton Energy in Atomically Thin Semiconductors. *ACS Photonics*. 2020, vol. 7, no. 5, pp. 1135-40.

SIMULATION AND DIAGNOSTICS OF PLASMACHEMICAL PROCESSES DURING MICROWAVE PLASMA SYNTHESIS OF GRAPHENE NANOSHEETS FROM ETHANOL

[1]Vít KUDRLE, [1]Miroslav SNIRER, [1]Jozef TOMAN, [1]Martin KUBEČKA, [1]Jana JURMANOVÁ, [1]Ondřej JAŠEK, [2]František KRČMA

[1]*Department of Physical Electronics, Faculty of Science, Masaryk University, Brno, Czech Republic, EU, kudrle@sci.muni.cz*

[2]*Institute of Physical and Applied Chemistry, Brno University of Technology, Brno, Czech Republic, EU*

https://doi.org/10.37904/nanocon.2020.3691

Abstract

Plasma synthesis by ethanol decomposition in microwave atmospheric torch is a simple, efficient, single-step scalable method suitable for volume production of graphene nanosheets. In our work, we studied influence of microwave power on several plasma parameters (e.g. gas temperature, concentration of active species) by optical emission spectroscopy (OES), Fourier transform infrared spectrometry (FTIR) and mass spectrometry (MS) to better understand the process of precursor decomposition and graphene formation in the gas phase. We observed significant change in kinetics and influence of input power on ethanol decomposition routes. Results were compared with theoretical model comprising hydrodynamics, plasma, heat transfer and chemical kinetics.

Keywords: Graphene, microwave plasma torch, OES, ethanol, modelling

1. INTRODUCTION

Atmospheric pressure plasma synthesis of advanced materials, including the graphene nanosheets, brings some advantages over competing methods e.g. liquid phase exfoliation and chemical vapour deposition. While commonly used, these techniques have their limitations in a need of a substrate or a post-treatment to obtain separated high-quality graphene. In contrast, a microwave plasma synthesis of graphene is a rather recent method [1,2,3] based on decomposition of organic precursors which in many aspects overcomes these limitations. It is mostly single step, without all the complexities of the wet process, uses simple equipment and affordable precursors, etc. However, the inherent nonlinearities of plasma, its spatial inhomogeneities and non-equilibrium kinetics make the process critically dependent on optimal local conditions. This in turn makes the analysing, controlling and up-scaling quite a challenge.

Material analyses of the graphene product by e.g. electron microscopy (SEM, TEM) and/or Raman spectroscopy can be carried out for various experimental conditions. While they provide ultimate results about the product quality, the causes can remain hidden. The diagnostics of the synthesis process itself is thus needed. The optical emission spectroscopy (OES) provides localised information, but only on radiating species, However, the more complex organic molecules involved in graphene growth are often formed later, outside the active plasma itself. These can be detected by standard chemical gas analysis techniques, such as Fourier transform infrared (FTIR), gas chromatography (GC) and mass spectroscopy (MS) but these are ex-situ and cannot provide localised information.

In this paper we combine these diagnostic techniques with a theoretical model, which couples heat transfer, gas dynamics and chemical kinetics, to get deeper insight into plasmachemical processes during the graphene synthesis.

2. EXPERIMENTAL SET-UP

The plasma torch was excited by a 2.45 GHz microwave generator with a power variable in the 10-500 W range. The generator fed a microwave waveguide line ending with a transition to rigid coaxial transition. Its central conductor (6 mm diameter) was hollow which enabled passing of multiple gas lines inside. It ended in an exchangeable carbon nozzle with dual flow configuration enhancing the plasma stability [3]. The central (axial) channel (0.8 mm diameter) was used for argon (300-1000 sccm). The precursor (ethanol vapour from a bubbler, 10-700 sccm argon carrier gas) is introduced to an outer (annular) channel, shown in **Figure 1**.

Plasma reactor consisted of fused silica tube (80 mm diameter, 200 mm long) terminated by a duralumin flange. The exhaust gas samples from the T-piece were collected in transportable cuvette for later FTIR and GC analysis. Optical emission spectra were recorded through the reactor walls and magnifying optical system using Jobin Yvon Triax 550 spectrometer. Digital imaging was performed using intensified CCD Pi-MAX 3 camera equipped with 100 mm macro UV lens. Set of interference filters was used for spectral imaging. Deposited nanomaterial was collected from the reactor walls for further analysis. Graphene nanosheets were imaged with scanning electron microscope (SEM) TESCAN MIRA3 with Schottky field emission electron gun. Raman spectroscopy was carried out using the HORIBA LabRAM HR Evolution system with 532 nm laser, using 100x objective, 600 gr/mm grating and 30 s acquisition time in the range from 1000 to 3200 cm^{-1}.

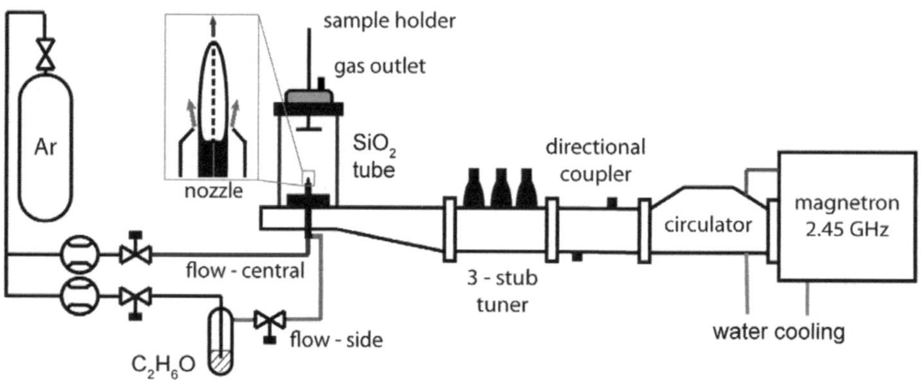

Figure 1 Experimental set-up

3. THEORETICAL MODEL

COMSOL Multiphysics was used for solving our model combining the gas dynamics, heat transfer and chemical reactions. Two-dimensional axially symmetric domain was used to simulate the geometry of our experimental reactor. The model takes the experimentally measured plasma plume dimensions as an input for the gas heat source. The gas flow is considered to be non-isotermal and turbulent. The main gas flow (500 sccm of argon) to the domain is introduced via the central (axial) channel, and the outer annular channel supplied 700 sccm of argon with 10 sccm of ethanol vapours. The reduced chemical reaction scheme of the ethanol decomposition was taken from A. Merino [4] and consists of 66 reactions and 31 species.

4. RESULTS AND DISCUSSION

The dual flow configuration, where the precursor was introduced into the outer channel while the active plasma itself was burning mostly in pure argon, proved to be very stable and efficient in ethanol conversion. The discharge had a form of stable, axially symmetric filament which length depended linearly on absorbed microwave power (behaviour typical for surface wave driven discharges [5]). Optical emission spectroscopy showed (**Figure 2**) that emissions were dominated by very intense molecular C_2 Swan band system (maximum at 516 nm). Despite the precautions (argon flushing, tightened seals, etc.), there were still traces of air in our apparatus, as exhibited by strong emissions of cyan violet system CN(B-X) (maximum at 388 nm). The atomic carbon C was also detected at 247 nm but with rather small intensity. High intensity of C_2 bands suggest higher concentrations of C_2 which serves as precursor for graphene formation while atomic C often leads to formation of amorphous structures [6].

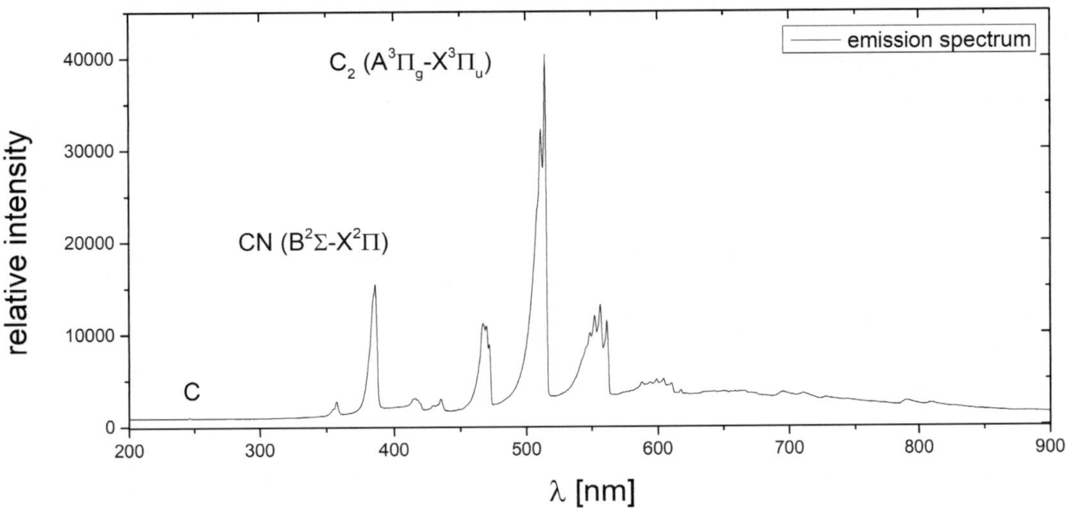

Figure 2 Overview emission spectra for 500 sccm Ar (central), 700 sccm Ar+EtOH (annular), 200 W

Rotational structure of the violet CN system is often used for calculation of rotational temperature which can estimate the gas temperature in carbon containing plasmas [3,7,8]. This procedure can be done manually, or by using e.g. Lifbase [9] or MassiveOES [10] software. The gas temperature is an important parameter which strongly influences plasma chemistry and ethanol decomposition routes. **Figure 3 (left)** shows temperature distributions of the filament along the axis for two different MW powers.

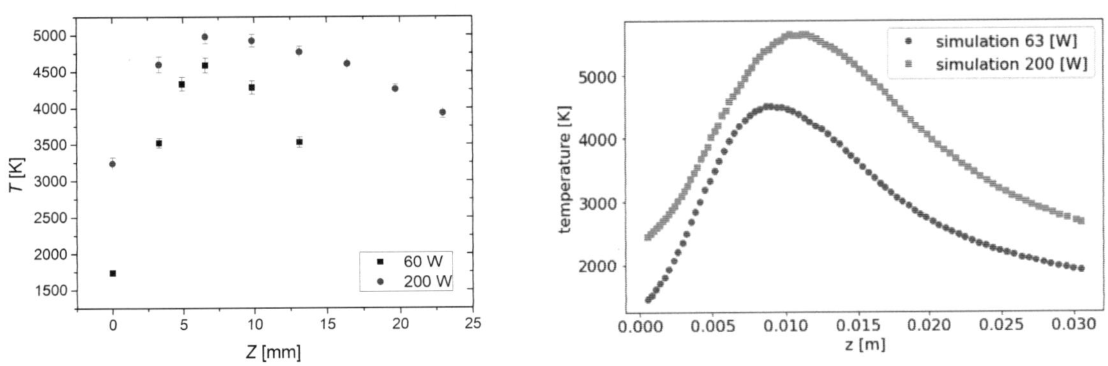

Figure 3 Gas temperature distribution - experimental (left (TROT (CN)), modelled (right) for 60 W a 200 W, 500 sccm Ar (axial), 700 sccm Ar+EtOH (annular)

The theoretical model can provide better insight into plasma phenomena, producing, among others, spatial distribution of temperature or chemical species abundance. A comparison between experimental and modelled axial temperature profile is shown in **Figure 3**. Current model tends to underestimate the temperature further from the nozzle. This may be solved with right coupling of the energy transfer from excited argon metastables to the other species.

While maximum temperature reached 4500 K threshold for effective formation of solid carbon [11] in both investigated conditions, higher microwave power fulfilled this condition in majority of its length, giving opportunity to formation of C2 and growth of planar structures over longer distance.

Analysis of exhaust gas showed that, as expected, the decomposition of ethanol was more complete for higher microwave power, see **Figure 4**. For lower microwave power (or high ethanol flow) the FTIR spectra are more complex as many intermediary species are present: methane, ethane, ethylene, acetylene, diacetylene, ethanol, CO, CO2, H2O, HCN. For higher microwave power (or low ethanol flow) only the acetylene, methane, ethylene, CO, CO2 can be found in the FTIR spectrum. Overall, the main gaseous products of ethanol plasma decomposition are the acetylene and CO.

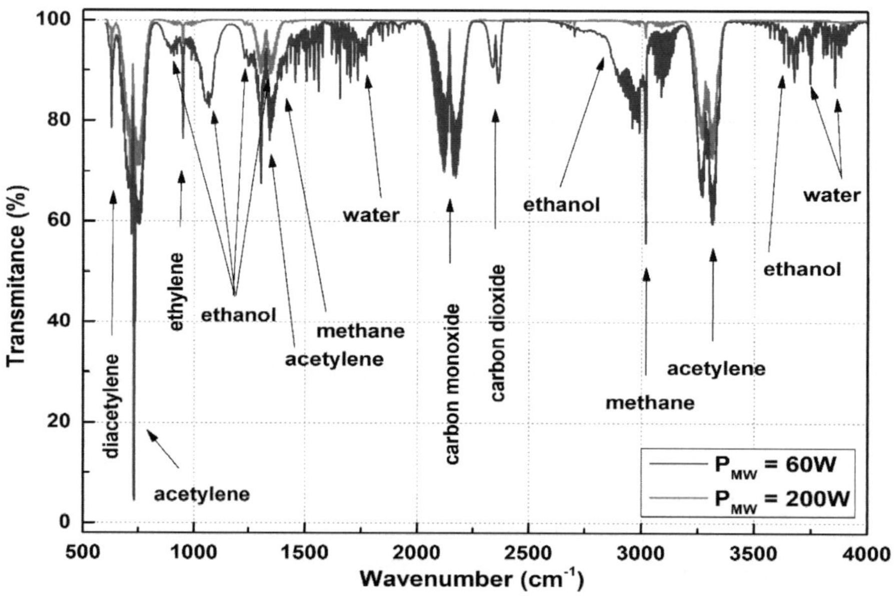

Figure 4 FTIR analysis of the exhaust gas for two microwave powers

The TOF MS spectra of the exhaust gas show a rich mixture of organic compounds with molecular weights mostly up to 132 amu. The repeating pattern with period of 26 amu suggests a significant role of -C_2H_2- group. Acetylene line (mass 26 amu) is present, too, but its signal can be masked by CN with the same mass. The presence of CN in the gas is known from OES spectra taken from the active plasma region. The limited mass range of the spectrometer together with 1 m long sampling tube precluded the direct detection of the heavy carbon clusters of forming graphene.

SEM images show substantial differences in the structure of solid carbon nanomaterial produced at 60 W or 200 W of microwave power (**Figure 5**). At low power mode, lower gas temperatures are achieved leading to incomplete decomposition of ethanol resulting in the synthesis of spherical amorphous carbon nanoparticles instead of planar graphene nanosheets. Previous FTIR and TOF MS investigations provide important information about the gaseous products and an insight into the construction process. The simpler product structure dominated by CO (inevitable biproduct) and C_2H_2 (growth) at higher power homogenizes the growth leading to the hexagonal graphene lattice. The Raman spectroscopy (**Figure 6**) reveals a substantial difference in material properties. Intensive 2D peak together with relatively low D peak are evidence for few-layer graphene nanosheets with a relatively low amount of lattice defects. On the other hand, the reduced intensity of 2D peak and the broad and intensive D peak suggests presence of highly amorphous bulk material synthesized at lower microwave power.

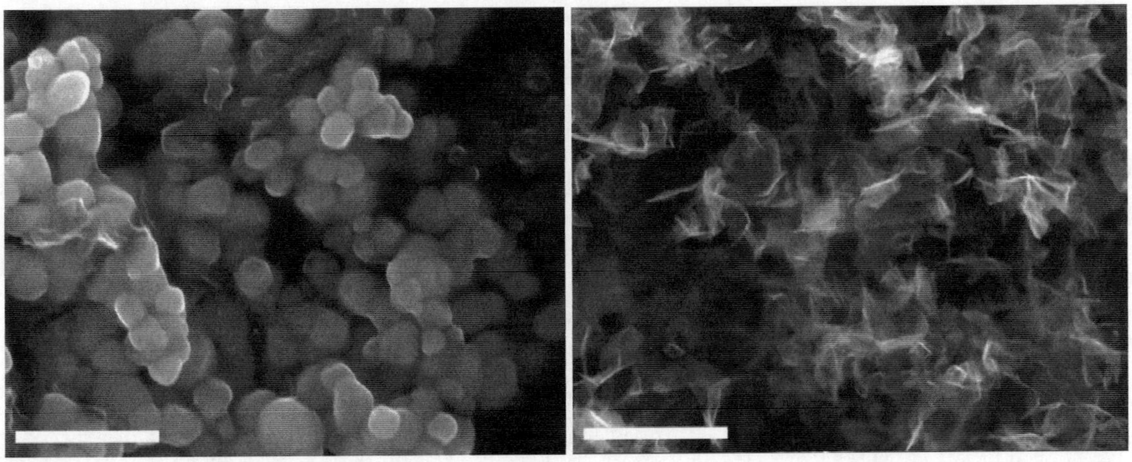

Figure 5 SEM image for 60 W (left) and 200 W (right), 500 sccm Ar (central), 700 sccm Ar+EtOH (annular). The scale bar represents 500nm

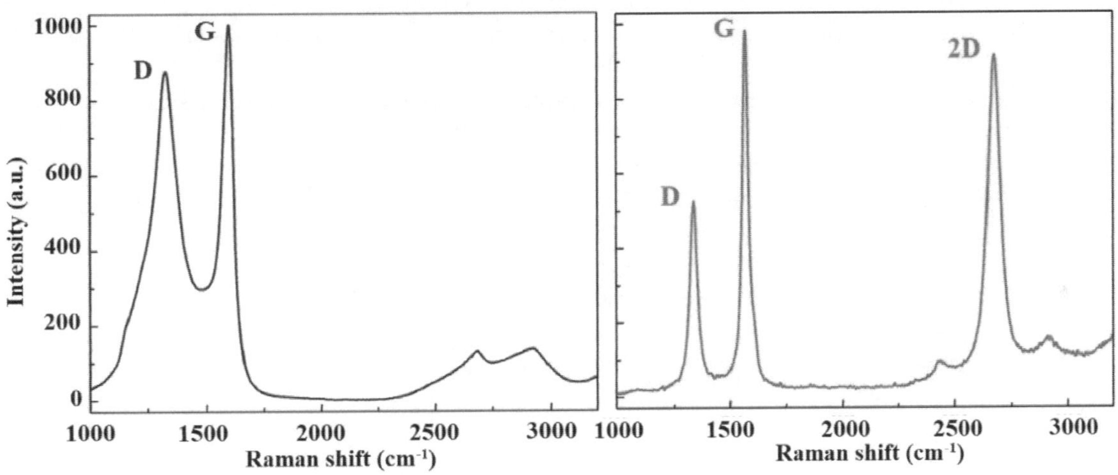

Figure 6 Raman spectra for 60 W (left) and 200 W (right), 500 sccm Ar (central), 700 sccm Ar+EtOH (annular)

5. CONCLUSION

Microwave power absorbed in the discharge can directly influence the gas temperature and gas kinetics during the synthesis of graphene nanosheets. Optical emission spectroscopy in conjunction with FTIR and mass spectrometry helped us identify the main species present in the process of ethanol decomposition under low and high plasma temperatures. The measured temperature profile of microwave discharge was in good agreement with modelling of plasma discharge under selected conditions showing maximum temperature in the main decomposition region 10 mm above the discharge nozzle. Nanosheets prepared in low power regime exhibited highly defective structure, high D/G Raman band ratio, in comparison to nanosheets prepared at a higher power, higher temperature regime. SEM images revealed structural change from amorphous nanoparticles to graphene which was directly related to generation of growth species (C_2H_2, C_2) as determined by OES and FTIR.

ACKNOWLEDGEMENTS

This work was supported by The Czech Science Foundation under project 18-08520S and in part by project LM2018097 funded by the Ministry of Education, Youth and Sports of the Czech Republic.

REFERENCES

[1] TATAROVA, E., et al. Microwave plasma based single step method for free standing graphene synthesis at atmospheric conditions. *Applied Physics Letters*. 2013, vol. 103, no. 13, p. 134101.

[2] MELERO, C., et al. Scalable graphene production from ethanol decomposition by microwave argon plasma torch. *Plasma Physics and Controlled Fusion*. 2016, vol. 60, p. 014009.

[3] TOMAN, J., et al. On the interplay between plasma discharge instability and formation of free-standing graphene nanosheets in a dual-channel microwave plasma torch at atmospheric pressure. *Journal of Physics D: Applied Physics*. 2019, vol. 52, no. 26, p. 265205.

[4] MERINO, A., et al. A multipurpose reduced mechanism for ethanol combustion. *Combustion and Flame*. 2018, vol. 193, pp. 112-122.

[5] MOISAN, M. et al. Contribution of surface-wave (SW) sustained plasma columns to the modeling of RF and microwave discharges with new insight into some of their features. A survey of other types of SW discharges. *Plasma Sources Science and Technology*. 2018, vol. 27, no. 7, p. 073001.

[6] TATAROVA, E., et al. Microwave plasmas applied for the synthesis of free standing graphene sheets. *Journal of Physics D: Applied Physics*. 2014, vol. 47, p. 385501.

[7] NASSAR, H. CN violet system spectrum used as a molecular pyrometer and the influence noise to signal ratio on the temperature values. *J. Phys. Conf. Ser.* 2012, vol. 370, p. 012050.

[8] MOON, S. Y., et al. Temperature measurement of an atmospheric pressure arc discharge plasma jet using the diatomic CN (BΣ+2-XΣ+2, violet system) molecular spectra. *J. Appl. Phys.* 2009, vol. 105, p. 053307

[9] LUQUE, J., LIFBASE, S. software, Database and Spectral Simulation for Diatomic Molecules.

[10] VORÁČ, J., et al. Deducing Rotational Quantum-State Distributions from Overlapping Molecular Spectra. *The Review of Scientific Instruments*. 2019, vol. 90, no. 12, p. 123102.

[11] RINCÓN, R., et al. Experimental research on ethanol-chemistry decomposition routes in a microwave plasma torch for hydrogen production. *Chemical Engineering Journal*. 2016, vol. 284, pp. 1117-26.

THE SENSING PROPERTIES OF CARBON NANOTUBE FILLED COPOLYMERS FOR VOC VAPORS DETECTION

Rostislav SLOBODIAN, Robert OLEJNÍK, Jiří MATYÁŠ, Petr SLOBODIAN

Tomas Bata University in Zlín, University Institute, Centre of Polymer Systems, Zlín, Czech Republic, EU,
rslobodian@utb.cz, olejnik@utb.cz, matyas@utb.cz, slobodian@utb.cz

https://doi.org/10.37904/nanocon.2020.3695

Abstract

Nowadays, carbon nanotubes are a widely available material, especially multiwall carbon nanotubes. In addition to many other applications, they find use in all kinds of sensors, like deformation, motion, tensile and pressure responsive elements. Numerous applications in sensors for volatile organic compounds (VOCs) are reported as well, nevertheless, they mainly suffer from low selectivity. Therefore, in this research, a sensor containing MWCNTs dispersed in a functional polymer matrix was prepared. As a polymer matrix, styrene-isoprene-styrene elastomer was chosen. The standard sensing mechanism of entangled MWCNTs is based on the quality of the contacts (charge transfer) between the individual nanotubes. In the prepared nanocomposite, the mechanism is modified due to the presence of the otherwise non-conductive matrix. The changes of conductivity depend on the response of the percolating nanotube filler network to the swelling of the polymer matrix due to adsorption of VOCs. The tested gas substances have high values of diffusion coefficient for the polymer, so they have a quick response. Then, the selectivity is ensured by differences in solubility of the tested VOCs in the polymer. The effect was demonstrated for four VOCs differing by their affinity to the polymer matrix, namely, heptane, toluene, acetone, and ethanol.

Keywords: Carbon nanotubes, copolymer nanocomposite, organic vapour sensing, gas sensor

1. INTRODUCTION

Carbon nanotubes (CNTs) are one of the allotropic forms of carbon that attract considerable attention nowadays. The arrangement of sp2 carbon atoms looks like a graphene "honeycombs" sheet that is twisted into a tube. The origin of CNTs can be traced to their discovery in Japan by Sumio Iijima in 1991 [1]. These nanotubes have unique electrical and mechanical properties and have become very popular for scientific activities around the world. The nanotubes can be produced either in the single-wall form or in the form of multiwall carbon nanotubes (MWCNTs). The production of MWCNTs is relatively simple, and they are available in a large variety of commercial brands. Moreover, they have a large specific surface area and good electrical conductivity [2].

The electrical conductivity of clusters and structures from CNT is very sensitive to the absorption of volatile organic compounds (VOCs), and these structures have excellent properties as sensors for the detection of vapours and gases [3]. Adsorption/desorption of gaseous molecules occurs due to the interaction of organic vapours with the surface of carbon nanotubes. This process causes a change in electrical resistance. On the other hand, the electrical conductivity response of structures made from bare CNTs to the gaseous molecules suffers from low selectivity. Interaction with any electron-donating molecule causes an increase of the conductivity while interaction with any electron acceptor molecules results in a decrease of the conductivity [4]. Therefore, we propose to prepare the entangled CNT structure in a polymer matrix, which will selectively interact with various VOC molecules. It is expected that a permeable thin soluble elastomeric material like styrene-isoprene-styrene (SIS) co-polymer is the most promising candidate for this purpose.

2. MATERIALS AND METHODS

For composite preparation, multiwall carbon nanotubes (MWCNTs) were used. The purified MWCNTs produced by chemical vapour deposition (CVD) from an acetylene precursor were delivered by Sun Nanotech Co. Ltd., China. The nanotube diameter was 10 - 30 nm, length 1 - 10 μm, purity > 90 % and specific electrical conductivity 0.12 $S.cm^{-1}$. [5,6]

The polymer matrix was copolymer Kraton D SIS (styrene-isoprene-styrene), which is a thermoplastic elastomer with a combination of advantageous properties such as high strength, low hardness and low viscosity in solution processing. MWCNTs dispersion was prepared in solution of Kraton in toluene, and it was sonicated at 40 °C for 15 minutes using the ultrasonic device UP 400 S. The concentration of MWCNTs in the dispersion was 11 wt. %. Interdigitated copper electrodes were made from Cuprexite (a layered structure made of 1 mm epoxy/glass laminate coated with a 35 μm thick Cu film by etching with a 30 % solution of $FeCl_3$ in water at room temperature. The copper electrodes were soaked in the copolymer MWCNTs dispersion for 10 seconds to form an active scanning layer on the surface, and they were then allowed to dry at 25 °C for 48 hours. The thickness of the ensuing nanocomposite layer was about 150 μm. [7]

To analyze the surface of the polymer composite, Phenom G2-Edlin scanning electron microscope (SEM) was used.

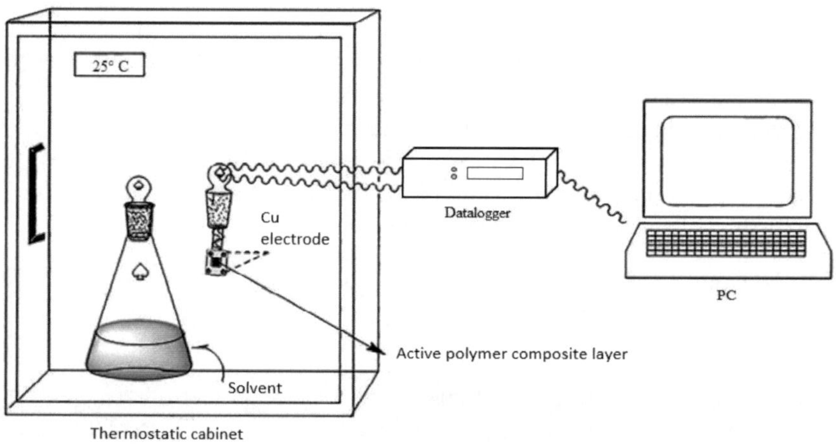

Figure 1 Experimental system for measuring resistance change

The electrical resistance was measured using a Multiplexed Data Logger 34980 connected to a PC (**Figure 1**), where the measured resistivity data was read every 1 s. The electrode with the active scanning layer was closed in an Erlenmeyer flask containing an organic solvent. These organic vapours were either an aliphatic hydrocarbon (heptane), aromatic hydrocarbon (toluene), ketone (acetone) or alcohol (ethanol). It took 6 min before the electrode with an active layer detected organic solvent vapours by changing its electrical resistance. The nanocomposite electrical resistance was quantified by the relative electrical resistance change defined as

$$\Delta R/R_0 = \frac{(R - R_0)}{R_0} \qquad (1)$$

where:

R_0 - is the electrical resistance of the composite before the exposition to vapour (Ω)

R - is the resistance during the exposition of the holder with the coated interdigitated electrode by the nanocomposite (Ω)

After this time, the electrode was pulled out of the flask and the desorption cycle was started in the thermostatic cabinet for 6 min at 25 °C. These cycles of absorption/desorption were repeated five times. The measurement was made under atmospheric pressure, at a temperature of 25 °C and relative humidity of 40 % in the thermostatic cabinet [7].

3. RESULTS AND DISCUSSION

Photographs of the interdigitated electrode substrate and the prepared sensor can be seen in **Figure 2a)** and **b)**, respectively. The soaking method was used to achieve a good surface coverage. The surface morphology of the cast polymer composite layer is shown in images in **Figures 2c)** and **d)**. The relief structure the composite resembles an irregular landscape of a coral reef. Fissures and valleys of white appearance can be observed within the continuous black polymer composite phase. Small bright homogeneously distributed spots are observable in the polymer matrix. These spots may be attributed to asperities caused by local entanglements of CNTs. Thus, the composite layer should be capable of detection of macroscopic electrical resistance change due to interconnected CNT structures.

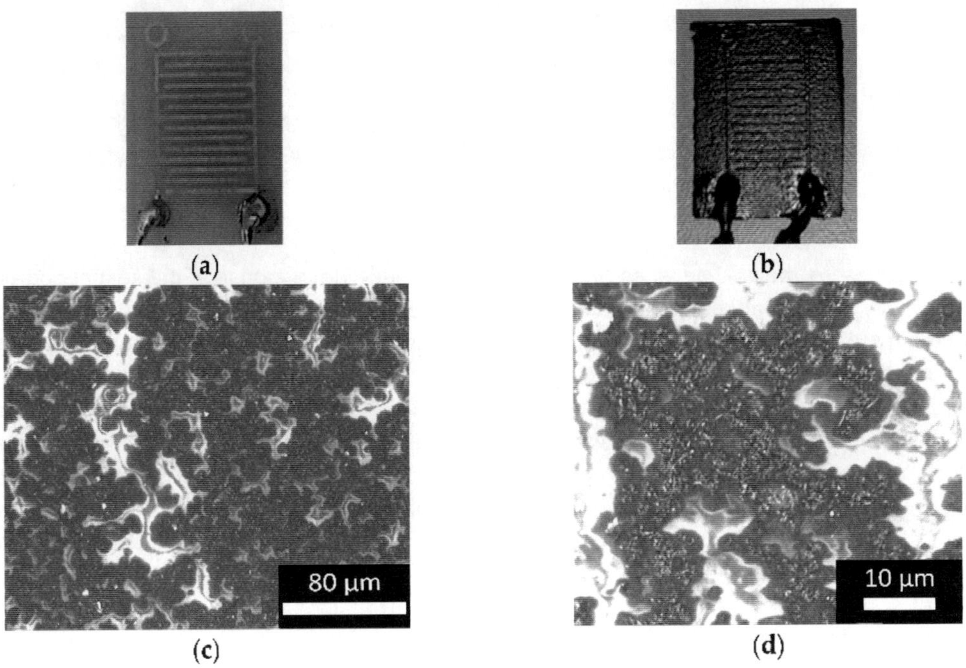

Figure 2 Photographs of (a) the copper interdigitated electrode substrate and (b) the electrode with a layer of polymer composite. SEM micrographs at lower (c) and higher (d) magnification

As stated earlier, the MWCNT/SIS composite sensor was exposed to the vapours of four organic solvents, namely toluene, acetone, ethanol, and heptane. The responses of the sensors to each of the tested vapours are plotted in **Figure 3**. The sensor response to the on/off cycle was recorded for five cycles. The curves have a typical shape of adsorption/desorption response. The adsorption of vapour molecules causes an increase in the electrical resistance while desorption of vapour molecules results in its decrease.

The different sensitivity of the sensor towards the tested chemicals is clearly manifested in the graph. The presence of ethanol vapours produces only little change in the resistance. Acetone vapours have a small yet pronounced impact on the resistance change. By far the highest sensitivity was observed for heptane. In other words, the selectivity of the sensor was clearly confirmed by this experiment.

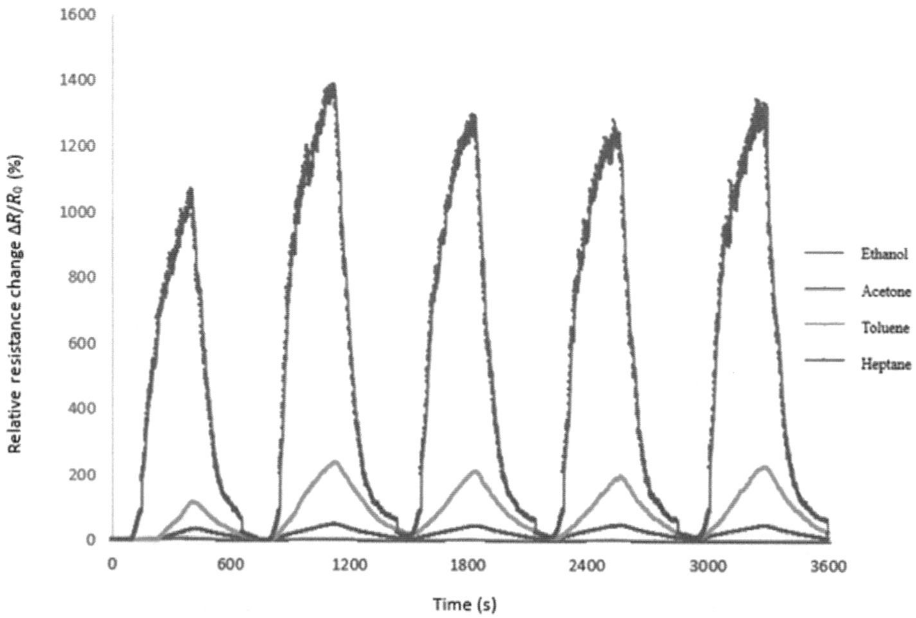

Figure 3 Time-dependent relative resistance of the MWCNT/SIS composite in the presence of heptane (purple), toluene (green), acetone (red) and ethanol (blue) during five consecutive adsorption/desorption cycles

Table 1 summarizes the maximum values $\Delta R/R_0$ for each solvent. The response of the sensor correlates with the hydrophobicity of the vapour molecules. Ethanol is a polar compound which does neither swell nor permeates the hydrophobic copolymer matrix. According to its molecular structure, acetone is of slightly less polar character than ethanol and is expected to permeate the copolymer matrix slowly, which results in the observed relatively small sensitivity among tested compounds. Toluene has a moderate influence on the resistance change, which is in accordance with its ability to dissolve both the styrene and isoprene blocks of the copolymer and moderate permeability through the copolymer [8]. The highest sensitivity of the sensor was observed for heptane. Heptane has the highest permeability through the copolymer among the tested chemicals, as reported earlier [8]. It is most likely due to its aliphatic hydrocarbon character that fits the molecular structure of the elastomer.

Table 1 Results of max. values $\Delta R/R_0$ of composite material in a given solvent

Solvents	**$\Delta R/R_0$ max. (%)**
Ethanol	8
Acetone	181
Toluene	761
Heptane	1388

4. CONCLUSION

This work aimed to facilitate the detection of volatile organic compounds by preparation of a new nanocomposite sensor. The results proved that the composite is able to detect ambient organic vapours, which in turn characteristically alter their electrical resistance. The sensor has the highest sensitivity for the vapour of heptane, followed by nearly two times lower sensitivity to toluene. A moderate response can be observed for vapour of acetone, and the lowest sensitivity is experienced for the vapour of ethanol. The choice of polymer matrix imparts the selectivity to the sensor due to differences in permeability and solubility of the tested VOCs in the styrene-isoprene-styrene copolymer. The conductivity of the percolating nanotube filler network responds significantly to the swelling of the polymer matrix.

Moreover, the gas sensor developed in our research is small in size and production costs are low. It can be practically used as a part of a universal device for identification of organic solvent vapours, so called "electronic nose". Further practical use of the sensor, such as in industry, is the subject of future research.

ACKNOWLEDGEMENTS

This research was funded by the Internal Grant Agency of the Tomas Bata University in Zlin, project number IGA/CPS/2019/007, and from the national budget of the Czech Republic, within the framework of the project CPS-strengthening research capacity (reg. number: CZ.1.05/2.1.00/19.0409). This work was also supported by the Ministry of Education, Youth and Sports of the Czech Republic - DKRVO (RP/CPS/2020/006). Assoc. Prof. Ivo Kuritka, Ph.D. is greatly acknowledged for fruitful discussions and help in recording SEM images.

REFERENCES

[1] WANG, Y., YEOW, J.T.W. A review of carbon nanotubes-based gas sensors. *Journal of Sensors.* [Online]. 2009, vol. 2009, Article ID 493904. Available from: https://doi.org/10.1155/2009/493904.

[2] LLOBET, E. Gas sensors using carbon nanomaterials: A review. *Sensors and Actuators B: Chemical.* 2013, vol. 179, pp. 32-45.

[3] SEPTIANI, N.L.W., YULIARTO, B. Review-The development of gas sensor based on carbon nanotubes. *Journal of the Electrochemical Society.* 2016, vol. 163, no. 3, pp. B97-B106.

[4] ZAPOROTSKOVA, I.V., BOROZNINA, N.P., PARKHOMENKO, Z.N., KOZHITOV, L.V. Carbon nanotubes: Sensor properties. A review. *Modern Electronic Materials.* 2016, vol. 2, no. 4, pp. 95-105.

[5] PRASEK, J., DRBOHLAVOVA, J., CHOMOUCKA, J., HUBALEK, J., JASEK, O., ADAM, V., KIZEK, R. Methods for carbon nanotubes synthesis-review. *Journal of Materials Chemistry.* 2011, vol. 21, pp. 15872-15884.

[6] CHOUDHARY, V., GUPTA, A. Polymer/Carbon Nanotube Nanocomposites. In: YELLAMPALLI, S. (ed.). *Carbon Nanotubes - Polymer Nanocomposites.* Rijeka: InTech, 2011. ISBN 978-953-307-498-6. Available from: http://www.intechopen.com/books/carbon-nanotubes-polymer-nanocomposites/polymer-carbon-nanotube-nanocomposites.

[7] OLEJNÍK, R., et al. Multi-wall carbon nanotube network prepared from pure MWCNT and their oxidised forms effect of compressive strain on electric resistence. In: *NANOCON 2010 - 2nd International conference.* Brno: TANGER Ltd., 2010, pp. 78-82.

[8] SLOBODIAN, P., RIHA, P., OLEJNIK, R. Electromechanical sensors based on carbon nanotube networks and their polymer composites. In: MUKHOPADHYAY, S.C., LAY-EKUAKILLE, A., FUCHS, A. (eds.) *New Developments and Applications in Sensing Technology.* New York, USA: SpringerVerlag, 2011, pp. 233-251.

DIELECTRICAL ANALYSIS OF COMPOSITE MATERIALS WITH RECYCLED CARBON FIBERS

[1]Jana NOVOTNÁ, [1]Blanka TOMKOVÁ, [2]Jana MÜLLEROVÁ

[1]Department of Material Engineering, Technical University of Liberec, Faculty of Textile engineering, Liberec, Czech Republic, EU, jana.novotna3@tul.cz, blanka.tomkova@tul.cz

[2]Technical University of Liberec, Institute for Nanomaterials, Advanced Technology and Innovation, Liberec, Czech Republic, EU, jana.mullerova@tul.cz

https://doi.org/10.37904/nanocon.2020.3690

Abstract

A series of thin epoxy resin samples were prepared. Short recycled carbon microfibers in concentrations from 0wt% to 33wt% were used as composite fillers. The geometry and structure of these fillers were characterized using SEM and Raman DXR microscopy images. It has been found that the dielectric properties of composites strongly depend on the RCF content and show an increase in values at and above the percolation threshold. Below the percolation threshold, the distance between the fibers is large enough so that there is no interaction of the local fields created by the adjacent fibers and the dielectric constant in this region increases slowly. As the filler concentration increases, the Maxwell Wagner effect increases and leads to a sharp increase in the real permittivity values. Furthermore, it was found in this work that the permittivity increases with increasing concentration of particles even after reaching the percolation threshold over the entire frequency band.

Keywords: Recycled carbon fibers (RCFs), epoxy composites, dielectrical properties

1. INTRODUCTION

By studying new materials concerning their use in electrical engineering, one of the most important properties is the dielectric constant of the material and its frequency dependence. This work describes the changes in dielectric properties of carbon fiber reinforced composites CFCRs as a function of filler content. The obtained data are analyzed from percolation theory [1], which was experimentally determined at a concentration of 20 wt % [2]. The dielectric behaviour of filled conductive composites is in the case of heterogeneous systems subject to interface polarization, where one of the components of the composite has a higher electrical resistance compared to the others [3] [4]. This is generally known as the Maxwell Wagner effect [5].

1.1. Carbon fiber (CFs)

CFs rovings are mainly used to reinforce polymers, similar to fibreglass (glass rovings embedded in various resins), and form high-performance composite materials. CFs have higher strength and lower density compared to glass fibers [6]. So far, however, insufficient attention has been paid to the use of recycled carbon fibers (RCF), which is an essential fibrous raw material, the amount of which will increase with the increasing use of CF in the composite industry [7]. To expand CF recycling it is necessarey to specify how recycled carbon fibers will be used. Carbon fibers are primarily used for the reinforcement of composite structures, due to the high ratio of strength to weight, the anisotropy of their properties is used. However, their electrical properties are usually not given much attention in the composite industry. Recycled carbon fibers have a limited length, and they are mainly used as isotropic reinforcement, limited in high concentrationsdue to decrease of the mechanical properties of plastic composites. Knowledge of their influence on dielectric properties of CFRCs expands the application potential of these materials.

1.2. Dielectric properties

The action of an external electric field shifts the electrically charged particles due to the movement of the Lorenz force or the applied field. The strength of strong bonds or the thermal motion of molecules counteracts this motion [8]. If the dielectric does not contain permanent dipoles, it is a non-polar dielectric, during polarization, there is a mutual displacement of the electron shells and nuclei of the atom. If the dielectric contains molecules with a permanent dipole, the dipoles rotate in the direction of the electric field intensity due to polarization, and it is a polar dielectric. Non-polar substances usually have low values of permittivity; they have electronic and ionic polarization. Polar substances have permittivity values in a wide range; they use mainly ionic polarization [9].

Polymers are dielectrics, i.e. both the matrix and the filler used in this work are dielectrics. RCF fibers are non-polar dielectrics, the matrix, like all polymers in general, is a polar dielectric.

Dielectric constant = permittivity

Relative permittivity is a material characteristic; it is a function of internal and external parameters of the measured material. In contrast, internal factors are filler concentration, bond polarity, molecular structure, crystal lattice type, and external criteria can be considered temperature, pressure, frequency and electric field intensity [9][10].

Complex permittivity and dielectric losses

As already mentioned, the permittivity depends on the type of dielectric, on the frequency at which it is measured and on the physical conditions. Due to the alternating field, free and bound charges move in the dielectric. The energy of the electric field changes into kinetic energy, partly into heat. As this heat is not used in any way, it is considered a loss. The development of new materials aims to eliminate these losses as much as possible. Then we formulate the complex permittivity as:

$$\varepsilon = \varepsilon' - j\varepsilon'', \qquad (1)$$

Anywhere ε' is real, and ε'' is the imaginary part of the permittivity. The real permittivity corresponds to the relative permittivity, and the imaginary part expresses the losses. The real permittivity shows how much energy of the external electric field is stored in the dielectric. The imaginary part of the permittivity is usually much smaller than the real component. In nonpolar dielectrics, both components of permittivity are low frequency-dependent due to electron polarization. In the case of polar dielectrics, these dependencies are more complicated due to the frequency, since there is an orientation dipole polarization involving the influence of the structure. At the same time, the following applies to the dissipation factor *tan δ*:

$$\tan\delta = \frac{\varepsilon''}{\varepsilon'}, \qquad (2)$$

2. EXPERIMENTAL PART

2.1. Materials

An epoxy matrix system made from bisphenol A-based low-viscosity epoxy resin LR 285 was used, along with cyclic-aliphatic polyamine curing agent H 508, with a mixing ratio 100:40 by weight. The density of the resin was 1,200 kg/m^3, and the density of the hardener was 1,030 kg/m^3. The specimens were filled with RCF in range of concentration from 0wt% to 33 wt%. Commercially available PAN-based Carbiso Milled Carbon Fibers (RCFs), with a density of 1,800 kg/m^3, were used. They have diameters of approximately 7,0 ± 0,3 μm and lengths of 100 ± 9 μm [5].

The mixture of epoxy, hardener, and fibers was stirred at room temperature for 5 min using a magnetic stirrer. Next it was poured into pre-separated circular glass molds and left to stand for 24 h at room temperature.

Curing followed, the mixture was left in the oven for 15 h at 60°C. The thickness of each sample varied but it was approximately 2-3.10^{-3} m.

2.2. Methods

SEM

A VEGA 3 TESCAN and VEGA TS 5130 microscope were used to photograph the composite samples.

Raman spectroscopy

It was measured on a Raman DXR microscopy (Thermo Fisher). Laser 532 nm, at each point, 20 exposures for 1 second. The Raman shift was 3600-0 cm^{-1}. A correction for fluorescence was made. The band intensities in the Raman spectra are related to the change in the polarizability of the material.

Dielectric properties

Capacity was measured using AGILENT 4294. The measurements were carried out in the frequency range of 100 Hz- 5 MHz according to ASTM D150-12. Permittivity ε' was calculated using equation (3):

$$C = \varepsilon 0 . \varepsilon' \frac{S}{h} \quad , \tag{3}$$

where ε_0 is the permittivity of the vacuum $\varepsilon_o = 8{,}854 \times 10^{-12}\ F/m$, h is the thickness of the sample and S is the area of the sample.

3. RESULTS

3.1. SEM

Some information about the strength of fiber-matrix interactions and fiber surfaces can be derived from SEM images. Images of the fracture surfaces of the tested composites obtained by SEM are shown in **Figure 1** (c) The figure shows the random orientation of the CFR fibers in the composite, while the detail of one fiber shows the adhesion of the interfacial interface.

(a)

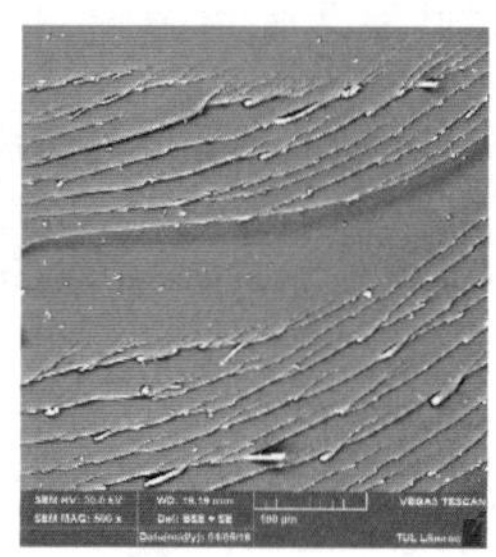

(b)

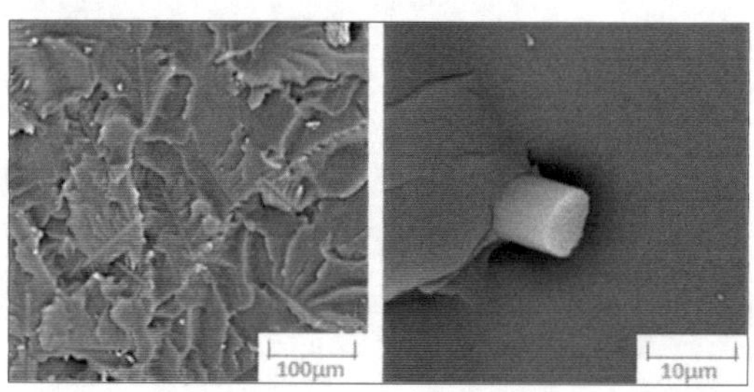

(c)

Figure 1 SEM photos: (a) RCF, (b) fracture surface of epoxy resin, (c) fracture surface of CFRCs composite

3.2. Raman spectroscopy

In **Figure 2** compares the Raman spectra of carbon fiber-filled epoxy composites with the spectra of the fibers themselves and the polymer matrix. In the wavelength range of 1600 cm^{-1}, there is a significant peak (G peak) in the samples of the polymer with the fibers and the fibers themselves, i.e. there is a typical double bond C = C for carbon fibers. The second most significant peak (D peak) is in the fiber polymer samples, and the fibers themselves are in the wavelength range of 1360 cm^{-1}. By all materials is in the wavelength range of 2900 cm^{-1} third considerable peak, i.e. also in the sample of the neat matrix. As we can see, this peak is the most pronounced peak for the polymer.

(a)

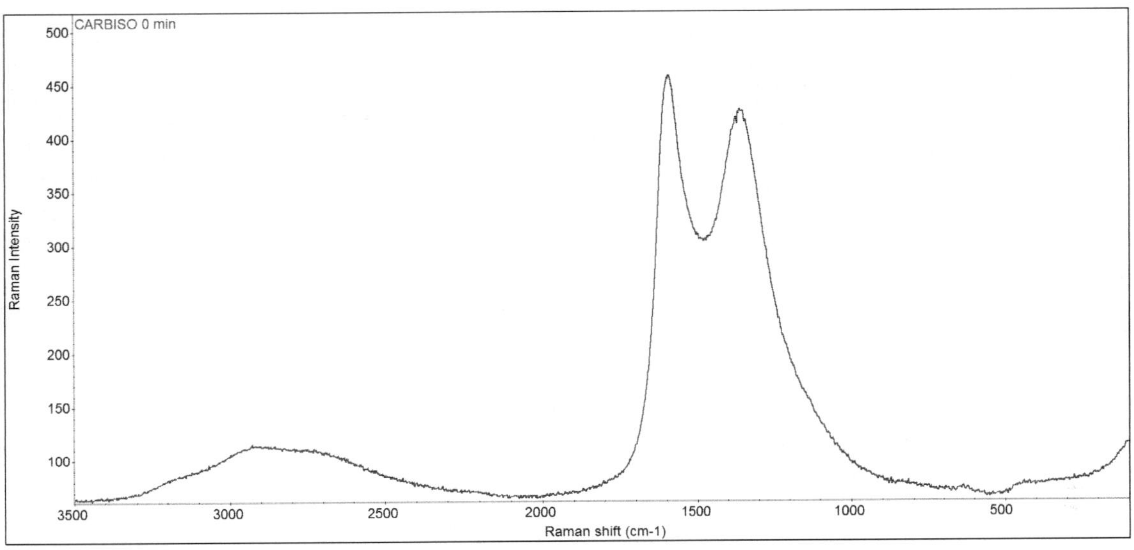

(b)

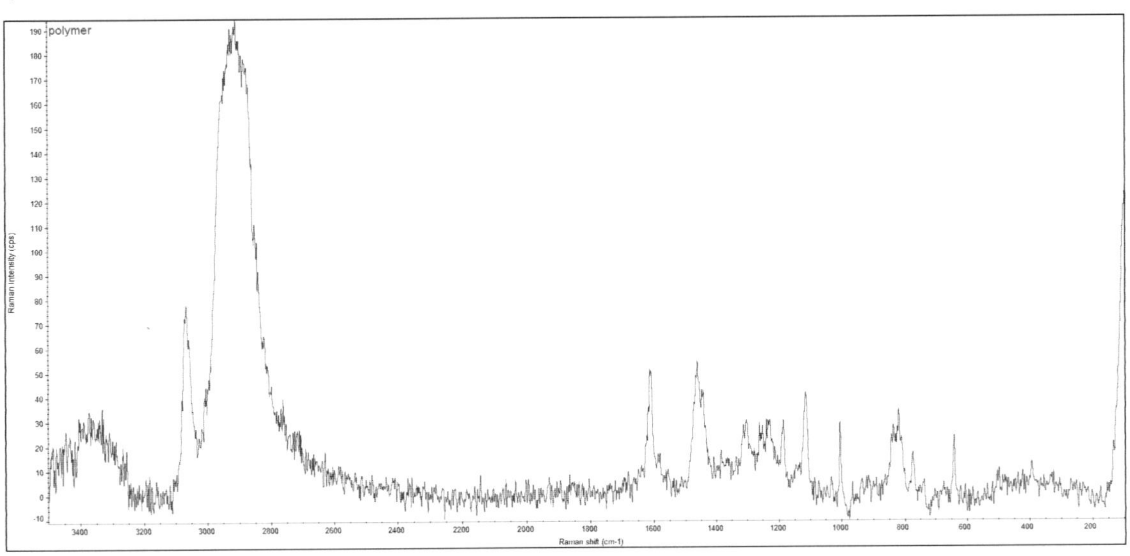

Figure 2/1 Raman spectroscopy: (a) RCF, (b) surface of epoxy resin, (c) surface of CFRCs composite

(c)

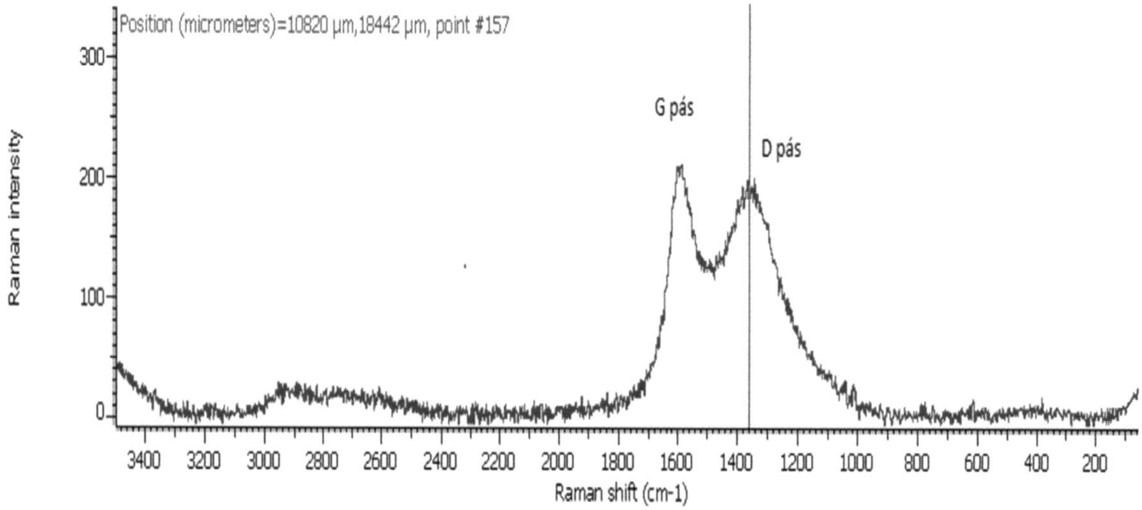

Figure 2/2 Raman spectroscopy: (a) RCF, (b) surface of epoxy resin, (c) surface of CFRCs composite

3.3. Dielectric properties

Dielectric constant

Figure 3 compares the real permittivity values of the whole spectrum of samples CFRCs at frequencies of 12Hz-5MHz. The same trend is seen; the dielectric constant decreases due to the increasing frequency. The Percolation threshold of these composites is 20 wt%. Up to the percolation concentration, the real permittivity increases substantially linearly, above the percolation threshold at lower frequencies (12Hz and 100Hz) it grows exponentially.

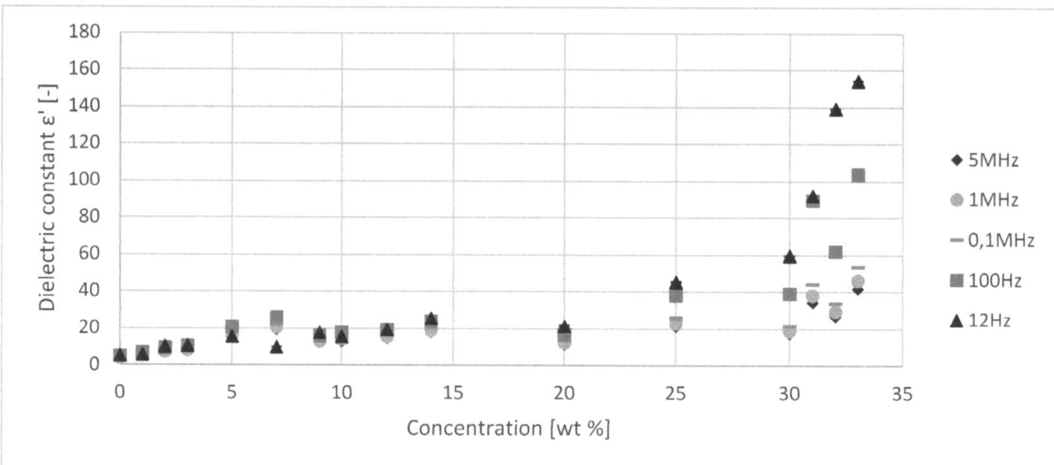

Figure 3 Variation of dielectric constant with fiber content

Loss Factor

Figure 4 compares the imaginary permittivity values of the whole spectrum of samples CFRCs at frequencies of 12Hz- 5MHz. In general, the imaginary permittivity is higher at lower frequencies due to the interface of the

Maxwell Wagner polarization between the epoxy resin and the RCFs. The value of έ′ decreases with increasing frequency, because the dipoles orient themselves with a certain delay due to their own relaxation time.

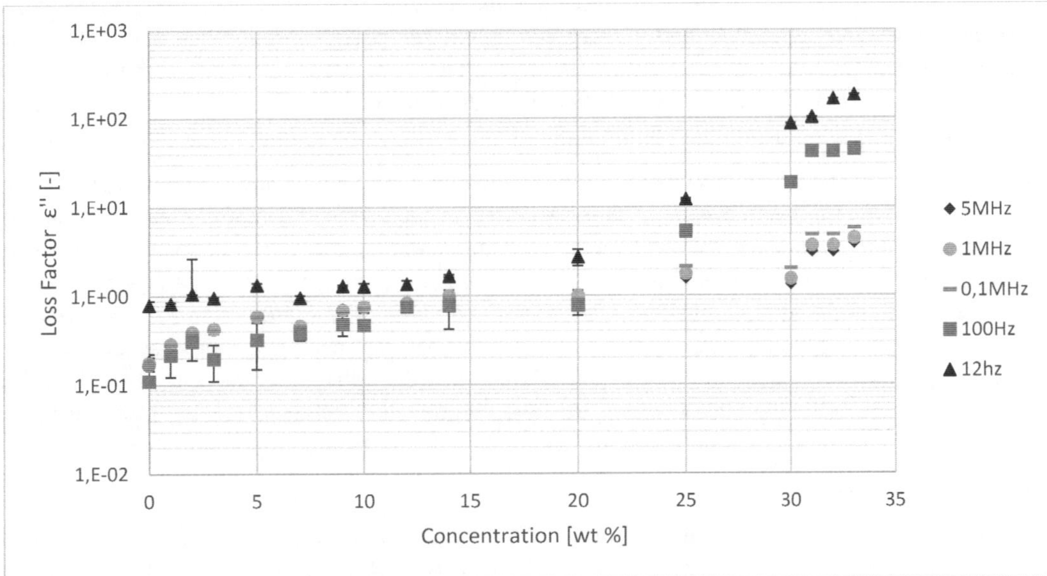

Figure 4 Variation of loss factor with fiber content

Dissipation factor

The figures show the tan δ values of the whole spectrum of samples CFRFs at frequencies of 12Hz-5 MHz. Due to the increasing frequency, the dissipation factor decreases. In general, the magnitude of tan δ, as well as other dielectric properties, is sensitive to polar sites in the polymer matrix [7]. These places increase the value of the dissipation factor. For concentrations above the percolation threshold, the tan δ decreases with increasing frequency because the induced charges do not gradually follow the reverse field, causing a decrease in electronic oscillation as the frequency increases.

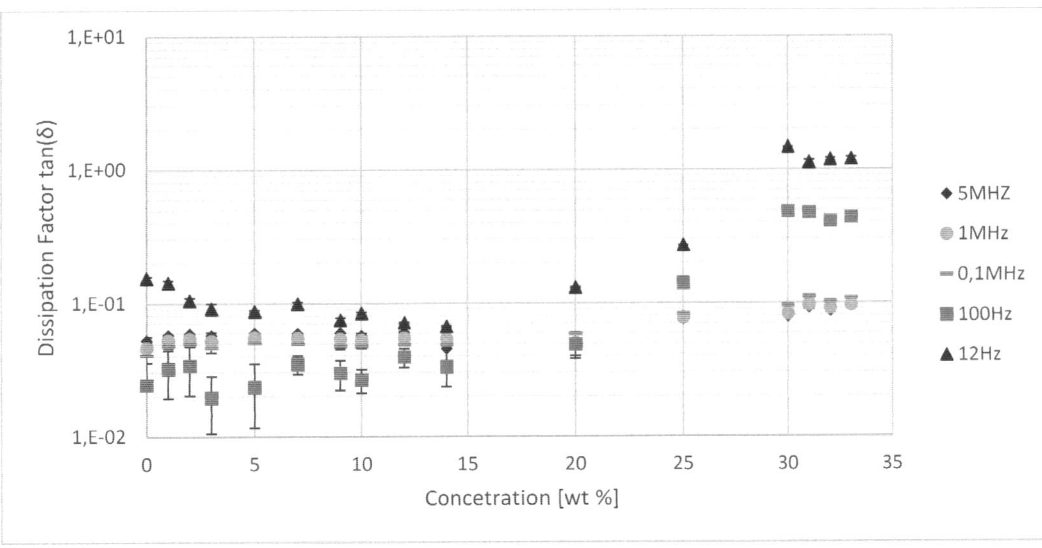

Figure 5 Variation of dissipation factor with fiber content

4. CONCLUSION

The real permittivity increases due to the spatial charge created in the interface between the conductive phase and the insulating phase due to the difference in conductivity of these two phases. Charge polarization occurs when more than one material component is present or when segregation occurs in a material containing incompatible chemical sequences and when charge carriers are trapped at the interface of these heterogeneous systems [11]. The deformation of the electric field caused by the accumulation of these charges increases the total capacity of the material, which manifests itself as an increase in the dielectric constant [12].

In this experiment, it was found that the real permittivity increases with increasing concentration of particles even after reaching the percolation threshold over the entire frequency band. Usually, above the percolation threshold (i.e., when the conductivity of composites increases sharply), a sharp increase in the value of the dielectric constant is observed. Then it is not possible to measure data due to the massive increase in the conductivity of the composites. However, in the case of composites prepared from recycled RCFs, the conductivity does not reach such high values. The explanation for this behaviour may be that as the concentration of fibers increases, the distances between them decrease, and the local fields created by adjacent particles increase the permittivity values. At lower frequencies, this effect is more pronounced.

ACKNOWLEDGEMENTS

Authors are grateful for the financial support from the Student research project 2020 No. 6050 supported by Czech Ministry of Education, and by Faculty of Textile, Technical University of Liberec.

REFERENCES

[1] KŘESÁLEK, V. *Electrical Conductivity of Two-Component Composites at the Percolation Threshold.* Brno, 2004. Habilitation thesis. Brno University of Technology.

[2] NOVOTNÁ, J. *Dielektrické vlastnosti epoxidových kompozitů plněných recyklovanými uhlíkovými vlákny*. Liberec, 2021. Dissertation. Technical University in Liberec.

[3] DRZAL, L. T., RICH, M.J., LLOYD, P.F. Adhesion of Graphite Fibers to Epoxy Matrices: I. The Role of Fiber Surface Treatment. *Journal of Adhesion Science and Technology*. 1983, vol. 16, no. 1, pp. 1-30.

[4] MEAKINS, R. J. *Progress in Dielectrics*. New York: John Wiley, 1961. vol. 3, pp. 151-155.

[5] BLYTHE, T., D. BLOOR. *Electrical properties of polymers*. 2nd edition. Cambridge: Cambridge university press, 2005.

[6] MORGAN, P. *Carbon fibers and their composites*. Boca Raton, Florida: Taylor & Francis Group, 2005.

[7] KUMAR, S., KRISHNAN, S. Recycling of carbon fiber with epoxy composites by chemical recycling for future perspective: a review. *Chemical Papers*. 2020, vol. 74, pp. 3785-3807.

[8] HASDENTEUFEL, J., KVĚT, K. *Elektrotechnické materiály*. Praha: SNTL, 1967.

[9] LIPTÁK, J., SEDLÁČEK J. *Úvod do elektrotechnických materiálů*. Praha: ČVUT, 2008.

[10] EDDIB A.A., CHUNG, D. D. L. Electric permittivity of carbon fiber. *Carbon*. 2019, vol. 143, pp. 475-480.

[11] ELIMAT, Z.M., HAMIDEEN, M.S., SCHULTE, K.I., WITTICH, H., DE LA VEGA, A., WICHMANN, M., BUSCHHORN, S. Dielectric properties of epoxy/short carbon fiber composites. *Journal of Materials Science*. 2010, vol. 45, pp. 5196-5203.

[12] DAHIYA, H. S., KISHORE, N., MEHRA, R.M. Effect of percolation on electrical and dielectric properties of acrylonitrile butadiene styrene/graphite composite. *Journal of Applied Polymer Science*. 2007, vol. 106, pp. 2101-2110.

FACILE MICROWAVE -ASSISTED SYNTHESIS OF CASEIN DERIVED CARBON NANODOTS

[1]R. Blessy PRICILLA, [1]David ŠKODA, [1]Pavel URBÁNEK, [1]Michal URBÁNEK, [1]Ivo KUŘITKA*

[1]*Centre of Polymer Systems, Tomas Bata University in Zlín, Czech Republic, EU,*
kuritka@utb.cz

https://doi.org/10.37904/nanocon.2020.3681

Abstract

Belonging to the carbon family, yet standing apart, carbon nanodots are materials with excellent properties. Among them, they are well known for their attractive optical properties. The insight into this outstanding strength has resulted in the discovery of unique design of materials. These nanodots can be prepared via various methods to obtain a good optical response. In our research, we synthesized them using a microwave reactor, which is simple, fast and productive. As a carbon source casein, a low-cost precursor was used. Since this is a protein composed of amino acids, no additional passivation was required. Polyvinylpyrrolidone was used as a stabilizer for the nanodots. The synthesis was carried out at 200 °C for 30 minutes. The color change of the resulting solution to orange brown indicates the formation of carbon nanodots. These nanodots were filtered and dialyzed to be used for further characterizations. The carbon nanodots were spherical with the average size of about 9.7 nm. They showed a strong blue emission in the visible region with an appreciable quantum yield. One of the important characteristics of this method is the availability of reasonably good product yield. The prepared carbon nanodots have potential applications in the field of electrochemistry, optoelectronics and biological imaging.

Keywords: Carbon nanodots, casein, microwave reactor, Polyvinylpyrrolidone

1. INTRODUCTION

In the recent decade, carbon nanodots (CNDs) have emerged as excellent luminescent materials. Since these materials manifest extraordinary merits, they are the hot topic of research studies. CNDs are materials with dimensions less than 10 nm. They were discovered in 2004 during the purification of single-walled carbon nanotubes [1]. Because of their alluring properties, CNDs are extensively used in applications like bioimaging [2], light emitting diodes [3] and sensing of metal ions [4]. Moreover, researchers all around the world have discovered different methods for synthesis such as hydrothermal [5], microwave irradiation [6] and laser ablation [7] The structure of CNDs contains a mixture of sp^2 and sp^3 hybridized carbon atoms with an amorphous core. To enhance the optical properties, their surface is usually passivated with various functional groups or heteroatoms. Furthermore, depending on the surface structure, hydrophilic [8], hydrophobic [9] and amphiphilic [10] CNDs can be obtained.

Amongst all the properties, the optical properties have been widely investigated. The core and surface states play a crucial role in the emission. Recently, different kinds of carbon precursors have been used to obtain better photoluminescence (PL) response [11,12]. Even though the mechanism of PL emission is still under debate, the three most important mechanisms include quantum confinement, surface state and molecular fluorophore [13]. CNDs usually follow the trend of excitation dependent PL spectra with strong emission in the blue region, whose intensity decreases with the red shift. This red shift in the PL spectra is observed due to high surface oxidation [14].

To further investigate the optical property, fluorescence lifetime decay studies are carried out, which helps in understanding the potential applications of CNDs. Multi-exponential decay of these studies is considered as a fingerprint of heterogeneity which is obtained from dot-to-dot differences in excited-state lifetimes [15]. Another important optical property is the fluorescence quantum yield. One group of researchers synthesized CNDs using citric acid and urea and studied the factors affecting the quantum yield. They discovered that high temperature and longer reaction time lead to a decrease in the quantum yield [16]. Achieving high fluorescence quantum yield with a good product yield has always been a challenge.

Even though CNDs have been synthesized from different precursors, their chemical, structural and optical properties have not been clearly understood yet. In our work, we synthesized CNDs from a protein named casein. Since casein is rich in amino acids, doping was avoided. The structural, chemical and optical properties of the synthesized material were studied using transmission electron microscope, fourier transform infrared spectroscopy, UV-Vis spectroscopy and photoluminescence spectroscopy.

2. EXPERIMENTAL

2.1. Materials required

MPC 85 Micellar Casein was purchased from a local seller in the Czech Republic. Polyvinylpyrrolidone (PVP) was bought from Sigma Aldrich. Solvents like ethylene glycol and isopropanol were procured from PENTA, Czech Republic. All reagents were used without any further purification.

2.2. Synthesis of casein based carbon nanodots

The synthesis of casein based carbon nanodots (CNDs) was carried out using a microwave reactor. In the typical synthesis, 0.1 g of casein and 0.2 g of PVP were taken in two separate beakers and dissolved in 20 ml of ethylene glycol separately using a sonication probe. Then, the two solutions were mixed and poured in a teflon lined container to be kept in the microwave reactor. This reaction mixture was maintained at 200 ° C for 30 minutes with 100% (600 W) power. After 30 minutes an orange-brown solution was obtained. This solution of carbon nanodots was filtered using a 0.22 µm membrane and dialyzed against water using a dialysis bag (3.5 KD) for two days to remove the excess of PVP. The resulting solution was freeze dried and the final product (40mg) was obtained.

2.3. CNDs characterization

The synthesized CNDs were characterized using various characterization techniques. The Ultraviolet-Visible (UV-Vis) absorption studies were carried out on Perkin-Elmer Lambda 1050 spectrometer. The photoluminescence (PL) emission spectra was recorded on FLS920, Edinburgh Instruments (excitation laser 332.2 nm, Xe lamp excitation 515 nm). The Fourier Transform Infrared (FTIR) spectra were obtained from Thermo Scientific Nicolet 6700 spectrometer utilizing the ATR method with the diamond crystal (4000-400 cm^{-1}, resolution 2 cm^{-1}, 64 scans). Transmission Electron Microscope (TEM) studies were carried out on the JEOL JEM 2100 microscope operated at 300 kV (LaB6 cathode, point resolution 2.3 Å equipped with OLYMPUS SYS TENGRA camera (2048 × 2048 pixels)). The particle analysis was carried out using Image J software.

3. RESULTS AND DISCUSSIONS

The morphology and the size of the synthesized CNDs was confirmed through TEM characterization. The TEM image is shown in **Figure 1**. As can be seen, the particles are randomly distributed with a spherical shape and of different sizes. The average particle size of the CNDs was found to be around 9.7 nm.

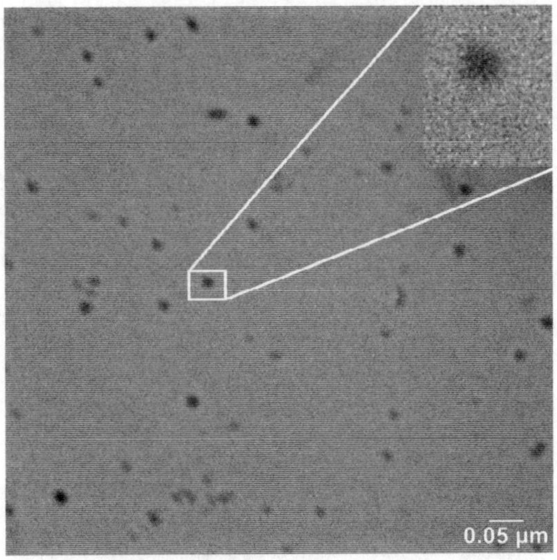

Figure 1 TEM image of CNDs

Figure 2 provides the FTIR spectrum of the CNDs. As shown, the spectrum indicates the presence of various functional groups. The peak at 3357 cm^{-1} shows O-H and N-H stretching vibrations. Characteristic casein peaks were observed at 2920 cm^{-1} and 1850 cm^{-1} due to the appearance of symmetric and asymmetric stretching of CH_2 [17]. The existence of C=O stretching vibrations can be found at 1656 cm^{-1}, O-H bending vibrations are seen at 1423 cm^{-1}. The peaks present at 1288 cm^{-1} and 1043 cm^{-1} indicate C-N stretching and C-O stretching, respectively.

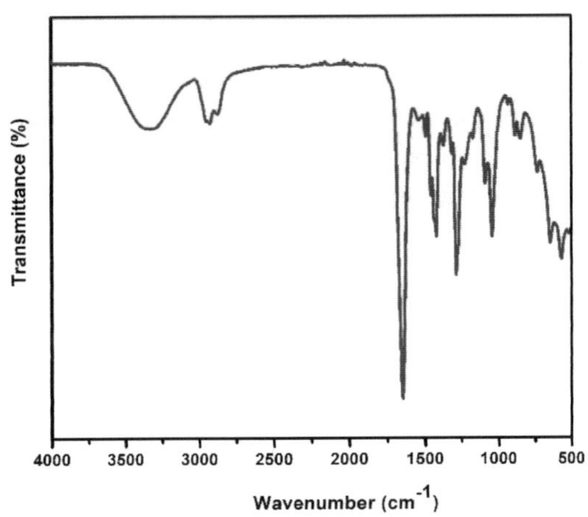

Figure 2 FTIR spectra of CNDs

The optical studies help in understanding the electronic transitions happening in CNDs. Therefore, we have investigated the absorption and emission spectra. When the CNDs were illuminated with a UV lamp of wavelength 365 nm, a blue color solution was observed. **Figure 3 (a)** shows the UV spectra of Casein based carbon nanodots. As can be seen, a peak is observed at 278 nm. This peak is due to the π-π^* transition of the aromatic C=C bond [18]. The PL emission spectra of the CNDs excited from 320-420 nm is shown in **Figure 3** (b). As revealed by the graph, an initial increase in the peak intensity is observed, followed by a gradual decrease. The presence of surface defects due to a high level of surface oxidation causes emission to shift to longer wavelengths [19]. When the CNDs were excited at 350 nm, the highest peak was obtained at 427 nm, which appears to be in the region of blue emission. The polydispersity of the sample can be one of the factors for the formation of excitation dependent emission spectra.

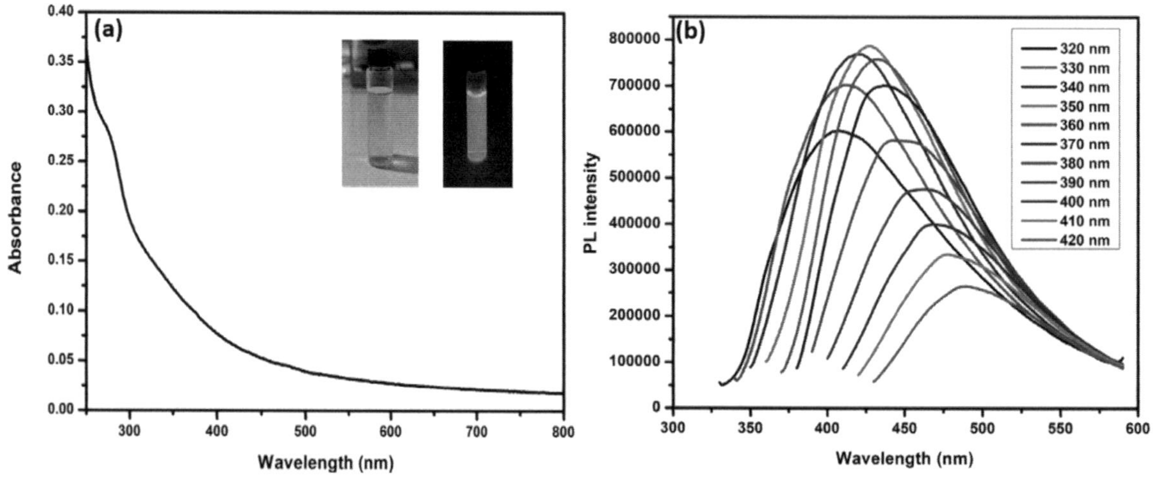

Figure 3 a) UV absorption spectra of CNDs **b)** PL emission spectra of CNDs

The quantum yield of the CNDs with water as a reference was found to be 4 %, which is comparable with those reported in the literature [17,20].

4. CONCLUSION

In summary, the study has reported a successful synthesis of CNDs using a simple and easy approach. The resulting CNDs are spherical in shape, they exhibit excitation dependent photoluminescence spectra with a red shift, indicating the heterogeneity of the sample. A strong blue color emission indicates the typical characteristic of the material. Compared to all the other methods, this technique is less time consuming and easily reproducible with a good yield. The bare casein CNDs show considerably less quantum yield than expected, hence it is concluded that in the next step, passivation is necessary to obtain an increase in this property. Passivating these CNDs with various functional groups or dopants can lead to their application in numerous arenas like biomarkers, optoelectronics, drug delivery and photosensitizer.

ACKNOWLEDGEMENTS

The authors gratefully acknowledge the financial support of the Ministry of Education, Youth and Sports of the Czech Republic Program- DKRVO (RP/CPS/2020/006).

REFERENCES

[1] XU, X., RAY, R., GU, Y., PLOEHN, H.J., GEARHEART, L., RAKER, K., SCRIVENS W.A. Electrophoretic analysis and purification of fluorescet single-walled carbon nanotube fragments. *J Am Chem Soc.* 2004, vol. 123, no. 40, pp. 12736-12737.

[2] ZHU, S., MENG, Q., WANG, L., ZHANG, J., SONG, Y., JIN, H., ZHANG, K., SUN, H., WANG, H., YANG, B. Highly Photoluminescent Carbon dots for multicolor patterning, sensors and bioimaging. *Angew. Chem. Int. Ed.* 2013, vol 52, no. 14, pp. 3953-3957.

[3] MIRASOL, S.P., FERRERO, E.M., PALOMARES, E. Direct white light emission from carbon nanodots (C-dots) in solution processed light emitting diodes. *Nanoscale.* 2019, vol 11, no. 23, pp. 11315-11321.

[4] SAI, L., CHEN, J., CHANG, Q., SHI, W., CHENA, Q., HUANG, L. Protein-derived carbon nanodots with an ethylenediamine-modulated structure as sensitive fluorescent probes for Cu_2^+ detection. ***RSC Adv.*** 2017, vol 7, no. 27, pp. 16608-16615.

[5] KUMAR, V.B., SHEINBERGER, J., PORAT, Z., TAL, Y.S., GEDANKEN, A. A hydrothermal reaction of an aqueous solution of BSA yields highly fluorescent N doped C-dots used for imaging of live mammalian cells. *J Mater Chem B.* 2016, vol 4, no. 17, pp. 2913-2920.

[6] MEDEIROS, T.V., MANIOUDAKIS, J., NOUN, F., MACAIRAN, J.R., VICTORIA, F., NACCACHE R. Microwave-assisted synthesis of carbon dots and their applications. ***J. Mater. Chem. C.*** 2019, vol 7, no. 24, pp. 7175-7195.

[7] REYES, D., CAMACHO, M., CAMACHO, M., MAYORGA, M., WEATHERS, D., SALAMO, G., WANG, Z., NEOGI, A. Laser Ablated Carbon Nanodots For Light Emission. *Nanoscale Res Lett.* 2016, vol 11, p. 424.

[8] YANG, Y.Z., XIAO, N., LIU, S.G., HAN, L., LI, N.B., LUO, H.Q. pH-induced aggregation of hydrophilic carbon dots for fluorescence detection of acidic amino acid and intracellular pH imaging. *Materials Science and Engineering: C.* 2020, vol 108, p. 110401.

[9] YANG, H., LIU, Y., GUO, Z., LEI, B., ZHUANG, J., ZHANG, X., LIU, Z., HU, C. Hydrophobic carbon dots with blue dispersed emission and red aggregation-induced emission. *Nat Commun.* 2019, vol 10, p. 1789.

[10] WANG, H.J., HE, X., LUO, T.Y., ZHANG, J., LIU, Y.H., YU, X.Q. Amphiphilic carbon dots as Versatile vectors for nucleic acid and drug delivery. *Nanoscale.* 2017, vol 9, no. 18, pp. 5935-5947.

[11] BAJPAI, S. K., D'SOUZA, A., SUHAIL, B. Blue light-emitting carbon dots (CDs) from a milk protein and their interaction with Spinacia oleracea leaf cells. *International Nano Letters.* 2019, vol 9, pp. 203-212.

[12] JIANG, K., SUN, S., ZHANG, L., LU, Y., WU, A., CAI, C., LIN, H. Red, Green, and Blue Luminescence by Carbon Dots: Full-Color Emission Tuning and Multicolor Cellular Imaging. *Angew. Chem.* 2015, vol 54, no. 18, pp. 5360-5363.

[13] CAYUELA, A., SORIANO, M.L., CARRILLO-CARRIO, C., VALCARCEL, M. Semiconductor and carbon-based fluorescent nanodots: the need for consistency. *Chem. Commun.* 2016, vol 52, no. 7, pp. 1311-1326.

[14] DING, H., YU, S.B., WEI, J.S., XIONG, H.M. Full-Color Light-Emitting Carbon Dots With a Surface-State-Controlled Luminescence Mechanism. *ACS Nano.* 2015, vol 10, no. 1, pp. 484-491.

[15] GHOSH, S., CHIZHIK, A.M., KAREDLA, N., DEKALIUK, M.O., GREGOR, I., SCHUHMANN, H., SEIBT, M., BODENSIEK, K., SCHAAP, I.A.T., SCHULZ, O. Photoluminescence of Carbon Nanodots: Dipole Emission Centers and Electron-Phonon Coupling. *Nano Lett.* 2014, vol 14. no. 10, pp. 5656-5661.

[16] WANG, W., WANG, B., EMBRECHTS, H., DAMM, C., CADRANEL, STRAUSS, V., DISTASO, M., HINTERBERGER, V., GULDI, D.M., PEUKERT, W. Shedding light on the effective fluorophore structure of high fluorescence quantum yield carbon nanodots. *RSC Adv.* 2017, vol 7, no. 40, pp. 24771- 24780.

[17] SIROČIĆ, A., KREHULA, LJ.K., KATANČIĆ, Z., MURGIĆB, Z.H. Characterization of Casein Fractions - Comparison of Commercial Casein and Casein Extracted from Cow's Milk. *Chem. Biochem. Eng. Q.* 2016, vol 30, no. 4, pp. 501- 509.

[18] ZHU, C., ZHAI, J., DONG, S. Bifunctional fluorescent carbon nanodots: green synthesis via soy milk and application as metal-free electrocatalysts for oxygen reduction. *Chem. Commun.* 2012, vol 48, no. 75, pp 9367-9369.

[19] ZHU, S., SONG, Y., ZHAO, X., SHAO, J., ZHANG, J., YANG, B. The photoluminescence mechanism in carbon dots (graphene quantum dots, carbon nanodots, and polymer dots): Current state and future perspective. *Nano Research.* 2015, vol 8, pp. 355-381.

[20] WANG, N., WANG, Y., GUO, T., YANG, T., CHEN, M., WANG, J. Green preparation of carbon dots with papaya as carbon source for effective fluorescent sensing of Iron (III) and Escherichia coli. *Biosensors and Bioelectronics.* 2016, vol 85, pp. 68-75.

POLYVINYLPYRROLIDONE COATING FOR NANODIAMOND STABILIZATION IN SALINE SOLUTION AND SILVER NANOPARTICLE DECORATION

[1]Katerina KOLAROVA, [1]Daria MILIAIEVA, [1]Stepan STEHLIK

[1]*Institute of Physics of the Czech Academy of Sciences, Prague, Czech Republic, EU,* kolarovak@fzu.cz

https://doi.org/10.37904/nanocon.2020.3696

Abstract

This work presents use of polyvinylpyrrolidone (PVP) for multipurpose coating of oxidized high-pressure high-temperature and detonation nanodiamonds. This simple way of nanodiamonds surface modification aims to improve their colloidal stability in biological environments and reduce their proneness to agglomeration. PVP immobilized on nanodiamond surface also provides for nanodiamond-supported AgNPs preparation by *in situ* synthesis using $AgNO_3$ as a metallic nanoparticles precursor. Dynamic light scattering (DLS) and UV-vis spectroscopy were used for evaluation of nanoparticles size distribution and dispersibility in water and after exposition of nanoparticles in saline solution. Images acquired by scanning electron microscopy and transmission electron microscope validate the possibility of binding ~ 10 nm AgNPs to nanodiamonds surface.

Keywords: Nanodiamonds, silver nanoparticles, colloid solution

1. INTRODUCTION

The diamond nanoparticles (so-called nanodiamonds, NDs) belong to a family of carbon-based nanomaterials The various structure and surface chemistry of ND particles can lead to their numerous applications [1]. Owing to their low chemical reactivity and unique physical properties, nanodiamonds could be useful in a variety of biological applications, novel imaging techniques, coatings for implantable materials and biodetectors [2]. Compared with other similarly sized materials, primary ND particles have a distinct advantage - they are inherently non-toxic; although this property depends on sufficient purification from sp^2 carbon, the toxicity also varies depending on the type of cell used.

NDs have been synthesized by various techniques, however the most important and available at industrial scale at the current time is the "bottom-up" method - detonation technique, and the "top-down" - high-energy ball milling of high-pressure high-temperature diamonds (HPHT) [3]. Primary particles of detonation nanodiamonds (DNDs) are single-digit nanometre in size with narrow size distribution and typically spherical in shape. These attributes stem from their origin in a rapid detonation process, which terminates within a fraction of microsecond, severely restricting the time of growth of ND particles. DNDs have diameters of 4-5 nm, but they tend to aggregate and therefore usual commercial suspensions of nanodiamonds contain larger aggregates [1]. DND nanoparticle is modelled by a diamond core, including various lattice defects, transient sp^3/sp^2 layer, and sp^2 surface shell that may carry various surface functional groups.

Primary HPHT particles are typically sharp and with huge size distribution. Their main advantage over DNDs is their expected uniform structure with low concentration of lattice defects such as dislocations or twinning.

Nanodiamonds have a superior mechanical and thermal properties combined with low cytotoxicity. Moreover, their variable surface chemistry is suited for preparation nanodiamond composites suitable for biomedical composition.

One of the main challenges in preparation of nanodiamond composites is the task of maintaining stability of colloidal solutions and also prevention of re-aggregation of NDs, especially in biological systems [4].

The aim of this work is to prepare nanodiamond composites that would be able to maintain their stability and dispersibility even in an unfavorable salt solution environment.

2. EXPERIMENTAL PART

The HPHT nanodiamonds (MSY18) were purchased form Microdiamant AG (size range: 0-25nm). The detonation nanodiamonds (DND) were purchased from New Metals and Chemicals Corp. The NDs were oxidized in air at 450 °C for 5 hours (for MSY18) or at 520 °C for 50 min for DND nanoparticles. Subsequently the NDs powder was mixed with deionized water (concentration 1mg/1mL) and ultrasonicated by an ultrasound horn for 1 hour. The ND-PVP colloids were prepared as shown in the scheme below (**Figure 1**). In short - the suspension of annealed nanodiamonds was added to a 2% w/w polyvinylpyrrolidone (PVP K25 from Carl Roth) water solution and stirred at 60 °C. The resulting colloid was overflowed three times by centrifugation to replace the PVP solution with a deionized water. The final ND-PVP colloid in water was used for preparation of silver decorated nanodiamonds. The PVP coated nanodiamond colloid was stirred at 60 °C and during this time a 2% w/w solution of PVP in ethanol was added into it. Then, silver nitrate was slowly dripped into the mixture (up to a final concertation of 0.1 M $AgNO_3$) in a dark place until Ag nanoparticles formed and the solution turned yellow. During addition of $AgNO_3$, the mixture was still stirred and heated. After 2 hours the silver decorated nanodiamonds were cleaned up by centrifugation as described above.

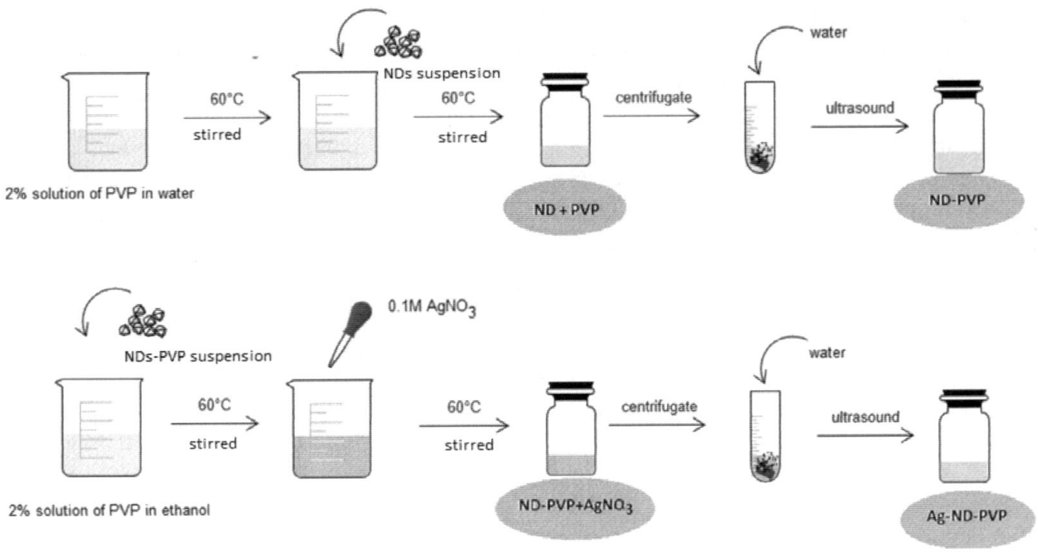

Figure 1 Scheme of sample preparation

Dynamic light scattering (DLS) was used for characterization of nanoparticles size distribution and zeta potential of the colloid solution, the measurements were performed by a Zetasizer Nano (Malvern Panalytical) equipped with a helium-neon laser (633 nm); the scattering angle was 173°.

For a colloidal stability test, NaCl was added to the nanodiamond solutions to a final concentration of 0.9% w/w. The evaluation was made by *UV-Vis spectroscopy* 2 hours after NaCl exposure. The measurements were done by Jasco V-730 UV-Vis double beam spectrophotometer with halogen and deuterium lamp as a light source.

The particle size and shape were observed with *scanning electron microscope (SEM)* and *transmission electron microscope (TEM)*. SEM images were acquired by SEM MAIA 3 with ultra-high resolution in high vacuum (TESCAN). Samples for SEM were prepared by dropping the NDs solution onto a silicon substrate.

TEM measurements were done by FEI Tecnai G2 20 with a LaB6 cathode at acceleration voltage 200 kV. The TEM is equipped with a CCD camera Olympus Veleta. Samples for TEM were prepared on carbon coated copper grid by immersion in ND colloid.

3. RESULTS

Nanoparticle size distribution was assessed by DLS measurements. **Figure 2** shows histograms of nanoparticle size by volume. Size distribution shifted towards larger sizes after PVP coating, especially for MSY18. After decoration of the nanodiamonds with silver nanoparticles, the size histogram remains unchanged. During the preparation of the samples, the pH changes of the NDs solutions (**Figure 3**) and their zeta potentials (**Figure 4**) were studied. Zeta potential is an important indicator of stability of colloidal solutions. Suspensions with their zeta potential above 30 mV or below -30 mV are considered stable. Colloidal stability is one of the critical factors for use of nanodiamonds. At pH 5, the colloidal solutions of annealed MSY particles sonicated in deionized water are well stable. The zeta potential of annealed DND nanoparticles is lower than in case of MSY (-23 mV for pH 6.5). The zeta potential is highly dependent on various chemical groups present on surface of the nanodiamonds. Carboxyl group is one such functional group and it determines the diamond surface charge [5]. Air oxidation of NDs at high temperature is responsible for creation of homogeneous layer of carboxyl groups on the surface of NDs. The difference between zeta potentials could be caused by varying methods of preparation and also by different particle sizes. After coating of NDs surface by PVP, the zeta potential for MSY nanodiamonds decreases while for DND it no change, up to a point where the value of zeta potential for both types of materials has stabilized at a similar number (see **Figure 3**). Carboxyl groups on the nanodiamond surface interact through bonding of hydrogen with pyridyl groups in PVP molecule [6]. PVP also acts as surface ligand to ensure dispersion of hybrid nanostructures in solution.

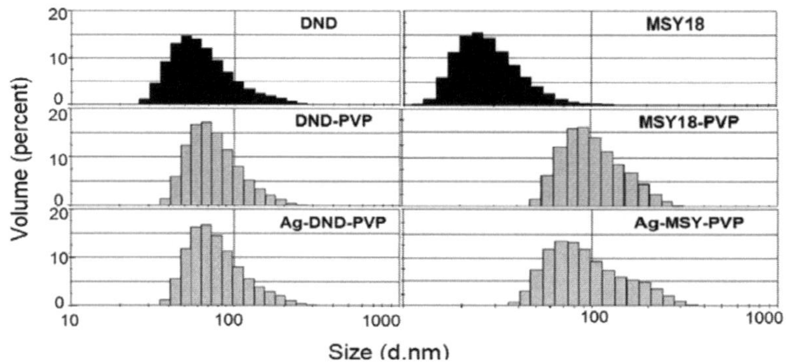

Figure 2 Size distribution histograms of prepared nanoparticles

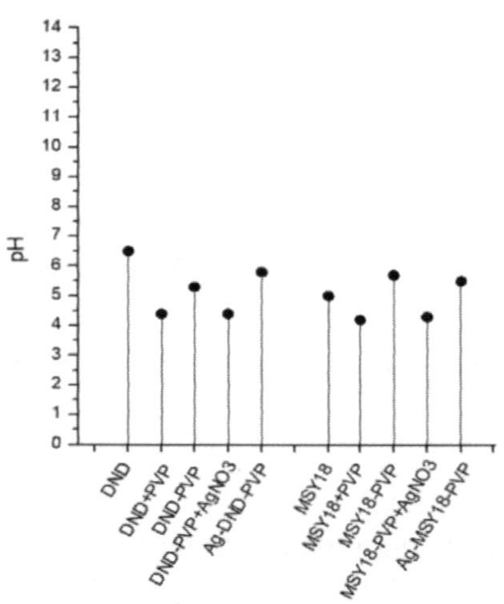

Figure 3 pH changes during samples preparation

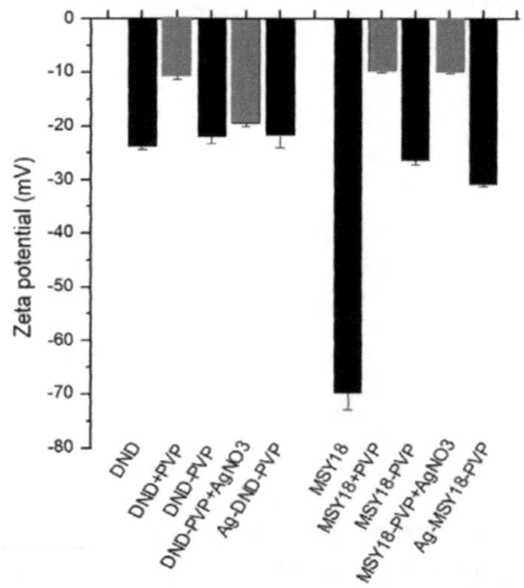

Figure 4 Zeta potential colloid solutions

Coated nanodiamonds (MSY18-PVP and DND-PVP) prepared by this way were used for decoration with silver nanoparticles *in situ* (see **Figure 1**). Growth of Ag nanoparticles on NDs is performed in ethanol solution with PVP molecules acting as a reducing agent. The nitrogen atoms on the unbound pyridyl groups in PVP molecule coated nanodiamond surface possess strong affinity to silver ions and allow silver nanoparticle formation on the diamond surface. To detect changes in the shape and size of the agglomerates, the samples were observed by microscopy. The SEM images of coated nanodiamonds after decoration by silver nanoparticles are presented in **Figures 5A** for Ag-DND-PVP and **5B** for Ag-MSY18-PVP. After decoration process, the surface of both nanodiamonds is covered with spherical silver nanoparticles. Backscattered-Electron (BSE) Imaging (right side of images) is used to detect contrast between areas with different chemical compositions. Since silver particles have higher atomic number, their electrons backscatter more strongly than those of lighter carbon, and thus appear brighter in the image. Bare NDs in colloids are electrostatically stabilized by zeta potential and thus have limited stability in solutions with ionic strength higher than 10^{-3} mol/L, the ND aggregate at higher ionic strengths [7]. However, SEM images of decorated nanoparticles did not confirm strong agglomeration effect in case of PVP-coated nanodiamonds; the agglomeration should usually occur with bare nanodiamonds during *in situ* reduction under similar experimental conditions. The silver nanoparticles have a diameter of about 10 nm. Images were also taken by TEM microscopy to confirm and refine images of silver decorated nanoparticles (see **Figures 6A** for Ag-DND-PVP and **6B** for Ag-MSY18-PVP).

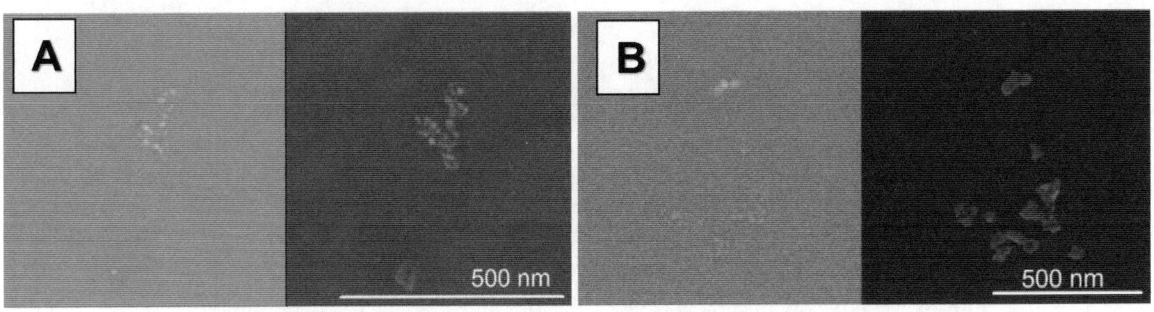

Figure 5 SEM images Ag-DND-PVP **(A)** and Ag-MSY18-PVP **(B)**

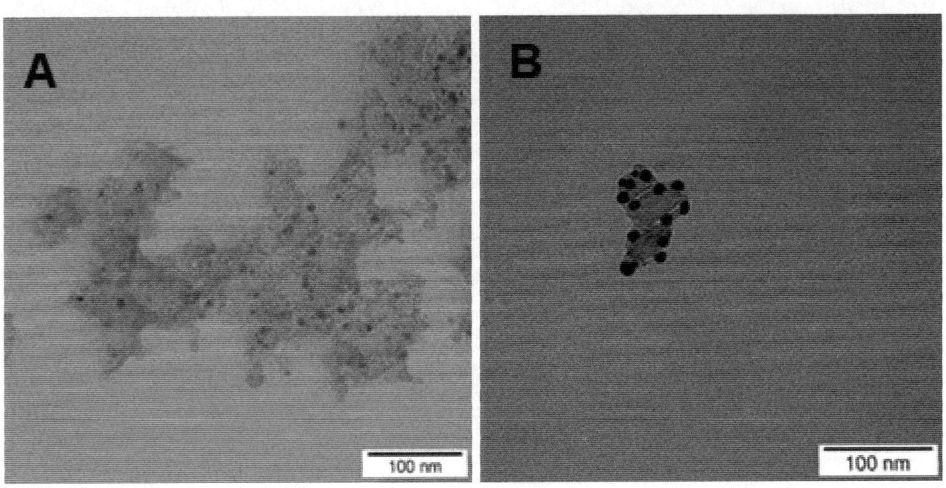

Figure 6 TEM images Ag-DND-PVP **(A)** and Ag-MSY18-PVP **(B)**

The DND nanodiamonds have form of tightly bound aggregates of particles called core agglutinates; this is typical for detonation-made nanoparticles. The agglutinate formation are attributed to facets-driven electrostatic interactions between individual DND particles and their liquid-phase sintering [8].

To determine the changes of stability of the studied nanoparticles in biological systems, NaCl was added to the aqueous suspension with pristine nanodiamonds, nanodiamonds in PVP and decorated nanodiamonds to a final NaCl concentration of 0.9 % (same osmolarity as physiological solution). After only a few minutes, there was a visible turbidity of the bare nanodiamond suspension. Contrary, the suspension of NDs coated with PVP and NDs coated with PVP and decorated with silver nanoparticles did not show any visible changes after exposure to saline solution. All solutions were measured by UV-vis spectroscopy in the range of 350-800 nm to detect changes after the addition of NaCl. From **Figure 7** it is obvious that both types of bare nanodiamonds in saline solution lost their dispersibility and agglomerated, the samples coated with PVP retained their transparency indicating good dispersibility. UV-vis spectroscopy of the decorated nanocomposite solutions displayed the typical surface plasmon resonance peak for AgNPs (~ 410 nm for nanoparticles with size of about 10 nm) and the nanocomposite showed stability even in physiological saline solution in which bare NDs already aggregated [9].

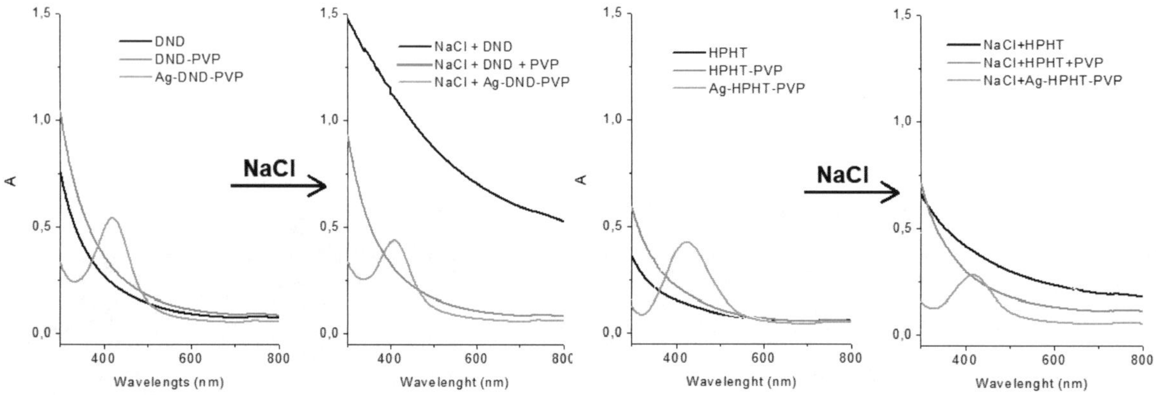

Figure 7 UV-Vis spectra of NDs solution before and after exposition of NaCl

4. CONCLUSION

The nanodiamonds coated with a polyvinyl pyrrolidone showed improved stability by preventing ND agglomeration even in physiological solution. The final zeta potential of coated nanodiamonds solution was -25 mV. By the polymer coating, we also achieved the attachment of AgNPs onto the ND surface. The final Ag-NDs composite material also showed good stability in deionized water and 0.9% NaCl. In this context, the PVP-coating of nanodiamonds seems as a promising way how to stabilize not only the HPHT, but also the detonation nanodiamonds in demanding biological environments and how to achieve controlled decoration of NDs by metal nanoparticles.

ACKNOWLEDGEMENTS

The work is supported by Operational Programme Research, Development and Education financed by European Structural and Investment Funds and the Czech Ministry of Education, Youth and Sports (Project No. SOLID21 CZ.02.1.01/0.0/0.0/16_019/0000760). We also acknowledge use of the CzechNanoLab research infrastructure supported by the MEYS (LM2018110).

REFERENCES

[1] MOCHALIN, V. N., SHENDEROVA, O., HO, D., GOGOTSI, Y. The properties and applications of nanodiamonds. *Nat. Nanotechnol.* 2012, vol. 7, pp. 11-23.

[2] SCHRAND, A. M., HUANG, H., CARLSON, C., SCHLAGER, J. J., ŌSAWA, E., HUSSAIN, S. M., DAI, L. Are Diamond Nanoparticles Cytotoxic? *J. Phys. Chem. B.* 2007, vol. 111, pp. 2-7.

[3] NUNN, N., TORELLI, M., MCGUIRE, G., SHENDEROVA, O. Nanodiamond: A high impact nanomaterial. *Curr. Opin. Solid State Mater. Sci.* 2017, vol. 21, pp. 1-9.

[4] ZHANG, Y., RHEE, K. Y., HUI, D., PARK, S.-J. A critical review of nanodiamond based nanocomposites: Synthesis, properties and applications. *Compos. Part B Eng.* 2018, vol. 143, pp. 19-27.

[5] ZHUKOV, A. N., GAREEVA, F. R., ALEKSENSKII, A. E., VUL', A. Ya. Surface charge of detonation nanodiamond particles in aqueous solutions of simple 1 : 1 Electrolytes. *Colloid J.* 2010, vol. 72, pp. 640-646.

[6] GONG, J., STEINSULTZ, N., OUYANG, M. Nanodiamond-based nanostructures for coupling nitrogen-vacancy centres to metal nanoparticles and semiconductor quantum dots. *Nat. Commun.* 2016, vol. 7, p. 11820.

[7] YOSHIKAWA, T., ZUERBIG, V., GAO, F., HOFFMANN, R., NEBEL, C. E., AMBACHER, O., LEBEDEV, V. Appropriate Salt Concentration of Nanodiamond Colloids for Electrostatic Self-Assembly Seeding of Monosized Individual Diamond Nanoparticles on Silicon Dioxide Surfaces. *Langmuir.* 2015, vol. 31, pp. 5319-5325.

[8] STEHLIK, S., HENYCH, J., STENCLOVA, P., KRAL, R., ZEMENOVA, P., PANGRAC, J., VANEK, O., KROMKA, A., REZEK, B. Size and nitrogen inhomogeneity in detonation and laser synthesized primary nanodiamond particles revealed via salt-assisted deaggregation. *Carbon.* 2021, vol. 171, pp. 230-239.

[9] BRADAC, C., RASTOGI, I. D., CORDINA, N. M., GARCIA-BENNETT, A., BROWN, L. J. Influence of surface composition on the colloidal stability of ultra-small detonation nanodiamonds in biological media. *Diam. Relat. Mater.* 2018, vol. 83, pp. 38-45.

GROWTH AND PROPERTIES OF DIAMOND FILMS PREPARED ON 4-INCH SUBSTRATES BY CAVITY PLASMA SYSTEMS

[1,2]Oleg BABČENKO, [1,2]Štěpán POTOCKÝ, [1]Kateřina AUBRECHTOVÁ DRAGOUNOVÁ, [1]Ondrej SZABÓ, [3]Philippe BERGONZO, [2]Bohuslav REZEK, [1]Alexander KROMKA

[1]*Institute of Physics of the Czech Academy of Sciences, Prague, Czech Republic, EU,* babcenko@fzu.cz

[2]*Faculty of Electrical Engineering, Czech Technical University in Prague, Czech Republic, EU*

[3]*Seki Diamond Systems, CORNES Technologies USA, San Jose, USA*

https://doi.org/10.37904/nanocon.2020.3701

Abstract

Diamond attracts the interest of researchers from different fields due to its extraordinary properties. However, many applications demand diamond films over large areas hence limiting usage of natural diamonds. Here we compare two microwave (2.45 GHz) plasma systems with ellipsoidal and multimode clamshell cavity for diamond synthesis by chemical vapor deposition. We use $H_2/CH_4/CO_2$ gas mixture for diamond film deposition on Si <100> wafers. Both systems are capable of high pressure (up to 20 kPa) operation and high growth rates (several µm/h). We compare the cavity systems from the point of diamond quality (Raman shift measurement), substrate size (2" versus 4") and grown film homogeneity together with surface morphology (SEM), deposition rate and parasitic doping levels (photoluminescence). For instance, we show that by using the multimode operation of the clamshell cavity system and specially design sample holder, it is possible to sustain a plasma in a cavity and reach good enough process reproducibility and diamond film quality over 4-inch substrates. We discuss effects of the cavity design on deposited layers for large area applications of diamond such as thermal management, electrodes and sensor arrays fabrication, photoluminescence, photonics and light sources.

Keywords: Large area diamond, microwave cavity plasma, high-power density plasma

1. INTRODUCTION

Diamond is a material with a wide range of extraordinary properties. It is the hardest natural material with the highest bulk thermal conductivity, broad optical transparency window and high resistance to chemical corrosion [1-3]. These properties would be enough to make a diamond an attractive material for various industrial applications. However, due to the high costs of natural diamonds proportional to size, the researchers had to develop synthetic diamond production methods [4-7]. Synthesis of diamond thin films was recognized as an appropriate alternative for various experimental needs [2-6]. Usage of synthetic diamond enabled discovery of other beneficial properties such as negative electron affinity, high radiation hardness, high breakdown field, biocompatibility, ability to form optical centers, adjustable electrical properties and surface chemistry, superconductivity with high boron doping levels, etc. [1-6]. It significantly expanded the list of diamond potential applications. Diamond films and coatings were thus proposed not only for cutting and drilling tools but also for heat spreaders and thermal management, optically transparent and electrically insulating encapsulation with high heat conductivity, high-power electronics, corrosion resistant electrodes, optoelectronic and quantum devices, various sensors or detectors and many more [1-6].

The diamond films are routinely grown by the chemical vapor deposition (CVD) method in various systems. The most popular are hot filament and microwave plasma reactors for which the fast growth rates (up to 10 µm/h) were reported [2-4, 7-9]. Characteristic features of such systems are hydrogen rich gas mixtures and high process temperatures that affect diamond growth kinetics. Although the diamond CVD is nowadays a well-established technology, the challenge is to grow diamond on large area with a fast growth rate and homogeneous properties. The hot filament CVD system can fulfill this demand via the filament length increase and/or new filaments addition. However, it is suffering from several significant limitations. The impurities from the filaments and/or its sensitivity to gas chemistry (in particular oxygen or high amount of methane) are not desirable or even prohibited in some cases, e.g. specific electronic devices, optical or photonic applications, etc. [1-3, 9]. Therefore, the solution for applications that requires diamond deposition on an area from 3 to 5 inches is searched by modifications of microwave plasma reactors.

The microwave plasma reactors exist in several configurations and have high potential to optimize diamond CVD technology [5,10]. In the current work we compare two microwave (2.45 GHz) cavity plasma CVD systems. The first system has a rotational ellipsoid cavity and the second one has a multimode clamshell cavity. Both systems are capable of high pressure (up to 20 kPa) and high power (up to 6 kW) operation, high growth rates (several µm/h) and in standard configuration diamond deposition on 2-inch substrates with the possibility of doping by boron. Our study focused on fast and reproducible diamond growth using oxygen containing chemistry in both these systems. We compare the systems from the point of diamond quality (Raman shift measurement), substrate size (2” versus 4”) and diamond film homogeneity together with surface morphology (SEM), deposition rate and parasitic doping levels (photoluminescence). We demonstrate the potential and discuss the effect of improvements in the system design for large area diamond deposition for such applications as thermal management, electrodes and sensor arrays fabrication, photoluminescence, photonics, light sources, etc.

2. EXPERIMENT

As substrates, 2” and 4” Si <100> wafers were used. In all cases the diamond nucleation layer was prepared by the substrate treatment in the ultrasound bath in water-based nanodiamond powder suspension (NanoAmando, with nominal particle size 5nm) for 40 min, as a reliable and reproducible seeding technique [6,11]. The wafers were held in the PTFE holder that enables easy manipulation and minimizes the damage of the seeding layer. Growth of diamond thin films was realized in the rotational ellipsoid cavity (P6, Diamond Materials GmbH) [5,10,12] and multimode clamshell cavity (SDS6K, Seki Diamond Systems) [2,5,10] 2.45 GHz microwave (MW) plasma CVD systems.

In the first set of experiments the 2” Si substrates were used. Diamond deposition in the rotational ellipsoid cavity (REC) reactor (ellipsoidal cavity resonator with the quartz bell jar as process chamber) was realized at the pressure 10.7 kPa (107 mbar), microwave power 6 kW, gas flow 500 sccm of H_2, 25 sccm of CH_4 and 5 sccm of CO_2. The average deposition temperature during the process was 740 °C. Process parameters for the multimode clamshell cavity (MCC) reactor, where the deposition chamber is a whole cavity itself, were the same: pressure 10.7 kPa (80 Torr), microwave power 6 kW, gas flow 500 sccm of H_2, 25 sccm of CH_4 and 5 sccm of CO_2. The average deposition temperature with advanced substrate holder cooling during the process was 890 °C. In both cases, prior to CO_2 addition into the process gas mixture the diamond nucleation layer was stabilized in the mixture of hydrogen and methane.

The diamond thin film deposition on the large 4” Si wafers was realized in the MCC reactor under the following conditions: pressure 6.7 kPa (50 Torr), microwave power 5 kW, gas flow 1000 sccm of H_2 and 25 sccm of CH_4. The average temperature during the 3 hours deposition process was 840 °C. A special holder for large wafers was used without additional cooling.

After the deposition the surface morphology of diamond films was characterized by the field-emission scanning electron microscopy (FE-SEM, Tescan MAIA3). The growth rates were calculated from the mass of the layers deposited on the known area taking the diamond film density equal to 3,5 g/cm^3 [4,13]. Material and photoluminescence properties were studied by the Raman spectroscopy (Renishaw InVia Reflex Raman microscope) using the excitation wavelength of 442 nm.

3. RESULTS AND DISCUSSION

3.1. Deposition on the 2-inch substrates

The CVD process using the $H_2/CH_4/CO_2$ gas mixture in both systems resulted in optically uniform coating on the used 2" Si substrates. In order to identify the possible changes in the films homogeneity, morphology and more precisely evaluate the growth rate, the deposition processes were repeated several times with different duration. SEM images of the layers deposited in the two employed reactors using the same deposition process settings and time are shown in **Figure 1** and **Figure 2**. The average size of diamond crystals for layer grown for 3 h in the REC reactor is in the range 1.0 - 1.5 µm, while layer grown during 9 h includes larger (up to 4 µm) and smaller (around 1 µm) diamond crystals (**Figure 1**). In case of the MCC reactor, already the layer grown for 3 h demonstrates high distribution of diamond crystals (from 0.5 to 4 µm). Layers grown for longer time show increase of maximum grain size with up to 15 µm large crystals (surrounded by smaller grains) observable on SEM images from 9 h deposited layer (**Figure 2**).

Figure 1 The SEM images of diamond films grown in the REC reactor for: a) 3 h, b) 6 h, and c) 9h

In general, the crystal size of diamond layers is affected by the grown film thickness [2,3,6]. Indeed, the thickness (denoted as "diamond" in **Figure 1** and **Figure 2**) that was calculated from the mass of layers deposited for the time from 3 to 9 h correlates with the morphology of diamond films investigated by the SEM. The estimated growth rates in case of REC reactor was around 0.39 - 0.40 µm/h, while for MCC reactor this value was between 2.07 - 2.25 µm/h. Commonly, to achieve by MW plasma CVD the thick diamond layers at high diamond growth rate the high-power density plasmas and thermally stable substrates (e.g. thick enough to sustain high temperature load) are used [2-5,8,12]. Nevertheless, as it can be seen from the comparison of the film thicknesses (and derived growth rates) and SEM images the diamond growth kinetics remained affected by the operation regime of the employed CVD system.

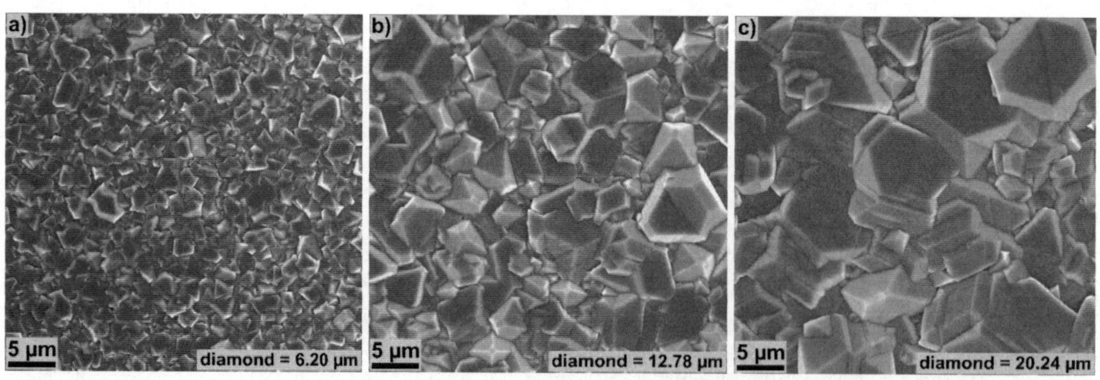

Figure 2 The SEM images of diamond film grown in the MCC reactor for: a) 3 h, b) 6 h, and c) 9h

The representative Raman spectra of the grown diamond films are shown in **Figure 3**. Raman spectroscopy in all cases indicates the high-quality diamond layer with a strong and sharp peak at 1332 cm^{-1}, characteristic for microcrystalline diamond films [14,15]. Considering the above SEM morphology this finding was expected. Diamond films with crystals as large as 500 nm already demonstrate a negligible amount of graphitic phases [14,15] whilst in the investigated cases, the size of diamond crystals is even larger. In agreement with previous reports, the second order Si peak from the substrate observable in the spectra of thinner diamond films grown in the REC reactor at around 980 cm^{-1} is diminishing with increasing diamond layer thickness [14,16]. However, the photoluminescence tail remains high even for thick films indicating "parasitic doping" due to plasma contact with quartz bell jar [5].

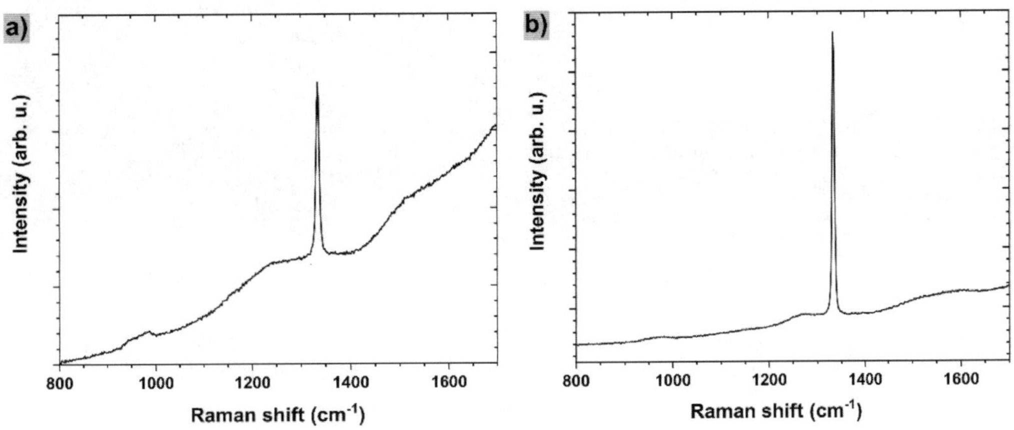

Figure 3 The Raman spectra measured after 3 h deposition on 2" Si in: a) REC reactor and b) MCC reactor

All aforementioned results indicate that the chosen deposition conditions are more suitable for the multimode clamshell cavity reactor than the rotational ellipsoid cavity reactor. Indeed, design of the REC reactor allows to maintain the stable plasma ball localized in the close vicinity to the substrate in the wide pressure range [12,16]. Therefore, the diamond deposition in the REC-reactor is realized in the round area with a diameter of approximately 5 cm while larger substrates can suffer from less homogeneous deposition [10,12,16]. However, at high power conditions the plasma discharge tends to be vertically expanded to the volume of the bell jar which decrease the plasma density and thus negatively affects the deposition temperature and growth rate [10,12]. Moreover, such expansion to the volume when plasma is approaching the quartz bell jar walls cause higher "parasitic doping" due to walls etching. The aforementioned issues can be overcome by the increase of deposition pressure that suppresses the plasma expanding and thus facilitate the growth rate [16].

Contrary to that, in the multimode clamshell cavity reactor operation at high power and lower deposition pressures cause more pronounced horizontal expansion of plasma discharge. Moreover, the pressure when such expansion becomes evident is lower than for the REC reactor [5,10]. The plasma expansion can be additionally altered by the design of the substrate holder. These properties of the MCC reactor were important in the research oriented at enlarging the deposition area and finally with specially designed substrate holder it became possible to expand the plasma discharge across the area of at least 4" in diameter [2,10]. For comparison, the system with rotational ellipsoid cavity for deposition on large wafers requires system with MW generators of lower frequency (915 MHz) and scaling up of resonator "egg" by factor of 2.7 [2,10,12]. It was reported that via employing large REC-type reactors and 915 MHz/60 kW generators the fast diamond deposition can be achieved on wafers up to 6" in diameter [2,10,12]. Such experiments cannot be commonly realized as they require complete change of the CVD system. Therefore, the experiments on the 4" wafers were realized only in the MCC reactor by changing the process parameters.

3.2. Deposition on the 4-inch substrates

The representative images of the expanded plasma discharge and the diamond film grown on 4" Si wafer for 3 h in the MCC reactor are shown in **Figure 4**. Visually, the thickness of diamond layer in this case seems to be not as high as in case of deposition on 2" substrates. Note also very few interference fringes seen due to diamond's high index of refraction. It indicates highly uniform film thickness as analyzed further below.

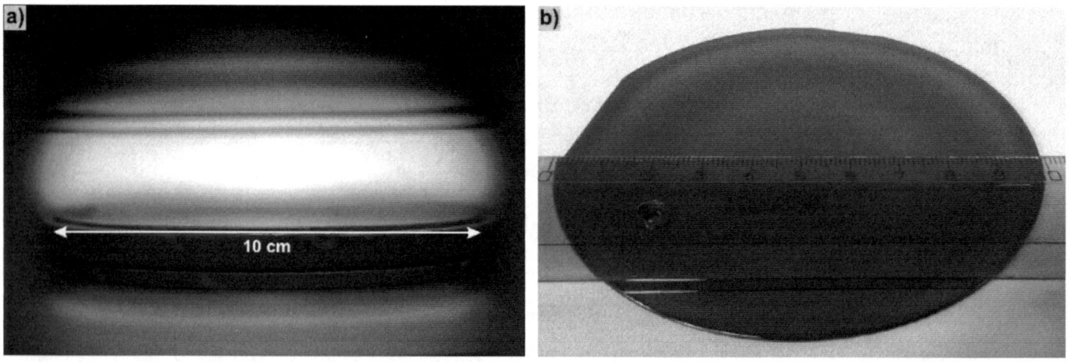

Figure 4 Photo of: a) plasma discharge in MCC reactor during the CVD and b) diamond film on the 4" Si

The SEM demonstrates that the grown layer is pinholes-free and consists of densely packed fine-grained crystallites in size up to 1 µm (**Figure 5a**). The Raman spectroscopy (**Figure 5b**), in addition to sharp diamond peak at 1332 cm^{-2}, characteristic to microcrystalline diamond, also demonstrate the presence of graphitic phases (broad band from 1400 cm^{-1} to 1600 cm^{-1}) and the second order Raman signal of Si substrate (band from 920 cm^{-1} to 1040 cm^{-1}) [14,15]. Stronger graphitic phases and second order signal from Si in the spectrum is another indication of lower diamond film thickness comparing to layers grown on 2" samples. The photoluminescence tail in case of diamond films from MCC reactor is low due to low level of parasitic doping (plasma is at far distance from the chamber walls) [5,10]. An additional analysis done by interference spectroscopy identifies the diamond thickness variation from 400 nm to 500 nm, i.e. the growth rate was significantly lower comparing to the deposition on 2" Si. The decrease of the growth rate is primarily related to the reduction of plasma density due to its expansion over the 4" sample (higher plasma volume) [10]. It should be noted that at lower applied power the plasma density is lower and the diamond thickness variation on large deposition areas became more evident [13]. Nevertheless, in our experiment the diamond growth was observed on the whole area of 4" Si wafer at the power of 5 kW and the quality remains close to the of MCC 2" samples rather than to the REC samples. It should be mentioned, that optimized process conditions result in layer thickness homogeneity as high as 95 %.

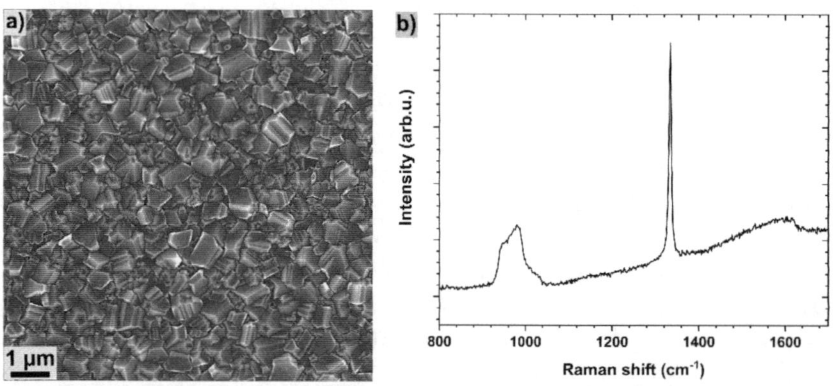

Figure 5 Diamond film grown on 4" Si wafer in the MCC reactor: a) SEM image and b) Raman spectrum

Compared to the REC reactor, that for deposition on large wafers (>3") requires scaling up (by factor 2.7) of the system and high-power MW generators (915 MHz/60 kW) to maintain the stable plasma of sufficient density [2,10,12], simple change of substrate holder in MCC reactor for deposition on 4" wafers, although with slower growth rate, is much more convenient. Lower photoluminescence of diamond from the MCC reactor indicates also higher material purity and provides lower background for possible applications. Therefore, the MCC reactor is potentially attractive for research also on small samples and for large-scale application of diamond films, e.g. thermal management for high-power electronics, optical windows and other optical elements, large arrays of photonic structures or photoluminescence nanostructures and electrically insulating chemically resistant coatings. The possibility of controlled boron doping reported for this type of CVD systems [4,8] enables fabrication of large area electrodes resistant to chemical corrosion, arrays of sensors or opto-electronic devices, etc.

4. CONCLUSION

We demonstrate the high diamond film growth rate by the high-power density plasma using two different deposition systems. We observe that despite the same $H_2/CH_4/CO_2$ process gas mixtures and other deposition conditions were used the diamond films were grown in both system with different growth rates and homogeneity. It was explained by the difference of operation regimes characteristic for used facilities that affect the deposition temperature and diamond growth kinetics. While the design of ellipsoidal cavity resonator allows to maintain stable plasma ball in the quartz bell jar in a wide pressure range the design of multimode clamshell cavity reactor tolerates change of plasma discharge shape and allows to expand it when suitable substrate holder is used. We have shown that the reproducible diamond films synthesis is well achievable in the MCC reactor on the substrates as large as 4" in diameter. We propose that the MCC reactor is a promising system for large area diamond growth for thermal management, electrodes fabrication, photonic applications, photoluminescence studies, etc.

ACKNOWLEDGEMENTS

This work was supported by the Operational Programme Research, Development and Education financed by European Structural and Investment Funds and the MEYES project SOLID21 (no. CZ.02.1.01/0.0/0.0/16_019/0000760) and by the CzechNanolab research infrastructure (no. LM2018110). We gratefully acknowledge R. Yatskiv and P. Bauerová for technical support with SEM and Raman measurements.

REFERENCES

[1] DAVIS, Robert F. (ed.). *Diamond films and coatings: development, properties, and applications.* Park Ridge, N.J : Noyes Pub, 1993. Materials science and process technology series. ISBN 978-0-8155-1323-0. TP873.5.D5 D52 1993

[2] MAY, P. W. Diamond thin films: a 21st-century material. *Philosophical Transactions of the Royal Society A: Mathematical, Physical and Engineering Sciences.* [online]. 15 January 2000, vol. 358, no. 1766, pp. 473-495. Available from: https://doi.org/10.1098/rsta.2000.0542.

[3] GRACIO, J J, FAN, Q H and MADALENO, J C. Diamond growth by chemical vapour deposition. *Journal of Physics D: Applied Physics.* [online]. 22 September 2010, vol. 43, no. 37, pp. 374017. Available from: https://doi.org/10.1088/0022-3727/43/37/374017.

[4] BUTLER, James E. and SUMANT, Anirudha V. The CVD of Nanodiamond Materials. *Chemical Vapor Deposition.* [online]. July 2008, vol. 14, no. 7-8, pp. 145-160. Available from: https://doi.org/10.1002/cvde.200700037.

[5] WERNER, M and LOCHER, R. Growth and application of undoped and doped diamond films. *Reports on Progress in Physics.* [online]. 1 December 1998, vol. 61, no. 12, pp. 1665-1710. Available from: https://doi.org/10.1088/0034-4885/61/12/002.

[6] WILLIAMS, O.A., NESLADEK, M., DAENEN, M., MICHAELSON, S., HOFFMAN, A., OSAWA, E., HAENEN, K. and JACKMAN, R.B. Growth, electronic properties and applications of nanodiamond. *Diamond and Related Materials*. [online]. July 2008, vol. 17, no. 7-10, pp. 1080-1088. Available from: https://doi.org/10.1016/j.diamond.2008.01.103.

[7] HIRMKE, J., SCHWARZ, S., ROTTMAIR, C., ROSIWAL, S.M. and SINGER, R.F. Diamond single crystal growth in hot filament CVD. *Diamond and Related Materials*. [online]. April 2006, vol. 15, no. 4-8, pp. 536-541. Available from: https://doi.org/10.1016/j.diamond.2006.01.003.

[8] SCHULTE, B., JUERGENSEN, H., BLACKBOROW, P. and SEVILLANO, E. Flexibility of microwave plasma chemical vapour deposition for diamond growth. *Surface and Coatings Technology*. [online]. October 1995, vol. 74-75, pp. 634-636. Available from: https://doi.org/10.1016/0257-8972(95)08311-1.

[9] MARTON, Marian, VOJS, Marian, KOTLÁR, Mário, MICHNIAK, Pavol, VANČO, Ľubomír, VESELÝ, Marian and REDHAMMER, Robert. Deposition of boron doped diamond and carbon nanomaterials on graphite foam electrodes. *Applied Surface Science*. [online]. September 2014, vol. 312, pp. 139-144. Available from: https://doi.org/10.1016/j.apsusc.2014.05.199.

[10] SILVA, F, HASSOUNI, K, BONNIN, X and GICQUEL, A. Microwave engineering of plasma-assisted CVD reactors for diamond deposition. *Journal of Physics: Condensed Matter*. [online]. 9 September 2009, vol. 21, no. 36, p. 364202. Available from: https://doi.org/10.1088/0953-8984/21/36/364202.

[11] KROMKA, A., BABCHENKO, O., KOZAK, H., HRUSKA, K., REZEK, B., LEDINSKY, M., POTMESIL, J., MICHALKA, M. and VANECEK, M. Seeding of polymer substrates for nanocrystalline diamond film growth. *Diamond and Related Materials*. [online]. May 2009, vol. 18, no. 5-8, pp. 734-739. Available from: https://doi.org/10.1016/j.diamond.2009.01.023.

[12] FÜNER, M., WILD, C. and KOIDL, P. Novel microwave plasma reactor for diamond synthesis. *Applied Physics Letters*. [online]. 9 March 1998, vol. 72, no. 10, pp. 1149-1151. Available from: https://doi.org/10.1063/1.120997.

[13] PHILIP, J., HESS, P., FEYGELSON, T., BUTLER, J. E., CHATTOPADHYAY, S., CHEN, K. H. and CHEN, L. C. Elastic, mechanical, and thermal properties of nanocrystalline diamond films. *Journal of Applied Physics*. [online]. 15 February 2003, vol. 93, no. 4, pp. 2164-2171. Available from: https://doi.org/10.1063/1.1537465.

[14] IŽÁK, Tibor, DOMONKOS, Mária, BABCHENKO, Oleg, VARGA, Marián, REZEK, Bohuslav, JURKA, Vlastimil, HRUŠKA, Karel and KROMKA, Alexander. Technological Aspects in Fabrication of Micro- and Nano-Sized Carbon Based Features: Nanorods, Periodical Arrays and Self-Standing Membranes. *Journal of Electrical Engineering*. [online]. 1 September 2015, vol. 66, no. 5, pp. 282-286. Available from: https://doi.org/10.2478/jee-2015-0046.

[15] KLAUSER, Frederik, STEINMÜLLER-NETHL, Doris, KAINDL, Reinhard, BERTEL, Erminald and MEMMEL, Norbert. Raman Studies of Nano- and Ultra-nanocrystalline Diamond Films Grown by Hot-Filament CVD. *Chemical Vapor Deposition*. [online]. 9 June 2010, vol. 16, no. 4-6, pp. 127-135. Available from: https://doi.org/10.1002/cvde.200906827.

[16] MORTET, V., KROMKA, A., KRAVETS, R., ROSA, J., VORLICEK, V., ZEMEK, J. and VANECEK, M. Investigation of diamond growth at high pressure by microwave plasma chemical vapor deposition. *Diamond and Related Materials*. [online]. April 2004, vol. 13, no. 4-8, pp. 604-609. Available from: https://doi.org/10.1016/j.diamond.2003.11.034.

TCO WORK FUNCTION TUNING BY NANODIAMONDS

[1]Jan ČERMÁK, [1]Daria MILIAIEVA, [2]Aurelien SOKENG DJOUMESSI, [2]Harald HOPPE, [1]Štěpán STEHLÍK

[1]Instutite of Physics, Czech Academy of Sciences, Prague, Czech Republic, EU,
cermakj@fzu.cz

[2]Center for Energy and Environmental Chemistry Jena, Friedrich-Shiller-University Jena, Germany, EU,
harald.hoppe@uni-jena.com

https://doi.org/10.37904/nanocon.2020.3688

Abstract

High-pressure high-temperature nanodiamonds (NDs) with hydrogen and oxygen surface termination are deposited on ITO coated glass substrates as well as on gold layers. Scanning probe microscopy is used for characterization of their microscopic electrical and electronic properties. Namely, conductive AFM was used to detect electric conductivity of NDs which prove that they act similarly to bulk diamond: hydrogen terminated NDs are electrically conductive whereas oxygen terminated NDs are electrically insulating. Work function (WF) of the ND-TCO systems were characterized by Kelvin probe force microscopy. It turned out, that WF of NDs on ITO is not stable in time. WF of H-NDs on ITO is changed by 150 mV to lower WF within 17 days. WF of O-NDs is varying in the range -250 mV up to +650 mV without any monotonous trend, which reflects their insulating character.

Keywords: Nanodiamonds, ITO, surface termination, Kelvin probe force microscopy, conductive atomic force microscopy, work function

1. INTRODUCTION

Photovoltaics covers large family of specific designs and material composition. Apart from the mostly used silicon photovoltaic (PV) cells, nowadays there is a remarkable increase in development of organic and perovskite PV cells. Their basic design consists of an opaque metal back electrode, active medium, and a transparent top electrode. To achieve best PV operation, the energy levels of the electrodes must be optimized for the best charge carrier collection [1]. The most common material for the transparent electrode is indium-tin-oxide (ITO). To enhance the PV operation additional interfacial layers are deposited between the active material and the ITO electrode like PEDOT:PSS [2] that is a hole conducting material and acts as an electron blocking layer. However, PEDOT:PSS is not an ideal solution as it is hygroscopic and acidic which causes degradation of the active medium [3]. Therefore, there is a demand to find a replacement [4].

Diamond is a well-known material due to its high durability, chemical stability, high thermal conductivity, or optical transparency across the visible spectrum due to its large energy bandgap (5.5 eV) [5]. From this point of view, diamond is a wide bandgap semiconductor that is electrically insulating at ambient conditions in its intrinsic form. However, it may become electrically conductive when doped or when its surface is terminated by hydrogen atoms [6]. In the latter case a thin (~10 nm) hole-conducting layer is formed on the surface. Yet, the conductivity of such a layer is not high enough (resistivity in the order of 10^4 kOhm/sq [7]) to be used as an effective electrode in PV cell directly.

Preliminary experiments indicated that nanodiamonds (NDs) inherit all these extraordinary properties of diamond including the hole conductivity when hydrogen terminated [8]. Moreover, computational modelling indicates that in a system of a diamond nanocrystal and an organic dye, there occurs a space separation of the highest occupied molecular orbital (HOMO) and the lowest unoccupied molecular orbital (LUMO) [9]. Thus, NDs are of high interest for many applications including photovoltaics for the use both as a hole conducting interlayer and as part of the active medium. They are available in large quantities at low pricing, their surface termination can be modified similarly to the bulk diamond and their processing is not technically demanding as they are purchased in the form of a powder or a colloid solution.

In this work the electronic properties of ND layers on ITO are characterized. Conductive atomic force microscopy (C-AFM) is used for testing their electrical conductivity and Kelvin probe force microscopy (KPFM) studies the change in surface potential that usually corresponds to a change in WF. The study is focused on NDs with two surface termination: hydrogenated NDs (H-NDs) and oxidized NDs (O-NDs).

2. EXPERIMENTAL DETAILS

High-pressure high-temperature NDs with a median size of 18 nm and size range 0-25 nm were purchased from Microdiamant AG. Initially, they were annealed in air at 450 ^{0}C for 5 hours. Hydrogenation was done in hydrogen atmosphere at atmospheric pressure at 800 ^{0}C for 6 hours. The colloid solutions were prepared by dissolving 1 mg of NDs in 1 ml of deionized water, ultrasonicating for 1 hour (at ~ 50 W) and decanting for 12 hours. The supernatant upon the decantation was used for samples preparation.

C-AFM was performed on an Icon system by Bruker equipped by a PeakForce TUNA (PF-TUNA) module using Multi75E-G probes (BudgetSensors). The system was operating in the PeakForce TUNA mode and for current detection the Contact current channel was used. The PeakForce setpoint was set to 18 nN and the bias voltage applied to the sample was -2.5 V. For PF-TUNA experiment NDs were drop-cast on a fresh thermally evaporated gold film on a glass substrate.

KPFM experiments were performed by an NTEGRA Prima system (NT-MDT) equipped with an infrared laser in the detection system using Multi75E-G probes (BudgetSensors). Here, ITO covered glass substrates were cleaned by ultrasonication in acetone, isopropanol and deionized water and dried by nitrogen flow. NDs were drop-cast on the surface and let evaporate on a hot plate (60 °C, 1 min). As the measurements were repeated within several weeks and consequently several probes (though of the same type) with different properties were used, we compare here the difference of surface potential between the NDs and the value measured on bare ITO surface on the same sample within the same measurement session, thus with the same tip and microscope parameters.

3. RESULTS AND DISCUSSION

Because NDs are not firmly attached to the ITO surface, the common conductive AFM method in contact mode cannot be used. The PF-TUNA regime is more suitable as the contact force is controlled at each probe approach-retract cycle [8]. Topography images **(Figure 1**) show that the measurement is performed on dense ND layers of O-NDs (**Figure 1a**) and H-NDs (**Figure 1b**) without protrusion to the underlying substrate. Topography of both samples are quite similar, the individual NDs are distinguishable by the AFM tip. In contrast, corresponding local current maps present a huge difference in electric conductivity. In similarity to bulk diamond, O-NDs are electrically insulating (**Figure 1c**; white color corresponds to electric current close to zero), while H-NDs are electrically conductive (**Figure 1d**; dark color corresponds to electric current below the bottom limit of the z-scale). Moreover, the electric conductivity is homogeneously detected on all the H-NDs, which is different from the data in literature, where only few of H-NDs were conductive [8]. This indicates that the used method of thermal hydrogen termination is more efficient than the plasma method used in [8].

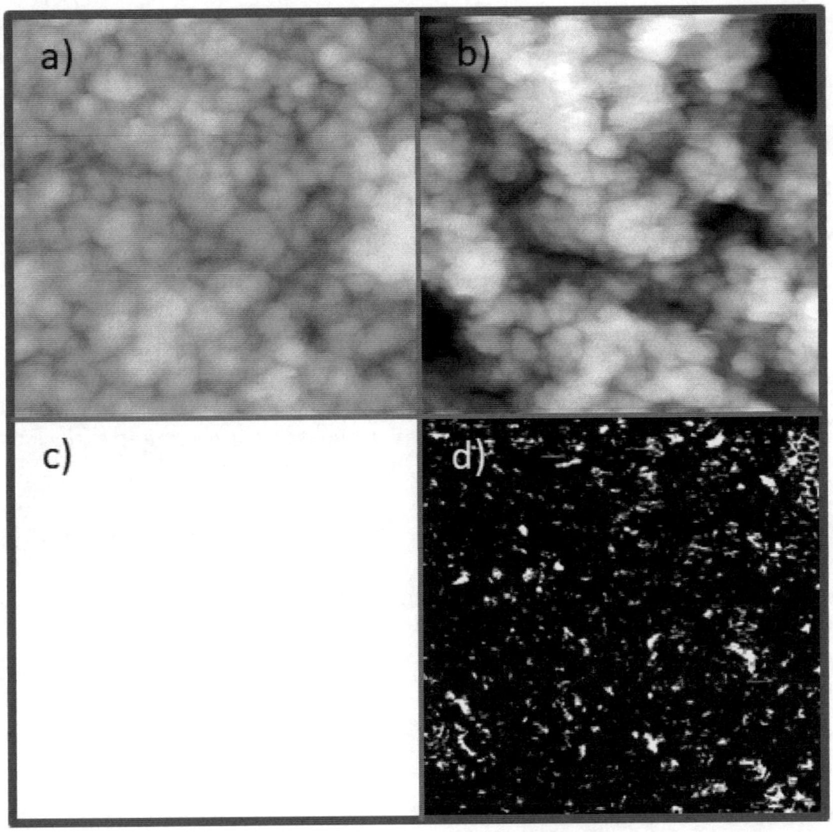

Figure 1 AFM topography (a, b) and local current maps (c, d) of O-NDs (a, c) and H-NDs (b, d). Z-scale for topography images is 150 nm, z-range for local current maps are from -5 pA to 0 pA.

For PV applications it is important to know and tune the work function of the PV systems and components. The WF of ITO (and hence the measured surface potential by KPFM) is known to vary within a range 4.1 to 4.7 eV when measured under vacuum by UPS or XPS [10]. Under ambient conditions, like in the case of KPFM or Kelvin Probe the obtained WF is typically higher: up to 5.2 eV [11]. It is also known that its WF may be influenced by as much as 0.8 eV by surface treatments [10]. Our control KPFM measurement showed that the ITO WF value is very close to the one of a gold reference, that is known to be 5.0 eV [12]. However, the measured value was different at each measurement session and varied also from sample to sample (**Figure 2a**). Therefore, in this work we compare and watch a trend in time of the difference between the WF of NDs and the WF if bare ITO on the same sample. The results are presented in **Figure 2b**. Note, that in our experimental setup the positive value of the difference corresponds to a decrease in WF and vice versa.

Right after the deposition the WF of H-NDs is approx. 50 mV lower than the one of ITO. During the period of 17 days the WF of H-NDs exhibit continuous differentiation from the WF of ITO up to approx. 150 mV that corresponds to an effective WF of 4.85 eV. This is close to a value 4.9 eV reported for bulk hydrogenated diamond surface [13].

O-NDs follow a trend that is expectable for an electrically insulating material: WF is not properly defined and thus the KPFM results display somehow random value at which the measurement feedback control is stabilized, possibly influenced by a trapped electrostatic charge. Both effects are not under control and, therefore, each additional measurement provides non-predictable results.

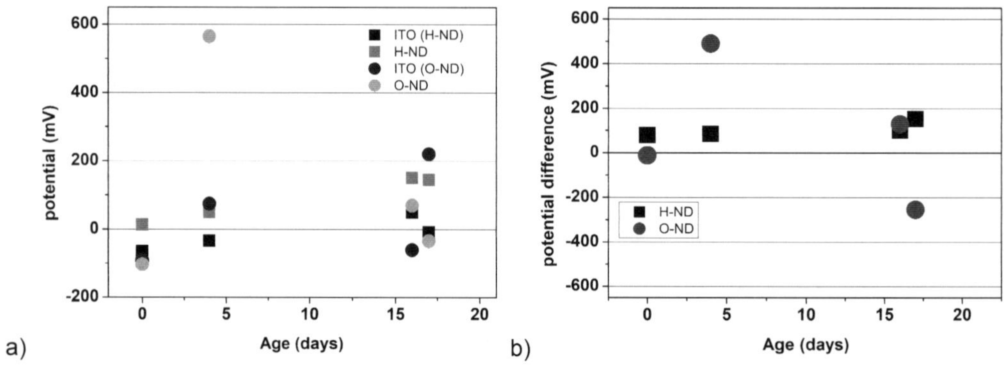

Figure 2 a) Potential values as measured by KPFM using a PtIr coated silicon tip on NDs and on the bare ITO on the corresponding substrates. b) Potential difference between the measured surface potential on ITO and on NDs as a function of time and ND surface termination.

From the data above it seems that H-NDs are the more promising candidate for application in PV as a hole transporting layer as they maintain electric conductivity and the WF of the ITO/H-NDs system is more stable in time. Also the results on O-NDs are important for further research, as recently, it was demonstrated that not specifically H-NDs or O-NDs, but their mixed surface termination provides the best opto-electronic response when interacting with polypyrrole [14]. Further experiments to study the details of interaction of NDs with ITO and other materials relevant for PV are in preparation.

4. CONCLUSION

We performed microscopic electronic characterization of H-NDs and O-NDs by means of PF-TUNA and KPFM on Au and ITO substrates, respectively. By PF-TUNA we showed that similarly to bulk diamond, properly hydrogenated H-NDs kept the surface conductivity down to nanoscale while the oxidized O-NDs remained insulating. These properties were further reflected in the KPFM characterization. It was demonstrated that deposition of differently surface terminated NDs could effectively modify the WF of the system. H-NDs shifted WF close to a common WF value reported for hydrogen terminated diamond, thus acting as a conductive capping layer. In contrast, the deposition of O-NDs resulted in scattered WF values most probably due to their insulating properties and subsequent poor definition of their WF with possible contribution of an uncontrolled electrostatic charging effect.

ACKNOWLEDGEMENTS

This study was supported by the Czech Science Foundation (GACR) grant number 20-20991J and by the Ministry of Education, Youth and Sports of the Czech Republic (MEYS) under the project CZ.02.1.01/0.0/0.0/16_019/0000760 (SOLID21). CzechNanoLab project LM2018110 funded by MEYS CR is gratefully acknowledged for the financial support of the measurements/sample fabrication at LNSM Research Infrastructure.

REFERENCES

[1] OPITZ, A., FRISCH, J., SCHLESINGER, R., WILKE, A. and KOCH, N. Energy level alignment at interfaces in organic photovoltaic devices. *Journal of Electron Spectroscopy and Related Phenomena.* [online] Oct. 2013, vol. 190, pp. 12-24. Available from: https://doi.org/10.1016/j.elspec.2012.11.008.

[2] KO, C.J., LIN, Y.K., CHEN, F.C. and CHU, C.W. Modified buffer layers for polymer photovoltaic devices. *Applied Physics Letters.* [online]. Feb. 2007, vol. 90, no. 6, p. 063509. Available from: https://doi.org/10.1063/1.2437703.

[3] LIN, Y. et al. 17% Efficient Organic Solar Cells Based on Liquid Exfoliated WS_2 as a Replacement for PEDOT:PSS. *Advanced Materials*. [online]. Nov. 2019, vol. 31, no. 46, p. 1902965. Available from: https://doi.org/10.1002/adma.201902965.

[4] NEOPHYTOU, M. et al. High mobility, hole transport materials for highly efficient PEDOT:PSS replacement in inverted perovskite solar cells. *Journal of Materials Chemistry C*. [online]. 2017, vol. 5, no. 20, pp. 4940-4945. Available from: https://doi.org/10.1039/C7TC00858A.

[5] WORT, C. J. H. and BALMER, R. S. Diamond as an electronic material. *Materials Today*. [online]. Jan. 2008, vol. 11, no. 1-2, pp. 22-28. Available from: https://doi.org/10.1016/S1369-7021(07)70349-8.

[6] STROBEL, P., RIEDEL, M., RISTEIN, J. and LEY, L. Surface transfer doping of diamond. 2004, vol. 430, p. 3.

[7] FIZZOTTI, F., LO GIUDICE, A., MANFREDOTTI, CH., MANFREDOTTI, C., CASTELLINO, M. and VITTONE, E. Diamond surface conductivity after exposure to molecular hydrogen. *Diamond and Related Materials*. [online]. Apr. 2007, vol. 16, no. 4-7, pp. 836-839. Available from: https://doi.org/10.1016/j.diamond.2006.11.094.

[8] ČERMÁK, J. et al. Microscopic Electrical Conductivity of Nanodiamonds after Thermal and Plasma Treatments. *MRS Advances*. [online]. 2016, vol. 1, no. 16, pp. 1105-1111. Available from: https://doi.org/10.1557/adv.2016.112.

[9] MATUNOVÁ, P., JIRÁSEK, V. and REZEK, B. DFT calculations reveal pronounced HOMO-LUMO spatial separation in polypyrrole-nanodiamond systems. *Physical Chemistry Chemical Physics*. [online]. 2019, vol. 21, no. 21, pp. 11033-11042, Available from: https://doi.org/10.1039/C8CP07622G.

[10] JUNG, H., MIN, H. and GAB, J. Effects of Surface Treatment on Work Function of ITO (Indium Tin Oxide) Films. *Journal of the Korean Physical Society*. 2005, vol. 47, p. 5.

[11] KIM, J. S. et al. Kelvin probe and ultraviolet photoemission measurements of indium tin oxide work function: a comparison. *Synthetic Metals*. [online]. Jun. 2000, vol. 111-112, pp. 311-314. Available from: https://doi.org/10.1016/S0379-6779(99)00354-9.

[12] ČERMÁK, J., REZEK, B., KROMKA, A., LEDINSKÝ, M. and KOČKA, J. Electrochemical synthesis and electronic properties of polypyrrole on intrinsic diamond. *Diamond and Related Materials*. [online]. Sep. 2009, vol. 18, no. 9, pp. 1098-1101. Available from: https://doi.org/10.1016/j.diamond.2009.01.035.

[13] REZEK, B., NEBEL, C. E. and STUTZMANN, M. Hydrogenated diamond surfaces studied by atomic and Kelvin force microscopy. *Diamond and Related Materials*. [online]. Apr. 2004, vol. 13, no. 4-8, pp. 740-745. Available from: https://doi.org/10.1016/j.diamond.2003.11.051.

[14] CHANG, Y.-C., MILIAIEVA, D. and REZEK, B. Study of photovoltage stability on nanodiamond-polypyrrole composites by Kelvin probe method. **In:** *10th anniversary international conference on nanomaterials - research & application (NANOCON 2018)*. Brno, Czech Republic: TANGER Ltd., 2019, pp. 164-168.

EFFECT OF THE SUBSTRATE CRYSTALLINE ORIENTATION ON THE SURFACE MORPHOLOGY AND BORON INCORPORATION INTO EPITAXIAL DIAMOND LAYERS

Jan VOVES[1], Alexandr POŠTA[1], Marina DAVYDOVA[2], Alexandr LAPOSA[1], Vojtěch POVOLNÝ[1], Pavel HAZDRA[1], Nicolas LAMBERT[1,2], Silvia SEDLAKOVÁ[2], Vincent MORTET[2,3]

[1]*Faculty of Electrical Engineering, Czech Technical University in Prague, Prague, Czech Republic, EU,* *voves@fel.cvut.cz*

[2]*Institute of Physics of the Czech Academy of Sciences, Prague 8, Czech Republic, EU,* *mortet@fzu.cz*

[3]*Faculty of Biomedical Engineering, Czech Technical University in Prague, Kladno, Czech Republic, EU*

https://doi.org/10.37904/nanocon.2020.3683

Abstract

Epitaxial growth of diamond is critically important for the fabrication of diamond-based electronic devices. The emerging study of the epitaxial diamond growth on the (113) vicinal surfaces evidences highly needed high growth rates and low structural defects concentrations with both p- and n-type doping. In this work, we compare the morphology and dopant concentration incorporation of heavily boron-doped (113) epitaxial diamond layers with conventionally studied (100) and (111) epitaxial layers. Epitaxial layers were grown using resonance cavity Microwave Plasma Enhanced Chemical Vapor Deposition (MWPECVD) system. The surface morphology of epitaxial layers was studied by optical microscopy and atomic force microscopy, whereas the boron incorporation homogeneity was determined by Raman spectroscopy mapping. Heavily boron-doped (113) epitaxial diamond layers can be grown at a high growth rate with a smooth surface, without pyramidal hillocks or non-epitaxial crystallite defects, and with homogeneous boron concentration. These results confirm that epitaxial diamond growth on (113) vicinal surfaces is a promising solution for the development and fabrication of diamond-based electronic devices.

Keywords: Diamond, epitaxy, defects, boron doping, Raman mapping

1. INTRODUCTION

In recent years, modern power electronics have been exploiting new semiconductor materials with a wide bandgap such as gallium nitride or silicon carbide for improving the blocking capability, decreasing of dimensions, and increasing the switching speed of power devices [1]. Due to its outstanding physical parameters, diamond is the best wide-bandgap materials for power electronic applications. However, the preparation of epitaxy layers with a low density of defects and homogenous doping is still under development [2,3]. The use of (113) oriented substrates for the epitaxial growth shows promising results with high boron incorporation efficiency, smooth and almost defect-free surface [4]. The Raman spectroscopy has been demonstrated as a simple and non-destructive characterization method to determine the atomic boron concentration as well as to monitor the strain connected with the presence of defects [5-7]. The increasing boron concentration red-shifts the diamond's zone-center phonon peak located at 1332 cm^{-1} to lower values and lower its relative intensity with respect to the asymmetric band centered around 1200 cm^{-1} attributed to a maximum of the phonon density of states. Another characteristic wide band centered around 500 cm^{-1} shows an almost linear Raman downshift with increasing boron concentration [7-9]. The inner strain in the epitaxy layer influences both the main peak and second asymmetric band [10]. In this work, we investigate and compare the surface morphology, and the spatial distribution of boron atoms in homo-epitaxial diamond layers grown on (100), (111), and (113) oriented substrates.

2. EXPERIMENTAL

Three epitaxial diamond layers with (111), (100), and (113) orientations were grown on polished diamond substrates using a 1.5 kW resonance cavity Microwave Plasma Enhanced Chemical Vapor Deposition (MWPECVD) system AX5010, Seki Diamond Systems. Prior diamond growth, all substrates were cleaned using the same multi steps procedure as follow: (i) cleaning in hot H2SO4 + KNO3 during 10 min, (ii) rinsing in deionized water in ultrasound bath for 10 min two times, (iii) cleaning in acetone with ultrasound for 10 min, (iv) cleaning in isopropyl alcohol with ultrasound for 10 min and finally the substrate is expose at high temperature to pure hydrogen microwave plasma for 10 min before the introduction of the precursor gases and the diamond growth. This cleaning process removes efficiently all surface contaminant as observed by X-Ray Photoelectron Spectroscopy (not shown here). The growth parameters for the different epitaxial layers are summarized in **Table 1**. The surface morphology of epitaxial layers was observed using an optical microscope Olympus BX60 and an atomic force microscope (AFM) NT-MDT Ntegra Prima. The boron incorporation homogeneity was studied by Raman surface mapping with a Raman Spectrometer Renishaw inVia Qontor equipped with a 532nm laser. The shift of the Raman wideband centered around 500 cm^{-1} was used to map the boron concentration, whereas the exact boron concentration was determined from the width of the diamond's zone-center phonon peak (1332 cm^{-1}) using the method described in [11] (see **Figure 1**).

Table 1 Diamond samples with different surface plane orientations, boron/carbon gas precursor concentration ratios, and epitaxy growth times

Crystalline orientation	Microwave power (W)	Pressure (mbar)	Methane concentr. (%)	B/C ratio (ppm)	Boron concentr.	Deposition rate (μm/h)
(111)	575	60	0.1 %	10,000	5.3×10^{20}	0.9 - 1
(100)	700	100	1 %	4,000	$1.3 - 10 \times 10^{20}$	1.8 - 2
(113)	700	100	1%	2,000	7.2×10^{20}	3 - 5

3. RESULTS AND DISCUSSION

All diamond samples were inspected by optical microscopy, and characteristic surface defects were further inspected by AFM and Raman spectroscopy.

3.1. (111) oriented homo-epitaxial boron-doped diamond

The (111) oriented homo-epitaxial diamond layer is optically very uniform over its 2×2 mm^2 surface with only one line defect trough (see **Figure 2a**). The AFM microscopy outside of the line defect shows on an inhomogeneous surface (**Figure 2b**) with approx. 100 nm deep and 1 μm wide trenches that were exhibiting a stochastic shape resulting in a root-mean-squared (RMS) roughness of 50 nm. Raman spectra recorded on randomly selected points are nearly identical (see **Figure 1 left**) and correspond to the heavily boron-doped diamond with a metallic conductivity and the boron concentration of ~ 5.3×10^{20} $cm^{-3,}$ which was established from the unperturbed width of the diamond's zone-center phonon (ZCP) peak. The map of the wide Raman peak centered around 500 cm^{-1} measured in the region including the line defect is homogeneous (**Figure 2c**). This confirms the results of the Raman point-by-point measurement and shows on very good homogeneity of boron incorporation with relatively small variations associated with the line defect.

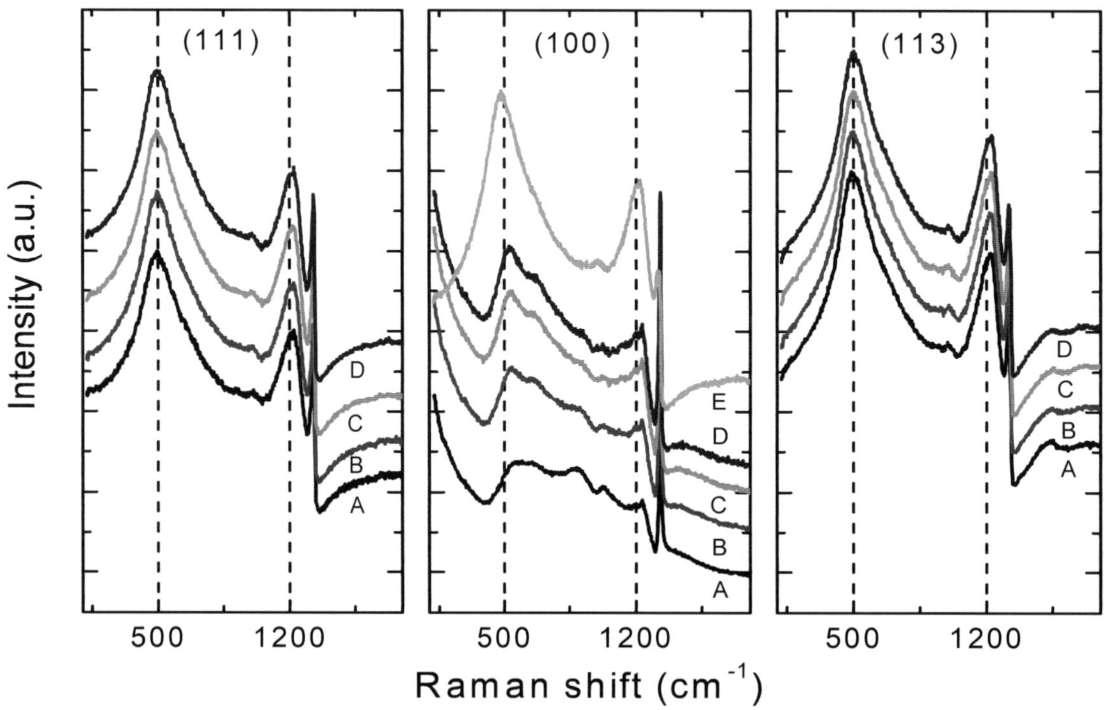

Figure 1 The Raman spectra of the homo-epitaxial boron-doped diamond layers grown on (111), (100), and (113) oriented substrates measured in the different points shown in Figures 2c, 3c, and 4c, respectively

3.2. (100) oriented homo-epitaxial boron-doped diamond

Optical microscopy observation (see **Figures 3a and 3b**) shows that this layer is covered by large rectangular based pyramidal hillocks with approx. 100x100 µm base and 100 nm height. The map of one hillock, including its vicinity (**Figure 3c**), shows on a large dispersion of the 500 cm^{-1} Raman peak, which is characteristic for inhomogeneous boron incorporation inside the hillock and its vicinity. The analysis of the zone-center-phonon line at different measurement points (**Figure 1 center**) shows that the boron concentration varies from 1.3×10^{20} to 10^{21} cm^{-3} and shows a minimal value on the top of the hillock.

3.3. (113) oriented homo-epitaxial boron-doped diamond

Apart from a few linear defects, the optical microscopy observation (see **Figure 4a**) demonstrates that the surface of the (113) oriented homo-epitaxial boron-doped diamond layer is flat and homogeneous. AFM inspection (see **Figure 4b**) confirms a very smooth surface with the RMS surface roughness of about 1 nm. The Raman map of the 500 cm^{-1} peaks, which was measured in the region including the line defect (see **Figure 4c**), indicates a very good boron homogeneity through the whole sample and a negligible dispersion along the line of the defect (**Figure 1 center**). The boron concentration determined by the analysis of the diamond ZCP peak is approximately 7.2×10^{20} cm^{-3}. This high boron concentration gives evidence that, during diamond growth on (113) surface, boron embeds with a high boron incorporation efficiency (BIE), which reaches approx. 2 %. This is a substantially higher value compared to the layers grown on the (100) surface (0.14 % < BIE < 1 %) and (111) surfaces (BIE = 0.28 %).

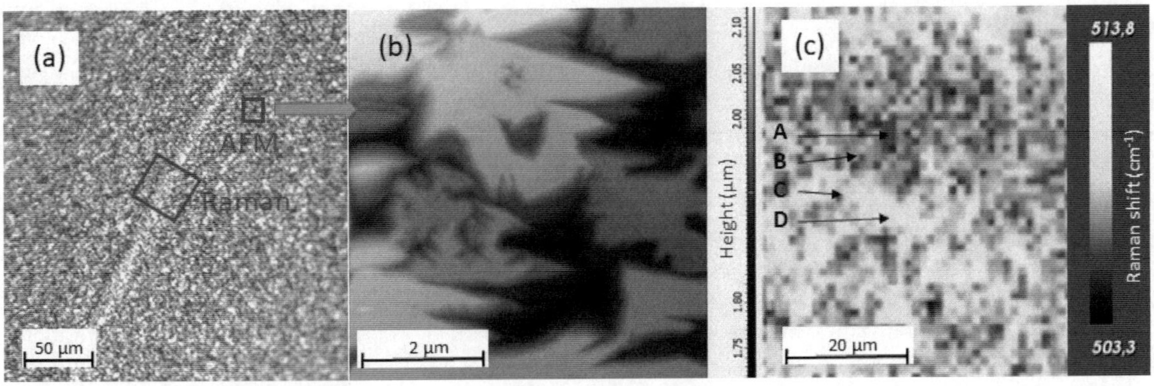

Figure 2 (a) Optical microscopy image of the (111) - oriented boron-doped diamond surface; (b) AFM image of the diamond's surface of the area indicated by the violet square on the optical microscopy image; (c) Raman 500 cm $^{-1}$ peak map of the area indicated by the red square in the optical microscopy image

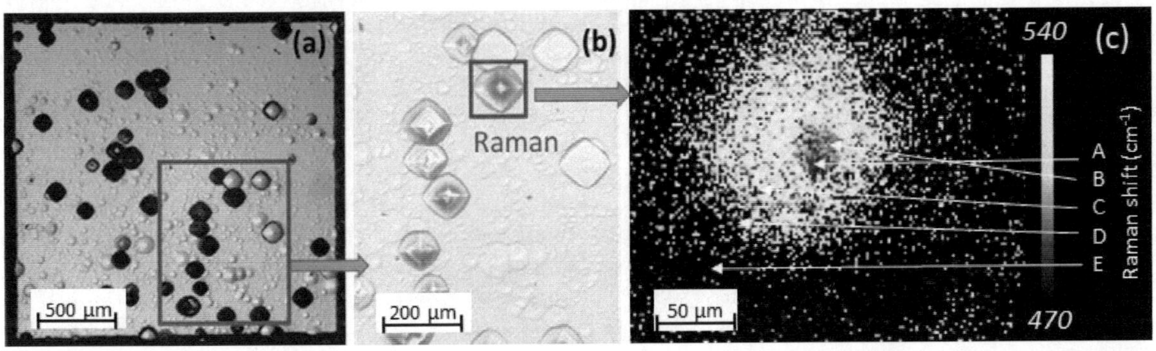

Figure 3 Large view (a) and magnified (b) of the area in the blue box optical microscopy images of the (100) - oriented boron-doped diamond surface; (c) Raman 500 cm $^{-1}$ peak map of the area indicated by the red square in the optical microscopy image

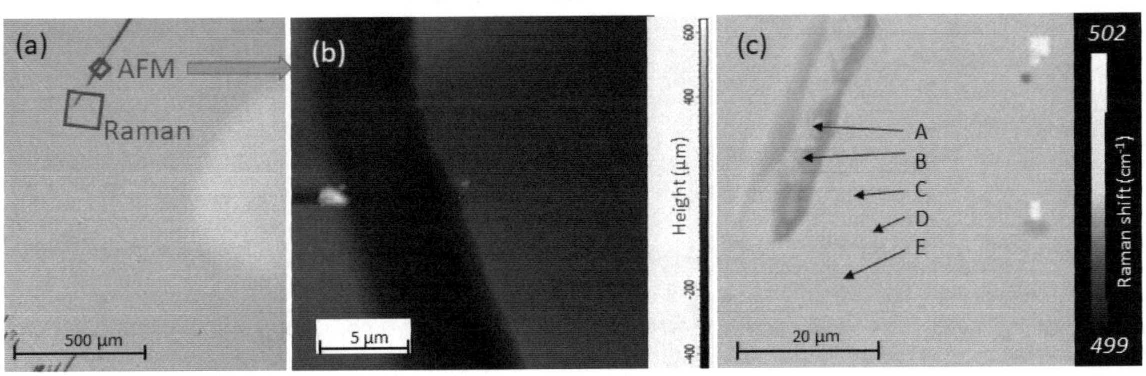

Figure 4 (a) Optical microscopy image of the (113) - oriented boron-doped diamond surface; (b) AFM image of the diamond's surface of the area indicated by the violet square on the optical microscopy image; (c) Raman 500 cm $^{-1}$ peak map of the area indicated by the red square in the optical microscopy image

4. CONCLUSION

In this work, we compared the surface morphology as observed by the optical microscopy, the atomic force microscopy images, and the boron incorporation as determined by Raman spectroscopy in MWPECVD homo-epitaxial boron-doped diamond layers grown on substrates with different crystalline orientations. We observed clearly marked and characteristic surface morphologies and the boron incorporation on the different epitaxial layers. Although macroscopically flat, the (111) epitaxial layer shows an irregular roughness at the sub-micrometer scale and a small boron concentration inhomogeneity. The (100) epitaxial layer is covered by characteristic rectangular based pyramidal hillocks, and the boron incorporation is very inhomogeneous. In contrast with the (111) and (100) epitaxial layers, the boron-doped (113) homo-epitaxial layer exhibits a very smooth surface combined with homogeneous boron incorporation. On top of it, the (113) layer grows more swiftly, and the boron incorporation efficiency is the highest. These results are very promising for the development of vertical diamond power devices, which necessitates thick highly boron-doped templates.

ACKNOWLEDGEMENTS

This work was primarily financially supported by the Czech Science Foundation grant No. 20-11140S and by the Czech Technical University Student Grant No. SGS20/176/OHK3/3T/13. This work has also been supported by Operational Program Research, Development, and Education financed by European Structural and Investment Funds and the Czech Ministry of Education, Youth and Sports (Project No. SOLID21 - CZ.02.1.01/0.0/0.0/16_019/ 0000760).

REFERENCES

[1] ZHANG, B., WANG, S. A Survey of EMI Research in Power Electronics Systems with Wide-Bandgap Semiconductor Devices. *IEEE J. of Emerging and Sel.Topics in Power Electronics.* 2019, vol. 8, pp. 626-643.

[2] UMEZAWA, H. Recent advances in diamond power semiconductor devices. *Materials Science in Semiconductor Processing.* 2018, vol. 78, pp. 147-156.

[3] VOLPE, P. N. et al. Extreme dielectric strength in boron doped homoepitaxial diamond. *Applied Physics Letters.* 2010, vol. 97, p. 223501.

[4] TALLAIRE, A. et al. Growth of thick and heavily boron-doped (113)-oriented CVD diamond films. *Diamond and Related Materials.* 2016, vol. 66, pp. 61-66.

[5] MORTET, V. et al. Determination of atomic boron concentration in heavily boron-doped diamond by Raman spectroscopy. *Diamond & Related Materials* 2019, vol. 93, pp. 54-58.

[6] WANG, X. et al. Surface Morphology of the Interface Junction of CVD Mosaic Single-Crystal Diamond. *Material.* 2020, vol. 13, p. 91.

[7] MORTET, V. et al. Insight into boron-doped diamond Raman spectra characteristic features. *Carbon.* 2017, vol. 115, pp. 279-284.

[8] BERNARD, M., DENEUVILLE, A., MUR, P. Non-destructive determination of the boron concentration of heavily doped metallic diamond thin films from Raman spectroscopy. *Diamond and Related Materials.* 2004, vol. 13, pp. 282-286.

[9] ACHATZ, P. et al. Isotopic substitution of boron and carbon in superconducting diamond epilayers grown by MPCVD. *Diamond & Related Materials.* 2010, vol.19, pp. 814-817.

[10] SRIMONGKON, K. et al. Boron inhomogeneity of HPHT-grown single-crystal diamond substrates: Confocal micro-Raman mapping investigations. *Diamond & Related Materials.* 2016, vol. 63, pp. 21-25.

[11] MORTET, V. et al. New perspectives for heavily boron-doped diamond Raman spectrum analysis. *Carbon.* 2020, vol. 168 pp. 319-327.

RAMAN MICROSPECTROSCOPY STUDY OF CALCINED ELECTRICALLY CONDUCTIVE NANOCOMPOSITE POLYPYRROLE/GHASSOUL

[1]Pavlína PEIKERTOVÁ, [1,2,3]Jonáš TOKARSKÝ, [4]Lenka KULHÁNKOVÁ, [1]Kateřina MAMULOVÁ KUTLÁKOVÁ

[1]*Nanotechnology Centre, VŠB-Technical University of Ostrava, Ostrava, Czech Republic, EU,* pavlina.peikertova@vsb.cz, jonas.tokarsky@vsb.cz, katerina.mamulova.kutlakova@vsb.cz

[2]*IT4Innovations, VŠB-Technical University of Ostrava, Ostrava, Czech Republic, EU,* jonas.tokarsky@vsb.cz

[3]*Institute of Environmental Technology, VŠB-Technical University of Ostrava, Ostrava, Czech Republic, EU,* jonas.tokarsky@vsb.cz

[4]*Faculty of Materials Technology, VŠB-Technical University of Ostrava, Ostrava, Czech Republic, EU,* lenka.kulhankova@vsb.cz

https://doi.org/10.37904/nanocon.2020.3679

Abstract

Moroccan clay ghassoul (GHA) was used in preparation process of electrically conductive nanocomposite contained polypyrrole (PPy/GHA). Based on our previous studies on electrically conductive nanocomposites, the calcination may lead to formation of graphite and few-layer graphene. Prepared PPy/GHA nanocomposite was compressed to the square tablets which were calcined in an inert atmosphere at 1300 °C. XRD measurements confirmed presence of graphite in the PPy/GHA sample. However, this method does not provide information about distribution of the graphitic and the few-layer graphene phases. Therefore, Raman microspectroscopy, which has an ability to distinguish the carbonaceous forms and allows showing their distribution on Raman spectral maps, was used as a major tool for the study of PPy/GHA. Several maps were created and studied. Spectral maps proved that the calcination leads to the formation of few-layer graphene on the surface of the tablet. Distribution of the graphitic phases was observed at the edge and on the surface of the tablet. Moreover, spectral maps were used to evaluate if and how the selected regions in one side correspond to each other.

Keywords: Ghassoul, polypyrrole, graphene, Raman microspectroscopy, electrical conductivity

1. INTRODUCTION

Polypyrrole (PPy) belongs to the groups of electrically conductive polymers, which can be used in various applications such as corrosion protectors or sensors (for biomolecules, VOCs, or gases) [1-6]. Arrangement of PPy chains may strongly affect its conductivity and can be performed by intercalation of the PPy into the interlayer space of clay matrix [7]. In our study, we used ghassoul (GHA), which is stevensite-rich Moroccan clay, as a carrier matrix for the PPy. Stevensite belongs to the trioctahedral smectite group and it is magnesium-rich phyllosilicate [8]. Prepared PPy/GHA nanocomposite powder was pressed into tablet and heat treated at 1300 °C. Afterwards, the prepared calcined tablet was characterized by XRD and Raman microspectroscopy Aim of the study is to determine the presence and nature of graphitic structures formed during heat treatment, and to evaluate how homogeneous the sample is in terms of graphitic structure distribution.

2. EXPERIMENTAL

Nanocomposite containing PPy and GHA was prepared in one-step process by oxidative polymerization of pyrrole (C_4H_5N; ≥ 98%, Sigma-Aldrich, Czech Republic) with ferric chloride ($FeCl_3$; Merci (Czech Republic) in aqueous suspension of ghassoul (Societé du ghassoul et de ses dérivés Séfrioui, Morocco) which was sieved to obtain < 40 µm size fraction. The initial materials were combined in mass ratio 1 (pyrrole) : 4.85 ($FeCl_3$) : 1.2 (GHA). Black product which was obtained after 6 h of stirring were rinsed with distilled water, collected on filter, and dried for 24 h at 40 °C.

The prepared nanocomposite was ground to a fine powder in a mortar, and 28×28 mm square tablets (m = 3 g) using ZWICK 1494 press for 10 min at 400 MPa and room temperature ~ 22 °C was prepared without any binder. Detailed description of the preparation process can be found in previous studies [7,9].

Prepared tablet was heated in the inert atmosphere (> 99.9999% Ar) under constant overpressure $1.06 \cdot 10^5$ Pa in high-temperature tube resistance furnace (CLASIC CZ, spol. s.r.o., Czech Republic). The tablet was exposed to 1300 °C (temperature rise with step 5 $°C \cdot min^{-1}$) for 1 h. We present only results obtained from the heated tablet. Therefore, the designation PPy/GHA will further mean the heated sample.

Heated tablet was characterized by X-ray diffraction (XRD) in reflection mode in symmetrical Bragg-Brentano arrangement using Cu lamp ($\lambda(Cu_{K\alpha})$ = 0.15406 nm; U = 40 kV; I = 40 mA) in Ultima IV diffractometer (Rigaku, Japan) equipped with scintillation detector. The phase composition of the sample was determined according to the ICDD PDF 2 Release 2014 database.

Raman spectral maps on the surface and on the edge of the tablet were measured using Smart Raman Microscopy System XploRA™ (HORIBA Jobin Yvon, France). Laser (532 nm, 100 mW) was reduced to the 1% of initial intensity. Objective with magnification 50× and grating 600gr./mm were used for the maps collection in the selected regions (21 × 21 µm) with 1 µm step.

3. RESULTS AND DISCUSSION

Diffraction pattern of the PPy/GHA is shown in **Figure 1**. As a result of the magnesium-silicate stevensite transformation, protoenstatite and forsterite were identified. Besides these phases, also graphite was determined in the diffraction pattern. Reflection at position 2-Theta = 26.34° reveals that its d_{002} value is d = 3.38 Å. The broad reflection under 20° 2-Theta can be ascribed to a disordered carbon structure derived from PPy, which has not been transformed into graphite.

XRD proved the presence of the graphitic structure, but it is not able to determine how many disorders are in the graphitic structure, how the structure is distributed in the sample, and whether the structure consist only from graphite or whether also some form of graphene is present. Raman microspectroscopy is very useful tool for the characterization of the carbonaceous samples. Big advantage is due to its connection with microscope, which allows the generation of the spectral maps and moreover very valuable information of the graphitic structure can be deduced from the Raman spectra.

Carbonaceous samples has three main bands; D (i.e. disorder), G (i.e. graphitic), and 2D band (overtone of D band). The most significant for the graphene determination is the 2D band [10], because its intensity may prove the presence of graphene. When intensity of 2D (I_{2D}) is four times higher than the intensity of G band (I_G) [11], the presence of single-layer graphene can be suggested. Moreover, ratio of the intensities of the D and G bands (I_D/I_G) show the degree of effects in the graphitic structure.

Raman spectral maps were collected from the three different regions on the surface and three different regions on the edge of the PPy/GHA tablet. And measured Raman spectra confirm the presence of the graphitic structure in the sample. But the spectra detected in the Raman maps show that the graphitic structure varies according the intensity of the 2D band (see **Figure 2**). Raman spectral maps from the surface and edge are shown in **Figure 3** and four different colors are observable (as is shown in **Figure 2**). Black color means that the 2D band was not detected in this measured point. Blue color means that the I_{2D}/I_G is lower than 0.5, green color means that the 0.5 < I_{2D}/I_G <1 and red color means that the I_{2D}/I_G > 1. Exemplary spectra are shown in **Figure 3.** Few-layer graphene can be suggested in the red areas [12], where the intensity I_{2D}/I_G is higher than 1, and in several cases almost reaches 2, in the case of shown Raman map from the surface (**Figure 2**, red spectrum).

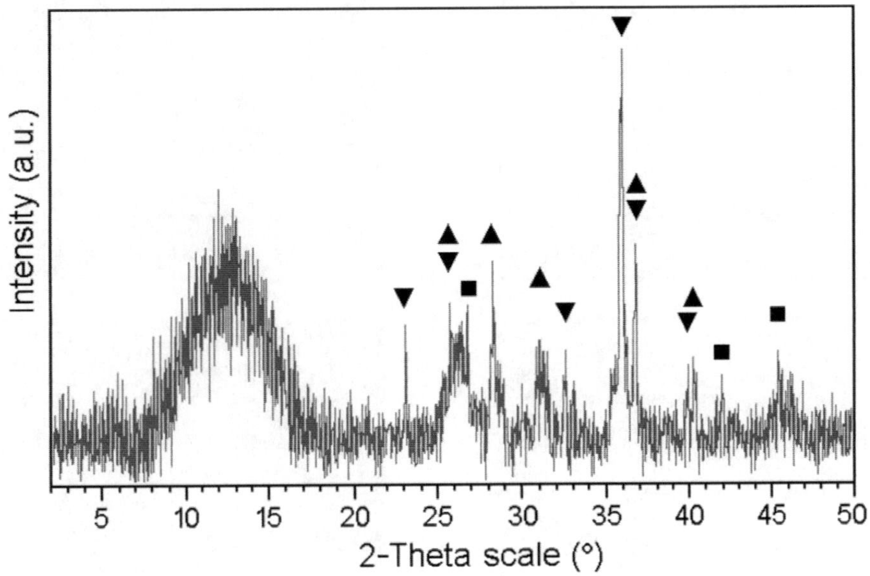

Figure 1 XRD pattern of PPy/GHA. ■ graphite, ▲ protoenstatite, ▼ forsterite

Raman spectral maps reveal the heterogeneity of the graphitic structure and also the difference between the surface and the edge of the tablets. On the surface was detected few-layer graphene *n* < 5 (*n*= numbers of graphene layers), which are observable as red color in **Figure 2** and **Figure 3**. Multi-layer graphene is connected to the green color [10]. Calculated ratios of I_{2D}/I_G for the whole region are in **Table 1**. There is very good correlation between the values from different regions on the surface/edge and copy the information from the Raman spectral maps, accordingly the higher values for the surface (presence of few-layer graphene) and lower for the edge.

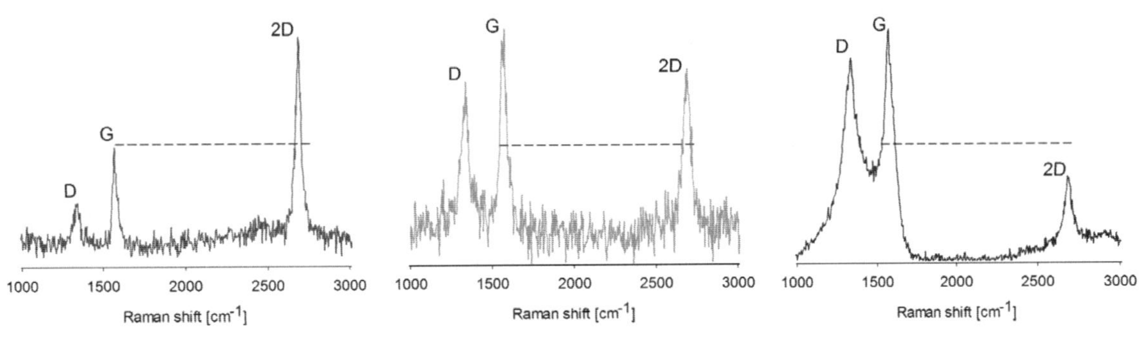

Figure 2 Chosen Raman spectra which show meaning of the colors of the maps (**Figure 3**) Red: I_{2D}/I_G > 1; green: 0.5 < I_{2D}/I_G < 1; blue: I_{2D}/I_G < 0.5

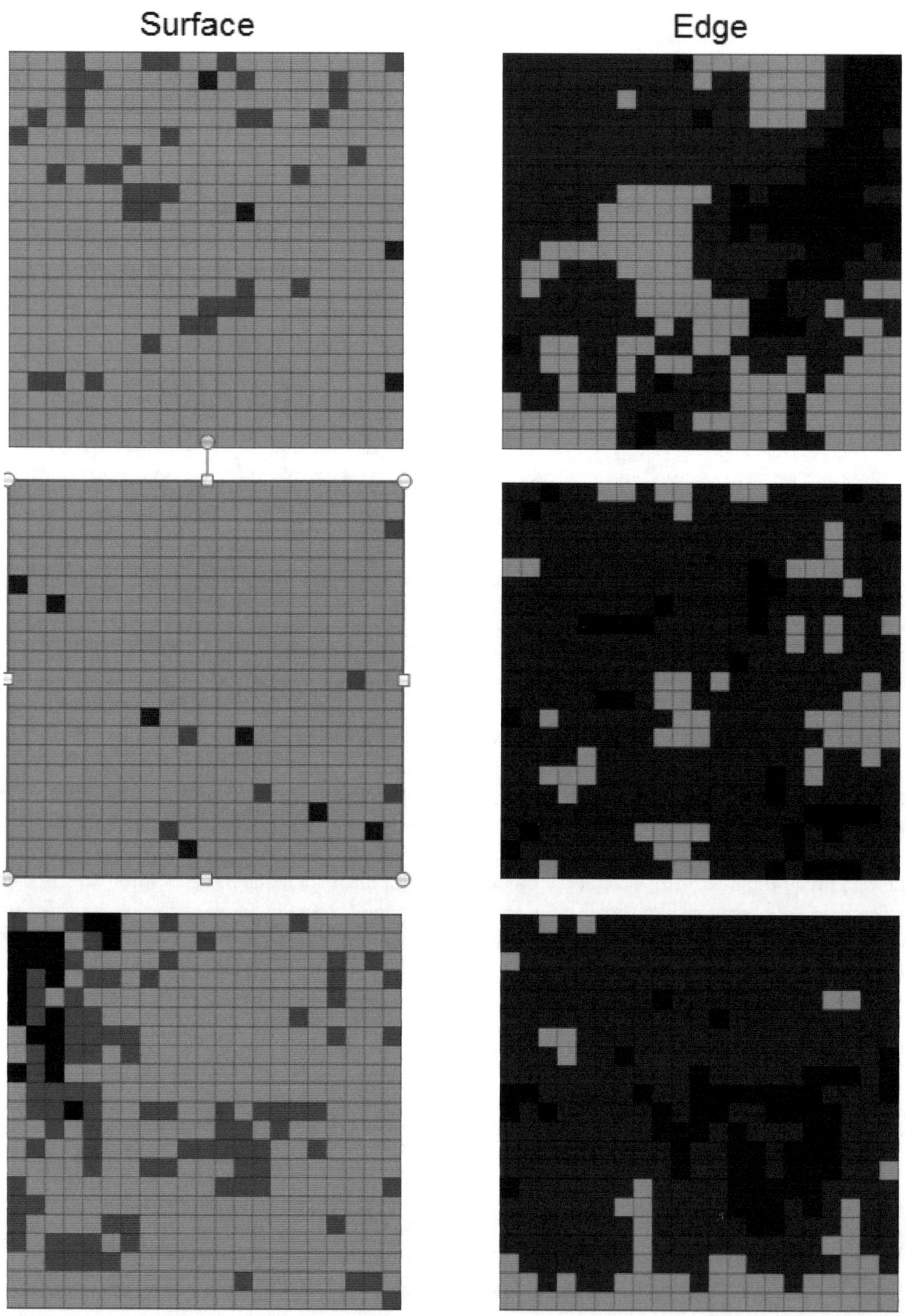

Figure 3 Raman spectral map of selected region (21 μm × 21 μm) in the surface (left), and in the edge (right) of PPy/GHA tablet. Red: $I_{2D}/I_G > 1$; green: $0.5 < I_{2D}/I_G < 1$; blue: $I_{2D}/I_G < 0.5$; black: no 2D band

Table 1 Calculated values for intensity ratio I_D/I_G and I_{2D}/I_G

	Surface	Edge
I_{2D}/I_G	0.82 ± 0.14	0.40 ± 0.17
	0.73 ± 0.11	0.37 ± 0.12
	0.90 ± 0.20	0.35 ± 0.13
I_D/I_G	0.73 ± 0.11	0.82 ± 0.16
	0.83 ± 0.12	0.81 ± 0.13
	0.71 ± 0.13	0.88 ± 0.11

Also the I_D/I_G were calculated to determine the degree of disorders and surprisingly the values for the surface and the edge are pretty similar, although little bit lower for the surface (less defects), which is connected to higher appearance of few-layer graphene. From the results is clearly visible that the random selected regions express the character of the surface/edge and in terms of surface or edge the structure is relatively homogeneous.

4. CONCLUSIONS

The PPy/GHA nanocomposite was successfully prepared by heating at 1300 °C in inert atmosphere. XRD analysis revealed the presence of graphite in the structure of heated nanocomposite, which was confirmed by Raman microspectroscopy. Moreover, generated Raman spectral maps reveal differences between the edge and surface of the tablet, when the few-layer graphene with less than 5 layers was observed on the surface. Calculated I_D/I_G reveals that the degree of defects is almost equal, but little bit lower for the surface. Taking into account the presence of forsterite and enstatite in heated PPy/GHA nanocomposite, the results suggest a promising way in which a ceramic material containing graphite and graphene prepared in situ from the polypyrrole could be achieved.

ACKNOWLEDGEMENTS

This work was supported by The Ministry of Education, Youth and Sports of the Czech Republic (projects SP2020/24, LQ1602, CZ.02.1.01/0.0/0.0/16_013/0001791).

REFERENCES

[1] GONZÁLEZ, M. B., SAIDMAN, S. B. Corrosion protection properties of polypyrrole electropolymerized onto steel in the presence of salicylate. *Progress in Organic Coatings*. 2012, vol. 75, no.3, pp. 178-183.

[2] BANDEIRA, R. M., van DRUNEN, J., GARCIA, A. C., TREMILIOSI-FILHO, G. Influence of the thickness and roughness of polyaniline coatings on corrosion protection of AA7075 aluminum alloy. *Electrochimica Acta*. 2017, vol. 240, pp. 215-224.

[3] KALANTAR-ZADEH, K. Polypyrrole nanofiber surface acoustic wave gas sensors. *Sensors and Actuators B: Chemical*. 2008, vol. 134, no. 2, pp. 826-831.

[4] AKBARINEJAD, A., GHOORCHIAN, A., KAMALABADi, M., ALIZADEH, N. Electrospun soluble conductive polypyrrole nanoparticles for fabrication of highly selective n-butylamine gas sensor. *Sensors and Actuators B: Chemical*. 2016, vol. 236, pp. 99-108.

[5] RAMANAVIČIUS, A., RAMANAVIČIENÉ, A., MALINAUSKAS, A. Electrochemical sensors based on conducting polymer-polypyrrole. *Electrochimica Acta*. 2006, vol. 51, no. 27, pp. 6025-6037.

[6] KOIRALA, K., SEVILLA III, F. B., SANTOS, J. H. Biomimetic potentiometric sensor for chlorogenic acid based on electrosynthesized polypyrrole. *Sensors and Actuators B: Chemical*. 2016, vol. 222, pp. 391-396.

[7] VILÍMOVÁ, P., KULHÁNKOVÁ, L., PEIKERTOVÁ, P., MAMULOVÁ KUTLÁKOVÁ, K., KONÍČKOVÁ, H., VALLOVÁ, S., PLAČEK, T., TOKARSKÝ, J. Effect of montmorillonite/polypyrrole ratio and oxidizing agent on structure and electrical conductivity of intercalated nanocomposites. *Applied Clay Science*. 2019, vol. 168, pp. 459-468.

[8] RHOUTA, B., KADDAMI, H., ELBARGY, J., AMJOUD, M., DAUODI, L., MAURY, F., SENCOCQ, F., MAAZOUZ, A., GERARD, J.F. Elucidating the crystal-chemistry of Jbel Rhassoul stevensite (Morocco) by advanced analytical techniques. *Clay Minerals*. 2008, vol. 43, no. 3, pp. 393-403.

[9] TOKARSKÝ, J., VILÍMOVÁ, P., PEIKERTOVÁ, P., MAMULOVÁ KUTLÁKOVÁ, K., KULHÁNKOVÁ, L. Stevensite-rich Moroccan clay intercalated by polypyrrole: towards the enhancement of electrical conductivity. *Journal of Nanoscience and Nanotechnology*. 2019, vol. 19, no. 5, pp. 2821-2832.

[10] FERRARI, A.C., MEYER, J.C., SCARDACI, V., CASIRAGHI, C., LAZZERI, M., MAURI, F., PISANEC, S., JIANG, D., NOVOSELOV, K.S., ROTH, S., GEIM, A.K. Raman spectrum of graphene and graphene layers. *Physical Review Letters*. 2006, vol. 97, pp. 187401.

[11] TAN, P.H., HU, C.Y., DONG, J., SHEN, W.C., ZHANG, B.F. Polarization properties, high-order Raman spectra, and frequency asymmetry between stokes and anti-stokes scattering of Raman modes in a graphite whisker. *Physical Review B*. 2011, vol. 64, pp. 214301.

[12] GUPTA, A., CHEN, G., JOSHI, P., TADIGADAPA, S., EKLUND, P.C. Raman scattering from high-frequency phonons in supported n-graphene layer films. *Nano Letters*. 2006, vol. 6, 12, pp. 2667-2673.

EXPANSION OF OPTICAL PROPERTIES IN TIO_X NANOPARTICLES BY THEIR LASER-MEDIATED ALLOYING WITH AG

[1]David ETTEL, [1]Ondrej HAVELKA, [2]Selingul ISIK, [1]Fatma YALCINKAYA, [1]Rafael TORRES-MENDIETA

[1]Institute for Nanomaterials, Advanced Technologies and Innovation, Technical University of Liberec, Liberec, Czech Republic, EU

[2]Faculty of Textile, Technical University of Liberec, Liberec, Czech Republic, EU, Rafael.Torres@tul.cz

https://doi.org/10.37904/nanocon.2020.3700

Abstract

TiOx nanoparticles are large bandgap materials that attract a great deal of attention for their use in light-powered applications. However, their utility is often restricted to employing energy from the ultraviolet (U.V.) or the second near-infrared solar spectrum region. In the current contribution, we expand the optical response of this material by its laser-mediated alloying with Ag nanoparticles, of which surface plasmon resonance activity allows the absorption of the visible solar spectrum region. For this, we produce the laser ablation of a Ti foil immersed in an aqueous solution of silver nitrate ($AgNO_3$). The analysis of the material using transmission electron microscopy, inductive coupled plasma mass spectroscopy, and UV-vis spectroscopy enabled recognizing that the use of the minimal $AgNO_3$ solution of 1 mM leads to the optimal synthesis of nanoalloys with the coexisting crystalline phases TiO (JPDS database: PDF 00-043-1296), and Ag (PDF 00-004-0783), the bimodal size distribution centered at 60 and 130 nm, the elemental composition of 31.22% Ag and 68.78% Ti, and finally, the absorbance edges centered at 400, and 638 nm.

Unlike conventional methodologies, in the presented approach, no special conditions or hazardous reducing agents are required. Therefore, we believe the current work will be of great interest in the facile and waste-reducing synthesis of nanoalloys composed by elements with contrasting optical properties.

Keywords: Nanoparticles, nanoalloys, Ti, Ag, Laser synthesis of nanoparticles

1. INTRODUCTION

In past years, nanomaterials research allowed the production of materials with unconventional optical properties compared to bulk materials [1]. One group of particular interest are nanoparticles (NPs) of Ti oxides, whose ability to generate photo-induced charge carriers upon exposure to light has led to their use in plenty of applications like photocatalysis, solar cell development, water purification, and photothermal conversion, among others [2]. Nevertheless, their real employability is often restricted to the percentage of the total electromagnetic spectrum that can absorb, e.g., in the case of TiO_2, which is the most popular form of titanium oxide, its absorption is limited to the ultraviolet region [3], in the case of other titanium oxide forms like black TiO_2 or Ti_2O_3, the absorption range gets extended to the visible and infrared regions [4]. However, their absorption efficiency is limited. The latest and most efficient trend to overcome these limitations is expanding their absorption capabilities through alloying with noble metal NPs [5]. These NPs display a phenomenon known as surface plasmon resonance (SPR), in which their free electrons in the conduction band oscillate collectively upon their exposure to light, and depending on the NPs size; electromagnetic waves with a specific wavelength resonates with the electronic oscillation. This phenomenon leads to its preferential absorption over the rest of the electromagnetic spectrum. When elements that experience SPR activity are mixed with materials like titanium oxides, synergistic effects can occur where photogenerated charge carriers can transfer from one element to the other, enhancing in this way the titanium oxide's harvesting of light [6].

The most straight forward ways of mixing these elements encompass either ball milling-based strategies or co-precipitation-based once, which often imply the use of special conditions, hazardous reducing agents, and large production of polluting by-products [7]. In the current contribution, we address these issues by the laser ablation of a Ti foil immersed in an aqueous solution of silver nitrate ($AgNO_3$). According to the relevant literature, when ablating a solid target in an aqueous medium, the detached material, including electrons, ions, and other energetic species, creates a plasma where all the forming species recombine, generating NPs [8]. In a traditional experimental procedure, the plasma's energy is released to the surrounding liquid medium forming a cavitation bubble where the NPs experience coalescence, reaching in this way their final size, and after the cavitation bubble extinguishes, the NPs get finally released to the liquid medium. However, when the liquid medium is filled with molecules that are precursors of other NPs, the plasma can render the precursor reduction/oxidation via charge transfer or through their interaction with sensitizers created by the solvent's molecular dissociation that surrounds the plasma (radicals or excited molecules) [9]. After the reduction/oxidation process occurs, the produced ions transfer into the plasma [10], resulting in nanoalloys' formation.

Since the proposed methodology enables the improvement of the optical capabilities in Ti oxide NPs by their mixing with Ag, while at the same time does not require any hazardous chemical agents, special conditions and greatly suppresses the generation of by-products, it is believed that the current investigation will be of great value for the eco-friendly design of new materials with tailored optical properties

2. EXPERIMENTAL

The nanoalloy synthesis took place by the laser ablation of a Ti foil (0.25 mm thickness, 99.7% trace metals basis, Sigma-Aldrich) immersed in 0 mM, 0.001 mM, 0.01 mM, 0.1 mM, 1 mM, and 10 mM solutions of $AgNO_3$, (≥99.0% pureness, Sigma-Aldrich) in distilled water (18.2 MΩ·cm). The Ti plate was irradiated by a High-energy industrial femtosecond laser (Onefive Origamy XP, NKT Photonics), which has a 400 fs pulse duration, a central wavelength centered at 1030 nm, a repetition rate of 1 MHz, a beam diameter of 1.5 mm at a width of $1/e^2$ and output power of 5.1 W. As displayed in **Figure 1**, the laser beam was focused by an F-Theta Scan Lens with a focal length of 160 mm over the surface of the Ti foil in a batch operation mode while continuously stirred by a magnetic stirrer. The laser beam was moved at a velocity of 2 m/s over the foil's surface, employing a dual-axis scanning galvanometer mirror positioning system (intelliSCAN 14, SCANLAB).

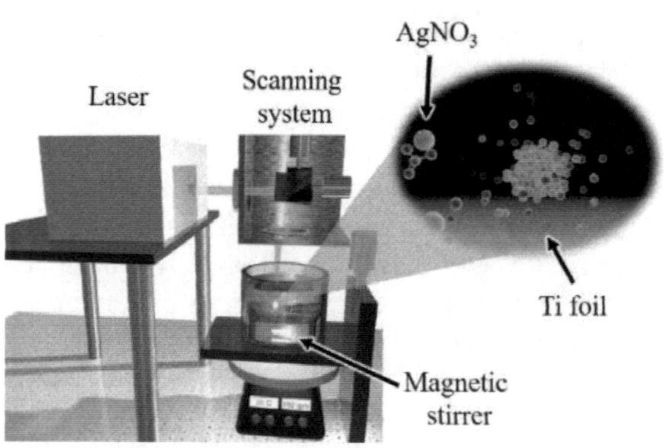

Figure 1 Laser ablation in an aqueous solution of $AgNO_3$ in a batch operation mode

The samples coming from the ablation in the different solutions are labeled as Ti NPs for 0 mM, and 0.001, 0.01, 0.1, 1, and 10 mM for the corresponding concentration's solutions.

After the synthesis, the elemental composition of individual particles was assessed by single-particle inductive-coupled plasma mass spectroscopy (spICP-MS) using a mass spectrometer with inductively coupled plasma (ICP-MS; NexION 3000D, Perkin Elmer). Their crystallographic structure was identified by X-ray diffraction in powder (XRD) using a diffractometer (Miniflex 600, Rigaku) with a wavelength of 1.540 Å operating at a scan speed of 1°·min−1 in a 2θ angle range of 30-90°. The ultraviolet-visible (UV-Vis) spectroscopy analysis was performed by acquiring the sample's absorption spectra using a spectrophotometer (DR 3900, Hach-Lange), in a wavelength range from 320 to 1000 nm with a wavelength resolution of 1 nm. Furthermore, the morphology and size distribution of selected samples were determined using a transmission electron microscope (TEM; JEM-2100Plus, JEOL), which was operated at an acceleration voltage of 200 kV.

3. RESULTS AND DISCUSSION

3.1. spICP-MS

The elemental composition displayed in **Table 1**, which was assessed in single particles by spICP-MS demonstrates that each element's weight percentage in the synthesized particles is relatively proportional to the $AgNO_3$ solution's concentration, except for the case of 0.01 mM, which seems to be comparable to the one observed for 0.1 mM. The solution's concentration that approaches the most to a 50 to 50 wt% elemental composition is 1 mM, which also establishes a border of the order of magnitude in the molar solution at which it is possible to control the percentage of Ag to Ti in the nanoalloys, thus leading to the design of truly tailored nanoalloys.

Table 1 Average concentration and the corresponding weight percentage of Ag and Ti found in the samples by spICP-MS (the weight percentage is provided without considering the contribution of oxygen due to its measurement's inaccuracy while employing spICP-MS).

Sample	Ag average concentration (mg/L)	Ti average concentration (mg/L)	Ag (wt%)	Ti (wt%)
Ti NPs	0.0	35.35	0	100
0.001 mM	0.14	35.20	0.40	99.60
0.01 mM	1.70	25.00	6.37	93.63
0.1 mM	2.11	31.87	6.21	93.79
1 mM	14.95	32.94	31.22	68.78
10 mM	331.62	41.14	88.96	11.04

3.2. XRD

Figure 2, which shows the comparison of the XRD patterns found in the different samples, exhibits in accordance with the results from spICP-MS, that the crystalline phases found in the samples with a high concentration of Ti, i.e., Ti NPs, 0.001 mM, 0.01 mM, and 0.1 mM, only belong to titanium oxides. On the contrary, the samples with a larger concentration of Ag also display the Ag crystalline phase.

For the samples Ti NPs, 0.001 mM, 0.01 mM, and 0.1 mM, it is possible to identify the crystalline families (111) at 43.46 °, (200) at 50.64 °, and (220) at 74.44 °, which correspond to the cubic crystalline phase $TiO_{1.04}$ with a space group Fm-3m, and cell lattice parameters a= b= c= 4.1940 Å (JCPDS database: PDF-00-043-1296). Also, the family (116) at 63.41 ° of the rhombohedral crystal phase Ti_2O_3 with the space group R-3c, and cell lattice parameters a= 5.139 Å, and c= 13.659 Å (JCPDS database: PDF-10-63).

The sample 1 mM, exhibits the presence of the crystalline phase $TiO_{1.04}$, and the families (111) at 44.8 °, (200) at 51.8 °, and (220) at 77 °, which belong to the crystalline cubic phase of Ag with a space group Fm and cell lattice parameters: a= b= c= 4.0862 Å (JCPDS database: 00-004-0783). Finally, the sample 10 mM only exhibits the Ag crystalline phase. Unlike the samples synthesized in lower $AgNO_3$ solution concentrations, the peaks belonging to the titanium oxide phases seem to be overshadowed by the once of Ag, which agrees with previous studies where the increment of Ag wt% results in higher visibility of the Ag crystalline phase [11].

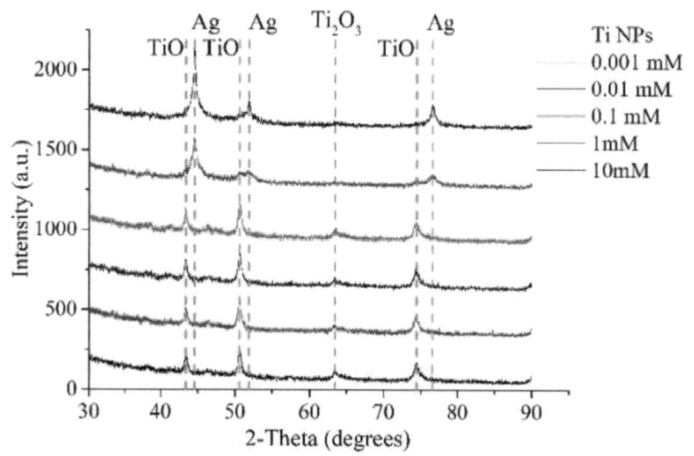

Figure 2 XRD spectra of the synthesized samples. The green vertical dashed lines indicate the TiO crystalline phase peaks, the orange lines the Ag, and dark yellow the Ti_2O_3 phases

3.3. UV-Vis

The absorbance spectra (**Figure 3**) demonstrates that the alloying with Ag heavily increments the synthesized particles' absorption in the wavelength region 350-600 nm, providing in this way coexisting absorbance edges centered at 400 and 663 nm in average, which may potentially enable the transfer of photo-induced charge carriers between the Ti oxide and Ag. Without the presence of $AgNO_3$, the sample labeled as Ti NPs displays a spectrum found in Ti NPs with coexisting crystalline phases of various oxides like TiO, Ti_2O_3, and TiO_2 that displays an absorbance edge at 400 nm (typical result when a Ti foil undergoes ablation in water) [12]. Within the addition of $AgNO_3$, the samples start to display an absorption peak that belongs to the SPR activity of Ag NPs, and with this, the possibility to generate photo-induced charge carriers from a broader range of the electromagnetic spectrum. In the sample labeled 0.001 mM, the absorbance maximum is centered at 533 nm with an edge at 717 nm, which, according to the Mie theory, corresponds to spherical Ag NPs with sizes around 117 nm, or core-shell nanostructure with an Ag core of 62 nm and a TiO_2 shell of 7 nm [13]. According to the spICP-MS results, a scenario where particles are mainly composed of Ag seems unlikely; therefore, it is more reasonable to deduce that the use of such minimal $AgNO_3$ solution's concentration does not lead to an adequate elemental mixing and may preferably lead to the separate synthesis of TiO_x NPs and Ag NPs. Moreover, the larger intensity of the titanium oxide crystalline phases and the lack of Ag phase in the XRD measurements support the incorrect mixing hypothesis. In the case of 0.01 mM, the Ag NPs SPR peak's presence at 430 nm and edge at 751 nm seems to get heavily reduced, which agrees with the behavior that Ag-based alloys should display for the elemental composition found by spICP-MS [14]. In the case of 0.1 mM, the plasmon peak is centered at 421 nm and have the edge at 627 nm, which according to the Mie theory, corresponds either to Ag Nps with sizes around 50 nm, or NPs with a TiO_2 core of 6 nm and Ag shell of 21 nm [13]. Similar to the case of 0.001 mM, according to the spICP-MS results, a scenario where the elements did not mix correctly seems more plausible. In the 1 mM and 10 mM cases, the SPR peaks are located at 433 and 426 nm, and the edges at 630 and 620 nm, respectively. According to the Mie theory, the location and intensity of the SPR peaks correspond to Ag NPs with sizes around 60 nm or NPs with a TiO_2 core of 9 nm and Ag shell of 26 nm for 1 mM, and Ag NPs with sizes around 55 nm or NPs with a TiO_2 core of 4 nm and Ag shell of 25 nm for 10 mM. Given the spICP-MS and XRD results, the presence of both elements in individual particles seems more plausible. Therefore, similar to the outcome drawn from the elemental composition analysis, 1 mM seems to be the solution's concentration threshold at which it is possible to get a high control over the elemental composition and optical properties in the synthesized alloys.

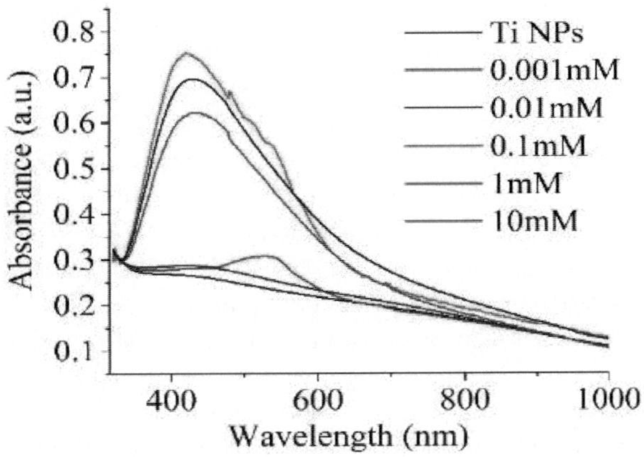

Figure 3 Absorbance spectra of the synthesized samples

3.4. TEM

Given the previous results, the samples labeled as Ti NPs and 1 mM were selected for their morphological analysis by means of TEM. **Figure 4**, which displays a micrograph picture of both samples accompanied by their corresponding size histogram, exhibits two essential aspects that significantly relate to the previous results.

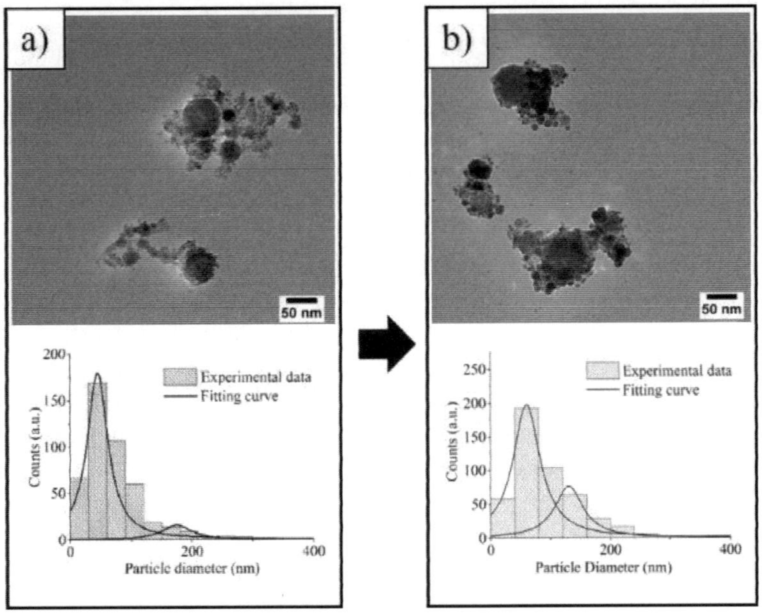

Figure 4 TEM micrograph (top side) and histogram of the size distribution (bottom side) of a) the samples synthesized in pure water and b) in a 1 mM aqueous solution of $AgNO_3$

On the one hand, both materials display a bimodal size distribution, which is typical for NPs synthesized by laser ablation in liquid mediums [15]. For Ti NPs, the average size is centered at (45 ± 20.7) nm, and (174 ± 30.2) nm, while for 1 mM at (60 ± 27.6) nm, and (130 ± 29.1) nm. On the other hand, the morphology of the titanium oxide NPs seems to be spine-like for the smaller elements and spherical for the bigger once, while it is spherical for 1 mM whether they are small or big particles. Similar to the case of monovalent salts usage for the quenching in the size of the laser-synthesized NPs, the usage of 1 mM $AgNO_3$ solution's concentration seems to interact intimately with the incoming titanium oxide NPs leading to their reshape in a spherical form [16].

4. CONCLUSION

The present study sheds light on the capabilities of the synthesis of NPs based on the ablation of solid targets in liquid media to expand the optical properties of materials such as titanium oxides. The analysis of samples coming from the ablation of a ti foil immersed in various concentrations of $AgNO_3$ aqueous solutions enables determining that 1 mm is a concentration's threshold where it is possible to control the elemental composition, crystalline structure, and optical absorption of the synthesized spherical alloys. Besides, since the alloying with Ag provides the Ti oxide NPs an absorption peak that coincides with the maximum of the solar spectral irradiance, i.e., 350-600 nm, and the coexistence of absorbance edges centered at 400 and 638 nm, it can be concluded that the current methodology increments the capabilities of titanium oxide NPs to harvest and turn into usable energy the radiation coming from widespread sources of energy like the sun.

Overall, the current study will be of great value for modifying titanium oxide NPs to increment their employability in more light-powered applications.

ACKNOWLEDGEMENTS

The research presented in this article was supported by the Internal Grant of the Technical University of Liberec (SGS-2020-4053)

REFERENCES

[1] ZHANG, Q., et al. Nanomaterials for energy conversion and storage. *Chemical Society Reviews.* 2013, vol. 42, no. 7, pp. 3127-3171.

[2] LUCIANI, G., IMPARATO, C., VITIELLO, G. Photosensitive Hybrid Nanostructured Materials: The Big Challenges for Sunlight Capture. *Catalysts.* 2020, vol. 10, no. 1, pp. 103.

[3] WANG, Z., et al. H-doped black titania with very high solar absorption and excellent photocatalysis enhanced by localized surface plasmon resonance. *Advanced Functional Materials.* 2013, vol. 23, no. 43, pp. 5444-5450.

[4] CHEN, X., et al. Increasing solar absorption for photocatalysis with black hydrogenated titanium dioxide nanocrystals. *Science.* 2011, vol. 331, no. 6018, pp. 746-750.

[5] MEYMIAN, M.R.Z., ABDOLVAHAB, R.H., MEHR, A.K. Fractal characteristics of TiO_2-Ag nanocomposite films deposited by a grid-assisted co-sputtering method. *Applied Surface Science.* 2019, vol. 480, pp. 593-600.

[6] DAL'TOÉ, A.T., et al. Lanthanum doped titania decorated with silver plasmonic nanoparticles with enhanced photocatalytic activity under UV-visible light. *Applied Surface Science.* 2018, vol. 441, pp. 1057-1071.

[7] PRABHU, B., VALANARASU, A. Stability analysis of TiO_2-Ag nanocomposite particles dispersed paraffin wax as energy storage material for solar thermal systems. *Renewable Energy.* 2020, vol. 152, pp. 358-367.

[8] ZHANG, D., GÖKCE, B., BARCIKOWSKI, S. Laser synthesis and processing of colloids: fundamentals and applications. *Chemical Reviews.* 2017, vol. 117, no. 5, pp. 3990-4103.

[9] TORRES-MENDIETA, R., et al. Laser-assisted synthesis of Fe-Cu oxide nanocrystals. *Applied Surface Science.* 2019, vol. 469, pp. 1007-1015.

[10] MATSUMOTO A., et al. Transfer of the species dissolved in a liquid into laser ablation plasma: an approach using emission spectroscopy. *The Journal of Physical Chemistry C.* 2015, vol. 119, no 47, pp. 26506-26511.

[11] GUPTA, K., et al. Photocatalytic antibacterial performance of TiO_2 and Ag-doped TiO_2 against S. aureus. P. aeruginosa and E. coli. *Beilstein Journal of Nanotechnology*. 2013, vol. 4, no. 1, pp. 345-351.

[12] HUANG, CH.-N., et al. Nonstoichiometric titanium oxides via pulsed laser ablation in water. *Nanoscale Research Letters*. 2010, vol. 5, no. 6, pp. 972.

[13] OLDENBURG, S.J. Light Scattering from Gold Nanoshells. Diss. Rice University, 2000.

[14] KULADEEP, R., et al. Laser-assisted synthesis of Au-Ag alloy nanoparticles with tunable surface plasmon resonance frequency. *Optical Materials Express*. 2012, vol. 2, no. 2, pp. 161-172.

[15] REHBOCK, CH, et al. Current state of laser synthesis of metal and alloy nanoparticles as ligand-free reference materials for nano-toxicological assays. *Beilstein Journal of Nanotechnology*. 2014, vol. 5, no. 1, pp. 1523-1541.

[16] LETZEL, A., et al. Time and mechanism of nanoparticle functionalization by macromolecular ligands during pulsed laser ablation in liquids. *Langmuir*. 2019, vol. 35, no. 8, pp. 3038-3047.

PRODUCTION AND ANALYSIS OF ELECTROSPUN MATERIALS CONTAINING OXIDIC NANOPARTICLES

[1]Alexandra BENEDIKOVÁ, [1]Jan GRÉGR, [1]Martin STUCHLÍK, [1]Pavel KEJZLAR, [2]Michaela KOZLOVSKÁ, [1]Eva KUŽELOVÁ KOŠŤÁKOVÁ

[1]*Technical University of Liberec, Liberec, Czech Republic, EU,*
alexandra.benedikova@tul.cz, jan.gregr@tul.cz, martin.stuchlik@tul.cz, pavel.kejzlar@tul.cz, eva.kostakova@tul.cz

[2]*National Institute for Nuclear, Chemical and Biological Protection, Kamenná, Milín, Czech Republic, EU, kozlovska@sujchbo.cz*

https://doi.org/10.37904/nanocon.2020.3702

Abstract

Metal oxides based on bismuth are considered to be potentially attractive candidates for developing new materials for radiation protection. In combination with electrospinning technology, it is possible to obtain interesting nanofibrous materials with high content of metal oxides based on bismuth nanoparticles in uniform distribution. This paper focuses on the fabrication and basic analysis of electrospun nanofibrous materials containing Bi2O3 and LuBiO3 nanoparticles. The aim of the research was to optimized high nanoparticle concentration in nanofibrous material (more than 50 wt%) via conventional needless electrospinning technology with optimal nanofibrous material morphology and uniform particle distribution.

Keywords: Nanofibres, PVA, oxidic nanoparticles, $LuBiO_3$, Bi_2O_3, X-Ray attenuation

1. INTRODUCTION

Recently, nanofibrous materials containing inorganic particles especially metal oxides have been investigated as a subject of various emerging applications or processes as for example gas sensors, ceramic biomaterials, magnetic membranes for medicine application, materials for visible-light responsible photocatalysts etc. [1-3]. However, there is also a possibility to use these composite nanofibrous materials with integrated metal oxide nanoparticles in the field of radiation protection [4]. Ionising radiation has accompanied human scientific and industrial activity for decades, nevertheless up to this date, a way to develop and produce a material that is non-toxic, light, breathable and protects against the negative effects of X-rays, is still being sought.

Currently, lead or patented composite materials [5] are used in the field of X-ray protection. Apart from the fact that lead is toxic to the human organism, there is a huge disadvantage of using these materials - lead sheets are extremely heavy because of their high density. Although polymer-based composites are more flexible and it is much easier to work with them and handle, they are still not sufficient. They are not breathable and flexible enough, which makes them very uncomfortable to wear. The solution could be based on nanomaterials. The enlarged particle surface and their dispersion in the polymer matrix can leads to a drastic reduction in material weight with equal efficiency and increased comfort. The most important is the uniform distribution of metal oxide nanoparticles over the material and relatively high content of particles in the final produced material, what is not easy task especially with regard to production on a larger scale, not only in laboratory one.

Following up on a previous research [6,7], the aim of this work is to fabricate and analyse PVB nanofibrous composites with incorporated heavy metal oxide nanoparticles (especially Bi_2O_3 and $LuBiO_3$) for ionising radiation attenuation. This nanofibrous composite constitutes a breathable, flexible, lightweight, non-toxic layer of a 'smart uniform' that could be primarily used by for protection of special units of the state apparatus in dangerous environments. Nevertheless, it could possibly serve in many different fields of human activities as for example, as a protection of medical professionals when working with the risk of being exposed to X-rays.

In order to compare the effectiveness of radiation attenuation in prepared materials, it is necessary to mention some properties. Besides linear attenuation coefficient and mass attenuation coefficient, the most important property is the attenuation length. Attenuation length is characterised as the depth of penetration of radiation into the material at which the intensity of radiation is reduced to approximately 37 % of the initial intensity [8]. **Figure 1** shows that both bismuth oxide and lutetium oxide have significantly increased values of attenuation length for certain energies and form so-called absorption edges. The waveform is much smoother for the $LuBiO_3$ oxide. If two or more heavy metal elements are combined in one oxide compound, the waveform is getting smoother. It means that there is not needed such a thick layer of material for the same attenuation effect.

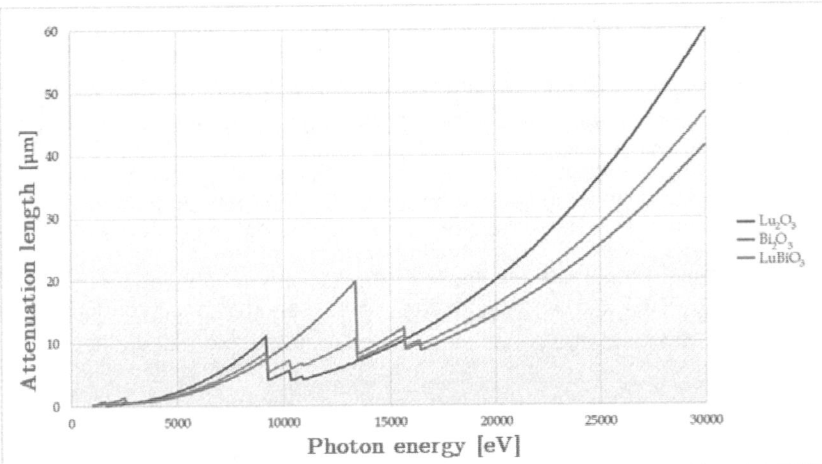

Figure 1 Attenuation length - photon energy graph: Parameters of oxides properties were specified on Web page [8] for Bi_2O_3 (density 8.9 g/cm^3), Lu_2O_3 (density 9.5 g/cm^3) and $LuBiO_3$ (density 9.4 g/cm^3). For scanning the energy the range from 30 to 30 000 eV in 100 steps at fixed angle 90°.

2. MATERIALS & METHODS

In the study, two types of metal oxides nanoparticles based on bismuth were used, bismuth oxide Bi_2O_3 and bismuth lutetium oxide $LuBiO_3$. Nanoparticles of bismuth oxide were purchased from Merck (nanopowder; 90-210 nm particle size, 99% trace metals basis, Merck, CZ). Since the nanoparticles of $LuBiO_3$ are not commonly available on the market, there was necessary to synthetize them in laboratory. Two methods of synthesis were used to prepare the $LuBiO_3$ nanoparticles - self-combustion synthesis and coprecipitation method. The reagents used for these methods were pure bismuth oxide Bi_2O_3 (pure, PENTA, CZ) and lutetium oxide Lu_2O_3 (99.999 %, Cerac Inc., USA). For the self-combustion synthesis experiments, metal oxides were transformed into precursors in form of nitrates, $Bi(NO_3)_3$ and $Lu(NO_3)_3$ by mixing starting oxides with analytical grade nitric acid (65 %, LACH:NER CZ) and heating the mixture up. For self-combustion reactions, different fuels were chosen - glycine CH_5NO_2 (LACH:NER, CZ), citric acid $C_6H_8O_7$ (LACH:NER, CZ) and tartaric acid ($C_4H_6O_6$, LACH:NER, CZ). Nitrate precursors were mixed with fuel and the reaction was initiated. Afterwards, the mixture was processed in agate mortar and heated up to 800 °C in an electric furnace. For the coprecipitation method, nitrate mixture solution was added by drops from burette to a beaker placed on a magnetic agitator containing aqueous solution of ammonium hydroxide NH_4OH (24 %, PENTA CZ). This process led to a white precipitate, that needed to be dried, and then it was placed into an electric furnace and heated up to 800 °C.

Polyvinyl butyral (PVB; Mowital B 60 H) manufactured by Kuraray was chosen as polymer material. The solvent for the spinning solutions was ethanol and the polymer concentration in the final solution was 10 % by weight. The concentration of polymer dry matter to nanoparticles in the final solutions was chosen as follows: 1:0; 1:3 and 1:9 by weight. An ultrasonic homogenizer was used to distribute the nanoparticles more evenly in the suspension to form a final stable solution necessary for needleless electrospinning technology. All the nanofibrous materials were processed by the electrospinning method on a needless electrospinning NS 1WS500U (Elmarco, CZ) device type. After the complex optimization process, the following process conditions were found. The spinning electrode was charged with a DC high voltage source positively (30kV) and the collector was charged negatively (-10 kV). The distance between the spinning electrode and the collector was 180 mm, the temperature during the spinning process was 22 °C and the relative humidity was 30 %. The used supporting material was spunbond (PFNonwovens, CZ) with 20 g/m^2 and withdrawal speed of supporting material was 10 mm/min.

The scanning electron microscopes were used for sample analysis to visualize the resulting nanoparticles and fibrous structures (FE-SEM Carl Zeiss ULTRA Plus and Tescan VEGA 3). Furthermore, the analysis of the chemical composition of the surface SEM-EDS analysis and TGA analysis (TGA 500, Ta Instruments) allowing the verification of the final amount of inorganic particles in spun nanofibers with temperature rise up to 650 °C during sample weighing about 10 mg.

3. RESULTS

Both methods of $LuBiO_3$ particles preparation led to a fine yellow powdered product that was analysed by XRD. On **Figure 2**, there is introduced the XRD analysis of self-combustion synthesis product prepared with tartaric acid as fuel. **Figure 2** shows, that prepared nanoparticles crystallize in cubic lattice with parameter a = 541 pm and density 9.06 g/cm^3.

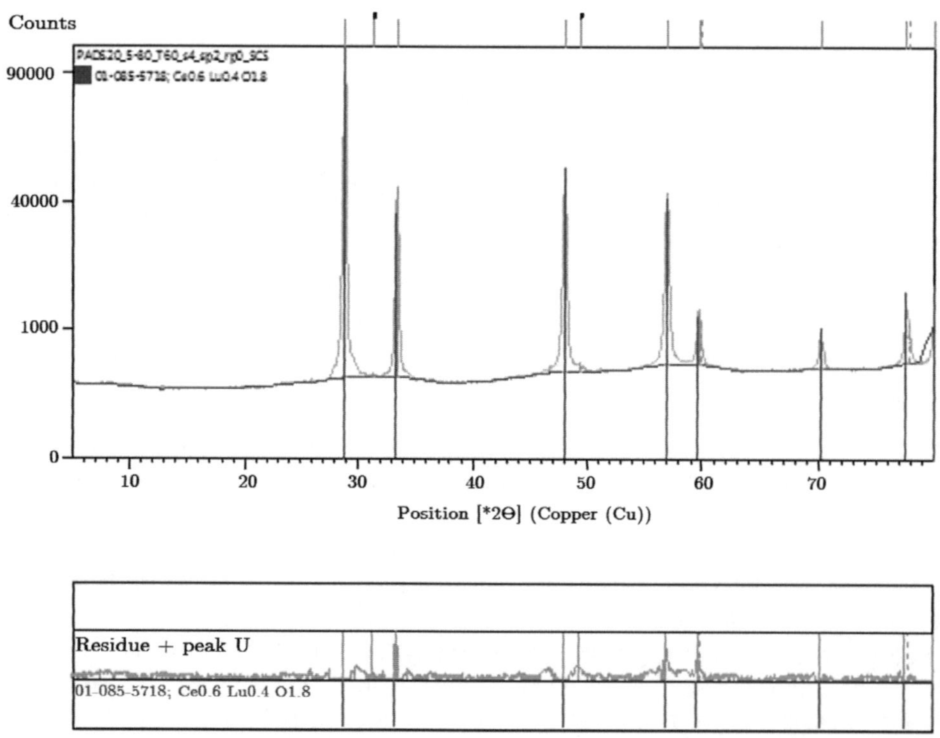

Figure 2 XRD analysis of self-combustion (tartaric acid) $LuBiO_3$ nanoparticles

Obtained $LuBiO_3$ as well as Bi_2O_3 nanoparticles are perfectly wettable in PVB/ethanol solution that was selected for electrospinning process. This property allows particles to be perfectly embedded in the resulting fibres. Most of the $LuBiO_3$ particles are in range of 50 - 500 nm. Both of the bismuth oxide particles are incorporated inside the electrospun material at all the concentrations very well (**Figure 3**).

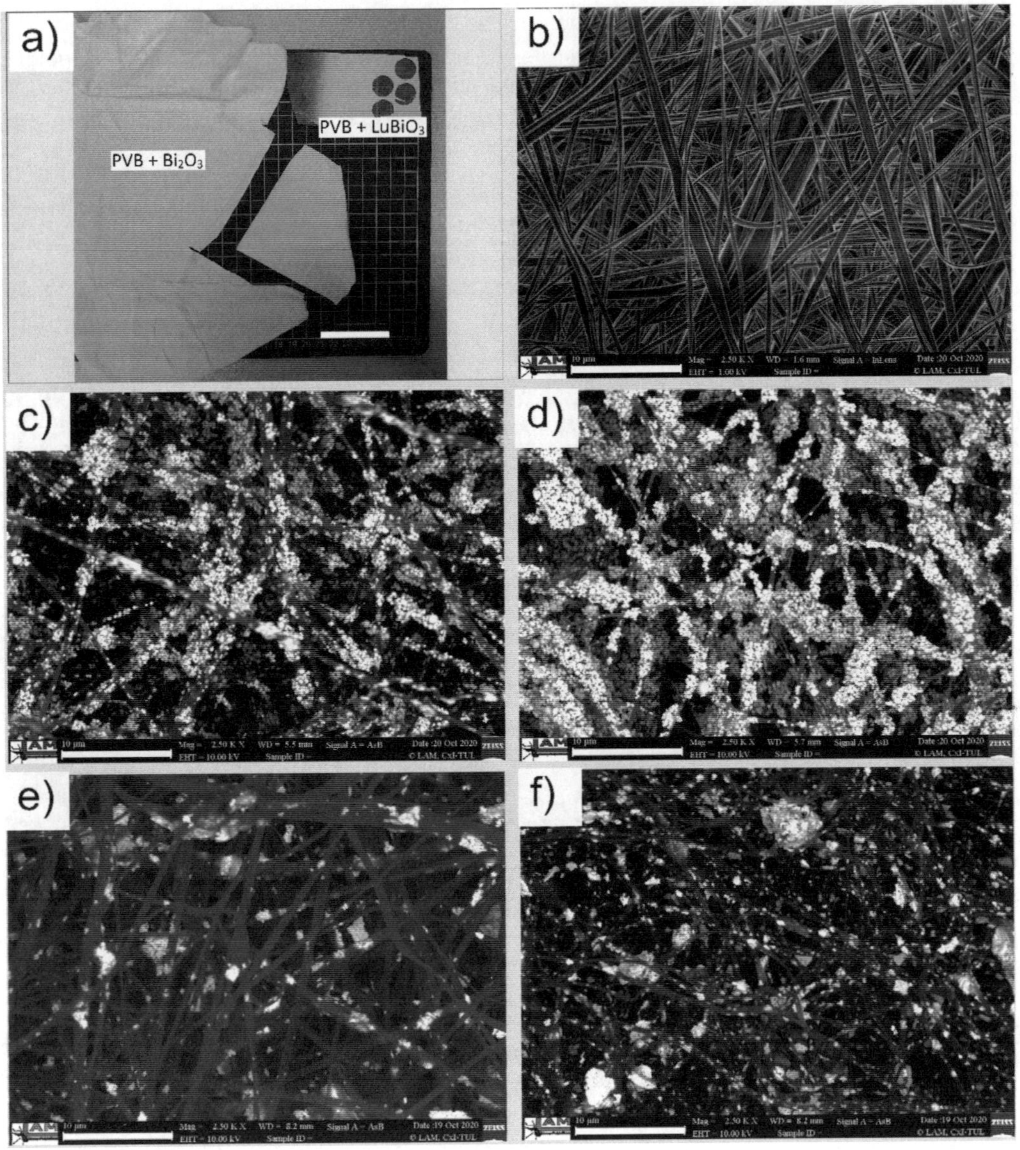

Figure 3 Electrospun materials: a) a photo of electrospun materials with Bi_2O_3 and $LuBiO_3$ in polymer to particles ratio 1:9 by weight; b) SEM image of PVB electrospun materials without particles (blind sample); c) SEM image of PVB with Bi_2O_3 nanoparticles in polymer to particles ration 1:3 by weight; d) SEM image of PVB with Bi_2O_3 nanoparticles in polymer to particles ration 1:9 by weight; e) SEM image of PVB electrospun material with $LuBiO_3$ in polymer to particle ratio 1:3 and f) SEM image of PVB electrospun material with $LuBiO_3$ in polymer to particle ratio 1:9 by weight. The scale bars show 5 cm (a) and 10 micrometres (b-f).

TGA analysis of all fabricated materials showed that real content of nanoparticles inside electrospun materials is exactly (for Bi_2O_3) or only a little smaller (for $LuBiO_3$) than ratio of polymer dry matter to nanoparticle concentration in prepared solutions (**Table 1**). **Table 1** also introduced individual surface densities of the electrospun materials with the same process parameters. The highest productivity, with the same electrospinning process parameters, was found for the material with integrated Bi_2O_3 nanoparticles. Their size was smaller and because of professional production, their distribution was not so wide.

Table 1 Comparison of chosen properties of fabricated basic and composite electrospun materials. The ratio PVB to particles represents the ratio in the original solutions for electrospinning by weight. TGA residue represents proof of real amount of particles in final electrospun nanofibrous materials. Volume ratio of particles inside fibre is calculated from the weight ratio and density. Final surface density of the electrospun materials was measured for each sample too.

Sample	Ratio PVB:particles	TGA residue (wt%)	Vol%	Surface density (g/m²)
PVB	-	0.79	-	
PVB - Bi_2O_3	1:3	75.8	25.6	102.4
	1:9	89.9	52.4	213.6
PVB - $LuBiO_3$	1:3	58.9	24.9	25.57
	1:9	81.7	33.1	51.87

The production study, which is mainly presented here, is added to illustrate the effect of medical diagnostic X-ray images. The electrospun materials were cut into pieces and put together in various numbers of layers to see how the attenuation effect would intensify. The effect of different number of electrospun material layers for the tested composite materials are visible in **Figure 4**.

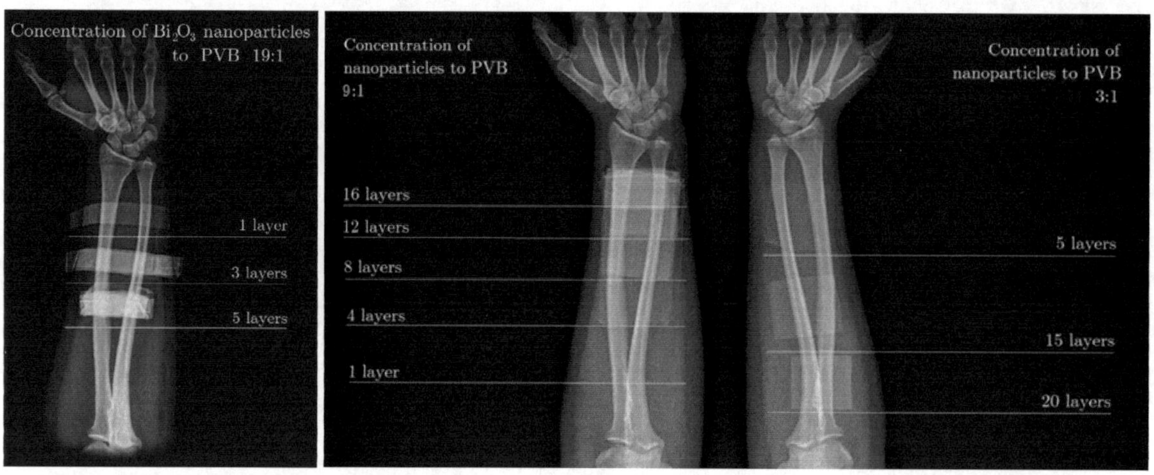

Figure 4 X-Ray image of radiation attenuation effect of electrospun PVB nanofibers with integrated nanoparticles Bi_2O_3 in polymer to particles ratio 1:9 by weight (left side) and electrospun PVB nanfoibers with integrated nanoparticles of $LuBiO_3$ in polymer to particles ratios 1:3 and 1:9 by weight (right side)

4. CONCLUSION

Nanoparticles $LuBiO_3$ were successfully prepared in nanometre size. Composite nanofibers containing two types of metal oxides based on bismuth (Bi_2O_3 and $LuBiO_3$) were successfully electrospun by needle-less electrospinning method. The optimization of the electrospinning technology was performed for pilot production and is therefore not limited to the laboratory production of small quantities of samples. The distribution of nanoparticles inside the nanofibers and all electrospun layer is uniform. The electrospun material contain almost all the particles, which were added into the solution what was confirmed by TGA analysis. The optimization of the electrospinning process and combination of the polymer, solvent and particles brings final materials, which are a good candidate as lead-free polymer/bismuth oxide based materials for use as potential X-ray shielding materials, because of their good X-ray attenuation ability. The testing for specific applications in the field of radiation protection is going to continue this study.

ACKNOWLEDGEMENTS

The result was obtained through the financial support of the grant "Intelligent textiles for protection against CBRN substances" of Ministry of Interior of the Czech republic; VI20172020059.

REFERENCES

[1] ABIDEEN, Z.U., JAE-HUN, K., JAE-HYOUNG, L., JIN-YOUNG, K., ALI, M., HYOUN, W.K., SANG, S.K. Electrospun Metal Oxide Composite Nanofibers Gas Sensors: A Review. *Journal of the Korean Ceramic Society.* [online]. 2017, vol.54, no. 5, pp. 366-79. Available from: https://doi.org/10.4191/kcers.2017.54.5.12.

[2] IM, Y.M., TAE, H.O., JIN, W.Ch., YOUNG, H.S., JUN, S.H., JOSEPH, A.N., SUNG, S.H., SOON, H.J. Preparation of Poly(Vinyl Alcohol)/ZrO_2 Composite Nanofibers via Co-Axial Electrospinning with Higher ZrO_2 Particle Content. *Fibers and Polymers.* [online]. 2014, vol.15, no.10, pp. 2066-71. Available from: https://doi.org/10.1007/s12221-014-2066-y.

[3] LIM, G.D., JAE-HYUN, Y., MYEONGJUN, J., YOUNG-IN, L. Visible Light Driven Photocatalytic Degradation Enhanced by α/β Phase Heterojunctions on Electrospun Bi_2O_3 Nanofibers. *Journal of Alloys and Compounds.* [online]. 2019, vol. 806, pp. 1060-67. Available from: https://doi.org/10.1016/j.jallcom.2019.07.319.

[4] HAZLAN, M.H., MUNIRAH, J., RAMZUN, M.R., NURUL, Z.N.A. X-Ray Attenuation Characterisation of Electrospun Bi_2O_3/PVA and WO_3/PVA Nanofibre Mats as Potential X-Ray Shielding Materials. *Applied Physics A.* [online]. 2018, vol.124, no.7, p. 497. Available from: https://doi.org/10.1007/s00339-018-1915-8.

[5] DEMEO, R.J, KUCHEROVSKY, J., KURUPATHI, A. Radiation detectable and protective articles. Patent US20050211930A1. 29. 9. 2005. [viewed 2020-05-29]. Available from: https://patentimages.storage.googleapis.com/16/1a/3c/d8e88313f57847/WO2006069007A3.pdf.

[6] GRÉGR, J., MÉSZÁROS, L., KOZLOVSKÁ, M., HAVLÍČEK, K., KUŽELOVÁ KOŠŤÁKOVÁ, E. Electrospun Fibrous Materials with Integrated Inorganic Particles. In: *Polymer Composites 2019.* Tábor: Czech Technical University in Prague, 2019, pp. 23-28. ISBN 978-80-01-06582-2.

[7] BENEDIKOVÁ, A. *$LuBiO_3$ nanoparticles for ionizing radiation attenuation.* Liberec, 2020. Bachelor thesis. Technical university of Liberec.

[8] ANON. *X-Ray Attenuation Length.* [online]. [viewed: 2020-05-30]. Available from: https://henke.lbl.gov/optical_constants/atten2.html.

ANODIC FORMATION OF HfO_2 NANOSTRUCTURE ARRAYS FOR RESISTIVE SWITCHING APPLICATION

Kirill KAMNEV, Zdeněk PYTLÍČEK, Jan PRÁŠEK, Alexander MOZALEV

CEITEC - Central European Institute of Technology, Brno University of Technology, Brno, Czech Republic, EU
kirill.kamnev@ceitec.vutbr.cz

https://doi.org/10.37904/nanocon.2020.3692

Abstract

Thin dielectric films are actively investigated as materials for novel resistive random-access memories based on resistive switching effect in metal/insulator/metal structures. Thin HfO_2 films are of particular interest due to the high thermal stability, low operating voltages of resulting devices, and complementary metal-oxide-semiconductor technology compatibility of this material. In this study, we investigate the resistive switching behavior of nanostructured HfO_2 film embedded in a porous anodic alumina matrix. The film was synthesized via self-organized electrochemical anodizing of a sputter-deposited Al/Hf bilayer on a Si substrate in an oxalic acid solution. The film was investigated by scanning electron microscopy. Simple metal/insulator/metal devices were prepared by sputter-deposition of Pt top electrodes through a shadow mask onto the nanostructured film. Assembled devices were characterized by I-V measurements. A bipolar eight-wise resistive switching was obtained, demonstrating a highly repeatable and stable low-voltage behavior in a set potential range. The achieved results indicate the high potential of the anodizing technique as an alternative to commonly used methods for producing insulating thin films for resistive random-access memory application.

Keywords: Resistive switching, anodizing, hafnium oxide, porous anodic alumina, memristor

1. INTRODUCTION

Resistive random-access memory (ReRAM) based on simple metal/insulator/metal (MIM) stacks is nowadays seen as a notable candidate for next-generation non-volatile memories, neuromorphic computing, alternative logic operations, or selector devices [1]. The demanded scalability of ReRAM systems to nano dimensions makes the fabrication, control, and prediction of their properties very challenging. Standard methods for producing the key elements of nanoscale ReRAM systems, such as atomic layer deposition, chemical vapor deposition, and pulsed laser deposition [2] require high-budged equipment, ultra-high vacuum conditions, and substantial consumption of energy. As an alternative approach, metal-oxide films for ReRAM can be formed by the cheap and accessible anodizing method [3]. The main benefit of the anodizing method is its simplicity since vacuum conditions or elevated temperatures are not required. Another notable advantage is that the substrate metal is already integrated into the device as the bottom electrode after the anodizing. Moreover, anodization of aluminum superimposed on a metal of interest can be utilized to create nanoscale arrays of various 3-D metal-oxide nanostructures inside the porous anodic alumina (PAA) film [4]. Such metal-oxide nanoarrays embedded in the PAA matrix may allow achieving resistive switching effects within the individual spatially separated nanostructures, thus introducing a new behavior advantageous to the continuous oxide films.

One of the most prominent oxides that can be utilized in metal/oxide/metal stacks for ReRAM fabrication is HfO_2. Owing to low operating voltages, high thermal stability, and full compatibility with complementary metal-oxide-semiconductor technology, HfO_2-based films can be utilized in a variety of low-cost resistive switching devices with simple circuitry [5]. Recently developed anodizing method for processing Al/Hf bilayer films [6] allows for creating thin HfO_2 layers densely covered by the nonstoichiometric nanoscale 3-D HfO_{2-x} structures. Such nanoscale 3-D features might significantly affect resistive switching behavior of the films provided the population density of the nanostructures may potentially be as high as 10^{11} cm^{-2}. Moreover, each HfO_2 nanostructure size is comparable with the size of a conductive filament, which forms within the metal-oxide under polarization and is a primary phenomenon responsible for resistive switching behavior [7]. Investigation of resistive switching in the nanostructured HfO_2 films can potentially offer insights needed to commercialize anodically prepared oxides in ReRAM devices.

Here we report the fabrication of MIM stacks based on HfO_2 nanostructured layers prepared via the PAA-assisted anodization of Al/Hf bilayers on substrates. MIM micro-devices were assembled by magnetron sputtering of top Pt electrodes. The nanostructured HfO_2-in-Al_2O_3 films and the assembled microdevices were examined by high-resolution scanning electron microscopy (SEM). The electrical properties of the devices were investigated by I-V measurements.

2. EXPERIMENTAL

2.1. Sample preparation

Si wafer covered with 380 nm of thermally grown SiO_2 was used as a starting substrate for the sputter-deposition. A 100 nm thick Hf layer followed by an 80 nm thick Al layer were deposited via magnetron sputtering from Hf and Al targets of respectively 99.95% and 99.999% purity. Anodization of sputter-deposited Al/Hf bilayer film was carried out in 0.6M $(COOH)_2$ aqueous solution by sweeping potential from 0 to 30 V at a rate of 0.5 V s^{-1} followed by 30 s of current decay. Subsequently, after the anodization process, reanodization was performed in the same electrolyte by sweeping potential from 30 to 80 V at a rate of 5 V s^{-1} followed by 60 s of current decay. A two-electrode polytetrafluoroethylene anodizing cell was used for anodization; a more detailed description of the anodizing setup is available elsewhere [8]. In selected samples, the PAA overlayer was completely dissolved in a selective etchant (0.45 M H_3PO_4, 0.2 M Cr_2O_3) heated to 65 °C. Prior to device fabrication, the PAA pore widening procedure was performed by dipping the samples in the selective etchant for 60 s.

2.2. Sample characterization

The morphology of the anodic films was examined by a FEI Verios 460L High-Resolution Scanning Electron Microscope utilizing InBeam secondary electron detector and magnetic immersion lens at 15 keV accelerated voltage.

2.3. Device fabrication and electrical characterization

Resistive switching devices were fabricated by depositing Pt top electrodes onto the oxide arrays via magnetron sputtering through a shadow mask. The I-V curves were recorded at ambient conditions by a Keithley Model 4200A-SCS Parameter Analyzer. Samples were mounted on a CASCADE M150 probe station equipped with magnetic micromanipulators and tested by applying a potential difference between the upper (Pt) and bottom (Hf) electrodes. In all measurements, the top Pt electrode was grounded while the voltage was applied to the bottom Hf electrode. To avoid an electric breakdown in the film, a compliance current of 10 mA was set during the positive polarization.

3. RESULTS AND DISCUSSION

3.1. The film morphology and device assembly

Anodizing of sputter-deposited Al/Hf bilayer films was expected to create a network of HfO_2 nanostructures protruding within the pores of the PAA matrix. Generally, the process involves converting the upper Al layer to

PAA by anodizing in an acidic solution followed by anodizing the underlying Hf through the alumina nanopores. The growing hafnium oxide mixes to some extent with the alumina barrier layer and further protrudes inside the pores. Additionally, reanodizing to higher voltages can be carried out to achieve a better fulling of the alumina pores with hafnium oxide. Full aspects of the PAA-assisted anodization of Al/Hf bilayer films were covered in our previous work [6].

Figure 1a shows a 3-D view of the film derived from the anodized/reanodized Al/Hf bilayer after dissolving the PAA layer. Thus, the approach resulted in an array of spatially separated 65 nm tall nanocones protruding from the oxide surface. The nanocones are separated from the Hf substrate by the oxide dimples of about 45 nm in depth.

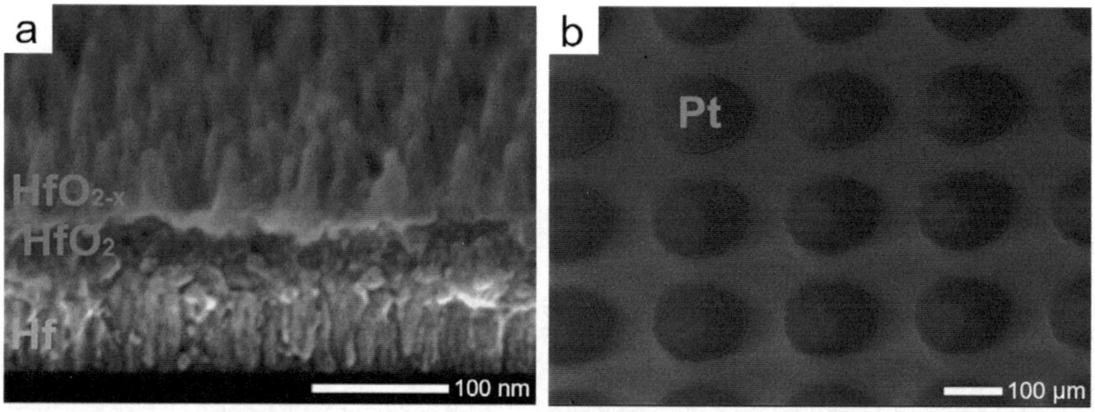

Figure 1 (a) SEM 3-D view of the anodized HfO_2 film after the PAA dissolution, (b) SEM top view of Pt contacts formed on the oxide surface via magnetron sputtering

To assemble MIM resistive switching devices, the PAA layer was not dissolved after anodizing but the pore widening procedure was carried out to make the pore mouths more expanded. Multiple microscale Pt/HfO_2-in-Al_2O_3/Hf stacks were assembled by sputter-deposition of round Pt contacts (**Figure 1b**), each of about 0.1 mm^2. During the sputter deposition, Pt was expected to permeate the PAA pore mouths, sandwiching the PAA-embedded HfO_2 nanostructures between the top Pt and the bottom Hf electrodes. The schematic design of the fabricated device based on the Pt/HfO_2-in-Al_2O_3/Hf stack alongside with the electrode setup for I-V characterization is presented in **Figure 2**.

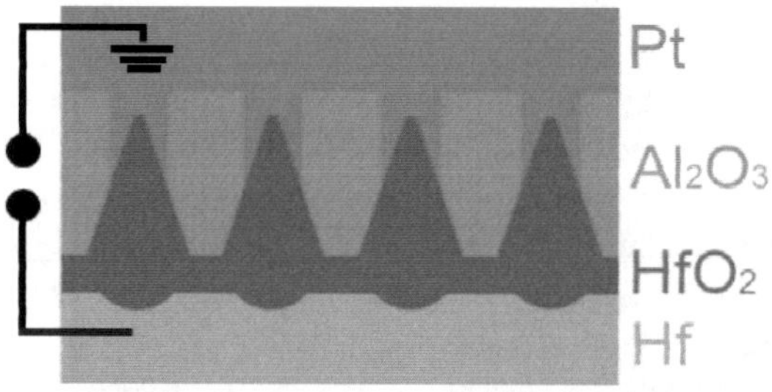

Figure 2 Schematic representation of the assembled MIM microdevice based on the Pt/HfO_2-in-Al_2O_3/Hf stack and the electrode setup for I-V characterization

3.2. Electrical characterization

Measured I-V characteristics of the assembled MIM microdevice are shown in **Figure 3**. The I-V cycling was performed in sequences following the pattern 0 → +1.7→ −1.9 → 0 V. A sweep rate of 250 mV s^{-1} and a compliance current of 10 mA was used for recording I-V data. The device appears to show a bipolar eight-wise switching. During the voltage sweep in the positive direction, the device demonstrates stable switching from the high resistance state (HRS) to the low resistance state (LRS), so-called SET process. The SET process is stable within low values of V_{SET} between 1.05 and 1.30 V. During subsequently sweeping the voltage in the negative direction, the device switches from acquired LRS back to the HRS via a RESET process. The RESET process is also highly stable with V_{RESET} values ranging between -1.70 and -1.75 V. The fabricated device demonstrates an excellent reproducibility of the resistive switching behavior throughout continuous I-V sweeps.

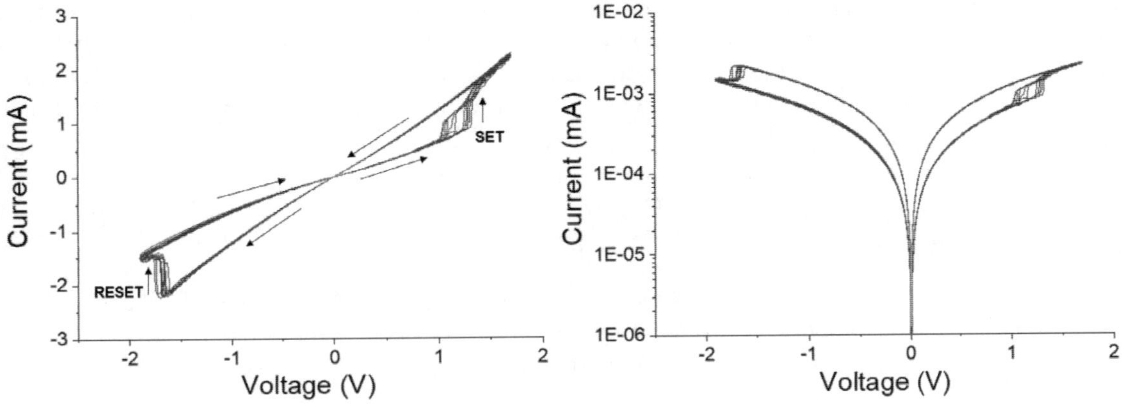

Figure 3 Measured I-V characteristics of MIM microdevices based on the Pt/HfO_2-in-Al_2O_3/Hf stacks

The mechanism responsible for the changes between the HRS and LRS states occurring in the HfO_2 nanostructured film sandwiched between the two metallic electrodes is not yet fully understood. However, the observed switching characteristics can be explained by forming and rupturing a conductive filament (CF) inside the individual HfO_2 nanostructures induced by the electric field, as the most generally accepted mechanism of resistive switching [9]. The initial distribution of oxygen vacancies in the dielectric HfO_2 layer might significantly affect its resisting switching behavior. The HfO_2 nanostructured films grown via the PAA-assisted anodizing of Al/Hf bilayers are known to possess unevenly distributed metastable HfO_{2-x} suboxides, resulting in a concentration gradient of oxygen vacancies across the film depth [6]. When a positive voltage is applied to the bottom Hf electrode, the abundant oxygen vacancies migrate towards the Pt cathode and serve as nuclei of CF. Possibly, the growing CF acts as an extension of the cathode towards the anode. With the assist of the applied electric field, the growing CF extends throughout the whole film thickness and creates a conductive path, setting a device to the LRS. Considering that the CF grows from the negatively charged Pt electrode to the positively charged Hf electrode, the thinnest region of the CF might be located at the Hf cathode. Thus, negatively biasing the Hf electrode would generate an extensive amount of Joule heat in the thinnest part of the CF, accelerating the mobility of vacancies in a localized region. Rapidly migrating vacancies then would be annihilated by oxygen ions on the film interface and grain boundaries, resulting in a rapture of the CF and resetting the device to the HRS [10]. Our MIM microdevice, based on the Pt/HfO_2-in-Al_2O_3/Hf stack, shows the excellent repeatability of forming and rapturing the CF throughout multiple I-V measurements.

In summary, the findings of the I-V tests demonstrated that a reliable low voltage resistive switching behavior could be obtained in the experimental memristive device utilizing the nanostructured HfO_2 films. In our work to date, the HfO_2 nanostructures have been scaled down to ~50 nm, which might already be comparable with the size of the conductive filament that forms within the oxide. In a future work, a much larger number of HfO_2 nanostructures, up to 10^{11} cm^{-2}, scaled-down to about 10 nm and embedded in a PAA matrix may be fabricated, potentially enhancing the device properties. Altering the electrical properties of the anodic nanostructured HfO_2 films by air or vacuum annealing is also to be considered for improving the memristive behavior.

CONCLUSION

Nanostructured HfO_2-in-Al_2O_3 films were prepared via the PAA-assisted anodizing of sputter-deposited Al/Hf bilayers and utilized as a solid electrolyte in memristive microdevices based on a simple metal/insulator/metal architecture. Top metallic electrodes were formed by sputter-deposition of Pt through a shadow mask. The fabricated Pt/HfO_2-in-Al_2O_3/Hf stacks were I-V cycled in a potential range of 1.7 to -1.9 V, revealing a reliable resistive switching behavior with a low onset voltage. The narrow dispersion of SET and RESET voltages was observed during the I-V cycling with V_{SET} between 1.05 and 1.30 V and V_{RESET} between -1.70 and -1.75 V. The devices demonstrate reproducible resistive switching over multiple I-V cycles.

This study contributes to understanding and utilizing anodically prepared nanostructured oxides as solid electrolytes in MIM based ReRAM devices. The nanostructured HfO_2-in-Al_2O_3 films fabricated via the PAA-assisted anodization can be used to manufacture low-cost and reliable memristive devices. It is of high interest to further explore their properties towards advancing the switching and memristive effects and creating relevant technology for incorporating the MIM-based nanostructured HfO_2 resistive switching stacks in a ReRAM prototype.

ACKNOWLEDGEMENTS

This research was supported in parts by project CEITEC VUT-J-20-6513 and by GAČR grant 20-25486S. We acknowledge CzechNanoLab Research Infrastructure supported by MEYS CR (LM2018110).

REFERENCES

[1] MAZUMDER P., KANG S. M., WASER R. Memristors: devices, models, and applications. In: *Proceedings of the IEEE*. 2012, vol. 100, no 6, pp. 1911-1919.

[2] MOHAMMAD, B., ABI JAOUDE, M., KUMAR, V., AL HOMOUZ, D. M., NAHLA, H. A., AL-QUTAYRI, M., and CHRISTOFOROU, N. State of the art of metal oxide memristor devices. *Nanotechnology Reviews*. 2016, vol. 5, no. 6, pp. 311-329.

[3] ZAFFORA, A., MACALUSO, R., HABAZAKI, H., VALOV, I., and SANTAMARIA, M. Electrochemically prepared oxides for resistive switching devices. *Electrochimica Acta*. 2018, vol. 274, pp. 103-111.

[4] MOZALEV, A., SMITH, A. J., BORODIN, S., PLIHAUKA, A., HASSEL, A. W., SAKAIRI, M., and TAKAHASHI, H. Growth of multioxide planar film with the nanoscale inner structure via anodizing Al/Ta layers on Si. *Electrochimica Acta*. 2009, vol. 54, no. 3, pp. 935-945.

[5] CHEN, L., DAI, Y. W., SUN, Q. Q., GUO, J. J., ZHOU, P., and ZHANG, D. W. Al2O3/HfO2 functional stack films based resistive switching memories with controlled SET and RESET voltages. *Solid State Ionics*. 2015, vol. 273, pp. 66-69.

[6] MOZALEV, A., BENDOVA, M., GISPERT-GUIRADO, F., and LLOBET, E. Hafnium-oxide 3-D nanofilms via the anodizing of Al/Hf metal layers. *Chemistry of Materials*. 2018, vol. 30, no. 8, pp. 2694-2708.

[7] SUN, W., GAO, B., CHI, M., XIA, Q., YANG, J. J., QIAN, H., and WU, H. Understanding memristive switching via in situ characterization and device modeling. *Nature communications*. 2019, vol. 10, no. 1, pp. 1-13.

[8] MOZALEV, A., CALAVIA, R., VAZQUEZ, R. M., GRACIA, I., CANÉ, C., CORREIG, X., VLIANOVA X., GISPERT-GUIRADO, F., HUBALEK, J., and LLOBET, E. MEMS-microhotplate-based hydrogen gas sensor utilizing the nanostructured porous-anodic-alumina-supported WO3 active layer. *international journal of hydrogen energy*. 2013, vol. 38, no. 19, pp. 8011-8021.

[9] MEENA, J. S., SZE, S. M., CHAND, U., and TSENG, T. Y. Overview of emerging non-volatile memory technologies. *Nanoscale research letters*. 2014. vol. 9, no. 1, pp. 526.

[10] PAN, F., GAO, S., CHEN, C., SONG, C., and ZENG, F. Recent progress in resistive random access memories: materials, switching mechanisms, and performance. *Materials Science and Engineering: R: Reports*. 2014, vol. 83, pp. 1-59.

EFFECT OF EXTRUSION PROCESS AND VARIOUS ELONGATION RATIOS ON THE STRUCTURAL AND DIELECTRIC PROPERTIES OF PVDF-BASED COPOLYMER CONTAINING MICRO AND NANO-SIZED CRYSTALLITES

[1]Miroslav MRLÍK, [1]Martin CVEK, [1]Josef OSIČKA, [2]Marcin MASLOWSKI, [3]Pavel TOFEL

[1]Tomas Bata University in Zlín, University Institute, Centre of Polymer Systems, Zlín, Czech Republic, EU, mrlik@utb.cz

[2]Lodz University of Technology, Institute of Polymer and Dye Technology, Lodz, Poland, EU

[3]Brno University of Technology, Department of Physics, Faculty of Electrical Engineering and Communication, Brno, Czech Republic, EU

https://doi.org/10.37904/nanocon.2020.3694

Abstract

In this contribution, the effect of the extrusion process of the poly(vinylidene fluoride-co-hexafluoropropylene) (PVDF-co-HFP) with the subsequent elongation/poling on its structural and dielectric properties is presented. The extrusion can be understood as continuous processing of polymer melts in the large scale (in comparison to solvent casting), when the thickness of the final product can be varied depending on the final operation conditions. Herein, the PVDF-co-HFP sheets of 5 cm in width were extruded using a single screw extruder. The fabricated sheets were cooled down and then, they were cut to the stripes and subsequently stretched to various elongations (100, 200 and 500 %) using a universal tensile testing machine. Such samples were investigated using FTIR in order to determine the effect of the elongation process on the transformation of the α-phase to the β-crystalline phase. The extend of the electro-active β-phase was quantified and its impact on the dielectric properties was investigated. The results clearly demonstrated that the elongation has a crucial effect on the final dielectric properties of the PVDF-co-HFP.

Keywords: Poly(vinylidene fluoride), poly(vinylidene fluoride-co-hexafluoropropylene), extrusion, dielectric properties, electromechanical coupling

1. INTRODUCTION

Smart systems can be classified as materials that can actively respond to the external stimuli, such as the electric [1] or magnetic field [2], temperature [3], pH change [4], light stimulation [5] or mechanical vibration [6]. In the last years, the majority of the electrical machines undergo the damaging due to the vibrations from the bearings causing the mechanical perturbances [7]. Therefore, the detection of the unwanted vibrations seems to be a crucial point to extend the operating lifetime of the machines. From this point of view, the vibration sensors based on the piezoelectric ceramics are typical materials of choice [8]. The ceramic-based sensors however have some drawbacks such as high cost and brittleness [9]. Especially, the brittleness is a very negative property, which can significantly decrease the efficiency of this type of sensor [10].

Therefore, certain polymeric materials such as poly(vinylidene fluoride) (PVDF) started to be very attractive, since they can be easily processed, they are flexible and provide suitable piezoelectric capability required for the vibration sensing [11]. The main issue of the PVDF is its inherent property; the materials requires the additional treatment, otherwise the PVDF consist mainly the non-piezoelectric α-phase [12]. By utilizing the elongation [13], polling in electric fields [14], particle addition [15] etc., the piezoelectric β-phase can be developed, and relatively good electromechanical coupling coefficients ($d_{33} \sim 25$ pC/N) can be achieved [16].

There are also other techniques of the PVDF post-processing that were successfully applied to increment the d_{33} coefficients including the electrospinning [17], melt-electrowriting [18] or the extrusion [19].

Besides the PVDF, also its copolymers are very promising for this purpose. The poly(vinylidene-co-hexafluoropropylene) (PVDF-co-HFP) is frequently used due to its good piezoelectric capability [20]. Its processing via the extrusion is however very limited, and just few research articles have addressed this topic [21], while only one paper was dealing with stretching during poling called SSP [22]. In the vast majority, this material is processed by solvent casting [23] or electrospinning [24]. From these reasons, this study is focused on the processing of the PVDF-co-HFP using industrially-viable extrusion process, and the impact of various relative elongations on the structural changes and dielectric properties.

2. EXPERIMENTAL

2.1. Materials

Poly(vinylidene-co-hexafluoropropylene) (PVDF-co-HFP) in the form of pellets (CAS number: 9011-17-0) with the molecular weight (Mw) of ~ 400 000 g/mol (Sigma Aldrich, USA) was used to construct the tested elements.

2.2. Characterization methods

The extrusion process was performed at 190°C using twin-screw extruder (Scientific, China) and using flat die having 5 cm in width and 0.5 mm in thickness. The continuous sheet was collected and cooled down without any interventions at laboratory conditions.

Then, the sheets were cut using the steel templates to the form of stripes with 15 mm in width, 100 mm in length. Such stripes were elongated using the universal testing machine M350-5 CT (Testometric, Lancashire, UK) coupled with a heat chamber (Omron) operating at a temperature of 65 °C. The cross-head speed of the clamps was set to 10 mm/min, with the relative elongations of 50, 100 and 300 %.

The Fourier-transform infrared spectroscopy (FTIR) was performed on Nicolet 6700 (Thermo-Scientific, USA) spectrometer equipped with ATR accessory and a germanium crystal. The spectra were recorded in a wavenumber range of 4000-500 cm^{-1} with a spectral increment of 2 cm^{-1}.
Dielectric properties were measured on the neat as well as on the stretched samples using Broadband Dielectric Impedance Analyzer (Novocontrol, Montabaur, Germany), in the frequency range of 0.01 Hz to 10 MHz, using a standard sample cell BDCS 140.

The neat PVDF-co-HFP as well as the stretched analogues were poled using a custom-build apparatus at the electric field strength of 7 kV/mm, and the temperature of 110 °C. Then, a thin conductive (silver) layer was deposited on the samples and their piezoelectric charge coefficient, d_{33}, was measured within 24 hour after the poling process. The d_{33} was analyzed in the transversal mode using the electrometer 6517b (Keithley, USA). Each sample was placed between two copper electrodes; the lower electrode had a diameter of 20 mm, while the upper one had a diameter of 10 mm. A mechanical force of 0.49 N was applied onto the upper electrode and the electric charge generated by the sample was recorded. Each sample was analyzed at ten positions, the presented d_{33} values represent the average values from the obtained data.

3. RESULTS AND DISCUSSION

The PVDF-co-HFP has similar crystalline structure as the neat PVDF. For this material, the transformation of α-phase to β-phase also plays a crucial role [25-27]. The typical main peaks of the α-phase corresponding to 762 cm^{-1} and for the β-phase at 840 cm^{-1} as displayed in **Figure 1**. A magnified visualization (inset figure) provides definite information of the successful α-β-phase transformation. As clearly seen, neat PVDF-co-HFP shows a negligible peak at 840 cm^{-1} and with further elongation this peak clearly increases exhibiting the highest intensity for the sample with 300 % deformation. On the other hand, the suppression of the α-phase is similarly important. In this case, the visible decrease of the peak intensity and thus confirmation, that α-β-phase transition was successful, was easily distinguishable only for the sample with the elongation of 300 %. The other samples did not exhibit almost any changes in the α-peak intensity, while slight decrease was observed for the sample that underwent the elongation of 100 %. This clearly indicates that extrusion process with consequent elongation has crucial impact on the distribution of the micro and nano-sized crystallites those presence is very important for development electro-active β-phase. Similar observation was also published on PVDF samples [28].

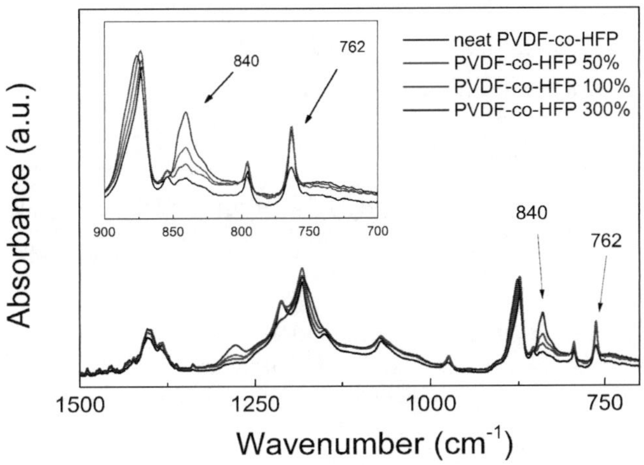

Figure 1 FTIR spectra of the PVDF-co-HFP samples before and after stretching process

Dielectric properties are assumed to be a crucial parameter affecting the electro-activity of the PVDF-co-HFP-based elements. Therefore, the relative permittivity was plotted against frequency; as obvious, the higher relative permittivity is achieved, therefore the better electrical output efficiency upon mechanical stimulation can be generated [29,30]. As can be seen in **Figure 2**, the relative permittivity measured on the prepared samples was increasing with the increasing deformation. This behavior demonstrates that the transformation of the β-phase was successful which is presented as a substantial increase of relative permittivity with higher strain deformation, and in fact, it confirms the trends obtained from the FTIR analysis.

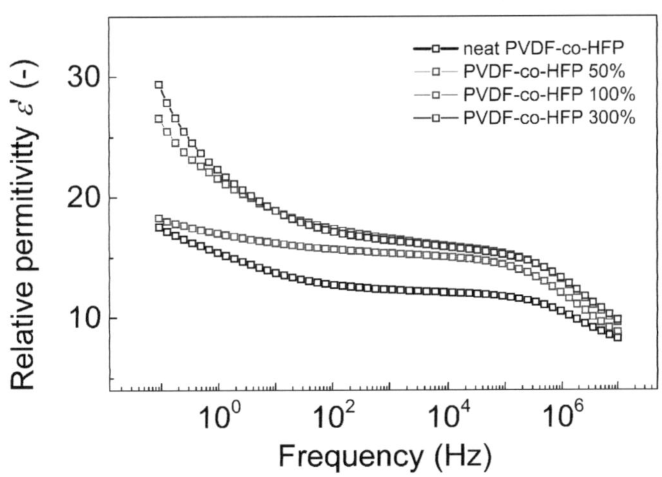

Figure 2 Dielectric spectra of relative permittivity against frequency of the PVDF-co-HFP samples before and after stretching/poling process

Finally, the electromechanical activity of the investigated samples is presented in **Table 1**. The dataset confirms that the industrially extruded PVDF-co-HFP samples can be effectively treated to increment their piezo-activity via elongation and subsequent polling process at 7 kV/mm. The maximal d_{33} values obtained for these materials upon the presented conditions are sufficient to show a comparable efficiency with the other commercial PVDF systems [31].

Table 1 Results of the piezo-activity for PVDF-co-HFP-based samples

Sample ID	Capacitance (pF) at 100 kHz	d_{33} coeficient (pC/N)	d_{33}^2/e_{33}
neat PVDF-co-HFP	6.19	1.1	3.47
PVDF-co-HFP 50 %	11.6	1.8	7.22
PVDF-co-HFP 100 %	11.8	1.9	8.11
PVDF-co-HFP 300 %	12.6	4.6	37.1

[a] permittivity $e_{33} = C \times h/A$, where C is the capacitance, h is the sample thickness, and A is the surface area

4. CONCLUSION

In this paper, the PVDF-co-HFP was extruded and further elongated using various deformations (50, 100, and 300 %). Then, the materials were poled and investigated from their electro-activity point of view. It was confirmed that the elongation positively influenced the transformation of the non-piezoelectric α-phase to its piezoelectric β-phase analogue, which was accompanied by increasing FTIR peak centered at 840 cm^{-1}. Analogously, the dielectric properties, specifically, the relative permittivity also increased with the elongation factor. Finally, the electromechanical investigation proved that d_{33} coefficient, and thus the effectivity of the systems was incremented, which was attributed to successfully developed β-phase. The most significant enhancement (4-fold) of d_{33} was recorded for the PVDF-co-HFP elongated by 300 %. Finally have to be concluded, that extrusion process and consequent elongation positively influencing the distribution of the micro and nano-sized crystallites to form proper β-phase enhancing the vibration sensing effectivity for sample elongated by 300%.

ACKNOWLEDGEMENTS

This work was supported by the Czech Science Foundation grant no. 19-17457S. The authors M. M. and J. O gratefully acknowledge the Ministry of Education, Youth and Sports of the Czech Republic - DKRVO (RP/CPS/2020/003) and finally, author M.C. would like to acknowledge project (RP/CPS/2020/006).

REFERENCES

[1] PLACHY, T.; SEDLACIK, M.; PAVLINEK, V.; STEJSKAL, J. The observation of a conductivity threshold on the electrorheological effect of p-phenylenediamine oxidized with p-benzoquinone. *J. Mater. Chem. C.* 2015, vol. 3, no. 38, pp. 9973-9980.

[2] CVEK, M.; MRLIK, M.; ILCIKOVA, M.; MOSNACEK, J.; BABAYAN, V.; KUCEKOVA, Z.; HUMPOLICEK, P.; PAVLINEK, V. The chemical stability and cytotoxicity of carbonyl iron particles grafted with poly(glycidyl methacrylate) and the magnetorheological activity of their suspensions. *RSC Adv.* 2015, vol. 5, no. 89, pp. 72816-72824.

[3] LUBTOW, M.M.; MRLIK, M.; HAHN, L.; ALTMANN, A.; BEUDERT, M.; LUHMANN, T.; LUXENHOFER, R., Temperature-Dependent Rheological and Viscoelastic Investigation of a Poly(2-methyl-2-oxazoline)-b-poly(2-iso-butyl-2-oxazoline)-b-poly(2-meth yl-2-oxazoline)-Based Thermogelling Hydrogel. *J. Func. Biomater.* 2019, vol. 10, no. 3, pp. 16.

[4] MRLIK, M.; SPIREK, M.; AL-KHORI, J.; AHMAD, A.A.; MOSNACEK, J.; ALMAADEED, M.A.; KASAK, P. Mussel-mimicking sulfobetaine-based copolymer with metal tunable gelation, self-healing and antibacterial capability. *Arab. J. Chem.* 2020, vol. 13, no. 1, pp. 193-204.

[5] KRUPA, I.; SOBOLCIAK, P.; MRLIK, M. Smart Non-Woven Fiber Mats with Light-Induced Sensing Capability. *Nanomaterials.* 2020, vol. 10, no. 1, p. 13.

[6] JI, S.H.; YUN, J.S. Fabrication and Characterization of Aligned Flexible Lead-Free Piezoelectric Nanofibers for Wearable Device Applications. *Nanomaterials.* 2018, vol. 8, no. 4, p. 9.

[7] PEARSON, M.R.; EATON, M.J.; PULLIN, R.; FEATHERSTON, C.A.; HOLFORD, K.M. IOP, Energy Harvesting for Aerospace Structural Health Monitoring Systems. In: *Modern Practice in Stress and Vibration Analysis 2012.* Iop Publishing Ltd: Bristol, 2012; Vol. 382.

[8] HE, Y.X.; YANG, Q.; LUO, M.D.; LIU, R.Y. Effect of the physical parameters of longitudinally polarized PZT tubes on PZT sensors. *J. Phys. D-Appl. Phys.* 2020, vol. 53, no. 27, p. 10.

[9] BAI, Y.; TOFEL, P.; PALOSAARI, J.; JANTUNEN, H.; JUUTI, J. A Game Changer: A Multifunctional Perovskite Exhibiting Giant Ferroelectricity and Narrow Bandgap with Potential Application in a Truly Monolithic Multienergy Harvester or Sensor. *Adv. Mater.* 2017, vol. 29, no. 29, p. 7.

[10] ZHANG, G.Z.; ZHAO, P.; ZHANG, X.S.; HAN, K.; ZHAO, T.K.; ZHANG, Y.; JEONG, C.K.; JIANG, S.L.; ZHANG, S.L.; WANG, Q. Flexible three-dimensional interconnected piezoelectric ceramic foam based composites for highly efficient concurrent mechanical and thermal energy harvesting. *Energy Environ. Sci.* 2018, vol. 11, no. 8, p. 12.

[11] YI, J.G.; LIANG, H. A PVDF-based deformation and motion sensor: Modeling and experiments. *IEEE Sens. J.* 2008, vol. 8, no. 3-4, pp. 384-391.

[12] WANG, Y.R.; ZHENG, J.M.; REN, G.Y.; ZHANG, P.H.; XU, C. A flexible piezoelectric force sensor based on PVDF fabrics. *Smart Mater. Struct.* 2011, vol. 20, no. 4, p. 7.

[13] SENCADAS, V.; GREGORIO, R.; LANCEROS-MENDEZ, S. alpha to beta Phase Transformation and Microestructural Changes of PVDF Films Induced by Uniaxial Stretch. *J. Macromol. Sci. Part B-Phys.* 2009, vol. 48, no. 3, pp. 514-525.

[14] PU, J.A.; YAN, X.J.; JIANG, Y.D.; CHANG, C.E.; LIN, L.W. Piezoelectric actuation of direct-write electrospun fibers. *Sens. Actuator A-Phys.* 2010, vol. 164, no. 1-2, pp. 131-136.

[15] AHN, Y.; LIM, J.Y.; HONG, S.M.; LEE, J.; HA, J.; CHOI, H.J.; SEO, Y., Enhanced Piezoelectric Properties of Electrospun Poly(vinylidene fluoride)/Multiwalled Carbon Nanotube Composites Due to High beta-Phase Formation in Poly(vinylidene fluoride). *J. Phys. Chem. C.* 2013, vol. 117, no. 22, pp. 11791-11799.

[16] TING, Y.; SUPRAPTO; NUGRAHA, A.; CHIU, C.W.; GUNAWAN, H., Design and characterization of one-layer PVDF thin film for a 3D force sensor. *Sens. Actuator A-Phys.* 2016, vol. 250, no., pp. 129-137.

[17] LEE, B.S.; PARK, B.; YANG, H.S.; HAN, J.W.; CHOONG, C.; BAE, J.; LEE, K.; YU, W.R.; JEONG, U.; CHUNG, U.I.; PARK, J.J.; KIM, O. Effects of Substrate on Piezoelectricity of Electrospun Poly(vinylidene fluoride)-Nanofiber-Based Energy Generators. *ACS Appl. Mater. Interfaces.* 2014, vol. 6, no. 5, pp. 3520-3527.

[18] FLORCZAK, S.; LORSON, T.; ZHENG, T.; MRLIK, M.; HUTMACHER, D.W.; HIGGINS, M.J.; LUXENHOFER, R.; DALTON, P.D. Melt electrowriting of electroactive poly(vinylidene difluoride) fibers. *Polym. Int.* 2019, vol. 68, no. 4, pp. 735-745.

[19] MARTINS, P.; LOPES, A.C.; LANCEROS-MENDEZ, S. Electroactive phases of poly(vinylidene fluoride): Determination, processing and applications. *Prog. Polym. Sci.* 2014, vol. 39, no. 4, pp. 683-706.

[20] ADHIKARY, P.; GARAIN, S.; MANDAL, D. The co-operative performance of a hydrated salt assisted sponge like P(VDF-HFP) piezoelectric generator: an effective piezoelectric based energy harvester. *Phys. Chem. Chem. Phys.* 2015, vol. 17, no. 11, pp. 7275-7281.

[21] HUAN, Y.; LIU, Y.Y.; YANG, Y.F.; WU, Y.N. Influence of extrusion, stretching and poling on the structural and piezoelectric properties of poly (vinylidene fluoride-hexafluoropropylene) copolymer films. *J. Appl. Polym. Sci.* 2007, vol. 104, no. 2, pp. 858-862.

[22] KUMAR, A.; PERLMAN, M.M. Simultaneous stretching and corona poling of PVDF and P(VDF-TriFE) films .2. *J. Phys. D-Appl. Phys.* 1993, vol. 26, no. 3, pp. 469-473.

[23] FRUBING, P.; WANG, F.P.; WAGENER, M. Relaxation processes and structural transitions in stretched films of polyvinylidene fluoride and its copolymer with hexafluoropropylene. *Appl. Phys. A-Mater. Sci. Process.* 2012, vol. 107, no. 3, pp. 603-611.

[24] SHI, L.; WANG, R.; CAO, Y.M. Effect of the rheology of poly(vinylidene fluoride-co-hexafluropropylene) (PVDF-HFP) dope solutions on the formation of microporous hollow fibers used as membrane contactors. *J. Membr. Sci.* 2009, vol. 344, no. 1-2, pp. 112-122.

[25] LI, H.X.; ZHANG, W.X.; DING, Q.; JIN, X.Y.; KE, Q.F.; LI, Z.L.; WANG, D.; HUANG, C. Facile Strategy for Fabrication of Flexible, Breathable, and Washable Piezoelectric Sensors via Welding of Nanofibers with Multiwalled Carbon Nanotubes (MWCNTs). *ACS Appl. Mater. Interfaces.* 2019, vol. 11, no. 41, pp. 38023-38030.

[26] CAI, J.; HU, N.; WU, L.K.; LIU, Y.H.; LI, Y.; NING, H.M.; LIU, X.Y.; LIN, L.Y. Preparing carbon black/graphene/PVDF-HFP hybrid composite films of high piezoelectricity for energy harvesting technology. *Compos. Pt. A-Appl. Sci. Manuf.* 2019, vol. 121, no., pp. 223-231.

[27] GAUR, A.; SHUKLA, R.; BRAJESH, K.; PAL, A.; CHATTERJI, S.; RANJAN, R.; MAITI, P. Processing and nanoclay induced piezoelectricity in poly(vinylidene fluoride-co-hexafluoro propylene) nanohybrid for device application. *Polymer.* 2016, vol. 97, pp. 362-369.

[28] GERHARD, R. IEEE, Improving essential properties of dielectrics for electro-electrets, piezo-electrets and ferroelectric polymer electrets via physico-chemical routes. In: *Proceedings of the 2013 Ieee International Conference on Solid Dielectrics.* Ieee: New York, 2013; pp 45-48.

[29] KOC, M.; PARALI, L.; SAN, O. Fabrication and vibrational energy harvesting characterization of flexible piezoelectric nanogenerator (PEN) based on PVDF/PZT. *Polym. Test.* 2020, vol. 90, p. 10.

[30] SAHOO, R.; MISHRA, S.; UNNIKRISHNAN, L.; MOHANTY, S.; MAHAPATRA, S.; NAYAK, S.K.; ANWAR, S.; RAMADOSS, A. Enhanced dielectric and piezoelectric properties of Fe-doped ZnO/PVDF-TrFE composite films. *Mater. Sci. Semicond. Process.* 2020, vol. 117, p. 9.

[31] MRLIK, M.; LEADENHAM, S.; ALMAADEED, M.A.; ERTURK, A. Figure of merit comparison of PP-based electret and PVDF-based piezoelectric polymer energy harvesters. In: *Active and Passive Smart Structures and Integrated Systems 2016.* Park, G., Ed. Spie-Int Soc Optical Engineering: Bellingham, 2016, Vol. 9799.

EMBEDDED SEMICONDUCTOR QUANTUM DOTS - CURRENT OVERVIEW

Eduard HULICIUS, Alice HOSPODKOVÁ, Markéta ZÍKOVÁ

Department of Semiconductors, Institute of Physics, Czech Academy of Sciences, v.v.i., Prague, Czech Republic, EU, hulicius@fzu.cz

https://doi.org/10.37904/nanocon.2020.3680

Abstract

This review paper focuses on semiconductor quantum dots (QDs) embedded inside semiconductor heterostructures prepared by Metalorganic Vapor Phase Epitaxy (MOVPE) technology and based on our contribution in [1]. Semiconductor direct-bandgap materials have much higher energy conversion efficiency than the light emission from atoms/molecules in a glass matrix or from most other light sources, but they have a broad band or multimode light emission spectra. QDs created and embedded inside semiconductor heterostructures can fundamentally improve the quality of emitted light spectrum, temperature dependencies and efficiency of emission.

QDs exhibit unique electronic and optical properties, intermediate between those of bulk semiconductors and discrete atoms or molecules. The reason for this is that the size of QDs is comparable with the de Broglie wavelength of an electron in a crystal. Electrons (and holes) inside QDs behave differently from that found in a "bulk" material. The most important difference is that inside the QDs, electrons (and holes) can occupy only discrete energy levels due to strong localization. The position of energy levels depends mainly on the smallest dimension of a QD. Applications include QD lasers for integrated silicon photonics and quantum computing, QD LEDs for highly efficient solid-state lighting, QDs for intermediate band solar cells and multi-exciton generation and QDs for bio-medical labeling, imaging, targeted drug delivery, sensing, and therapy.

Keywords: Semiconductors, quantum dots, quantum levels, epitaxy, applications

1. INTRODUCTION

This contribution focuses only on quantum dots (QDs) embedded inside a semiconductor structure. Freestanding QDs (semiconductor, colloidal, metal etc.) with a much larger application field, which can be prepared from the same material, are not subject of this talk. A research report about the whole family of QDs market can be found at (paid) [2].

QDs are small pieces of semiconductor nanocrystals (mainly) with sizes in the range from ones to tens of nanometers. Ekimov and Onushchenko published the first idea of (freestanding) QDs, having properties different from that of the bulk material, in 1981 [3]. During the early 1990s, embedded QDs were prepared by molecular beam epitaxy (MBE) [4-5] in several laboratories, as described in [6].

Light emission (LED or laser type) from separated atoms in a glass matrix, e.g. neodymium doped YAG, ruby, etc., or from atoms or molecules in a gas, is nearly monochromatic thanks to these media having sharp energy levels.

Semiconductor direct-bandgap materials have much higher energy conversion efficiency than indirect-bandgap ones, but many possible recombination energies, thus they have broadband or multimode light emission. Electron energy levels in isolated atoms, the bulk semiconductor material (direct) and inside a QD are shown in **Figure 1**.

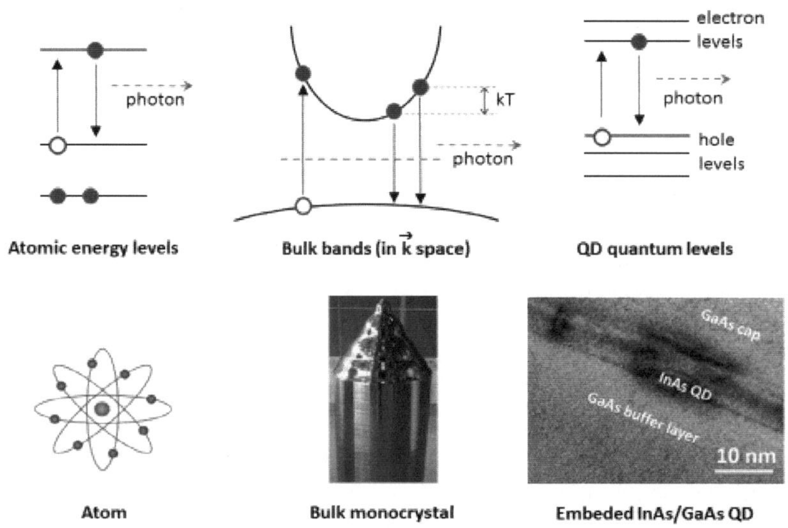

Figure 1 Paradigm of quantum dots, from [1]

A QD, resembling an artificial atom in its ability to confine the electron (or hole) wavefunction, emits more monochromatic light than the bulk material.

Reasons and examples of QD parameters for semiconductor lasers are as follows: The emission from quantum levels in QWs, QWrs or QDs is monochromatic and still very efficient. One of the effects of strong quantum confinement are discrete energy levels. Another effect is a lower threshold current density of a QD-based semiconductor laser, when achieving the inversion of population in QDs, which is needed for a stimulated emission, as well as suppression of loss mechanisms such as Auger recombination and intervalence band absorption.

The photon energy (emitted wavelength) can be changed mainly by the size of QDs and not only by chemical composition. This is a similar principle as in quantum well lasers, but the temperature dependence of these lasers is also much lower than for "classical" two-dimensional QW based lasers. Another very important property of QD-based semiconductor lasers is that very small QDs can emit single photons, which is necessary for quantum cryptography.

2. $A^{III}B^{V}$ MATERIALS AND STRUCTURES

2.1. QDs embedded in the structure

The three main growth technological procedures used for MOVPE preparation of QDs embedded in the structure are: 1) self-assembled Stranski-Krastanov growth mode; 2) formation of QDs in prepatterned inverted pyramids and 3) droplet epitaxy. The most widely used procedure is a self-assembling of QDs in SK growth mode. This growth mode can be used for highly strained QDs such as InAs on GaAs, InSb on GaSb, or InGaAs on GaP. In this technological procedure, QDs form from the material of a strained epitaxial layer, when the system has enough time to find the minimum energy, this means either the growth of strained layer has to be slow or the growth is interrupted for a few seconds after the epitaxial growth of the strained layer. By this method, different QD densities can be obtained (108-1011 cm-2) depending on the amount of deposited strained material and the time of the growth interruption. It is possible to grow stacks of vertically aligned QDs when the separation layer thickness between QDs is sufficiently thin (3-10 nm). In such a case, QDs form on the top of the QDs in previous layer thanks to the advantageous lattice deformation. An atomic force microscopy (AFM) picture of the surface of a vertically correlated QD structure with the last uncovered QD layer is shown in **Figure 2a**). It nicely demonstrates that the vertical correlation of QDs is high. No surface QDs form between hillocks, which are formed above buried QDs in previous layers and the QDs are formed on those hillocks only. A transmission electron microscopy (TEM) example of the cut of a similar structure is shown in **Figure 2b)**.

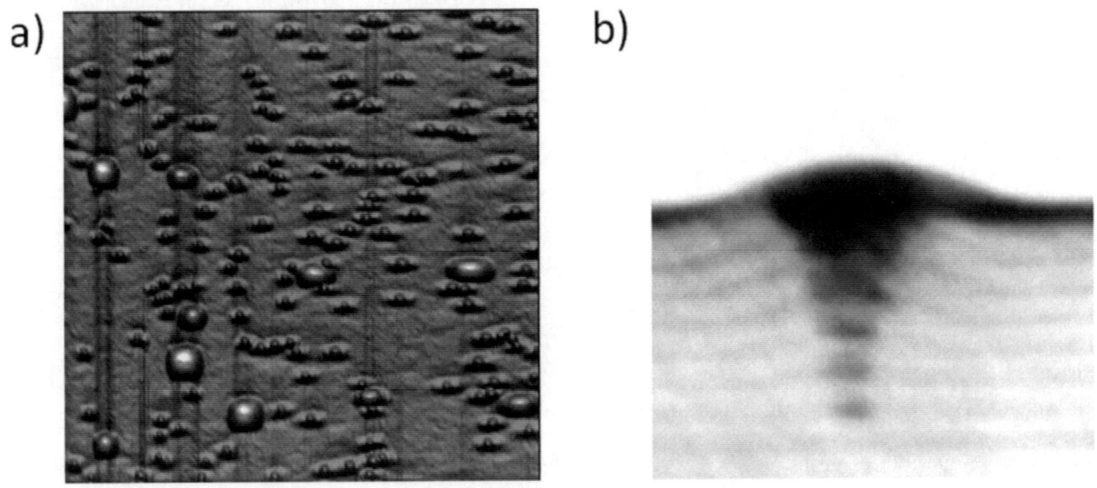

Figure 2 AFM picture of a surface with vertically correlated QDs with the last uncovered QD layer (**a**); TEM picture of the cut of a 7-layer vertical QD structure (**b**). Taken from [1].

2.2. Strain reducing and capping layers

There are two commonly used ternary materials for the growth of strain-reducing layers from the V-III group semiconductors, InGaAs and GaAsSb that have been studied simultaneously during recent years. The mechanism of the strain relaxation is the same for both InGaAs and GaAsSb ternary alloys, but at the same time different from the GaAs-covering mechanism. While GaAs is covering the surface with QDs from the bottom upwards and is leveling off the surface, both InGaAs and GaAsSb layers copy the topography of the surface, see **Figure 3**, which then enables the preservation of the size and shape of InAs QDs.

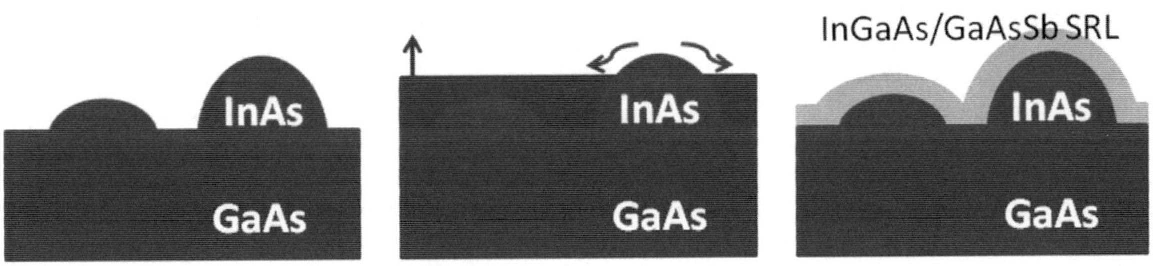

Figure 3 Covering mechanism of different types of covering layers from left: no capping layer, GaAs capping layer, InGaAs/GaAsSb strain-reducing layer. Taken from [1].

For InGaAs SRL, a similar study of the capping-layer thickness, as was carried out for the GaAs CL, was performed. The thickness of the InGaAs was kept at 5 nm, while the thickness of the GaAs was varied. The results for InGaAs with 13% of In are shown in **Figure 4**. When InGaAs strain-reducing layers are used, it is possible to achieve lower recombination energy. The main problem of the InGaAs SRL is in the weak confinement of electrons in the QD for higher In content due to the lowering of the conduction-band edges, which can then lead to a higher dependency on the ambient conditions such as temperature. Another reason

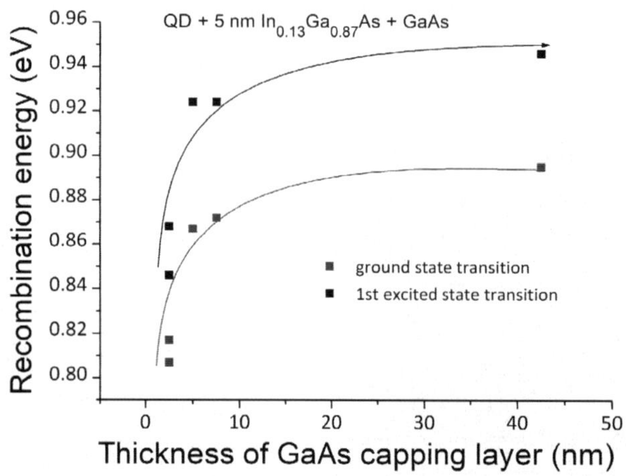

Figure 4 Dependence of recombination energy of a structure with InGaAs strain-reducing layer on the thickness of GaAs capping layer. Taken from [1].

for the weak confinement could be also a poor InAs/InGaAs interface that could lead to delocalization of electrons in the structure. Then, the structure shows photoluminescence (PL) with low intensity because the recombination rate of electrons and holes decreases. This can be seen in **Figure 5** from PL spectra measured for different InGaAs composition. There, the PL energy is decreased for higher In content, but from 13% of In the PL intensity is steadily decreasing. Concerning the PL maximum shift and intensity, the most suitable composition of the InGaAs layer would be around 13% or slightly higher.

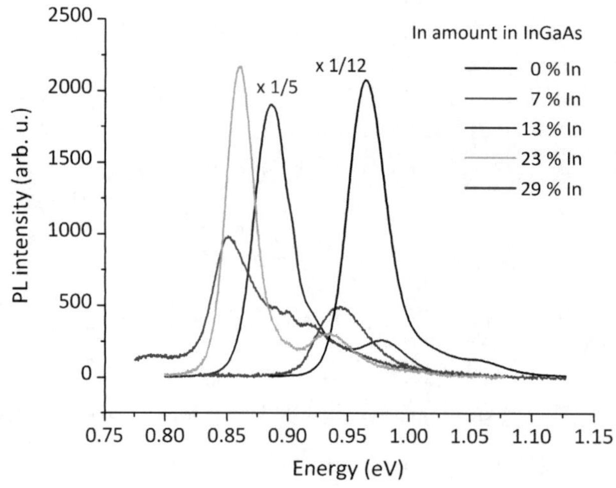

Figure 5 PL spectra of InAs QDs covered by InGaAs SRL with different In content. Taken from [1].

3. REFLECTANCE ANISOTROPY SPECTROSCOPY FOR QD GROWTH CONTROLLING

Compared to conventional reflectance measurements, Reflectance Anisotropy Spectroscopy (RAS) monitors in situ the properties of surfaces, interfaces and doping-induced surface electric fields, which makes it a unique optical in-situ technique. Moreover, because RAS includes the conventional reflectance measurement in addition to its surface and doping level sensitivity, the method allows for determination of layer thickness, growth rate and composition through reflectance analysis. Note that RAS can only be applied to cubic crystals, as they are grown e.g. on GaAs and InP. For bulk material of cubic crystals, the reflectance should be the same along two axes perpendicular to each other. However, at the surface region symmetry is reduced due to the crystal termination. This region of the crystal is responsible for the occurrence of the RAS signal. It carries information about symmetry and stoichiometry of the uppermost atomic layers. As tiny changes in surface stoichiometry can have a considerable effect on the surface symmetry, RAS enables growth monitoring and growth control - see **Figure 6**, even on a sub-monolayer level - see **Figure 7**.

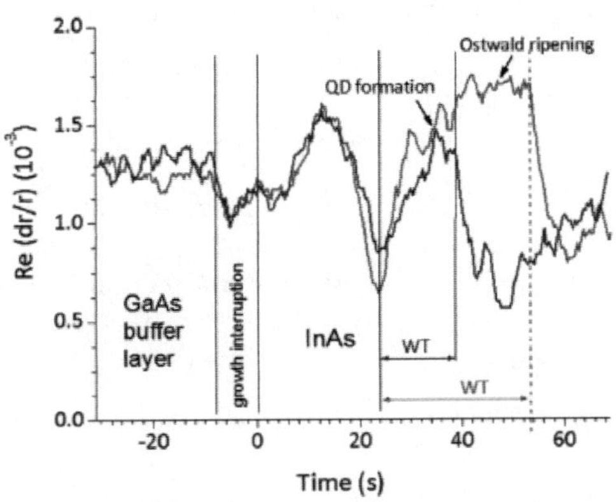

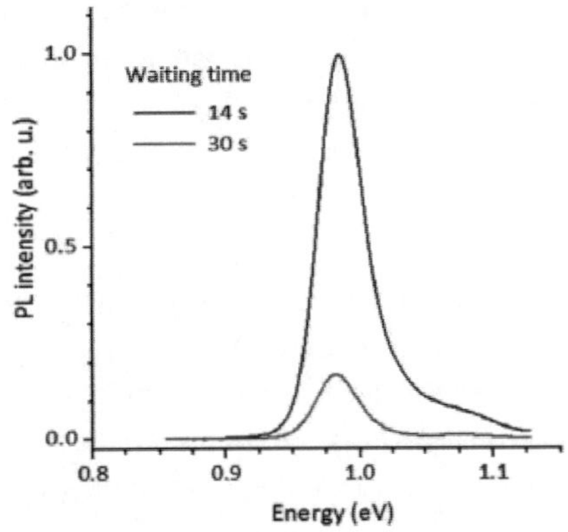

Figure 6 Left: RAS spectra (for 2.65 eV) of samples with different waiting times (WT) - time during which QDs are formed - for **14 s WT** (blue line) QD were formed, for **30 s WT** (red line) the time was overly long and QD coalesced into large objects. (This process is called Ostwald ripening.). **Right**: QDs were formed and evince PL for a sample with 14 s waiting time (WT), (blue line), for the WT of 30 s (red line). QDs coalesced into large objects that do not have a PL. Taken from [7].

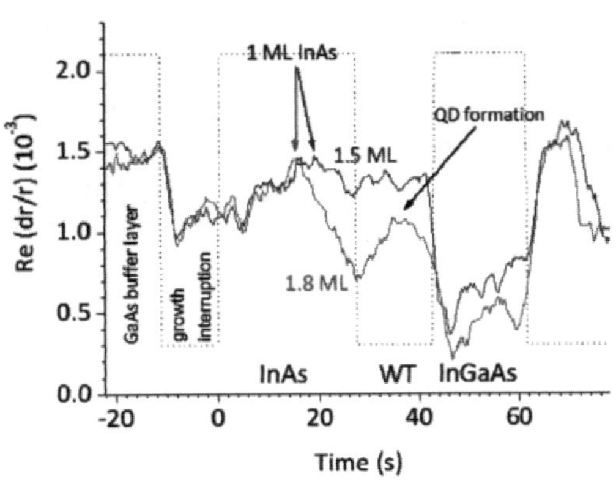

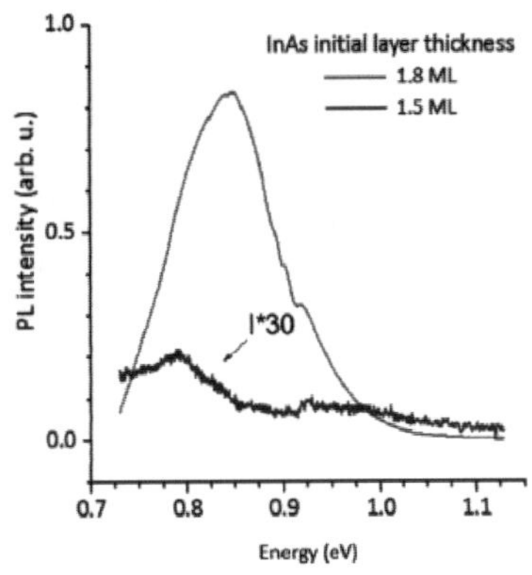

Figure 7 Left: RAS spectrum (for 2.65 eV) for estimation of the proper amount of InAs for a QD formation for **1.8 ML** thick InAs layer (red line), **1.5 ML** InAs (blue line). Right: PL spectra of samples with **1.8 ML** and **1.5 ML** of InAs for a QD formation, only inside the sample with **1.8 ML** QDs were created and contribute to PL. Taken from [7].

4. CONCLUSION

This paper explained importance of QDs embedded in semiconductor heterostructures prepared by MOVPE). It shows some technology parameters important for QD properties and explains the basic in-situ characterization technique RAS, which can be used for controlling of QD growth.

Applications include QD lasers for integrated silicon photonics and quantum computing. QD LEDs for highly efficient solid-state lighting. QDs for intermediate band solar cells and multi-exciton generation. QDs for bio-medical labeling, imaging, targeted drug delivery, sensing, and therapy.

Future applications:

- QD-based single-photon or -electron devices. Mainly single-photon QD lasers for quantum cryptography.
- QD MIR photomultipliers can be more useful than other QD photomultiplier wavelengths applications.
- QD long-life memories are very promising.
- Telecom lasers very probably for 1.3 μm, maybe also for 1.55 μm.
- Prospects of QD solar cells: at a very early stage of research, complications to be expected.

Future research:

- Extension of QD device wavelengths to the far-MIR and to the UV using different materials as well as size and shape of QDs.
- Improvement of structure parameters over the standard ones.
- The cost of devices has to be reduced, as usually, thus research of low-cost and mature (Si or GaAs wafers based?) technology has to be improved.

ACKNOWLEDGEMENTS

The authors acknowledge the support of MSMT project no. NPU LO1603 - ASTRANIT.

REFERENCES

[1] E. HULICIUS, A. HOSPODKOVÁ, M. ZÍKOVÁ. Quantum dots. In: IRVINE, S.J.C., CAPPER, P., eds, *Metalorganic Vapor Phase Epitaxy (MOVPE): Growth, Materials Properties and Applications*. John Wiley & Sons, Hoboken. 2020, Chapter 6, p. 584.

[2] Press release from: WiseGuyResearch Consultants Pvt Ltd_Project Portfolio Quantum Dots 2017 Global Market Expected to Grow at CAGR 11.39% and Forecast to 2019, Quantum Dots *Market Research Report* 2017.

[3] EKIMOV, A.I. and ONUSHCHENKO, A.A. Quantum size effect in three-dimensional microscopic semiconductor crystals. *JETP Letters*. 1981, vol. **34**, pp. 345-349.

[4] LEONARD, D., KRISHNAMURTHY, M., REAVES, C.M., *et al.* Direct formation of quantum-sized dots from uniform coherent islands of InGaAs on GaAs surfaces. *Applied Physics Letters*. 1993, vol. **63**, pp. 3203-3205.

[5] GRUNDMANN, M., CHRISTEN, J., LEDENTSOV, N.N., *et al.* (1995) Ultranarrow Luminescence Lines from Single Quantum Dots. *Physical Review Letters*. 1995, vol. 74, pp. 4043-4046.

[6] PETROFF, P.M. and DENBAARS, S.P. MBE and MOCVD growth and properties of self-assembling quantum dot arrays in III-V semiconductor structures. *Superlattices and Microstructures*. 1994, vol. **15**, pp. 15-21.

[7] ZÍKOVÁ, M., HOSPODKOVÁ, A. PANGRÁC, J., VYSKOČIL, J., HULICIUS, E., OSWALD, J., KOMNINOU, P, KIOSEOGLOU, J. The Metalorganic Vapour Phase Epitaxy Growthof AIIIBVHeterostructuresObserved by Reflection Anisotropy Spectroscopy. In: *Proceedings the 44th International School and Conference on the Physics of Semiconductors "Jaszowiec 2015". Wisła 2015.*

SESSION B
INDUSTRIAL AND ENVIRONMENTAL APPLICATIONS OF NANOMATERIALS

Chairmen

Prof. Dr. Radek ZBORIL	Palacky University in Olomouc, RCPTM, Czech Republic, EU
Prof. Dr. Miroslav CERNIK	Technical University of Liberec, Czech Republic, EU
Prof. Dr. Miloslav PEKAR	Brno University of Technology, Czech Republic, EU

ELIMINATION OF FIBERS CREATED FROM THE ELECTRODE ROD AND INFLUENCE ON ELECTROSPINNING

Ondřej BAŤKA, Josef SKŘIVÁNEK

TUL - Technical University of Liberec, Department of Textile Machine Design, Liberec, Czech Republic, EU, ondrej.batka@tul.cz

https://doi.org/10.37904/nanocon.2020.3729

Abstract

The article deals with the production of nanofibers using the AC-electrospinning method. It focuses on research into the possibility of eliminating the formation of fibers, which are not desirable. Ways to prevent the formation of these fibers have been proposed and tested experimentally. The influence on the electrospinning process and also on the size of production productivity was proved. Simultaneously, simulations were performed, which showed the electric field's dependence on the electrode's active part at its height. The dependence of the productivity of electrospinning on the height of the spinning electrode experimentally was found.

Keywords: Electric field, spinning electrode, electrospinning

1. INTRODUCTION

This research aimed to eliminate fiber drift from the spinning electrode's rod during AC-electrospinning [1]. These electrodes consist of parts for the transport and outflow of the polymer solution and an active part from which the spinning occurs [2]. They are usually used for the production of linear nanofiber structures [3]. The electrode diagram is shown in **Figure 1 a)**. Since the polymer solution flows down the electrode rod's surface, long bundles of fibers sometimes form from this part. However, these bundles are not caught by the siding of fibers formed on the conical part of the electrode and fall off onto the lid of the container with the polymer solution and the machine table. Thus, there is contamination and excessive consumption of material that is not used in the final product. A single-stage electrode with a diameter value of 22 millimeters (**Figure 1 b)**) was used for the tests.

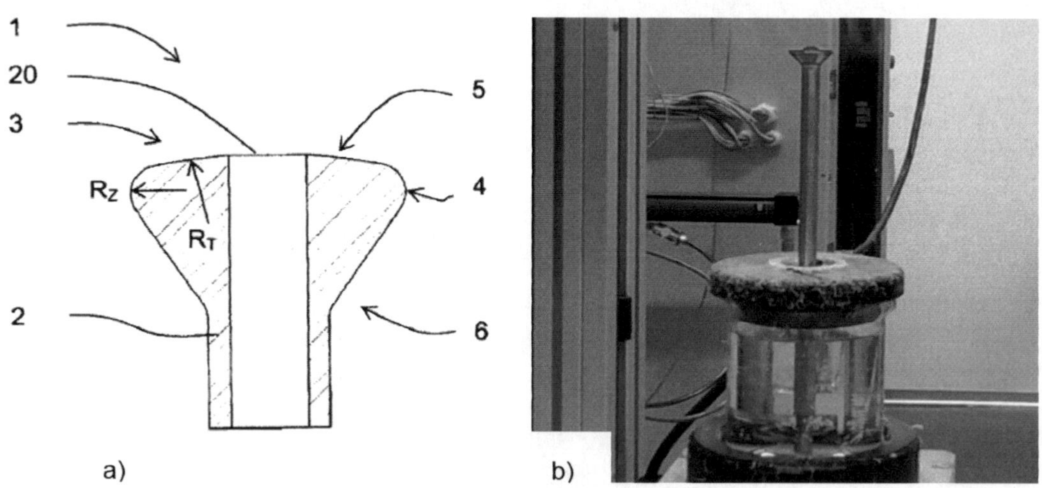

Figure 1 a) scheme of spinning electrode: (2) electrode rod, (5) (6) polymeric solution transporting surfaces, (4) active spinning surface [1]; b) picture of real spinning electrode used for experiments

2. SOLVING POSSIBILITIES

Some options to prevent flights have been tested. One of them is shown in **Figure 2 a)**. A metal tube was inserted around the stem of the electrode, which should prevent flying. However, as can be seen from the figure, some of the fibers formed on the cone are caught by the top of the tube and gradually deposited on it until the whole process of nanofiber production practically stops. **Figure 2 b)** shows a variant where the pipe has been shortened. As can be seen from the figure, the fibers are also deposited on and on the shorter tube. Although this is done in a visibly smaller amount, it can be assumed that after a more extended period of time, the increase will also be considered. The pipe, therefore, does not provide any solution to avoid pollution and excessive consumption of material.

Figure 2 electrode with the covering tube a) longer variant, b) shorter variant

Figure 3 electrode with disc

Another tried and tested way to prevent fiber escapes was to use a shielding disk, which should electrically shield the electrode rod and ensure that the rod's electric field is low enough to prevent spinning. **Figure 3** shows this.

The upper surface of the disk was 40 mm from the top of the electrode. The tests with the shielding disk observed that long bundles of fibers do not fall off. However, after a longer spinning time, a small amount of dirt was observed on the disc. However, this is a phenomenon that cannot be completely suppressed. These are probably fine fibers formed on the electrode's active surface and are not captured by the stream of nanofibers. The shield disk essentially simulates the polymer container's lid, suggesting that the electrode rod could be shorter.

3. MEASUREMENT OF SPINNING PRODUCTIVITY

Experiments with electrode rod shielding have been supplemented with productivity measurements to determine how tube or disk shielding affects nanofiber production productivity. The voltage signal applied to the electrode had the shape of a sine function with a frequency of 50 Hz. For each electrode treatment variant, experiments were performed for voltage values with voltage values of 28.5 kV, 32 kV and 35.4 kV. A 10% solution of Movital H60B PVB in ethanol was used for the experiments. The results of the experiments are shown in the graph in **Figure 4**. The productivity dependences on voltage for the three electrode variants are shown - the base electrode, the electrode with the covering tube and the electrodes with the disk 40 mm away from the top of the electrode. It can be seen from the graph that both selected solutions to eliminate unwanted fiber drop have an impact on productivity. In both cases, it was reduced by approximately ten percent. Furthermore, productivity measurements were performed for different disk positions and electrode heights at two voltage values on the electrode. **Figure 5** shows the dependences of production productivity on electrode height. It should be noted that at the electrode's height of 30 millimeters, the electrospinning process was already so unstable, and the nanofibers produced were so small that it was not possible to deposit them on a collection drum and perform weighing. At the height of 20 millimeters, the electrospinning process no longer occurs. The fibers were not produced. For this reason, the graph for this distance shows a zero productivity value. The graph shows that with the height of the electrode, productivity increases up to a specific value when no further increase has an effect.

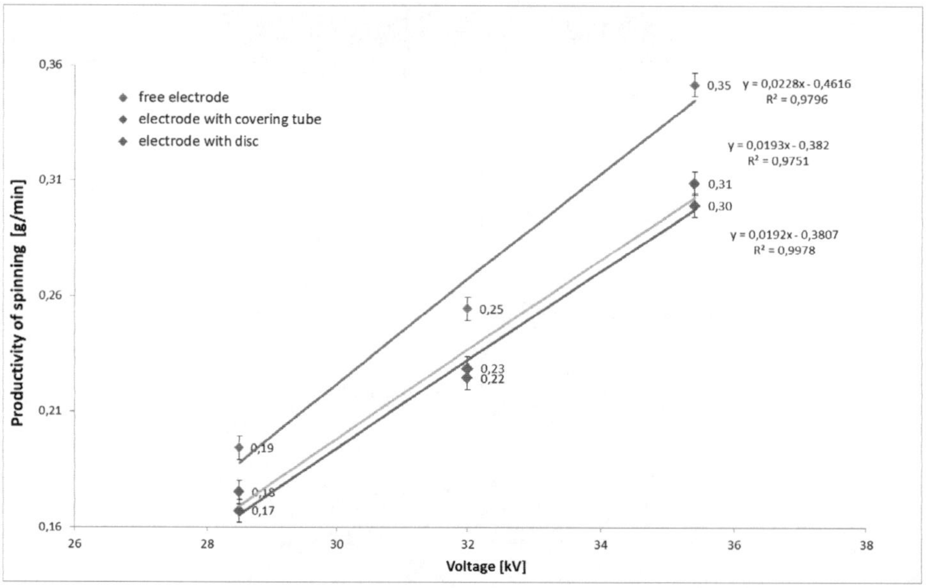

Figure 4 Dependence of productivity on voltage for different variants of the electrode covering

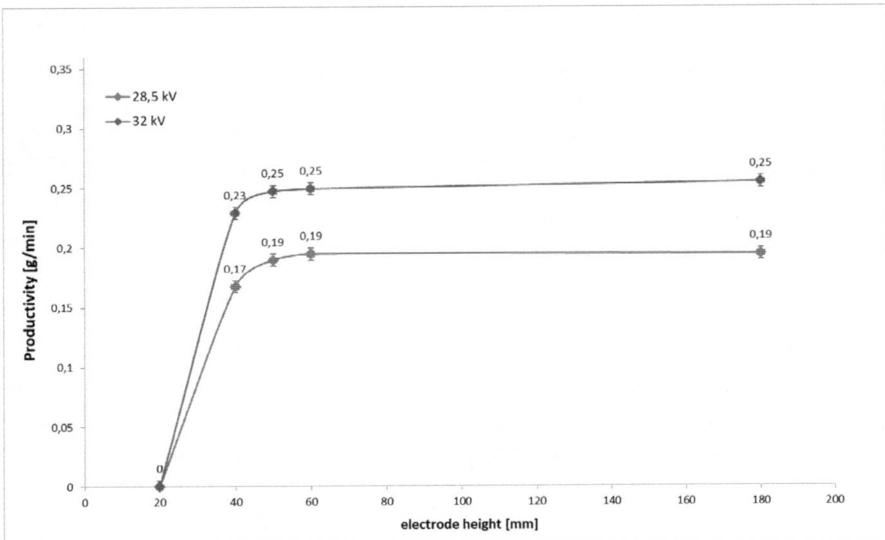

Figure 5 Dependence of productivity on electrode height

4. SIMULATIONS

The research was supplemented by simulations of the electric field distribution around the spinning electrode. Simulations were performed for different electrode heights to determine the dependence of the electric field's value in the active part of the electrode on its height. Autodesk Simulation Mechanical software was used for the simulations. They were performed for electrode voltages of 30 kV and 0 V at the boundary of the distant surroundings. **Figure 6** shows the dependence of the electric field active surface of the electrode on electrode height. It is evident from the dependence that the electric field's value on the electrode's active surface increases with the electrode's increasing height. It can be assumed that the cover of the electrode, located on the bottom, or the shielding disk influences the electric field's distribution. This dependence is probably also related to the effect on productivity, which was described in the previous chapter.

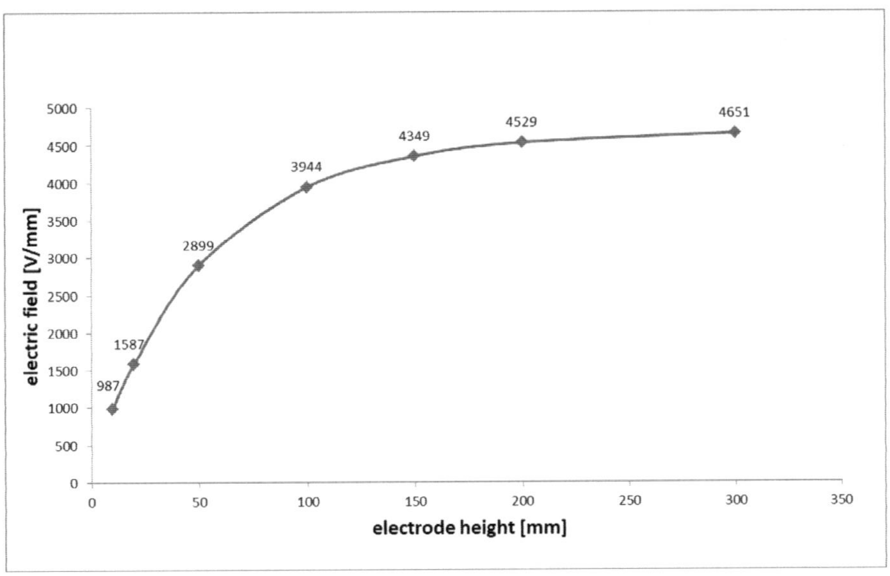

Figure 6 Dependence of the electric field of the active electrode surface on the height of the electrode

5. CONCLUSION

Experiments show that it is possible to find ways to eliminate unwanted emissions of nanofibers from the rod of the spinning electrode. The use of a tube threaded around the electrode rod proved inappropriate, as nanofibers were trapped at the edge of the tube. The use of a disk or the possibility of shortening the spinning electrode rod has proven to be effective. However, it has been shown that as the height of the electrode decreases, the productivity of nanofiber production decreases. Corresponding to this is also the result of simulations, which showed that the electric field's value on the electrode's active surface decreases with the shortening of the electrode rod.

ACKNOWLEDGEMENTS

This publication was written at the Technical University of Liberec as part of the project with the support of the Specific University Research Grant, as provided by the Ministry of Education, Youth and Sports of the Czech Republic in the year 2020.

REFERENCES

[1] KOCIS, L., POKORNY, P., LUKÁŠ, D., MIKEŠ, P., CHVOJKA, J., KOŠŤÁKOVÁ, E., MÍČKOVÁ, A., Method for production of polymeric nanofibres by spinning of solution or melt of polymer in electric field, and a linear formation from polymeric nanofibers prepared by this method. EP 2931951

[2] BERAN, J., VALTERA, J., BÍLEK, M., SKŘIVÁNEK, J., KOŠŤÁKOVÁ, E., Method for producing polymeric nanofibres by electrospinnig a polymer solution or melt, a spinning elektrode for performing the metod and a device for producing polymeric nanofibers equipment with at least one cush spinning electrode. EP 3394328

[3] VALTERA, J., KALOUS, T., POKORNY, P., BATKA, O., BILEK, M., CHVOJKA, J., LUKAS, D. Fabrication of dual-functional composite yarns with a nanofibrous envelope using high throughput AC needleless and collectorless electrospinning. *Scientific Reports*. [online]. 2019, vol. 9, no. 1. Available from: https://doi.org/doi:10.1038/s41598-019-38557-z.

[4] KOMAREK, J., VALTERA, J., SOUKUPOVA, J., VYSLOUZILOVA, L., SKRIVANEK, J., ZABKA, P., BERAN, J., LUKAS, D. Verification of the mathematical model of the rod electrode in the electrospinning process. In: *Nanocon 2015, 7th International Conference on Nanomaterials.* Ostrava: TANGER, 2015.

[5] RŮŽIČKOVÁ, J. *Electrostatic spinning of nano fibres.* Liberec: Technical University of Liberec, 2006, p 11. ISBN 80-7372-066-3.

[6] POKORNY, P. Effective AC needleless and colector less electrospinning for yarn production. *Physical Chemistry Chemical Physics.* 2014, vol. 16, pp. 816-822.

[7] PEJCHAR, K., VYSLOUŽILOVÁ, L., POKORNÝ, P., BÍLEK, M., BERAN, J., LUKÁŠ, D. The slit needleless electrode for the electrospinning. In: *NANOCON 2013 - 5th International Conference.* Tanger, 2013, pp. 172-177.

RESEARCH OF ELECTRODES ENABLING THE PRODUCTION OF NANOFIBRES WITH DEFINED FINENESS

Josef SKŘIVÁNEK, Jiří KOMÁREK, Ondřej BAŤKA

TUL - Technical University of Liberec, Department of Textile Machine Design, Liberec, Czech Republic, EU, *Josef.skrivanek@tul.cz*

https://doi.org/10.37904/nanocon.2020.3730

Abstract

The main scope of work is to verify the possibility of production diverse fibres, which have different fineness and are produced simultaneously on one electrode. In the first phase of the research, a basic design of the geometry of the two-stage electrode was performed and subsequently, using FEM software, an analysis was performed to determine the electrical field at the individual stages of the electrode. Based on the distribution of the electrical field, 3 different types of the two-stage electrode geometry were found, the mutual structure of stages on one electrode. In the second phase, these 3 types were created and then an experiment was performed and a subsequent evaluation of the frequency and fineness of the fibres related to the solved types of electrodes.

Keywords: Fineness, electrical field, spinning electrode, electrospinning

1. INTRODUCTION

Nanomaterials are currently a very interesting and not yet fully explored field of scientific activity. There are specific materials that have at least one dimension smaller than 10 nm. Most often, these materials have the shape of a cylinder, tube or sphere in cross sections. Cylindrical nanomaterials are called nanofibers. "The principle of nanofiber production is their elongation and thinning with the help of external forces [1].

Forms of nanofiber products are diverse. Commonly known are flat nanofiber fabrics, which are usually applied to a backing material in the form of a nonwoven fabric. Another very important product from the portfolio of nanofibers is bi-component yarn produced by the so-called ballooning method. In general, it can be stated that nanofibers are a promising element for current materials engineering. "They are used, for example, in the development of protective materials, sensors, cosmetics, hygiene products, tissue culture media, filters and energy storage materials [2].

Currently, the widest use for multistage electrodes is the production of yarns. The production of yarn, which consists of nanofibers, is a relatively important option in the field of spinning. Nanofiber yarns can be the basis for the production of fabrics or knitwear. These fabrics made from nanofiber yarns can be used to make high value-added products such as protective clothing, high performance fabrics and composites, or they can be used in areas such as tissue engineering. Increasing the technological level of nanofiber yarn production requires finding a way to transform polymer nozzles into linear nanofiber assemblies and achieve a satisfactory level of process productivity [3].

This study aims to create a nanofiber structure with a majority of fibers of two different finenesses. A particular two-stage electrode (**Figure 1**) should be used for this, consisting of two different electrodes placed one above the other. Each stage of this so-called multistage electrode has a different value of the electrical field, so it is assumed that there is a probability to produce fibers with varying fineness at each stage.

2. ANALYSIS OF A SPECIAL TWO-STAGE ELECTRODE

Simulation Multiphysics software was used to determine the electrical field on the particular two-stage electrode. This simulation software provides precise and flexible tools for calculating boundary value problems using the finite element method (FEM). The assembled mathematical model allows simulating the charge distribution in an electrical field.

Due to the experimental device's axial symmetry, the mathematical model can be solved as a two-dimensional problem with axial symmetry. The FEM model's 2D geometry was created by the experimental equipment dimensions described in the experiment (Chapter 3). The material properties of the individual parts of the device were defined in the model using relative permittivity. The critical states of the electrospinning process were described in a mathematical model by the applied voltage. A grounded protective box was defined as a sphere with an outer diameter of 2000 mm and an applied voltage of 0 V at its outer boundary [4]. The boundary condition for the spinning electrode was 30 kV, the same value was subsequently used in the experiment.

The type of analysis "Electrical field and voltage" was chosen for the simulation. The electrical field distribution in the model is shown in **Figures 1 a, b, c**. The results of the analysis shown in the figures correspond to the cases in the assembly 3, 4 and 5 in the **Table 1**. The assembly 5 shows the considerable difference in electrical field value between the first and second electrode stages, which is in the case shown in **Figure 1 a)**.

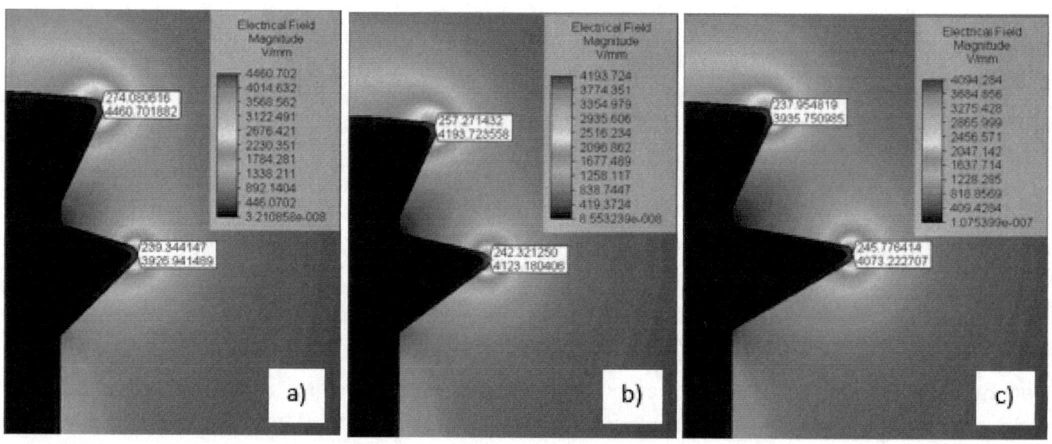

Figure 1 Electrical field distribution

3. EXPERIMENT

For the experiment, a group of special elements was designed and manufactured, from which it is possible to assemble a two-stage electrode [5]. Thanks to the interchangeability of parts, the parameters of individual electrode stages can be changed. The two-stage electrode has an axially symmetrical geometry and consists of support and a working part. The supporting part consists of a steel tube with an outer diameter of 8 mm and a height of 150 mm. The working part consists of interchangeable cone-shaped steel electrodes- stages. These stages are placed on top of each other on the support part to form the so-called "tree shape".

During the experiment, the two-stage electrode was assembled so that 1 stage was formed by an electrode with a diameter of 15 mm with a functional radius of 0.5 mm. The second stage was replaced by electrodes with diameters of 20, 24, and 28 mm with an operating radius of 0.3 mm on the outer perimeter. A voltage of 30 kV was applied to the electrode. The experiment itself was performed in a grounded protective box.

Polyvinyl butyral (PVB, Mowital B60H) was used for the experiment. The solution contained 9 % (w/w) of polymer, the remainder of the solvent. The solvent was stirred from ethanol and isopropyl alcohol in a ratio of

4: 1. The polymer was conveyed to the electrode through the center of the steel tube (support part) by means of a peristaltic pump. The experiment was done at an ambient temperature of 23 °C and relative humidity of 40 % [6].

In the experiment, five different sets of electrodes were measured. For each set, three samples of a planar fibrous structure were taken on a black base paper. The task was to compare three different assemblies of the tree electrode with three other differences in electrical field. It was assumed that the samples would show a different percentage of fibers of a certain fineness [7]. The electrical field distribution on the tree electrode and the maximum values of the electrical electrical on the individual stages of the electrode are described in detail in the analysis.

3.1. Used electrode assemblies

Table 1 Assemblies of used electrodes within the experiment

Case	Figure		Assemblies
1	2 a)		The rod itself with a diameter of 8 mm - verification of operation
2	2 b)		Single-stage electrode - diameter 28 mm - verification of operation
3	1 a)	2 c)	Two-stage electrode - 1 st. diameter 15 mm, 2 st. diameter 28 mm
4	1 b)		Two-stage electrode - 1 st. diameter 15 mm, 2 st. diameter 24 mm
5	1 c)		Two-stage electrode - 1 st. diameter 15 mm, 2 st. diameter 20 mm

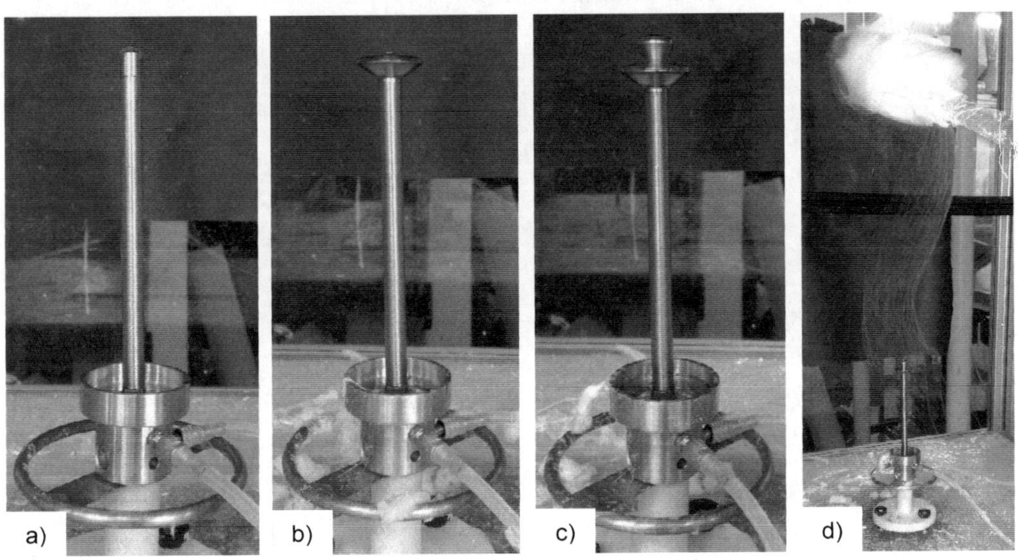

Figure 2 a) rod, b) single-stage electrode, c) two-stage electrode, d) spinning process

4. EVALUATION

Three samples were taken for each assembly and subsequently scanned with an electron microscope (**Figure 3**). 15 images were taken for each assembly. The obtained images were evaluated using software where fiber thicknesses were measured. One hundred values were measured on each image. The evaluated results are shown in **Figures 3 to 5**, the graphs in the mentioned figures present the quantity of fibers' representation of the certain fineness in the samples taken from assemblies (**Table 1**, case 3, 4 and 5).

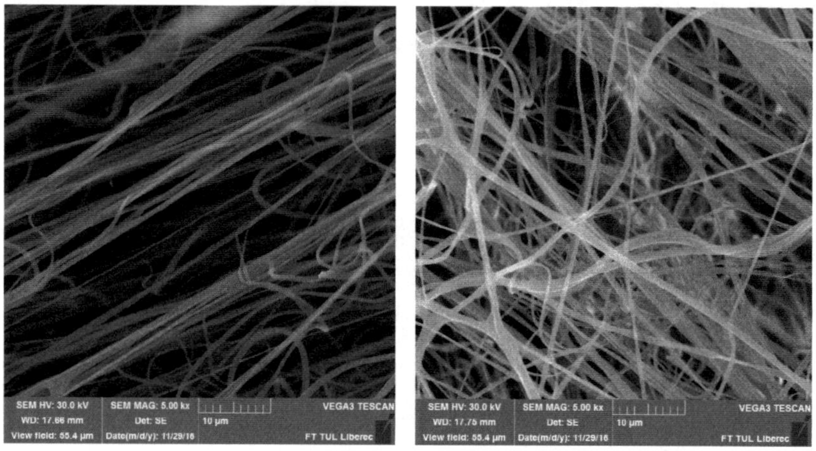

Figure 3 SEM images - assembly 3

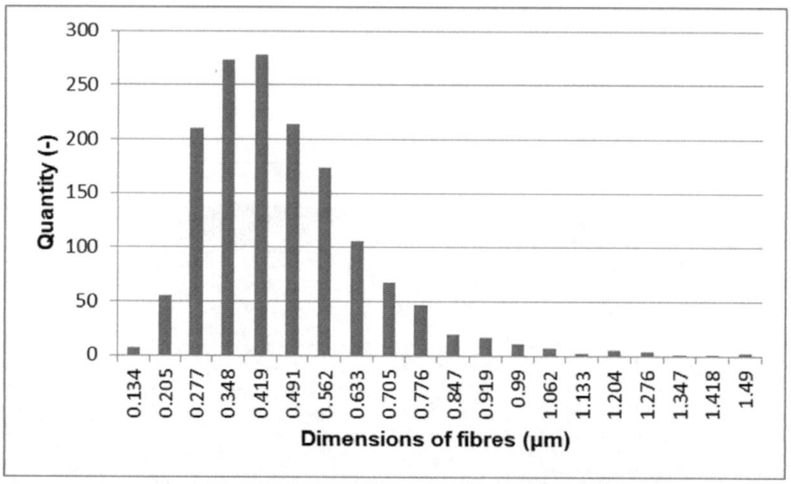

Figure 4 Distribution of fiber fineness - case 1 (Table 1)

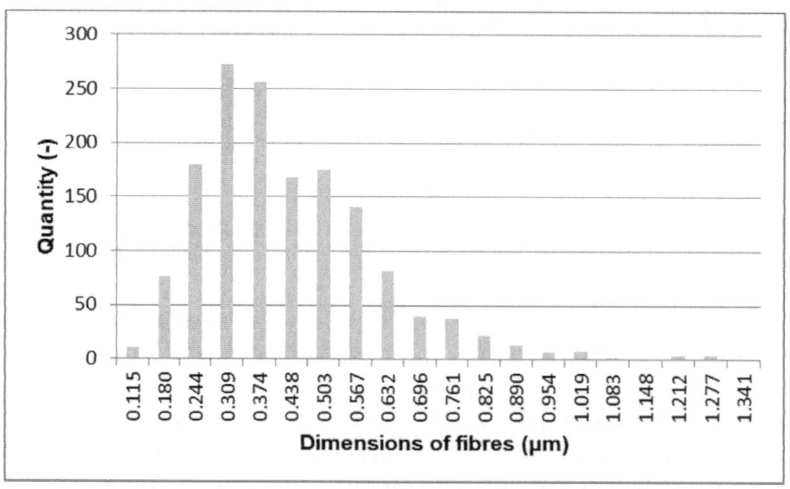

Figure 5 Distribution of fiber fineness - case 2 (Table 1)

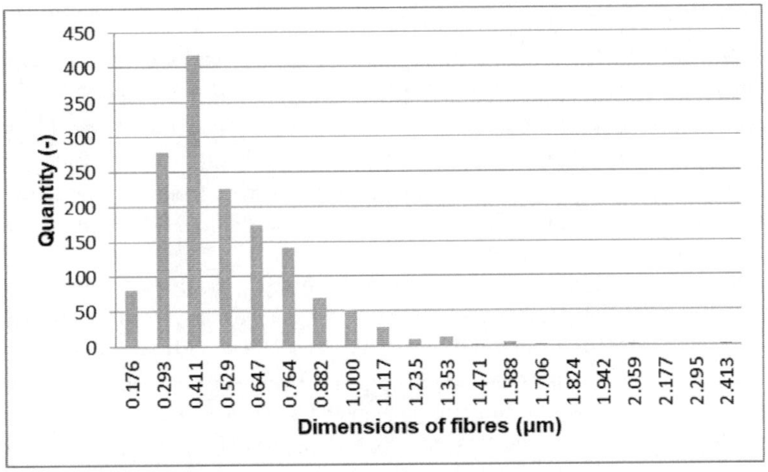

Figure 6 Distribution of fiber fineness - case 5 (Table 1)

5. CONCLUSION

The two-stage electrode in case 5 (**Table1, Figure 1a**) has a lowest difference in electrode diameters on the first and second stages. The diameter of the first stage is 15mm and the second one is 20mm (**Figure 1a**). On the other hand, the difference between the maximum values of electrical field at the individual stages is the largest for this assembly, yet this difference is 12 %. The evaluated samples have the largest proportion of fibers with a fineness 0.411 µm (**Figure 6**).

A large proportion of fibers with two different finenesses is not significantly apparent from the sample. The cause may be a small difference in the maximum electrical field at the individual electrode stages. This fact could also be influenced by the different production of fibers at each stage of the electrode. The quantity of fibers from the second stage of electrode would be in such a small amount that it would not significantly stand out from the other values of fineness in the represented results. Productivity is related to an electrical field so that the higher the intensity value, the higher the productivity [3]. From the small difference in the electrical field between the individual stages of the electrode, the previous consideration could be ruled out. Productivity could also be affected by shading one electrode by another. From the analysis results shown in **Figure 1** also implies that with increasing diameter of the lower stage of the electrode there is a decrease of the electrical field at the upper stage of the electrode.

It is also worth mentioning the evaluated samples of assemblies case 1 and case 2 (**Table 1**), although it is not a tree electrode. The results can be compared in **Figures 4 and 5**. The values of the fineness of the most represented fibers differ slightly here. Thus, there is some hope that the idea of creating a nanofiber structure with a large proportion of fibers of different fineness is not wrong. It would be interesting to further deal with this task and design a two-stage electrode with an enormous difference in electric field between the individual stages for further tests.

ACKNOWLEDGEMENTS

This publication was written at the Technical University of Liberec as part of the project with the support of the Specific University Research Grant, as provided by the Ministry of Education, Youth and Sports of the Czech Republic in the year 2020.

REFERENCES

[1] TECHNICAL UNIVERSITY OF LIBEREC. Method of nanofibers production from polymeric solution using electrical spinning and device for carrying out the method. JIRSAK, O. Czech Republic, 2015. WO2005024101.

[2] LUKAS, D. Physical principles of Electrospinning. *Journal of Applied Physics*. 2008, ISSN (E-ISSN) 1089-7550.

[3] VALTERA, J., KALOUS, T., POKORNY, P., BATKA, O., BILEK, M., CHVOJKA, J, LUKAS, D. Fabrication of dual-functional composite yarns with a nanofibrous envelope using high throughput AC needleless and collectorless electrospinning. *Scientific Reports.* [online]. 2019, vol. 9, article no. 1801. Available from: https://doi.org/10.1038/s41598-019-38557-z.

[4] KOMAREK, J., VALTERA, J., SOUKUPOVA, J., VYSLOUZILOVA, L., SKRIVANEK, J., ZABKA, P., BERAN, J., LUKAS, D. Verification of the mathematical model of the rod electrode in the electrospinning process. In: *Nanocon 2015: 7th International Conference on Nanomaterials.* Ostrava: TANGER, 2015.

[5] TECHNICAL UNIVERSITY OF LIBEREC. Method for producing polymeric nanofibres by electrospinnig a polymer solution or melt, a spinning elektrode for performing the metod and a device for producing polymeric nanofibers equipment with at least one cush spinning electrode. BERAN, J., VALTERA, J., BÍLEK, M., SKŘIVÁNEK, J., KOŠŤÁKOVÁ, E. Czech Republic, 2017. EP 3394328.

[6] MACDIARMID, A.G., JONES, W.E., NORRIS, I.D., GAO, J., JOHNSON, A.T. JR., PINTO, N.J., HONE, J., HAN, B., OKUZAKI, H., LLAGUNO, M. Electricalally-generated nanofibers of electronic polymers. *Synthetic Metals.* Pennsylvania: University of Pennsylvania, 2001, p. 27.

[7] JIN, H.-J., FRIDRIKH, S.V., RUTLEDGE, G.C., KAPLAN, D.L. Electrospinning Bombyx mori Silk with (Polyethylene oxide). *Biomacromolecules.* American Chemical Society, 2002, p.408.

PRODUCTION OF FIBROUS COMPOSITE MATERIAL WITH INCORPORATED ACTIVATED CARBON

[1]Pavel HOLEC, [2]Ivan ULMAN, [3]Radek JIRKOVEC, [4]Jakub VANĚK

[1,2,3]*Technical University of Liberec, Liberec, Czech Republic, EU,*
pavel.holec@tul.cz, ivan.ulman@tul.cz, radek.jirkovec@tul.cz

[4]*National Institute for Nuclear, Chemical and Biological Protection, Milin, Czech Republic, EU,*
vanek@sujchbo.cz

https://doi.org/10.37904/nanocon.2020.3705

Abstract

The increasing emphasis on human health and safety presupposes, among other things, the development of new safety technologies and aids that should protect people in high-risk occupations, such as firefighters, soldiers, paramedics, chemical plant workers or researchers themselves. One of the most common type of protective equipment is protective clothing. In the second half of the 20th century, garments made of composite textiles with incorporated activated carbon particles have been used for the sorption of hazardous gaseous or liquid substances.

This work followed up on previous research and dealt with the design and production of a composite material with incorporated activated carbon, which was applied to the nonwoven material. The final product consisted of several layers: spun-bond, nonwoven needled fabric, activated carbon and nanofibers produced by polymer spinning technology using alternating current (AC spinning). The work also focused on the design of the order of individual layers, the method of application of activated carbon and the strengthening of the resulting composites. The finished material was finally subjected to tests of breathability, vapour permeability, loss of activated carbon particles and the passage of chemical warfare agents (simulants of sarin, soman or yperite). At the same time, the resulting composite was compared with the FOP-96 military protective clothing used today. The final product could serve as a protective layer for military purposes, firefighting, clothing for paramedics or the material for filtration.

Keywords: Chemical warfare agents, nanofibers, activated carbon, composite

1. INTRODUCTION

This article deals with design and production of composite material with the incorporation of sorbent - activated carbon, which was applied to the nonwoven material. The final product was composed of several layers - spundbond, nonwoven textile with activated carbon [1] and nanofibers produced by AC spinning technology. The article deals with the design of layers, incorporation of activated carbon and the bonding of finished composites. The finished material was finally subjected to several tests, such as breathability, vapour permeability, decrease of activated carbon particles and penetration of chemical warfare agents [2]. The resulting material was compared with FOP-96 military clothing [3]. The final product should serve as a protective layer for military purposes.

2. EXPERIMENT

2.1. Preparation of composite samples with activated carbon

Samples of composite materials were prepared by layering of three types of nonwoven fabrics - spunbond (polyethylene-polypropylene, 16 $g \cdot m^{-2}$), needlepunched nonwovens (polyester, 80 $g \cdot m^{-2}$) and nanofiber layers (polyvinyl butyral, 50 $g \cdot m^{-2}$) produced by electrospinning using alternating voltage source (AC spinning).

The polymer solution for nanofiber production was composed of polyvinyl butyral (Mowital B 60 H, M_n = 60,000 g·mol^{-1} purchased from Kuraray) at a weight concentration of 10 %, dissolved in denatured ethanol of 96 % weight concentration (purchased from Technisolv). The polyvinyl butyral nanofibers showed a high degree of adhesion to other materials, which was later advantageously used to capture activated carbon particles in the structure of nanofiber layers. The polymer solution was spun using a screw pump [4] and alternating high voltage power source (VTS 36, purchased from KPB Intra) with an added residual-current device. The nanofibers were deposited on a spunbond base nonwoven fabric placed on a rotating collector. After reaching the required basis weight, the nanofiber layer was removed from the spunbond and further treated as other nonwoven layers.

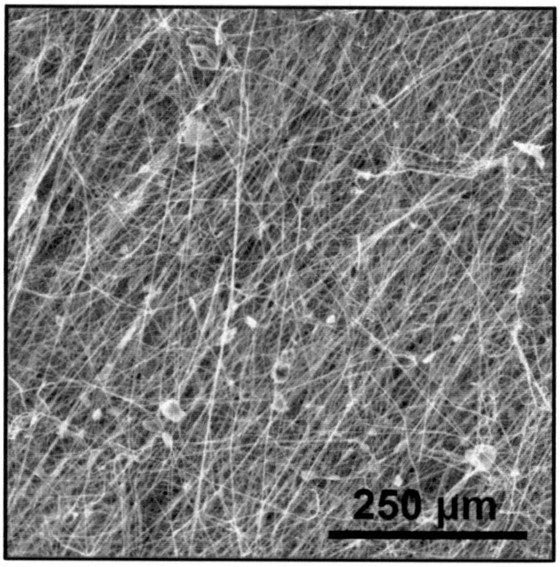

Figure 1 Nanofibers produced by AC spinning technology

It was necessary to find a compromise between bulk size of the composite, the possible application of the sorbent and maintaining its functionality after the application of the activated carbon. After testing the various combinations of mentioned nonwovens, the following was subjectively selected as suitable: spunbond layer, needlepunch nonwoven, nanofiber layer, needlepunch layer with activated carbon and again nanofiber layer, needlepunch nonwoven and spunbond. The composite consisted of seven layers at all. Activated carbon was applied to the needled fabric in an amount of 90 g·m^2 by the raking technique. Blank samples were made for further experiments. Its composition of layers was identical, but activated carbon was not added.

Subsequently, the samples were reinforced by lamination, hot-melt technology or a combination of sewing with ultrasonic bonding. Lamination was done by a laminator RPS-L 600 (Maschinenfabrik Herbert Meyer GmbH) without added pressure, at a temperature of 130 °C and a conveyor speed of 2.3 m·min^{-1}. Poly-α-olefin Helmitin 42048 (Forbo International SA) applied with a spray gun was used for hot-melt bonding. The Couptiss Ultra Sons HS 30 (30 W, 40 kHz) with a relief sonotrode set at 15.5 % power at a displacement speed of 2.5 m·min^{-1} and a pressure of 2 bar was used for ultrasonic bonding. Hagal UNIPOLY 120 thread (120 tex) was used for sewing. The holes caused by the penetration of the needle through the material were sealed using ultrasound, preventing the passing harmful substances.

2.2. Testing methods

Samples of manufactured composite materials reinforced by lamination, hot-melt technology or a combination of sewing and ultrasound were subjected to tests of activated carbon loss, breathability and vapour permeability. After comparing the results of individual types of composite reinforcement, two were selected, for further testing of the penetration of warfare agents or their simulants. These tests were performed by the National Institute for Nuclear, Chemical and Biological Protection.

Static activated carbon loss test - Samples were clamped in testing head of the device. They were then subjected to a vacuum at a given airflow rate for 1 minute. The vacuum value was set to achieve a constant airflow rate of 0.2 mm·s^{-1}. The samples were weighed to three decimal places before and after testing and the absolute and relative loss of activated carbon from the sample was found. Initial amount of activated carbon was of 3 g per sample.

Dynamic activated carbon loss test - The dynamic test was performed on a Vibramax 100 shaker (Heidolph Instruments GmbH & CO. KG). The samples were clamped to the vibrating plate of the device and the device subsequently performed a horizontal circular motion at a frequency of 1010 oscillations per minute for 10 minutes. Again, the absolute and relative loos of sorbent was found.

Breathability - Materials were tested for breathability using an SDL Atlas M021A (SDL Atlas). The measurement was performed according to the ČSN EN ISO 9237 standard. The pressure drop was 200 Pa. The currently used military jacket FOP-96 was measured as well.

Vapour permeability - The measurement was performed on a Permetest (Sensora) device according to the ČSN EN ISO 11092 standard. Concerning the sample size, the measurement was performed only twice on each sample.

Iodine resistance test - The resistance of the produced materials to the penetration of gaseous iodine was tested according to the internal methodology of National Institute for Nuclear, Chemical and Biological Protection [5]. The indicator solution was prepared from 1 g starch from potato (Sigma-Aldrich), which was dissolved in 50 ml of distilled water. The resulting solution was then poured into 500 ml of boiling distilled water and allowed to cool. The test apparatus consisted of two glass vessels, two silicone spacers and a distance ring. 3 ml of the prepared starch solution were dispensed into the bottom vessel. A sample of the composite material was placed between a silicone spacer placed on the bottom vessel. A distance ring with an iodine tablet was placed on the upper silicone intermediate ring. The assembly was covered with a top cover vessel (see **Figure 2**). Colour changes on the indicator solution were monitored at 10 min intervals. The resistance time of the examined material to iodine vapour was determined as the time from the beginning of the experiment to the first signs of blueing of the indicator solution.

Figure 2 Schematic representation of a test chamber for testing of samples against the passage of dangerous substances - upper and lower glass cover vessel (1), a chamber with tablet or frit with warfare agent or its simulant on a distance ring (2), tested material (3) and chamber with an indicator solution with arrows indicating the direction of penetration of the used chemicals through the sample (4)

Soman resistance test - Indication solution was prepared from components A (0.2 g of benzidine hydrochloride dissolved in 40 ml of redistilled water and made up to 100 ml with distilled ethyl alcohol), B (0.25 g of sodium perborate dissolved in 100 ml of redistilled water) and C (10 g of sodium citrate dissolved in 100 ml of redistilled water). Subsequently, all three components were mixed in a ratio of 1:2:2. Finally, a reference solution of 0.004 weight % potassium dichromate in water was prepared. The apparatus for testing the resistance of the clamps to soman penetration was similar to the apparatus from the iodine resistence test. 2.5 ml of indicator solution was poured into the lower vessel. 2.5 ml of dichromate solution was poured into a comparison apparatus with a blank without activated carbon (i.e. only bonded layers of nonwovens). After tempering the whole apparatus and the used chemicals to 30 °C, 5 times 0.5 µl of soman was applied to the tested sample in the testing and comparison apparatuses. The samples were sealed and tempered again.

The resistance time of the samples to soman penetration was determined as the time from the start of the test to the colouring of the indicator solution to the same colour as the dichromate solution.

Material resistance test for DMMP, DCH and yperite - Measurements were performed under static conditions of 25 °C on a Kit Carousel 2000 [6]. Samples were tested by contamination with a frit dipped in dimethyl methyl phosphonate (DMMP), 1,6-dichlorohexane (DCH) or yperite. The wet frit was then placed on the distance ring above the measured sample. The testing scheme is shown in **Figure 2**.

3. RESULTS AND DISCUSSION

3.1. Activated carbon loss test

The results of the loss of activated carbon particles are shown in **Table 1**. Static and dynamic tests of particle loss showed that the formed composite maintained the sorbent in its structure. The decrease of carbon particles was smaller than 2 weight %. The largest loss of particles occurred in the laminated sample (12 %), was done by the high value of the pressure drop required to achieve a given air flow rate.

Table 1 The results of activated carbon loss tests

Testing method	Bonding method	Vacuum [kPa]	Initial weight [g]	Final weight [g]	Absolute loss [g]	Percentage loss [%]
Static	lamination	17.0	15.083	14.720	0.363	12.1
	hot-melt	4.0	31.317	31.282	0.035	1.2
	sewing+ultrasound	3.3	17.616	17.587	0.029	1.0
Dynamic	lamination	—	15.149	15.096	0.053	1.8
	hot-melt	—	29.732	29.696	0.036	1.2
	sewing+ultrasound	—	18.813	18.782	0.031	1.0

3.2. Breathability

The measured values of breathability for samples and blanks are given in **Table 2**. Along with the samples, an army jacket FOP-96 was measured. Product properties can be found on the manufacturer's website. The breathability of the material is greater than 100 $l \cdot m^{-2} \cdot s^{-1}$ [3]. The FOP-96 sample showed the highest rate of air passage, followed by hot-melt samples and laminated samples. Upon closer inspection, it was found that by laminating at 130 °C, the polyvinyl butyral nanofibers melted and formed an integral air barrier layer. The best results of the test from the point of view of breathability appeared to be laminated, then sewn with ultrasound and finally the sample bonded using the hot-melt technique. FOP-96 sample performed the worst.

Table 2 The results of breathability tests

Sample	Without activated carbon [$l \cdot m^{-2} \cdot s^{-1}$]	With activated carbon [$l \cdot m^{-2} \cdot s^{-1}$]
lamination	5.6	4.9
hot-melt	26.3	20.3
sewing+ultrasound	20.0	16.8
FOP-96	—	200

3.3. Paropropustnost

Table 3 shows the results of the vapour permeability test for samples of composites with and without activated carbon (blank). The laminated samples proved to have low permeability to water vapour and would therefore be unsuitable for use in the clothing industry. The hot-melt samples showed approximately the same properties as the FOP-96 military garment. The best results were achieved by samples bonded by combination of sewing and ultrasound, which even belong to degree of better comfort compartment than military clothing. Due to the results of vapour permeability measurements, the laminated sample was excluded from further penetration tests of warfare agents.

Table 3 Evaporative resistance and relative permeability to water vapour

	lamination	hot-melt	sewing +ultrasound	blank lamination	blank hot-melt	blank sewing +ultrasound	FOP-96
Evaporative resistance [$Pa \cdot m^2 \cdot W^{-1}$]	38	14.5	11.4	83.3	12	8.5	14.4
Relative permeability to water vapour [%]	13.3	28.5	32.9	6.5	32.3	40.2	28.6

3.4. The resistance of samples against penetration of warfare agents or their simulants

The **Table 4** summarizes the comparison of the results of tested samples bonded by the hot-melt method or a combination of sewing and ultrasound against the penetration of warfare agents and their simulants. The penetration of yperite was also tested on military clothing FOP-96. The samples bonded by sewing and ultrasound were able to resist to the tested chemical agents longer than hot-melt sample. Only exception was the iodine test. Both composites held yperite almost 5 times longer than the used army jacket FOR-96.

The evaluation of the resistance of samples was based on the standard ČSN EN 16523-1 and ČSN EN 16523-2. The evaluation criterion was the permeation rate $F = 1\ \mu g \cdot cm^2 \cdot min^{-1}$ [7,8]. In the case of chemical warfare agents, the lower permeation rate $F = 0.1\ \mu g \cdot cm^2 \cdot min^{-1}$ [9] may also be used as a criterion.

Table 4 Results of the resistance of the samples against penetration of warfare agents or their simulants

Retention time [min]					
Sample	**iodine**	**soman**	**DMMP**	**DCH**	**yperite**
hot-melt	240	930	198	558	398
sewing+ultrasound	195	1350	281	727	420
FOP-96	-	-	-	-	80

4. CONCLUSION

The work describes the production of composite materials with activated carbon particles for capturing warfare agents. A composite material consisting of several layers of spun-bond nonwovens, needlepunch fabrics and nanofibers spun using alternating current electrospinning. Activated carbon was evenly introduced into the samples by raking. The layers were finally reinforced by lamination, hot melt technique or a combination of sewing and ultrasound.

Testing of breathability properties of samples shown its wind resistance (durability). Vapour permeability test demonstrated good properties of the product. Two of the composites were suitable for further clothing processing. Both static and dynamic measurements of particle loss shown, that the used nanofibers were able to keep the activated carbon particles in the material. The samples bonded by hot-melt technology and especially the samples bonded by combination of sewing and ultrasound shown better properties than in all directions the FOP-96.

The dependence of vapour permeability on the breathability of materials or a dependence of vapour permeability and breathability on pore sizes could be measured. The next step could be the development of a decontamination layer with metal oxides, which would help with the decomposition of hazardous substances. It would be appropriate to test a final material, which would consist of a covering ripstop layer with an oleophobic and hydrophobic coating, functional composite material described in this article, decontamination layers with metal oxide particles and lining.

ACKNOWLEDGEMENTS

The research was supported by the project reg. no. VI20172020059 provided by the Ministry of the Interior of the Czech Republic. Thanks also belongs to State Institute for Nuclear, Chemical and Biological protection in Brno for cooperation.

REFERENCES

[1] YANG, R. T. *Adsorbents: fundamentals and applications.* Hoboken, 2003. ISBN 04-712-9741-0

[2] HOENIG, S. L. *Handbook of chemical warfare and terrorism.* Westport, Conn.: Greenwood Press, 2002. ISBN 0313324077.

[3] BOIS - FILTRY, NBC ochranné oděvy - FOP-96. *Bois - filtry* [online]. Available from: http://www.bois-filtry.cz/nbc-ochranne-odevy.php

[4] TECHNICAL UNIVERSITY OF LIBEREC. *A method of producing polymer nanofibres by electric or electrostatic spinning of a polymer solution or melt, a spinning electrode for this method, and a device for the production of polymer nanofibres fitted with at least one such spinning electrode.* Inventors: BERAN, J., LUKAS, D., POKORNY, P. KALOUS, T., VALTERA, J., MAZDAMUNDI, S. CZ 307745. 27.2.2019.

[5] NATIONAL INSTITUTE FOR NUCLEAR, CHEMICAL AND BIOLOGICAL PROTECTION. *Iodine testing method.* Kamenná: SÚJCHBO. Internal method.

[6] SLABOTINSKÝ, J. a CEJPEK, J. Automatická aparatura pro vícemístné hodnocení kvality ochranných materiálů proti toxickým látkám Carousel 2000. In: *Ochrana obyvatelstva - Dekontam 2013.* SPBI Ostrava: 2013. ISBN 978-80-7385-122-4.

[7] ČSN EN 16523-1. *Determination of resistance to chemical permeation of material - Part 1: Permeation of gaseous chemicals under permanent contact conditions.* Czech Standards Institute, 2015.

[8] ČSN EN 16523-2. *Determination of resistance to chemical permeation of material - Part 2: Permeation of liquid chemical under permanent contact conditions.* Czech Standards Institute, 2015.

[9] ASTM F739. *Standard Test Method for Permeation of Liquids and Gases through Protective Clothing Materials under Conditions of Continuous Contact.* American National Standards Institute, 2012.

THE NEW METHOD OF SURFACE-ASSISTED COF SYNTHESIS FOR OPTICAL SENSOR MODIFICATION

[1,2]Elena MILIUTINA, [1]Polina BAINOVA, [1]Vasilii BURTSEV, [1,2]Anna ZABELINA, [1]Vaclav ŠVORČÍK, [1,2]Oleksiy LYUTAKOV

[1]*VŠCHT - University of Chemistry and Technology, Prague, Czech Republic, EU, lyutakoo@vscht.cz*

[2]*Tomsk Polytechnic University, Research School of Chemistry and Applied Biomedical Sciences, Tomsk, Russian Federation*

https://doi.org/10.37904/nanocon.2020.3712

Abstract

Covalent organic frameworks (COFs) are an emerging class of crystalline networks that are covalently built from organic components and featured by merits of low density, well-defined pore aperture, large surface area, inherent porosity, facilely tailored functionality, and ordered channel structure. Among other applications, COF compounds can be utilized for CO_2 detection. It Is known that the preparation of COFs compounds is commonly associated with hard experimental conditions (high pressure, inert atmosphere, and high temperature). In this work, we suggest an alternative method of COFs under normal pressure and temperature. The experimental concept implements the surface-assisted COF growth. The created surface-immobilized COF structures were subsequently used for measurement of CO_2 presence.

Keywords: Optical fibers, COFs, plasmons, selectivity

1. INTRODUCTION

Covalent organic frameworks (COF) are a new class of crystalline porous organic polymers with controlled porosity and highly ordered structure [1,2]. Today, COFs have found a wide range of applications in catalysis, separation and absorption gases [3]. However, the manufacture of COF requires difficult experimental conditions and is quite expensive [4,5]. In addition, the formation of COF layer on functional materil or devices surface still remain a challenging task [6,7]. So, the development of a technology for producing COFs on the solid surface(s) is urgently required. The main goal of this work is to develop the simple and scalable procedure for COF synthesis on directly the sensor surface and subsequent utilization of created hybrid materials for ClOs sensing.

2. EXPERIMENTAL

2.1. Materials

Gold targets for metal deposition (purity of metals, 4 N) were purchased from Deionized water, methanol (reagent grade, ≥ 99.8 %), acetone (97 %), were purchased from Sigma-Aldrich and used without further purification. 4-cyanobenzenediazonium tosylate (ADT-CN) was prepared according to published procedure [3]. CO2 gas was obtained from SIAD.

2.2. Samples preparation

The deposition of Au was accomplished from Au target (purity of 99.99 %, provided by Safina, Czech Republic).

At the first stage, covalent organic structures of the CTF-1 (carbon triazine framework) type were obtained on the sensor surface (**Figure 1**). First, the samples were spontaneously modified by soaking in a 3 mM freshly prepared aqueous solution of ADT-CN for 30 min. After modification, the samples were washed with water, methanol, and acetone for 20 minutes and dried in a desiccator for 2 hours. At the next stage, the COF building units were dissolved in chloroform with addition of activation agent and samples were immersed in this solution for 3 h.

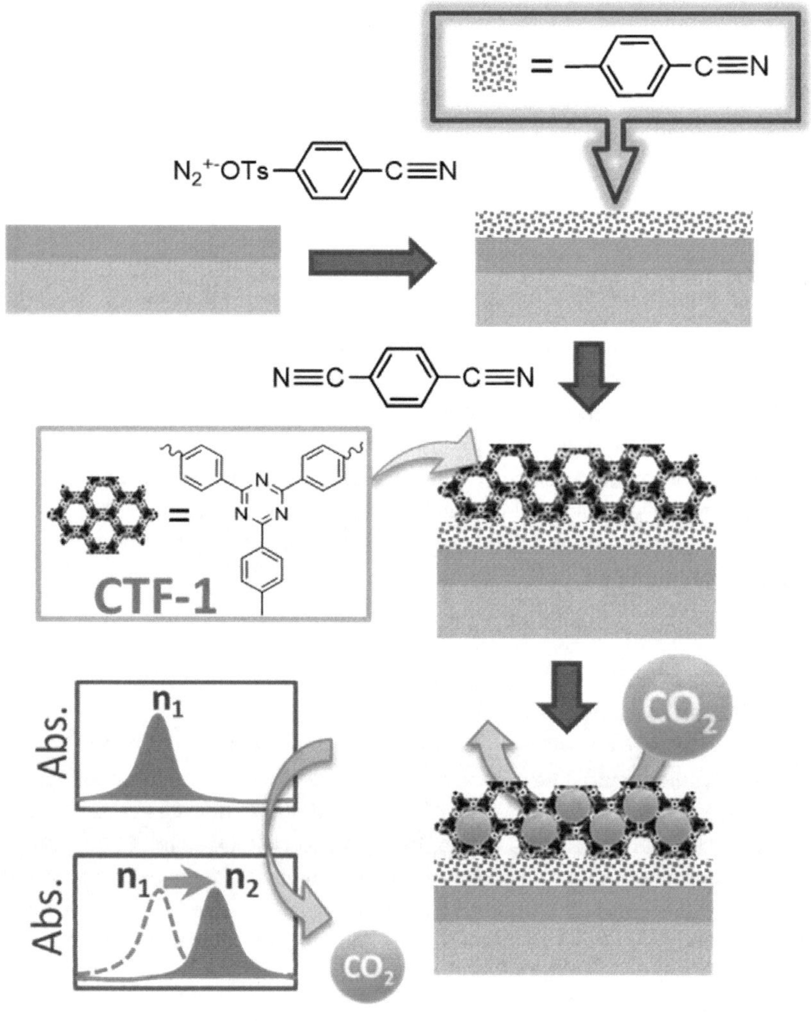

Figure 1 Schematic representation of the fabrication of a sensor with a sensitive surface in the form of CTF-1 covalent organic structures

2.3. Measurement Techniques

The X-ray photoelectron spectroscopy (XPS) was performed using an Omicron Nanotechnology ESCAProbeP spectrometer fitted with monochromated Al K Alpha X-ray source working at 1486.6 eV.

Raman spectra were measured on ProRaman-L spectrometer (Laser power 35 mW) Raman spectrometer with 785 nm excitation wavelengths. Spectra were measured 30 times, each of them with 3 s accumulation time.

UV-Vis absorbance spectra of the samples were measured using a HR2000 (Ocean Optics) spectrometer in 400-800 nm wavelengths range using the AvaLight-DHS light source (Avantes).

3. RESULTS AND DISCUSSION

Successful growth of CTF-1 has been verified using XPS, Raman and UV-Vis methods. **Figure 2 (parts A, B, C)** shows the XPS spectra of pristine surface, surface grafted with -Ph-CN and final samples with immobilized CTF-1 layer. The corresponded table (part D) shows the change in the concentration of surface elements depending on the step of surface modification. It is obvious that a gradual increase of concentrations of carbon, oxygen, and nitrogen confirms the shielding of initial sample surface and formation of a CTF-1 layer. We assume that the reaction proceeds according to the following principle:

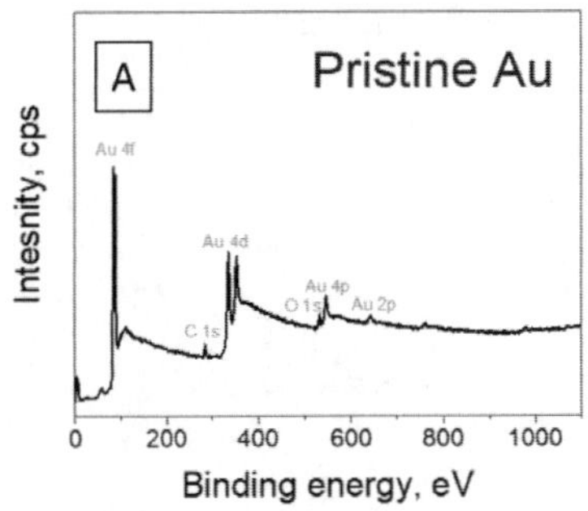

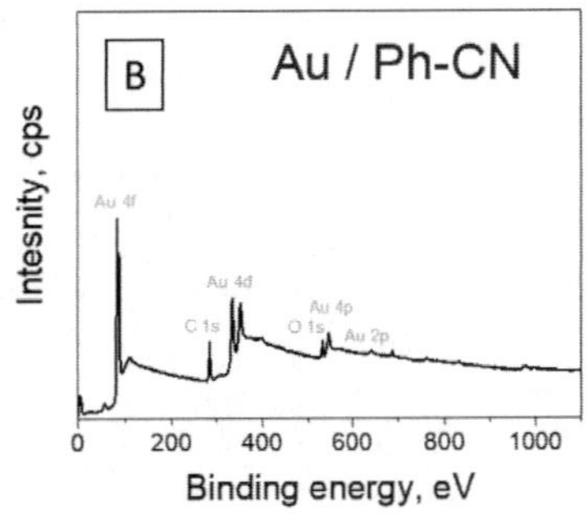

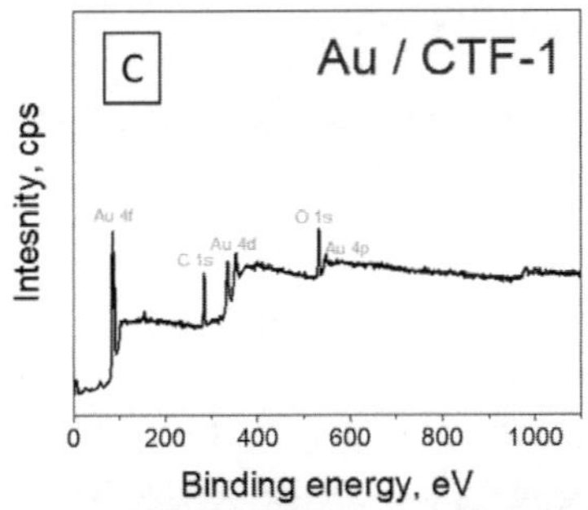

D

Surface atom element concentration (at %)	Sample		
	Pristine Au	*Au / Ph-CN*	*Au / CTF-1*
Au (4f)	52,0	22,6	14.7
C (1s)	33,1	63,5	57.3
O (1s)	14,9	11,7	24.7
N (1s)	-	2,2	3.3

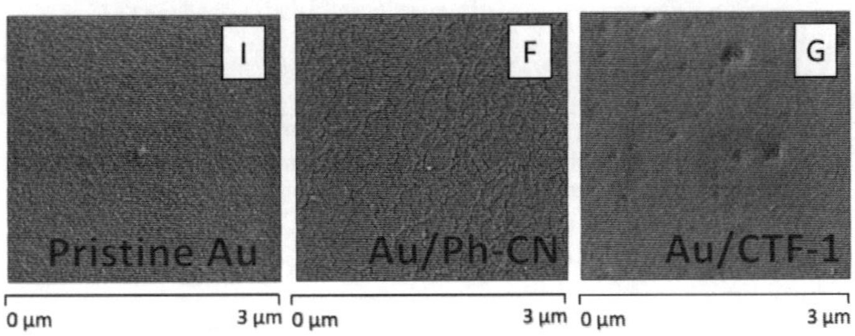

Figure 2 XPS spectra of the surface (A) - pure gold, (B) - gold surface grafted with ADT-CN, (C) gold surface decorated with CTF-1 film. D - Table shows the percentage of elements on the surface. SEM images of the gold surface before (A) and after (B) decoration of the CTF-1 film.

The surface morphology of the samples, before and after decoration with CTF-1 was investigated by SEM. The results are presented in **Figure 2 (parts I, F, G)** and show that the pristine surface has a slightly rough morphology. This morphology is conserved after the -Ph-CN grafting. After the growth of the CTF-1 film, visible changes in the surface morphology were observed (**Figure 2G**), indicating that the COF layer is dominantly formed in the surface valleys.

Figure 3 shows the results of Raman spectroscopy (and the corresponding referencing of the spectral positions of the Raman bands). As is evident, the pristine sample surface does not have any spectral features. Grafting of the sample with ADT-CN leads to the appearance of several bands, corresponded to chemical fragments of benzene rings and cyano chemical moieties. Further growth of CTF-1 leads to the appearance of several additional Raman bands, the spectral positions of which completely coincide with those in the Raman spectra of CTF-1 powder, also shown in **Figure 3B**.

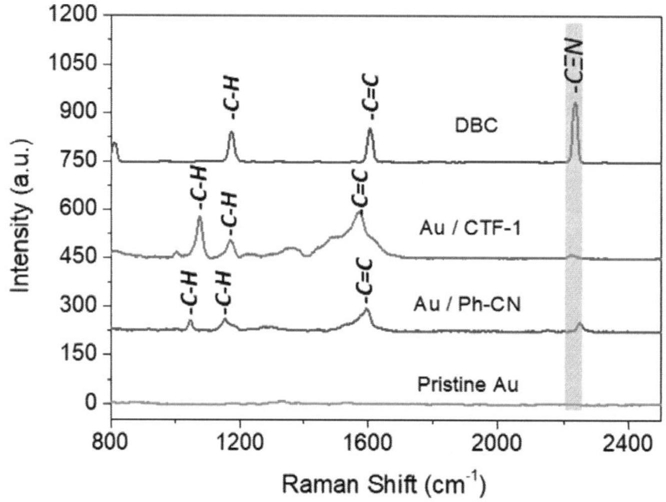

Figure 3 Raman spectra of the surface of primordial gold; a gold surface grafted with ADT-CN and a gold surface decorated with a CTF-1 film

In the next step, sample with CTF-1 were tested for sensitivity to CO_2 in water. As seen from **Figure 4A**, absorption spectrum before and after CO_2 purging for 30 minutes did not change the light transmission spectrum. The absorption spectra after COF decoration show a slight broadening of the absorption peak due to CO_2 presence. **Figure 4B**. So, it is also evident that the sensors decorated with COF shows sensitivity to CO_2. After blowing with air, the absorption peak returns to its original position, confirming the ability of sensor reutilization.

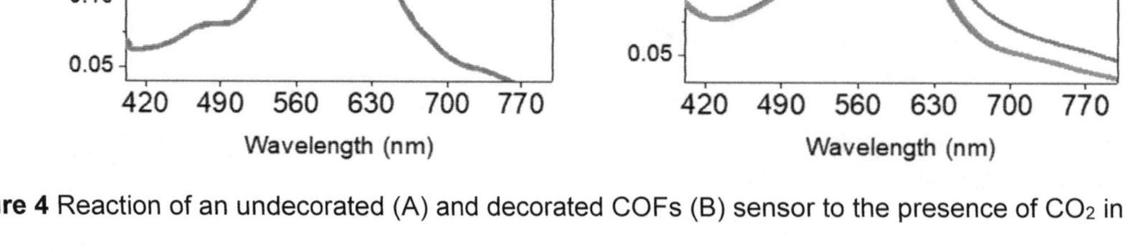

Figure 4 Reaction of an undecorated (A) and decorated COFs (B) sensor to the presence of CO_2 in water

4. CONCLUSION

In this work, a new method for surface-assisted COF growth is proposed and verified. The COF layer were formed under the ambient condition, without utilization of high temperature or temperature. The COF layer were grown on the sensor surface, increasing the affinity of device to CO_2. In particular, proposed method allows to identify CO_2 presence in water.

ACKNOWLEDGEMENTS

This work was supported by the project Russian Science Foundation (RSF-19-73-00238) and the project Internal Grant Agency 126 88 2005.

REFERENCES

[1] GENG, K., HE, T., LIU, R., DALAPATI, S., TAN, K.T., LI, Z., TAO, S., GONG, Y., JIANG, Q., JIANG, D. Covalent Organic Frameworks: Design, Synthesis, and Functions. *Chem. Rev.* 2020, vol. 120, no. 16, pp. 8814-8933.

[2] YAO, B.-J., ZHANG, X.-M., LI, F., LI, C., DONG, Y.-B. Fe3O4/Porphyrin Covalent Organic Framework Core-Shell Nanospheres as Interfacial Catalysts for Enzymatic Esterification. *ACS Appl. Nano Mat.* 2020, vol. 3, no. 10, pp. 10360-10368.

[3] GUSELNIKOVA, O., KALACHYOVA, Y., ELASHNIKOV, R., CIESLAR, M., KOLSKA, Z., SAJDL, P., POSTNIKOV, P., SVORCIK, V., LYUTAKOV, O. Taking the power of plasmon-assisted chemistry on copper NPs: Preparation and application of COFs nanostructures for CO2 sensing in water. *Microporous and Mesoporous Mat.* 2020, vol. 309, p. 110577.

[4] LI, X., YANG, C., SUN, B., CAI, S., CHEN, Z., LV, Y., ZHANG, J., LIU, Y., Expeditious synthesis of covalent organic frameworks: a review. *J. Mater. Chem. A.* 2020, vol. 8, no. 32, pp. 16045-16060.

[5] DÍAZ, U., CORMA, A., CORMA, A. Ordered covalent organic frameworks, COFs and PAFs. From preparation to application. *Coord. Chem. Rev.* 2016, vol. 311, pp. 85-124.

[6] MILIUTINA, E., GUSELNIKOVA, O., SOLDATOVA, N.S., BAINOVA, P., ELASHNIKOV, R., FITL, P., KURTEN, T., YUSUBOV, M.S., ŠVORČÍK, V., VALIEV, R.R., CHEHIMI, M.M., LYUTAKOV, O., POSTNIKOV, P.S. Can Plasmon Change Reaction Path? Decomposition of Unsymmetrical Iodonium Salts as an Organic Probe. *J. Phys. Chem. Lett.* 2020, vol. 11, no. 14, pp. 5770-5776.

[7] BI, S., YANG, C., ZHANG, W., XU, J., LIU, L., WU, D., WANG, X., HAN, Y., LIANG, Q., ZHANG, F. Two-dimensional semiconducting covalent organic frameworks via condensation at arylmethyl carbon atoms. *Nat. Commun.* 2019, vol. 10, no. 1, p. 2467.

HYDROPHILIC NANOFIBER MEMBRANES FOR OILY WASTEWATER TREATMENT

[1]Evren BOYRAZ, [2]Fatma YALCINKAYA, [2]Jakub HRUZA

[1]Faculty of Mechatronics, Technical University of Liberec, Liberec, Czech Republic, EU, evren.boyraz@tul.cz

[2]Institute for Nanomaterials, Advanced Technology and Innovation, Technical University of Liberec, Liberec, Czech Republic, EU, fatma.yalcinkaya@tul.cz

https://doi.org/10.37904/nanocon.2020.3703

Abstract

Electrospun nanofiber seems interesting in the filter domain area due to its highly porous structure, narrow pore size, and high specific surface area. In this work, polyamide 6 (PA6), polyvinylidene fluoride (PVDF), and polyacrylonitrile (PAN) nanofibers were prepared as hybrid membranes. Hydrophobic PVDF and PAN nanofiber membrane surface was hydrophilized using a chemical modification method and performance for the treatment of oily wastewater was compared. The surface modification of the membrane improved membrane anti-fouling property. Results indicated that nanofibrous membranes may become interesting materials for the treatment of oily wastewater.

Keywords: Nanofiber, membrane, wastewater, oil separation, hydrophilic

1. INTRODUCTION

A large amount of oily wastewater has been generated from various industries such as automotive, mining, food and beverages, pharmaceutical, petrochemical, metallurgical, oil and natural gas exploration, and processing. The release of oily wastewater into nature cause of severe damage to the environment and human health. Oily wastewater with a droplet size less than 10 μm is in a highly stable state and very difficult to separate. For this reason, it has to be properly treated before discharge or recycling. There are several techniques to treat oil-water emulsion namely electrostatic coalesce, heat treatment, chemical emulsification, centrifugal settling, and membrane filtration [1]. Some of these methods have certain limitations such as using toxic compounds, high cost, low separation efficiency, demand large space, and generation of secondary pollutants.

Recently, membrane technology has gained huge interest as an effective separation process for the emulsified oil droplets that are smaller than ~10 μm. Membrane separation offers, high selectivity, easy to operate, cost-effectiveness, low energy demand, and no secondary pollution. However, membranes have suffered from fouling due to the deposition of foulant (such as particles, oil droplets, aggregates) on the surface or in the pores of the membranes causing a decline in flux. As a result, the membrane life-span is shortened, and a frequently cleaning process is needed which increases energy demanded and secondary pollution. To overcome membrane fouling, several attempts have been done. These attempts include physical and chemical modification of the membrane surface or blending with other polymers or incorporating additives into the membrane. Zhao et al. [2] grafted perfluoroalkyl groups onto polyacrylonitrile (PAN) membrane surface through the acylation reaction. The fluorinated PAN membranes displayed desirable fouling release property with almost complete flux recovery for oil/water emulsion (separation of oil) due to non-polar hydrophobic perfluoroalkyl groups which reduced the surface free energy and increased the degree of chemical heterogeneity. Similarly, Xu et al. [3] prepared (separation of oil) modified membranes which were highly water repellent, oleophilic, and showed excellent self-cleaning properties. There are plenty of attempts that have been reported for the separation of oil-in-water or water-in-oil [4,5]. Yet, there is a demand to improve highly permeable and fouling resistance membrane material for the separation of oily wastewater.

Nanofiber membranes offer an effective separation process with high permeability due to their tight pore size, and porous structure. The main advantages of nanofibers in membrane technology are their specific surface area, tight pore size, narrow pore size distribution, and highly porous structure (over 80%). The tight pore size and narrow pore size distribution can capture foulants in micron size on their surface that improves the filtration efficiency. A highly porous structure increases membrane flux and permeability. The high specific surface area serves many micropores in the fiber network which improves filtration efficiency and performance. More interestingly, nanofiber that has highly specific surface area can be modified by surface-active chemical compounds to improve their functionality.

In the present work, polyamide 6 (PA6), polyvinylidene fluoride (PVDF), and PAN nanofiber membranes were prepared by using the lamination method, and hydrophobic membranes were modified to be superhydrophilic for separation of oil-water emulsion. PVDF and PAN nanofibers have low wettability compared to PA6. PA6 membranes are swelling in alkaline conditions, due to the dissociation of carboxylic groups in polymer chains which yields in chains to be charged negatively. As a result average pore size of the membrane increases. For the reasons above, only PVDF and PAN membranes have been modified using an alkaline treatment. The nanofiber membranes were modified with no complex preparation method or expensive equipment. Modified membranes showed good permeability and fouling resistance regardless of their original properties. Prepared nanofiber membranes are promising for the practical application of the oil-water separation system.

2. EXPERIMENTAL

The polymers PA6, PVDF, and PAN have been prepared by Nanospider electrospinning device at the Technical University of Liberec. The lamination process has been done using the heat-press method onto a hydrophobic nonwoven material. All the nanofibers had an area weight 3 gsm. The surface modification for PVDF and PAN membranes have been done using an alkaline solution prepared as 2g of potassium hydroxide (KOH) dissolved in 20 mL of isopropyl alcohol (Penta s.r.o.). Samples were kept in the alkaline solution for 1h, then rinsed several times and kept in the distilled water. The treated samples are called PVDF-OH and PAN-OH. The water contact angle of the membranes has been measured by Krüss Drop Shape Analyzer DS4 (Krüss GmbH, Hamburg, Germany) and showed in **Table 1**.

Table 1 Water contact angle of the modified and unmodified nanofiber membranes.

Membrane	WCA (°)
PA6	78.92
PVDF	89.41
PAN	80.72
PVDF-OH	0
PAN-OH	0

A scanning electron microscope (SEM) is used to detect if any changes or damages on the membrane surface. Fiber diameters are measured using the ImageJ program. The oil-water emulsion was prepared as half-to-half oil and water in weight by adding 2% wt of triton X surfactant (Sigma). The oil/water/surfactant mixture was left to be mixed on the magnetic stirrer for 24h, speed @500 rpm. Amicon mini stirrer dead-end unit used for the filtration test. Flux (f) ($Lm^{-2}h^{-1}$) and permeability (k) ($Lm^{-2}h^{-1}\ bar^{-1}$) were calculated according to Eq. (1) and (2).

$$f = \frac{1}{A}\frac{dV}{dt} \qquad (1)$$

$$k = \frac{f}{P} \qquad (2)$$

where

V- the total volume of the permeate (L)

A- the active membrane area (m2),

t- the filtration time (h),

P-the transmembrane pressure (bar).

3. RESULTS AND DISCUSSION

The surface of the membranes has been examined using SEM images after the lamination process (**Figure 1**). Lamination and modification do not damage the surface of nanofiber membranes.

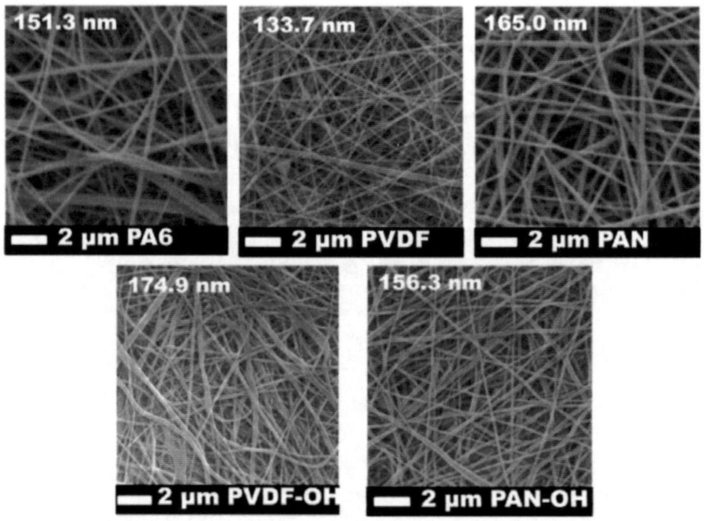

Figure 1 SEM images of the nanofiber membranes

The modified membranes submerged in distilled water which showed a highly hydrophilic structure. The reason is due to alkaline treatment which incorporates hydrophilic groups (such as hydroxyl or carboxyl) on PVDF and PAN membrane surface. It was found that the alkaline solution treated PAN membrane showed superhydrophilic/underwater superoleophobic characteristics due to -CN groups of PAN hydrolyzed to -COOH groups [6,7]. Using alkaline treatment on the PVDF membrane caused dehydrofluorination, and hydroxyl groups formed on the surface [8,9]. The interaction between the alkaline solution and PVDF and PAN membrane has been given in **Figure 2**. From **Table 1**, it is visible that the modification process improved membrane hydrophilicity. Membrane hydrophilicity plays an important role in membrane flux, permeability, and selectivity. It was found that hydrophilic membranes reduce membrane fouling [10,11].

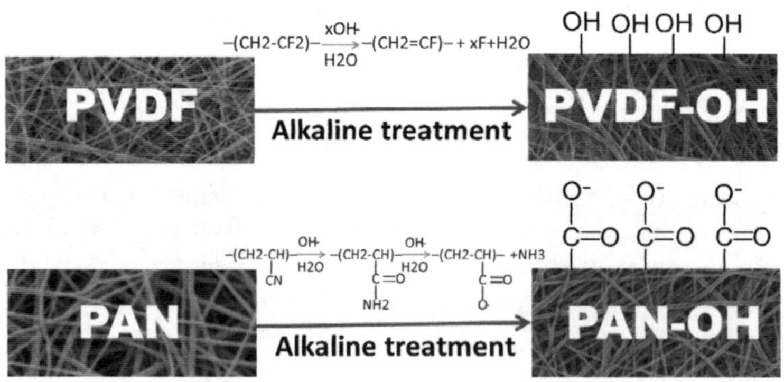

Figure 2 Surface modification of PVDF and PAN membranes

Further experiments have been done to evaluate membrane permeability and selectivity for oil-water emulsion (**Figure 3**). For the filtration test, first distilled water, then emulsion was used. This step was followed 3 times. For each step, the same membrane has been used to observe membrane fouling. The applied pressure was almost zero (0.02 bar). All the membranes permeated water from the oil-water emulsion. The permeability of unmodified membranes decreased in each cycle due to membrane fouling. Oil droplets were trapped into membrane pores and caused membrane fouling. Increasing membrane wettability improves the attachment of water molecules to the membrane surface while repels the oil droplets and reduce their attachment to the membrane surface. As a result, membrane fouling resistance improves. Herein, after surface modification, both PAN and PVDF membranes showed remarkable membrane fouling resistance. The PVDF nanofiber membrane's permeability has not been changed in each cycle. On the other side, the permeability of the PAN membrane increased in each cycle. The reason could be due to the interaction of surfactant with PAN-OH nanofiber membranes which improved membrane wetting in time.

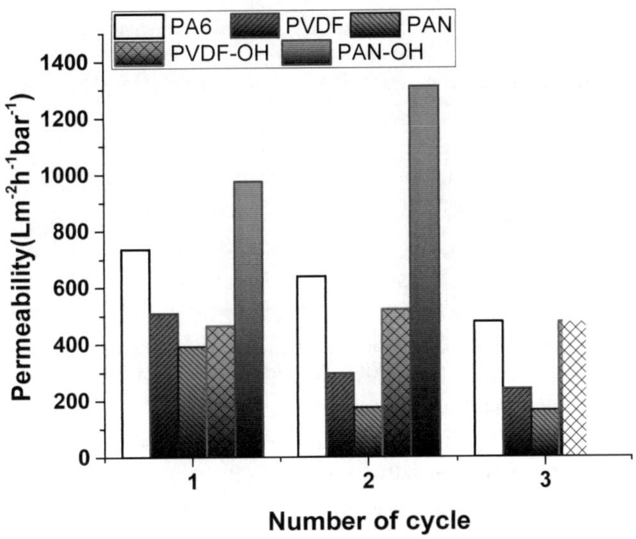

Figure 3 Permeability of modified and unmodified membranes

It was found that the surfactant showed to render the surface of the membranes more 'homogeneously' permeable, reduced flux decline, increased the flux, reduced the surface rugosity, and increased hydrophilicity [12,13].

4. CONCLUSION

In this work, we have successfully prepared PVDF, PAN, and PA6 nanofiber membranes for the separation of oil-water emulsion. The surfaces of the PVDF and PAN membranes have been modified using the alkaline treatment to improve membrane hydrophilicity. The surface of the membranes did not damage after the lamination and modification process. Membrane modification reduced membrane fouling during filtration. Moreover, membrane water permeability was improved due to hydrophilic groups attached to the PVDF and PAN membranes. Overall, the super hydrophilic PVDF and PAN membranes with effective oil-water separation highlight the greatly promising potential for further applications in industrial wastewater treatment.

ACKNOWLEDGEMENTS

This work was supported by the Ministry of Education, Youth and Sports for Institutional support for Long-term Conceptual Development of a Research Organization of the Czech Republic, 2020.

REFERENCES

[1] SINGH, V., PURKAIT, M.K., DAS, C. Cross-Flow Microfiltration of Industrial Oily Wastewater: Experimental and Theoretical Consideration. *Separation Science and Technology*. 2011, vol. 46, no. 8, pp. 1213-23.

[2] ZHAO, X., SU, Y., CHEN, W., PENG, J., JIANG, Z. Grafting perfluoroalkyl groups onto polyacrylonitrile membrane surface for improved fouling release property. *Journal of Membrane Science*. 2012, vol. 415-416, pp. 824-34.

[3] XU, Z., MIYAZAKI, K., HORI, T. Fabrication of polydopamine-coated superhydrophobic fabrics for oil/water separation and self-cleaning. *Applied Surface Science*. 2016, vol. 370, pp. 243-51.

[4] SADEGHI, I., AROUJALIAN, A., RAISI, A., DABIR, B., FATHIZADEH, M. Surface modification of polyethersulfone ultrafiltration membranes by corona air plasma for separation of oil/water emulsions. *Journal of Membrane Science*. 2013, vol. 430, pp. 24-36.

[5] TANG, H., HAO, L., CHEN, J., WANG, F., ZHANG, H., GUO, Y. Surface Modification to Fabricate Superhydrophobic and Superoleophilic Alumina Membranes for Oil/Water Separation. *Energy Fuels*. 2018, vol. 32, no. 3, pp. 3627-36.

[6] ZHANG, F., GAO, S., ZHU, Y., JIN, J. Alkaline-induced superhydrophilic/underwater superoleophobic polyacrylonitrile membranes with ultralow oil-adhesion for high-efficient oil/water separation. *Journal of Membrane Science*. 2016, vol. 513, pp. 67-73.

[7] HU, X.M., XIAO, C.F. Characterization and Hydrolization of PAN by Sodium Hydroxide. *Advanced Materials Research*. [online]. 2011 [viewed 2019 Jul 19]. Available from: https://www.scientific.net/AMR.332-334.1032.

[8] BOYRAZ, E., YALCINKAYA, F., HRUZA, J., MARYSKA, J. Surface-Modified Nanofibrous PVDF Membranes for Liquid Separation Technology. *Materials*. 2019, vol. 12, no. 17, p. 2702.

[9] MARCHAND BRYNAERT, J., JONGEN, N., DEWEZ, J.-L. Surface hydroxylation of poly(vinylidene fluoride) (PVDF) film. *Journal of Polymer Science Part A: Polymer Chemistry*. 1997, vol. 35, no. 7, pp. 1227-35.

[10] YALCINKAYA, F., SIEKIERKA, A., BRYJAK, M. Preparation of Fouling-Resistant Nanofibrous Composite Membranes for Separation of Oily Wastewater. *Polymers (Basel)*. [online]. 2017 [viewed 2019 Jul 15], vol. 9, no. 12. Available from: https://www.ncbi.nlm.nih.gov/pmc/articles/PMC6418811/.

[11] YALCINKAYA, F., SIEKIERKA, A., BRYJAK, M. Surface modification of electrospun nanofibrous membranes for oily wastewater separation. *RSC Advances*. 2017, vol. 7, no. 89, pp. 56704-12.

[12] FANE, A.G., FELL, C.J.D., KIM, K.J. The effect of surfactant pretreatment on the ultrafiltration of proteins. *Desalination*. 1985, vol. 53, no. 1, pp. 37-55.

[13] KOLEY, D., BARD, A.J. Triton X-100 concentration effects on membrane permeability of a single HeLa cell by scanning electrochemical microscopy (SECM). *PNAS*. 2010, vol. 107, no. 39, pp. 16783-7.

THE EFFECT OF NANOVOID ELONGATION ON ELECTRON MULTIPLICATION DURING (SUB)NANOSECOND ELECTRICAL BREAKDOWN

[1]Ján TUNGLI, [1]Petr BÍLEK, [1]Zdeněk BONAVENTURA

[1]*Department of Physical Electronics, Fac. Sci., Masaryk University, Brno, Czech Republic, EU,* *tun@mail.muni.cz*

https://doi.org/10.37904/nanocon.2020.3726

Abstract

We investigate how the geometry of nanovoids present during the (sub)nanosecond electrical breakdown in liquid water influences the electron multiplication. Our analysis uses a particle-tracing Monte Carlo simulation toolkit Geant4-DNA. The electron multiplication in nanovoids is one of the possible scenarios describing the charge generation in liquid water. In our simplified model, we assume a constant homogeneous electric field, an ellipsoidal shape of nanovoids, and isotropic distribution of the primary electron's velocity. The quantity of interest is the number of ionizations per number of launched primary electrons. We study this yield of electrons as we vary the ellipsoid eccentricity parameter while keeping the volume constant. The nanovoids with zero eccentricity (spherical case) produce smaller yield since the suppressed length does not favor electron multiplication. On the other hand, a very prolonged ellipsoid causes the loss of most electrons because of early collisions with the void-liquid interface. Therefore, for a particular value of eccentricity, the yield is maximal. The results of this study contribute to the elucidation of the initial phases of discharge evolution in polar liquids and is one of the first steps towards quantitative assessment of the importance of microscopic parameters involved. The understanding of this phenomenon promises the explanation of macroscopic parameters observed in the (sub)nanosecond electrical breakdown experiments

Keywords: Nanovoids, electrostriction, liquid water electric breakdown, nanosecond pulsed electric field

1. INTRODUCTION

Historically, plasma discharges has been used as a medium to generate chemically active species in various gas mixtures. During past few decades, attempts to generate plasma also in liquid environment has emerged, followed immediately by applications such as nanomaterials syntheses. Research of pulsed discharges in water is of interest to many applications. These include: purification of hazardous organic compounds [1,2], high power switch systems [3], and electric impulse fragmentation applied in recycling [4], or electrohydraulic lithotripsy [5].

Dielectric fluids in inhomogeneous electric field are subject to ponderomotive forces [6]. In a homogeneous fluid and in the absence of free electric charge this force causes the fluid to move to regions with higher electric field. However, if the electric pulse is strong and fast enough, the fluid does not have time to move and large negative pressures appear that can lead to cavitation [7]. It is known that with application of a strong nanosecond electric pulse, discharge develops. During these small time scales a model where the water is heated up and the discharge is created in a resultant gas bubble can be shown to be inconsistent with experimental findings [8]. Explaining the initial stages of discharge formation therefore involves processes occurring at sub-nanosecond and sub-micrometer scales and makes the topic challenging.

One of the models worth investigating is the electron avalanche formation inside nanovoids formed by the cavitation process. Electrons ejected into a nanovoid could gain enough energy to ionize water molecules upon collision. Although the shape and size of these nanovoids is still unknown, cavitation models usually assume a spherical shape. Furthermore, in the presence of electric field, a spherical void would become elongated in the direction of electric field and so to assume an ellipsoidal shape is reasonable. In this work, we study electron multiplication occurring inside an ellipsoidal nanovoid by means of particle tracking Monte Carlo simulation. We focus mainly on the effect of nanovoid elongation on the average yield, which we define as the number of secondary electrons produced per the number of primary electron injected into the nanovoid.

2. MODEL

To accurately simulate electron acceleration and multiplication a simulation toolkit called *Geant4-DNA* [9,10] [11,12]. Geant4 is an open-source project that allows simulation of particles passing through matter. The extension - Geant4-DNA - is aimed primarily at biological application and includes physical processes for liquid water. The toolkit is widely used in many fields of physics, including nuclear, space and medical research.

In our setup, an ellipsoid of variable eccentricity is placed at the center of the simulation box using material WaterSteam, which simulates a nanovoid that could be born during the application of highly inhomogeneous electric field. The rest of the box is filled with water, see **Figure 1**.

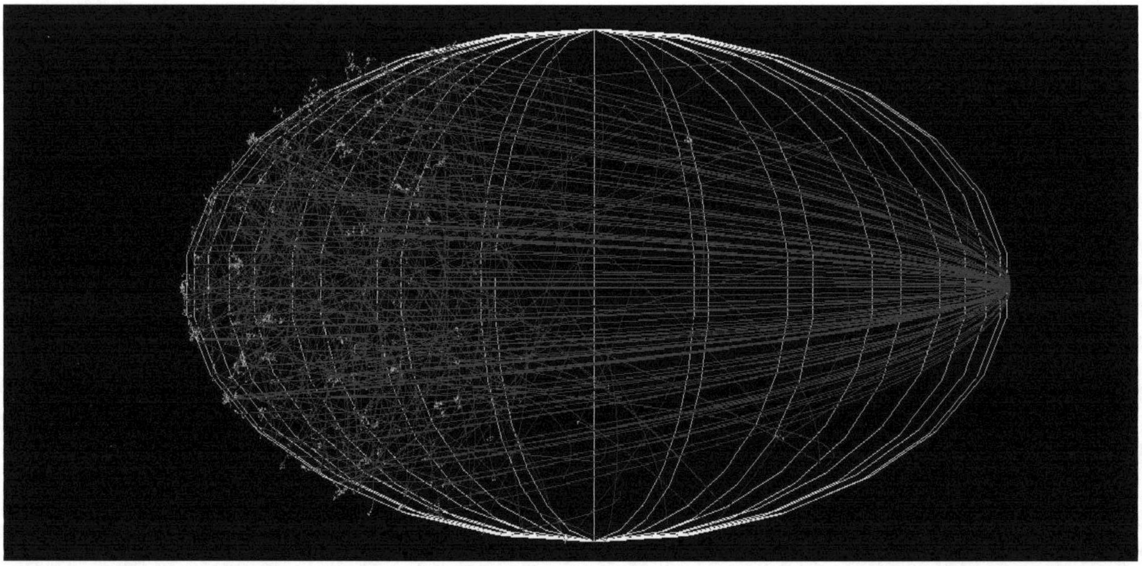

Figure 1 A beam of 100 electrons accelerated in an ellipsoidal void in Geant4. The trajectory of the electrons is represented with red lines while the yellow dots represent collisional events

The main purpose of this work is to study the effect of elongation of the nanovoid. In order to isolate this geometric effect on electron multiplication, the following two-step procedure is used:

1) In a sphere (ellipsoid of zero eccentricity), find the radius for which, on average, the number of electrons created is equal to the number of primary electrons, i.e, for which the yield is equal to 1.

2) Vary the elongation of the nanovoid by changing the eccentricity in a way that the volume of the ellipsoid stays constant and monitor the yield. Also, in both cases, a constant electric field of 0.2 V/nm is applied in the direction the ellipsoid is elongationed.

The first step is accomplished by running a series of runs with variable radius of the sphere and finding the radius R where the function:

$$f(R) = Y(R) - 1$$

is equal to zero. Each run consists of launching 10000 electrons from the ellipsoid vertex. The initial momenta of electrons are distributed isotropically and the initial energy of electrons is left as a parameter and multiple values are tested.

Once the radius is found, the second step can be undertaken. As the eccentricity is changed, the volume-preserving transformations for the ellipsoid parameters are:

$$a = \frac{R_0}{\sqrt[3]{1-e^2}},$$

$$b = \sqrt{(1-e^2)}a,$$

where a and b are the semi-axes and $b < a$. Because of the symmetry of the problem, the third semi-axis is simply set equal to the second semi-axis (the smaller one).

In Geant4, a cut-off energy threshold for electrons propagating in bulk water needs to be specified. It is assumed that electrons in water below this energy threshold are immediately solvated. The assumptions made and their effect on the result will be discussed further below.

3. RESULTS

The radius where the yield is balanced is found to be approximately 0.09 μm at energies about 1 eV and decreases for higher energies. Also, as is shown in **Figure 2**, the yield in a sphere is approximately a linear function of radius in the range of values investigated. As the eccentricity of the ellipsoid is increased, the yield increases until it reaches a maximum value (**Figure 3**). Further increasing eccentricity, while maintaining constant volume, means that more electrons will not have enough time to gain energy from electric field. As expected, the lower the energy of the electron, the more it benefits from elongation since the average electron motion is more directed by the applied electric field. As a consequence, the eccentricity at which the yield is maximal is dependent on the initial energy (**Figure 4**).

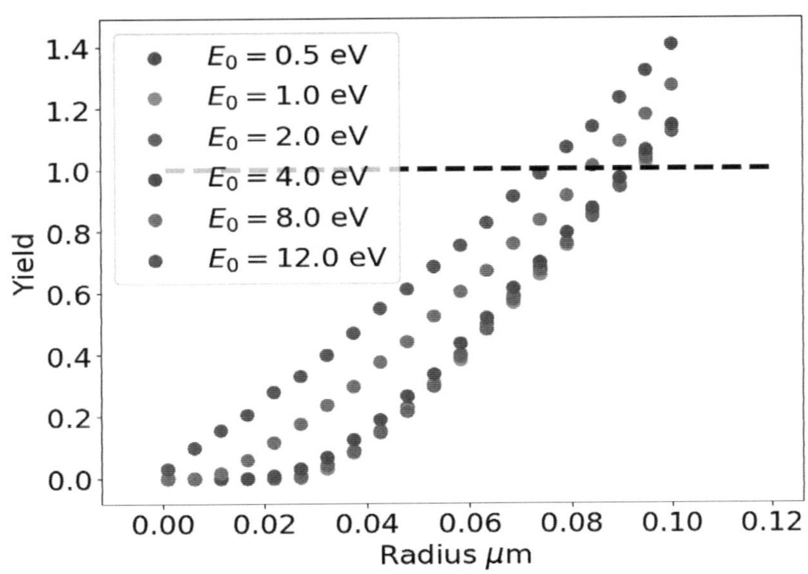

Figure 2 Secondary electron yield as a function of spherical radius

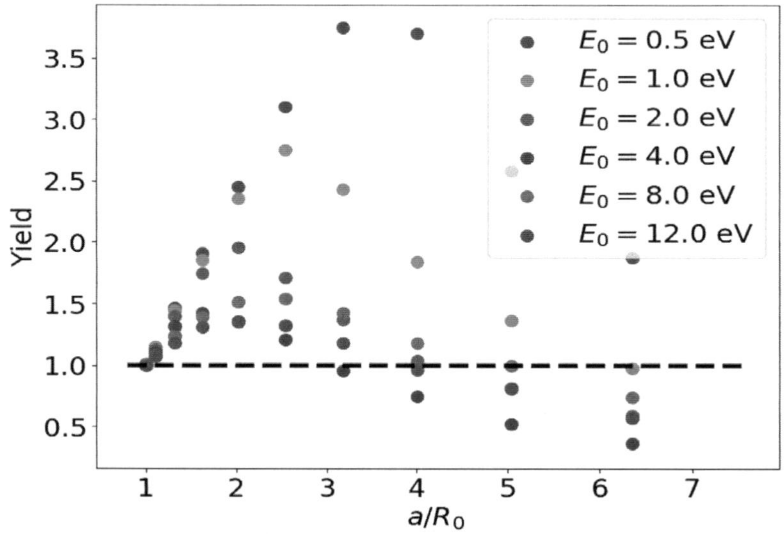

Figure 3 Secondary electron yield as a function of ellipsoid elongation

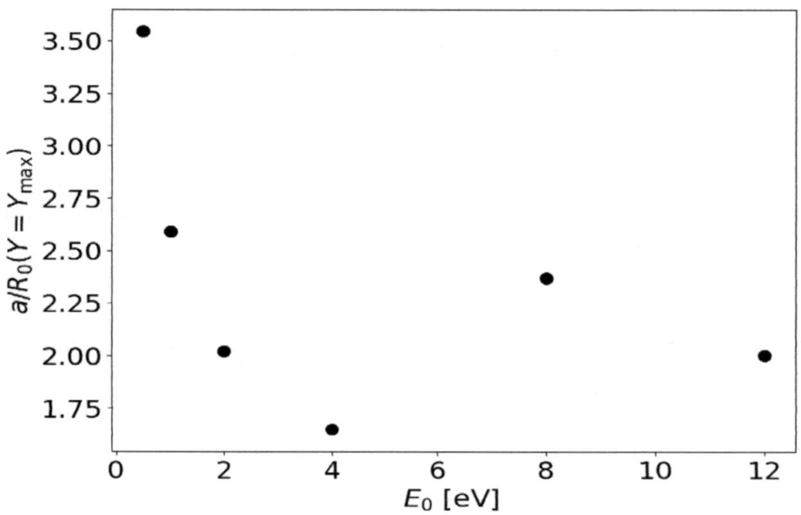

Figure 4 Elongation parameter where the yield is maximal as a function of initial energy

4. DISCUSSION

For a correct interpretation of the results, it is important to discuss the effects of assumed parameters in our simulations.

Electron solvation

Because of the lack of cross-sectional data for processes in water, Geant4 terminates the flight of an electron in bulk water below a certain energy threshold. The electron is assumed to be solvated. Since this energy, in our case, is well below the ionization energy, it may seem that this parameter is of no consequence on the results of the simulation. Unfortunately, this is not the case and electron solvation energy acts as an important numerical parameter. The effect of this parameter has been studied already by other scientists and it seems to provide quantitative correlation with experimental data the value would have to be set below the smallest value allowed by Geant4 [13]. It is therefore important to bare in mind that the secondary electron yield obtained from these simulations is only a lower limit and experimentally measure yields will most likely be larger.

Initial energy and momentum distribution

In this study, the assumption of the isotropic distribution of electron momenta is chosen for simplicity. Nonetheless, the question whether this assumption is justified remains. To our knowledge, there are no experimental data describing the properties of primary electrons originating in bulk water. Therefore, to what extend are the primary electrons guided to the void by the external electric field is unknown.

In addition, because of cavitation effects produced by inhomogeneous electric field, spatial fluctuations of electric field can play a major role in the resulting dynamics of electron propagation inside the nanovoid.

The initial energy of electrons turns out to be an important parameter. Electrons with low energy are more likely to fly longer and possibly gain more energy from the electric field. On the other hand, due to theisotropic distribution used here, electrons with higher energy can hit the bulk water surface sooner and may not have enough energy for ionization (**Figure 5**).

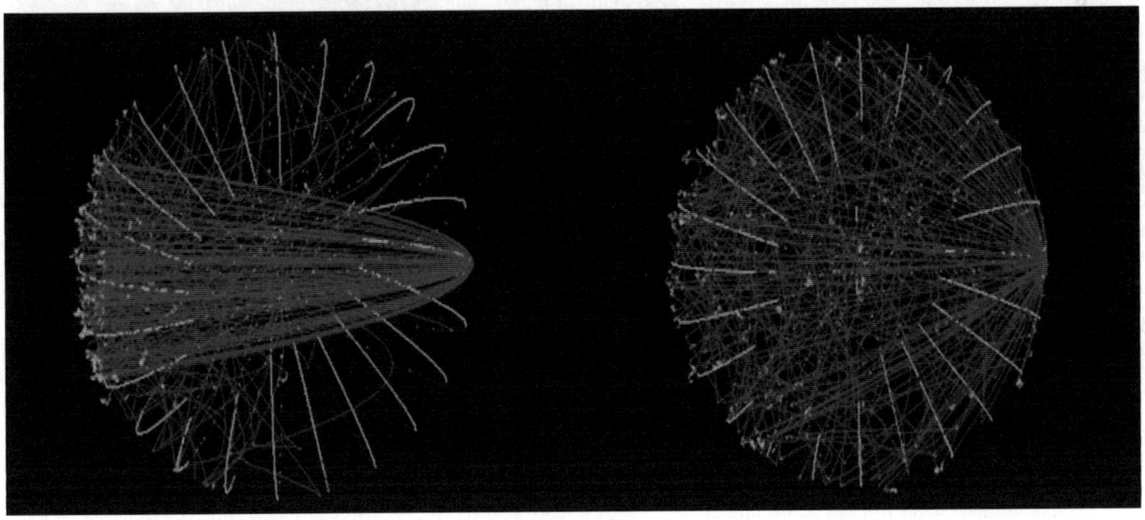

Figure 5 Electron trajectories - low initial energy (left) and high initial energy (right)

5. CONCLUSION

A quantitative assessment of electron multiplication inside ellipsoidal nanovoids has been done by means of particle-tracing Monte Carlo simulation. Influence of ellipsoid elongation and the effect of initial energy of electrons has been studied. From the results obtained, several conclusions are apparent:

- The initial momenta of electrons have a significant effect on the number of electrons produced.
- The number of secondary electrons generated in a void of ellipsoidal shape can be up to ~ 5 times higher compared to a spherical void of the same volume. Also, because of cavitation effects produced by inhomogeneous electric field, spatial fluctuations of electric field can play a major role in the resulting dynamics of electron propagation inside the nanovoid.

ACKNOWLEDGEMENTS

This work was supported by the Czech Science Foundation (Project ID 18-04676S).

REFERENCES

[1] VELDHUIZEN VAN, E. M. *Electrical discharges for environmental purposes : Fundamentals and applications.* Huntington: Nova Science, 2000.

[2] ŠUNKA, P. Pulse electrical discharges in water and their applications. *Physics of Plasmas.* 2001, vol. 8, no. 5, pp. 2587-2594.

[3] JOHNSON, D. L., VANDEVENDER, J. P., MARTIN, T. H. High power density water dielectric switching. *IEEE Transactions on Plasma Science.* 1980, vol. 8, no. 3, pp. 204-209.

[4] BLUHM, H., FREY, W., GIESE, H., HOPPE, P., SCHULTHEISS, C., STRASSNER, R. Application of pulsed HV discharges to material fragmentation and recycling. *IEEE Transactions on Dielectrics and Electrical Insulation.* 2000, vol. 7, no. 5, pp. 625-636.

[5] COLEMAN, A. J., CHOI, M. J., SAUNDERS, J. E., LEIGHTON, T. G. Acoustic emission and sonoluminescence due to cavitation at the beam focus of an electrohydraulic shock wave lithotripter. *Ultrasound in Medicine & Biology.* 1992, vol. 18, no. 3, pp. 267-281.

[6] LANDAU, L. D., et al. *Electrodynamics of continuous media.* Oxford, England: Butterworth-Heinemann, 1984.

[7] SHNEIDER, M. N., PEKKER, M. Dielectric fluid in inhomogeneous pulsed electric field. *Physical Review E.* 2013, vol. 87, no. 4, p. 043004.

[8] AN, W., BAUMUNG, K., BLUHM, H. Underwater streamer propagation analyzed from detailed measurements of pressure release. *Journal of Applied Physics.* 2007, vol. 101, no. 5, p. 053302.

[9] BERNAL, M., BORDAGE, M., BROWN, J., DAVIDKOVA, M., DELAGE, E., EL BITAR, Z., ENGER, S., FRANCIS, Z., GUATELLI, S., IVANCHENKO, V., et al. Track structure modeling in liquid water: A review of the Geant4-DNA very low energy extension of the Geant4 Monte Carlo simulation toolkit. *Physica Medica.* 2015, vol. 31, no. 8, pp. 861-874.

[10] INCERTI, S., IVANCHENKO, A., KARAMITROS, M., MANTERO, A., MORETTO, P., TRAN, H., MASCIALINO, B., CHAMPION, C., IVANCHENKO, V., BERNAL, M., et al. Comparison of geant4 very low energy cross section models with experimental data in water. *Medical Physics.* 2010, vol. 37, no. 9, pp. 4692-4708.

[11] INCERTI, S., BALDACCHINO, G., BERNAL, M., CAPRA, R., CHAMPION, C., FRANCIS, Z., GUÈYE, P., MANTERO, A., MASCIALINO, B., MORETTO, P., et al. The Geant4-DNA project. *International Journal of Modeling, Simulation, and Scientific Computing.* 2010, vol. 1, no. 02, pp. 157-178.

[12] INCERTI, S., KYRIAKOU, I., BERNAL, M., BORDAGE, M., FRANCIS, Z., GUATELLI, S., IVANCHENKO, V., KARAMITROS, M., LAMPE, N., LEE, S. B., et al. Geant4-DNA example applications for track structure simulations in liquid water: A report from the geant4-dna project. *Medical Physics.* 2018, vol. 45, no. 8, pp. e722-e739.

[13] YANG, L., ZOU, Y., DA, B., MAO, S., LI, H., ZHAO, Y., DING, Z. A comparative study on monte carlo simulations of electron emission from liquid water. *Medical Physics.* 2020, vol. 47, no. 2, pp. 759-771.

ON ELECTRON ACCELERATION IN LIQUID RUPTURES CAUSED BY ELECTROSTRICTIVE FORCES

[1]Petr BÍLEK, [1]Ján TUNGLI, [1]Zdeněk BONAVENTURA

[1]*Department of Physical Electronics, Fac. Sci., Masaryk University, Brno, Czech Republic, EU,* *petrbilek248@gmail.com*

https://doi.org/10.37904/nanocon.2020.3728

Abstract

Water is often used as a medium for preparation of nanoparticles in plasma. One way to obtain plasma in liquids is a nanosecond high voltage pulse applied on micrometer sharp electrode, so that the electric discharge is developed. Liquid water under the action of sharp pulse of the electric field may be disrupted so that cavities of nanometer scale would eventually appear and expand. Owing the electric field forces, those nanocavities rapidly elongate to the form of long needle-like ruptures in the liquid bulk. We study electron acceleration in these ruptures and analyze the production of secondary electrons in the water near the nanocavity surfaces. For electron transport in the nanocavity and for electron water-interactions we use Monte Carlo model based on Geant4-DNA simulation toolkit. Nanocavities are modelled as hollow cylindrical voids in liquid water with homogeneous electric field inside oriented along the cylindrical axis. Due to the nanometric scale of these voids, electrons can move collisionless inside, where are also accelerated by the action of the electric field. Primary electrons are injected as monoenergetic isotropic source from the inner surface of the void. We seek physical conditions, a combination of electric field strength and geometry of the cavity that would lead to the production of more than one secondary electron per single primary electron. This study is relevant for understanding of initial phases of electric discharge development in liquid water.

Keywords: In-liquid plasma, nanocavities, electrostriction, electron multiplication

1. INTRODUCTION

Applications of plasma in many distinct technological areas has increased gradually, ever since the term 'plasma' has been coined by an American chemist and Nobel Prize winner Irving Langmuir in 1920s. Historically, plasma has been used as a medium to generate chemically active species in various gas mixtures. During past few decades, attempts to generate plasma also in liquid environment has emerged, followed immediately by applications such as nanomaterials syntheses and wastewater treatment [1,2]. Many of the currently reported devices for plasma generation in liquids use presence of diluted bubbles in the liquid, where accelerated electrons ionize vapors of the liquid. Then, the electric breakdown, in fact, takes place in gaseous environment instead of directly in the liquid bulk. Typical voltage pulses used for the generation of such plasmas are of microsecond duration, applied to a sharp metallic electrode, e.g. in point-plane electrode geometry [3]. Another interesting case to consider for plasma generation in liquids is an ultra sharp high-voltage pulse of (sub)nanosecond duration. Currently, the prevailing opinion is that, in that case, for polar liquids such as water, the initial stage of the plasma discharge formation is associated with the appearance of nanoruptures or nanovoids, which occur because of the ponderomotive electrostrictive forces. Inside of these nanovoids, then the electrons might gain sufficient energy to ionize. Due to the action of the electric forces, these nanocavities rapidly elongate and form long needle-like ruptures of the liquid bulk [4,5]. Note that this mechanism of plasma generation is different from the bubble-electric-breakdown, because nanovoids serve as collision-free environment merely for acceleration of electrons and ionization occurs in the liquid, instead.

In this contribution, we study electron acceleration in these elongated ruptures and we analyze resulting production of secondary electrons in the water near the nanocavity/water interface.

2. MODEL AND METHODS

Cavities are considered as long cylindrical voids with homogeneous electric field loaded inside and oriented along their axis. Electrons in the cavity accelerate freely, i.e. without collisions, and can only interact with water molecules when they hit the wall of the cavity. This assumption of uncolissionality is justified because the characteristic spatial scale of these cavities is much shorter than the mean free path of electrons in the corresponding equilibrium vapor pressure. The electron motion in the cavity with the homogenous electric field is an analogy to the projectile motion in a vertical tube subjected to the action of the gravitation force. It can be shown that the product of the electric field strength E and the cavity radius R, i.e., $E \cdot R$ is appropriate for discussion of results for different cavity dimensions and electric field strengths. For description of electron interactions with water, we use state of the art simulation framework Geant4-DNA [6-9]. This framework offers a variety of models to simulate the physical interactions of electrons in liquid water. We use Geant4-DNA physics 'option 4' constructor, which includes models for elastic and inelastic scattering of electrons, together with a model for vibrational excitation and attachment. We assume that sub-excitation electrons, i.e. electrons with energy below 7.4 eV, cannot contribute to further ionization in water. Therefore, no tracking of sub-excitation electrons in water is performed in the simulation. Overall, the electron interaction with the surface of the cavity can have two distinct outcomes: (a) the electron penetrates the water bulk and terminates there, or (b) the electron is bounced back to the void of the cavity and is accelerated by the electric field once again. In both cases, in termination or in bouncing, certain number of secondary electrons is created in the water by electron impact ionization of water molecules. In addition, some portion of those secondary electrons is emitted from the surface of the cavity to the void. In the following, we analyze this production of secondary electrons in detail, and we look for suitable condition to ensure that the number of secondary electrons emitted to the cavity per one impacting primary electron would be equal to one or higher. Primary electrons are launched from the surface of the cavity with isotropic velocity distribution and the initial energy at the lowest threshold energy 7.4 eV. This initial condition is motivated by three facts. First, every secondary electron can serve as a primary electron for the next generation of secondary electrons. Second, electron collisionality in the water is very high so that any electron that is emitted or bounced-back from the cavity/water interface to the cavity will have no memory of momentum prior to the latest collisional event. Therefore, we can assume isotropic initial velocity distribution of primary electrons. And third, any electron with sub-excitation energy will thermalize in the water bulk and cannot further produce secondary electrons. Minimal energy that allows electrons to be released to the cavity is therefore at the threshold of 7.4 eV in our model. Then the initial condition formulated this way allows us to study the production of secondary electrons and make some conclusions regarding the conditions that are favorable for electron multiplication inside the nanocavity.

3. RESULTS

Figure 1 shows distribution of secondary electrons generated along the cavity in water by the impact of primary electrons released from the cavity surface at position z=0. The distribution is normalized such a way that the integral of all secondary electrons emitted in the cavity is divided by the total number, N_0, of primary electrons launched. Panels on **Figure 1** represent secondary electron distribution for $E \cdot R$ in {15,18,20,25} V. Total number of secondaries per single primary electrons are {0.75, 1.01, 1.15, 1.5}, this number is obtained as a sum of all secondary electrons generated and emitted along the cavity. In this regard it is interesting to look at the cumulative sum of secondary electrons along the cavity length, as shown in **Figure 2** for $E \cdot R$ in {15,18,20,25} V. Clearly for $E \cdot R$ higher or equal to 18, there is a finite length of the tube on which the number of secondary electrons per single primary electron sums up to one or higher number. On the other hand for $E \cdot R = 15$ V, there will be less secondary electrons then primary electrons, no matter how long the cavity would be. This allows us to conclude that there exists a condition on a minimal value of E · R that is required for electrons released into the cavity to be multiplied by ionization along the cavity surface.

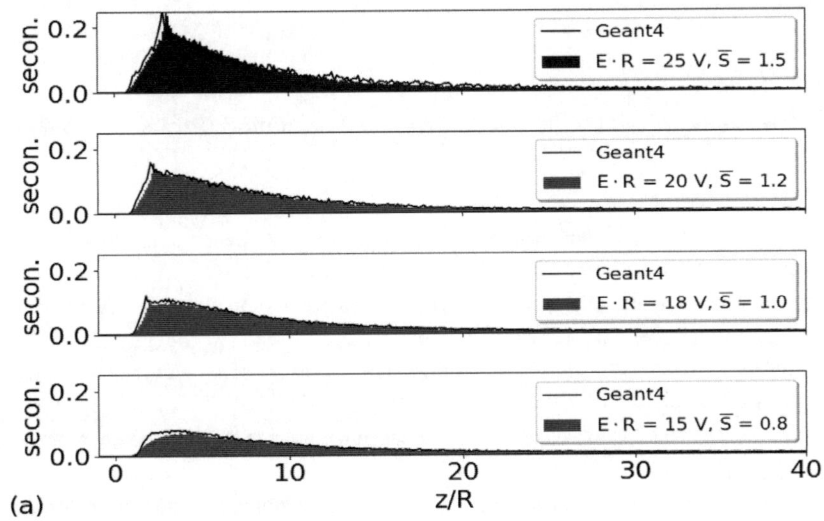

Figure 1 Distribution functions of secondary electrons along z-axis for four different E ·R values. Integrals of the distribution functions along z-axis give number of secondary electrons generated per primary electron

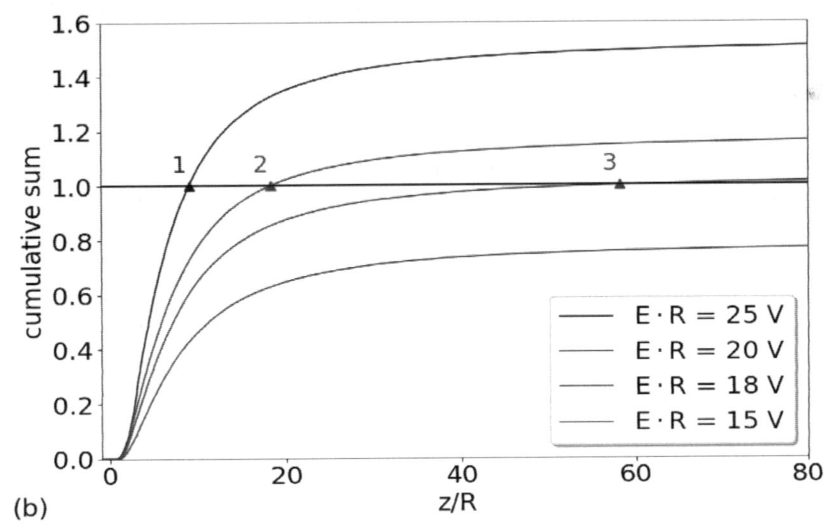

Figure 2 Cumulative sums of the distribution functions and the dots denote the length of the cavity for which the primary electron produces exactly one secondary electron

4. CONCLUSION

We have simulated motion of primary electrons released in the capillary rupture created by electrostrictive stress in water by strong and ultrafast pulse of the electric field. Electrons are accelerated by the electric field in the void of the rupture under collisionless conditions. Then by impact on the surface of the cavity, we calculate number of secondary electrons emitted from the cavity surface by these accelerated impacting primary electrons. Considering several values of electric field strength times cavity radius (E · R), we observe that there exists a minimal value of E · R (~ 18 V) at which the number of primary electrons is ensured to be multiplied. These results has strong implications for understanding of initial phases of electric discharge and plasma state development in liquid water.

ACKNOWLEDGEMENTS

This work was supported by the Czech Science Foundation (Project ID 18-04676S).

REFERENCES

[1] HORIKOSHI, S., SERPONE, N. In-liquid plasma: a novel tool in the fabrication of nanomaterials and in the treatment of wastewaters. *RSC Advances.* 2017, vol. 7, pp. 47196-47218.

[2] SAITO, G., AKIYAMA, T. Nanomaterial synthesis using plasma generation in liquid. *J. Nanomater.* 2015, pp. 1-21.

[3] DEVINS, J.C., RZAD, S.J., SCHWABE, R.J. Breakdown and pre-breakdown phenomena in liquids. *J. Appl. Phys.* 1981, vol. 52, pp. 4531-4545.

[4] SHNEIDER, M.N., PEKKER, M. Pre-breakdown processes in a dielectric fluid in inhomogeneous pulsed electric fields. *Journal of Applied Physics.* 2015, vol. 117, 224902.

[5] M.ŠIMEK et al. Investigation of the initial phases of nanosecond discharges in liquid water. *Plasma Sources Sci. Technol.* 2020, vol. 29, 064001.

[6] INCERTI, S., KYRIAKOU, I., BERNAL, M., BORDAGE, M., FRANCIS, Z., GUATELLI, S., IVANCHENKO, V., KARAMITROS, M. LAMPE, N., LEE, S. B., et al. Geant4-DNA example applications for track structure simulations in liquid water: A report from the Geant4-DNA Project. *Medical physics.* 2018, vol. 45, pp. e722-e739.

[7] BERNAL, M., BORDAGE, M., BROWN, J., DAVÍDKOVÁ, M., DELAGE, E., EL BITAR, Z., ENGER, S., FRANCIS, Z., GUATELLI, S., IVANCHENKO, V., et al. Track structure modeling in liquid water: A review of the Geant4-DNA very low energy extension of the Geant4 Monte Carlo simulation toolkit, *Physica Medica.* 2015, vol. 31, pp. 861-874.

[8] INCERTI, S., IVANCHENKO, A., KARAMITROS, M., MANTERO, A., MORETTO, P., TRAN, MASCIALINO, B., CHAMPION, C. IVANCHENKO, V., BERNAL, M., et al. Comparison of GEANT4 very low energy cross section models with experimental data in water. *Medical physics.* 2010, vol. 37, pp. 4692-708.

[9] INCERTI, S., BALDACCHINO, G., BERNAL, M., CAPRA, CHAMPION, C., FRANCIS, Z., GUATELLI, S., GUÈYE, P., MANTERO, A., MASCIALINO, B., MORETTO, P., NIEMINEN, P., ROSENFELD, A., VILLAGRASA C., ZACHARATOU, C. THE GEANT4-DNA PROJECT. *Int. J. Model. Simul. Sci. Comput.* 2010, vol. 1, pp. 157--178.

ELECTROCHEMICAL STUDY OF CUSCN INORGANIC HOLE-TRANSPORT MATERIAL FOR SOLAR CELLS PREPARED BY ELECTRODEPOSITION FROM AQUEOUS SOLUTION

Zuzana VLČKOVÁ ŽIVCOVÁ, Věra MANSFELDOVÁ, Milan BOUŠA, Ladislav KAVAN

J. Heyrovský Institute of Physical Chemistry of the CAS, Prague, Czech Republic, EU

https://doi.org/10.37904/nanocon.2020.3727

Abstract

A comparative study is reported for electrodeposited copper(I) thiocyanate layers (ca. 500 nm) on two types of conductive/semiconductive substrates; i) carbon (boron-doped diamond_BDD, glass-like carbon_GC), and ii) carbon-free F-doped SnO_2 conducting glass (FTO). SEM and Raman evidence that electrodeposition from aqueous solution results in homogenous CuSCN layers with dominant thiocyanate ion bounded to copper through its S-end (Cu−SCN bonding), as in spin-coated CuSCN layers. Electrochemical impedance spectroscopy (EIS) confirms the *p*-type semiconductivity of layers with a flatband potential from 0.1 to 0.18 V vs. Ag/AgCl depending on the substrate type, and the acceptor concentration (N_A) of ~ 5 x 10^{20}cm^{-3} in all cases. The flatband potentials determined from Mott-Schottky plots (EIS) are in good agreement with the Kelvin probe measurements. The blocking quality of CuSCN layers was tested using $Ru(NH_3)_6^{3+/2+}$ redox probe. CuSCN deposited on BDD substrate exhibits better blocking properties compared to CuSCN deposited on FTO.

Keywords: Electrodeposition, CuSCN, hole transport material, electrochemistry, impedance spectroscopy

1. INTRODUCTION

Copper(I) thiocyanate (CuSCN) is a *p*-type semiconductor with wide band gap of ~3.9 eV, hole mobility 0.001−0.1 $cm^2 \cdot V^{-1} \cdot s^{-1}$ [1] and good optical transparency [2] applicable as a hole transport material (HTM) in dye-sensitized solid-state solar cells [3,4] and perovskite solar cells [5,6]. Cathodic electrodeposition from aqueous solution containing SCN^- and Cu^{2+} is one of the low-temperature deposition techniques for CuSCN layers [2,3,7-10] in addition to spray deposition [11], drop-casting [12] or spin coating [13]. The electrodeposition benefits from avoiding organic solvents (e.g. alkyl sulfides). EIS is a useful technique to study the double-layer structure and charge transfer at the electrochemical interface. Based on Mott-Schottky plot (MS) obtained by fitting impedance spectra using appropriate equivalent circuit, the flatband potential (E_{fb}), and acceptor (N_A) or donor (N_D) concentration can be determined [14]. However, the experimental flatband potentials depend on various factors, such as i) the presence of deliberately added dopants, ii) differences in the crystallographic orientation, iii) a difference in the pH of zero charge, etc. [15]. The flatband positions can be also determined from the work function using Kelvin probe measurements after the corresponding conversion to the electrochemical potential scale. This technique is based on measurement of changes in contact potential difference (CPD) between the studied surface and a reference probe [16,17]. Here we report the electrodeposition from aqueous solution of hole-transporting CuSCN layers under the same conditions on different types of substrates (boron-doped diamond as *p*-type semiconductor, FTO glass as *n*-type semiconductor, and glass-like carbon). The structure and electrochemical properties of the electrodeposited CuSCN layers were compared with those prepared by the spin-coating method [5].

2. EXPERIMENTAL

2.1. CuSCN layer preparation

CuSCN thin films were prepared by electrodeposition from aqueous electrolyte solution according Ni et al. [2] on: i) boron-doped diamond with B/C ratio of 1000 ppm (BDD 1000) and 4000 ppm (BDD 4000) as detailed elsewhere [18], ii) glass-like carbon (GC, 3000C from Goodfellow, 400 μOhm/cm), and iii) F-doped SnO_2 conducting glass (FTO, TEC 15 from Libbey-Owens-Ford, 15 Ohm/sq). The electrodeposition of CuSCN was performed potentiostatically at -0.5V vs. Ag/AgCl for 30 minutes; Pt mesh was a counter electrode and Ag/AgCl with 3M KCl was a reference electrode. The electrolyte solution consists of cupric sulfate pentahydrate (99.9%, Sigma-Aldrich) and potassium thiocyanate (99.0%, Sigma-Aldrich) as precursors and TEA (99.0%, Sigma-Aldrich) as a chelating reagent for Cu^{2+} cations. Before electrodeposition, the $CuSO_4$/TEA + 0.1M KSCN solution was stirred for 1 h and then stored for 24 h.

2.2. Structural and chemical characterization

The surface morphology was investigated by field emission scanning electron microscopy (FESEM, S-4800 Hitachi). SEM images were acquired at an acceleration voltage of 3 kV at a working distance of 5-6 mm. Raman spectra were excited by 514 nm laser (power of 1 mW) and recorded by a Labram HR spectrometer (Horiba Jobin-Yvon) interfaced to an Olympus microscope (objective 100×). The spectrometer was calibrated by the F_{1g} mode of Si at 520.2 cm^{-1}. Kelvin probe measurements used KP020 instrument (KP Technology Ltd.). The gold probe was positioned close to the sample surface and the contact potential difference was measured. Work functions were calibrated using a freshly peeled-off highly oriented pyrolytic graphite; its work function was set to 4.6 eV [17]. All electrochemical measurements were performed in a three-electrode cell (working electrode: CuSCN film, counter electrode: Pt mesh, reference electrode: Ag/AgCl with 3M KCl). The electrolyte solution was 0.5M KCl (Sigma Aldrich) saturated with CuSCN (pH 6). Electrochemical experiments were carried out on AUTOLAB PGSTAT128N potentiostat (Metrohm) controlled by GPES4 software (cyclic voltammetry, CV) and FRA software (EIS). The electrochemical impedance spectra were measured at frequencies from 100 kHz to 0.1 Hz. Electrochemical test of blocking used of 0.5mM $[Ru(NH_3)_6]$ Cl_3 (Sigma Aldrich, 98%) in 0.5M KCl (Sigma Aldrich, ≥99%) sat. with CuSCN. Electrochemical measurements were carried out in a closed cell under argon atmosphere.

3. RESULTS AND DISCUSSION

3.1. Structural characterization of CuSCN layers

Figure 1A displays plan view of dense fine-crystalline morphology (trigonal crystallites) of homogeneously electrochemically grown CuSCN layer onto FTO substrate. The CuSCN layer thickness observed from cross sectional SEM image (**Figure 1B**) is about 550 nm and is comparable (same as morphology) with CuSCN layers prepared on BDD and GC substrate (not shown). The surface morphology of electrodeposited CuSCN layers is distinctly different from layers prepared by spin coating from diethyl sulfide solution and the crystal size is significantly larger [5].

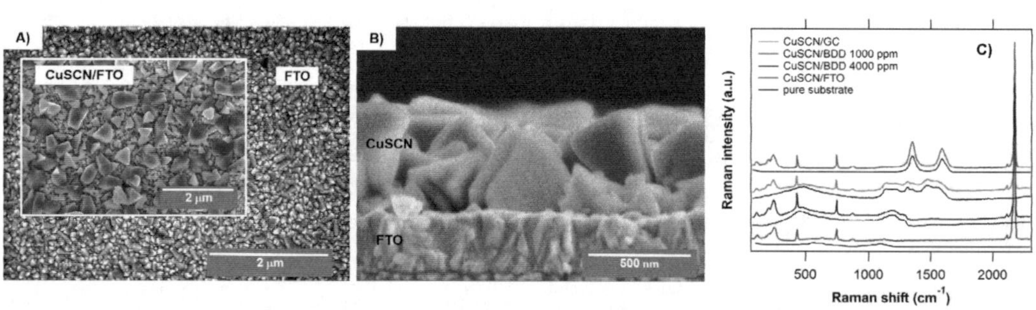

Figure 1 SEM (A_plain view, B_cross section) of CuSCN on FTO glass substrate (CuSCN/FTO). Inset of A) shows CuSCN on FTO substrate (background of the chart A). Chart C) shows the Raman spectra of CuSCN on GC (green line), BDD 1000 (light blue line), BDD 4000 (dark blue line), and FTO (red line) substrates. Black lines show the reference spectra of blank substrates. The spectra are offset for clarity.

Figure 1C shows Raman spectra of CuSCN layers deposited on different types of substrates (CuSCN/GC, CuSCN/BDD 1000, CuSCN/BDD 4000, and CuSCN/FTO). The Raman spectra of blank substrates are also shown for comparison. Independent of the substrate type the Raman spectra exhibit the same peak positions as the CuSCN films prepared by spin coating [5]. The peaks of C≡N stretching are located at higher frequency region, i.e. the weaker peak at 2115 cm^{-1} for isothiocyanate which is a less energetically favourable resonance form of SCN ion (Cu−NSC bonding) and the most intense peak at 2173 cm^{-1} for the second resonant form thiocyanate (Cu−SCN bonding). In the low frequency range region 100-1000 cm^{-1} where are located peaks indicating the presence of two possible SCN resonant forms are clearly visible the Raman peaks corresponding to the Cu-S stretching at 202 and 745 cm^{-1}, SCN bending at 431 cm^{-1}, and Cu-N stretching at 243 cm^{-1}.

3.2. Cyclic voltammetry (CV) and electrochemical impedance spectroscopy (EIS)

The CuSCN layers were electrochemically studied in 0.5M KCl sat. with CuSCN aqueous electrolyte solution in various potential ranges from -0.3V to 0.5V. The set of cyclic voltammograms (CVs) is illustrated in **Figure 2A** for CuSCN/BDD substrates, in **Figure 2B** for CuSCN/GC and CuSCN/FTO substrates. In all cases, with increasing potential window the capacitances, determined at 0 V and related to the projected geometric surface area, increase (**Figure 2C**) due to electrochemical reactions occurring on the electrode surface. As CuSCN is *p*-type semiconductor, cyclic voltammograms show no capacitive charging in cathodic direction, while with increasing positive potential the anodic current increases depending on the substrate type. For the anodic vertex potentials from 0.3 V to 0.5 V (**Figure 2D**), the increase of capacitance is more evident for CuSCN/FTO (0.6 mF/cm^2) and CuSCN/GC (0.8 mF/cm^2) than for CuSCN/BDD (0.3 mF/cm^2). This difference is caused by the variability of substrates used for CuSCN electrodeposition, i.e., the width of potential window (PW) of capacitive charging depends on the substrate type. The reason for the lowest capacitance values of CuSCN/BDD is that BDD has a wide electrochemical potential window in aqueous media (more than 3V for high quality and highly doped BDD) and low double-layer capacitance (< 12 $\mu m/cm^2$), as previously reported [14,18-21]. Depending on BDD film quality (sp^2 carbon content) and doping level (B/C ratio in the gas phase) we distinguish between high- and low-quality diamonds, as well as semiconducting (< 3 x 10^{20} B atoms cm^{-3} [22]) or metallic. For CuSCN electrodeposition, we used two types of BDD; 1) with lower quality and doping level denoted BDD 1000, and 2) high quality with high doping (BDD 4000). The structure and electrochemical properties of these BDDs were described in [18]. From the inset of **Figure 2C** it is obvious, that CuSCN/BDD 4000 layer exhibits slightly lower capacitance than the CuSCN/BDD 1000. The reason is the higher quality of the pristine BDD 4000 (compared to BDD 1000) containing no sp^2 carbon impurities (Raman spectrum in **Figure 1C**), where oxygen-containing groups are formed causing a decrease in the potential BDD window and an increase in background capacitive currents [18]. The GC (20 $\mu F/cm^2$ [5]) and FTO (30 $\mu F/cm^2$ [5]) substrates increase the capacitance of CuSCN layer in the whole range of potential windows compared to the BDD substrates due to various structure of surface containing oxygen groups where redox reactions occur.

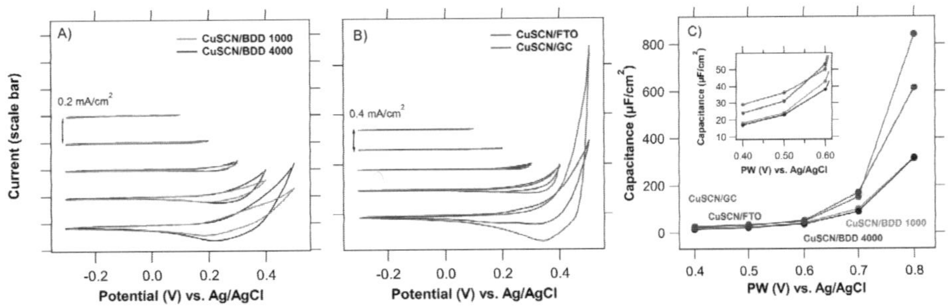

Figure 2 Cyclic voltammograms of CuSCN on A) boron-doped diamond (CuSCN/BDD 1000_light blue line, CuSCN/BDD 4000_dark blue line), B) glass-like carbon (CuSCN/GC_green line) and FTO glass substrate (CuSCN/FTO_red line). The scan rate of 100 mV/s. Plots in A) and B) are offset for clarity, but the current scale is identical for all voltammograms (see the scale bar). C) shows the capacitance of CuSCN in potential ranges from -0.3V-0.1V (PW=0.4) to -0.3V-0.5V vs. Ag/AgCl (PW=0.8) calculated from CVs in A) and B).

The blocking properties of electrodeposited CuSCN layer were tested using FTO and BDD 4000 substrates (**Figure 3**). In our previous work [5] the blocking function of spin-coated CuSCN was found to depend on details of spin-coating deposition. Here we used the same $Ru(NH_3)_6{}^{3+/2+}$ redox system due to suitable redox potential and stability of aqueous solution. **Figure 3** shows that CuSCN/BDD 4000 layer (blue line) has a better blocking function which is quantified as the relative pinhole area [23] (A_u/A_0) of 42% compared to CuSCN/FTO (red line) with A_u/A_0 = 64%, referenced to blank FTO (black line). The pinhole defect type A of the CuSCN layer was detected for both substrates [23]. The larger A_u/A_0 values obviously reflect the coarse morphology of our film (**Figure 1**) compared to spin-coated ones; nevertheless, this parameter is also known to depend dramatically on details of the spin-coating protocol [5].

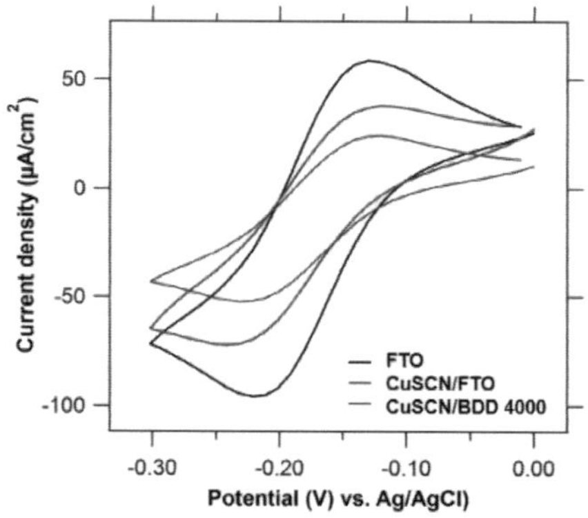

Figure 3 Cyclic voltammograms of CuSCN on FTO (red line) and BDD 4000 (blue line) substrates. Blank FTO substrate (black line) is shown for comparison. Electrolyte solution 0.5mM $Ru(NH_3)_6Cl_3$ in 0.5M KCl sat. with CuSCN (pH 6) and the scan rate 100 mV/s.

Figure 4 shows the Mott-Schottky plots determined from electrochemical impedance spectroscopy (EIS) and fitted using the RC equivalent circuits, where the space charge capacitance is represented by constant phase element (CPE) [14]. The negative slope of MS plots of CuSCN in all cases confirmed the *p*-type conductivity. Similarly, blank BDD (1000 and 4000) shows the *p*-type semiconducting behaviour (inset of **Figure 4A** and **Figure 4B**). For the calculation of the acceptor concentration N_A and flatband potential E_{fb} (**Table 1**), we used the Mott-Schottky equation [14]. The found flatband potentials depend on the substrate type, ie. the E_{fb} is lower in the case of carbon (BDD, GC) substrates compared to carbon-free FTO substrate. This trend is the same as in our previous work on spin-coated CuSCN layers [5]. For the CuSCN/BDD are the E_{fb} values as follows: 0.1 V (BDD 1000) and 0.13 V (BDD 4000) vs. Ag/AgCl compared to E_{fb} of blank BDDs (1.04 V for BDD 1000 and 1.3 V for BDD 4000) (**Figure 4A** and **Figure 4B**). The deposition on conductive GC substrate leads to the higher E_{fb} = 0.15 V (**Figure 4C**). Despite the fact, that the FTO is a *n*-type semiconductor (E_{fb} = -0.5 V vs. Ag/AgCl, **Figure 4D**), the *p*-semiconducting character of the CuSCN layer dominates and the flatband potential is 0.18 V vs. Ag/AgCl. This value is slightly higher, but still in good agreement with the value of 0.12 V measured on spin-coated CuSCN layers on FTO [5]. The acceptor concentrations of CuSCN layers on GC, BDD, and FTO are in the range of 4.7 to 5.4 x 10^{20} cm^{-3} (**Table 1**) comparable to spin-coated CuSCN layers [5]. KP measurements give the work function for CuSCN layers on FTO, GC, and BDD substrates as; 4.931 eV, 4.833 eV, and 4.575 eV, respectively. These work functions can be converted to the corresponding flatband potential. **Table 1** confirms that both techniques give well comparable data.

Table 1 The acceptor concentrations (N_A) and flatband potentials (E_{fb}) for CuSCN on various substrates (CuSCN/BDD 1000, CuSCN/BDD 4000, CuSCN/GC, and CuSCN/FTO) determined by electrochemical impedance spectra from Mott-Schottky (MS) plots and Kelvin probe (KP) method

	CuSCN/BDD 1000	**CuSCN/BDD 4000**	**CuSCN/GC**	**CuSCN/FTO**
N_A **(cm^{-3})** (MS)	4.8 x 10^{20}	4.8 x 10^{20}	4.7 x 10^{20}	5.4 x 10^{20}
E_{fb} **(V) vs Ag/AgCl** (MS)	0.1 ± 0.01	0.13 ± 0.04	0.15 ± 0.02	0.18 ± 0.02
E_{fb} **(V) vs.Ag/AgCl** (KP)	-	0.14 ± 0.03	0.13 ± 0.03	0.24 ± 0.05

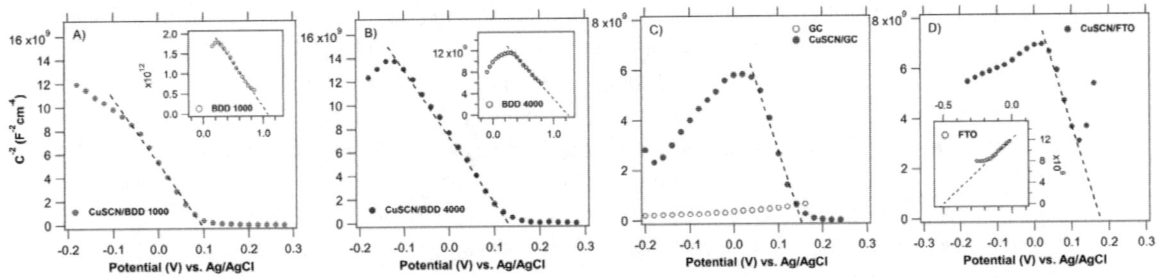

Figure 4 Mott–Schottky (MS) plots from EIS of CuSCN on A) boron-doped diamond CuSCN/BDD 1000_light blue full symbols, B) CuSCN/BDD 4000_dark blue full symbols, C) glass-like carbon (CuSCN/GC_green full symbol) and D) FTO substrate (CuSCN/FTO_red full symbols). The open symbols show the MS of substrates. Electrolyte solution was 0.5M KCl sat. with CuSCN (pH 6).

4. CONCLUSION

Electrochemical deposition on different substrates (boron-doped diamond, glass-like carbon, and FTO conductive glass) from aqueous solution yielded homogenous CuSCN layers with a thickness of about 550 nm measured by SEM. The capacitances and flatband potentials depend on the substrate type. The determined flatband potentials from two different methods (electrochemical impedance spectroscopy and Kelvin probe) considering the experimental errors were in good agreement. The CuSCN deposited on BDD substrate exhibits better blocking function (smaller relative pinhole area) compared to CuSCN deposited on FTO substrate.

ACKNOWLEDGEMENTS

The authors acknowledge the support from the Czech Science Foundation (Contract No. 18-08959S).

REFERENCES

[1] WIJEYASINGHE, N., EISNER, F., TSETSERIS, L. et al. p-Doping of Copper(I) Thiocyanate (CuSCN) Hole-Transport Layers for High-Performance Transistors and Organic Solar Cells. *Advanced Functional Materials*. 2018, vol. 28, pp. 1802055.

[2] NI, Y., JIN, Z., FU, Y. Electrodeposition of p-Type CuSCN Thin Films by a New Aqueous Electrolyte With Triethanolamine Chelation. *Journal of the American Ceramic Society*. 2007, vol. 90, no. 9, pp. 2966-2973.

[3] SUN, L., ICHINOSE, K., SEKIYA, T., et al. Cathodic Electrodeposition of p-CuSCN Nanorod and Its Dye-Sensitized Photocathodic Property. *Phys. Proc.* 2011, vol. 14, pp. 12.

[4] PERERA, V.P.S., SENEVIRATHNA, M.K.I., PITIGALA, P.K.D.D.P., et al. Doping CuSCN Films for Enhancement of Conductivity: Application in Dye-Sensitized Solid-State Solar Cells. *Sol. Energy Mater. Sol. Cells*. 2005, vol. 86, pp. 443.

[5] KAVAN, L., ŽIVCOVÁ, Z.V., HUBÍK, P., et al. Electrochemical Characterization of CuSCN Hole-Extracting Thin Films for Perovskite Photovoltaics. *ACS Applied Energy Materials*. 2019, vol. 2, pp. 4264-4273.

[6] MATEBESE, F., TAZIWA, R., MUTUKWA, D. Progress on the Synthesis and Application of CuSCN Inorganic Hole Transport Material in Perovskite Solar Cells. *Materials*. 2018, vol. 11, pp. 2592.

[7] CHAPPAZ-GILLOT, C., SALAZAR, R., BERSON, S., et al. Room temperature template-free electrodeposition of CuSCN nanowires. *Electrochemistry Communications*. 2012, vol. 24, pp. 1-4.

[8] SUN, L., HUANG, Y., ANOWER HOSSAIN, M., et al. Fabrication of TiO2/CuSCN Bulk Heterojunctions by Profile-Controlled Electrodeposition. *Journal of The Electrochemical Society*. 2012, vol. 159, pp. D323-D327.

[9] RAMÍREZ, D., ÁLVAREZ, K., RIVEROS, G., et al. Electrodeposition of CuSCN seed layers and nanowires: A microelectrogravimetric approach. *Electrochimica Acta*. 2017, vol. 228, pp. 308-318.

[10] SHLENSKAYA, N.N., TUTANTSEV, A.S., BELICH, N.A., et al. Electrodeposition of porous CuSCN layers as hole-conducting material for perovskite solar cells. *Mendeleev Communications*. 2018, vol. 28, pp. 378-380.

[11] YANG, I.S., SOHN, M.R., SUNG, S.D., et al. Formation of pristine CuSCN layer by spray deposition method for efficient perovskite solar cell with extended stability. *Nano Energy*. 2017, vol. 32, pp. 414-421.

[12] CHAVHAN, S., MIGUEL, O., GRANDE, H.J., et al. Organo-metal halide perovskite-based solar cells with CuSCN as the inorganic hole selective contact. *Journal of Materials Chemistry A*. 2014, vol. 2, pp. 12754-12760.

[13] ARORA, N., DAR, M.I., HINDERHOFER, A., et al. Perovskite solar cells with CuSCN hole extraction layers yield stabilized efficiencies greater than 20%. *Science,* 2017. vol. 358, pp. 768-771.

[14] ŽIVCOVÁ, Z.V., PETRÁK, V., FRANK, O., et al. Electrochemical impedance spectroscopy of polycrystalline boron-doped diamond layers with hydrogen and oxygen terminated surface. *Diamond and Related Materials*. 2015, vol. 55, pp. 70-76.

[15] HANKIN, A., ALEXANDER, J.C., KELSALL, G.H. Constraints to the flat band potential of hematite photo-electrodes. *Physical Chemistry Chemical Physics*. 2014, vol. 16, pp. 16176-16186.

[16] BONNET, J., SOONCKINDT, L., LASSABATÈRE, L. The Kelvin probe method for work function topographies: technical problems and solutions. *Vacuum*. 1984, vol. 34, pp. 693-698.

[17] BEERBOM, M.M., LÄGEL, B., CASCIO, A.J., et al. Direct comparison of photoemission spectroscopy and in situ Kelvin probe work function measurements on indium tin oxide films. *Journal of Electron Spectroscopy and Related Phenomena*. 2006, vol. 152, pp. 12-17.

[18] ŽIVCOVÁ, Z.V., FRANK, O., PETRÁK, V., et al. Electrochemistry and in situ Raman spectroelectrochemistry of low and high quality boron-doped diamond layers in aqueous electrolyte solution. *Electrochimica Acta*. 2013, vol. 87, pp. 518-525.

[19] MACPHERSON, J.V. A practical guide to using boron-doped diamond in electrochemical research. *Physical Chemistry Chemical Physics*. 2015, vol. 17, pp. 2935-2949.

[20] KAVAN, L., VLCKOVA ZIVCOVA, Z., PETRAK, V., et al. Boron-doped Diamond Electrodes: Electrochemical, Atomic Force Microscopy and Raman Study towards Corrosion-modifications at Nanoscale. *Electrochimica Acta*. 2015, vol. 179, pp. 626-636.

[21] VLČKOVÁ ŽIVCOVÁ, Z., MORTET, V., TAYLOR, A., et al. Electrochemical characterization of porous boron-doped diamond prepared using SiO_2 fiber template. *Diamond and Related Materials*. 2018, vol. 87, pp. 61-69.

[22] ACHATZ, P., BUSTARRET, E., MARCENAT, C., et al. Metal-insulator transition and superconductivity in highly boron-doped nanocrystalline diamond films. *physica status solidi (a)*. 2009, vol. 206, pp. 1978-1985.

[23] KAVAN, L., TÉTREAULT, N., MOEHL, T., et al. Electrochemical Characterization of TiO_2 Blocking Layers for Dye-Sensitized Solar Cells. *The Journal of Physical Chemistry C*. 2014, vol. 118, pp.16408-16418.

THE CREATION OF AU@TIO$_2$ PLASMON-ACTIVE STRUCTURE FOR HYDROGEN PRODUCTION

[1]D. ZABELIN, [1]A. ZABELINA, [1]R. ELASHNIKOV, [1]V. SVORCIK, [2]D. NAZAROV, [3]M. MAXIMOV, [1,4]O. LYUTAKOV

[1]Department of Solid State Engineering, University of Chemistry and Technology, Prague, Czech Republic, EU, lyutakoo@vscht.cz

[2]Research Park «Innovative Technologies of Composite Nanomaterials» Saint-Petersburg State University, Russian Federation

[3]Peter the Great Saint-Petersburg Polytechnic University, Russian Federation

[4]Research School of Chemistry and Applied Biomedical Sciences, Tomsk Polytechnic University, Russian Federation

https://doi.org/10.37904/nanocon.2020.3709

Abstract

In this work substrates able to efficiently perform so-called photo-electrochemical process are proposed. The hybrid substrates consist of a plasmon-active gold structure and a certain number of TiO_2 layers deposited by the atomic layer deposition (ALD) method. Above the influence of LED lamp irradiation (λ=850 nm) in the water splitting process, the enhancement of hydrogen production is observed (0.11 ppm/sec VS. 0.22 ppm/sec) which can be explained by creation of surface plasmon-polariton resonance (SPP), which occurs as a result of the excitation of collective electronic vibration on the periodical gold nanostructure under the incident light. Also, it is suggested that the combination of gold and titanium dioxide can lead to plasmon triggering of TiO_2 catalytic activity, which will lead to decreasing energy costs on the photolysis of water and to the overall acceleration of the process.

Keywords: Electrochemistry, plasmonic, atomic layer deposition, titanium dioxide, photolysis of water

1. INTRODUCTION

One of the most important global environmental problems nowadays is the search for sources of ecological "green" fuels [1-7]. This problem is closely related to the high amount of emission gases that cause global warming effect and creating of greenhouse effect. One of the most promising «green» fuels is hydrogen, which releases water vapor as a by-product when burned [8-11].

One of the richest sources of hydrogen is water. By cleaving water molecules under the influence of electric current, the so-called «green» hydrogen can be released. Today, there are many studies related to the cleavage of water by electrolysis. However, these methods have relatively high energy requirements [12-15]. Therefore, studying related to the increasing the rate of green hydrogen production at lower energy costs is very relevant [16-19].

The main goal of this work was to create a hybrid structure with a combination of plasmon-active gold structure and additional catalytic TiO_2 layer. The water splitting process proceeds under the simultaneous plasmon triggering and an electric field application. In perspective, proposed structures will be applied for the hydrogen production and generation of ecologically pure fuel in the future.

2. EXPERIMENTAL

2.1. Materials

Gold targets for metal deposition (purity of metal, 4 N) were purchased from Safina (Czech Republic). SU-8 2005 was purchased from Microchem (Newton, USA). Titanium chloride ($TiCl_4$, Vecton, Russia 99.99%) and deionized water were used as precursors, Rhodamine 6G was purchased from Sigma-Aldrich.

2.2. Sample preparation

The SU-8 polymer was deposited on a clean glass surface by using spin-coating method (1400 rpm for 20 minutes). The prepared samples then were dried at 60 °C for 24 hours and then irradiated with UV light for 30 minutes, followed by heat treatment at 90 °C for 2 hours (**Figure 1A**). Creation of periodic polymer structure was performed by excimer KrF laser with a wavelength of 248 nm (**Figure 1B**). Then, thin layers of gold were deposited on the periodically structured surface by vacuum sputtering (**Figure 1C**). In the last stage, a different number of TiO_2 layers were deposited on the gold surface using ALD equipment (**Figure 1D**). The atomic layer deposition was performed in the hot-wall, flow-type reactor Nanoserf having slot-type geometry (Nanoengineering Ltd, Russia). The temperature of the reactor was maintained at 200 °C. Nitrogen (99.9999%) was used as a carrier and purging gas. The total reactor N_2 flow rate at purge and pulse was 300 sccm (standard cubic centimeters per minute). The pulse and purge durations were 100 ms and 20 s respectively.

LED light source (λ=850 nm, FWHM=30 nm, irradiance=1450 μW/cm^2, current=1200 mA) was used for plasmon-polariton resonance excitation.

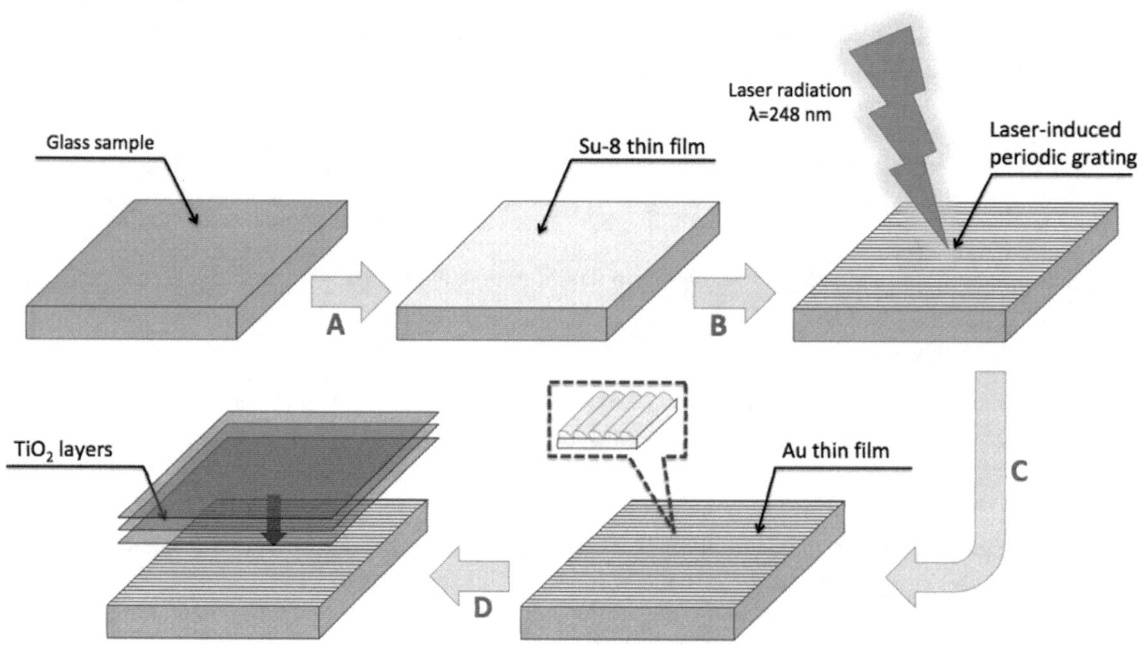

Figure 1 Formation of a combined plasmon-active surface based on TiO_2

A - Deposition of Su-8 polymer on the glass surface; B - creation of a periodic grating under laser irradiation; C - Deposition of the gold layer by vacuum sputtering; D - Deposition of monoatomic TiO_2 layers by ALD method

2.3. Measurement techniques

Raman scattering was measured by using ProRaman-L spectrometer (Laser power 30 mW) Raman spectrometer with 785 nm excitation wavelengths. SEM images and EDX mapping were obtained using energy dispersive spectroscopy (EDX, analyzer X-MaxN, 20 mm^2 SDD detector, Oxford Instruments). The amount of generated hydrogen was measured by gas chromatography (Tianmei GC 7900, TCD detector, N_2 as a carrier).

3. RESULTS AND DISCUSSION

Figure 2 shows results of SEM measurements and EDX element mapping for Au and Ti. **Figure 2A** shows that as a result of laser modification of the polymer, an even and straight periodic grating was formed. After the deposition of titanium oxide by atomic layer deposition, significant changes in the structure are observed (**Figure 2B**). Moreover, based on the results of the EDX analysis (**Figures 2C, 2D**), it can be seen that gold was evenly distributed over the surface of the periodic structure. The EDX element mapping for titanium (**Figure 2F**) also shows that atomic layer deposition process results in an uniform distribution of titanium over the gold surface, while no traces of titanium were found on pristine sample (**Figure 2E**).

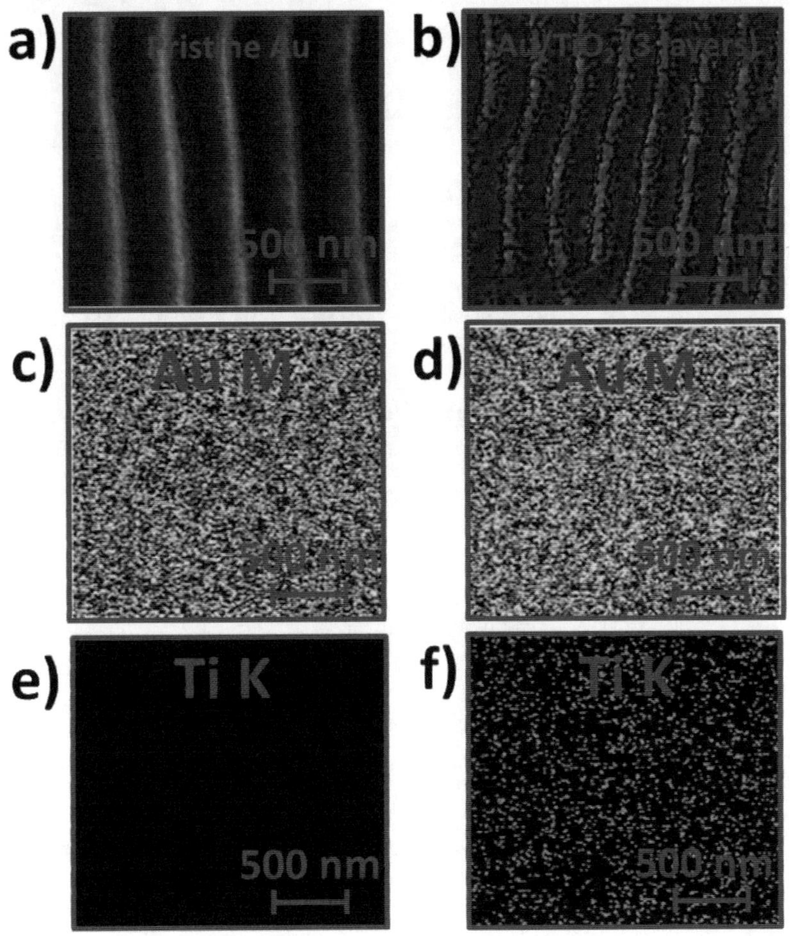

Figure 2 Results of SEM for (a) pristine grating covered by gold and (b) gold grating covered by 3 layers of TiO_2 and EDX element mapping (Au, Ti) for (c, e) pristine grating covered by gold and (d, f) gold grating covered by 3 layers of TiO_2

Figure 3 shows the results of the SERS measurements. No peaks were observed on the gold sample without a periodic grating. However, a sample containing a periodic lattice coated with gold is capable to generate surface plasmon resonance, resulting in the appearance of pronounced peaks of the dye (Rhodamine 6G - R6G). Also, according to the measurement results, it was found that a combined structure based on a gold periodic grating and titanium oxide contributes to a significant increase in the SERS signal due to the influence of surface plasmon-polariton resonance and significant amplification of the electromagnetic field.

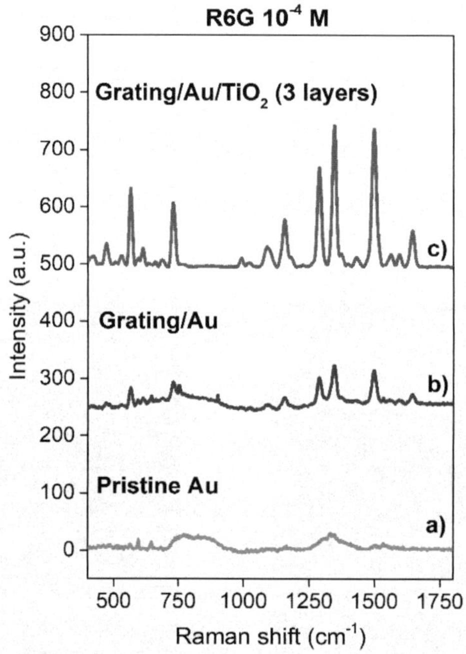

Figure 3 SERS measurements for a) pristine sample with Au without grating, b) pristine sample with Au on the periodic grating and c) sample with gold periodic grating covered by 3 layers of TiO_2

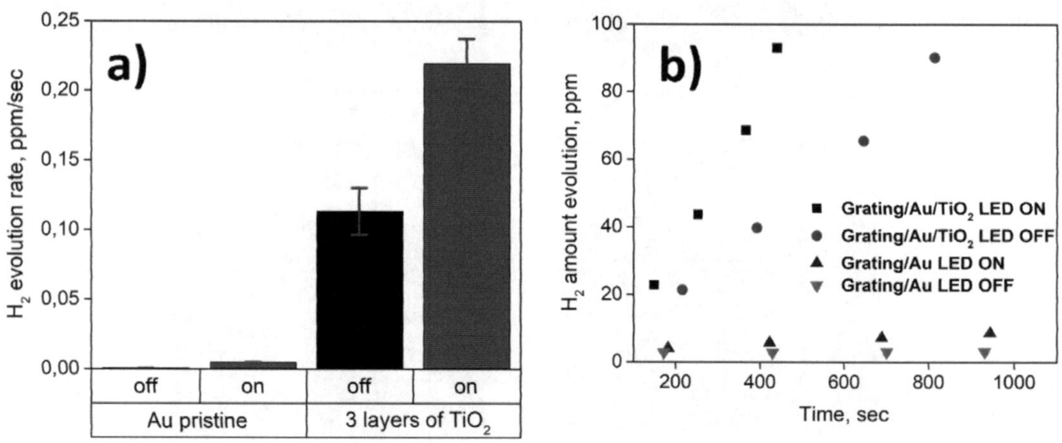

Figure 4 Results of hydrogen amount evolution: a) H_2 evolution rate production by using pristine gold grating and combination of gold grating with titanium dioxide layers with and without LED lamp; b) H_2 evolution amount of samples with and without LED lamp

Figure 4 shows the results of measuring the amount of hydrogen produced in the process of water splitting. **Figure 4A** shows a comparison of hydrogen evolution efficiency with applied voltage of 0.6V by using samples with and without titanium oxide on the gold grating. The measurement results show that the samples with titanium oxide on the surface generate more hydrogen than the original sample due to plasmon triggering of titanium dioxide. Moreover, the effect of an LED lamp switching is also well visible. **Figure 4B** shows the time dependences of the hydrogen concentration in the electrolytic bath, which allows estimating approximately the reaction kinetics.

4. CONCLUSION

In this work, we created a hybrid structure with a combination of plasmon-active component and photocatalytic component TiO_2. Grating was created in using excimer KrF laser with a wavelength of 248 nm. Gold was deposited by vacuum sputtering. TiO_2 layer was produced from titanium (IV) chloride and was deposited by using atomic layer deposition process (ALD). Experiments were performed in dark or under illumination with LED lamp (λ=850 nm, FWHM=30 nm, irradiance=1450 μW/cm^2, current=1200 mA) which corresponded to plasmon absorption band. It is shown that the combination of gold and titanium dioxide can lead to the triggering of catalytic activity of TiO_2 and enhanced generation of green hydrogen.

ACKNOWLEDGEMENTS

This work was supported by the project Internal Grant Agency UCT № 126 088 2009. Also this research was partly conducted using the equipment of the resource center of the Research Park of the St. Petersburg State University «Innovative Technologies of Composite Nanomaterials».

REFERENCES

[1] SUKLA, Lala Behari, ENKETESWARA, Subudhi, PRADHAN, Debabrata, (Eds.). *The role of microalgae in wastewater treatment*. Springer Nature Springapore Pte Limited, 2019.

[2] NGUYEN, D. C. Potential of Biomass Sources for Fural-Based Fuel Production in the Consideration as a Green Fuel. *European Journal of Engineering Research and Science*. 2019, vol. 4, no. 1, pp. 42-48.

[3] GORJI, Y. M., GHAZIASKAR, H. S. Optimization of solketalacetin synthesis as a green fuel additive from ketalization of monoacetin with acetone. *Industrial & Engineering Chemistry Research*. 2016, vol. 55, no. 25, pp. 6904-6910.

[4] PIKER, A., TABAH, B., PERKAS, N., GEDANKEN, A. A green and low-cost room temperature biodiesel production method from waste oil using egg shells as catalyst. *Fuel*. 2016, vol. 182, pp. 34-41.

[5] MILIUTINA, E., GUSELNIKOVA, O., CHUFISTOVA, S., KOLSKA, Z., ELASHNIKOV, R., BURTSEV, V., POSTNIKOV, P., SVORCIK, V., LYUTAKOV, O. Fast and All-Optical Hydrogen Sensor Based on Gold-Coated Optical Fiber Functionalized with Metal-Organic Framework Layer. *ACS sensors*. 2019, vol. 4, no. 12, pp. 3133-3140.

[6] ELASHNIKOV, R., ZAHORJANOVA, K., MILIUTINA, E., KOLSKA, Z., CIESLAR, M., SVORCIK, V., LYUTAKOV, O. Proton exchange membrane with plasmon-active surface for enhancement of fuel cell effectivity. *Nanoscale*. 2020, vol. 12, no. 22.

[7] GUSELNIKOVA, O., TRELIN, A., MILIUTINA, E., ELASHNIKOV, R., SAJDL, P., POSTNIKOV, P.S., KOLSKA, Z., SVORCIK, V., LYUTAKOV, O. Plasmon-induced water splitting-through flexible hybrid 2D architecture up to hydrogen from seawater under NIR light. *ACS Applied Materials & Interfaces*. 2020, vol. 12, no. 25, pp. 28110-28119.

[8] HOSSEINI, S. E., WAHID, M. A. Hydrogen production from renewable and sustainable energy resources: promising green energy carrier for clean development. *Renewable and Sustainable Energy Reviews*. 2016, vol. 57, pp. 850-866.

[9] AHMED, A., AL-AMIN, A. Q., AMBROSE, A. F., SAIDUR, R. Hydrogen fuel and transport system: A sustainable and environmental future. *International journal of hydrogen energy*. 2016, vol. 41, no. 3, pp. 1369-1380.

[10] DINCER, I., ACAR, C. Review and evaluation of hydrogen production methods for better sustainability. *International journal of hydrogen energy*. 2015, vol. 40, no. 34, pp. 11094-11111.

[11] JADHAV, P., SARKAR, J., PATIL, R., VINCHURKAR, S. Microbial Disintegration of Bio-Waste for Hydrogen Generation for Application in Fuel Cell. *Int. Res. J. Eng. Technol.* 2017, vol. 4, no. 3, pp. 229-232.

[12] RASHID, M. M., AL MESFER, M. K., NASEEM, H., DANISH, M. Hydrogen production by water electrolysis: a review of alkaline water electrolysis, PEM water electrolysis and high temperature water electrolysis. *Int. J. Eng. Adv. Technol.* 2015, vol. 4, no. 3, pp. 2249-8958.

[13] CHI, J., YU, H. Water electrolysis based on renewable energy for hydrogen production. *Chinese Journal of Catalysis*. 2018, vol. 39, no. 3, pp. 390-394.

[14] SHARMA, S., GHOSHAL, S. K. Hydrogen the future transportation fuel: From production to applications. *Renewable and sustainable energy reviews*. 2015, vol. 43, pp. 1151-1158.

[15] NIKOLAIDIS, P., POULLIKKAS, A. A comparative overview of hydrogen production processes. *Renewable and sustainable energy reviews*. 2017, vol. 67, pp. 597-611.

[16] IATSUNSKYI, I., JANCELEWICZ, M., NOWACZYK, G., KEMPIŃSKI, M., PEPLIŃSKA, B., JAREK, M., SMYNTYNA, V. Atomic layer deposition TiO_2 coated porous silicon surface: Structural characterization and morphological features. *Thin Solid Films*. 2015, vol. 589, pp. 303-308.

[17] HACKLER, R. A., KANG, G., SCHATZ, G. C., STAIR, P. C., VAN DUYNE, R. P. Analysis of TiO_2 atomic layer deposition surface chemistry and evidence of propene oligomerization using surface-enhanced Raman spectroscopy. *Journal of the American Chemical Society*. 2018, vol. 141, no. 1, pp. 414-422.

[18] ZHANG, X.-Y., HU, A., ZHANG, T., LEI, W., XUE, X.-J., ZHOU, Y., DULEY. W. W. Self-assembly of large-scale and ultrathin silver nanoplate films with tunable plasmon resonance properties. *ACS Nano*. 2011, vol. 5, no. 11, pp. 9082-9092.

[19] ELASHNIKOV, R., TRELIN, A., OTTA, J., FITL, P., MARES, D., JERABEK, V., SVORCIK, V., LYUTAKOV, O. Laser patterning of transparent polymers assisted by plasmon excitation. *Soft Matter*. 2018, vol. 14, no. 23, pp. 4860-4865.

THE EFFECT OF ATMOSPHERIC COLD PLASMA CLEANING OF FTO SUBSTRATES ON THE QUALITY OF TiO2 ELECTRON TRANSPORT LAYERS FOR PRINTED CARBON-BASED PEROVSKITE SOLAR CELLS

[1]Matej HVOJNIK, [2]Július VIDA, [2]Tomáš HOMOLA, [1]Michaela PAVLIČKOVÁ, [1]Michal HATALA, [1]Milan MIKULA, [1]Katarína TOMANOVÁ, [1]Pavol GEMEINER

[1]*Faculty of Chemical and Food Technology, Slovak University of Technology in Bratislava, Slovakia, EU,* matej.hvojnik@stuba.sk

[2]*Department of Physical Electronics, Faculty of Science, Masaryk University, Brno, Czech Republic, EU*

https://doi.org/10.37904/nanocon.2020.3716

Abstract

In this work, TiO_2 electron transport layers (ETL) of printed perovskite solar cells with back carbon electrode (C-PSCs) were prepared on uncleaned, chemically cleaned, and plasma-treated FTO substrates. The effect of cleaning procedure type on the quality of TiO_2 ETL has been characterised by XPS and SEM. The C-PSCs with FTO substrates treated by low-temperature atmospheric plasma at ambient air for 10 s reached approximately the same efficiency (4.4%) as with the chemically cleaned FTO (4.5%). From optical microscope and SEM images, it was observed that the plasma cleaned the FTO substrate to some extent, thereby reducing the number of defects and pinholes occurring in the blocking layer. XPS measurements confirmed that chemical and plasma treatment significantly reduced organic species on the FTO surface.

Keywords: Atmospheric cold plasma, TiO_2, electron transport layer, carbon electrode, perovskite solar cells

1. INTRODUCTION

The role of the electron transport layer (ETL) of carbon-based perovskite solar cell (C-PSC) is to extract and transport electrons from the perovskite layer towards the transparent conductive oxide (TCO) electrode (glass or PET substrate with FTO or ITO layer). The quality of the ETL depends on two main parameters: 1) the preparation process and the composition of the used dispersion, which determine its thickness, roughness, and compactness; 2) the surface properties of the used substrate [1]. The most suitable ETL layer is very thin (<50 nm), which results in defects that cause internal short-circuits after the undesirable contact between the perovskite and TCO [2,3]. On the other hand, if the layer is too thick, the series resistance increases, the electrons recombine with the holes, resulting in a reduction of the current density and the fill factor of the solar cell [4,5]. The ETL with a thickness of several tens of nanometres is applied on the pre-treated substrates, and even the smallest impurity related to insufficient cleaning can significantly affect the quality of the ETL as well as the performance of the entire PSC. The most commonly used method of cleaning is chemical cleaning, which is very effective, but on the other hand, it is time-consuming (~1 hour) and requires the use of harmful organic solvents [6].

In this work, we showed that rapid (in order of seconds) atmospheric plasma treatment in ambient air has a potential to replace chemical cleaning of FTO substrates, and we examined the effect of plasma on FTO surface and the quality of TiO_2 ETL deposited on FTO. In addition to substrate cleaning, plasma also increases the surface energy and ensures better ETL homogeneity and charge transport at its interface with FTO.

2. EXPERIMENTAL SECTION

2.1. Materials

FTO/glass substrates (fluorine-doped tin oxide, 7 Ω/sq.), titanium diisopropoxide bis(acetylacetonate) (75 wt.% TiAcAc in isopropanol), isopropyl alcohol (≥ 99,7% $(CH_3)_2CHOH$), diethanolamine (≥ 98 wt.%, DEA) were purchased from Sigma-Aldrich. Titanium tetrachloride (≥ 97%, $TiCl_4$) was ordered form Merck KGaA. Ethanol (≥ 97%, CH_3CH_2OH) was from mikroCHEM. Mesoporous titania nanoparticle paste (Ti-Nanoxide T165/SP), mesoporous zirconium dioxide nanoparticle paste (Zr-Nanoxide ZT/SP), mesoporous carbon-black paste (Elcocarb B/SP) and perovskite solution $((5 - AVA)_x (MA)_{1-x}PbI_3)$ were purchased from Solaronix.

2.2. Device fabrication

Printed mesoporous perovskite solar cells with carbon back electrode (C-PSCs) were prepared on the commercial FTO/glass substrates cleaned by three different methods: chemically cleaned, plasma-treated, and uncleaned. The preparation process of solar cells with the structure (**Figure 1**): FTO glass substrate/electron transport - blocking layer TiO_2/mesoporous TiO_2 layer/scaffold ZrO_2 layer/carbon back electrode/perovskite ran under laboratory conditions. The chemical cleaning procedure was managed as follows: applied substrates were precisely and sequentially cleaned with a surfactant, acetone, and isopropyl alcohol in an ultrasonic bath for 20 min in every solvent. The drying of the substrates took place on the ambient air, and additionally before deposition of the functional layers were treated by ultraviolet radiation for 15 min to remove all organic residues. Plasma-treated substrates were exposed to 10 s low-temperature ambient-air surfaceplasma generated by RPS40+ (Roplass s.r.o., Czech Republic). The surface of the uncleaned substrates was not treated in any way. First, a compact TiO_2 sol-gel blocking layers prepared from the mixture of TiAcAc and $TiCl_4$ precursors were spin-coated on the different pre-treated FTO substrates and sintered at 500 °C for 30 min. Second, other functional layers of the C-PSC, such as mesoporous TiO_2, ZrO_2 and carbon back electrode were deposited by screen-printing. Third, the perovskite solution was directly dropped and infiltrated trough the carbon layer and dried at 100 °C for 30 min. A detailed method of C-PSC and TiO_2 blocking layer preparation is described in the author's previous work [7].

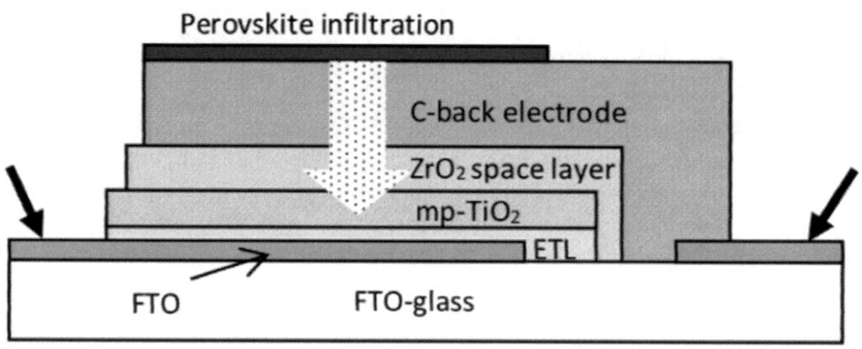

Figure 1 The structure of the printed C-PSC

2.3. Characterisation

The conversion efficiency of solar to the electric energy of the C-PSC was determined by measuring photocurrent density-voltage load characteristics under 1000 W/m^2 of standard daylight exposition with a 1.5G air-mass (AM). Optical microscope (*LEICA DM 2700 M*) and scanning electron microscope (*JEOL, JSM67500FA, Analytical field emission scanning electron microscope, Japan*) were used for the analysis of the FTO/TiO_2 sol-gel surface. The X-ray photoelectron spectrometer Axis Supra from *Kratos Analytical* was used to study the surface chemistry of chemically cleaned, plasma-treated and uncleaned FTO samples.

3. RESULTS AND DISCUSSION

We analysed the reference, chemically cleaned and plasma-cleaned samples by X-ray photoelectron spectroscopy (XPS) to study the changes in the stoichiometry and bonding states on the surface of FTO glass. **Table 1** presents the elemental composition of the surface of FTO for different cleaning methods used. The uncleaned sample was highly contaminated, containing as much as 74% of carbon on the surface. Chemical cleaning process led to a decrease in carbon concentration on the surface to 26%. The uncleaned surface also contained traces (below 1%) of potassium and calcium, which were also reduced and in case of potassium completely removed after chemical cleaning. The oxygen concentration on the surface also increased, which can be attributed to the relative change in carbon concentration. Plasma cleaning of FTO for 10 s led to a decrease in carbon concentration to around 14%. The increase of oxygen on the surface was more significant compared to the chemical cleaning process. Exposure of the surface to the ambient air plasma, which contains reactive oxygen species causes oxidation of the surface and is known to induce polar oxygen-containing functional groups to the treated surface [8-10]. The O:C ratio (**Table 1**) therefore increased significantly. Compared to chemical cleaning, plasma treatment was not so efficient for the total removal of the potassium and calcium contamination. Around 4% of nitrogen was introduced to the surface of plasma-treated samples, a known effect of treatment by plasma generated in ambient air. These results correspond well with the plasma-cleaning of ITO with the same plasma source reported by *Homola et al.* [11].

Table 1 Atomic concentrations from XPS with standard deviation measured at two points for each sample

	C [%]	O [%]	Sn [%]	Ca [%]	K [%]	N [%]	O:C	O:Sn
No clean	74 ± 7	19 ± 4	5 ± 3	0.7 ± 0.1	0.2 ± 0.0	1.0 ± 0.3	0.3	3.7
Chem clean	26 ± 1	49 ± 1	23 ± 1	0.3 ± 0.1	0.0 ± 0.1	2.1 ± 0.7	1.8	2.1
10 s plasma	14 ± 1	57 ± 0	23 ± 1	1.1 ± 0.3	0.8 ± 0.2	4.0 ± 1.0	4.0	2.5

The high-resolution C 1s region in the XPS spectrum is shown in **Figure 2a**. Four components were used for deconvolution, specifically C-C/C-H, C-OH/C-O-C, C=O and O-C=O species at 285.0 eV, 286.5 eV, 288.0 eV and 289.0 eV of binding energy, respectively. The reference sample without any cleaning displayed a significant C-C/C-H component with around 82% relative intensity. Chemical cleaning led to the removal of C-C/C-H groups from the surface, while the relative intensity of the oxygen-containing functional groups increased. The oxidation effect of the plasma can be seen in the increase of the relative intensity of the oxygen-containing functional groups in the C 1s region of the plasma-treated sample.

The high-resolution O 1s region is shown in **Figure 2b**. The SnO_2 in FTO typically displays a peak in the O 1s region at around 530.5 eV [12,13]. Furthermore, oxygen on metallic surfaces can be found in the form of metal-hydroxides $(OH)^-$, that are often found in around 531.5 eV and in adsorbed H_2O at around 533.0 eV [14,15]. Oxygen can also be found bound to carbon in a multitude of environments of the organic species, positions of which can vary between 531.0 eV up to 534.0 eV. We can expect significant contributions from the organic oxygen to the $(OH)^-$ and H_2O components. Both chemical cleaning and plasma treatment led to a more pronounced SnO_2 component due to the removal of organic species. A shift of the SnO_2 component to higher binding energies can be seen after the plasma treatment. We believe that the surface of FTO prior to plasma treatment consisted of a mixture of Sn^{4+} oxide and Sn^{2+} oxide. Several author have shown that the signal in the XPS spectrum from the SnO is shifted from the signal from SnO_2 by around 0.4 eV towards lower binding energies [15-17]. The reactive oxygen species in plasma cause oxidation of the SnO into SnO_2 and therefore the shifted signal is observed.

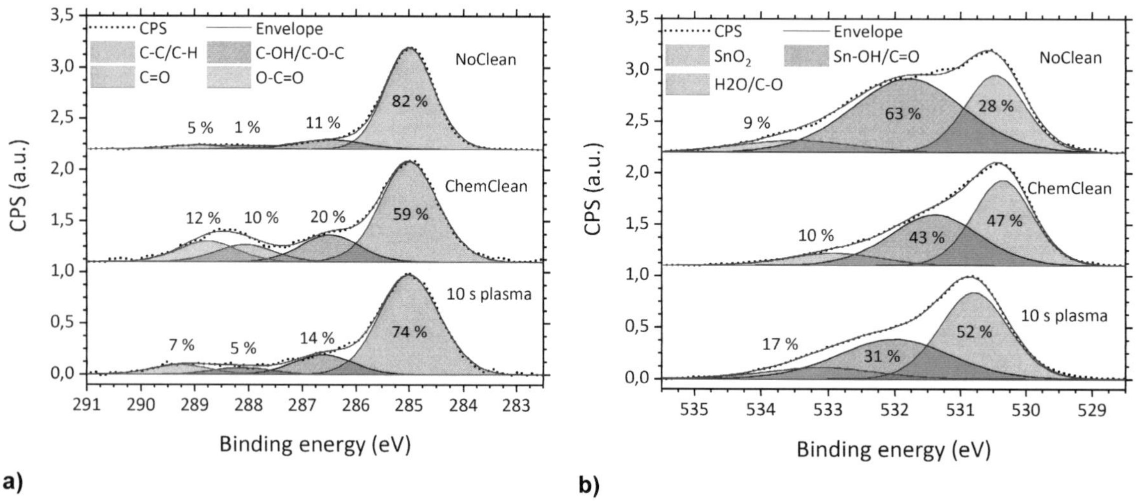

Figure 2 Comparison of narrow regions of **a)** C 1s and **b)** O 1s in the XPS spectrum of the uncleaned, chemically cleaned and plasma-cleaned surface of FTO

The photocurrent-voltage load characteristics of C-PSCs with all types of treated and uncleaned substrates are shown in **Figure 3**. It is evident, that the purity of the substrate's surface has a crucial effect on the quality of the deposited functional layers. Specifically on the blocking layers, as their thickness is several tens of nanometers and any impurity adversely affects all the photovoltaic parameters. The blocking layer with high quality without any cracks or failures prevents the recombination of electrons with holes, and also the internal short circuits what is necessary for high performance of C-PSC. Devices with substrates treated by the chemical way and by plasma for 10 s reached approximately the same efficiency 4.4 - 4.5% with relatively good shapes of photocurrent-voltage load characteristics, fill factor (FF) and short-circuit current density (J_{sc}) (**Table 2**). The open-circuit voltage (V_{oc}) has changed only partially from 0.65 to 0.70 V in all cases. Results achieved by the chemical cleaning can be attributed to a thin, homogeneous, and almost failure-free blocking layers, which was confirmed by optical and top-view SEM images (**Figures 4, 5a**). In the case of the substrates plasma-treated for 10 s, a small occurrence of impurities and defects in the blocking layers is seen in **Figures 4, 5b**. On the other hand, the effect of plasma improved the wettability of the FTO surface (contact angle decreased for plasma-treated FTO = 10° vs chemically cleaned FTO = 35°), and interfacial contact between the FTO and the blocking layer what led to better charge transport between the layers. The efficiency of C-PSCs with uncleaned substrates was at the level of 1% due to the presence of a large number of impurities, failures and pin-holes in the blocking layer **(Figures 4, 5c**). The presence of failures and pin-holes in the blocking layer created the trapping sites for charge recombination and current leakage what further led to a decrease in FF, J_{sc}, and to the linearisation of the load characteristics (**Table 2, Figure 3**). It can also be observed from optical images that the plasma, to some extent, cleans the surface of the substrate itself (**Figures 4b vs 4c**).

Table 2 Photovoltaic parameters of the C-PSCs with differently treated and uncleaned substrates

Treatment	J_{sc} (mA.cm^{-2})	V_{oc} (V)	Efficiency (%)	FF
Uncleaned	8.4	0.70	1.4	0.23
Cleaned	15.8	0.68	4.4	0.41
Plasma 10 s	17.0	0.65	4.5	0.41

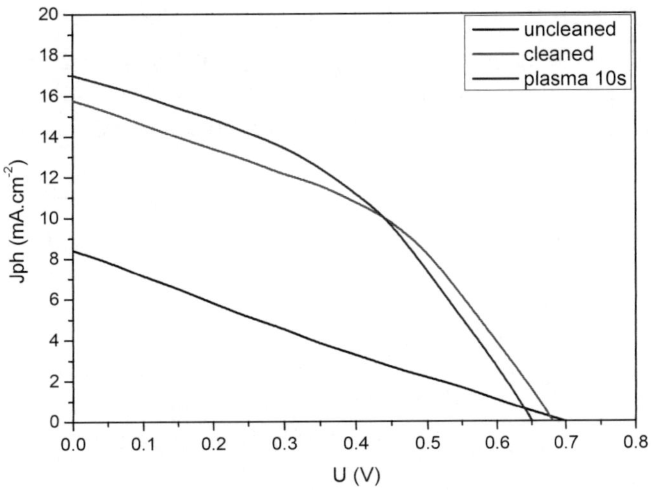

Figure 3 J-V loading photo-curves of solar cells with differently cleaned and uncleaned substrates

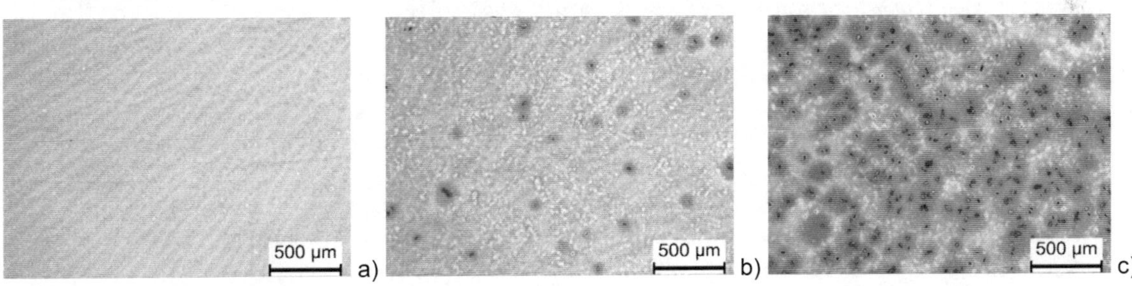

Figure 4 Optical microscopy images of the TiO_2 sol-gel blocking layers prepared on: a) chemically cleaned substrate, b) 10 s plasma treated substrate and c) uncleaned substrate

Figure 5 Top-view SEM images (scale bar 3 µm) of the TiO_2 sol-gel blocking layers prepared on: a) chemically cleaned substrate, b) 10 s plasma-treated substrate and c) uncleaned substrate

4. CONCLUSION

In this work, the mesoporous perovskite solar cells with carbon back electrode were prepared on chemically cleaned, plasma-treated and uncleaned substrates by screen-printing and coating technics. The obtained results showed that solar cells prepared on chemically cleaned substrates reached the approximately same efficiency and FF as on the substrates treated by 10 s low-temperature ambient air plasma. It means that the few second plasma treatments of FTO glass substrate can successfully replace protracted one hour chemically cleaning in different solvents and an ultrasonic bath.

ACKNOWLEDGEMENTS

This research was supported by the Slovak Grant Agency, VEGA 1/0488/19, STU Grant Scheme for Support of Young Researchers "PRINTCELL", Czech Science Foundation project 19-14770Y and LM2018110 project funded by the Ministry of Education, Youth and Sports of the Czech Republic.

REFERENCES

[1] MIKULA, M., BEKOVÁ, Z., HVOJNIK, M., HATALA, M., MIKOLÁŠEK, M., MULLEROVÁ, J., JERGEL, M., GEMEINER, P. Differently sintered TiO_x hole blocking layers for solution processed solar cells. *Applied Surface Science*. 2018, no. 461, pp. 54-60.

[2] LIU, H., FU, X., BALA, H., ZONG, B., HUANG, L., FU, W., WANG, S., GUO, Z., SUN, G., CAO, J., ZHANG, Z. An effective TiO_2 blocking layer for hole-conductor-free perovskite solar cells based on carbon counter electrode. *Organic Electronics*. [online]. 2018. Available from: https://doi.org/10.1016/j.orgel.2018.04.042.

[3] LIAN, J., LU, B., NIU, F., ZENG, P., ZHAN, X. Electron-Transport Materials in Perovskite Solar Cells. *Small Methods*. 2018, Vol. 2, 1800082.

[4] MOHAMAD NOH, M.F., TEH, C.H., DAIK, R., LIM, E.L., YAP, C.C., IBRAHIM, M.A.A., AHMAD LUDIN, N., MOHD YUSOFF, A.R.B., JANG, J., MAT TERIDI, M.A. The architecture of the electron transport layer for a perovskite solar cell. *Journal of Materials Chemistry C*. 2018, vol. 6, pp. 682-712.

[5] FAGIOLARI, L., BELLA, F. Carbon-based materials for stable, cheaper and large-scale processable perovskite solar cells. *Energy and Environmental Science*. 2019, vol. 12, pp. 3437-3472.

[6] HOMOLA, T., SHEKARGOFTAR, M., POSPÍŠIL, J. Atmospheric plasma treatment of ITO thin films for rapid manufacturing of perovskite solar cells. **In:** *11th International Conference on Nanomaterials - Research & Application*. [online]. Brno:Tanger, 2019, pp. 43-47. Available from: https://doi.org/10.37904/nanocon.2019.8645.

[7] HVOJNIK, M., POPOVIČOVÁ, A.M., PAVLIČKOVÁ, M., HATALA, M., GEMEINER, P., MÜLLEROVÁ, J., TOMANOVÁ, K., MIKULA, M. Solution-processed TiO_2 blocking layers in printed carbon-based perovskite solar cells. *Applied Surface Science*. 2020, vol. 536, 147888.

[8] VESEL, A., MOZETIC, M. New developments in surface functionalization of polymers using controlled plasma treatments. *J. Phys. D. Appl. Phys.* [online]. 2017, vol. 50, no. 29. Available from: https://doi.org/10.1088/1361-6463/aa748a.

[9] KHOMIAKOVA, N., HANUŠ, J., KUZMINOVA, A., KYLIÁN, O. Investigation of Wettability, Drying and Water Condensation on Polyimide (Kapton) Films Treated by Atmospheric Pressure Air Dielectric Barrier Discharge. *Coatings*. 2020, vol. 10, no. 7, p. 619.

[10] KUZMINOVA, A., VANDROVCOVÁ, M., SHELEMIN, A., KYLIÁN, O., CHOUKOUROV, A., HANUŠ, J., BAČÁKOVÁ, L., SLAVINSKÁ, D., BIEDERMAN, H. Treatment of poly(ethylene terephthalate) foils by atmospheric pressure air dielectric barrier discharge and its influence on cell growth. *Applied Surface Science*. 2015, vol. 357, part A, pp. 689-695.

[11] HOMOLA, T., MATOUŠEK, J., MEDVECKÁ, V., ZAHORANOVÁ, A., KORMUNDA, M., KOVÁČIK, D., ČERNÁK, M. *Appl. Surf. Sci.* [online] 2012, vol. 258, no. 18, pp. 7135-7139. Available from: https://doi.org/10.1016/j.apsusc.2012.03.188.

[12] SWALLOW, J.E.N., WILLIAMSON, B.A.D., WHITTLES, T.J., BIRKETT, M., FEATHERSTONE, T.J., PENG, N., ABBOTT, A., FARNWORTH, M., CHEETHAM, K.J., WARREN, P., et al. Self-Compensation in Transparent Conducting F-Doped SnO2. *Advanced Functional Materials*. [online]. 2017, vol. 28. Available from: https://doi.org/10.1002/adfm.201701900.

[13] MARTÍNEZ, A.I., HUERTA, L., O-RUEDA DE LEÓN, J.M., ACOSTA, D., MALIK, O., AGUILAR, M. Physicochemical characteristics of fluorine doped tin oxide films. J. *Phys. D. Appl. Phys.* [online]. 2006, vol. 39, no. 23, pp. 5091-5096. Available from: https://doi.org/10.1088/0022-3727/39/23/029.

[14] JADHAV, H., SURYAWANSHI, S., MORE, M.A., SINHA, S. Pulsed laser deposition of tin oxide thin films for field emission studies. *Appl. Surf. Sci.* [online]. 2017, vol. 419, pp. 764-769. Available from: https://doi.org/10.1016/j.apsusc.2017.05.020.

[15] GAGGIOTTI, G., GALDIKAS, A., KAČIULIS, S., MATTOGNO, G., ŠETKUS, A. Surface chemistry of tin oxide based gas sensors. *J. Appl. Phys.* [online]. 1994, vol. 76, no. 8, pp. 4467-4471. Available from: https://doi.org/10.1063/1.357277.

[16] SZUBER, J., CZEMPIK, G., LARCIPRETE, R., KOZIEJ, D., ADAMOWICZ, B. XPS study of the L-CVD deposited SnO2 thin films exposed to oxygen and hydrogen. **In:** *Thin Solid Films*. [online]. Vol. 391, pp. 198-203. Available from: https://doi.org/10.1016/S0040-6090(01)00982-8

[17] LIANG, L.Y., LIU, Z.M., CAO, H.T., PAN, X.Q. Microstructural, Optical, and Electrical Properties of SnO Thin Films Prepared on Quartz via a Two-Step Method. *ACS Appl. Mater. Interfaces.* [online]. 2010, vol. 2, no. 4, pp. 1060-1065. Available from: https://doi.org/10.1021/am900838z.

NICKEL-COBALT OXIDE THIN-FILMS ANODES FOR LITHIUM-ION BATTERIES

[1]Ilya MITROFANOV, [1]Denis NAZAROV, [1]Yury KOSHTYAL, [1]Ilya EZHOV, [1]Pavel FEDOROV, [2]Aleksander RUMYANTSEV, [1]Anatoliy POPOVICH, [1]Maxim MAXIMOV*

[1]Peter the Great Saint-Petersburg Polytechnic University, Saint-Petersburg, Russia, maximspbstu@mail.ru
[2]Ioffe Institute, Saint-Petersburg, Russia

https://doi.org/10.37904/nanocon.2020.3714

Abstract

Thin-film transition metal oxides can be applied as transparent conductive coatings, photocatalysts, thermoelectric generators, and battery electrodes. In power sources application binary transition metal oxides are attractive due to high theoretical capacities. Among them nickel-cobalt oxides possess the highest ($NiCoO_2$, 717mAh/g or 471.4 μAh cm^{-2} $μm^{-1}$). This work is devoted to Atomic layer deposition (ALD) of thin-films of nickel-cobalt oxides and evaluating their performance as negative electrodes for solid-state lithium-ion batteries. Ni-Co-O thin films were synthesized with different NiO/CoO ALD cycles ratio (5/1, 3/1, and 1/1) using nickelocene, cobaltocene and oxygen plasma. Both NiO and CoO crystal phases were observed in deposited films. The content of chemical elements (C, O, Ni and Co) in the film's depth are uniform, except for sample 5/1. The electrochemical performance of synthesized thin films was studied by cyclic voltammetry and galvanostatic cycling. It was found that with an increase of the nickel content in the coatings, the electrode's specific capacity is increasing. The highest capacity at high discharge currents (35C) is observed for the sample obtained with NiO/CoO - 5/1 ratio (660 $μA \cdot h \cdot μm^{-1} \cdot cm^{-2}$)

Keywords: Atomic layer deposition, Nickel-cobalt oxide, lithium-ion batteries, solid-state lithium-ion batteries

1. INTRODUCTION

Solid-state thin-film lithium-ion batteries (SSLIBs) can be applied to power various miniature devices [1]: medical implants [2], "smart" bank cards, RFID tags, etc. The increase of operating time (that is usability) requires power sources with higher energy density.

SSLIBs can be manufactured using chemical vapor deposition, pulsed laser deposition, dip coating, and atomic layer deposition [3-5] (ALD). ALD is a promising technology that allows the deposition of films of various materials with high thickness accuracy on flat and three-dimensional substrates.

Nickel oxide and cobalt oxide are promising materials for SSLIBs [6-8] and have high theoretical capacities (715-746 mAh/g [9], 425-480 $μAh \cdot μm^{-1} \cdot cm^{-2}$). The chemical composition of the active material can affect the electrochemical activity and service life of the electrodes. In this regard, we studied the effect of the chemical composition of films of mixed nickel and cobalt oxide obtained by the ALD method using the supercycle approach [3].

2. MATERIALS AND METHODS

Silicon (surface orientation (100), 40 × 40 mm^2, Telecom-STV Co., Ltd., Zelenograd, Russia) and stainless-steel (316SS, 16 mm diameter plates, Tob New Energy Technology Co., Ltd., Xiamen, China) were used as substrates. The substrates were cleaned in an ultrasonic bath in acetone and deionized water for 10 and 5 min, respectively. The native oxide layer was removed by immersion of silicon wafer in 10% HF solution for 5 min. Then, to remove organic contaminants and produce a hydroxylic surface, silicon substrates were cleaned using piranha solution (H_2SO_4/H_2O_2, volume ratio 7:3) for 20 min, rinsed in deionized water, and dried under an argon atmosphere [10].

ALD processes of nickel-cobalt oxide (NCO), nickel oxide (NO), and cobalt oxide (CO) were performed by a commercial R-150 setup (Picosun Oy, Espoo, Finland) at a temperature 300 °C and a reactor base pressure of 8-12 hPa. Bis(cyclopentadienyl) nickel(II) and Bis(cyclopentadienyl) cobalt(II) ($Ni(Cp)_2$, $Co(Cp)_2$; 99%, Dalchem, Nizhny Novgorod, Russia) were used as the nickel- and cobalt-containing precursors. $Co(Cp)_2$ and $Ni(Cp)_2$ were kept in stainless-steel bottles (PicohotTM 200, Picosun Oy) and heated to 160 and 110 °C, respectively. Pulse times and purge times were 1s and 10s, respectively, for both $Co(Cp)_2$ and $Ni(Cp)_2$. Remote oxygen plasma was used as a counter-reagent (pO_2). The plasma power was 3 kW, with a frequency range of 1.9-3.2 MHz. The total oxygen plasma pulse time was 19.5 s (Ar purge during 0.5 s with flow rate 40 sccm; Ar and O2 plasma purge during 14 s with flow rate 90 sccm; Ar purge during 5 s with flow rate 40 sccm). Deposition conditions were based on our previous studies devoted to obtaining cobalt and nickel oxide [11,12]. Synthesized films were denoted as NCO 1/1, 3/1, 5/1, which correspond to NiO/CoO pulse ration in supercycle ([n·(Ni- pO2)+m·(Co-pO_2)]).

The thickness of the films was determined using an Ellips-1891 SAG ellipsometer (CNT, Novosibirsk, Russia) in a wavelength range from 370 to 1000 nm (at an incidence angle of 70°) and the Spectr software package (1.10, CNT, Novosibirsk, Russia). The growth per cycle (GPC) and growth per supercycle (GPSC) were calculated by dividing film thickness by the number of cycles/supercycles.

X-ray diffraction (XRD) studies were performed by Bruker D8 DISCOVER (Cu-Kα, Billerica, MA, USA) diffractometer. Surface-sensitive grazing incidence XRD (GIXRD) mode was used for XRD measurements using 2θ range of 15-65° with a step of 0.1° and an exposure of 1s at each step.

Escalab 250Xi spectrometer (Thermo Fisher Scientific, Waltham, MA, USA) was used to obtain X-ray photoelectron spectra (XPS). The samples were etched by Ar+ ions with 3 keV energy for 30 and 90 s for depth profiling studies. The samples were excited by Al-Kα (1486.7 eV) X-rays at a pressure of 7×10^{-8} Pa.

The thin films deposited on stainless-steel plates were used for electrochemical studies in CR2032 coin cells. Lithium foil, polyolefin porous film 2325 (Celgard, Charlotte, NC, USA), and TC-E918 (Tinci, Guangzhou, China) solution were used as the counter electrode, separator, and electrolyte, respectively. Coin cells were assembled in an argon atmosphere using OMNI-LAB glove box (VAC). Cyclic voltammetry (CV) was performed using PGSTAT302N+ potentiostat (Autolab, Utrecht, the Netherlands) in the range of 0.01-3 V with a scan rate of 0.5 mV/s. Cyclic charge/discharge was performed using the battery testing system CT-3008W-5V10mA (Neware, Shenzhen, China) at room temperature in the potential range of 0.01-3 V, current range 20-1600 µA.

3. RESULTS AND DISCUSSION

3.1. Film characterization

The deposition of films was effectuated with the use of the supercycle approach. To deposit NCO 1/1, NCO 3/1 and NCO 5/1, the 900 (1800), 470 (1880) and 310 (1860) supercycles (cycles) of synthesis were conducted. According to spectral ellipsometry measurements, the thicknesses of the NCO 1/1, NCO 3/1 and, NCO 5/1 films were 45.9 nm, 44.2 nm and, 36.3 nm, respectively.

The GPC determined from spectral ellipsometry analysis of NiO and CoO films are 0.12 ± 0.01 Å/cycle [11] and 0.25 ± 0.02 Å[12], respectively. Thus, the decrease of GPC of mixed oxide with number of NiO cycles increment in supercycle is expected (**Figure 1**). The observed augmentation of GPSC is also evident since the number of deposition cycles in one supercycle is augmented. For most samples, a good agreement between calculated values of GPC of mixed oxide films (basing on GPC of monoxides) and derived from ellipsometry measurements of deposited mixed oxide films is observed (0.01-0.03 Å/cycle difference). The slight increase of GPC and GPSC of deposited mixed oxide films may occur due to their lower density.

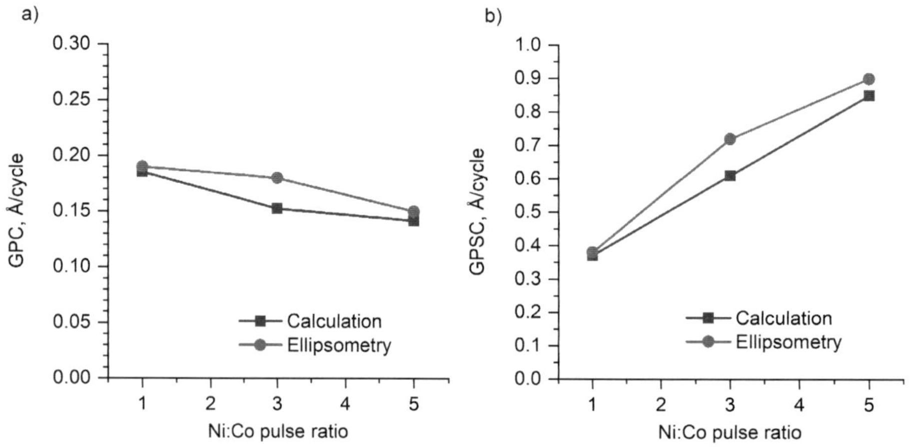

Figure 1 Growth per cycle(a) and growth per supercycle (b) of NCO thin films

Several reflexes were observed on the XRD patterns of deposited films. The peaks situated in 55, 56.5, and 62° are appeared due to defects of silicon substrates. The rest reflexes presented at 37, 43, 63° are associated with crystal phases of nickel oxide (PDF 01-071-1179) and cobalt oxide (PDF 01-061-1227). Thus, the deposition conducted at 300°C resulted in the formation of crystal phases of NiO and CoO.

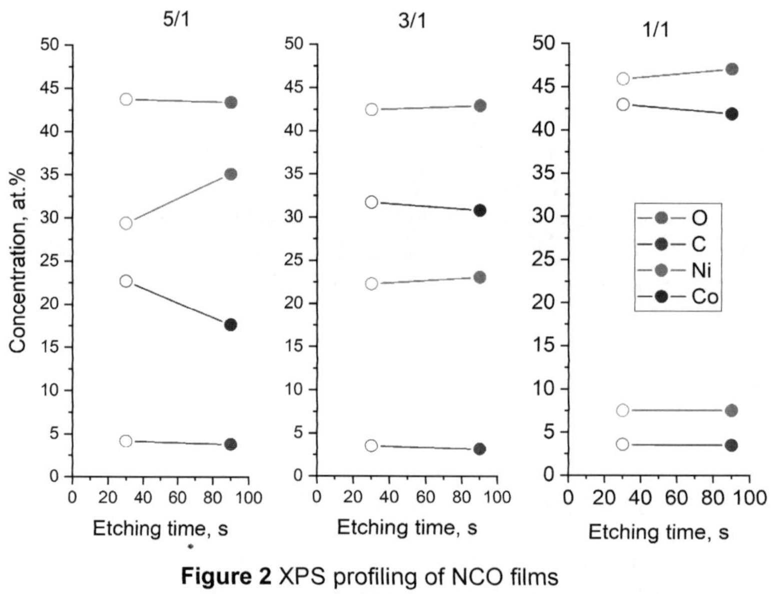

Figure 2 XPS profiling of NCO films

The Chemical composition of the films was estimated using XPS after etching during 30 and 90s (Ar^+, 3keV) (**Figure 2**). The first etching allows the elimination of hydrocarbon residues adsorbed from the atmosphere. According to the results of the experiments, the etching rate of nickel-cobalt oxide films in the chosen conditions is 0.77 Å/s. Therefore, XPS measurements performed after 90s of etching shows the composition of the film at a depth of 5-10 nm. For all samples and etching time, the concentration of carbon is stable, doesn't exceed 4.2 At.%, and might be caused by residues of Ni and Co precursor ligands. The concentration of transition metal (Ni, Co) augments with an increment of cycles effectuated for transition metal oxide deposition. The content of all elements in the film's depth is uniform, except for sample 5/1, where an increase in the proportion of nickel in the depth of the film is observed in proportion to a decrease in the proportion of cobalt (about 5%). An oxygen concentration varies from 42.5 to 47 at.%. The sum of transition metal concentration varies from 49 to 54 at.%. The ratio of concentrations - transition metals/oxygen is higher than 1. Thus part of metals may retain metal-carbon bonds or present in zero oxidation state.

3.2. Electrochemical analysis

With a potential decrease from 3.0 to 0V, an intense increase of current observed in the 0.2-0.8V area is observed. It can be related to the reduction of electrolyte components on the surface of materials [11]. The form of the observed current maximum is asymmetrical, and it may characterize at least to reduction reaction (with the participation of nickel or cobalt atoms). The subsequent increase of potential is accompanied by the increase of current in the 1.5-2.5V region. A shoulder at 1.62V is observed, and it is related to SEI electrochemical activity. The position of the main maximum shifts from 2.1 to 2.21 with an increment of nickel content. Thus, it can be concluded that maximum in the 2.1-2.21 region is related to oxidation reaction with transition metals (2.0V CoO [13], 2.05V Co_3O_4.[13], 2.22V NiO [11]). On the CV cathode curves of the 2nd-9th cycle, asymmetrical peak (peaks) are observed in the 0.6-1.5 V region while the increase of current observed during the first cycle is no longer presented. The noted current increase may be related to the reaction of transition metal oxide with lithium [14]. On the anode curves, the peaks observed on the first cycle are remained at following cycles, but their positions are slightly shifted to higher potentials.

After CV, the samples charged-discharged at different currents (20-1600 μA correspond to 25-42C). The specific discharge capacity of NCO 1/1, NCO 3/1, and NCO 5/1 at highest discharge currents were equal 470 μA h μm^{-1} cm^{-2} (25.5C), 650 μA h μm^{-1} cm^{-2} (29C), and 660 μA h μm^{-1} cm^{-2} (35C). Therefore, the increase in nickel content provides better C-rate performance due to possible solid electrolyte interphase (SEI) contribution which increases with nickel content. The theoretical capacities of nickel oxide and cobalt oxide are approximately equal (718 and 715 mAh/g). Probably, NiO better promotes the decomposition of the electrolyte to form an SEI film. When studying the electrochemical characteristics of thin films, SEI makes a significant contribution to the measured capacitance. Accordingly, higher NiO (SEI) content promotes higher capacity values.

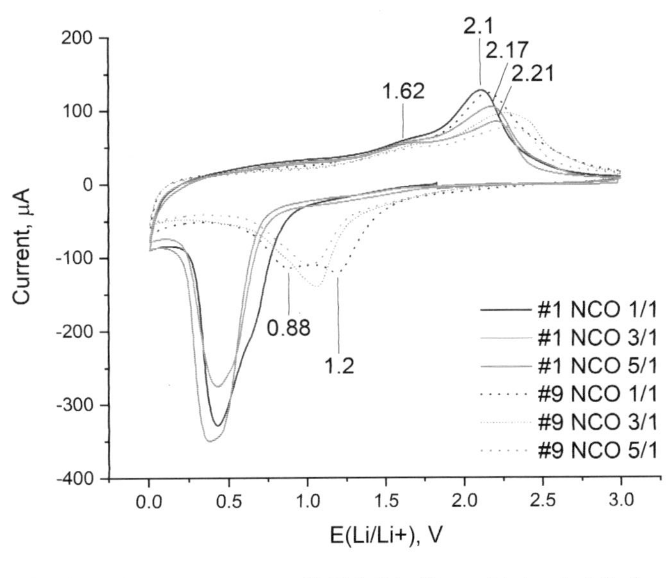

Figure 3 Cyclic voltamperograms of NCO thin films obtained at first and ninth cycle

4. CONCLUSION

Thin films (36-46 nm) of mixed nickel and cobalt oxides with a different ration of Ni/Co were deposited on silicon and stainless steel substrates using the ALD method. The growth per supercycle of the mixed oxide film was close to the linear combination of NiO and CoO cycles deposition. Both NiO and CoO crystal phases were observed in deposited films.

The increase in the number of transition metal (Ni, Co) oxide deposition cycles led to increased transition metal content in the film. Carbon (less than 4.2 at.%) was observed on the external surface and in the films' depth. An atomic concentration of transition metal exceeds oxygen concentration; thus, part of transition metal may be presented in a lower oxidation state.

According to electrochemical investigations, the specific capacity and rate performance increase with nickel content, due to possible solid electrolyte interphase (SEI) contribution which increases with to nickel content. The highest capacity at high discharge currents (35C) is observed for the sample obtained with NiO/CoO - 5/1 ratio (660 $\mu A \cdot h \cdot \mu m^{-1} \cdot cm^{-2}$).

ACKNOWLEDGEMENTS

The research was conducted under the financial support of the Russian Science Foundation grant (project No. 18-73-10015).

REFERENCES

[1] GOLDSTEIN, M. *IEEE Computer Society Phoenix Chapter - Internet of Things Innovations & Megatrends Update.* [online]. [viewed 03.08.2020]. Available from: https://www.slideshare.net/markgirc/ieee-computer-society-phoenix-chapter-internet-of-things-innovations-megatrends-update-121119.

[2] KHAN, Y., OSTFELD, A.E., LOCHNER, C.M., PIERRE, A., ARIAS, A.C. Monitoring of Vital Signs with Flexible and Wearable Medical Devices. *Advanced Materials.* [online]. 2016, vol. *28*, pp. 4373-4395. Available from: https://doi.org/10.1002/adma.201504366.

[3] MACKUS, A.J.M., SCHNEIDER, J.R., MACISAAC, C., BAKER, J.G., BENT, S.F. Synthesis of Doped, Ternary, and Quaternary Materials by Atomic Layer Deposition: A Review. *Chemistry of Materials.* [online]. 2019, vol. 31, pp. 1142-1183. Available from: https://doi.org/10.1021/acs.chemmater.8b02878.

[4] NAZAROV, D., EZHOV, I., MITROFANOV, I., LYUTAKOV, O., MAXIMOV, M.Y. The Use of the TMA as Stabilizing Reagent for the Li-O System Obtained by Atomic Layer Deposition. *Key Engineering Materials.* [online]. 2019, vol. 822, pp. 787-794. Available from: https://doi.org/10.4028/www.scientific.net/KEM.822.787.

[5] MAXIMOV, M., NAZAROV, D., RUMYANTSEV, A., KOSHTYAL, Y., EZHOV, I., MITROFANOV, I., KIM, A., MEDVEDEV, O., POPOVICH, A. Atomic Layer Deposition of Lithium-Nickel-Silicon Oxide Cathode Material for Thin-Film Lithium-Ion Batteries. *Energies.* [online]. 2020, vol. 13. Available from: https://doi.org/10.3390/en13092345.

[6] TANG, H., JIANG, M.J., ZHANG, Y., LAI, X.X., CUI, C., XIAO, H.Y., JIANG, S.X., REN, E.H., QIN, Q., GUO, R.H. CNTs anchored on defective bimetal oxide NiCoO2-x microspheres for high-performance lithium-ion battery anode. *Electrochimica Acta.* [online]. 2020, vol. 354. Available from: https://doi.org/10.1016/j.electacta.2020.136760.

[7] HUANG, Z.D., ZHANG, K., ZHANG, T.T., YANG, X.S., LIU, R.Q., LI, Y., LIN, X.J., FENG, X.M., MA, Y.W., HUANG, W. Hierarchical NiCoO2 mesoporous microspheres as anode for lithium ion batteries with superior rate capability. *Energy Storage Materials.* [online]. 2016, vol. 3, pp. 36-44. Available from: https://doi.org/10.1016/j.ensm.2016.01.001.

[8] POIZOT, P., LARUELLE, S., GRUGEON, S., TARASCON, J.M. Rationalization of the low-potential reactivity of 3d-metal-based inorganic compounds toward Li. *Journal of the Electrochemical Society.* [online]. 2002, vol. 149, pp. A1212-A1217. Available from: https://doi.org/10.1149/1.1497981.

[9] PARK, C.M., KIM, J.H., KIM, H., SOHN, H.J. Li-alloy based anode materials for Li secondary batteries. *Chemical Society Reviews.* [online]. 2010, vol. 39, pp. 3115-3141. Available from: https://doi.org/10.1039/b919877f.

[10] NAZAROV, D.V., MAXIMOV, M.Y., NOVIKOV, P.A., POPOVICH, A.A., SILIN, A.O., SMIRNOV, V.M., BOBRYSHEVA, N.P., OSMOLOVSKAYA, O.M., OSMOLOVSKY, M.G., RUMYANTSEV, A.M. Atomic layer deposition of tin oxide using tetraethyltin to produce high-capacity Li-ion batteries. *Journal of Vacuum Science & Technology A*. [online]. 2017, vol. 35. Available from: https://doi.org/10.1116/1.4972554.

[11] KOSHTYAL, Y., NAZAROV, D., EZHOV, I., MITROFANOV, I., KIM, A., RYMYANTSEV, A., LYUTAKOV, O., POPOVICH, A., MAXIMOV, M. Atomic Layer Deposition of NiO to Produce Active Material for Thin-Film Lithium-Ion Batteries. *Coatings*. [online]. 2019, vol. 9. Available from: https://doi.org/10.3390/coatings9050301.

[12] MITROFANOV, I., EZHOV, I., YURY, K., NAZAROV, D., Kim, A., RUMYANTSEV, A., POPOVICH, A., MAXIMOV, M. Synthesis of lithium and cobalt oxides systems by the ald method to obtain lithium cobalt oxide cathode for thin-film libs. In: *NANOCON 2019 - 11th International Conference on Nanomaterials - Research & Application*. Brno, Czech Republic: TANGER, 2019, pp. 251-256.

[13] REDDY, M.V., PRITHVI, G., LOH, K.P., CHOWDARI, B.V.R. Li Storage and Impedance Spectroscopy Studies on Co3O4, CoO, and CoN for Li-Ion Batteries. *Acs Applied Materials & Interfaces*. [online]. 2014, vol. 6, pp. 680-690. Available from: https://doi.org/10.1021/am4047552.

[14] CAO, K.Z., JIN, T., YANG, L., JIAO, L.F. Recent progress in conversion reaction metal oxide anodes for Li-ion batteries. *Materials Chemistry Frontiers*. [online]. 2017, vol. 1, pp. 2213-2242. Available from: https://doi.org/10.1039/c7qm00175d.

ELECTROCHEMICAL ACTIVITY OF LITHIUM NICKEL OXIDE THIN-FILM CATHODES OBTAINED BY ALD

[1]Ilya MITROFANOV, [1]Yury KOSHTYAL, [1]Denis NAZAROV, [1]Ilya EZHOV, [1]Artem KIM, [1,2]Aleksander RUMYANTSEV, [1]Oleg MEDVEDEV, [3]Oleksiy LYUTAKOV, [1]Anatoliy POPOVICH, [1]Maxim MAXIMOV*

[1]Peter the Great Saint-Petersburg Polytechnic University, Saint-Petersburg, Russia, maximspbstu@mail.ru
[2]Ioffe Institute, Saint-Petersburg, Russia

[3]Department of Solid State Engineering, Institute of Chemical Technology, Czech Republic, EU

https://doi.org/10.37904/nanocon.2020.3718

Abstract

Energy density is one of the essential characteristics of thin-film power sources which provides the duration of the autonomous performance of sensors, energy harvesters, IoT devices, etc. The Atomic layer deposition (ALD) allows the growth of conformal coatings with a controlled composition on high aspect ratio substrates and can be used to manufacture some components of thin-film batteries. Modern high energy active cathode materials include Li, transition metal, and oxygen. The production of such films by the ALD method can be carried out using a linear combination of lithium oxide structures and transition metal oxide structures (supercycle approach), followed by annealing. The control of the composition and properties of the films can be achieved by varying the ratio of cycles conducted for deposition of binary oxides during supercycle. In present work, were used 1/10 and 1/30 ratio of lithium oxide/nickel oxide ALD cycles during supercycle to obtain thin films of Li-Ni-O system. X-ray photoelectron spectroscopy of the as-deposited films demonstrates low nickel content in films. The annealed films at 800 and 900 °C for 10 minutes show the presence of the lithium silicates and nickel silicide phases. It was found that the best electrochemical performance show samples of LNO 1/30 series annealed at 800 °C: at a discharge current of 20 µA (5C), the capacity was equal to 35 $\mu A \cdot h \cdot \mu m^{-1} \cdot cm^{-2}$. The obtained results demonstrate a low effect of an increase in the number of cycles on the proportion of nickel in the films and, consequently, on the electrochemical characteristics.

Keywords: Atomic layer deposition, lithium nickel oxide, Li-ion batteries, thin films

1. INTRODUCTION

The Internet of Things (IoT) is a rapidly growing area in which every object, thing, is a source of information and can communicate with other objects within the network [1,2]. Improving devices' performance in the Internet of Things requires miniature autonomous power supplies with increased lifetime, specific energy, and power. Solid-state lithium-ion batteries (SSLIBs) can be used to power IoT devices [1,3,4]. The advantages of SSLIBs include a wide range of operating temperatures and safety. One of the critical characteristics of the SSLIBs is the specific energy, which ensures the duration of autonomous operation.

Since IoT power supply can be mounted on printed circuit boards, the essential characteristics are the capacity, energy, and power density per specific mounting area ($A \cdot h/cm^2$, $W \cdot h/cm^2$, W/cm^2). These parameters can be improved by increasing the number of electrode pairs [5], the thickness of the electrodes, or by creating thin-film batteries on high aspect structures (3D batteries) [6].

Another way to increase the specific energy is to create batteries using active anode and cathode materials with higher energy. Among the promising cathode materials that can be used for SSLIBs production are lithiated mixed oxides with high nickel content.

The ALD method allows the deposition of films of various compositions on substrates with a high aspect ratio trenches and can be used to obtain high-energy-density thin-film electrodes. Previously, it was shown that an electrochemically active film could be obtained by a linear combination of deposition cycles of lithium oxide and nickel oxide structures [7]. When using the ratio of the cycles of synthesis of lithium oxide structures and nickel oxide structures equal to 1/10 or less, the atomic fraction of nickel was small and amounted to about 0.2% [7]. An increase of nickel content can be achieved by increasing the number of nickel oxide synthesis cycles in the supercycle. This work describes ALD synthesis and studies (physicochemical and electrochemical) of films obtained by ALD with a ratio of lithium oxide/nickel oxide synthesis cycles of 1/10 and 1/30.

2. MATERIALS AND METHODS

Monocrystalline silicon wafers (surface orientation 111, the diameter 40 mm, Svetlana Co., LTD, Saint-Petersburg, Russia) and stainless-steel plates (316SS, Tob New Energy Technology Co., LTD, diameter 15.8 mm) were used as substrates. Before deposition, silicon substrates were cleaned in an ultrasonic bath in acetone and deionized water for 15 min.

The deposition of lithium nickel oxide (Li-Ni-O) films was conducted by the ALD method using Picosun R-150 setup at 300 °C and at a base pressure in the reactor of 8-12 hPa. Lithium hexamethyldisilazide (LiHMDS, 97%, Sigma Aldrich) and bis(cyclopentadienyl)nickel (II) (NiCp2, 99% Sigma-Aldrich) were used as metal-containing reagents. Remote oxygen plasma applied as a counter-reactant. The supercycle started with 10 or 30 nickel oxide structures (Ni-O, n) cycles deposition followed by one cycle of lithium oxide structures (Li-O, m) deposition. The conditions of Li-O and Ni-O deposition were selected, considering results reported elsewhere [8,9]. Deposition of lithium oxide system: T_{source} - 160 °C; pulse/purge with N_2/remote O_2 plasma pulse/purge with N_2 - 0.1/6/15/6 s. Deposition of nickel oxide system: T_{source} - 110 °C; pulse/purge with N_2/remote O_2 plasma pulse/purge with N_2 -1/10/15/10 s. The Synthesized samples were heated in an oven for 10 minutes at 800-900 °C (T). The samples are denoted according to the following form of designation Li-Ni-O m/n T.

The growth rates were calculated from film thickness measured by spectral ellipsometry (350-1000 nm) using Ellips-1891 SAG ellipsometer (CNT, Novosibirsk, Russia).

X-ray photoelectron spectra (XPS) were registered with a Thermo Fisher Scientific Escalab 250Xi spectrometer in the Physical Methods of Surface Investigation Resource Centre, SPbSU (Thermo Fisher, Waltham, MA, USA). Before performing the first measurement, the surface layer of samples was etched by Ar+ ions with 500 eV energy for 30 s to remove adventitious carbon. The samples were excited by Al-Kα (1486.7 eV) X-rays in the vacuum of $7x10^{-8}$ Pa. The sample charging was automatically compensated.

X-ray diffraction (XRD) studies in surface-sensitive grazing incidence XRD (GIXRD) modes were performed using a Bruker D8 DISCOVER (Cu-Kα, Billerica, MA, USA) high-resolution diffractometer.

The electrochemical performance of 316SS substrates with deposited Li-Ni-O films was studied in CR2032 coin cells. Lithium foil, polyolefin porous film 2325 (Celgard, Charlotte, NC, USA), and TC-E918 (Tinci, Guangzhou, China) were used as the counter electrode, separator, and electrolyte, respectively. Coin cells were assembled in an argon glove box OMNI-LAB (VAC). Cyclic voltammetry (CV) was performed using a potentiostat PGSTAT302N+ (Autolab, Utrecht, the Netherlands) in the range of 2.5 - 4.3 V with a scan rate of 0.5 mV/s. Cyclic charge/discharge was performed using the battery testing system CT-3008W-5V10mA (Neware, Shenzhen, China) at room temperature in the potential range of 2.5-4.3 V, at current 20-80 μA.

3. RESULT AND DISCUSSION

3.1. Films deposition and thermal treatment

The program for the synthesis of films is summarized in **Table 1**. For both series of samples, the growth per supercycle determined from thickness of films measured by spectral ellipsometry was lower than calculated from linear combination of growth per rate of lithium oxide (LiOx - 1.23 ± 0.01- Å / cycle [9]) and nickel oxide (NiO - 0.12 ± 0.01 Å / cycle [8]). The difference between values augmented with the increase of nickel oxide deposition cycles in the supercycle. Therefore, we assume that Li-contained species grafted on the surface may slow nickel oxide structure growth.

Table 1 Synthesis program and thin films growth characteristics

Name	Cycles		Supercycles/Cycles	Growth per cycle/supercycle, Å			
				Calculation		Ellipsometry	
	Li-Ox	Ni-Ox		SC	C	SC	C
LNO 1/10	1	10	250/2750	2.56	0.23	2.32	0.21
LNO 1/30	1	30	175/5250	4.56	0.14	3.06	0.1

The stainless-steel substrates with deposited structures were investigated by XPS analysis **(Figure 1)**. It was found that for both series of samples, atoms of carbon, lithium, and oxygen are presented in significant quantities on the films external surface. The presence of Carbon may be due to adsorbed hydrocarbon and carbonate impurities as well as residues of Carbon from precursor ligand. The quantiles of nickel and silicon are moderate and don't exceed 2.3 at.%. The concentration of nickel (0.7 at.%) on the surface of LNO 1/30 is 3.5 times higher than for LNO 1/10 but still not sufficient to form the stoichiometric LiNiO2 phase.

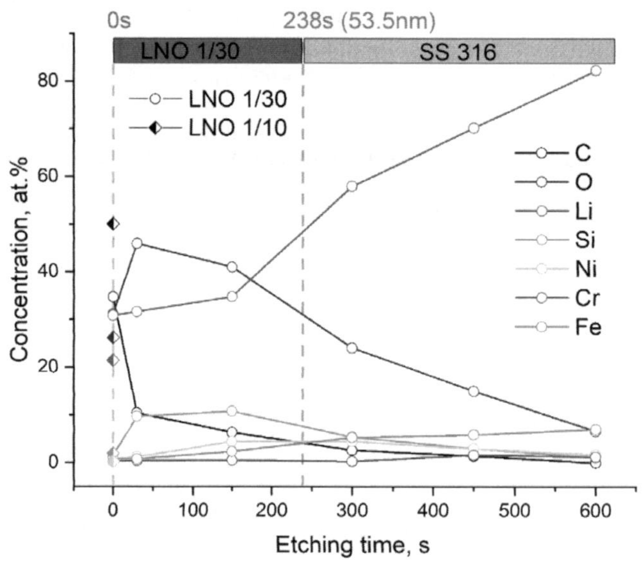

Figure 1 Concentration depth profile measured by X-ray photoelectron (XPS)

The LNO 1/30 sample was investigated by XPS after different times of etching (3 keV). The rate of etching determined for model samples of similar composition was 0.225 nm/s. Thus, the maximal etching time (600 s) exceeds the etching time required for reaching the substrate.

After 30 seconds of etching, the quantity of carbon decreases significantly (from 32 to 10 at.%) and declines moderately with subsequent etching time. According to calculated data, the deposited films' carbon content is varied from 5 to 10 at.%, and its presence may be due to ligand residues. The quantity of nickel slightly increased from 0.7 at.% to 4.5 at.%, but the increment may be due to nickel content in the stainless-steel substrate. The concentration of silicon in the films reaches 11 at.%. Thus, the ligand of the LiHMDS precursor also is not entirely removed during plasma treatment. Lithium (1s) and Iron (3p) bands in XPS spectra are superimposed, and the increment of lithium shown in **Figure 1** may be explained by the contribution of iron from the substrate. Nevertheless, one can conclude that lithium's atomic concentration is much higher than other elements' concentrations.

The as-deposited thin films exhibited no reflexes on XRD patterns. Therefore, no detectable crystal phase was observed in the films. On the diffractograms of the samples obtained after thermal treatment at 800-900 °C for 10 minutes, several reflexes have appeared. The observed reflexes could be assigned to silicon support and the phases of lithium silicates and nickel silicide ($L_2O_5Si_2$ [PDF-2 00-030-0767], Li_2SiO_3 [Li_2SiO_3 PDF 01-070-0330] $NiSi_2$ [PDF 01-077-9324]). Since a deposited film contains silicon (**Figure 2**), the lithium silicates can be formed due to phase transformation in film and not due to the interaction of deposited film and a silicon substrate. Nickel silicide could be formed due interaction of nickel and silicon substrate. The reflexes of NiO (PDF 01-071-1179) и $LiNiO_2$ (PDF 00-062-0468) were not found on the roentgenograms. Probably contained nickel, lithium, and oxygen phases are not formed during deposition, and subsequent calcination or their quantity is the bellow of the detection limit.

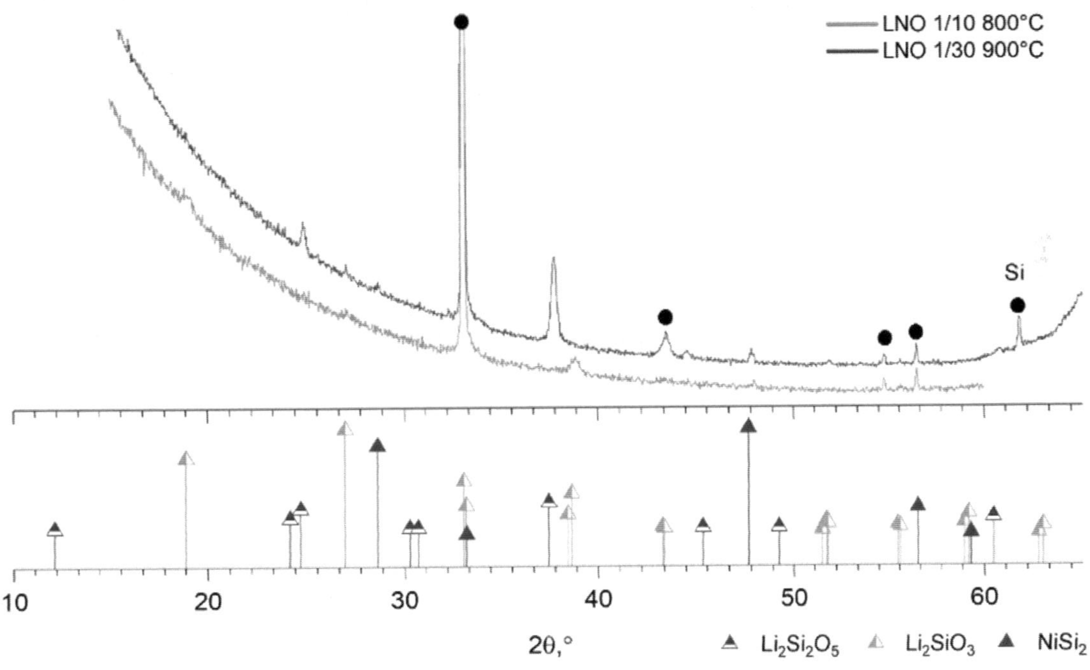

Figure 2 XRD patterns of LNO 1/10 and LNO 1/30

3.2. Electrochemical performance

According to the results of nickel-containing cathode materials investigations using cyclic voltammetry [10] the maximum current increase is observed in 4.15-4.25V region of the anode curve. It corresponds to the oxidation of nickel ($Ni^{2+}/Ni^{3+}/Ni^{4+}$). During the reverse process, the current increases at 4.2V (Ni^{4+}/Ni^{3+}) and 3.65-3.75V regions (Ni^{3+}/Ni^{2+}). Although both regions with increment of current are observed in cyclic voltammetry of samples only after calcination taking into account the nickel quantity it is possible that observed increment of current characterizes other phases electrochemical activity such as lithium silicates.

The charge/discharge at various C-rate was performed after 15 cycles of CV measurement. To compare the performance of films, the specific volumetric (μAh·μm⁻¹·cm⁻²) discharge capacities were used. At higher discharge currents, all samples showed a lower discharge capacity. The LNO-1/30 samples showed higher discharge capacities at various C-rates (**Figure 3**). As deposited, films have not possessed any notable electrochemical activity and could not store energy. For both series of the sample, the higher discharge capacity exhibit samples calcinated at 800 °C. The calcination at 900 °C led to a small decrease in discharge capacity. The capacity observed at moderate discharge currents (20 μA, 5-7C) varied from 23 $\mu Ah \cdot \mu m^{-1} \cdot cm^{-2}$ (LNO 1/10 900°C) to 35 $\mu Ah \cdot \mu m^{-1} \cdot cm^{-2}$ (LNO 1/30 800°C) and less than the calculated value from density and specific gravimetrical capacity for $LiNiO_2$ film - 103 $\mu Ah \cdot \mu m^{-1} \cdot cm^{-2}$ (at 0.5C discharge rate [7,11]). The lower discharge capacities of deposited films may be due to another active compound (smaller nickel content) and higher discharge rates.

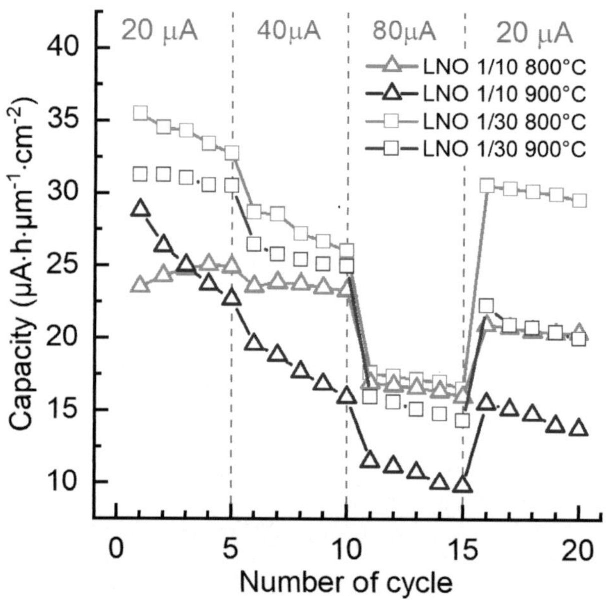

Figure 3 The effect of discharge current on the capacity of annealed LNO 1/10 and LNO 1/30 samples

4. CONCLUSION

With the use of LiHMDS, $NiCp_2$, O_2 (remote plasma) precursors, and the supercycle approach, the thin films were deposited at 300 °C by Atomic layer deposition on the silicon and stainless steel substrates. The growth of NiO structures is hindered by LiHMDS/O_2 treatment. The increase of NiO cycles deposition from 10 to 30 in supercycle led to an augmentation of nickel content from 0.2 at.% to 0.7 at.% at surface (4.5 at. % in the depth of the film - LNO 1/30). According to XPS results, the films are contaminated by silicon and carbon - lithium and nickel precursors' residues. The as-deposited films were amorphous. Calcination of films for 10 minutes at 800 and 900 °C led to a probable formation of lithium silicate phases and $NiSi_2$. Before thermal treatment, the synthesized films have not possessed any electrochemical activity. After annealing, the discharge capacity increased to 32-35 $\mu Ah \cdot \mu m^{-1} \cdot cm^{-2}$ at 5-7C rate currents, which is smaller than the estimated value for $LiNiO_2$ - 103 $\mu Ah \cdot \mu m^{-1} \cdot cm^{-2}$ (0.5C) possible due to low content of electrochemical active phase and higher discharge rate.

ACKNOWLEDGEMENTS

The research was conducted under the financial support of the Russian Science Foundation grant (project No. 18-73-10015).

REFERENCES

[1] SHIRVANIMOGHADDAM, M., SHIRVANIMOGHADDAM, K., ABOLHASANI, M.M., FARHANGI, M., BARSARI, V.Z., LIU, H.Y., DOHLER, M., NAEBE, M. Towards a Green and Self-Powered Internet of Things Using Piezoelectric Energy Harvesting. *Ieee Access.* [online]. 2019, vol. 7, pp. 94533-94556. doi: 10.1109/access.2019.2928523.

[2] GOLDSTEIN, M. IEEE Computer Society Phoenix Chapter - Internet of Things Innovations & Megatrends Update. [online]. [viewed 2020.09.25]. Available from: https://www.slideshare.net/markgirc/ieee-computer-society-phoenix-chapter-internet-of-things-innovations-megatrends-update-121119

[3] MAXIMOV, M.Y., NOVIKOV, P.A., NAZAROV, D.V., RYMYANTSEV, A.M., SILIN, A.O., ZHANG, Y., POPOVICH, A.A. Characterization and Electrochemical Performance at High Discharge Rates of Tin Dioxide Thin Films Synthesized by Atomic Layer Deposition. *Journal of Electronic Materials. [online].* 2017, vol. 46, pp. 6571-6577. Available from: https://doi.org/10.1007/s11664-017-5701-8.

[4] MAXIMOV, M.Y., KOSHTYAL, Y., MITROFANOV, I., EZHOV, I., RUMYANTSEV, A., POPOVICH, A. Features of the synthesis of lithium-based ternary oxide nanofilms by atomic layer deposition with LHMDS for thin-film LIBs. *Materials Today-Proceedings.* [online]. 2020, vol. *25*, pp. 6-12. Available from: https://doi.org/10.1016/j.matpr.2019.10.107.

[5] PEARSE, A., SCHMITT, T., SAHADEO, E., STEWART, D.M., KOZEN, A., GERASOPOULOS, K., TALIN, A.A., LEE, S.B., RUBLOFF, G.W., GREGORCZYK, K.E. Three-Dimensional Solid-State Lithium-Ion Batteries Fabricated by Conformal Vapor-Phase Chemistry. *Acs Nano.* [online]. 2018, vol. 12, pp. 4286-4294. Available from: https://doi.org/10.1021/acsnano.7b08751.

[6] OUDENHOVEN, J.F.M., BAGGETTO, L., NOTTEN, P.H.L. All-Solid-State Lithium-Ion Microbatteries: A Review of Various Three-Dimensional Concepts. *Advanced Energy Materials.* [online]. 2011, vol. 1, pp 10-33. Available from: https://doi.org/10.1002/aenm.201000002.

[7] MAXIMOV, M., NAZAROV, D., RUMYANTSEV, A., KOSHTYAL, Y., EZHOV, I., MITROFANOV, I., KIM, A., MEDVEDEV, O., POPOVICH, A. Atomic Layer Deposition of Lithium-Nickel-Silicon Oxide Cathode Material for Thin-Film Lithium-Ion Batteries. *Energies.* [online]. 2020, vol. 13, 2345. Available from: https://doi.org/10.3390/en13092345.

[8] KOSHTYAL, Y., NAZAROV, D., EZHOV, I., MITROFANOV, I., KIM, A., RYMYANTSEV, A., LYUTAKOV, O., POPOVICH, A., MAXIMOV, M. Atomic Layer Deposition of NiO to Produce Active Material for Thin-Film Lithium-Ion Batteries. *Coatings.* [online]. 2019, vol. 9, 301, Available from: https://doi.org/10.3390/coatings9050301

[9] NAZAROV, D., EZHOV, I., MITROFANOV, I., LYUTAKOV, O., MAXIMOV, M.Y. The Use of the TMA as Stabilizing Reagent for the Li-O System Obtained by Atomic Layer Deposition. *Key Engineering Materials.* [online]. 2019, vol. 822, pp.787-794. Available from: https://doi.org/10.4028/www.scientific.net/KEM.822.787.

[10] CHONG, S.K., LIU, Y.N., YAN, W.W., CHEN, Y.Z. Effect of valence states of Ni and Mn on the structural and electrochemical properties of Li1.2NixMn0.8-xO2 cathode materials for lithium-ion batteries. *Rsc Advances.* [online]. 2016, vol. 6, pp. 53662-53668. Available from: https://doi.org/10.1039/c6ra09454f.

[11] REMPEL, J., PULLEN, A., KAPLAN, D., BARNETT, B., SRIRAMULU, S. High-Nickel Cathode / Graphite Anode Cells for Diverse DoD Applications (24-1). In: *Proceedings of 48th Power Sources Conference.* Marriott Tech Center Hotel, Denver, Colorado, 2018, pp. 404-407.

SPINEL FERRITES NANOPARTICLES FOR ALLOY STEEL PROTECTIVE LAYERS

[1]Martin OCHMANN, [1]Fredericus M. A. LINDERHOF, [1,2]Libor MACHALA

[1]Department of Experimental Physics, Faculty of Science, Palacký University, Olomouc, Czech Republic, EU
[2]Regional Centre of Advanced Technologies and Materials, Palacký University, Olomouc, Czech Republic, EU

https://doi.org/10.37904/nanocon.2020.3722

Abstract

Covering layers might have very important role in improving performance of many mechanical parts. These layers are usually designed to protect a substrate from the environment and enhance mechanical properties such as hardness. Blackening is a classical approach that is very demanding on resources. This process is based on the alkalisation of surface atoms and the transformation of formed hydroxides to oxides. Such an approach inspired us to carry out experiments resulting in preparation of protective layers with similar properties, by using stoichiometric spinel ferrite nanoparticles ($MeFe_2O_4$). Thus mechanical parts were covered with ferrite nanoparticles and heated in a furnace. Ferrite samples, which were used as precursor for the preparation of layers, were analysed with X-ray powder diffraction, energy dispersive X-ray spectroscopy and ^{57}Fe Mössbauer spectroscopy. The samples were analysed with ultrasonic hardness test, electron microscopy, and Mössbauer spectroscopy. The protection layers showed a higher hardness compared to untreated parts.

Keywords: Spinel ferrites, protective layer, Mössbauer spectroscopy, hardness test

1. INTRODUCTION

Spinel ferrites are a family of compounds similar to magnetic iron oxides, thus chemically magnetite can be considered as a spinel ferrite. The chemical formula of spinel ferrites is $MeFe_2O_4$, where Me is a divalent metal cation, e.g. Zn, Mg, Ni or Mn [1]. If the metal cation does not have a trivalent state, we can presume that the compound has high chemical stability. Spinel ferrites exist in normal, inverse or mixed modification. Both spinel modifications have the same *Fd-3m* space group, but the distribution of cations can be determined by low temperature Mössbauer spectroscopy [2]. The physico-chemical properties of spinel ferrites are very convenient for passivation of surfaces, long lasting sensors, supercapacitors or contrast agents [1]. Thus the synthetic procedure is the key to tailor nanoparticles for specific purposes. The coprecipitation technique is very convenient for environmentally friendly synthesis of narrowly distributed nanoparticles [3], so it was employed in the study.

A surface treatment of mechanical parts is crucial to fabricate high quality products. Many metals lack rust resistance. Commonly used techniques are able to improve only the mechanical or chemical properties, e.g. galvanisation or painting. Other techniques are able to improve both mechanical and chemical properties, but require a relatively high amount of energy and resources, namely nitriding, anodising or blackening [4]. Blackening is a powerful technique to improve surface properties, hardness and chemical stability [5]. This process is applied to carbon steel such as high quality alloy steel used for guns. Military standards also mention blackening for surface treatment and testing of chemical resistance to moisture, salts and operating fluids (e.g. oil, gasoline). Blackening consists of submerging the part into highly alkaline solution with a high temperature. Leading to the formation of a hydroxide on the surface, which is then heated to form an oxide layer, which is chemically stable. This process is transformed into deposition of spinel ferrite nanoparticles and heating in a furnace for moderate temperature and time.

The goal of the study is to investigate the influence of depositing zinc ferrite nanoparticles on the surface of an alloy steel plate. Basic properties of the prepared zinc ferrite nanoparticles were obtained with X-ray powder diffraction, Mössbauer spectroscopy and scanning electron microscopy. The phase composition of covered alloy steel plate was determined via the same analytical tools. The hardness is the main feature of prepared samples as the only mechanical property investigated during the study.

2. MATERIALS AND METHODS

2.1. Preparation of spinel ferrite nanoparticles

$FeCl_3{\cdot}6H_2O$, $ZnCl_2$ and NaOH (pure analytically) chemicals were purchased from PENTA, s.r.o. (Prague, Czech Republic). Ethanol was purchased from the company Verkon. Nanoparticles were prepared by precipitation of Zn^{2+} and Fe^{3+} ions by sodium hydroxide. The amount of ions were $n(Fe^{3+})$ = 2 mmol, $n(Zn^{2+})$ = 1 mmol and $n((OH)^-)$ = 9 mmol. The admixture was homogenised for 5 min, then washed by deionised water. Finally, vacuum filtration was applied to collect the precipitate.

2.2. Surface treatment of CL20ES plates

CL20ES is an austenitic stainless steel powder of the chemical composition indicated in **Table 1**. The powder was sintered with a laser to form 25 mm x 25 mm x 3 mm metallic plate. This plate was then thermally treated and finally the plate was sandblasted by corundum abrasive of grain size of 70 - 150 um. The prepared nanoparticles were dispersed in ethanol and deposited on the plate, then the dispersions were dried at 80 °C and finally the plates were heated in a furnace at the desired temperature for 2 h. Sample Zn_Et_200 was heated at 200 °C and sample Zn_Et_400 was heated at 400 °C.

Table 1 The chemical composition of CL20ES powder

Component	Fe	Cr	Ni	Mo	Mn	Si	P	C, S
Indicative value (%)	Balance	16.5-18.5	10.0-13.0	2.0-2.5	0.0-2.0	<=1.0	<=0.045	<=0.030

2.3. X-ray diffraction (XRD)

X-ray powder diffraction (XRD) was used to determine the crystal structure and phase composition. The measurements were conducted using a Bruker D8 ADVANCE powder diffractometer operating in the Bragg-Brentano parafocusing geometry. The diffractometer was equipped with a LYNXEYE position sensitive detector and with a Co "Kalpha" radiation source. In addition, the divergence slit and Soller slits for the primary beam and the Fe "Kbeta" filter and Soller slits for the secondary beam were applied for the measurements.

2.4. ^{57}Fe Mössbauer spectroscopy

To distinguish positions and chemical states of ^{57}Fe within the crystal structure in the samples, two Mössbauer spectrometers were used. The first spectrometer is a MS96 transmission Mössbauer spectrometer, the second a Conversion Electron Mössbauer Spectrometer (CEMS). Both operate in constant acceleration mode and make use of a ^{57}Co radioactive source in a Rh matrix. Samples were measured at room temperature [6]. The MS96 spectrometer was calibrated using a α-Fe calibration foil zeroing the isomer shift values. No external magnetic field was applied during measurement. The samples were measured at room temperature without applying an external magnetic field. MossWin 4.0 software was used for spectra evaluation [7].

The CEMS works in a reflective geometry and measures a Mössbauer spectrum based on conversion electrons which come from a depth up to 300 nm in the sample [8]. The CEMS makes use of a ФЭУ-85 photomultiplier as its detector. It is build into a Pfeiffer Vacuum Chamber to make the mean free path of the conversion electrons longer and an electric field is created using an Ortec 556H High Voltage Power Supply between the detector and the sample to accelerate electrons towards the photomultiplier tube.

2.5. Ultrasonic hardness test

Hardness tests were performed with a ultrasonic portable hardness tester MET-U1A (Centre "MET", Russia). The tester is equipped with a probe that operates according to the ultrasonic contact impedance method (ASTM A 1038, DIN 50159). The hardness was measured on each side several times and an estimated hardness was used to calculate the improvement in hardness as a percentage.

2.6. Energy dispersive X-ray spectroscopy

VEGA3 LMU (TESCAN, Czech Republic) was used to collect EDS spectra, equipped with Si(Li) XFlash 410 EDS detector (Bruker, Germany). The primary energy of electrons was 30 keV with a takeoff angle of 35°.

3. RESULTS

3.1. Zinc ferrite characterisation

Zinc ferrite was synthesised as described in the experimental section. XRD pattern corresponds to *Fd-3m* space group, which is associated with spinel structure, because spinel ferrites have the same space group varying per cell parameter. The recognised peaks correspond exclusively to *Fd3-m* space group pattern (**Figure 1a**).

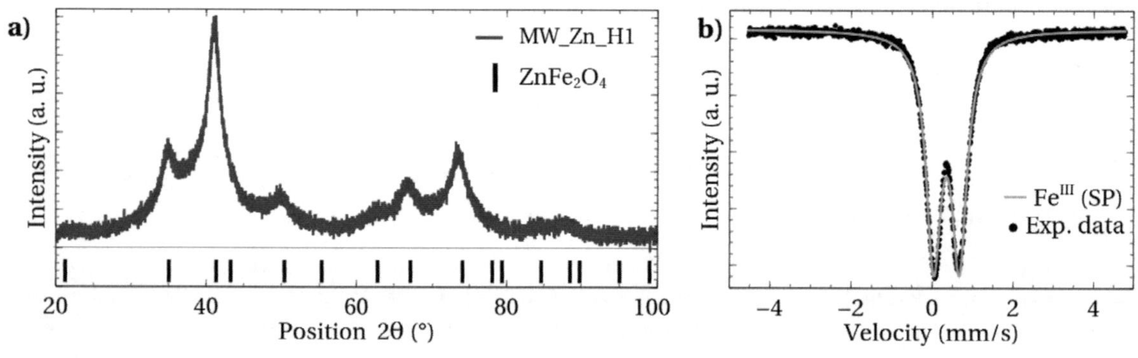

Figure 1 Prepared zinc ferrite MW_Zn_H1 (a) XRD pattern (b) ^{57}Fe Mössbauer spectroscopy

Room temperature transmission ^{57}Fe Mössbauer spectroscopy revealed only superparamagnetic nanoparticles containing Fe^{III} (doublet spectral component) in **Figure 1b**. Generally, the size of superparamagnetic nanoparticles is under 20 nm. The detailed parameters of Mössbauer spectral components are included in **Table 2**.

Table 2 Components and parameters of Mössbauer spectra of prepared zinc ferrite

Sample	Component	δ ± 0.01 (mm/s)	ΔEQ ± 0.01 (mm/s)	Bhf ± 0.3 (T)	FWHM ± 0.01 (mm/s)	RA ± 1 (%)	Identification
MW_Zn_H1	Doublet	0.35	0.60	---	0.46	100	Fe^{III} (SP)

δ is the isomer shift (related to α-Fe calibration foil at room temperature), ΔE_Q is the quadruple splitting energy, B_{hf} hyperfine magnetic field and RA is relative area.

The element composition was evaluated by EDS, it identified peaks, that belongs to silicon, iron, copper, oxygen, zinc and carbon and the amount of individual elements are listed in **Table 3**. The spectrum has identified high intensity peaks, because the peaks of copper have low intensity they are not marked in **Figure 2**. The amount of iron, zinc and oxygen meet the synthetic procedure expectations, i. e. the ratio of Fe : Zn is approximated to 2 : 1.

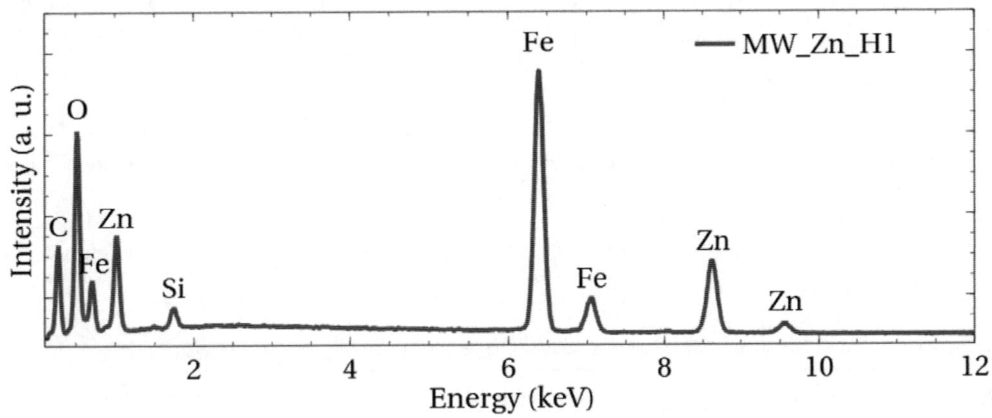

Figure 2 EDS spectrum of prepared zinc ferrite

Table 3 Quantification of EDS spectra of prepared zinc ferrite in weight % with incertenity 0.5 %

Sample	Fe	Zn	Si	C	O	Cu
MW_Zn_H1	6.5	3.1	0.5	43.0	46.8	0.1

3.2. Covering layers characterisation

The CL20ES sample plates with covering layer were analysed using conversion ^{57}Fe Mössbauer spectroscopy to obtain information about the surface phase composition. The investigation of layers was performed with a CEMS. The obtained spectra has 2 spectral components, a singlet is austenite, a doublet corresponding to zinc ferrite (**Figure 3**). The ferrite at the layers has different parameters as compared to the original spinel ferrite. The Zn_Et_200 doublet has similar parameters as untreated ferrite, but a higher temperature leads to a slight modification in the structure as presented in **Table 4**.

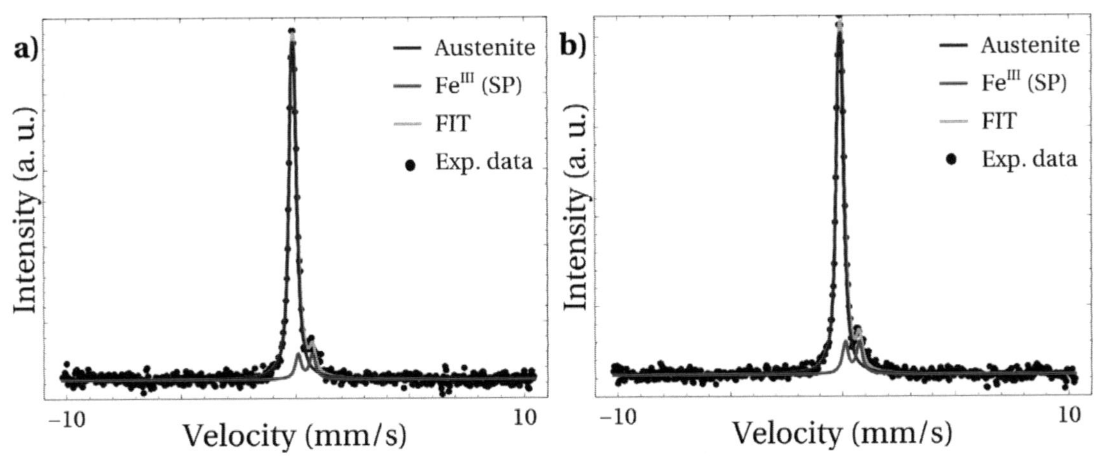

Figure 3 CEMS spectra of samples (a) Zn_Et_200 (b) Zn_Et_400

Table 4 Components and parameters of CEMS spectra of plates covered with prepared zinc ferrite

Sample	Component	δ ± 0.02 (mm/s)	ΔEQ ± 0.02 (mm/s)	Bhf ± 0.3 (T)	FWHM ± 0.02 (mm/s)	RA ± 2 (%)	Identification
Zn_Et_200	Doublet 1	-0.13	0.14	---	0.28	89	Austenite
	Doublet 2	0.41	0.63	---	0.30	11	Fe^{III} (SP)
Zn_Et_400	Doublet 1	-0.11	0.15	---	0.27	86	Austenite
	Doublet 2	0.52	0.63	---	0.30	14	Fe^{III} (SP)

δ is the isomer shift (related to α-Fe calibration foil at room temperature), ΔE_Q is the quadruple splitting energy, B_{hf} hyperfine magnetic field and RA is relative area.

Hardness tests performed on each side of each plate show an improvement in hardness as indicated in **Table 5** with the respective conditions of preparation.

Table 5 Improvement in hardness of prepared covering layers compared to untreated sides

Sample	Alcohol	Temperature (°C)	Improvement in hardness (%)
Zn_Et_200	Ethanol	200	8.6
Zn_Et_400	Ethanol	400	9.4

4. CONCLUSION

The detailed composition of the prepared zinc ferrite is provided including phase and elemental composition. The fabrication of the covering layer on a CL20ES plate was successful as demonstrated in the result section by phase composition and hardness test. The results indicate improved hardness in all cases, in addition the relative hardness is even higher as the annealing temperature is higher. CEMS provided very useful information about the surface. The study revealed a need for covering layers not only to enhance mechanical properties, but also to passivate the surface. Spinel ferrites can be considered a good candidate to provide higher hardness and chemical stability to mechanical parts even in the case of alloy steel, which is considered as stainless.

ACKNOWLEDGEMENTS

The research has been supported by the Operational Programme Research, Development and Education - European Regional Development Fund, project "Hydrodynamic Design of Pumps" No. CZ.02.1.01/0.0/0.0/17049/0008408 of the Ministry of Education, Youth and Sports of the Czech Republic.

The authors appreciate the contribution in analysis and results of Vít Procházka, Vlastimil Vrba, Miroslav Mašláň, Tomáš Ingr and employees of VTP (University Palacký).

REFERENCES

[1] TATARCHUK, T., BOUOUDINA, M., VIJAYA, J. J. Spinel Ferrite Nanoparticles: Synthesis, Crystal Structure, Properties, and Perspective Applications. In: FESENKO, O., YATSENKO,L. *Nanophysics, Nanomaterials, Interface Studies, and Applications.* Springer International Publishing, 2017.

[2] DURRANI, S., NAZ, S., et al. Structural, impedance and Mössbauer studies of magnesium ferrite synthesized via sol-gel auto-combustion process. *Journal of Saudi Chemical Society*. 2017, vol. 21, no. 8, pp. 899-910.

[3] ATALAY, S., ERSÖZ, G. *Novel Catalysts in Advanced Oxidation of Organic Pollutants*. Springer, 2016.

[4] A. FATTAH-ALHOSSEINI, H. Y. Comparison of anti-corrosive properties between hot alkaline nitrate. *Journal of Alloys and Compounds*. 2016, vol. 676, pp. 474-480.

[5] REGHURAJ, A., SAJU, K. Black oxide conversion coating on metals: A review of coating techniques and adaptation for SAE 420A surgical grade stainless steel. **In**: *Materials today: proceedings*. 2017, vol. 4, no. 9, pp. 9534-9541.

[6] PECHOUŠEK, J., JANČÍK, D., FRYDRYCH, J., NAVAŘÍK, J., NOVÁK, P. Setup of Mössbauer spectrometers at RCPTM. In: *Mossbauer Spectroscopy in Materials Science - 2012.* American Institute of Physics, 2012, pp 186 - 193.

[7] KLENCSÁR, Z. Mössbauer spectrum analysis by Evolution Algorithm. *Nuclear Instruments and Methods in Physics Research Section B Beam Interactions with Materials and Atoms*. 1997, vol. 129, no. 4, pp. 527-533.

[8] PROCHÁZKA, V. *Neobvýklá Mössbauerova spektroskopie.* Olomouc: Univerzita Palackého v Olomouci, 2014.

AB-INITIO STUDY OF SURFACE ENERGIES AND STRUCTURAL INFLUECE OF VACANCIES IN TITANIUM NITRIDE NANOLAYER

[1,2]Miroslav LEBEDA, [1]Petr VLČÁK, [2]Petr VEŘTÁT, [3]Jan DRAHOKOUPIL

[1] *Department of Physics, Faculty of Mechanical Engineering, Czech Technical University in Prague,* lebedmi2@fjfi.cvut.cz, petr.vlcak@fs.cvut.cz

[2] *Department of Solid State Engineering, Faculty of Nuclear Sciences and Physical Engineering, Czech Technical University in Prague,* vertapet@fjfi.cvut.cz

[3] *Department of Material Analysis, Institute of Physics, Czech Academy of Sciences,* draho@fzu.cz

https://doi.org/10.37904/nanocon.2020.3706

Abstract

Titanium nitride (TiN) is largely applied as protective nanolayer of medical titanium implants due to its significant positive influence on the surface properties such as friction and corrosion resistance. During the process of its phase formation, occurrence of the point defects is probable and can potentially affect various material properties, e.g. change the lattice parameters. The surface energies of 8 crystallographic planes and effects of nitrogen vacancies on the lattice parameter in rock salt-like structure of TiN (δ-TiN) were studied using *ab-initio* method of density functional theory (DFT) with the generalized gradient approximation functional (GGA) as parametrized by Perdew, Burke and Ernzerhof (PBE). TiN supercell with 64 atomic positions was used for the calculation of defects influence and the results are thoroughly discussed in the context of available theoretical and experimental literature data. The linear decrease of lattice parameter with the increasing presence of nitrogen vacancies up to ca. 80 % was observed. The surface energy of (100) crystallographic plane is two times lower (1.499 J/m^2) than for the rest of the studied planes.

Keywords: Titanium nitride, TiN_x, ab initio simulation, density functional theory, DFT, vacancies, lattice parameter, surface energy

1. INTRODUCTION

Titanium and its alloys are nowadays widely used as implant materials in biomedical industry due to their generally great mechanical, physical and chemical properties. By various types of surface treatment, their surface properties (such as friction or corrosion resistance) are often suitably modified without changing the required bulk ones (such as internal bulk modulus) [1]. One of the most prominent and controllable surface modification methods is the implantation of charged particles (e.g. ions of nitrogen, hydrogen, oxygen, potassium, carbon, argon, silver) under the top surface layer intervening depth of the sample typically about 100 nm [2]. Changes of material properties are primarily caused by the formation of point defects, dislocations and potential new phases in the affected area, all of which are directly related to the depth concentration profiles of implanted ions and their dose [3]. In case of N ion implantation into the α-Ti matrix ($P6_3/mmc$, #194) [4], titanium nitride (TiN) with rock salt-like structure (δ-TiN, $Fm\bar{3}m$, #225) is primarily formed [5].

Metallic TiN has wide range of interesting properties such as high melting point, ultra-hardness, excellent mechanical resistance or good electric and thermal conductivity [6]. Therefore, it is being largely applied as coating nanolayer. During the modification of α-Ti with N ion implantation, the occurrence of high-density of N and Ti vacancies, substitutions or interstitials can significantly modify physical properties in the implanted zone, e.g. change the lattice parameters. Thus, knowledge of point defects and their influence is essential for understanding the behavior of our material. Particularly other important characteristics are the surface energies as they play significant role in epitaxial film growth of TiN or in the explanations of particle (e.g. hydrogen, oxygen) absorptions on its given surface layer [7].

It is often desirable to have theoretical predictions of all the mentioned characteristics and effects as they can provide a meaningful insight to the material behaviour or the processes occurring during its modifications. Development of *ab-initio* simulation methods, such as density functional theory (DFT), allowed performing aforementioned predictions and had become broadly used in the last decades. In this study, we provide DFT predictions of the mean effects of vacancies on the lattice parameter in rock salt-like structure of TiN. We also present the calculations of surfaces energies of TiN for 8 crystallographic planes and compare all our results with published studies for the cases where data was available.

2. COMPUTATIONAL DETAILS

DFT simulations were performed within the CASTEP (Cambridge Serial Total Energy Package) code [8]. The exchange-correlation energy functional was approximated by means of the GGA in PBE parametrization [9]. Iterative solutions of Kohn-Sham equations are derived with plane-wave basis for linear expansion of the electronic wavefunctions. Suitable value of energy cutoff E_{cut}, determining the number of plane waves used in the expansion, was found by the following algorithm: The total free energy of the fcc-TiN unit cell (with 8 atoms) was calculated with predefined ultra-fine settings while changing only the values of E_{cut} ranging from 140 to 600 eV with the step of 20 eV (**Figure 1, Left**, red marks). We set the energy cut-off at 360 eV to achieve the calculation convergence of at least 0.02 eV per atom with respect to this parameter. Similar convergence algorithm was used to find the suitable parameters of the Monkhorst-Pack k-point mesh [10] for the sampling of Brillouin zone. We selected 8 × 8 × 8 (**Figure 1, Left**, blue marks) as the energy convergence per atom with respect to the k-point sampling is here lesser than 0.01 eV. To further reduce the number of plane wave coefficients, we used the ultrasoft pseudopotential of the Vanderbilt type [11]. The system was considered be fully relaxed when the magnitude of the forces acting on all atoms was smaller than 0.01 eV/Å and the difference of energy per atom between consecutive iterates has decreased under $5 \cdot 10^{-6}$ eV/atom.

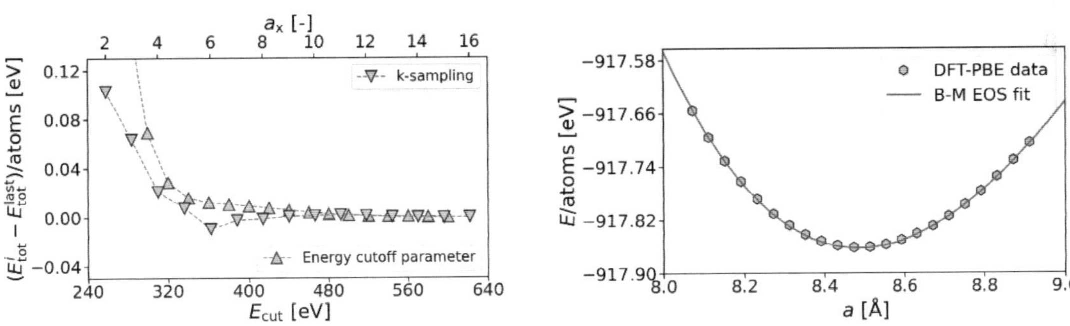

Figure 1 Left: Convergence of the fcc TiN total energy per atom with respect to the cutoff energy parameter E_{cut} and $a_x \times a_x \times a_x$ k-points from the Monkhorst-Pack grid. **Right:** Quality of DFT data fit with Birch-Murnaghan equation of state.

For the surface energies calculations, we have used a grid of 8 × 8 × 1, where × 1 is the usual choice in the direction perpendicular to the surface. This accounts the fact that the length of the supercell along this direction includes a vacuum region. Calculations of vacancies were performed on the TiN supercell containing 64 atomic sites. Monkhorst-Pack grid was reduced to 4 × 4 × 4 as the lattice parameters are now twice the bigger the unit cell containing 8 atoms. This provides a set of k-points with equal density in each axis direction of the reciprocal space. The placement of defects for their given number was randomized using a custom script in PERL language. Being interested only in mean effects of vacancies on lattice parameters, we kept the supercells as cubic and calculated their dependences of total energy per atom on the lattice parameter a.

The range of changes of a was within 10 % of the computed equilibrium value of non-defected TiN (8.492/2 = 4.246 Å) with the step of 0.04 Å. The obtained dependences were fitted by the Birch-Murnaghan equation of states (EOS) [12]:

$$E(a) = E_c + \frac{9a_e B}{16}\left\{\left[\left(\frac{a_e}{a}\right)^{\frac{2}{3}} - 1\right]^3 B' + \left[\left(\frac{a_e}{a}\right)^{\frac{2}{3}} - 1\right]^2 \left[6 - 4\left(\frac{a_e}{a}\right)^{\frac{2}{3}}\right]\right\}, \quad (1)$$

where fitting parameters have the following physical meaning: E_c is the cohesive energy, a_e the equilibrium lattice parameter, B the bulk modulus and B' its derivation. Quality of this fit is illustrated for the one case in **Figure 1, Right.**

3. RESULTS AND DISCUSSION

3.1. Calculations of TiN surface energies

We have studied the TiN surface energies $E_{\mathrm{DFT}}^{\mathrm{Surf}}$ of (100), (110), (111), (211), (221), (311), (321) and (322) cleavage planes. The bulk energy per atom was set as the energy of geometrically optimized TiN structure. Resulting lattice parameter $a = 4.246$ Å was in very good agreement with the experimental value 4.238 Å [13] (relative deviation of 0.2 %). After that, all the crystallographic planes were cleaved from this optimized structure. Neither the symmetric nor the asymmetric surface relaxations were allowed as well as the surface reconstructions. In all the considered planes (except for (111) and (311)), we have used the smallest possible surface cell for all slab calculations and tested the effect of different numbers of atomic layers ranging from 4 to 12 (with 8 to 24 atoms) on the surface energy. For (111) and (311), we had to choose non-primitive surface cell in order to keep the consistence of the same number of atoms in layers with the rest of the studied planes. Since (111) and (311) surfaces have single species termination in rock salt-like structure, there are three possibilities of cleavage. Both sides are either Ti or N terminated, or one is terminated with Ti layer while the other one with N. We have chosen the later, mixed state. This should lead to an average value of surface energy between the two different terminations with the same atomic species [3].

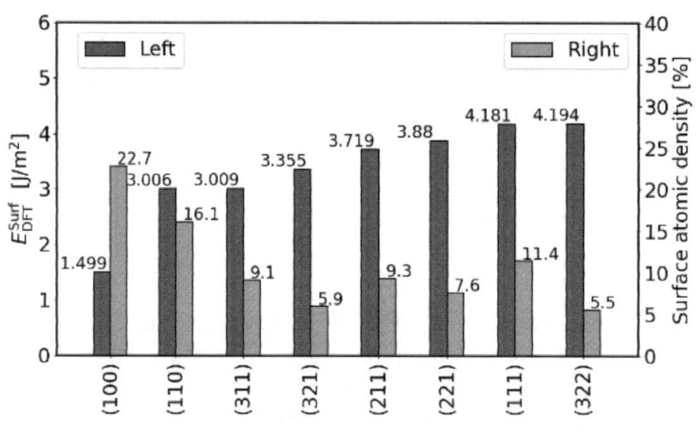

Figure 2 Descending order from the most stable surface to the least stable one in TiN. Given data are calculated by means of the GGA-PBE functional with 12 atomic layers (24 atoms in the slab) and 10 Å thickness of vacuum. For each plane, corresponding atomic surface density is also shown.

Resulted surface energies are summarized in **Table 1**. Our values are well converged with respect to the numbers of atomic layers in the slab as the surface energy changes are not greater than 0.1 J/m^2 from 8 layers (16 atoms). Descending order from the most stable surface to the lowest stable one is shown in **Figure 2** with the corresponding atomic surface densities (energies are in units J/m^2 = 16.022 eV/Å^2 and for the vacuum thickness of 10 Å with 24 atoms in the slab). Typically, the most stable surfaces are the ones with highest surface densities. This agrees for the (100) (1.499 J/m^2) as it has significantly higher density (22.7 %) than the second most stable (110) (3.006 J/m^2) surface with 16.1 %.

Table 1 DFT GGA-PBE calculations of TiN surface energies. Vacuum thickness was set to 10 Å. Surface relaxations and reconstructions are not considered. For the (111) and (311), one side was terminated with N atomic plane while the other with Ti. Comparison (percentage of the relative deviation) with the closest reference value [3,7] is given for the cleavage planes where data was found.

N. of layers (atoms)	$E_{PBE}^{(100)}$ J/m^2)	$E_{PBE}^{(110)}$ (J/m^2)	$E_{PBE}^{(111)}$ (J/m^2) Ti-N term.	$E_{PBE}^{(211)}$ (J/m^2)	$E_{PBE}^{(221)}$ (J/m^2)	$E_{PBE}^{(311)}$ (J/m^2) Ti-N term.	$E_{PBE}^{(321)}$ (J/m^2)	$E_{PBE}^{(322)}$ (J/m^2)
4 (8)	1.580 (+3.3 %)	3.013 (+5.0 %)	4.420 (+5.3 %)	3.925	3.977	3.151	3.538	4.519
6 (12)	1.525 (-0.3 %)	3.011 (+4.9 %)	4.163 (-0.8 %)	3.782	4.072	3.098	3.387	4.341
8 (16)	1.529 (-0.1 %)	3.030 (+5.6 %)	4.206 (+0.2 %)	3.730	3.926	3.013	3.313	4.382
10 (20)	1.497 (-2.2 %)	3.011 (+4.9 %)	4.176 (-0.5 %)	3.736	3.896	3.002	3.365	4.277
12 (24)	1.499 (-2.0 %)	3.006 (+4.7 %)	4.181 (-0.4 %)	3.719	3.880	3.009	3.355	4.194
Refer.	1.530[3], rPBE 1.602[7], PW91	2.870[3], rPBE	4.198[7], PW91 5.080[3], rPBE	-	-	-	-	-

3.2. Nitrogen vacancies in TiN and their influence on lattice parameter

We present DFT prediction of the mean effects of nitrogen vacancies on the lattice parameter a in fcc TiN_{1-x}. To minimize the interactions between vacancies themself for periodic boundary calculations, the TiN supercell with 64 atomic sites was chosen. Within this supercell, vacancies had been created ranging from 3.13 % to 100.00 % with the step of 3.13 % up to the 12.50 % and from this point, with the step of 6.25 % (corresponding to creation of two vacancies from initial 32 N atoms). Resulted dependence of the lattice parameter a on N vacancies concentration (as 100 × x in TiN_{1-x}) from the least-square best-fit with Birch-Murnaghan EOS is presented in **Figure 3**. We observed linear decrease in a with possible linear regression $a = -0.00009261x + 4.247$ up to the 80 % of vacancy concentration x (up to $TiN_{0.2}$ stoichiometry). The stability of δ-TiN_{1-x} phase was experimentally observed up to 63 % of N vacancy concentration [14]. Our calculation shows that the cubic phase of TiN_{1-x} could be stable/metastable with even higher concentration of N vacancies, up to ca. 80 %, as the slope of the lattice parameter starting to decrease from this point in much steeper way.

In [15,16], similar calculations were performed on smaller supercell consisting of 8 atomic positions of fcc TiN using the Full Potential-Linear Muffin Tin Orbital (FP-LMTO) implementation of DFT with local density approximation (LDA). However, there arising direct disadvantages using this type of cell as the number of vacancy concentrations is strictly limited (0 %, 25 %, 50 %, 75 % and 100 %), and the self-interactions of defects within periodic boundary conditions are less eliminated. Very recently, such simulations were extended in [17] using GGA-PBE functional on the supercell with the same size as ours (64 atomic positions). We used all these theoretical reference data as well as available experimental results [17-20] and have compared them with linear regression of own calculated lattice parameter dependence in **Table 2**. Our results are for 0.00, 1.00, 20.00, 49.00 and 50.00 % of N vacancy concentration in very good agreement with experimentally derived lattice parameters, as the maximum relative deviation was 0.61 % for $TiN_{0.80}$ [19]. Comparing to the theoretical prediction [17], their data starting at very similar value (0.00 % deviation at x = 3.13 %) and slightly differs at x = 25.00 % with -0.26% error from our results. Overall, with the highest relative deviation of 2.14 % for $TiN_{0.25}$ [16], there is no discrepancy between data in literature and our calculated prediction.

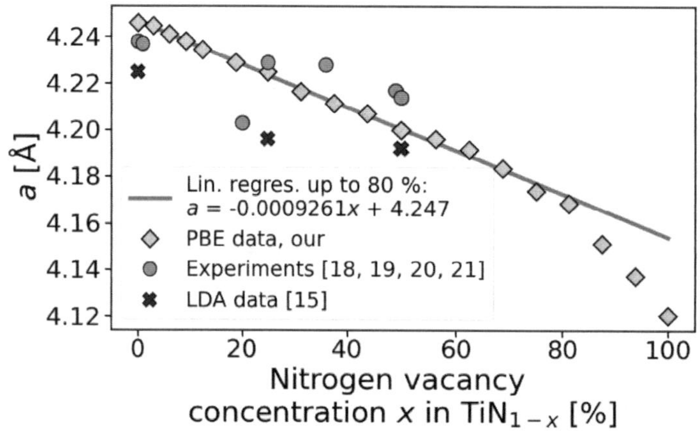

Figure 3 DFT GGA-PBE calculations of TiN_{1-x} lattice parameter changes with increasement presence of nitrogen vacancies (100 × x) performed on the supercell with 64 atomic position sites.

Table 2 Comparison of our GGA-PBE calculations of TiN_{1-x} lattice parameter dependence on N vacancy concentration with theoretical and experimental data from available literature

x in TiN_{1-x} (× 100 %)	a_{ref}, references (Å)	a_{our}, our PBE results, linear fit (Å)	$\frac{a_{our}-a_{ref}}{a_{ref}}$ (%)
0.00	4.238exp, [18], 4.225LDA, [15], 4.180LDA, [16], 4.244PBE, [17]	4.247	+0.21, +0.52, +1.60, +0.07
1.00	4.237exp, [19]	4.246	+0.21
3.13	4.244PBE, [17]	4.244	0.00
6.26	4.243PBE, [17]	4.241	-0.04
12.50	4.242PBE, [17]	4.235	-0.16
20.00	4.203exp, [19]	4.228	+0.61
25.00	4.229exp, [18], 4.196LDA, [15], 4.160LDA, [16], 4.235PBE, [17]	4.224	-0.12, +0.66, +1.53, -0.26
36.00	4.228exp, [21]	4.214	-0.34
49.00	4.217exp, [20]	4.202	-0.36
50.00	4.214exp, [18], 4.192LDA, [15], 4.128LDA, [16]	4.201	-0.32, +0.21, +1.76
75.00	4.090LDA, [16]	4.178	+2.14

4. CONCLUSION

We have determined surface energies of 8 crystallographic planes in TiN by means of the *ab-initio* simulation method of DFT with GGA-PBE exchange-correlation functional. The most stable is (100) which agrees with the fact it has significantly higher atomic surface density than the rest of the studied surface planes. Comparing with available published data for (100), (110) and (111) surfaces, our calculations are in very well agreement. We also used DFT GGA-PBE method to calculate influence of nitrogen vacancies on the lattice parameter a

in rock salt-like structure of TiN_{1-x}. Linear decrease of a with increasement in N vacancy concentration is observed and the linear regression of those data is possible up to 80 % of vacancies presence. From this point, the slope of the lattice parameter is much steeper and one can predict that the metastability of cubic TiN_{1-x} phase will be close to $TiN_{0.20}$ composition. To conclude, we have reached excellent correspondence with theoretical and experimental published literature data and extended calculated lattice parameter dependence of δ-TiN_{1-x} on the full range of nitrogen vacancies with very good linear fit regression.

ACKNOWLEDGEMENTS

This work was supported by the Ministry of Health of the Czech Republic [project number NV19-08-00070] and the Grant Agency of the Czech Technical University in Prague [grant No. SGS19/190/OHK4/3T/14] and by the Operational Program Research, Development and Education financed by European Structural and Investment Funds and the Czech Ministry of Education, Youth and Sports [Project No. SOLID21 - CZ.02.1.01/0.0/0.0/16_019/0000760].

REFERENCES

[1] VLCAK, P. et al. Influence of surface pre-treatment with mechanical polishing, chemical, electrochemical and ion sputter etching on the surface properties, corrosion resistance and MG-63 cell colonization of commercially pure titanium. *Mater. Sci. Eng. C.* 2020, p. 111065.

[2] VLCAK, P. et al. Structural characterization and mechanical properties of a titanium nitride-based nanolayer prepared by nitrogen ion implantation on a titanium alloy. *J. Nanomater.* 2016, vol. 2016.

[3] MARLO, M., MILMAN, V. Density-functional study of bulk and surface properties of titanium nitride using different exchange-correlation functionals. *Phys. Rev. B - Condens. Matter Mater. Phys.* 2000, vol. 62, no. 4, pp. 2899-2907.

[4] VOHRA, Y. K., SPENCER, P. T. Novel γ-phase of titanium metal at megabar pressures. *Phys. Rev. Lett.* 2001, vol. 86, no. 14, pp. 3068-3071.

[5] BOLOKANG, A. S., PHASHA, M. J. Formation of titanium nitride produced from nanocrystalline titanium powder under nitrogen atmosphere. *Int. J. Refract. Met. Hard Mater.* 2010, vol. 28, no. 5, pp. 610-615.

[6] BÈS, R. et al. First-principles study of rare gas incorporation in titanium nitride. *Phys. Rev. B - Condens. Matter Mater. Phys.* 2013, vol. 87, no. 2, pp. 1-10.

[7] GALL, D. et al. Pathways of atomistic processes on TiN(001) and (111) surfaces during film growth: An ab initio study. *J. Appl. Phys.* 2003, vol. 93, no. 11, pp. 9086-9094.

[8] CLARK, S. J. et al. First principles methods using CASTEP. *Zeitschrift für Krist. Mater.* 2005, vol. 220, no. 5-6, pp. 567-570.

[9] PERDEW, J. P. et al. Generalized gradient approximation made simple. *Phys. Rev. Lett.* 1996, vol. 77, no. 18, p. 3865.

[10] MONKHORST, H. J., PACK, J. D. Special points for Brillouin-zone integrations. *Phys. Rev. B.* 1976, vol. 13, no. 12, p. 5188.

[11] VANDERBILT, D. Soft self-consistent pseudopotentials in a generalized eigenvalue formalism. *Phys. Rev. B* 1990, vol. 41, no. 11, p. 7892.

[12] BIRCH, F. Finite elastic strain of cubic crystals. *Phys. Rev.* 1947, vol. 71, no. 11, p. 809.

[13] KOSOLAPOVA, T. Y. *Handbook of high temperature compounds: properties, production, applications.* CRC Press, 1990.

[14] PALTY, A. E. et al. *Titanium-nitrogen and titanium-boron systems.* New York University, 1954.

[15] GUEMMAZ, M. et al. Theoretical and experimental investigations on elastic properties of substoichiometric titanium nitrides: Influence of lattice vacancies. *Int. J. Inorg. Mater.* 2001, vol. 3, no. 8, pp. 1319-1321.

[16] DRIDI, Z. et al. First-principles calculations of vacancy effects on structural and electronic properties of TiCx and TiNx. *J. Phys. Condens. Matter* 2002, vol. 14, no. 43, pp. 10237-10249.

[17] CATELLANI, A. et al. Tailoring the plasmonic properties of metals: The case of substoichiometric titanium nitride. *Phys. Rev. Mater.* 2020, vol. 4, no. 1, p. 15201.

[18] WRIEDT, H. A., MURRAY, J.L. The N-Ti (nitrogen-titanium) system. *Bull. Alloy Phase Diagrams.* 1987, vol. 8, no. 4, pp. 378-388.

[19] HÖCHST, H. et al. Photoemission study of the electronic structure of stoichiometric and substoichiometric TiN and ZrN. *Phys. Rev. B.* 1982, vol. 25, no. 12, pp. 7183-7191.

[20] GUEMMAZ, M. et al. Ion implantation processing of sub-stoichiometric titanium nitrides and carbonitrides: Chemical structural and micromechanical investigations. *Appl. Phys. A Mater. Sci. Process.* 1997, vol. 64, no. 4, pp. 407-415.

[21] JIANG, C.-C. et al. Non-stoichiometry of titanium nitride plates prepared by chemical vapour deposition. *J. Alloys Compd.* 1993, vol. 190, no. 2, pp. 197-200.

PATTERNING OF CONDUCTIVE NANO-LAYERS ON GARNET

Jana CHLUMSKÁ, Ondřej LALINSKÝ, Milan MATĚJKA, Stanislav KRÁTKÝ, Vladimír KOLAŘÍK

Institute of Scientific Instruments of CAS, Brno, Czech Republic, EU, chlumska@isibrno.cz

https://doi.org/10.37904/nanocon.2020.3731

Abstract

Synthetic crystalline materials of the garnet group are used as scintillators in scanning electron microscopy. If a thick conductive layer is applied on the garnet surface, slower electrons don't have enough energy to pass through this relatively thick conductive layer on the scintillator surface. Therefore, either thinner conductive layer or appropriate patterning of the thicker layer has to be used. Within this contribution we study the patterning process of such conductive nano-layer. Resolution of the patterning process is of high interest. Two approaches are compared: direct writing electron beam lithography and mask projection UV lithography.

Keywords: Electron beam lithography, nano-patterning, yttrium aluminium garnet

1. INTRODUCTION

Scintillation detectors are one of the most widely used types of backscattered electron (BSE) and secondary electron (SE) detectors. Their basic element is a scintillator. The scintillator is a material in which a cathodoluminescence (CL) response occurs after an electron impact. The integral intensity of CL is a very important physical quantity and its magnitude affects the performance of the overall scintillation detector. The problem arises in the detection of low-energy electrons, since the integral intensity of CL decreases significantly with decreasing energy of incident electrons. SEs, having an energy of the order of tens of eV, are accelerated by the applied positive voltage on the scintillator, so that upon impact on the scintillator they elicit an intense CL response. BSEs have an energy close to that of the primary beam and are often detected by a scintillator without a positive potential applied. When the low energy of the primary beam is selected, the detected BSEs also have a low energy, which causes a weak CL response.

Another important factor influencing the CL response is the depth of electron penetration into the scintillator, which also decreases significantly with decreasing energy of the incident electrons. Then in single-crystalline scintillators, CL does not occur deep in the bulk, but closer to the surface of the scintillator. The energy quantum states at the surface do not have to create radiative recombination centers as in the bulk, but can change their nature from radiative to non-radiative. In addition to the surface treatment of the scintillator after its growth (cutting, grinding, polishing, thermochemical treatment), it also depends on the chemical composition and crystal structure of the scintillator. For the detection of electrons with an energy in hundreds of eV, a completely different scintillator may be suitable due to its CL response than for the detection of electrons with an energy of 10 keV.

Various approaches were presented for the etching of the ITO (Tin-doped indium oxide) conductive layer [1-3]. Alternatively, highly luminescent thin films of zinc tungstate have been deposited on top of conventional scintillators for electron detection in order to replace the need for a top conducting layer [4].

The aim of this contribution is to develop a technology for patterning of an ITO nano-layer on a single crystalline scintillator substrate. Microlithography shall be used for this purpose, both direct write e-beam lithography and mask projection UV lithography (using the EBL originated photo mask) are of interest. Pattern line width is expected in the range 1-2 microns; the final surface coverage of the patterned ITO layer should be less than 20 %. The ITO layer with specific parameters is coated on the sample surface before the lithography steps.

2. METHOLOGICAL BASIS

Basically, a lithographic process is used for patterning of the thin conductive layer. The electron-beam direct-write patterning generally provides higher resolution and flexibility. The advantage of the optical projection lithography is basically lower processing cost.

3. EXPERIMENTS

The garnet sample (**Figure 1**, left) was coated by a conductive ITO layer of 30-50 nm. A specific sample holder was designed for the spin coating process (**Figure 1**, right).

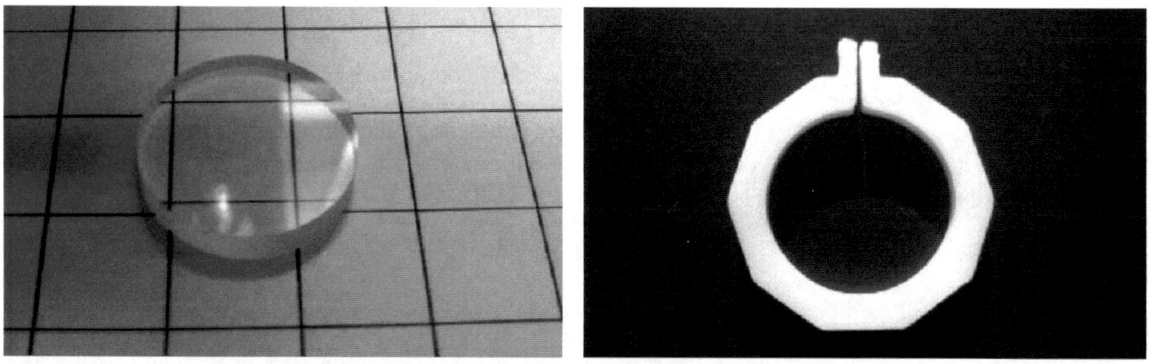

Figure 1 Garnet sample (left); sample holder for spin-coating process

3.1. Direct Writing Electron Beam Lithography

First, the sample was coated by an electron resist layer. Two types of positive-tone resist were evaluated, PMMA and Shipley S1813. The adhesivity of both types on the ITO layer was very poor. Known approaches for improving the adhesivity, i.e. plasma treating and adhesive promoter, were not effective. The resist layer was peeled off, partially or fully, either during the resist development process or during the ITO etching process. Partial results were achieved only for rough patterns; testing pattern in successive technological steps is shown in **Figure 2**. Moreover, the positive tone resist is not very suitable for the intended grid pattern, due to proximity effect of back scattered electrons during the exposure, the technological window of the applied dose is very narrow. The appropriate etching of the ITO layer was achieved using the $HCl+H_2O$ 1:1 solution.

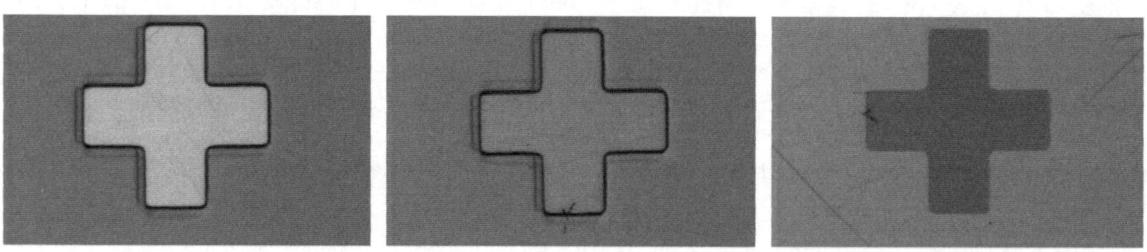

Figure 2 Sample test mark (see text): after resist development (left), after wet etching (center), after resist removing (right)

3.2. Mask Projection UV Lithography

The resolution of grid patterns was aimed at line width of less than 2 microns, with the spacing between lines in order of 20 microns; the final coverage of the ITO layer should be in the range 10-20 %.

The projection photo mask was prepared by using the e-beam lithography. The glass substrate was covered by the chromium layer of 100 nm and subsequently by a PMMA resist layer of 400 nm. The patterning was performed by using the e-beam pattern generator Vistec EBPG5000+ES with 100 keV energy of electrons. After the development of the resist mask, the pattern was transferred into the chromium layer by wet etching process, using a commercial solution *TechniStrip* from *MicroChemicals*.Detail of the photo mask is depicted in **Figure 3**.

Figure 3 Chromium photo mask (light microcopy); grid size 12 um; line width 2.0 um

The garnet sample with the ITO layer was coated by 200 nm layer of the photoresist AZ 1518 from *MicroChemicals*. The photo lithography transfer of pattern from the mask to the photoresist was done by using the mask aligner MA/BA6 form *Süss*. The exposure time was set to 7 seconds; the resist was developed by AZ 726 MIF developer for 15 seconds. The ITO layer was etched with $HCl+H_2O$ solution 1:1 for 30 seconds. The photo resist adhesion was found to be acceptable.

4. RESULTS AND DISCUSSION

The designed mask line of 3 microns was transferred as 1.5-2.0 micron lines in the ITO layer, thus achieving the final line width below 2 micrometers. The AFM measurements are shown in **Figure 4**; the micro photo is shown in **Figure 5**. The surface electrical conductivity of the sample was successfully checked.

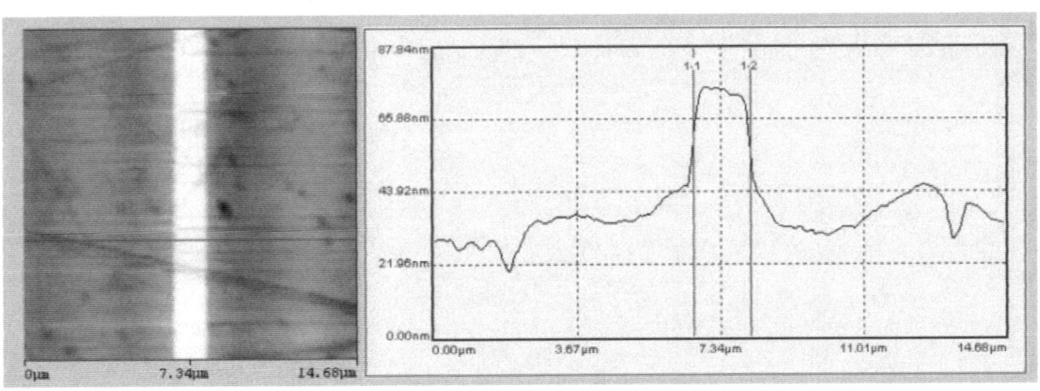

Figure 4 Conductive line on garnet (AFM); grid size 20 um; line width 1.5 um; thickness ~ 30 nm

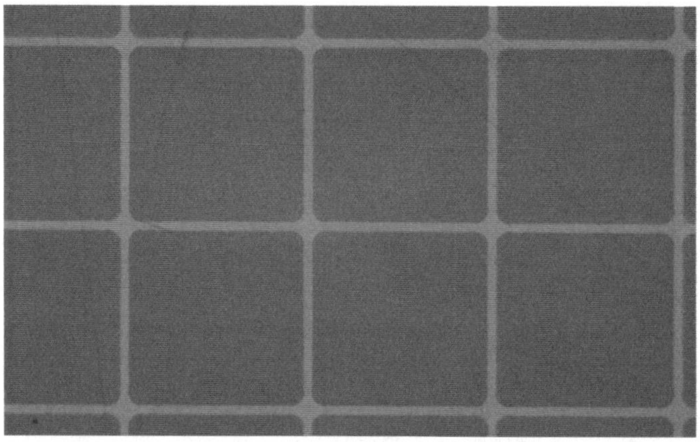

Figure 5 Conductive grid-patterned nano layer on garnet (light microcopy); grid size 20 um; line width 1.5 um; thickness ~ 30 nm

5. CONCLUSIONS

The paper summarizes the results of patterning conductive nano layer on the garnet substrate. Direct write lithography using electron beam patterning was unsuccessful. The projection optical lithography using the e-beam originated photo mask was shown to be adequate and precise process. The resulting sample is used as a cathodoluminiscence detector with defined surface conductivity.

ACKNOWLEDGEMENTS

The research was funded by the Technology Agency of the Czech Republic (project TN01000008). The research infrastructure was funded by the Czech Academy of Sciences (project RVO:68081731).

REFERENCES

[1] TSAI, T.-H., WU, Y.-F. Wet etching mechanisms of ITO films in oxalic acid. *Microelectronic Engineering*. March 2006, vol. 83, no. 3, pp 536-541.

[2] HUANG, C.J., SU, Y.K., WU, S.L. The effect of solvent on the etching of ITO electrode. *Materials Chemistry and Physics*. March 2004, vol. 84, no. 1, pp. 146-150.

[3] SCHOLTEN, M., MEERAKKER, J.E.A.M. van den. On the Mechanism of ITO Etching: The Specificity of Halogen Acids. *J. of the Electrochemical Society*. 1993, vol. 140, no. 2, pp. 471-475.

[4] TZOLOV, M. B. et al. First-Surface Scintillator for Low Accelerating Voltage Scanning Electron Microscopy (SEM). Imaging. *Microscopy and Microanalysis*. 2018, vol. 24, no. 5, pp. 488-496.

CONDUCTIVE SILVER FILMS ON PAPER PREPARED BY ATMOSPHERIC PRESSURE ARGON PLASMA CONVERSION OF SILVER NITRATE

[1]Július VIDA, [2]Aleš STÝSKALÍK, [1]Masoud SHEKARGOFTAR, [3]Juho Antti SIRVIÖ, [1]Tomáš HOMOLA

[1]*Department of Physical Electronics, Faculty of Science, Masaryk University, Brno, Czech Republic, EU,* *jvida@mail.muni.cz*

[2]*Department of Chemistry, Faculty of Science, Masaryk University, Brno, Czech Republic, EU,* *styskalik@chemi.muni.cz*

[3]*Fibre and Particle Engineering Research Unit, University of Oulu, Finland, EU,* *Juho.Sirvio@oulu.fi*

https://doi.org/10.37904/nanocon.2020.3725

Abstract

We present a novel approach for deposition of metallic silver films from silver nitrate ($AgNO_3$) ink. The conversion of $AgNO_3$ is induced by argon plasma of the diffuse coplanar surface barrier discharge (DCSBD) generated at atmospheric pressure. The macroscopically homogeneous and diffuse plasma of high power density allows fast reduction of $AgNO_3$ into conductive metallic silver within two minutes. The process is carried out at temperatures below 70 °C and without the need for a complex vacuum chamber and is therefore highly suitable for deposition onto temperature-sensitive materials. In our study we used paper prepared from nanocellulose fibres, which offers mechanical flexibility, translucency and recyclability while having lower surface roughness and enhanced mechanical properties and thermal stability compared to regular paper. As a figure of merit, the resistivity of prepared films was measured. The X-ray photoelectron spectroscopy was used to study the conversion of $AgNO_3$ into metallic silver. Scanning electron microscopy revealed the morphology of the surface of the films giving insight on the nucleation and the growth process. The silver films prepared according to our methodology are an attractive possibility for applications in sensing devices or as conductive lines and other features in flexible electronics.

Keywords: Conductive films, silver nitrate, reduction, argon plasma, nanocellulose

1. INTRODUCTION

Printed electronics is an emerging technological field that focuses on utilizing deposition methods compatible with solution processing to prepare functional coatings for electronic devices. While conventional electronics are based on rigid substrates as silicon wafers; printed electronics aim towards flexible substrates such as polymer (PET, PEN) foils or (nano)paper, which can be designed for the highly desirable roll-to-roll processing with high throughput.

Printing of the metals is essential to create conductive features and paths in electronic circuits. There are several approaches for the formulation of metal inks for printing. Nanoparticle inks are the most studied in the metal ink technology [1]. Nanoparticles are dispersed within an organic solution together with some capping agents to control their shape and size. Another approach is formulation of particle-free inks, where metals exist in a form of ions from metal-metorganic complexes dissolved in volatile solvents. After printing the complexes can be transformed into pure metal patterns by decomposition at elevated temperature [2] or by chemical reduction [3].

Of particular interest are metal particle-free inks based on inorganic metal salts [4]. They have the same advantages against NP inks as the metal-organic complex inks, while the metal salts are readily available and do not require careful design and synthesis. Numerous metals have been printed by simple dissolving of the metal salt in water with addition of volatile organic solvents to adjust the fluid properties of the inks including gold, silver, copper, palladium, platinum, lead, bismuth and tin [5]. The drawback of metal salt inks is relatively high sintering temperature required for the decomposition.

Post-deposition sintering is typically required for removal of the organic parts of the inks that decrease the conductivity of the printed films. In case of particle-free inks the sintering is also needed for the conversion of the ionic metals to pure metal films. Sintering at elevated temperatures restricts the possible substrates used, as polymers or paper often cannot withstand temperatures exceeding 100 °C. Alternative sintering approaches have therefore been used such as photonic sintering [6], microwave sintering [7], chemical sintering [8] and plasma sintering [5,9-11].

In this contribution we present a method to prepare conductive silver films by reduction of silver nitrate $AgNO_3$ printed from a simple water-based ink by plasma treatment at low temperature (< 70 °C) at atmospheric pressure. The approach we present can completely convert silver nitrate film into pure metallic silver in just two minutes. It is highly suitable for printing on temperature-sensitive substrates and is capable of fast treatment of large areas and is compatible with roll-to-roll processing.

As a substrate we used nanocellulose paper. Compared to naturally-occurring cellulose, which consists of cellulose fibres 20-50 µm in diameter, the microfibrils that make up nanocellulose paper have diameters that lie in a measurement range of only tens of nanometres. This allows nanocellulose paper to match the desirable properties of plastic substrates, such as low surface roughness and thermal stability, while adding recyclability and enhanced flexibility [12,13].

2. EXPERIMENTAL PROCEDURE

2.1. Materials

Silver nitrate was purchased from *Merck KGaA* (Germany). By dissolving 0.212 g of $AgNO_3$ in a mixture of 0.429 g water and 0.946 g ethylene glycol (*Lach-ner s.r.o*, Czech Republic) we obtained an ink with 15 wt.% of $AgNO_3$. The ink was very stable and retained its properties after up to a year of storage.

The nanocellulose paper was kindly provided by Dr. Juho Antti Sirviö of the Fibre and Particle Engineering Research Unit at the University of Oulu, Finland. The preparation process is thoroughly described in the works of *Sethi et. al.* and *Li et. al.* [14,15].

2.2. Deposition and plasma treatment

We deposited the silver nitrate ink using a spin-coater. A droplet with volume of 10 µl was placed in the middle of a 0.5 cm × 0.5 cm square nanocellulose substrate and spun for 45 s at 2000 RPM to distribute the ink.

Immediately after the deposition the coated samples were attached to the sample holder by a double-sided tape and inserted into the gas chamber, schematically visualized in **Figure 1**. The gas chamber had a volume of 50 cm^3. An argon gas was continually flowing through the gas chamber at a rate of 1 l/min to achieve an argon atmosphere inside the chamber. The chamber was operated at atmospheric pressure. Plasma was generated by diffuse coplanar surface barrier discharge (DCSBD) - a dielectric barrier discharge withcoplanar arrangement of electrodes; commercialized by Roplass s.r.o. (Czech republic) [16].

The plasma region of the DCSBD unit was around 0.3 mm thick. To ensure a good contact of the sample surface with the plasma region the sample holder was distanced from the ceramics of the DCSBD unit by 0.3 mm of Kapton tape. The exposure time of the treated sample surface was varied from 0 s to 128 s.

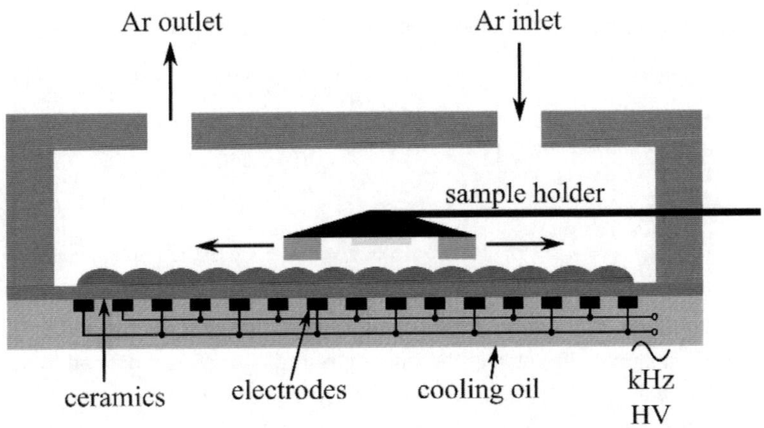

Figure 1 Scheme of the setup of the DCSBD plasma unit operating in argon. Samples are attached to the sample holder, which can be moved horizontally over the plasma region to achieve a uniform treatment.

2.3. Film analysis

Mira3 scanning electron microscope (SEM) from *Tescan* (Czech Republic) was employed for the analysis of the morphology of the reduced silver film and the evaluation silver nanoparticles dimension. The images were captured at with 20x up to 100x magnification, 5 kV accelerating voltage and at a working distance of 5 mm.

The surface chemistry of the reduced silver films was determined from X-ray photoelectron spectra (XPS) obtained by AXIS Supra spectrometer from *Kratos Analytical Ltd.* (United Kingdom). The instrument uses Al Kα spectral line (1486.6 eV photon energy) and an electron flood gun was utilized for charge compensation. The acquisition of narrow regions of the spectrum was performed with the pass energy 20 eV. For analysis of the spectra CasaXPS software was used. The spectra were calibrated to C-C/C-H peak of C 1s at 284.8 eV binding energy.

The sheet resistance of the reduced silver films was determined by the four-point probe measurement using the Four-Point Probe System from *Ossila Ltd (*United Kingdom).

3. RESULTS AND DISCUSSION

The sheet resistance of the as-deposited $AgNO_3$ film and the converted silver films after treatment for 16 s, 64 s and 128 s are shown in **Table 1**. Because of the insulating nature of the $AgNO_3$ caused the sheet resistance of the reference sample was too high to be measured. With increasing exposure to the reduction atmosphere of the argon plasma the sheet resistance of the film decreased down to 0.6 ± 0.1 Ω/□ for the film treated for 128 s. The energetic species in the plasma, specifically the argon ions and electrons are thought to be responsible for the conversion of the $AgNO_3$ into metallic silver. The plasma has a limited penetration depth into the treated film given by the porosity of the substrate and the film. There is a possibility that the converted metallic silver film forms a crust around non-converted $AgNO_3$ below, that has not been exposed to the plasma species.

The XPS spectra of the film treated for 128 s were analysed for the atomic concentrations and displayed 48% of silver, 35% of carbon, 14% of oxygen and 3% of fluorine. The carbon and oxygen that were detected can be attributed to surface contamination as well as the signal from the underlying nanocellulose substrate, which can be significant due to its porosity. The fluorine signal was also detected in the XPS spectra of the nanocellulose without the coating, therefore it can be attributed to the substrate as well. Interestingly, no nitrogen was detected in the coating. This suggests complete removal of the $AgNO_3$ during the conversion process.

Table 1 Sheet resistance of as-deposited $AgNO_3$ reference film and plasma reduced silver films

Treatment time	Sheet resistance [Ω/□]
Reference	n/a (> 10 MΩ/□)
16 s	160 ± 30
64 s	50 ± 20
128 s	0.6 ± 0.1

The narrow XPS region of the Ag 3d 5/2 of the 128 s treated sample is shown in **Figure 2a**. A metallic Ag displays a single peak at around 368.4 eV and the signal from $AgNO_3$ is typically shifted by 0.4 eV towards higher binding energies. This small difference in the binding energies makes it difficult to assess the chemical form of the film. If we look at the Ag MNN auger peak in **Figure 2b** we can better see the pronounced features typical for the metallic silver rather than those in the position for the $AgNO_3$ [17].

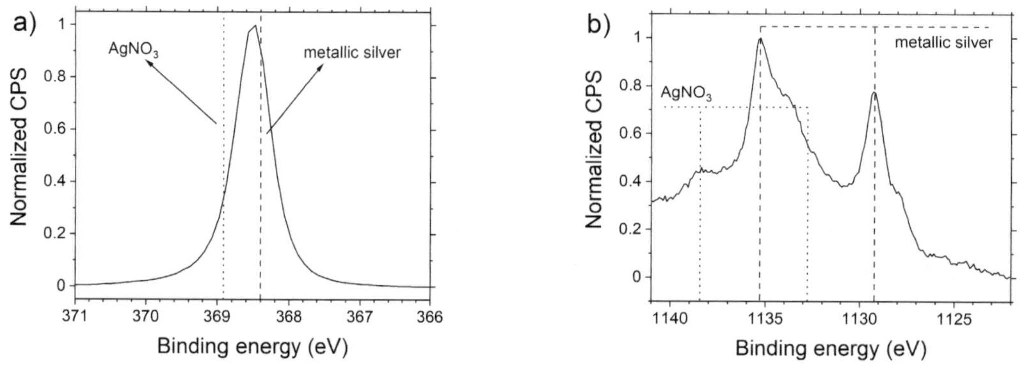

Figure 2 Narrow XPS regions of the film treated for 128 s **a)** Ag 3d 5/2 peak **b)** Ag MNN auger peak

The SEM images of the film treated for 128 s are shown in **Figure 3**. The image with lower magnification in **Figure 3a** shows the homogeneity of the converted film. The reduced silver film copies the fibres of the underlying nanocellulose substrate. The image with higher magnification in **Figure 3b** shows details of the nanoparticles of silver which formed by agglomeration of silver atoms during the conversion from $AgNO_3$ by plasma. The average diameter of nanoparticles was 36 ± 1 nm. The tight packing of the nanoparticles that can be seen in **Figure 3b** and the necks that formed between them explain the excellent sheet resistance of the film.

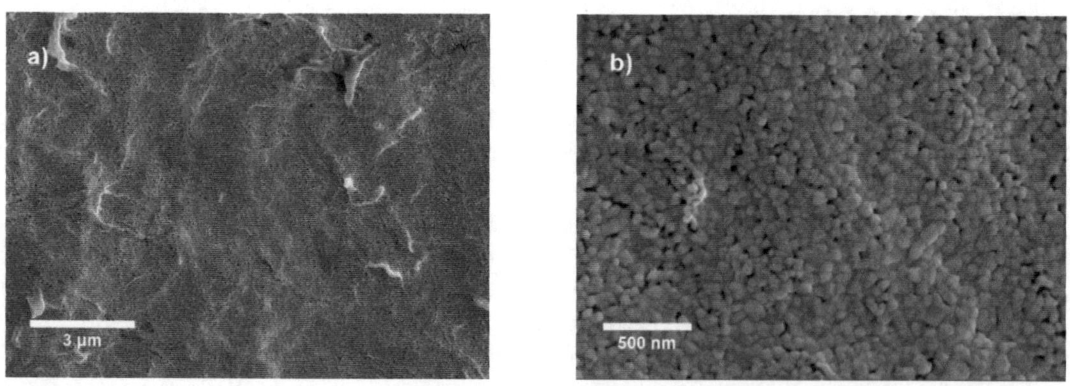

Figure 3 SEM images of the reduced silver film after 128 s treatment with **a)** 20 kx magnification and **b)** 100 kx magnification

4. CONCLUSION

Silver nitrate dissolved in a mixture of water and ethylene glycol was printed using spin-coating on the nanocellulose substrate. Exposure of the printed film to the argon plasma generated by the diffuse coplanar surface barrier discharge led to the conversion of the silver salt to metallic silver as a result of reduction by energetic species from the plasma, specifically electrons and argon ions. The sheet resistance of 0.6 Ω/□, which is about 10x the resistance of bulk silver, was achieved after treatment for just 128 s. X-ray photoelectron spectroscopy suggested a complete conversion of the $AgNO_3$, as there was no nitrogen detected on the surface and the auger peak of silver displayed a shape typical for metallic silver, not a mixture of silver and silver nitrate. The nanocellulose paper substrate was used because of its compatibility with the ink, good mechanical and thermal properties and it's flexibility and recyclability. Scanning electron microscopy images showed homogeneous coating copying the rough surface of the nanocellulose. The agglomerated nanoparticles were densely packed and formed connections during conversion. The high conductivity of the prepared films and the compatibility with the roll-to-roll processing makes this method very attractive for applications in flexible and printed electronics.

ACKNOWLEDGEMENTS

This research has been supported by Czech Science Foundation project 19-14770Y and projects LM2018097 and LM2018110 funded by Ministry of Education, Youth and Sports of Czech Republic.

REFERENCES

[1] RAJAN, K., ROPPOLO, I., CHIAPPONE, A., BOCCHINI, S., PERRONE, D., CHIOLERIO, A. Silver nanoparticle ink technology: State of the art. *Nanotechnology, Science and Applications.* 2016, vol. 9, pp. 1-13.

[2] SMITH, P. J., SHIN, D. Y., STRINGER, J. E., DERBY, B., REIS, N. Direct ink-jet printing and low temperature conversion of conductive silver patterns. *Journal of Materials Science.* 2006, vol. 41, no. 13, pp. 4153-4158.

[3] BLACK, K., SINGH, J., MEHTA, D., SUNG, S., SUTCLIFFE, C. J., CHALKER, P. R. Silver Ink Formulations for Sinter-free Printing of Conductive Films. *Scientific Reports.* 2016, vol. 6, pp. 1-7.

[4] SUI, Y., KREIDER, L. P., BOGIE, K. M., ZORMAN, C. A.. Fabrication of a silver-based thermistor on flexible, temperature-sensitive substrates using a low-temperature inkjet printing technique. *IEEE Sensors Letters.* 2019, vol. 3, no. 2.

[5] SUI, Y., DAI, Y., LIU, C. C., SANKARAN, R. M., ZORMAN, C. A. A New Class of Low-Temperature Plasma-Activated, Inorganic Salt-Based Particle-Free Inks for Inkjet Printing Metals. *Advanced Materials Technologies.* 2019, vol. 4, no. 8.

[6] MAEKAWA, K., YAMASAKI, K., NIIZEKI, T., MITA, M., MATSUBA, Y., TERADA, N., SAITO, H. Drop-on-Demand Laser Sintering With Silver Nanoparticles for Electronics Packaging. *IEEE TRANSACTIONS ON COMPONENTS, PACKAGING AND MANUFACTURING TECHNOLOGY.* 2012, vol. 2, no. 5.

[7] PERELAER, J., DE GANS, B. J., SCHUBERT, U. S., Ink-jet printing and microwave sintering of conductive silver tracks. *Advanced Materials.* 2006, vol. 18, no. 16, pp. 2101-2104.

[8] SHI, L., LAYANI, M., CAI, X., ZHAO, H., MAGDASSI, S., LAN, M., An inkjet printed Ag electrode fabricated on plastic substrate with a chemical sintering approach for the electrochemical sensing of hydrogen peroxide. *Sensors and Actuators, B: Chemical.* 2018, vol. 256, pp. 938-945.

[9] KNAPP, C. E., CHEMIN, J. B., DOUGLAS, S. P., ONDO, D. A., GUILLOT, J., CHOQUET, P., BOSCHER, N. D., Room-Temperature Plasma-Assisted Inkjet Printing of Highly Conductive Silver on Paper. *Advanced Materials Technologies.* 2018, vol. 3, no. 3.

[10] WÜNSCHER, S., STUMPF, S., TEICHLER, A., PABST, O., PERELAER, J., BECKERT, E., SCHUBERT, U. S., Localized atmospheric plasma sintering of inkjet printed silver nanoparticles. *Journal of Materials Chemistry.* 2012, vol. 22, no. 47, pp. 24569-24576.

[11] MA, S., BROMBERG, V., LIU, L., EGITTO, F. D., CHIAROT, P. R., SINGLER, T. J., Low temperature plasma sintering of silver nanoparticles. *Applied Surface Science.* 2014, vol. 293, pp. 207-215.

[12] ZHU, H., LUO, W., CIESIELSKI, P. N., FANG, Z., ZHU, J. Y., HENRIKSSON, G., HIMMEL, M. E., HU, L. Wood-Derived Materials for Green Electronics, Biological Devices, and Energy Applications. *Chemical Reviews.* 2016, vol. 116, no. 16, pp. 9305-9374.

[13] ZHU, H., FANG, Z., PRESTON, C., LI, Y., HU, L. Transparent paper: Fabrications, properties, and device applications. *Energy and Environmental Science.* 2014, vol. 7, no. 1, pp. 269-287.

[14] SETHI, J., FAROOQ, M., SAIN, S., SAIN, M., SIRVIÖ, J. A., ILLIKAINEN, M., OKSMAN, K. Water resistant nanopapers prepared by lactic acid modified cellulose nanofibers. *Cellulose.* 2018, vol. 25, no. 1, pp. 259-268.

[15] LI, P., SIRVIÖ, J. A., HONG, S., ÄMMÄLÄ, A., LIIMATAINEN, H., Preparation of flame-retardant lignin-containing wood nanofibers using a high-consistency mechano-chemical pretreatment. *Chemical Engineering Journal.* 2019, vol. 375.

[16] ČERNÁK, M., ČERNÁKOVÁ, Ľ., HUDEC, I., KOVÁČIK, D., ZAHORANOVÁ, A. Diffuse coplanar surface barrier discharge and its applications for in-line processing of low-added-value materials. *EPJ Applied Physics.* 2009, vol. 47, no. 2.

[17] FERRARIA, A. M., CARAPETO, A. P., BOTELHO DO REGO, A. M. X-ray photoelectron spectroscopy: Silver salts revisited. *Vacuum.* 2012, vol. 86, no. 12, pp. 1988-1991.

APPLICATION OF MANGANESE OXIDE THIN-FILMS OBTAINED BY ALD FOR LI-ION BATTERIES ANODE

Ilya EZHOV, Paul VISHNIAKOV, Ilya MITROFANOV, Yury KOSHTYAL, Denis NAZAROV, Aleksander RUMYANTSEV, Anatoliy POPOVICH, Maxim MAXIMOV*

Peter the Great Saint-Petersburg Polytechnic University, Saint-Petersburg, Russia, maximspbstu@mail.ru

https://doi.org/10.37904/nanocon.2020.3715

Abstract

Thin-film solid-state lithium-ion batteries can provide autonomous operation of miniature devices (biosensors, smartwatches, medical devices, etc.). In this work, we investigated the processes of obtaining thin films of manganese oxide by atomic layer deposition (ALD), and their electrochemical activity as an anode of a lithium-ion battery (LIBs). Tris (2,2,6,6-tetramethyl-3,5-heptanedionato) manganese (III) ($Mn(thd)_3$) was used as an Mn precursor, and remote oxygen plasma was used as a co-reactant. Each pulse of $Mn(thd)_3$ and remote plasma treatment were separated by N_2 purge and evacuation of the reactor. The deposition of manganese oxide films was carried out on silicon (100) and stainless steel (316SS, 16 mm in diameter) substrates at the temperature of 250-300 °C. The effect of the precursor sublimation temperature, the pulse of manganese precursor, and purge time on the growth rate per cycle was studied. The average growth per cycle calculated from film thickness measurements (spectral ellipsometry) varied from 0.06 to 0.12 Å/cycle. Using X-ray photoelectron spectroscopy (XPS), the compositions of the deposited films were determined. According to XPS results, the formation of Mn_2O_3 oxide occurred during deposition. The change in the shape of the curves of cyclic voltammetry as a result of cyclic charge/discharge relative to lithium is discovered. The maximum capacity observed at 0.8 C-Rate (30 µA) was 110 $\mu Ah \cdot \mu m^{-1} \cdot cm^{-2}$ for a steel substrate with a manganese oxide layer.

Keywords: Atomic layer deposition, manganese oxide, thin films, solid-state li-ion battery

1. INTRODUCTION

Nowadays, most electronics companies try to reduce the size of their product. Due to this fact, the downsizing of power-supply sources is the current problem for them. There is a need for methods that can accurately recreate the structure of the battery and its materials while improving the parameters compared to old ones. The synthesis of thin-film cathode and anode materials by atomic layer deposition (ALD) allows solving this problem. The method is based on self-limiting reactions of a gas-phase reagent with a substrate surface [1,2]. Due to its peculiar properties, the process makes it possible to create uniform coatings on substrates of complex shapes such as high-aspect structures [3,4]. Therefore, the energy capacity of the battery can be increased, which has a positive effect on the device's autonomy. Studies [5-7], have shown that ALD coatings the oxides of transition metals such as Ni, Co, have high electrochemical activity. Manganese oxides have similar electrochemical characteristics [8]. Thus, it can appear for high-capacity anode material of a thin-film lithium-ion battery.

Various compounds are used to synthesis thin films of manganese oxides by the ALD. The most common are manganese carbonyl $Mn_2(CO)_{10}$ [9], Bis(ethylcyclopentadienyl)manganese (II) $Mn(EtCp)_2$ [10,11], and Tris(2,2,6,6-tetramethyl-3,5-heptanedionato)manganese (III) $Mn(thd)_3$ [12-14]. The main disadvantage of $Mn_2(CO)_{10}$ is the difficulty of controlling the uniform growth of films at elevated temperatures due to the reagent decomposition. In the case of using $Mn(EtCp)_2$, the resulted manganese oxides generally have a stoichiometric formula close to MnO. Thus, stronger oxidation conditions are required to obtain manganese oxides with higher oxidation states.

In this work, $Mn(thd)_3$ was chosen as a precursor due to the stable average growth per cycle rate and uniformity of the films. Another advantage is the possibility of synthesis of manganese oxides in a wide range of oxidation states from +2 to +4 by varying the second reagent [10]. This work describes ALD synthesis and studies (physicochemical and electrochemical) of films obtained by ALD synthesis thin films of manganese oxide using $Mn(thd)_3$ as a reagent, as well as to identify the optimal synthesis parameters.

2. MATERIALS AND METHODS

Silicon monocrystal plate (111, 40 мм, ZAO "Svetlana") and stainless-steel plate (316SS, Tob New Energy Technology Co., LTD, 15.8 mm) were used as a surface for the thin film deposition. Steel plates were cleaned in Ultrasonic cleaner, acetone, and deionized water for 15 minutes successively.

ALD of the thin film was performed in the «Functional materials» laboratory, SPbPU using Picosun R-150 setup at the reactor temperature of 270°C and the reactor pressure of 8-12 GPa. Tris(2,2,6,6-tetramethyl-3,5-heptanedionato)manganese(III) ($Mn(thd)_3$) (CAS № 14324-99-3, DalChem) was used as a precursor. Oxygen plasma was used as a co-reactant (Power- 3 kW, pulse - 15 s).

Spectroscopic ellipsometry parameters for the Mn_2O_3 film was measured by ellipsometer SAG Ellips-1891 (CNT, Novosibirsk, Russia) in wave range from 350 to 1000 nm.

Electrochemical measurements were carried out on coin cells with CR2032 dimensions relative to lithium. Mn-O samples on the 316SS surface were used as an electrode. Lithium foil, polyolefin porous film 2325 (Celgard, Charlotte, North Carolina, USA), and TC-E918 solution (Tinci, Guangzhou, China) were used as a counter electrode, separator, and electrolyte, respectively. Disc cells were collected in the OMNI-LAB (VAC) glove box under argon atmosphere. Cyclic voltammetry (CV) was performed using the PGSTAT302N+ potentiostat (Autolab, Utrecht, Netherlands) in the range of 0-3.0 V at a scan velocity of 0.5 mV / s.

X-ray photoelectron spectra (XPS) were detected with "Thermo Fisher Scientific Escalab 250Xi". The surface of samples was etched by Ar ions with an energy of 500-3000 eV before the measurements. Then samples were illuminated by the x-ray emission of Al Kα (1486.7 eV) in vacuum $7 \cdot 10^{-8}$ Pa. Sample charging was automatically compensated. Analysis for each sample was carried out at 2-3 randomly selected points on the surface.

X-ray diffraction (XRD) studies were performed using a Bruker D8 ADVANCE (Cu-Kα, Billerica, MA, USA).

3. RESULT AND DISCUSSION

3.1. Mn-O thin films synthesis

Different deposition parameters were varied during the experiment to determine their influence on the growth parameters of the films. Experimental parameters and growth results are presented in **Table 1.**

Deposition parameters consisted of the temperatures of the evaporator (170-190 °C), the temperature of the reagent supply line to the reactor (200-210 °C), and the pulse time of the manganese precursor (0.5-4 s). The growth rate was studied on films resulting from 500 ALD cycles. Thicker films were grown (over 1700 cycles) to research chemical, phase compositions and determine the electrochemical characteristics. The purge time for all experiments was 3 seconds after the $Mn(thd)_3$ injection. The time of the pulse and purging of oxygen plasma was 15 and 5 seconds, respectively. Experimental parameters and growth conditions are presented in **Table 1**.

The study showed that the growth rate doubled from 0.06 to 0.12 Å/cycle, with an increase in the evaporator temperature from 170 to 190 °C. Such a difference is caused by the vapor pressure rise of $Mn(thd)_3$ in the evaporator and, consequently, in the reactor. Furthermore, the uniformity of the coatings improves with an increase of the pulse duration at the minimum investigated temperature of the evaporator (170 °C). Still, the average growth per cycle does not increase significantly. An increase in the precursor's pulse time from 0.5 to 2 s at 190 °C leads to a nonlinear increase in the growth rate. The maximum growth per cycle was recorded at a 1 s pulse with maintaining the uniformity of the coating constant. This time is sufficient to saturate the substrate with reagent vapors. Subsequent increase pulse time may cause a purge effect, which promotes reagent desorption and a decrease in the growth rate per cycle.

Table 1 Influence of synthesis parameters on the growth rate of manganese oxide films

T_{source}/ T_{line}	Pulse $Mn(thd)_3$/ Purge	Thickness	Growth per cycle	Cycle
°C	s	nm	Å/ cycle	n
170/210	1.0/3.0	2.0-3.8	0.06±0.01	500
170/210	4.0/3.0	2.9-3.7	0.07±0.01	500
180/200	1.0/3.0	3.3-3.8	0.07±0.01	500
190/200	0.5/3.0	3.2-4.6	0.08±0.01	500
190/200	1.0/3.0	5.0-6.3	0.12±0.01	500
190/200	2.0/3.0	3.8-4.9	0.09±0.01	500
190/200	1.0/3.0	12.6-20.7	0.10±0.01	1700

It should be noted that the reagent is stable up to 240 °C [15]. Hence, a further increase in the evaporator temperature would lead to unwanted decomposition of the reagent.

Consequently, deposition conditions with the highest growth rate were chosen to grow a thick manganese oxide film (1700 cycles): the deposition temperature is 190 °C, the precursor pulse and purge times are 1 and 3 seconds, respectively. The average growth per cycle for samples obtained at 500 and 1700 cycles is approximately the same and varies in the range of 0.10-0.12 Å / cycle.

3.2. Mn-O thin films characterization

To determine the chemical composition, the obtained samples were examined using X-ray photoelectron spectroscopy. Before measurements, the surface was etched with argon ions (3 keV) for 30 seconds to remove surface contamination. It was found that the coating in the analyzed region contains 63.8 at. % oxygen, 26.8 at. % manganese and 9.4 at. % carbon. Thus, the ratio of oxygen to manganese is 1.43 (63.8/26.8), closest to Mn_2O_3. The high carbon content in the film is associated with carbon-containing contaminants during etching and incomplete removal of the residues of the precursor ligands. Two peaks are observed on the C1s spectrum (**Figure 1a**), corresponding to C-C, C-H bonds, and carbonates (CO_3^{2-}).

On the O1s spectrum (**Figure 1b**) appear two peaks at 529.8 eV and 531.9 eV. The former refers to the compounds of oxygen with manganese in Mn_2O_3. The latter corresponds to oxygen in hydroxyl groups and/or carbonate.

The Mn2p spectrum (**Figure 1c**) contains two peaks with maxima at 641.4 eV (Mn 2p3/2) and 653.1 eV (Mn 2p1/2), which correspond to the compound Mn_2O_3. As a result, separation of the Gaussian curves, it was found that the analyzed part of the sample might contain a small proportion of MnO_2.

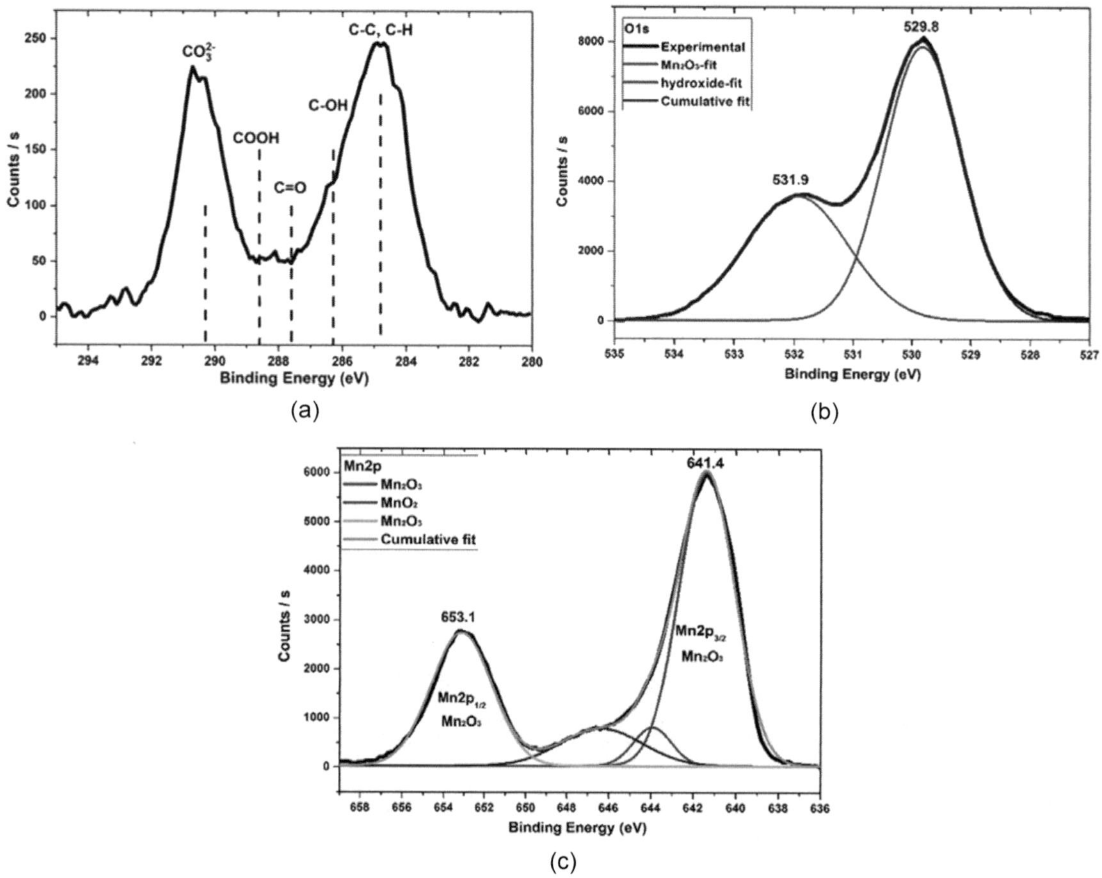

Figure 1 XPS spectra (a) C1s, (b) O1s, (c) Mn2p obtained after etching the film surface

The oxidation state of manganese can also be estimated based on the difference between the values of the Mn2p3/2 maximum and the Mn-O peak in the O1s spectrum. In the study of various manganese oxides, it was found that with a decrease in the oxidation state, this difference decreases and amounts to 112.2 eV for MnO_2, 111.7 eV for Mn_2O_3, and 111.1 eV for MnO [16]. In our case, it is 111.6 eV, which indicates the predominant presence of manganese in the Mn_2O_3 compound. In the process of ALD with the use of $Mn(thd)_3$ and O_2 plasma, there is practically no change in the oxidation state of manganese, and a Mn_2O_3 film is formed.

According to the results of an X-ray phase analysis study, no reflections corresponding to manganese oxides were found on the X-ray diffraction patterns. In this regard, it can be concluded that an X-ray amorphous film is possibly formed during the ALD at 275 °C.

3.3. Electrochemical characteristics

The electrochemical characteristics of thin films of manganese oxide Mn_2O_3 obtained on steel substrates during 1700 ALD cycles are shown in **Figure 2**. CV (cyclic voltammetry) studies (**Figure 2a**) showed that during the first scan, as well as in the subsequent 15, there are intense increases in the current in the anodic region with maxima of 1.3, 1.6, and 2.0 V. Inverse processes are present in the cathodic curve of 0.3 and 0.7 V. The presence of a maximum in the anodic region of 1.6 V (cathodic curve 0.7 V) is associated with the formation of the solid electrolyte interface (SEI film) [5]. In the anodic process, two distinct peaks at 1.3 V and 2.1 V could be described to the oxidation of Mn^0 to Mn^{2+} and Mn^{2+} to Mn^{4+}, respectively [17]. It should be noted that after 15 CV scans intensity of anodic peak at 1.3 V decreased, and cathodic peaks became more intensive.

The areas of the anode and cathode parts are comparable in area, which indicates high reversibility of the processes.

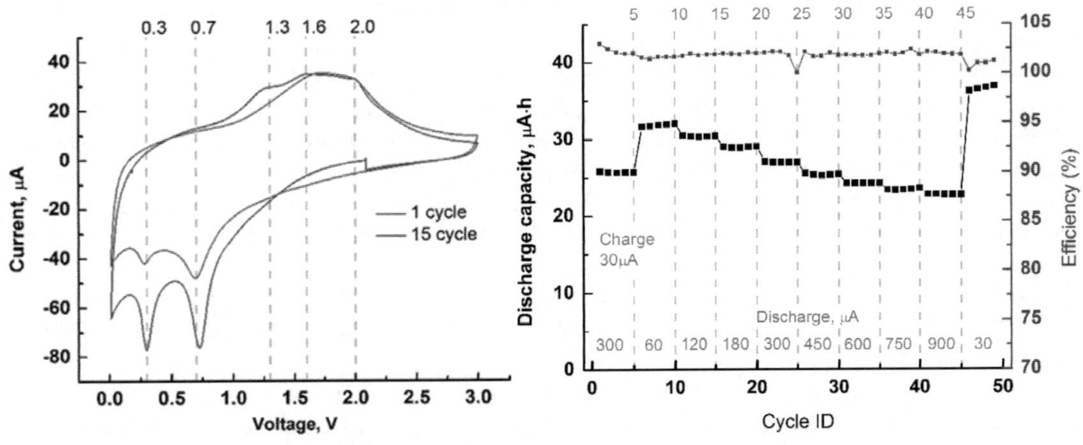

(a) (b)

Figure 2 a - CV curves of manganese oxide coatings, b - electrochemical charge-discharge tests with different currents

Cyclic charge-discharge tests at various current densities were carried out after 15 CV cycles in **Figure 2b.** The figure shows the discharge capacity at different current densities from 30 to 900 µA (from 0.8 C-Rate to 28 C-Rate) and coulombic efficiency. An increase in the discharge current density led to the decrease in capacity. The maximum capacity of 37 µAh corresponded to the lower current of 30 µA (0.8 C-Rate), the minimum 24 µAh for 900 µA (28 C-Rate). Thus, the capacitance drop was 35% of the maximum with 30 times increase in current, which corresponds to the high discharge characteristics of the obtained coatings. The maximum specific volume discharge capacity was 110 $\mu Ah \cdot \mu m^{-1} \cdot cm^{-2}$ corresponding to the discharge capacity of 37 µAh. For example, NiO prepared by us early has the specific discharge capacity 94 $\mu Ah \cdot \mu m^{-1} \cdot cm^{-2}$ (0.8 C-Rate) [5]. Cyclic tests showed the values of the coulombic efficiency are more than 100%, which is associated with the formation of the SEI film and/or associated with adsorption processes occurring on the electrode surface.

4. CONCLUSION

ALD growth of Mn-O films was carried out using Bis (2,2,6,6-tetramethyl-3,5-heptanedionato) manganese (III) ($Mn(thd)_3$) and remote oxygen plasma as an oxidizing agent. The largest average growth per cycle, 0.12 Å/cycle, is achieved at a reactor temperature of 270 °C, an evaporator temperature of 190 °C, a pulse time $Mn(thd)_3$ - 1 second, and a purge time (N_2) - 3 seconds. According to XPS, the film contains predominantly Mn_2O_3. The presence of carbon is due to incomplete removal of the residues of the precursor ligands. The crystalline phase of manganese oxides was not found, and the films is amorphous.

According to the results of CV, the films had high electrochemical reversibility. The resulting two peaks at 1.3 V and 2.1 V could be described to the oxidation of Mn^0 to Mn^{2+} and Mn^{2+} to Mn^{4+}. The highest specific discharge capacity is 110 $\mu Ah \cdot \mu m^{-1} \cdot cm^{-2}$ (0.8 C). The capacity drop was 35% of the maximum with an increase in current 30 times, which corresponds to the high discharge characteristics of the obtained coatings.

ACKNOWLEDGEMENTS

The research was supported by the Ministry of Science and Higher Education of the Russian Federation (State Assignment for basic research 0784-2020-0022).

REFERENCES

[1] MALYGIN, A.A., DROZD, V.E., MALKOV, A.A., SMIRNOV, V.M. From V. B. Aleskovskii's "Framework" Hypothesis to the Method of Molecular Layering/Atomic Layer Deposition. *Chemical Vapor Deposition.* 2015, vol. 21, pp. 216-240.

[2] GEORGE, S.M. Atomic Layer Deposition: An Overview. *Chemical Reviews.* 2010, vol. 110, pp. 111-131.

[3] MAXIMOV, M., NAZAROV, D., RUMYANTSEV, A., KOSHTYAL, Y., EZHOV, I., MITROFANOV, I., KIM, A., MEDVEDEV, O., POPOVICH, A. Atomic Layer Deposition of Lithium-Nickel-Silicon Oxide Cathode Material for Thin-Film Lithium-Ion Batteries. *Energies.* 2020, vol. 13, p. 2345.

[4] NAZAROV, D., EZHOV, I., MITROFANOV, I., LYUTAKOV, O., MAXIMOV, M.Y. The Use of TMA as Stabilizing Reagent for the Li-O System Obtained by Atomic Layer Deposition. *Key engineering Materials.* 2019, vol. 822, pp. 787-794.

[5] KOSHTYAL, Y., NAZAROV, D., EZHOV, I., MITROFANOV, I., KIM, A., RYMYANTSEV, A., LYUTAKOV, O., POPOVICH, A., MAXIMOV, M. Atomic Layer Deposition of NiO to Produce Active Material for Thin-Film Lithium-Ion Batteries. *Coatings.* 2019, vol. 9, no. 5, p. 301.

[6] NAZAROV, D.V., MAXIMOV, M.Y., NOVIKOV, P.A., POPOVICH, A.A., SILIN, A.O., SMIRNOV, V.M., BOBRYSHEVA, N.P., OSMOLOVSKAYA, O.M., OSMOLOVSKY, M.G., RUMYANTSEV, A.M. Atomic layer deposition of tin oxide using tetraethyltin to produce high-capacity Li-ion batteries. *Journal of Vacuum Science & Technology A.* 2017, vol. 35, pp. 1-11.

[7] MAXIMOV, M.Y., NOVIKOV, P.A., NAZAROV, D.V., RYMYANTSEV, A.M., SILIN, A.O., ZHANG, Y., POPOVICH, A.A. Characterization and Electrochemical Performance at High Discharge Rates of Tin Dioxide Thin Films Synthesized by Atomic Layer Deposition. *Journal of Electronic Materials.* 2017, vol. 46, pp. 6571-6577.

[8] REDDY, M.V., RAO, G.V.S., CHOWDARI, B.V.R. Metal Oxides and Oxysalts as Anode Materials for Li Ion Batteries. *Chemical Reviews.* 2013, vol. 113, pp. 5364-5457.

[9] JIN, H., HAGEN, D., KARPPINEN, M. Low-temperature atomic layer deposition of crystalline manganese oxide thin films. *Dalton Transactions.* 2016, vol. 45, pp. 18737-18741.

[10] BURTON, B.B., FABREGUETTE, F.H., GEORGE, S.M. Atomic layer deposition of MnO using Bis(ethylcyclopentadienyl) manganese and H2O. *Thin Solid Films.* 2009, vol. 517, pp. 5658-5665.

[11] LU, H.L., SCAREL, G., LI, X.L., FANCIULLI, M. Thin MnO and NiO films grown using atomic layer deposition from ethylcyclopentadienyl type of precursors. *Journal of Crystal Growth.* 2008, vol. 310, pp. 5464-5468.

[12] MATTELAER, F., VEREECKEN, P.M., DENDOOVEN, J., DETAVERNIER, C. Deposition of MnO Anode and MnO2 Cathode Thin Films by Plasma Enhanced Atomic Layer Deposition Using the Mn(thd)(3) Precursor. *Chemistry of Materials.* [online]. 2015, vol. 27, pp. 3628-3635, Available from: https://doi.org/10.1021/acs.chemmater.5b00255.

[13] NIEMINEN, H.E., MIIKKULAINEN, V., SETTIPANI, D., SIMONELLI, L., HONICKE, P., ZECH, C., KAYSER, Y., BECKHOFF, B., HONKANEN, A.P., HEIKKILA, M.J., et al. Intercalation of Lithium Ions from Gaseous Precursors into beta-MnO2 Thin Films Deposited by Atomic Layer Deposition. *Journal of Physical Chemistry C.* 2019, vol. 123, pp. 15802-15814.

[14] MIIKKULAINEN, V., RUUD, A., OSTRENG, E., NILSEN, O., LAITINEN, M., SAJAVAARA, T., FJELLVAG, H. Atomic Layer Deposition of Spinel Lithium Manganese Oxide by Film-Body-Controlled Lithium Incorporation for Thin-Film Lithium-Ion Batteries. *Journal of Physical Chemistry C.* 2014, vol. 118, pp. 1258-1268.

[15] NILSEN, O., FJELLVAG, H., KJEKSHUS, A. Growth of manganese oxide thin films by atomic layer deposition. *Thin Solid Films.* 2003, vol. 444, pp. 44-51.

[16] MATTELAER, F., BOSSEREZ, T., RONGE, J., MARTENS, J.A., DENDOOVEN, J., DETAVERNIER, C. Manganese oxide films with controlled oxidation state for water splitting devices through a combination of atomic layer deposition and post-deposition annealing. *Rsc Advances.* 2016, vol. 6, pp. 98337-98343.

[17] CHEN, J.B., WANG, Y.W., HE, X.M., XU, S.M., FANG, M., ZHAO, X., SHANG, Y.M. Electrochemical properties of MnO2 nanorods as anode materials for lithium ion batteries. *Electrochimica Acta.* 2014, vol. 142, pp. 152-156.

ACTIVATION OF AIR-STABLE ZERO-VALENT IRON NANOPARTICLES: COMPARISION OF DIFFERENT APPROACHES

[1,2]Viktorie VÍCHOVÁ, [2]Jana OBORNÁ, [2]Petr JAKUBEC, [2]Jan FILIP

[1]*Department of Experimental Physics, Faculty of Science, Palacký University in Olomouc, Czech Republic, EU, viktorie.vichova@upol.cz*

[2]*Regional Centre of Advanced Technologies and Materials, Palacký University in Olomouc, Czech Republic, EU*

https://doi.org/10.37904/nanocon.2020.3721

Abstract

Nanoscale zero-valent iron (nZVI) particles represent a strong reducing agent which makes them highly promising in the process of degradation of organic compounds such as persistent chlorinated compounds (e.g. chlorinated ethylenes) as well as immobilisation of inorganic pollutants (e.g. hazardous elements). In this contribution, we compare several types of activation procedures to restore the reactivity of air-stable nZVI particles. Different approaches to increase the reactivity of nZVI particles have been tested for hexavalent chromium (Cr(VI)) removal. The study was supplemented by complex characterisation of nZVI particles including electrochemical impedance spectroscopy, X-ray powder diffraction, transmission electron microscopy and specific surface area measurement. Based on experiments of contaminant removal capacity and the characterization of activated nZVI particles, we can conclude that the short-time high-temperature activation process is the most efficient.

Keywords: Air-stable zero-valent iron nanoparticles, activation process, hexavalent chromium removal, groundwater remediation

1. INTRODUCTION

Nanoscale zero-valent iron (nZVI) particles are typically used for removal of environmentally hazardous substances (e.g. hazardous elements) because of their high reactivity and the strong reducing effect. During the chemical reduction, nZVI particles reduce pollutants to less toxic products and nanoparticles themselves are oxidized to environmentally benign iron oxides. The nanoscale of the particles leads to their high reactivity and allows them to migrate in aqueous media easily. The high specific surface area of nZVI particles causes their high reactivity and also a high sorption capacity. Reactivity of nZVI particles could be further controlled by modifying their surface and/or by combination with other abiotic or biotic processes [1-3].

The most common modification of nZVI surface is to create a compact oxide shell. Such nanoparticles are air-stable containing a metallic-iron core and a compact oxide shell [4]. The oxide shell is formed by iron oxides protecting nZVI core against fast oxidation by oxygen leading to their easier transport, storage and manipulation. On the other hand, this shell leads to the decrease of the nZVI reactivity when they are used for contaminant removal. A process called the activation of air-stable zero-valent iron nanoparticles is essential for recovering their reactivity with contaminants during the remediation process [5].

In this paper, we compared a traditional activation [5] with two new approaches to the activation of air-stable zero-valent iron nanoparticles. Evaluation of changes in their reactivity was monitored by hexavalent chromium reduction to trivalent chromium [6,7].

2. MATERIALS AND METHODS

2.1. Chemicals

NANOFER STAR (air-stable zero-valent iron nanoparticles consisting of metallic iron core and thin oxide shell) were purchased from NANOIRON, Ltd. (Czech Republic). The solution with an initial Cr(VI) concentration equal to 10 mg/L was prepared from potassium dichromate ($K_2Cr_2O_4$, Sigma Aldrich, USA) with the minimum purity of 98 %. Chemicals used for electrochemical impedance spectroscopy: phosphate buffer solution (Penta s.r.o, Czech Republic) and potassium ferricyanide(III) (Sigma Aldrich, USA). Solutions for colourimetric test contained 1,5-diphenylcarbazide (Sigma Aldrich, USA) and 0.04 mol solution of HCl (Lach-Ner, Czech Republic).

2.2. Characterization Techniques

Microscopy characterization was performed on a transmission electron microscope (TEM) JEOL JEM 2100 at 200 kV of accelerating voltage. To each sample in small Eppendorf tube was added ethanol (methylated ethanol, Tereos TTD, Czech Republic) and was not followed by sonication. Suspensions were dropped on carbon grid and dried on air. The average thickness of the oxide layer on nZVI particles was measured from TEM images using ImageJ software (version 1.53e, Wayne Rasband, USA).

Electrochemical impedance spectroscopy (EIS) was measured in a three-electrode configuration, in which the glassy carbon electrode modified with iron-based samples, platinum wire electrode, and Ag/AgCl (3 M KCl) electrode (all purchased from 2THETA ASE s.r.o., Český Těšín, Czech Republic) served as working, counter, and reference electrodes, respectively. EIS experiments were carried out using a Metrohm Autolab PGSTAT128N potentiostat/galvanostat (Metrohm Autolab B.V., Netherlands). Phosphate buffer solution (PBS, pH 7) was used as a supporting electrolyte containing 5 mmol/L $K_3[Fe(CN)_6]$ as a redox probe. All experiments were carried out at room temperature (22 ± 2 °C). All EIS spectra were collected using a 5 mV amplitude and were recorded over the frequency range from 0.1 Hz to 10 kHz using the half-wave potential of potassium ferricyanide(III) (0.2 V). The glassy carbon electrode (GCE) was modified as follows: a 10 µL drop of a powder suspension (2 mg/mL) was drop-coated onto the surface of the GCE electrode and allowed to dry at ambient temperature to form a thin film.

For measurement of the specific surface area, samples were dried under a nitrogen atmosphere in a glove box (SylaTech GmbH, Germany). The specific surface area of samples was measured using a surface area and porosity analyser Autosorb IQ (Quantachrome, USA) and determined by Brunauer-Emmett-Teller (BET) theory. Process of degassing was held at a temperature of 130 °C for 13 hours.

The X-ray powder diffraction (XRD) was measured employing X`Pert PRO diffractometer (Malvern Panalytical, UK) equipped with Co radiation source, programmable divergence and diffracted beam anti-scatter slits, and X`Celerator detector. The wet samples were dropped on a zero-background silicon slide and covered with Myllar foil to protect them against drying. Every pattern was captured by the measurement of six fast repetitive scans (5 min each) in the range between 5 and 105 °2Theta. NANOFER STAR nZVI particles (NFSTAR) were measured as a typical dry powder sample, i.e., the sample was prepared by the back-loading method of the sample holder and the pattern was measured as a single scan in the range between 5 and 105 °2Theta. The data were processed employing High Score Plus software in conjunction with PDF-4+ and ICSD databases.

2.3. Activation Process

Three different approaches of activation of zero-valent iron nanoparticles were examined in this study. To obtain nZVI slurries, nZVI particles were added to deionized water leading to the final concentration of 250 g/L nZVI particles to distilled water. Before the activation process, nZVI slurries were dispersed using T 10 basic ULTRA-TURRAX (IKA, Germany) for 2 minutes at 11 000 rpm.

The first method of activation of nZVI particles in water for 24 hours was adopted from Ribas et al. [5]. Briefly, 5 g of nZVI particles was added to 20 mL of distilled water in 40 mL glass vial and dispersed. The activation process was held at the room temperature for 24 hours (sample labelled as A_TIME).

The second approach utilized heating of ferromagnetic nZVI particles in an electromagnetic field (EMF) (samples labelled as A_EMF) [8,9]. nZVI suspension (10 g of nZVI and 40 mL of distilled water in 60 mL glass vial) with the final concentration of nZVI equal 250 g/L was dispersed. Then, glass vial was placed inside the copper coil of the induction heating device CX-2015A (Chengdu Jinkezhi Electronic Co., China). The activation process was performed for 30 minutes with the regulation of secondary current in the coil equal 310 A.

To simulate the heating effect of the electromagnetic field on nZVI particles (samples labelled as A_TEMP), the third method of zero-valent iron nanoparticles activation was tested The nZVI suspension was prepared by the same approach as in the first method. Glass vial was placed in a water bath and heated for 35 minutes with a setting of the temperature of water bath equal to 105 °C (sample labelled as A_TEMP). Heating time and temperature rate were chosen according to temperatures reached during the activation process in EMF.

All experiments were conducted in triplicates. Measurements of temperature, pH and oxidation-reduction potential (ORP) were done for every sample before and after the process of activation (Multi 3410, WTW, Germany). ORP values normalized to standard hydrogen electrode (SHE) adding +207 mV (for 25 °C, sample A_TIME), +188 mV (for 50 °C, sample A_EMF) and +184 mV (for 55 °C, sample A_TEMP).

2.4. Hexavalent Chromium Removal

To determine the reactivity of treated nZVI particles for contaminant removal, batch experiments with model contaminant Cr(VI) were held. Slurries with nZVI particles were dispersed after the activation process in the same procedure as described in Section 2.1. The initial concentration of Cr(VI) was 10 mg/L and concentration of nZVI was equal to 2 g/L. The pH of Cr(VI) solution was adjusted to 7 using 0.4 mol HCl (Lach-Ner, Czech Republic). Experiments were conducted in 40 mL glass vials at room temperature (RT). Experiments for Cr(VI) removal by nZVI particles were managed for 1, 2.5, 5, 15, 30 and 60 minutes, 24, 48 and 72 hours. Blank samples without nZVI particles were measured in the time period of 0, 1, 24, 48 and 72 hours. Samples were shaken at the horizontal shaker Unimax 2010 (Heidolph, Germany) at 300 rpm. Samples were filtrated using PTFE membrane filters with 0.1 µm pore size (Whatman, United Kingdom). Colourimetric test EPA METHOD 7196A was performed to measure the residual concentration of Cr(VI) in samples using UV-Visible spectrophotometer (Biochrom WPA Lightwave II, UK) at wavelength $\lambda = 542$ nm.

3. RESULTS AND DISCUSSION

3.1. Characterization of Nanoparticles Before and after Activation Process

TEM images of nZVI particles before and after the activation process are presented in **Figure 1**. Initial nZVI particles (samples labelled as NFSTAR) show a uniform oxide layer on their surface with a thickness approximately 4.3 nm (**Table 1**). The oxide shell of activated nanoparticles reveals substantial changes as can be seen from **Figure 1**. This is mainly reflected in the presence of significant fractures and defect of the oxide shell for all three activated samples. Such changes are accompanied by the increased thickness of the oxide layer compared to un-activated nZVI (ranging from 5.1 to 5.6 nm).

Charge transfer resistance (R_{ct}) values obtained from electrochemical impedance spectroscopy (EIS) are shown in **Figure 2**. The average value of R_{ct} of unactivated nZVI particles (NFSTAR) is the lowest compared to activated samples. During the activation process, the value of R_{ct} increased. This change is significant for the growth of the oxide shell but also for its structural changes and growth of other material phases such as e.g. iron hydroxides. This increased thickness of the oxide layer is also observable in TEM images (**Figure 1**).

The changes in the specific surface area of nZVI particles during the activation process are shown in **Table 1**. This value increased for all types of the activation process and is comparable for all activated samples.

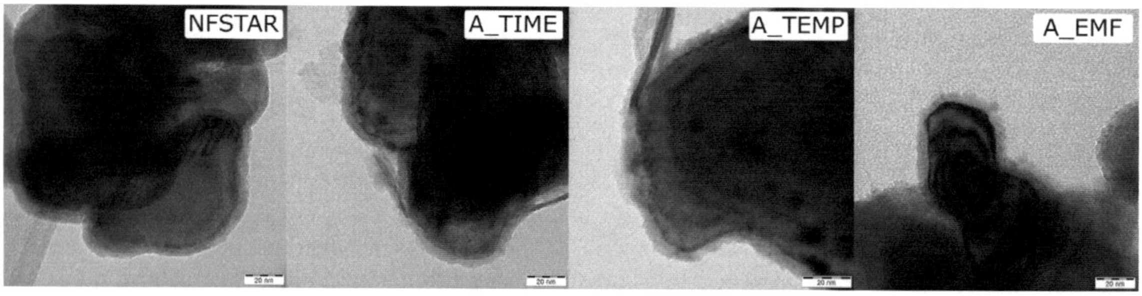

Figure 1 Comparison of TEM images of initial and activated nZVI nanoparticles

Table 1 The average thickness of the oxide layer on nZVI particles measured from TEM images and the average specific surface area of nZVI particles before and after the activation process

Sample	Average thickness of the oxide layer (nm)	Number of measurements	SSA ($m^2 \cdot g^{-1}$)
NFSTAR	4.3 ± 0.6	93	20.8
A_TIME	5.3 ± 0.7	53	37.3 ± 5.6
A_TEMP	5.1 ± 0.9	57	30.5 ± 6.0
A_EMF	5.6 ± 0.9	74	36.3 ± 8.6

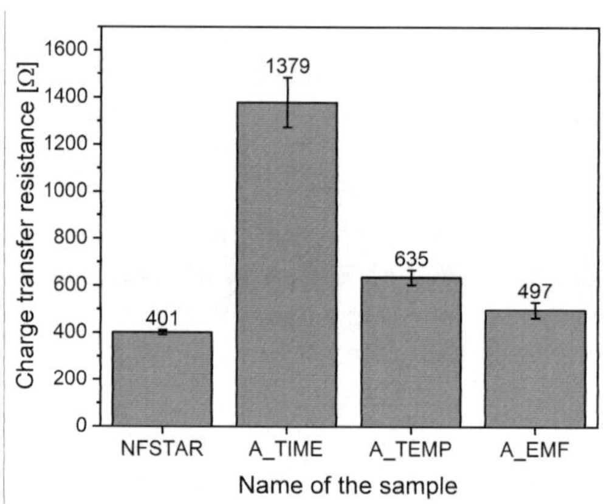

Figure 2 Average charge transfer resistance (R_{ct}) of un-activated (NFSTAR) and activated nZVI particles measured by EIS

XRD patters of un-activated and activated nZVI particles are shown in **Figure 3**. In is worth to note, that XRD records of activated samples and NFSTAR sample, do not exhibit any significant crystallographic changes or changes in phase composition.

Evolution of pH and ORP values proved enhanced reactivity of nZVI particles after the activation process. Increasing values of pH and decreasing values of ORP (**Table 2**) are significant for higher reactivity of zero-valent iron nanoparticles in an aqueous environment. Comparing different approaches of activation of nZVI particles, there is only a small increase of pH value and slower decrease of ORP for nZVI particles activated for 24 hours (A_TIME) compared to other two activation procedures. For activation in the water bath

(A_TEMP) and EMF (A_EMF), the change of pH and ORP have similar trend and are more significant than for method A_TIME. While the activation process A_TIME was held at the RT, the other two samples reached temperatures up to 95 °C during the activation process. According to this, it can be concluded that a higher temperature is increasing the reactivity of nZVI particles. The changes in the oxide shell morphology seem to be analogous to the oxide shells prepared at elevated temperatures by Kašlík et al. in [10] leading to the same changes in reactivity.

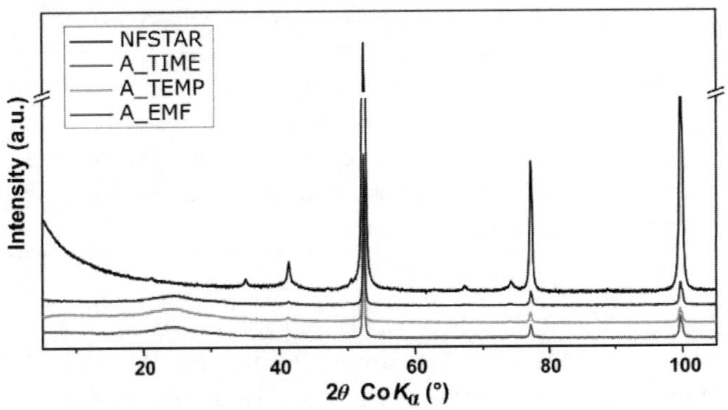

Figure 3 XRD patterns of initial and activated nZVI nanoparticles. NFSTAR was measured in a different mode which is leading to higher peak intensities (counts) compared to activated samples

Table 2 pH and ORP development during the activation process. Data logged before and after the activation processes in nZVI suspensions (Multi 3410, WTW, Germany)

Sample	Average ORP (mV SHE)		Average pH	
	Before	After	Before	After
A_TIME	270 ± 109	-38 ± 1	6.91 ± 0.04	7.2 ± 0.4
A_TEMP	143 ± 40	-125 ± 32	6.90 ± 0.08	8.5 ± 0.2
A_EMF	263 ± 75	-269 ± 12	6.9 ± 0.2	8.5 ± 0.2

3.2. Evaluation of Cr(VI) Removal

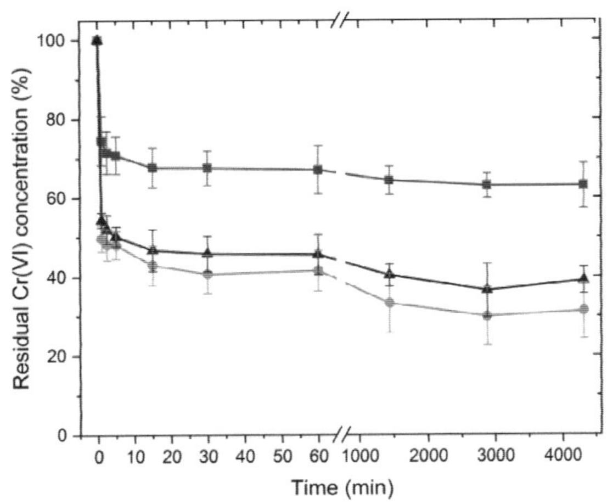

Figure 4 The change of residual concentration of Cr(VI) in time for nZVI particles activated in three different approaches. Initial concentration of Cr(VI) was equal to 10 mg/L

The trend of the residual concentration of Cr(VI) in time for nZVI particles activated in three different approaches is shown in **Figure 4**. The lowest reaction rate corresponds to A_TIME nZVI particles with removal capacity of 37 % of Cr(VI) after 3 days. However, the Cr(VI) removal capacity was higher for nZVI particles activated at higher temperatures reaching 69 % (A_TEMP) and 61 % (A_EMF) of removed Cr(VI) after 3 days.

4. CONCLUSION

Three different approaches of the activation process were performed on air-stable zero-valent iron nanoparticles to recover their reactivity. The activation process of nZVI particles commonly used in practice was compared with two new methods of activation performed at high temperatures for the period of 30-35 minutes. Short-time high-temperature methods revealed an increase of the contaminant removal capacity tested on Cr(VI) reduction. In all cases, the oxide shell of nanoparticles changed its character with increasing specific surface area and more defects leading to their higher reactivity without significant structural changes or phase composition of nZVI particles.

ACKNOWLEDGEMENTS

This research was supported by the ERDF project No. CZ.02.1.01/0.0/0.0/16_019/0000754 of the Ministry of Education, Youth and Sports of the Czech Republic, and by the project No. FV30034 from Ministry of Industry and Trade of the Czech Republic. The authors also gratefully acknowledge the financial support from the internal IGA grant of Palacký University (IGA_PrF_2020_034). Authors thank Josef Kašlík for XRD measurement and Jana Stráská for TEM images.

REFERENCES

[1] SUN, Y. P., LI, X. Q., CAO, J., ZHANG, W. X., WANG, H. P. Characterization of zero-valent iron nanoparticles. *Advances in colloid and interface science*. 2006, vol. 120, no. 1-3, pp. 47-56.

[2] ZOU, Y., WANG, X., KHAN, A., WANG, P., LIU, Y., ALSAEDI, A., HAYAT, T., WANG, X. Environmental remediation and application of nanoscale zero-valent iron and its composites for the removal of heavy metal ions: a review. *Environmental science & technology*. 2016, vol. 50, no. 14, pp. 7290-7304.

[3] O'CARROLL, D., SLEEP, B., KROL, M., BOPARAI, H., KOCUR, C. Nanoscale zero valent iron and bimetallic particles for contaminated site remediation. *Advances in Water Resources*. 2013, vol. 51, pp. 104-122.

[4] KIM, H. S., AHN, J. Y., HWANG, K. Y., KIM, I. K., HWANG, I. Atmospherically stable nanoscale zero-valent iron particles formed under controlled air contact: characteristics and reactivity. *Environmental science & technology*. 2010, vol. 44, no. 5, pp. 1760-1766.

[5] RIBAS, D., ČERNÍK, M., BENITO, J. A., FILIP, J., MARTI, V. Activation process of air stable nanoscale zero-valent iron particles. *Chemical Engineering Journal*. 2017, vol. 320, pp. 290-299.

[6] DI PALMA, L., PETRUCCI, E., VERDONE, N., VILARDI, G. Iron Nanoparticles for Cr (VI) Removal from Contaminated Soil. In: LITTER, M. I., QUICI, N., MEICHTRY, M. *Iron Nanomaterials for Water and Soil Treatment*. Jenny Stanford Publishing, 2018, pp. 201-231.

[7] LI, S., WANG, W., LIANG, F., ZHANG, W. X. Heavy metal removal using nanoscale zero-valent iron (nZVI): theory and application. *Journal of hazardous materials*. 2017, vol. 322, pp. 163-171.

[8] PHENRAT, T., THONGBOOT, T., LOWRY, G. V. Electromagnetic induction of zerovalent iron (ZVI) powder and nanoscale zerovalent iron (NZVI) particles enhances dechlorination of trichloroethylene in contaminated groundwater and soil: Proof of concept. *Environmental science & technology*. 2016, vol. 50, no. 2, pp. 872-880.

[9] PHENRAT, T., LOWRY, G. V. *Nanoscale zerovalent iron particles for environmental restoration*. Springer, 2019.

[10] KAŠLÍK, J., KOLAŘÍK, J., FILIP, J., MEDŘÍK, I., TOMANEC, O., PETR, M., ... & TRATNYEK, P. G. Nanoarchitecture of advanced core-shell zero-valent iron particles with controlled reactivity for contaminant removal. *Chemical Engineering Journal*. 2018, vol. 354, pp. 335-345.

HYDROTHERMAL AND MICROWAVE SYNTHESIS OF ZnS NANOPARTICLES

[1]Julie SMIJOVÁ, [1]Pavlína PEIKERTOVÁ, [1]Kateřina MAMULOVÁ KUTLÁKOVÁ, [1,2,3]Jonáš TOKARSKÝ

[1]*Nanotechnology Centre, VŠB - Technical University of Ostrava, Ostrava, Czech Republic, EU,* julie.smijova.st@vsb.cz, pavlina.peikertova@vsb.cz, katerina.mamulova.kutlakova@vsb.cz, jonas.tokarsky@vsb.cz

[2]*IT4Innovations, VŠB - Technical University of Ostrava, Ostrava, Czech Republic, EU,* jonas.tokarsky@vsb.cz

[3]*Institute of Environmental Technology, VŠB - Technical University of Ostrava, Ostrava, Czech Republic, EU,* jonas.tokarsky@vsb.cz

https://doi.org/10.37904/nanocon.2020.3704

Abstract

Zinc sulfide (ZnS) is a well-known semiconductor with the wide band gap ~3.6 eV. Since the ZnS exhibits excellent transmission properties, high electron mobility, non-toxicity, water insolubility, and it is relatively inexpensive, it has been considered as an important photocatalyst for water and wastewater treatment. In this study, ZnS nanoparticles were successfully prepared by hydrothermal synthesis using zinc chloride and sodium sulfide. Nevertheless, in order to further reduce the size of prepared ZnS nanoparticles and thus to further increase their photocatalytic activity, also the microwave synthesis was tested. Phase composition, morphology, particle size, and photoactivity of ZnS nanoparticles prepared by both methods were compared. FTIR spectroscopy, Raman microspectroscopy, scanning electron microscopy, and X-ray powder diffraction analyses were used. The efficiency of prepared photocatalysts was established by the decomposition of organic azo dye Acid Orange 7 under ultraviolet irradiation.

Keywords: ZnS, hydrothermal synthesis, microwave synthesis, photocatalytic activity

1. INTRODUCTION

Nanostructured materials have attracted much attention due to their unique properties that are different from bulk materials. Zinc sulfide (ZnS) is semiconductor with wide band gap (~3.6 eV) [1]. This is the one of reasons why ZnS has been used for the light emitting diodes, flat panel displays, electroluminescent, and infrared devices [1]. Nanoparticles ZnS have also a great potential in antibacterial application due to the large surface to volume ratio in comparison with bulk ones. Antibacterial effects of ZnS nanoparticles (2-4 nm) against some pathogen bacteria (*Pseudomonas aeruginosa, Actinomycet, Salmonella typhi*) have been observed [2]. Various precursors are used for ZnS nanoparticles preparation. For example, zinc acetate [3-5], zinc chloride [6], zinc sulphate [7], or zinc nitrate [6] can be used as a source of zinc ions. Sulfur source can be, for example, thioacetamide [3,4] or thiourea [6]. In this paper, we report a rapid microwave method compared with hydrothermal synthesis for simple preparation of ZnS nanoparticles synthesized from sodium sulfide (Na_2S) and zinc chloride ($ZnCl_2$). Hydrothermal synthesis is a simple one-pot method which does not acquire temperatures above 100 °C. Main principle of microwave synthesis is transferring energy from microwaves to the material, which causes particle reduction. In comparison to hydrothermal synthesis, the microwave-assisted synthesis is much faster, cleaner, energy efficient, and more economical [8]. Preparation process of hydrothermal synthesis was optimized [9], and the microwave synthesis parameters were chosen according to previous studies [3,4,6]. The precursors were chosen to develop economically acceptable production without by-products and harmful effects on the environment. The aim of this work was to compare the nanostructured material of ZnS prepared by hydrothermal and microwave synthesis. The resulting nanostructured materials were characterized by scanning electron microscopy (SEM), X-ray powder diffraction (XRPD), Fourier transform infrared spectroscopy (FTIR), and Raman microspectroscopy. Photocatalytic activities of both prepared nanostructured materials were compared.

2. MATERIALS AND METHODS

A solution of $ZnCl_2$ (0.5 M) and solution of Na_2S (1M) were combined, and later the formed solution was diluted with distilled water. Total volume of the solution was 200 ml. The obtained solution was heated in a microwave oven (SENCOR, 700W) operating at 50%. The heating time in the microwave was 30 minutes, the solution was stirred and temperature was measured after every 10 minutes. The same preparation of solution was applied to hydrothermal synthesis. Solution was heated (up to 100 °C) and stirred on a magnetic stirrer (Heidolph, MR Hei-Standard) for 3.5 hours. Precipitates were separated from solution by centrifugation and washed repeatedly with water. SEM analysis was performed using JEOL JSM-7610Fplus. Samples were coated by thin layer (20 nm) of Pt to make surface conductive, and to prevent charge accumulation. GWYDDION software was used to determine particle sizes. XRPD patterns were recorded (range 5-80°2θ) in reflection mode in symmetrical Bragg-Brentano arrangement using Bruker D8 Advance diffractometer equipped with fast position sensitive detector VÅNTEC 1. Radiation CoKα was used (λ = 0.1789 nm). Sizes of ZnS crystallites were calculated from the most intensive reflection, i.e. ZnS(111), using Scherrer equation [10].

$$L_c = \frac{K \cdot \lambda}{\beta \cdot \cos\theta} \quad (1)$$

where:

K - dimensionless shape factor (0.9)

λ - radiation wavelength (nm)

β - full width at half maximum (FWHM) of the ZnS(111) reflection (°)

θ - position of the ZnS(111) reflection (°).

FTIR spectra in range 400 - 4000 cm^{-1} were recorded by Nicolet 6700 - Thermo Fisher Scientific with diamond ATR crystal (spectral resolution 4 cm^{-1}, 32 scans). The measured data were processed by the OMNIC software. Raman spectra were acquired on Smart Raman System XploRA™ in range 120 - 1200 cm^{-1}. Laser (785 nm) was reduced to 50 % of the initial intensity. Grating with 600 grooves/mm and objective with magnification 50x were used. The acquisition time was set to 10 s with 10 times repetition. Photocatalytic activity (PA) was tested as follows. For each sample, two suspensions containing Acid Orange 7 (AO7) aqueous solution ($V = 5 \cdot 10^{-3}$ dm^3, $c = 6.259 \cdot 10^{-4}$ mol/dm^3), 50 ml of demineralized water, and 50 mg of the sample were stirred for 1 h in the dark to obtain the adsorption equilibrium. One suspension was further stirred under UV irradiation (λ = 254 nm) for 1 h, the second one (control) was stored in the dark. Discoloration was evaluated using CINTRA 303 UV-VIS spectrometer according to the equation

$$PA\ (\%) = \left(1 - \left(\frac{A_i}{A_c}\right)\right) \cdot 100 \quad (2)$$

where:

A_i - intensity of AO7 absorption maximum (480 nm) for irradiated suspension

A_c - intensity of AO7 absorption maximum (480 nm) for control suspension.

3. RESULTS AND DISCUSSION

3.1. Scanning electron microscopy

SEM images of ZnS_H and ZnS_M samples (**Figure 1**) show high degree of agglomeration. In both samples, the sizes of agglomerates are in micrometer range. However, sizes of the observed particles vary. While agglomerates in ZnS_H sample contain small round shaped (nano)particles having size in range 50 - 200 nm, agglomerates in ZnS_M sample consist of (nano)particles having size < 150 nm. EDS spectra showed the presence of Zn, S, and Na elements in both samples, only in the selected spectrum of the ZnS_M sample (shown in **Figure 1**) Zn band overlaps Na band. Occurrence of Pt and C elements is associated with sample preparation for the SEM analysis. Oxygen may indicate the atmospheric water on the surface of particles.

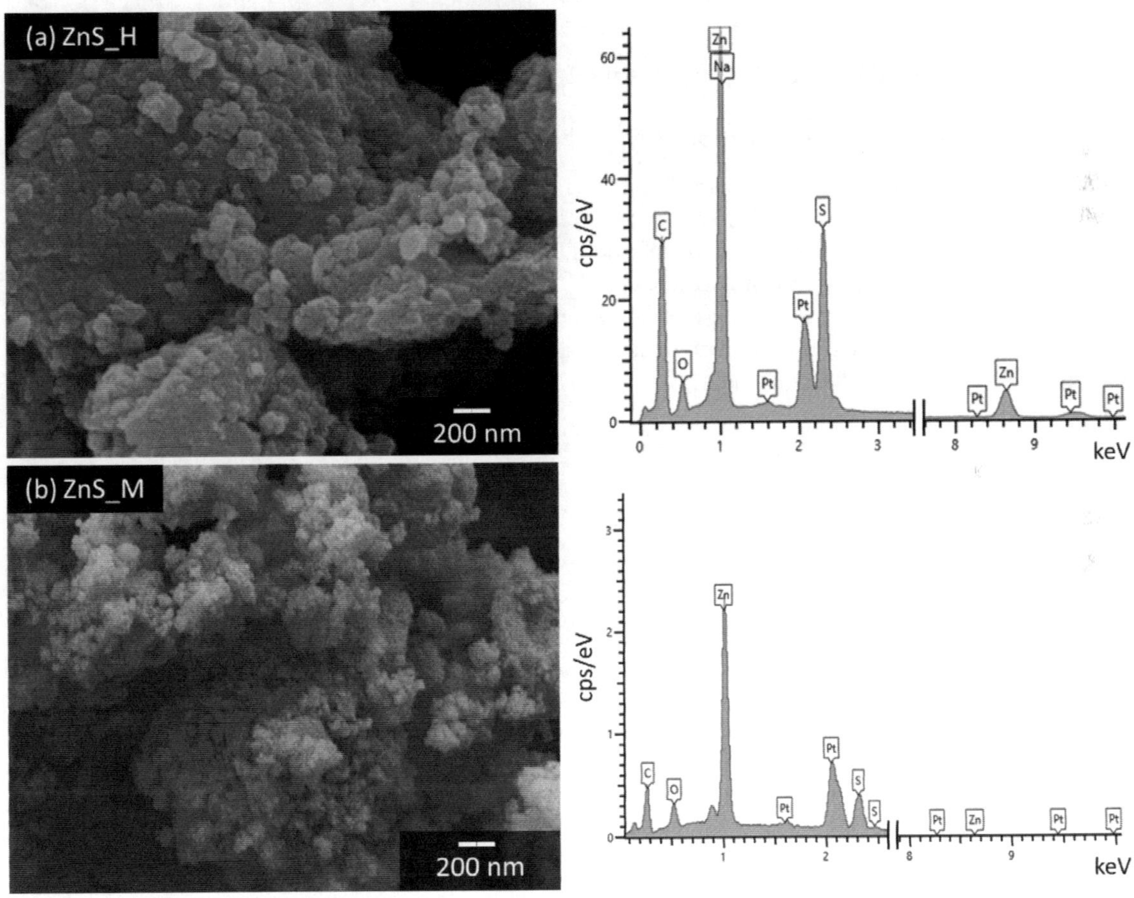

Figure 1 SEM images with corresponding EDS spectra of synthesized ZnS_H (a) and ZnS_M (b) samples

3.2. Phase analysis

XRPD analysis (**Figure 2**) revealed that both ZnS_M and ZnS_H samples contain the same ZnS phase: the cubic phase sphalerite (PDF no. 005-0566). Width of the reflections indicates a low degree of crystallinity. FWHM value for the ZnS_H and ZnS_M sample are 2.894° and 2.824°, respectively. L_c values, calculated according to the equation (1), are similar for both samples, 3.33 nm (ZnS_H sample) and 3.41 nm (ZnS_M sample). Apart from ZnS, the XRPD analysis did not show the presence of any other phases.

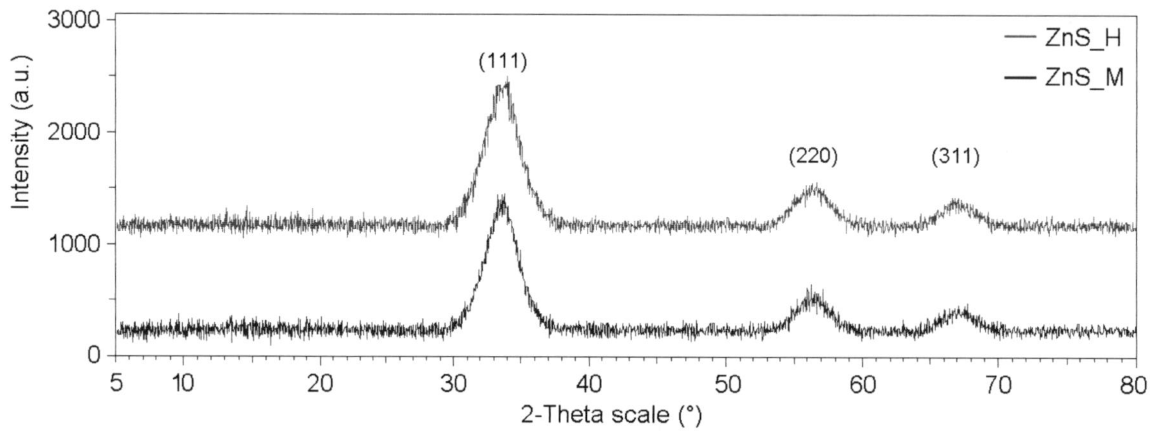

Figure 2 XRPD patterns of synthesized ZnS_M and ZnS_H samples

3.3. Fourier Transform Infrared Spectroscopy

Measured FTIR spectra are shown in **Figure 3**, and it is clearly evident that both samples have similar band position. Thus, the different preparation methods lead to the same composition of the sample, which is in agreement with XRPD results. The most intensive bands at ~3230 cm^{-1} and ~1629 cm^{-1} correspond to the stretching and bending vibration of -OH, respectively. Presence of -OH group indicates the absorbed water on the surface of (nano)crystals originating from atmospheric humidity. Based on the data from literature, the obtained spectra corresponds to the ZnS spectra, and the Zn-S bond can be observed at positions ~1111 cm^{-1}, ~977 cm^{-1}, and ~635 cm^{-1} [11,12].

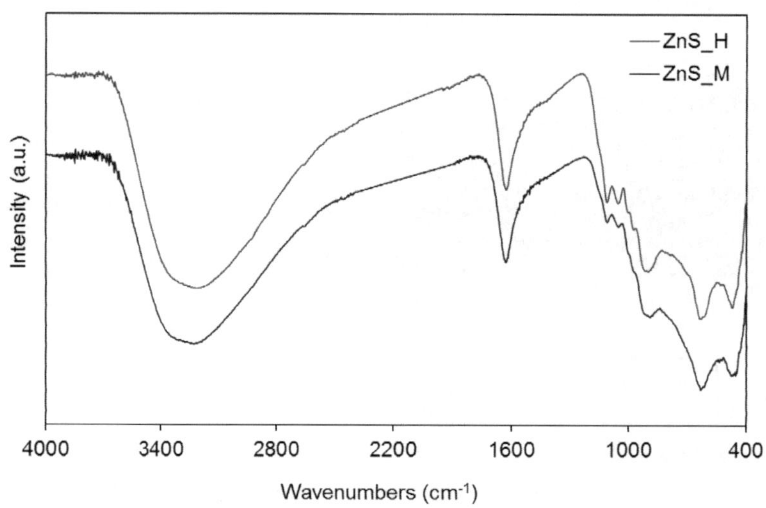

Figure 3 Infrared spectra of synthesized ZnS_M a ZnS_H samples

3.4. Raman microspectroscopy

Raman spectra for both ZnS_M and ZnS_H samples are shown in **Figure 4**. Similarly to the results of XRPD and IR analyses, Raman spectra reveal that both ways of preparation lead to the same ZnS phase as the spectra has similar shape and band positions. According to the bands appearance and bands positions, the ZnS cubic phase, i.e. sphalerite, is confirmed due to the presence of bands at 276 cm^{-1} and 352 cm^{-1}, which corresponds to the transverse and longitudinal optical zone center phonons of the cubic ZnS sphalerite phase

[13]. The shape of the Raman spectra (**Figure 4**) is partially caused by the amorphous-like structure of the ZnS and partially by size of the synthetized particles (in nano range) [14].

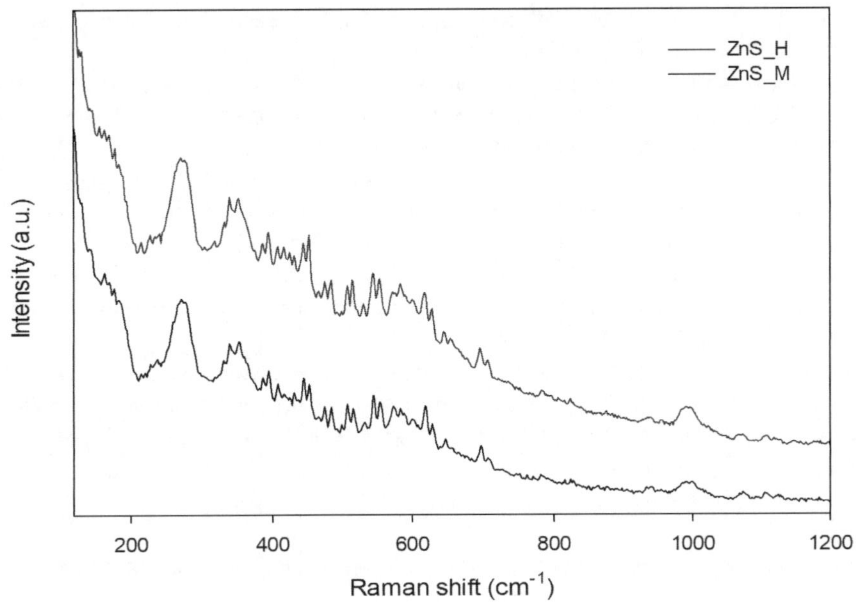

Figure 4 Raman spectra of synthesized ZnS_M a ZnS_H samples

3.5. Photocatalytic activity

ZnS samples prepared by hydrothermal and microwave synthesis do not show a significant difference in photocatalytic activity. Although no change in the color of the AO7 solution was visually observed during the first half of the total duration (1 h) of the experiment, the resulting PA values for both ZnS_H and ZnS_M sample were very satisfactory. PA values, calculated according to the equation (2), are 99.27% (ZnS_H) and 98.06% (ZnS_M). The photocatalytic efficiency of both ZnS_H and ZnS_M samples can therefore be considered very good.

4. CONCLUSION

Hydrothermal and microwave synthesis led to the successful synthesis of ZnS nanoparticles. The ZnS nanoparticles are not separate; the resulting ZnS_H and ZnS_M samples consist of their nanostructured agglomerates. While SEM analysis showed slight morphological differences between the samples, XRPD, IR, and Raman analyzes consistently confirmed cubic (sphalerite) ZnS phase in both samples, and revealed no significant differences between them. Both samples show high photocatalytic activity. After 1 h of UV irradiation, more than 99% (ZnS_H) and more than 98% (ZnS_M) of the AO7 dye was degraded. The microwave synthesis is faster and more energy efficient than the hydrothermal synthesis. Microwave radiation ensuring uniform heating of the reaction mixture makes the microwave synthesis a promising method for preparing large amount of this highly efficient ZnS photocatalyst.

ACKNOWLEDGEMENTS

This work was supported by The Ministry of Education, Youth and Sports of the Czech Republic (projects SP2020/24, LQ1602, CZ.02.1.01/0.0/0.0/16_013/0001791).

REFERENCES

[1] YAMAMOTO, T., KISHIMOTO, S., IIDA, S. Control of valence states for ZnS by triple-codoping method. *Physica B: Condensed Matter*. 2001, vol. 308-310, pp. 916-919.

[2] AMIR, G.R., FATAHIAN, S., KIANPOUR, N. Investigation of ZnS Nanoparticle Antibacterial Effect. *Current Nanoscience*. 2014, vol. 10, no. 6, pp. 796-800.

[3] SOLTANI, N., SAION, E., YUNUS, W.M.M., ERFANI, M., NAVASERY, M., BAHMANROKH, G., REZAEE, K. Enhancement of visible light photocatalytic activity of ZnS and CdS nanoparticles based on organic and inorganic coating. *Applied Surface Science*. 2014, vol. 290, pp. 440-447.

[4] RATH, T., KUNERT, B., RESEL, R., FRITZ-POPOVSKI, G., SAF, R., TRIMMEL, G. Investigation of Primary Crystallite Sizes in Nanocrystalline ZnS Powders: Comparison of Microwave Assisted with Conventional Synthesis Routes. *Inorganic Chemistry*. 2008, vol. 47, no. 8, pp. 3014-3022.

[5] GOHARSHADI, E.K., MEHRKHAH, R., NANCARROW, P. Synthesis, characterization, and measurement of structural, optical, and phtotoluminescent properties of zinc sulfide quantum dots. *Materials Science in Semiconductor Processing*. 2013, vol. 16, no. 2, pp. 356-362.

[6] LA PORTA, F.A., FERRER, M.M., DE SANTANA, Y.V.B., RAUBACH, C.W., LONGO, V.M., SAMBRANO, J.R., LONGO, E., ANDRÉS, J., LI, M.S., VARELA, J.A. Synthesis of wurtzite ZnS nanoparticles using the microwave assisted solvothermal method. *Journal of Alloys and Compounds*. 2013, vol. 556, pp. 153-159.

[7] VÁZQUEZ, A. a J. AGUILAR-GARIB. Preparation of ZnS nanoparticles using microwave assisted synthesis: effects of the irradiation power and the precursors. *Revista Mexicana de Física*. Mexico: Mayo, 2009, vol. S55, no. 1, pp. 57-60.

[8] RAO, J.K., VAIDHYANATHAN, B., GANGUL, M., RAMAKRISHNAN, P.A. Synthesis of Inorganic Solids Using Microwaves. Chemistry Of Materials. 1999, vol. 11, no. 4, pp. 882-895.

[9] MAMULOVÁ KUTLÁKOVÁ, K., TOKARSKÝ, J. Simple one-pot hydrothermal synthesis and photocatalytic activity of ZnS and ZnS/kaolinite nanocomposite. **In:** *NANOCON 2019: 1th International Conference on Nanomaterials - Research & Application*. Ostrava: TANGER, 2019, pp. 146-151.

[10] SCHERRER, P. Estimation of size and internal structure of colloidal particles by means of Röntgen rays. *Nachrichten von der Gesellschaft der Wissenschaften zu Göttingen*. 1918, vol. 2, pp. 96-100.

[11] IRANMANESH, P., SAEEDNIA, S., NOURZPOOR, M. Characterization of ZnS nanoparticles synthesized by co-precipitation method. *Chinese Physics B*. 2015, vol. 24, no. 4.

[12] MOTE, V.D., PURUSHOTHAM, Y., DOLE, B.N. Structural, morphological and optical properties of Mn doped ZnS nanocrystals. *Cerâmica*. 2013, vol. 59, no. 351, pp. 395-400.

[13] KUMAR, S.S., KHADAR, M.K., DHARA, S.K., RAVINDRAN, T.R., NAIR, K.G.M. Photoluminescence and Raman studies of ZnS nanoparticles implanted with Cu^+ ions. *Nuclear Instruments and Methods in Physics Research Section B: Beam Interactions with Materials and Atoms*. 2006, vol. 251, no. 2, pp. 435-440.

[14] ABDULKHADAR, M., THOMAS, B. Study of Raman spectra of nanoparticles of CdS and ZnS. *NanoStructured Materials*. 1995, vol. 5, no. 3, pp. 289-298.

THE EFFECTS OF MOLECULAR AND PROCESSING PARAMETERS ON ENERGY HARVESTING CAPABILITY OF PVDF-BASED NANOGENERATORS

[1]Martin CVEK, [1]Josef OSIČKA, [1]Peter SRNEC, [1]Miroslav MRLÍK, [2]Pavel TOFEL

[1]Tomas Bata University in Zlín, University Institute, Centre of Polymer Systems, Zlín, Czech Republic, EU, cvek@utb.cz

[2]Brno University of Technology, Department of Physics, Faculty of Electrical Engineering and Communication, Brno, Czech Republic, EU

https://doi.org/10.37904/nanocon.2020.3720

Abstract

In the research of the alternative vibration sensing systems, the major potential is attributed to piezoelectric materials that can generate the electrical output from the waste vibration sources of the industrial machines. Poly(vinylidene fluoride) (PVDF), mostly in the electroactive β-phase, is a great option due to its excellent piezoelectric properties and good flexibility. The β-phase PVDF can be obtained by simple stretching of the α-phase PVDF films, and the conditions of this process are well documented. Surprisingly, the implications of molecular parameters of the PVDF have not been addressed yet. This study investigates the effect of the molecular weight (Mw) of the PVDF on the β-phase development and consequential vibration sensing capabilities after uniaxial stretching. The successful phase transformation was confirmed using FTIR and XRD. In the FTIR spectra, a typical α-phase peak at 762 cm^{-1} diminished giving rise to the β-phase peak at 840 cm^{-1} after the stretching. The results also showed a remarkable impact of the Mw on d33 coefficient making Mw an important parameter that should not be overlooked in designing the PVDF-based sensing elements. The obtained data are highly important for the optimization of the PVDF-based vibration sensors applicable in the efficient structural and health monitoring nanosystems.

Keywords: Nanosystem, vibration sensing, poly(vinylidene fluoride), crystallites, d33, electromechanical coupling

1. INTRODUCTION

At the present time, the increasing demand for the electrical energy is one of the most serious challenges that world faces. To cover this demand, fossil fuels, such as petroleum, coal and natural gas, are used as the main primary-energy source. The use of these traditional fuels is however connected to many environmental problems including air pollution, water pollution, or accidental oil spills [1,2]. From these reasons, there is an urgent need for the alternative energy sources. Probably, the most fascinating alternative concept to obtain energy is represented by the energy harvesting systems. Such devices utilize waste mechanical energy, such as vibrations, air/fluid movement, body motion etc., and converts it into the electrical form [3]. To construct the energy harvesting nanogenerator, various inorganic semi-conducting materials (ZnO, InN, GaN, CdS) or free ceramics ($NaNbO_3$, $KNbO_3$) have been studied [4]. Although these materials demonstrated high efficiency, they are brittle, heavy and difficult to process, which limits the breadth of applications [3,5]. To eliminate these drawbacks, the materials of choice can be found in ferroelectric types of polymers, mainly poly(vinylidene fluoride) (PVDF) and its copolymers [6]. PVDF is a polymorphic material existing in five phases (α, β, γ, δ and ε) depending on the processing methods. The α and ε-phases are non-polar due to the antiparallel packing of dipoles. On the other hand, the β, γ and δ-phase are polar, and hence electroactive [7]. The γ-phase of PVDF is referred to as the mixture of the α and β-phases, while δ-phase is regarded as polar version of α-phase. Amongst all conformations, the β-phase PVDF is the most desirable one for the construction of the energy harvesting and vibration sensing devices, since it exhibits the best piezoelectric properties [8,9]. The significant research efforts have been therefore targeted to facilitate formation of the β-phase content in PVDF. The β-phase can be obtained directly from the polymer melt, however, the process requires high temperature, high pressure and other specific conditions [9]. Conversely, the α-phase can be obtained very easily, because it is the most stable primary phase of PVDF [10]. And subsequently, it can be transferred into the β-analogue by simple stretching (uniaxial or biaxial) at the elevated temperatures [11]. Other method to increment the β-phase content is through poling of the PVDF films in high external electric fields [12]. Also, the fabrication of films through electrospinning, which is also a form of mechanical elongation, was successfully applied [13]. Certain improvements in the α-β-phase transformation were observed after the addition of graphene oxide or cellulose particles [14,15]. The β-phase is also achievable from the γ and δ-phase using a plethora of other processing techniques [9,16]. However, from the technological point of view, the uniaxial stretching is the most convenient method to convert the α-phase into its electroactive β-counterpart. The stretching process of the PVDF was performed within wide temperature range (50-150 °C), with different stretching speeds (1-1000 μm/s) and various (1-5) stretching ratios [10]. Although the effects of these parameters on the formation of β-phase PVDF have been described, the implications of its molecular weight (M_W) on the β-phase development, energy harvesting and vibration sensing capabilities have not been, surprisingly, addressed yet. Moreover, the M_W of the applied PVDF is hardly ever mentioned in the literature. This paper therefore aims to clarify the correlations between the M_W of the PVDF and the formation of the electroactive β-phase and consequential d33 coefficient after stretching at various uniaxial ratios.

2. EXPERIMENTAL PART

2.1. Materials

The PVDF beads (CAS number: 24937-79-9) of different average molecular weights (M_W); 71 000, 107 000 and 530 000 g/mol (sample ID: M71, M107 and M530) were purchased from Sigma-Aldrich (USA). The density of beads was 1.78 g/cm^3 and they were used as received.

2.2. Fabrication and stretching process

The PVDF films with thickness of 0.8 mm were prepared using compression molding. In a typical procedure, the calculated mount of PVDF beads was placed into a mold, pre-heated (5 minutes) and compressed with a pressure of 10 MPa (for additional 5 minutes), while the temperature was set to 210 °C. Afterwards, the mold was cooled down in a controlled manner to ensure repeatability of the process. The characterization/testing of the samples was performed at least 24 h after their successful fabrication.

The rectangular strips (dimensions of 10 mm × 100 mm) were cut out from PVDF films. Stretching of as-prepared PVDF elements was performed using a tensile device M350-5 CT (Testometric, Lancashire, UK) coupled with a heat chamber (Omron) operating at a temperature of 65 °C. The cross-head speed of the clamps was set to 10 mm/min, with the relative elongations of 50, 100, 200, 300 and 500 %. In the case of M71, the elongation of 500 % could not be achieved, since it was above its breaking point. Therefore, for this sample, we have selected the maximum elongation at 400 %.

2.3. General characterization

The crystalline phase development of PVDF films was studied via X-Ray diffractions (XRD) using Miniflex 600 (Rigaku, Japan) diffractometer with a Co-Kα radiation source (λ = 1.789 Å) operating within 2θ range of 10-95° with a scan speed of 3°/min. The Fourier transform infrared spectroscopy (FTIR) was performed on Nicolet 6700 (Thermo-Scientific, USA) spectrometer equipped with ATR accessory and a germanium crystal. The spectra were recorded in a wavenumber range of 4000-500 cm^{-1} with a spectral increment of 2 cm^{-1}. Both analyzes were performed at laboratory conditions.

2.4. Energy harvesting setup

Firstly, the poling of the stretched PVDF strips was performed using a custom-build apparatus at the electric field strength of 7 kV/mm, and the temperature of 110 °C. Secondly, a thin conductive (silver) layer was deposited on the samples and their piezoelectric charge coefficient, d33, was measured within one hour after the poling process. The d33 was analyzed in the transversal mode using the electrometer 6517b (Keithley, USA). Each sample was placed between two copper electrodes; the lower electrode had a diameter of 20 mm, while the upper one had a diameter of 10 mm. A mechanical force of 0.49 N was applied onto the upper electrode and the electric charge generated by the sample was recorded. Each sample was analyzed at ten positions, the presented d33 values represent the average values from the obtained data.

3. RESULTS AND DISCUSSION

The PVDF strips of different M_W were stretched at the temperature of 65°C to generate the piezoelectric β-phase with subsequent poling process performed at 110 °C. The efficiency of phase transformation was determined by means of the FTIR spectroscopy. **Figure 1** compares the FTIR spectra recorded for the M71, M107 and M530 samples. As clearly seen, the mechanical stretching significantly altered the FTIR profile indicating changes in the polymer chain conformations. In detail, the α-phase PVDF can be identified through a large number of characteristic peaks. In the studied wavenumber region, the relevant peaks of the α-phase were centered at 762, 795, 855, 974 and 1210 cm^{-1} [2,17]. After stretching, these peaks diminished giving rise to their electroactive β-phase counterparts centered at 840 and 1276 cm^{-1} [11].

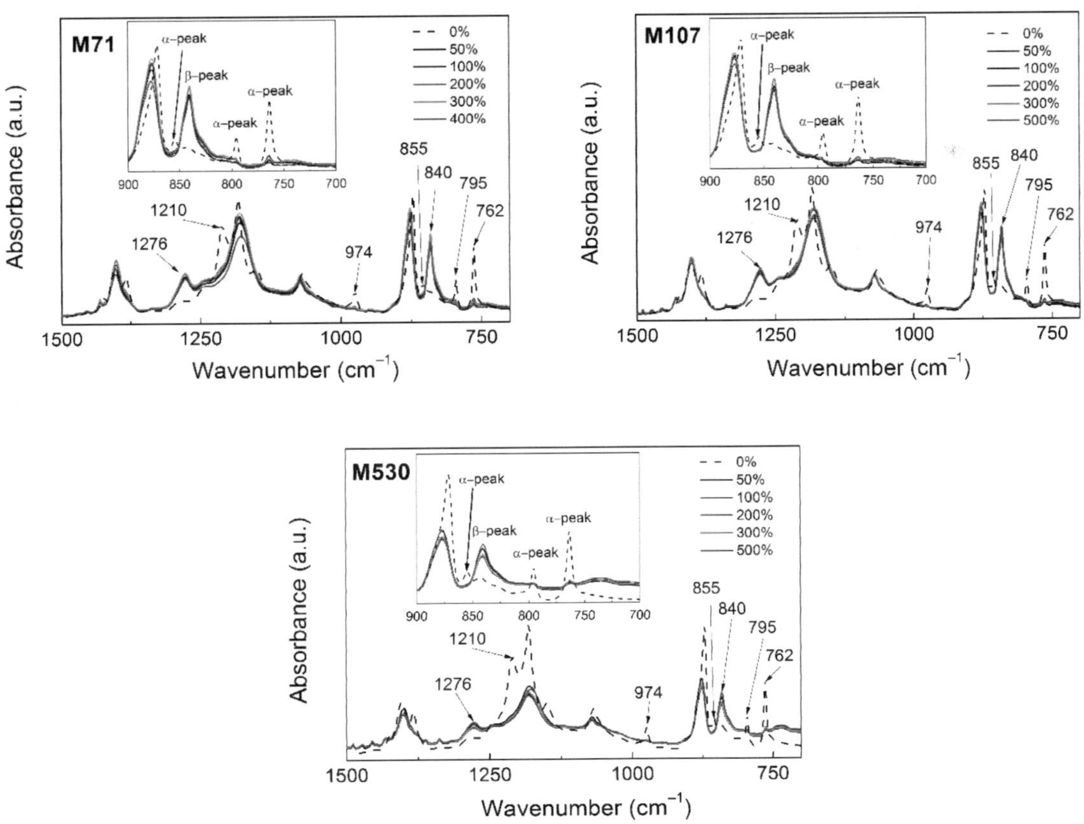

Figure 1 Comparison of the FTIR spectra for the PVDFs of different M_W

The interpretation of peak at 840 cm^{-1} is not always straightforward; in some papers this peak is classified as pure β-phase [17], while in others it is considered as the β-γ-phase mixture [18]. However, the signature of the γ-phase in terms of peaks at 776, 812, 833 and 1233 cm^{-1} was not identified. Also, the peak at 840 cm^{-1} was sharp without any distinct shoulder that would be coming from the γ-phase. Based on these findings, we tend to believe that the content of the γ-phase in the PVDF was rather minimal.

The XRD is usually used as a complementary technique to determine the crystal phase of the PVDF. As shown in **Figure 2**, all samples exhibited typical XRD diffractograms ($K\alpha_1$, λ = 1.790 Å). Prior to stretching, the α-phase was the most prevailing and exhibited typical double-peak corresponding to diffractions in planes (100) and (020), respectively. After the stretching, the β-phase was successfully developed, which was reflected in the single sharp peak that is assigned to the total diffraction in (110) and (200) planes [13]. The phase transformation was remarkably affected by the M_W of the samples. For M71, the manifestation of the β-peak changed without any trend in peak intensity. In the samples M107 and M530, the intensity of the β-peak generally increased with the relative elongation, which implies a greater efficiency of the α-β-phase transformation. These results indicate that the M_W of the PVDF has a significant influence on the structural changes during the stretching process.

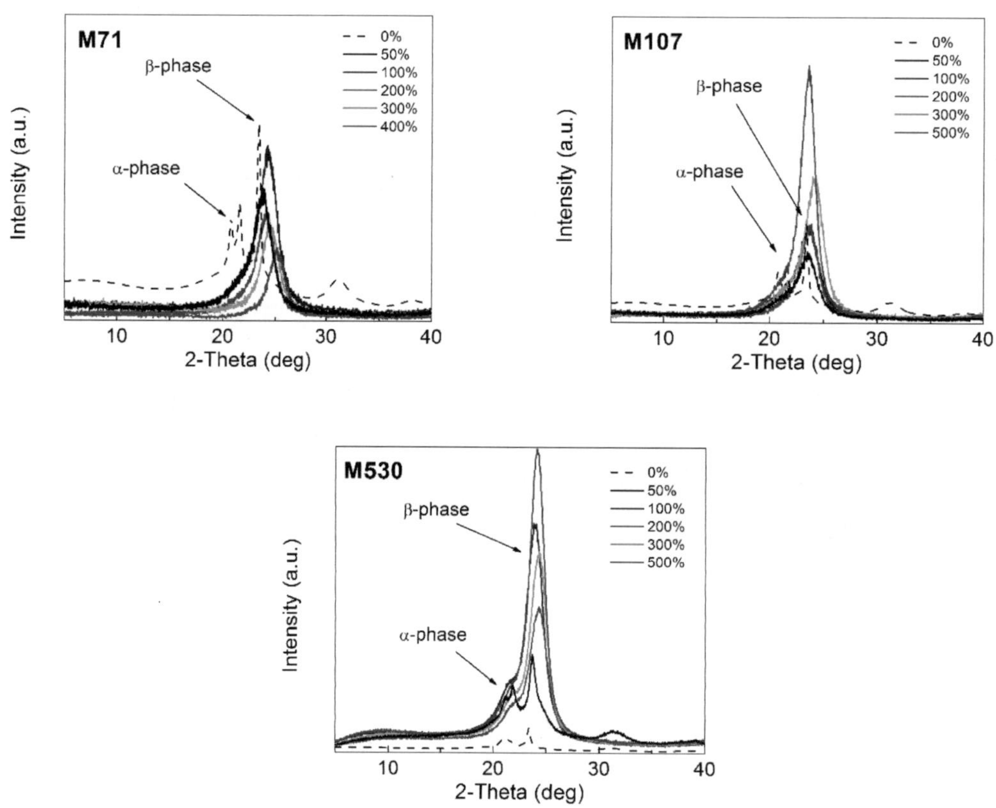

Figure 2 Comparison of the XRD patterns for the PVDFs of different M_W

The electromechanical performance of the PVDF mainly depends on the β-phase content [12]. In our case, the formation of the β-phase was facilitated by stretching in a combination with poling process. **Table 1** summarizes the d33 data for the investigated samples. It can be claimed that the applied stretching positively affected the d33 values, since they increased by a factor of 4-5 for the M71 and M530, when stretched from 50 to 500 % relative elongation. The highest d33 value was however detected for the M107, which exhibited the d33 of 9.10 pC/N at maximal relative elongation. This value is below the theoretical d33 maximum that is over 25 pC/N for pure β-phase PVDF. Such difference indicates the persistent co-existence of the α-phase, and the presence of trapped charges induced during the processing [19]. It should be mentioned that samples M107 and M530 have potential for further improvements since they have capability to achieve even higher relative elongations, and thus better conditions for the β-phase development. To conclude, we have shown that the M_W of the PVDF is highly important parameter affecting the d33 performance, and thus, it is of high relevancy for the fabrication of vibration sensing and energy harvesting elements.

Table 1 Summarized d33 values for the investigated PVDF samples

Sample ID	50 %	100 %	200 %	300 %	500 %
M71	1.20 pC/N	5.10 pC/N	5.62 pC/N	6.20 pC/N	*6.50 pC/N
M107	7.00 pC/N	7.80 pC/N	7.60 pC/N	8.50 pC/N	9.10 pC/N
M530	2.00 pC/N	4.18 pC/N	3.20 pC/N	3.60 pC/N	8.20 pC/N

*the value taken for sample with the relative elongation of 400 %

4. CONCLUSION

In this study, the PVDF strips of different M_W were stretched and subjected to poling in order to facilitate formation of the piezoelectric β-phase. The phase transformation was monitored using FTIR spectroscopy demonstrating the changeover between the dominating peaks of the α and β-phase at 762 cm^{-1} and 840 cm^{-1}, respectively. Also, the XRD data showed the successful β-phase development. In particular, samples M107 and M530 exhibited increasing peak-signal intensity with the relative elongation. The implications of different M_W of the samples were reflected in the d33 values that exhibited significant variations. Samples M71 and M530 experienced several-fold increase in the electromechanical performance, however, the highest value of the d33 was 9.10 pC/N generated by the M107. Based on these preliminary findings, further research is clearly required to better understand the interrelations among the Mw, relative elongation, crystallinity, poling conditions and d33 value of the PVDF-based nanosystems.

ACKNOWLEDGEMENTS

The authors gratefully acknowledge the Czech Science Foundation (grant no. 19-17457S) for the financial support. This work was also supported by the Ministry of Education, Youth and Sports of the Czech Republic - DKRVO (RP/CPS/2020/003) and (RP/CPS/2020/006).

REFERENCES

[1] FRAGOULI, D., ATHANASSIOU, A. Oil spill recovery: Graphene heaters absorb faster. *Nature Nanotechnology*. 2017, vol. 12, no. 5, pp. 406-407.

[2] GAUR, A., TIWARI, S., KUMAR, C., MAITI, P. A bio-based piezoelectric nanogenerator for mechanical energy harvesting using nanohybrid of poly(vinylidene fluoride). *Nanoscale Advances*. 2019, vol. 1, no. 8, pp. 3200-3011.

[3] GAUR, A., KUMAR, C., TIWARI, S., MAITI, P. Efficient energy harvesting using processed poly(vinylidene fluoride) nanogenerator. *ACS Applied Energy Materials*. 2018, vol. 1, no. 7, pp. 3019-3024.

[4] ZENG, W., TAO, X.M., CHEN, S., SHANG, S.M., CHAN, H.L.W., CHOY, S.H. Highly durable all-fiber nanogenerator for mechanical energy harvesting. *Energy & Environmental Science*. 2013, vol. 6, no. 9, pp. 2631-2638.

[5] WANKHADE, S.H., TIWARI, S., GAUR, A., MAITI, P. PVDF-PZT nanohybrid based nanogenerator for energy harvesting applications. *Energy Reports*. 2020, vol. 6, pp. 358-364.

[6] RAMADAN, K.S., SAMEOTO, D., EVOY, S. A review of piezoelectric polymers as functional materials for electromechanical transducers. *Smart Materials and Structures*. 2014, vol. 23, no. 3, 03301.

[7] MARTIN, J., ZHAO, D., LENZ, T., KATSOURAS, I., DE LEEUW, D.M., STINGELIN, N. Solid-state-processing of delta-PVDF. *Materials Horizons*. 2017, vol. 4, no. 3, pp. 408-414.

[8] EL MOHAJIR, B.E., HEYMANS, N. Changes in structural and mechanical behaviour of PVDF with processing and thermomechanical treatments. 1. Change in structure. *Polymer*. 2001, vol. 42, no. 13, pp. 5661-5667.

[9] RUAN, L.X., YAO, X.N., CHANG, Y.F., ZHOU, L.Q., QIN, G.W., ZHANG, X.M. Properties and applications of the beta phase poly(vinylidene fluoride). *Polymers*. 2018, vol. 10, no. 3, 228.

[10] LI, L., ZHANG, M.Q., RONG, M.Z., RUAN, W.H. Studies on the transformation process of PVDF from alpha to beta phase by stretching. *RSC Advances*. 2014, vol. 4, no. 8, pp. 3938-3943.

[11] MOHAMMADI, B., YOUSEFI, A.A., BELLAH, S.M. Effect of tensile strain rate and elongation on crystalline structure and piezoelectric properties of PVDF thin films. *Polymer Testing*. 2007, vol. 26, no. 1, pp. 42-50.

[12] SHARMA, M., MADRAS, G., BOSE, S. Process induced electroactive beta-polymorph in PVDF: Effect on dielectric and ferroelectric properties. *Physical Chemistry Chemical Physics*. 2014, vol. 16, no. 28, pp. 14792-14799.

[13] FANG, J., NIU, H.T., WANG, H.X., WANG, X.G., LIN, T. Enhanced mechanical energy harvesting using needleless electrospun poly(vinylidene fluoride) nanofibre webs. *Energy & Environmental Science*. 2013, vol. 6, no. 7, pp. 2196-2202.

[14] ISSA, A.A., AL-MAADEED, M.A.A.S, MRLIK, M., LUYT, A.S. Electrospun PVDF graphene oxide composite fibre mats with tunable physical properties. *Journal of Polymer Research*. 2016, vol. 23, 232.

[15] ISSA, A.A., AL-MAADEED, M.A.A.S, LUYT, A.S., MRLIK, M., HASSAN, M.K. Investigation of the physico-mechanical properties of electrospun PVDF/cellulose (nano)fibers. *Journal of Applied Polymer Science*. 2016, vol. 133, 43594.

[16] FLORCZAK, S., LORSON, T., ZHENG, T., MRLIK, M., HUTMACHER, D.W., HIGGINS, M.J., LUXENHOFER, R., DALTON, P.D. Melt electrowriting of electroactive poly(vinylidene difluoride) fibers. *Polymer International*. 2019, vol. 68, no. 4, pp. 735-745.

[17] MARTINS, P., LOPES, A.C., LANCEROS-MENDEZ, S. Electroactive phases of poly(vinylidene fluoride): Determination, processing and applications. *Progress in Polymer Science*. 2014, vol. 39, pp. 683-706.

[18] GREGORIO, R., CAPITAO, R.C. Morphology and phase transition of high melt temperature crystallized poly(vinylidene fluoride). *Journal of Materials Science*. 2010, vol. 35, pp. 299-306.

[19] GOMES, J., SERRADO NUNES, J., SENCADAS, V., LANCEROS-MENDEZ, S. Influence of the β-phase content and degree of crystallinity on the piezo- and ferroelectric properties of poly(vinylidene fluoride). *Smart Materials and Structures*. 2010, vol. 19, 065010.

CATALYTIC ACTIVITY OF THE NOBLE METAL NANOPARTICLES

[1]Libor KVÍTEK, [1]Tomáš STRYŠOVSKÝ, [1]Martina KUBÍKOVÁ, [1]Miroslav ORSÁG, [1]Aleš PANÁČEK, [1]Robert PRUCEK

[1]*Department of Physical Chemistry, Faculty of Science, Palacky University in Olomouc, Czech Republic, EU, libor.kvitek@upol.cz*

https://doi.org/10.37904/nanocon.2020.3732

Abstract

Noble metal nanoparticles are excellent catalysts for many industrial important reactions. Because heterogenous catalysis is dependent strongly on the surface of catalyst the nanomaterials are better catalysts in comparison with the bulk materials. However, it is important for optimization of the effectivity of catalytic process to have a comparison of the nanostructured catalysts of different nature for application in the particular reaction. As a model for this process was conducted primary testing of catalytic activity of five noble metal nanoparticles (Ru, Rh, Os, Ir, Pt) in redox reaction (reduction of 4-nitrophenol by the borohydride). It is interesting that for this model reaction the best catalyst is rhodium with the shortest induction period and fastest main part of the reaction course. On the other hand, platinum nanoparticles are not the best catalyst for the studied model reaction.

Keywords: Nanoparticles, noble metals, catalytic activity, model reaction, 4-nitrophenol

1. INTRODUCTION

Nanoparticles of metals, especially noble metals from the platinum group, show high catalytic activity with high potential for use in practical applications. Typically, these materials are tested as suitable catalysts for fuel cells [1]. These catalytic metals are currently difficult to replace in the redox reactions [2], but a similar situation prevails in the field of other types of catalytic reactions. Hydrogenations of unsaturated hydrocarbons can be mentioned as reaction mostly applicated in practice [3]. However, the catalytic action of this type of nanoparticles is also studied in other types of reactions - preparation of hydrogen by hydrolysis of ammonium borane [4] or in catalytic oxidation of organic compounds [5]. These metal nanocatalysts are frequently studied in reactions useful in environmental technologies [6]. In this respect, they are involved in a number of studies where a model reaction is used to assess their basic catalytic activity. Typically, the most used model reaction is reduction of 4-nitrophenol to 4-aminophenol. [7].

Preparation of nanoparticles of these noble metals is most easily accomplished by the method of chemical reduction of a salt of a given metal using a suitable reducing agent. When $NaBH_4$ is used as a reducing agent, the smallest particles in the range of about 1.5-5 nm are formed for all metals in this group [1,8]. However, since the metal nanoparticles prepared by this method easily aggregate, they are stabilized using protective layers formed by surfactants [9] or polymers [7,10]. Stabilization ca be also realized by anchoring of nanoparticles on the surface of a solid inert substrate of the type of carbonaceous materials [3] or inorganic substances such as ZnO [11]. On the other way, the reducing action of weak reducing agents, as are polyols, are often used in this field [2,12]. Due to the highly positive redox potential of noble metal ions, the so-called "green synthesis", which has recently become very popular, using natural substances as reducing agents and stabilizers of the resulting nanoparticles, can also be used in the preparation of this type of nanoparticles. Thus, for example, Pd nanoparticles can be prepared by reduction with polyphenols from black tea extract. [13]

However, very few studies can be found in the available literature offering a basic comparison of the catalytic activity of platinum metal nanoparticles prepared by the same method in the same standard reaction. Therefore, this study is aimed at platinum metal nanoparticles which were prepared using reduction synthesis with $NaBH_4$ and then they were tested for their catalytic activity in the most commonly used model reaction - reduction of 4-nitrophenol with $NaBH_4$.

2. EXPERIMENTAL

2.1. Chemicals

The chemicals that were used for the preparation of nanoparticles and subsequent kinetic experiments are listed in **Table 1**. Deionized water (18 MΩ·cm, Millipore) was used to prepare all solutions.

Table 1 Chemicals for nanoparticle preparation and kinetics experiments

Formulae	Name	Producer	Molar weight (g/mol)
$NaBH_4$	Sodium borohydride	Sigma-Aldrich	37.83
$C_6H_5Na_3O_7{\cdot}2H_2O$	Trisodium citrate dihydrate	Lach-Ner	294.1
$RuCl_3{\cdot}xH_2O$	Ruthenium(III) chloride hydrate	Merck KGaA	207.43
$RhCl_3{\cdot}3H_2O$	Rhodium(III) chloride trihydrate	Merck KGaA	263.32
$PdCl_2$	Palladium(II) chloride anhydr.	Sigma-Aldrich	177.33
$OsCl_3{\cdot}xH_2O$	Osmium(III) chloride hydrate	Sigma-Aldrich	296.59
$IrCl_3{\cdot}xH_2O$	Iridium(III) chloride hydrate	Merck KGaA	298.58
$PtCl_4$	Platinum(IV) chloride	Merck KGaA	336.89
$C_6H_5NO_3$	4-nitrophenol	Lachema	139.11

2.2. Nanoparticles preparation

Nanoparticles of all metals used in this study were prepared in the same way - reduction of a salt of a given metal with borohydride and citrate. Citrate also serves as a stabilizer of the resulting nanoparticles. The reaction takes place at room temperature. In a 50 ml beaker, mix 5 ml of $NaBH_4$ solution with a concentration of 10^{-2} mol.dm^{-3} and 5 ml of sodium citrate solution with a concentration of 2.10^{-2} mol.dm^{-3} while stirring. To the solution is then added water to obtain total volume 20 ml and then left to stand for about 20 minutes. Subsequently, 5 ml of a $4.96.10^{-3}$ mol.dm^{-3} salt solution of the metal are added dropwise. The reaction is stopped after stirring for another about 20 minutes.

2.3. Nanoparticles characterization

The resulting colloidal dispersions were characterized by UV-Vis spectroscopy and the dynamic light scattering (DLS, Zetasizer Nano ZS, Malvern Instruments, UK) method. However, the particle sizes measured by DLS were taken as indicative only, and the actual particle size was determined only from transmission electron microscope images (TEM, JEM 2100, Jeol Ltd., Japan). UV-Vis spectra (Specord S600, Analytic Jena AG, Germany) were obtained after 10-fold dilution of resulting dispersions.

2.4. Catalytic experiments

For the purpose of evaluating the catalytic activity of the prepared nanoparticles, a solution of 4-nitrophenol with a concentration of 1.5.10^{-3} mol.dm^{-3} was prepared, which was used in all experiments. The $NaBH_4$ solution (8.10^{-3} mol.dm^{-3}) was prepared fresh before each experiment due to its considerable instability. The reaction system was prepared by mixing 0.03 ml of the prepared nanoparticle dispersion, 0.09 ml of 4-nitrophenol (4-NP) solution and 1.28 ml of water. A cuvette with this solution was placed in a UV-Vis spectrophotometer (Specord S600, Analytic Jena AG, Germany), the measurement being started immediately after the addition of 1.6 ml of $NaBH_4$ solution. The $NaBH_4$ solution must be allowed to stand for 20 minutes after preparation so that the kinetic experiment takes place at a time when its reducing power is the best. All measurements were performed in a quartz cuvette in the wavelength range of 250-600 nm. The duration of the experiment was set to 20 minutes, measured every 10 seconds.

3. RESULTS AND DISSCUSSION

3.1. Nanoparticles preparation

Noble metal nanoparticles prepared by the above reduction method were characterized by UV-vis spectroscopy and their size was evaluated from TEM images (**Figure 1**). The one same procedure was used to prepare nanoparticles of all platinum metals with the exception of palladium, whose nanoparticles in the given method of preparation quickly aggregated and the resulting aggregates sedimented to the bottom of the reaction vessel. Because the aim of this study was to evaluate the catalytic activity of unmodified metal nanoparticles, no attempt was made to stabilize these nanoparticles with surfactants or polymers that can fundamentally affect the resulting catalytic activity [14]. In all cases, a strong absorption peak in the region of 190-210 nm appeared in the UV-vis spectra (**Figure 2**), which is typical for very small platinum metal nanoparticles. [link below] The average size of the prepared nanoparticles is given in **Table 2**.

Table 2 Average size of the prepared nanoparticles (measured in nanometers)

Ruthenium	Rhodium	Osmium	Iridium	Platinum
5.1±1.1	4.8±1.3	1.3±0.6	1.2±0.3	4.4±1.3

Except for iridium, whose dispersion was yellow, all the dispersions prepared were in shades of brown, and except for iridium and osmium, the dispersions were color stable. The iridium dispersion began to change color from yellow to light blue approximately one week after preparation. The reason for this color change is probably the recrystallization of nanoparticles. The dispersion of osmium was changed the intensity of color over time, this color change is observable about three weeks after preparation. The reason is probably the deposition of nanoparticles on the walls of the vessel.

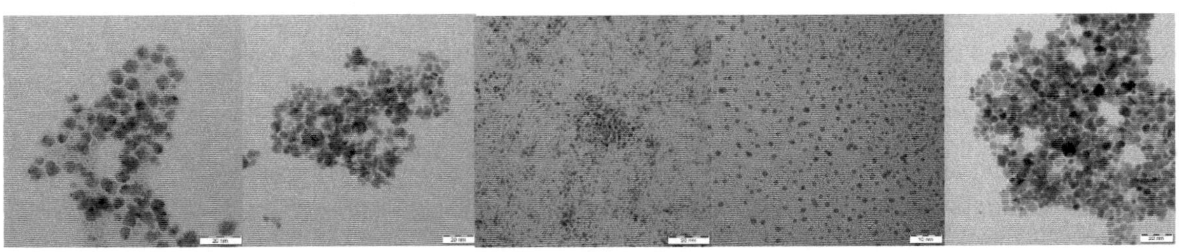

Figure 1 TEM images of nanoparticles a) Ru, b) Rh, c) Os, d) Ir, e) Pt (scale is 20 nm, only for Ir 10 nm)

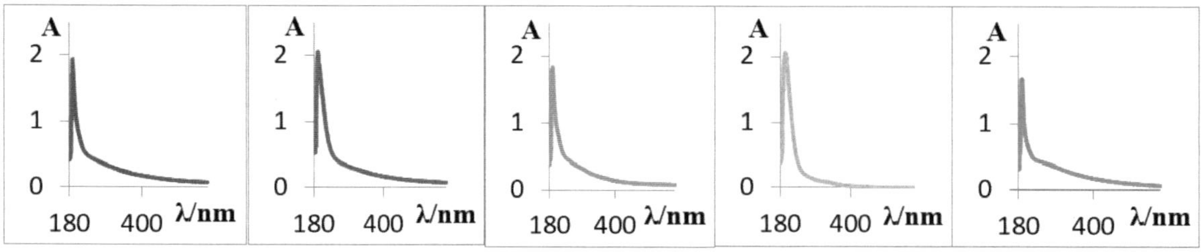

Figure 2 UV-vis spectra of aqueous dispersions of nanoparticles a) Ru, b) Rh, c) Os, d) Ir, e) Pt

3.2. Catalytic activity of nanoparticles

The catalytic activity of the prepared nanoparticles was studied using a model reaction, which was the reduction of 4-Nitrophenol (4-NP) to 4-Aminophenol. 4-Nitrophenol has a significant absorption peak at 401 nm, which decreases with reduction and a new peak appears around 300 nm, which belongs to 4-aminophenol. Since reductant NaBH4 is in significant excess, it was possible to evaluate the used model reaction according to the kinetics of the pseudo-first order. For this reason, it was possible to subtract the rate constants as exponents in absolute value from the exponential regression equation from the graphs of the absorbance of 4-nitrophenol versus time. Absorbance values at 401 nm were used for this evaluation. When calculating the value of the rate constant, only the time interval in which the value of the logarithm of the absorbance decreased linearly was used from the graph of the dependence of the logarithm of absorbance on time. Thus, the time interval corresponding to the initiation period, in which the catalyst surface is activated in a strongly reducing environment and the primarily adsorbed particles are replaced by reactant molecules, was omitted from the calculation. To evaluate the effect of this slow part of the reaction, the reaction half-times t1/2 were also subtracted from the measured kinetic curves, which better reflect the overall course of the catalytic reaction. The records of the spectra from the catalytic experiments are shown in **Figure 3**.

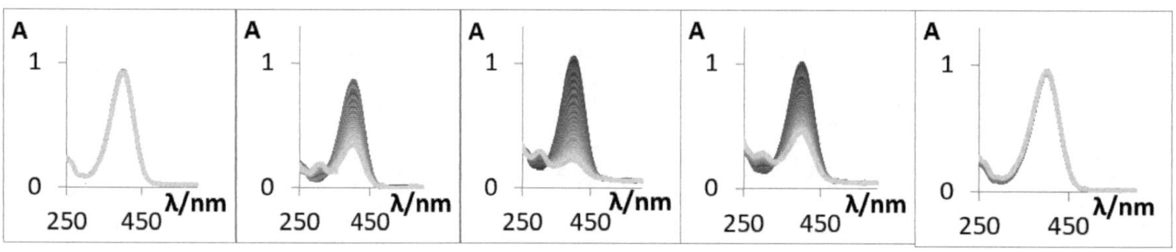

Figure 3 UV-vis spectra taken from the catalytic reaction of 4-NP reduction by borohydride a) without catalyst, b) catalysis of RuNPs, c) RhNPs, d) OsNPs, e) PtNPs, f) IrNPs

The average value of the rate constant for the reaction catalysed by ruthenium nanoparticles was the same as for the reaction catalysed by rhodium nanoparticles. However, the very long time was required to activate the Ru nanoparticle surface caused the reaction to be generally slower than in the case of Rh. This fact is also evidenced by the average value of the reaction half-time, which is almost 2.5 times higher for Ru than for Rh (**Table 3**).

As was already mentioned, the average value of the rate constant for the reaction catalysed by ruthenium nanoparticles is the same as in the case of Ru, but due to the much shorter time required for its activation, the reaction is faster. As a result, Rh nanoparticles (in this study) proved to be the best catalyst. A similar result was obtained in the study of Maegawa et al. [3].

The average value of the rate constant of the reaction catalysed by osmium nanoparticles makes it the third best catalyst. Iridium nanoparticles have proven to be the worst catalyst and the reaction catalysed by them practically does not run, even compared to the uncatalyzed reaction. These nanoparticles appear to be an inhibitor of the observed reaction. However, the probable cause of a slight increase in absorbance (approximately 2%) is rather influenced by the aggregation of iridium nanoparticles in the reaction system. Platinum nanoparticles have proven to be the second worst catalyst in the reaction system used, but unlike other metals, this catalyst shows no initiation period.

Table 3 Rate constants and reaction half-times of 4-nitrophenol reduction with $NaBH_4$ in the presence of noble metal nanocatalysts

Metal	Rate constants (s^{-1})						k_{av} (s^{-1})	k_s (s^{-1})	$t_{1/2av}$ (s)
Ruthenium	0.001	0.001	0.001	0.002	0.002	0.001	0.0013	0.0004	1250
Rhodium	0.001	0.001	0.002	0.002	0.001	0.001	0.0013	0.0004	485
Osmium	0.0005	0.0006	0.0006	0.0005	0.0006	0.0004	0.00053	0.0001	1275
Platinum	0.0002	0.0003	0.0002	0.0002	0.0003	0.0003	0.00025	0.00005	2990

k_s - rate constants normalised per 1 µg of catalyst

$t_{1/2av}$ - reaction half-times obtained from the experimental kinetic curves (evaluated as average from six measurements)

4. CONCLUSION

The presented study was focused on methods of preparation of noble metal nanoparticles and study of their catalytic activity. The objective was to compare catalytic activity of these nanoparticles for redox reactions. Metal nanoparticles were prepared by the same method using sodium borohydride as primary reducing agent in the presence of sodium citrate as secondary reducing agent and stabilizer of the prepared nanoparticles. Successfully was prepared nanoparticles of ruthenium with an average diameter of 5.1 nm, nanoparticles of rhodium with an average diameter of 4.8 nm, nanoparticles of osmium with an average diameter of 1.3 nm, nanoparticles of iridium with an average diameter of 1.2 nm and nanoparticles of platinum of average size 4.4 nm. Palladium nanoparticles wasn't involved in this work because of problems with their preparation. The catalytic activity of the prepared nanoparticles was studied using model reaction based on reduction of 4-nitrophenol to 4-aminophenol with sodium borohydride at room temperature. Rate constants for reactions catalysed by nanoparticles of each metal were calculated using pseudo-first order kinetics. Rhodium nanoparticles have proven to be the best catalyst. Although the reaction catalysed by ruthenium nanoparticles had the same average rate constant as the reaction catalysed by rhodium nanoparticles, the very long time was required for activation of Ru catalyst. By this reason, ruthenium nanoparticles were worse catalyst than rhodium nanoparticles. Osmium nanoparticles were the third best catalyst. The second worst catalyst were platinum nanoparticles. The worst catalyst were iridium nanoparticles, which had no catalytic activity in the used reaction system.

ACKNOWLEDGEMENTS

The authors acknowledge financial support from ERDF project "Development of pre-applied research in nanotechnology and biotechnology" (No. CZ.02.1.01/0.0/0.0/17_048/0007323), and from Internal Grant of Palacky University in Olomouc (IGA_PrF_2020_034).

REFERENCES

[1] LUO, M., YANG, Y., GUO, S. Precious metal nanocrystals for renewable energy electrocatalysis: structural design and controlled synthesis. *Dalton Transaction*. 2020, vol. 49, pp. 267-273.

[2] QUINSON, J., INABA, M., NEUMANN, S., SWANE, A.A., BUCHER, J., SIMONSEN, S.B., KUHN, L.T., KIRKENSGAARD, J.J.K., JENSEN, K.M.O., OEZASLAN, M., KUNZ, S., ARENZ, M. Investigating Particle Size Effects in Catalysis by Applying a Size-Controlled and Surfactant-Free Synthesis of Colloidal Nanoparticles in Alkaline Ethylene Glycol. *ACS Catalysis*. 2018, vol. 8, pp. 6627−6635.

[3] MAEGAWA, T., AKASHI, A., YAGUCHI, K., IWASAKI, Y., SHIGETSURA, M., MONGUCHI, Y., SAJIKI, H. Efficient and Practical Arene Hydrogenation by Heterogeneous Catalysts under Mild Conditions. *Chemistry: an European Journal*. 2009, vol. 15, pp. 6953-6963.

[4] AKBAYRAK, S., ÖZÇIFÇI, Z., TABAK, A. Noble metal nanoparticles supported on activated carbon: Highly recyclable catalysts in hydrogen generation from the hydrolysis of ammonia borane. *Journal of Colloid and Interface Science*. 2019, vol. 546, pp. 324-332.

[5] SO, M-H., HO, C-M., CHEN, R., CHE, C-M. Hydrothermal Synthesis of Platinum-Group-Metal Nanoparticles by Using HEPES as a Reductant and Stabilizer. *Chemistry: an Asian Journal*. 2010, vol. 5, pp. 1322-1331.

[6] ANANTHARAJ, S., NITHIYANANTHAM, U., EDE, S.R., AYYAPPAN, E., KUNDU, S. π-stacking intercalation and reductant assisted stabilization of Os organosol for catalysis. *RSC Advances*. 2015, vol. 5, pp. 11850-11860.

[7] CUI, Y., LIANG, B., ZHANG, J., WANG, R., SUN, H., WANG, L., GAO, D. Polyethyleneimine-stabilized palladium nanoparticles for reduction of 4-nitrophenol. *Transition Metal Chemistry*, 2019. vol. 44, pp. 655-662.

[8] ANANTHARAJ, S., JAYACHANDRAN, M., KUNDU, S. Unprotected and interconnected Ru0 nano-chain networks: advantages of unprotected surfaces in catalysis. *Chemical Science*. 2016, vol. 7, pp. 3188-3205.

[9] SEO, J., LEE, S., KOO, B., JUNG, W-C. Controlling the size of Pt nanoparticles with an cationic surfactant, C_nTABr. *CrystEngComm*. 2018, vol. 20, pp. 2010-2015.

[10] LIEW, K.H., ROCHA, M., PEREIRA, C., PIRES, A.L., PEREIRA, A.M., YARMO, M.A., JUAN, J.C., YUSOP, R.M., PEIXOTO, A.F., FREIRE, C. *ChemCatChem*. 2017, vol. 9, pp. 3930-3941.

[11] DEMILLE, T.B., HUGHES, R.A., PRESTON, A.S., ADELUNG, R., MISHRA, Y.K., NERETINA, S. Light-Mediated Growth of Noble Metal Nanostructures (Au, Ag, Cu, Pt, Pd, Ru, Ir, Rh) From Micro- and Nanoscale ZnO Tetrapodal Backbones. *Frontiers in Chemistry*. 2018, vol. 6, Article 411.

[12] FU, J., WANG, S., WANG1, X., YAN, Y., WANG, K., GAO, M., XU, Q. Facile preparation of highly dispersed Pt nanoparticles supported on heteroatom-containing porous carbon nanospheres and their catalytic properties for the reduction of 4-nitrophenol. *Journal of Porous Materials*. 2018, vol. 25, pp. 1081-1089.

[13] LEBASCHI, S., HEKMATI, M., VEISI, H. Green synthesis of palladium nanoparticles mediated by black tea leaves (Camellia sinensis) extract: Catalytic activity in the reduction of 4-nitrophenol and Suzuki-Miyaura coupling reaction under ligand-free conditions. *Journal of Colloid and Interface Science*. 2017, vol. 485, pp. 223-231.

[14] NEAL, R.D., HUGHES, R.A., SAPKOTA, P., PTASINSKA, S., NERETINA, S. Effect of Nanoparticle Ligands on 4-Nitrophenol Reduction: Reaction Rate. ACS Catalysis. 2020, vol. 10, pp. 10040−10050.

EFFECT OF ANNEALING ON LUMINESCENCE AND PHOTOCATALYTIC ACTIVITY OF ZNS NANOCRYSTALS UNDER UV LIGHT IRRADIATION

Hassan ALI, Milan MASAR, Michal URBANEK, Ali Can GULER, Pavel URBANEK, Michal MACHOVSKY, Ivo KURITKA

Centre of Polymer Systems, Tomas Bata University in Zlin, Czech Republic, EU, hali@utb.cz

https://doi.org/10.37904/nanocon.2020.3707

Abstract

Zinc sulfide (ZnS) nanocrystals were prepared at a large-scale via precipitation of Zn^{2+} ions water solution with gaseous hydrogen sulfide, H_2S. The effect of annealing time on the ZnS phase structure, morphology, and optical properties was investigated in detail by XRD, SEM, UV-vis, and photoluminescence (PL) spectroscopy. It was observed that pristine ZnS possessed a pure cubic phase structure and an increase in annealing time resulted in a phase mixture with increased content of wurtzite phase structure. Moreover, the crystallinity of the prepared samples, as well as PL intensities, increased with increasing annealing time. Photocatalytic activities of the pristine ZnS annealed at different time intervals were evaluated by the means of methyl violet 2B (MV 2B) degradation under UV LED illumination wavelengths at λ_{max}~ 343 nm and 365 nm. It was observed that the photocatalytic activities of the annealed ZnS samples increased with increasing annealing time. The improved photocatalytic performance can be attributed to the improved crystallinity of annealed ZnS samples.

Keywords: ZnS, annealing, photocatalysis, luminescence

1. INTRODUCTION

Zinc sulfide (ZnS) is an important wide bandgap semiconductor with optoelectronic properties suitable for diverse applications in light-emitting diodes (LEDs), electroluminescent flat panel displays, sensors, photovoltaic devices, photocatalysis, and water splitting [1,2]. Due to its luminescent properties, which were first recognized by Sidot in the 19th century followed by the discovery of phosphor-based high field electroluminescence in 1936, ZnS is probably the most studied sulfide semiconductor material to date [3]. ZnS exists in two crystalline forms, i.e., cubic ZnS (sphalerite) and hexagonal ZnS (wurtzite) phase with an optical bandgap of 3.72 eV and 3.77 eV at room temperature, respectively. The wurtzite phase is thermodynamically metastable and forms at a higher temperature than sphalerite (1020 °C in bulk ZnS). Moreover, the crystallography of ZnS is complicated by its propensity to crystallize in a variety of polymorphic modifications and polytypes, with substantially deviated phase structures. Due to this extensive polytypism, defect structures associated with intergrowths of several crystal forms are commonly encountered [4]. These defects, together with native point defects are responsible for the luminescence even in pristine, undoped ZnS, especially when thermally post-treated. Although ZnS itself exhibits luminescence over a broad range of wavelengths, emission wavelength and intensity can be finely tuned by modifying its structural properties.

While ZnS is traditionally used in various electroluminescent devices, it has also been widely studied for its ability of water splitting and photocatalytic degradation of the pollutants. ZnS has been already demonstrated to possess excellent photocatalytic activity towards degradation of dyes, phenol, or halogenated compounds under UV light irradiation, as well as hydrogen evolution capability [5-8].

ZnS nanocrystals are typically synthesized by hot injection method or heat-up method, with both employing various types of precursors. The most commonly used method of hot injection can produce nanocrystal batches with good crystallinity and high PL quantum yields but there is a drawback of limited scalability. This restriction of large scale production is due to the inevitable occurrence of nucleation and growth stages at different temperatures and times [9-11]. Herein, we report a facile preparation method of nanocrystalline ZnS, which is based on the precipitation of Zn^{2+} cations in an aqueous solution by gaseous hydrogen sulfide, H_2S, at room temperature. The effect of annealing time on luminescence properties and photocatalytic activity was also investigated in detail.

2. EXPERIMENTAL

2.1. Materials

Zinc nitrate hexahydrate ($Zn(NO_3)_2.6H_2O$), sodium sulfide hydrate ($Na_2S.xH_2O$), hydrochloric acid (HCl, 38% aqueous solution) were all purchased from Sigma Aldrich (St. Louis MO, USA) and used as received without further purification.

2.2. Synthesis of ZnS nanocrystals

ZnS nanocrystals were synthesized by the precipitation of zinc ions by hydrogen sulfide at room temperature according to the method described previously for the preparation of CuS nanoplates by our group [12] as follows: 4.569 g of zinc nitrate hexahydrate was dissolved in 100 mL of water and transferred into a cylindrical flask. Afterward, the gaseous hydrogen sulfide evolved by the reaction of sodium sulfide with hydrochloric acid was bubbled through the solution containing zinc ions. During this, the solution pH increased steeply, and the precipitation reaction occurred in a short time interval after reaching pH high enough at which S^{2-} ions predominated in solution. The resultant white precipitate was washed several times by distilled water prior to filtration and the collected powder was dried in an oven at 60 °C. The obtained dried powder was later put into a glass test tube and annealed using a Bunsen burner for 30 and 90 s. The glass test tube was placed within flame at the position of highest temperature, i.e., at the tip of the inner flame cone. The temperature of samples measured immediately following the annealing process by the contactless thermometer was approximately 350 °C and 700 °C, for 30 and 90 s, respectively. The annealed samples were labeled as ZnS-30 and ZnS-90.

2.3. Characterization methods

The crystalline phases of the as-prepared samples were characterized by the X-ray diffractometer Miniflex 600 (Rigaku, Japan) with a Co-Kα X-ray source (λ = 1.5418 Å) in the diffraction angle range 5-85° 2θ. The morphology was investigated by scanning electron microscope NOVA NanoSEM 450 (FEI, The Netherland). The study of UV-vis absorption of prepared powders was performed by the UV-vis spectrometer LAMBDA 1050+ (PerkinElmer, UK). Photoluminescence (PL) measurements were carried out by fluorescence spectrometer FLS920 (Edinburgh Instruments Ltd).

2.4. Photocatalytic experiment

The photocatalytic activity of the as-prepared samples was evaluated via degradation of methyl violet 2B (MV 2B) at a concentration of 3.5 $mg.L^{-1}$ under UV light (Roithner LaserTechnik, UVLUX 340-HL-3) with maxima wavelength of 343 and 365 nm. An original experimental arrangement intended for the online measurement of photocatalytic activity under irradiation with LED comprised of various wavelengths was used. It is based on the homemade cuvette holder housing equipped with LED mounted directly inside the UV-vis spectrometer. The cuvette serves as a miniature photochemical reactor with its content being mixed continuously or in a duty cycle with a small magnetically driven stirrer bar. In a typical experiment, a quartz glass cuvette containing 10 mg of photocatalyst and 5 mL of model dye solution was inserted inside the UV-vis spectrophotometer, covered by cuvette holder housing, and stirred in the dark for 1 hour in order to reach adsorption/desorption equilibrium. After that, an LED was switched on with continuous stirring. Degradation of model dye was monitored every

15 minutes interval without the need for sampling and extra evaluation. During the experiment, the temperature was precisely controlled to 25 °C by dual cell Peltier.

3. RESULTS AND DISCUSSION

The crystalline phase structures of the pristine ZnS powder and the products of its annealing were investigated by powder XRD. The diffractogram of pristine ZnS and the products of its annealing for 30 and 90 s are shown in **Figure 1**. XRD pattern of the pristine ZnS exhibits three peaks at diffraction angles 2θ= 33.34°, 55.86° and 66.63° which corresponds to most intense (111), (220) and (311) planes of the (sphalerite) cubic ZnS phase (PDF Card No.: 01-071-4763), respectively. The broadness and the low intensities of the peaks indicate small particle size and poor crystallinity. Phase quantification for the pristine and annealed samples was done by the RIR (reference intensity ratio) method and the calculated values are given in **Table 1**. It should be mentioned that the unambiguous identification of ZnS phase structures is accompanied by some difficulties, as both polymorphs possess tetrahedral arrangements of Zn and S and differ only in the stacking sequence of atomic layers in cubic and hexagonal structures. Based on the RIR calculation, even pristine ZnS is not composed entirely of cubic phase but contains about 10 % of the wurtzite hexagonal phase. Average crystalline scattering domain sizes, D_c, were also estimated according to the well-known Debye-Scherrer formula and the values are given in **Table 1**.

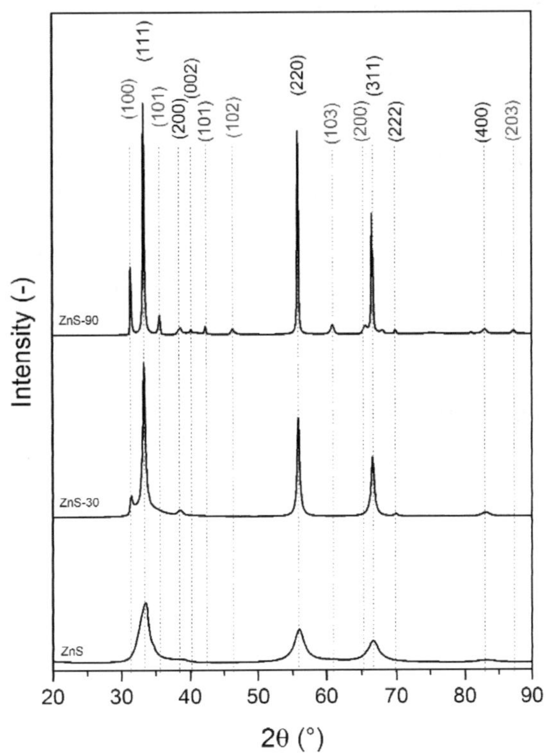

Figure 1 Powder XRD patterns of samples ZnS, ZnS-30, and ZnS-90. Stick pattern correspond to PDF Card No.: 01-071-4763 (sphalerite cubic phase ZnS, black), PDF Card No.: 00-036-1450 (wurtzite hexagonal ZnS, red), and PDF Card No.: 01-079-0207 (wurtzite hexagonal ZnO, blue)

The morphology of the as-prepared samples was investigated using SEM as shown in **Figure 2**. Pristine ZnS exhibits flake-like morphology with a smaller grain size, which is consistent with poor crystallinity as evidenced by the XRD results. For the annealed samples, ZnS-30 and Zn-90, an increase in the temperature led to coarser grain size. This increase may result in the extension of the absorption edge due to the formation of defects and scattering centers.

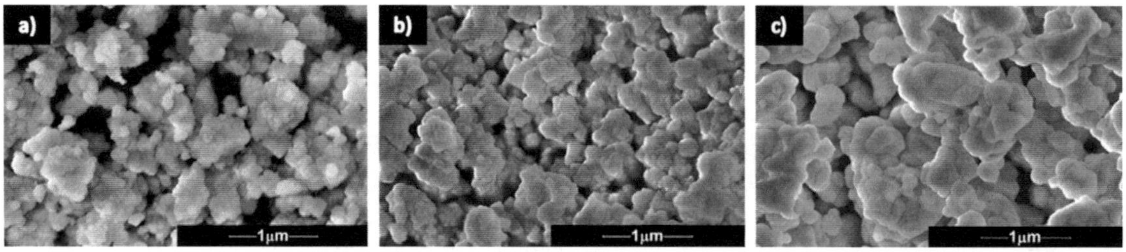

Figure 2 SEM images of precipitated ZnS (a) and products of its annealing for 30 and 90 s, ZnS-30 (b) ZnS-90 (c)

Table 1 XRD data and photocatalytic activity of the prepared samples

Sample	Crystalline phase structure			Average Crystallite size [nm]	Rate Constant r, λ~343 nm [s^{-1}]	Rate Constant r, λ~365 nm [s^{-1}]
	Cubic ZnS	Hexagonal ZnS	Hexagonal ZnO			
ZnS	90	10	-	6.2	-	-
ZnS-30	85	15	-	27.5	0.44 ± 0.05	0.09 ± 0.01
ZnS-90	62	35	3	64.0	0.94 ± 0.03	0.17 ± 0.01

The photocatalytic activity of prepared materials was evaluated via degradation of MV 2B at the concentration of 3.5 mg. L^{-1} under UV light irradiation (Roithner LaserTechnik, UVLUX 340-HL-3) with maxima wavelength of 343 (3.6 eV) and 381 nm (3.4 eV). From **Figure 3**, it is obvious that the photocatalytic activity at 365 and 343 nm is greatest for the sample, ZnS-90. From **Table 1**, it can be seen that the rate constant for dye degradation with ZnS-90 sample is one-fold higher than for the sample ZnS-30, at both 365 and 343 nm light irradiation. The limited activity of ZnS-30 sample can be ascribed to the slow rate of electron-hole pairs creation and low crystallinity.

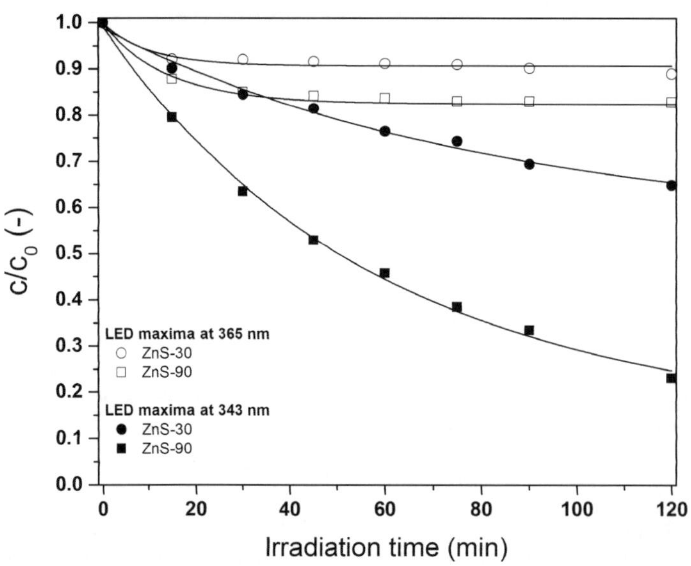

Figure 3 Photocatalytic activities of ZnS, ZnS-30, and ZnS-90 samples

The as-prepared samples were also characterized by PL emission spectra to investigate the charge carrier's separation and recombination rate. A stronger intensity of PL indicates more rapid recombination of photoexcited electro-hole pairs while a lower PL intensity is associated with slow charge recombination rate. From **Figure 4**, it can be seen that pristine ZnS and ZnS-30, exhibit the lowest PL intensity while ZnS-90 has the highest PL intensity implying that pristine ZnS has a low recombination rate as compared to annealed ZnS samples. This result indicates that the high photocatalytic activity of ZnS-90 sample is due to the rapid creation of electron-hole pairs which led to an increase in photocatalytic activity as compared to pristine ZnS and ZnS-30 samples.

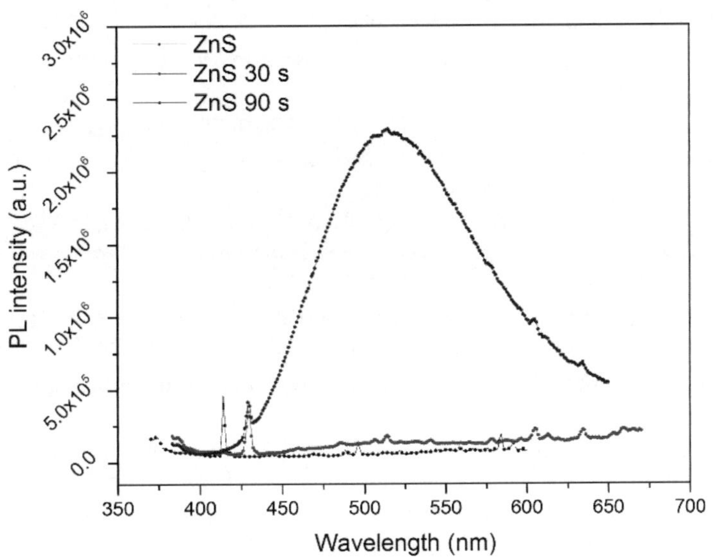

Figure 4 PL spectra for ZnS, ZnS-30 and ZnS-90 samples

4. CONCLUSION

ZnS nanocrystals were prepared and the effect of annealing on the ZnS phase structure, morphology, and optical properties was investigated. Pristine ZnS samples exhibited pure cubic phase structure with slight wurtzite content which increased with increasing annealing time. Pristine ZnS annealed for 90 s exhibited the highest photocatalytic activity as compared to unannealed ZnS. Optical investigation of the as-prepared samples suggested that annealing resulted in the formation of luminescence and charge recombination centers.

ACKNOWLEDGEMENTS

This research obtained funding from the Ministry of Education, Youth and Sports of the Czech Republic in the frame of the project LTT20010. This article was also written with the support of Operational Program Research and Development for Innovations co-funded by the European Regional Development Fund (ERDF) and the national budget of Czech Republic, within the framework of project CPS - strengthening research capacity (reg. number: CZ.1.05/2.1.00/19.0409). The work was also supported by the Internal Grant Agency of Tomas Bata University in Zlin; contract grant number: IGA/CPS/2017/007. This work was supported by the Ministry of Education, Youth and Sports of the Czech Republic - Program NPU I (LO1504).

REFERENCES

[1] UMMARTYOTIN, S, BUNNAK, N, JUNTARO, J, SAIN, M, MANUSPIYA, H. Synthesis and luminescence properties of ZnS and metal (Mn, Cu)-doped-ZnS ceramic powder. *Solid State Sci.* 2012, vol. 14, no. 3, pp. 299-304.

[2] FANG, X, ZHAI, T, GAUTAM, UK, LI, L, WU, L, BANDO, Y, et al. ZnS nanostructures: From synthesis to applications. *Prog Mater Sci.* 2011, vol. 56, no. 2, pp. 175-287.

[3] SMET, PF, MOREELS, I, HENS, Z, POELMAN, D. Luminescence in Sulfides: A Rich History and a Bright Future. *Materials.* 2010, vol. 3, no. 4, pp. 2834-2883.

[4] DENZLER, D, OLSCHEWSKI, M, SATTLER, K. Luminescence studies of localized gap states in colloidal ZnS nanocrystals. *J Appl Phys.* 1998, vol. 84, no. 5, pp. 2841-5.

[5] CHEN, F, CAO, Y, JIA, D. Facile synthesis of ZnS nanoparticles and their excellent photocatalytic performance. *Ceram Int.* 2015, vol. 41, no. 5, Part A, pp. 6645-52.

[6] PALANISAMY, VK, MANOHARAN, K, RAMAN, K, SUNDARAM, R. Efficient sunlight-driven photocatalytic behavior of zinc sulfide nanorods towards Rose Bengal degradation. *J Mater Sci Mater Electron.* 2020, vol. 31, pp. 14795-14809.

[7] HOJAMBERDIEV, M, CZECH, B, GÖKTAŞ, A.C., YUBUTA, K, KADIROVA, Z.C. SnO2@ZnS photocatalyst with enhanced photocatalytic activity for the degradation of selected pharmaceuticals and personal care products in model wastewater. *J Alloys Compd.* 2020, vol. 827, p. 154339.

[8] ZHOU, J, ZHAO, J, LIU, R. Defect engineering of zeolite imidazole framework derived ZnS nanosheets towards enhanced visible light driven photocatalytic hydrogen production. *Appl Catal B Environ.* 2020, vol. 278, p. 119265.

[9] MUNRO, AM. Synthetic approaches for growing zinc sulfide and zinc selenide colloidal nanocrystals. *J Vac Sci Technol A.* 2020, vol. 38, p. 020805.

[10] FLAMEE, S, CIRILLO, M, ABE, S, DE NOLF, K, GOMES, R, AUBERT, T, et al. Fast, high yield, and high solid loading synthesis of metal selenide nanocrystals. *Chem Mater.* 2013, vol. 25, no. 12, pp. 2476-2483.

[11] BANSKI, M, AFZAAL, M, MALIK, MA, PODHORODECKI, A, MISIEWICZ, J, O'BRIEN, P. Special Role for Zinc Stearate and Octadecene in the Synthesis of Luminescent ZnSe Nanocrystals. *Chem Mater.* 2015, vol. 27, no. 11, pp. 3797-3800.

[12] MASAR, M, URBANEK, M, URBANEK, P, MACHOVSKA, Z, MASLIK, J, YADAV, RS, et al. Synthesis, characterization and examination of photocatalytic performance of hexagonal covellite CuS nanoplates. *Mater Chem Phys.* 2019, vol. 237, p. 121823.

THERMO-CATALYTIC DEGRADATION OF POLYSTYRENE OVER α-Fe_2O_3

Kateřina KLEMENCOVÁ, Barbora GRYCOVÁ, Amer INAYAT, Pavel LEŠTINSKÝ

VSB - Technical University of Ostrava, Ostrava, Czech Republic, EU,
katerina.klemencova@vsb.cz

https://doi.org/10.37904/nanocon.2020.3719

Abstract

Polystyrene (PS) is an important plastic material, which is widely used in packaging, home, construction, electrical appliances, medical equipment etc. The widespread use of PS generates large amounts of PS wastes, which is due to poor recycling rates globally end up in landfills as well as in the oceans. The increasing amounts of wastes polystyrene and other wastes plastics thus represent a serious threat to the environment, and also to human and animal health. Chemical recycling is an environmentally friendly approach that can be applied for the recycling of plastics. For chemical recycling, thermal or thermo-catalytic pyrolysis/degradation can be used. During the degradation process, polymeric materials are converted into their monomers or other valuable compounds. This paper deals with the synthesis of α-Fe_2O_3 nanoparticles and their use as catalyst in thermo-catalytic degradation of PS in a semi-batch reactor. The aim was to study the influence of synthesis parameters on the catalytic properties of α-Fe_2O_3 in PS degradation. The α-Fe_2O_3 catalyst samples were prepared by the chemical precipitation method using $FeCl_3.6H_2O$ as a precursor salt and NaOH as precipitating agent and by calcining the precipitates at different temperatures. All catalyst samples prepared were characterized by XRD and physisorption of nitrogen. It is shown that by increasing the calcination temperature of precipitates, pure α-Fe_2O_3 (hematite phase) can be obtained. Furthermore, it is demonstrated that PS degradation using pure hematite as catalyst in comparison with mixed phase or non-catalytic degradation gives higher yields of oil and styrene monomer.

Keywords: Degradation, chemical recycling, polystyrene, catalyst, pyrolysis

1. INTRODUCTION

Nowadays, plastics are an integral part of everyday life. Due to their widespread use in modern society, they have become irreplaceable. In recent years, the amount of produced plastics has been continuously increasing due to the wide possibilities of their use in different sectors. The largest amount of plastics is produced for the packaging industry, which amounts to be approximately 40 %. Among various types of plastics, polystyrene (PS) is one of the most important and versatile polymeric material that is used in numerous applications which include packaging, construction, medical equipment etc. The continuously increasing demand for plastics as well as poor recycling rate has caused the accumulation of landfilled plastic waste, which contributes to the environmental problem.

Recycling is one of the possibilities to reduce the amount of produced (virgin) plastics and the associated negative impact on the environment. There are four main categories of plastic recycling, namely primary, secondary, tertiary and quaternary recycling. In recent years, the tertiary recycling which is also known as chemical or feedstock recycling has attracted much attention. This is because it represents a potential effective way of processing waste plastics efficiently from ecological and economic point of view..

In chemical recycling, the waste polymeric materials are converted back to their original monomers or oil /hydrocarbon components which can be reused for the production of pure (virgin quality) polymers or new polymers respectively. Chemical recycling can be realized by thermal or thermo-catalytic degradation/pyrolysis of waste polymeric materials. In comparison with thermal degradation, thermo-catalytic degradation offers the possibility of reducing the process temperature and improving the selectivity towards desired compounds. Among various thermoplastics, PS has a unique property to be fully recycled. Therefore, PS wastes are good candidates for the chemical recycling.

In literature, thermo-catalytic degradation of PS has been widely studied. In these studies, the use of solid acids and bases as catalysts has been extensively reported. Ukei et al 2000 concluded that solid bases are effective catalysts for the thermochemical conversion of PS into styrene monomer (SM). Furthermore, it has also been reported that some transition metal oxides have basic sites on their surfaces and therefore can be alternative catalytic materials for converting PS into oil with high fraction of SM. In this regard, α-Fe_2O_3 nanoparticles can be attractive catalytic material for PS degradation, which exhibit remarkable structural properties that can be beneficial in the decomposition of PS into SM at low reaction temperature of about 400 °C. Therefore, it is the aim of the present work to synthesis α-Fe_2O_3 nanoparticles using different synthesis parameters and test the resulting materials in thermo-catalytic degradation of PS. For this purpose, as a first step, α-Fe_2O_3 nanoparticles were prepared by using the chemical precipitation method followed by calcination at different temperatures. As a second step, the influence of calcination temperature on the structural, textural and catalytic properties of synthesized α-Fe_2O_3 materials was studied.

2. MATERIALS AND METHODS

2.1. Feedstock and catalyst

Granular PS (purchased from Sigma Aldrich) with an average diameter of 3-4 mm and an average molecular weight of 192000 $g.mol^{-1}$ was used as feedstock. For the catalytic degradation of PS, α-Fe_2O_3 nanoparticles synthesized in house were used as catalyst.

The α-Fe_2O_3 catalyst samples were synthesized by the chemical precipitation method using $FeCl_3.6H_2O$ as a precursor salt. For the synthesis, 4 g $FeCl_3.6H_2O$ was dissolved in 100 ml of distilled water. The resulting solution was stirred and heated to 70 °C for 30 minutes. During this time, the pH of the solution was adjusted to 11 using 0.4 Molar solution of NaOH. The precipitate obtained was filtered and washed extensively with distilled water until neutrality (pH $\sim$ 7) as indicated by paper indicator. Afterwards, the precipitate was dried in a drying furnace at 70 °C for 12 hours. Finally, the dried α-Fe_2O_3 precipitates were calcined at three different temperatures i.e. 250, 400 and 500 °C to obtain three catalyst samples, namely α-Fe_2O_3-250, α-Fe_2O_3-400 and α-Fe_2O_3-500 respectively. All samples were characterized by X-ray powder diffraction (XRD) on a Rigaku SmartLab diffractometer (Rigaku, Japan) with detector D/teX Ultra 250. The source of X-ray irradiation was Co tube (CoKα, $\lambda1$ = 0.178892 nm, $\lambda2$ = 0.179278 nm) operated at 40 kV and 40 mA. The textural properties of the samples were determined by physisorption of nitrogen using Micrometrics 3Flex analyzer. For the catalytic experiments, all catalyst samples were pelletized to give a pellet size in the range 0.63-1 mm.

2.2. Thermal and thermo-catalytic degradation

Both thermal and thermo-catalytic degradation of PS were carried out in a semi-batch reactor setup under continues nitrogen gas flow at a flowrate of 50 $ml.min^{-1}$. The schematic diagram of the reactor setup is shown in **Figure 1**. All experiments were performed at 400 °C using a heating rate of 10 °C/min and a dwelling time of 1 hour. The operating conditions used in the present work were optimized in our previous study. For all experiments, 4 g of PS was used that was placed between two layers of quartz wool in a quartz glass reactor tube with a length of 250 mm and internal diameter of 17 mm. For catalytic experiments, 0.4 g of catalyst pellets, packed between two quartz wool layers, were placed after the PS bed in the nitrogen flow direction. The reactor was heated using a cylindrical heating jacket which was equipped with a temperature controller.

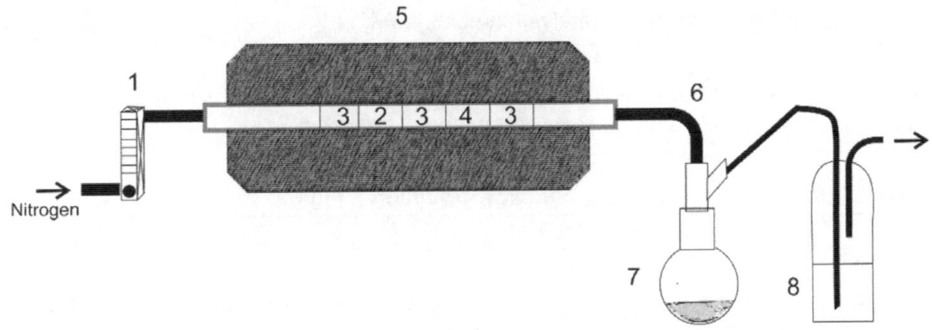

Figure 1 Schematic diagram of semi-batch reactor setup: (1) Flowmeter, (2) Polystyrene, (3) Quartz wool, (4) Catalyst, (5) Electrical heating zone, (6) Air cooling, (7) Round bottom flask with condensate, (8) Washing bottle

2.3. Product analysis

For each experiment, two oil (condensate) fractions were obtained. The first fraction was collected in a glass flask by condensing the pyrolysis vapors through air cooling, while the second fraction was condensed inside the reactor tube within the quartz wool. In order to extract the second fraction, the quartz wool loaded with oil was soaked and washed with acetone and the oil was obtained by subsequent evaporation of acetone. The amount of both fractions was determined gravimetrically, and the overall oil yield was determined as the sum of both fractions. The amount of carbon deposited on the spent catalysts was determined using RC612 Multiphase Carbon and Water Analyzer (LECO Instruments). The gas yield was obtained by subtracting the mass of oil and carbon from the mass of feedstock used. The analyses of both oil fractions were performed using gas chromatography. For this purpose, a YL 6100 GC equipped with a HP-5 column and a flame ionization detector was used.

3. RESULTS AND DISCUSSION

3.1. Characterization of catalyst

The XRD patterns obtained for all three catalysts calcined at three different temperatures are shown in **Figure 2**. The samples calcined at 400 and 500 °C exhibited pure hematite phase, whereas the one calcined at 250 °C showed a mixture of goethite and hematite phases. Moreover, the sample calcined at 500 °C i.e. α-Fe_2O_3-500 showed enhanced crystallinity as compare to the other samples. The textural properties of the catalysts as obtained from the nitrogen adsorption are summarized in **Table 1**. The results show that with increasing calcination temperature the BET surface area decreased, whereas the pore size increased.

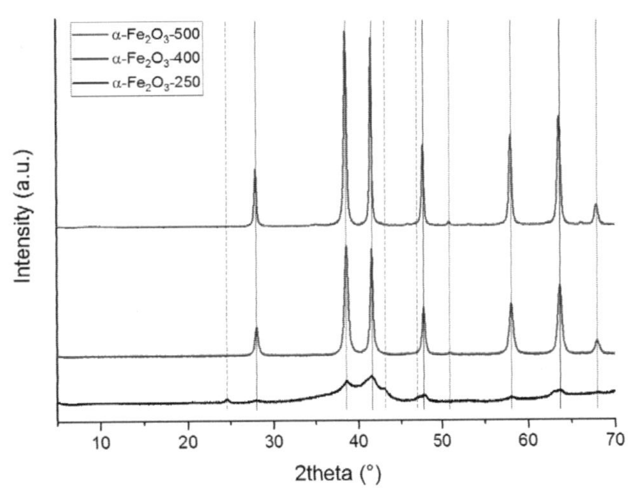

Figure 2 X-ray diffraction patterns of catalyst samples with reference lines indicating Hematite (solid lines) and Goethite (dotted lines) reflexes

Table 1 Textural properties of synthesized catalyst samples

Catalyst	S_{BET} (m^2g^{-1})	V_{net} ($cm^3(STP).g^{-1}$)	d_{pore} (nm)
α-Fe_2O_3-250	165	211	4.5
α-Fe_2O_3-400	66	212	14.4
α-Fe_2O_3-500	36	197	29.3

3.2. Product analysis

The pyrolytic products from thermal and thermo-catalytic degradation of PS are shown in **Figure 3**. For all experiments main products obtained were oil and gas. No char was produced in any of the experiments. Only a small amount of carbon was observed on the surface of spent catalysts. The amount of deposited carbon was found to be less than 0.5 wt. %. The main components of oil produced were SM and oligomers (di-and trimers). In addition to SM and oligomers, some minor compounds including benzene, toluene, ethyl benzene and alpha-methylstyrene (not shown here) were also produced. The total amount of all minor compound was less than 5 wt. %.

From the results as depicted in **Figure 3**, a trend of higher oil and SM yields with increasing calcination temperature can be observed. This can be attributed to the enhanced crystallinity (at higher calcination temperature) that may lead to higher basicity of the sample. It has been reported that base catalysts are effective catalysts for PS degradation, and as some transition metal oxides have basic sites on their surfaces, they can be potential catalytic material for this reaction in order to improve the selectivity for oil as well as styrene monomer.

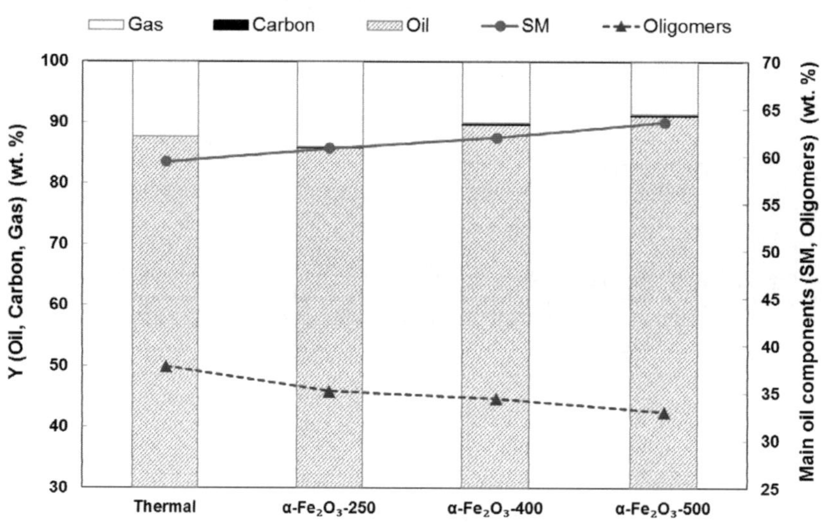

Figure 3 Pyrolytic products obtained from thermal and thermo-catalytic degradation of PS

Table 2 Composition of oligomers produced

Catalyst	Total oligomers (wt. %)	Dimers (wt. %)	Trimers (wt. %)
Thermal	37.8	22.6	15.2
α-Fe_2O_3-250	35.2	16.2	19.0
α-Fe_2O_3-400	34.4	19.6	14.8
α-Fe_2O_3-500	33.0	14.9	18.1

4. CONCLUSION

Thermo-catalytic degradation of PS was studied over α-Fe_2O_3 nanoparticle used as catalyst. The catalyst samples were synthesized by precipitation followed by calcination at 250, 400 and 500 °C. Different calcination temperatures led to different phases and textual properties of the samples. From XRD analyses it was shown that pure α-Fe_2O_3 phase could be achieved at higher calcination temperature. The results of thermo-catalytic degradation of PS over α-Fe_2O_3 showed that all three catalysts produced different amounts of oil, gas and SM. A trend of higher oil and SM yield was observed with increasing the calcination temperature. The present study shows that α-Fe_2O_3 nanoparticles can be interesting catalytic materials for thermo-catalytic degradation of PS. However, it is important to tune the properties (through synthesis parameters) of such materials in order to improve the selectivity for target products, as different phases and textural properties will lead to different product spectra.

ACKNOWLEDGEMENTS

This paper has been elaborated in the framework of the projects "Institute of Environmental Technology - Excellent Research" (CZ.02.1.01/0.0/0.0/16_019/0000853) and "Development of the UniCRE Centre" (LO1606). Experimental results were accomplished by using Large Research Infrastructures ENREGAT (LM2018098) and CATPRO (LM2015039) which were financially supported by the Ministry of Education, Youth and Sports of the Czech Republic.

REFERENCES

[1] PARK, K. B., JEONG, Y.S., GUZELCIFTCI, B., KIM, J.S. Two-stage pyrolysis of polystyrene: Pyrolysis oil as a source of fuels or benzene, toluene, ethylbenzene, and xylenes. *Applied Energy*. 2020, vol. 259.

[2] SHARUDDIN, S.C.A., ABNISA, F., DAUD, W.M.A.W., AROUA, M.K. A review on pyrolysis of plastic waste. *Energy Conversion and Management*. 2016, vol. 115, pp. 308-326.

[3] HAMAD, K., KASEEM, M., DERI, F. Recycling of waste from polymer materials: An overview of the recent works. *Polymer degradation and stability*. 2013, vol. 98, pp. 2801-2812.

[4] OKAN, D.K., VINU, R. Resource recovery via catalytic fast pyrolysis of polystyrene using zeolites. *Journal of analytical and applied pyrolysis*. 2015, vol. 113, pp. 349-359.

[5] WANG, J., JIANG, J., SUN, Y., ZHONG, Z., WANG, X., XIA, H., LIU, G., PANG, S., WANG, K., LI, M., XU, J., RUAN, R., RAGAUSKAS, A.J. Recycling benzene and ethylbenzene from in situ catalytic fast pyrolysis of plastic waste. *Energy Conversion and Management*. 2019, vol.200.

[6] UKEI, H., HIROSE, T., HORIKAWA. S. Catalytic degradation of polystyrene into styrene and a design of recyclable polystyrene with dispersed catalysts. *Catalysis today*. 2000, vol. 62, pp. 67-75.

[7] GU, R., LEE, O., SALEHZADAH, Y. An investigation into Polystyrene Recycling at UBC [online]. [viewed 2020-9-30]. Available from: https://open.library.ubc.ca/clRcle/collections/undergraduateresearch/18861/items/1.0108209

[8] OJHA, D.K., VINU, R. Resource recovery via catalytic fast pyrolysis of polystyrene using zeolites. *Journal of Analytical and Applied Pyrolysis*. 2015, vol. 113, pp. 349-359.

[9] KIJENSKI, J., KACZOREK, T. Catalytic degradation of polystyrene. *Polimery*. 2005.

[10] CONNEL, G., DUMESIC, J.A. The generation of Brønsted and Lewis acid sites on the surface of silica by addition of dopant cations. *Journal of Catalysis*. 1987, vol. 105, pp. 285-298.

[11] VALÁŠKOVÁ, M., CHLEBÍKOVÁ, L., LEŠTINSKÝ, P. α-Fe2O3 nanoparticles/vermiculite composites prepared for catalytic decomposition of polystyrene. *Materialstoday Proceeding*. 2020.

[12] INAYAT, A., KLEMENCOVÁ, K., GRYCOVÁ, B., SOKOLOVÁ, B., LEŠTINSKÝ, P. Thermo-catalytic pyrolysis of polystyrene in batch and semi-batch reactors: A comparative study. *Waste Management & Research*. 2020.

FACILE HPLC TECHNIQUE FOR SIMULTANEOUS DETECTION OF ESTROGENTIC HORMONES IN WASTEWATER

[1*]Muhammad YASIR, [1]Tomáš ŠOPÍK, [1,2]Dušan KIMMER, [1]Vladimír SEDLAŘÍK

[1]*Centre of Polymer Systems, University Institute, Tomas Bata University in Zlín, Zlín, Czech Republic, EU,* *yasir@utb.cz*

[2]*SPUR a.s., Zlin, Czech Republic, EU*

https://doi.org/10.37904/nanocon.2020.3711

Abstract

The ever-increasing population has aroused demand for contraceptive chemicals which pollute the water reservoirs through industrial effluents. This has caused a severe threat to marine life and high concern about the availability of fresh drinkable water for people all over the world. Not only this, the unwanted intake of these water containing hormones leads to fertility disorder, rapid femininity, loss in male sperm count, high chances of breast, and ovarian cancer. Therefore, in this study, a one-step high-pressure liquid chromatography (HPLC) technique was devised for simultaneous detection and quantification of various estrogenic hormones from wastewater. Four representative hormones Estrone (E1), β-Estradiol (E2), Estriol (E3), and 17α-Ethinylestradiol (EE2) were used. To address the solubility of these hormones, a study was conducted in three solvents systems viz. ethanol, ethanol: water (20:80), and water, respectively. Similarly, calibration curves were made for these three solvent systems with regression coefficients ≥0.99. Interestingly, it was found that water can be used as a solvent for the estrogenic hormones at a detection limit as low as 5 μg/L, which makes this study quite significant.

Keywords: Wastewater, effluents, contraceptives, estrogenic hormones, liquid chromatography

1. INTRODUCTION

Nowadays, in this modern era, manufacturing is increasing in all sectors of the industry due to high demand, pollution is also a huge threat to the people and their environment. Estrogenic hormones such as Estrone (E1), Estradiol (E2), Ethinylestradiol (EE2), Estriol (E3) present in water effluents are a danger to the environment [1]. There have been reported high potencies and significant occurrence of E2, E3, and E1 in flowing waters [2]. Due to their high level of presence, they have been observed and monitored at many wastewater treatment locations [3,4]. EE2 is another synthetic hormone mainly used as an oral contraceptive but also used for the treatment of menstrual problems and prostate cancer. The remains of this hormone are a huge source in the environment because of its partial degradation while treated at sewage plants so its metabolites interact in nature and de-conjugate to become active again [5]. They are classified as endocrine-disrupting chemicals used as medicine for reproduction control and infertility in females, which harms marine life when released in water channels. Studies on marine species have proved fertility disorder, rapid femininity in the fish breed, dropped the weight of testicles in Japanese quails [1]. Also, linkage to humans has proved loss in male sperm count, high chances of breast and ovarian cancer [6,7]. Therefore, it requires proper removal and disposal [5].

In previous works, either one of the hormones was detected and removed whereas, in this paper, the aim is to detect and quantify these estrogenic hormones simultaneously in 3 mediums in a one-step method using the technique of high-pressure liquid chromatography (HPLC) [5].

2. MATERIALS AND METHODS

2.1. Materials and reagents

The estrogenic hormones were estrone (E1), β-estradiol (E2), estriol (E3), and 17α-ethinylestradiol (EE2) purchased from Sigma Aldrich, Czech Republic. Furthermore, the HPLC solutions: acetonitrile and ethanol of HPLC grade were purchased from VWR, Czech Republic. Deionized water (pH 7.3, 18.3 MΩ/cm) was sourced from a laboratory Milli-Q water purification system. Glass microfiber (GMF) filters (Whatman, Czech Republic) with pore size 0.45 μm and 25 mm diameter were used prior to HPLC. Selected values for the properties of the hormones are shown in **Table 1** below.

Table 1 Certain properties of hormones [8]

Estrogenic Hormone	Molecular formula	Molecular weight (g/mol)	Melting point (°C)	Solubility in water (mg/l)
Estrone	$C_{18}H_{22}O_2$	270.37	258.0-260.0	12.42
B-Estradiol	$C_{18}H_{24}O_2$	272.38	178.5	12.96
17α-Ethinyl-Estradiol	$C_{20}H_{24}O_2$	296.40	182.0-183.0	4.83
Estriol	$C_{18}H_{24}O_3$	288.38	282.0	13.25

2.2. Solution preparation and sampling

Hormone solution was prepared in three different mediums viz. ethanol, ethanol: water (20:80), and water. For the ethanol, 5 mg/L stock solution was prepared after stirring solution for 1 h and it was seen that hormones dissolve immediately. For the ethanol: water system, the concentration of 20 mg/L in solvent 10:90, 10 mg/L 10:90, 20 mg/L 20:80, and 10 mg/l 20:80 were prepared but didn't dissolve completely and stayed as a suspension. However, at a higher volume ratio of ethanol: water 20: 80, solubility was better as can be seen in **Figure 1** below.

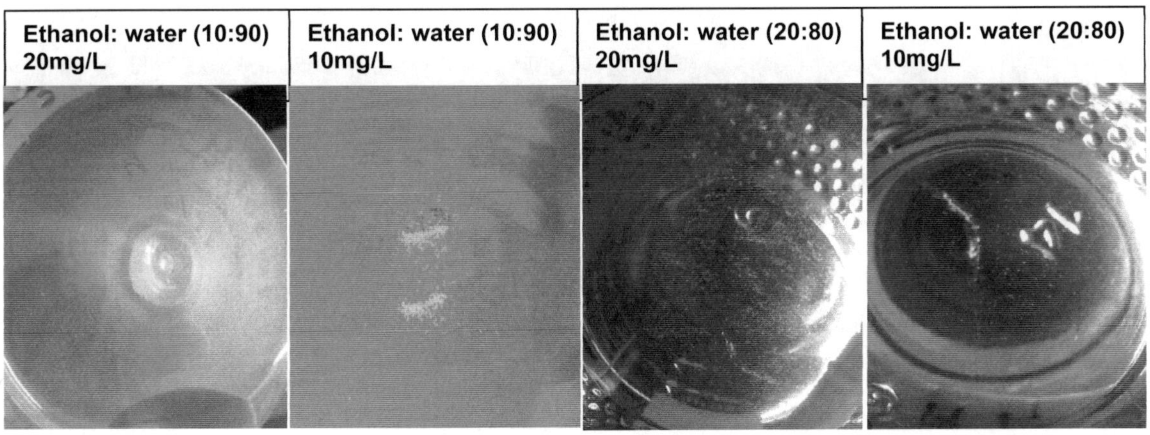

Figure 1 Solubility of all 4 hormones together in a solution at different concentrations

Hence, using ethanol: water 20:80, 5 mg of each hormone was dissolved in a total of 1000 ml by initially dissolving in 200 ml ethanol, followed by 800 ml of water properly stirred at 800 r.p.m for 24 hours to make sure complete homogenous mixing and solubility. It was also observed that if hormones are first dissolved in water followed by ethanol then, hormones are only partially dissolved. The descending order of solubility using HPLC is EE2>E3>E2>E1. In the case of water, solubility was a problem because individual solubility of each hormone is available in literature but considering all 4 hormones together in a single solution was challenging especially for distilled and deionized water. Solubility was lower than the values available in the data and it was seen that preparing a solution of 1mg/L concentration of each hormone even after stirring for 1 complete day was still having some particles at the bottom of the container which could be referred to as E1 because of its least solubility [7]. It was also checked by individually dissolving each hormone in 1 L water separately and also when the solution was sonicated for 30 mins, there was an increase in peak for E1 proving that its solubility improved. Therefore, finally, a concentration of 0.2 mg/L of each hormone was prepared by adding 1 mg of each hormone in 5 L of water. Samples were collected in 1.5 ml vials after passing through the GMF filter before HPLC and were triplicated to report the mean concentrations with standard deviation for obtaining the calibration.

2.3. High-Pressure Liquid Chromatography (HPLC) analysis

HPLC analysis of hormones (E3, E2, EE2, E1) calibration standards and samples were carried out on an HPLC DionexUltiMate 3000 Series (Thermo Fisher Scientific, Germany). The separation was performed on a reversed-phase column Kinetex 2.6 µm C18 100 A (150x4.6mm; Phenomenex USA) equipped with a pre-column security guard ULTRA, UHPLC C18 (Phenomenex. the USA) at 30 °C. A mixture of acetonitrile and water was used as mobile phase (45:55, v/v) at a flow rate of 0.8 ml/min with a total isocratic run of 12 min. The sampler chamber was set at 5°C and a volume of 20 µl was injected into the column. Eluates were detected using wavelengths of 200 nm. Data were recorded and processed in chromeleon 7.2 software (Thermo Fisher Scientific, USA).

3. RESULTS AND DISCUSSION

3.1. Characterization of adsorbent

To know the surface shape of Hormones, imaging from SEM (FEI, Thermo Fisher Scientific, USA) was carried out. **Figure 2** below shows the appearance and surface morphology of each hormone. The figure was captured at 8 kV applied potential and at a magnification of 10000x except for E1 which was 1000x due to the large size of particles.

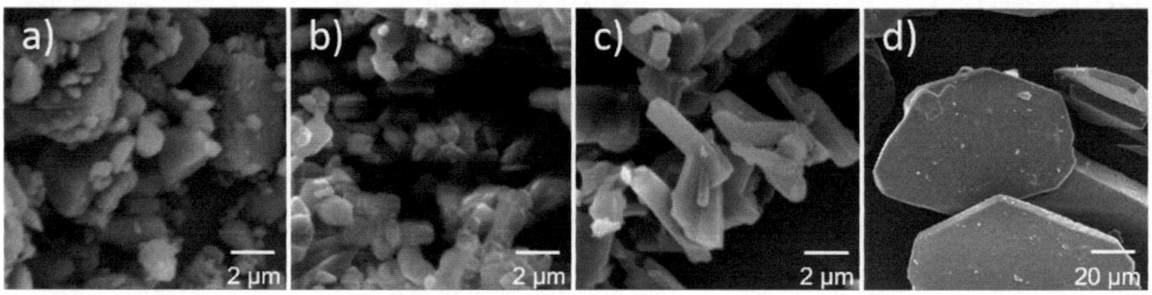

Figure 2 SEM of a) E3, b) E2, c) EE2 and d) E1 hormones, respectively

3.2. Detection and quantification

To identify the peak of hormones, firstly each hormone solution was tested to detect and identify the retention time (r.t), and then a combined solution of hormones was tested. Also, the limit of detection (LOD) and limit of quantification (LOQ) were calculated from 0.01 mg/L standard as given in the formulas below:

$$LOD = ((\frac{c}{S/N}) \times 3) \quad (1)$$

$$LOQ = ((\frac{c}{S/N}) \times 10) \quad (2)$$

Where:

c- concentration (mg/L)

S/N- signal-to-noise ratio

Figure 3 represents intensity peaks, calibration equations along with LOD and LOQ of each hormone at their particular retention time in the ascending order of time of E3, E2, EE2, and E1, respectively in a given medium.

	(a) Ethanol	**Equation**	**LOQ/LOD**
E3	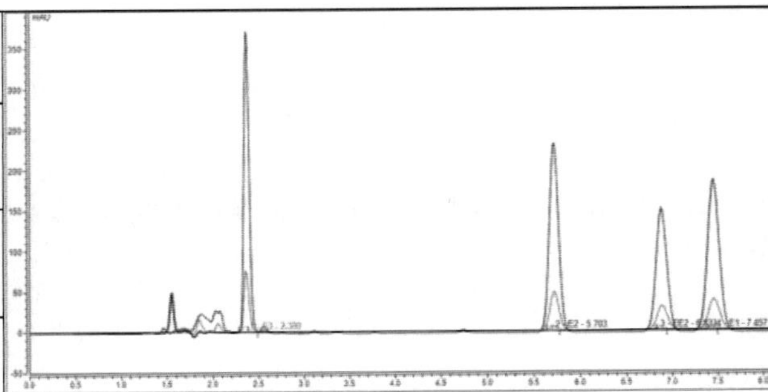	y = 5.11x + 0.02 (R^2 = 1)	**LOD:** 0.001 mg/L **LOQ:** 0.004 mg/L
E2		y = 5.52x + 0.04 (R^2 = 1)	**LOD:** 0.002 mg/L **LOQ:** 0.006 mg/L
EE2		y = 4.2557x - 0.0004 (R^2 = 1)	**LOD:** 0.003 mg/L **LOQ:** 0.009 mg/L
E1		y = 5.64x + 0.04 (R^2 = 1)	**LOD:** 0.002 mg/L **LOQ:** 0.007 mg/L
	(b) Ethanol: water 20: 80	**Equation**	**LOQ/LOD**
E3	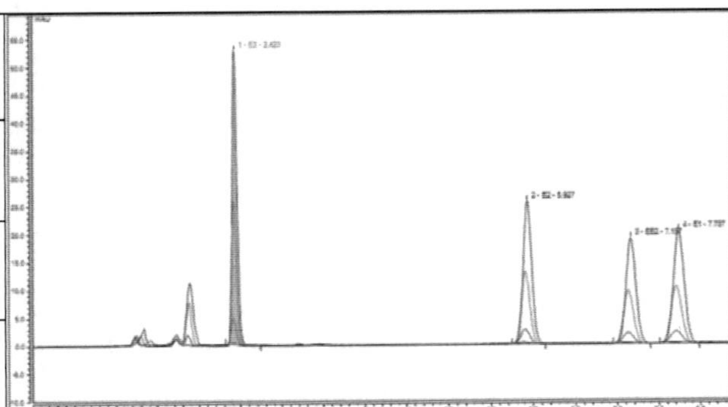	y = 3.44x + 0.07 (R^2 = 1)	**LOD:** 0.002 mg/L **LOQ:** 0.006 mg/L
E2		y=2.92x + 0.06 (R^2=0.9999)	**LOD:** 0.003 mg/L **LOQ:** 0.011 mg/L
EE2		y=2.58x +0.05 (R^2=0.9999)	**LOD:** 0.005 mg/L **LOQ:** 0.015 mg/L
E1		y = 2.99x + 0.06 (R^2 = 1)	**LOD:** 0.004 mg/L **LOQ:** 0.014 mg/L
	(c) Water	**Equation**	**LOQ/LOD**
E3	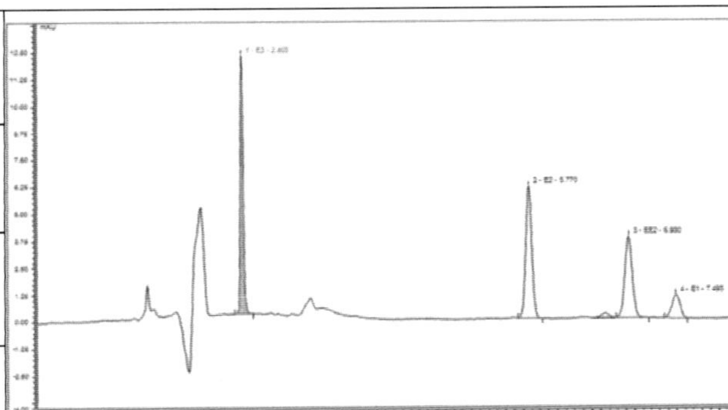	y=2.00x +0.04 (R^2= 0.9885)	**LOD:** 0.0005 mg/L **LOQ:** 0.002 mg/L
E2		y=2.06x +0.05 (R^2= 0.9918)	**LOD:** 0.001 mg/L **LOQ:** 0.004 mg/L
EE2		y=1.60x +0.04 (R^2=0.9939)	**LOD:** 0.002 mg/L **LOQ:** 0.005 mg/L
E1		y= 0.61x +0.02 (R^2=0.9901)	**LOD:** 0.005 mg/L **LOQ:** 0.017 mg/L

Figure 3 Intensity peak, calibration equation, and LOD and LOQ of each hormone when mixed in a specific solution medium (a) ethanol, (b) ethanol: water 20: 80, and (c) water

4. CONCLUSION

A method has been developed on HPLC to successfully detect, separately identify and quantify E1, E2, E3, and EE2 hormones together in a single sample with a detection limit of about 5 µg/L. It is noteworthy to say that this study has examined only neutral solutions with pH around 7.3, which is close to the actual wastewater having pH 6-9, and it can later be used for adsorption study, kinetics, and also for photocatalytic degradation experiments of these hormones using this method. However, this study has addressed the question of detection and quantification only. Therefore, this study is limited to the presence of hormones in the amounts of micrograms. In general, future research with this approach can also be applied to waste river waters for comparison and to address this issue more deeply and comprehensively.

ACKNOWLEDGEMENTS

The authors gratefully acknowledge the financial support of the Internal Grant Agency, IGACPS2020002 from the Centre of Polymer System (CPS), Tomas Bata University in Zlin, Czech Republic.

REFERENCES

[1] NGHIEM, L. D., SCHÄFER, A. I. Adsorption and transport of trace contaminant estrone in NF/RO membranes. *Environmental Engineering Science*. 2002, vol. 19, no. 6, pp. 441-451.

[2] CARTINELLA, J. L., CATH, T. Y., FLYNN, M. T., MILLER, G. C., HUNTER, K. W., CHILDRESS, A. E. Removal of natural steroid hormones from wastewater using membrane contactor processes. *Environmental Science and Technology*. 2006, vol. 40, pp. 7381-7386.

[3] JOHNSON, A. C., AERNI, H. R., GERRITSEN, A., GIBERT, M., GIGER, W., HYLLAND, K., JÜRGENS, M., NAKARI, T., PICKERING, A., SUTER, M.J.-F., SVENSON, A., WETTSTEIN, F. E. Comparing steroid estrogen, and nonylphenol content across a range of European sewage plants with different treatment and management practices. *Water Research*. 2005, vol. 39, no. 1, pp. 47-58.

[4] SARMAH, A. K., NORTHCOTT, G. L., LEUSCH, F. D. L., TREMBLAY, L. A. A survey of endocrine-disrupting chemicals (EDCs) in municipal sewage and animal waste effluents in the Waikato region of New Zealand. *Science of the Total Environment*. 2006, vol. 355, no. 1-3, pp. 135-144.

[5] HAN, J., QIU, W., CAO, Z., HU, J., GAO, W. Adsorption of ethinylestradiol (EE2) on polyamide 612: Molecular modeling and effects of water chemistry. *Water Research*. 2013, vol. 47, no. 7, pp. 2273-2284.

[6] SOLOMON, G. M., SCHETTLER, T. Environment and health: 6. Endocrine disruption and potential human health implications. *CMAJ*. 2000, vol. 163, no. 11, pp. 1471-1476.

[7] HAN, J., QIU, W., GAO, W. Adsorption of estrone in microfiltration membrane filters. *Chemical Engineering Journal*. 2010, vol. 165, no. 3, pp. 819-826.

[8] TABAK, H. H., BLOOMHUFF, R. M., BUNCH, R. L. Studies on the persistence and stability of natural urinary and synthetic ovulation-inhibiting hormones in untreated and treated wastewaters in Chapter 43 'Steroid Hormones as Water Pollutants II'. *Developments in Industrial Microbiology*. 1981, vol. 22, pp. 497-519.

THE DEVELOPMENT OF OPTICAL SENSOR FOR INORGANIC SALTS DETECTION IN WATER

[1]Polina BAINOVA, [1,2] Elena MILIUTINA, [1] Vaclav ŠVORČÍK, [1,2] Pavel POSTNIKOV, [1,2]Oleksiy LYUTAKOV

[1]*VŠCHT - University of Chemistry and Technology, Prague, Czech Republic, EU, lyutakoo@vscht.cz*

[2]*Tomsk Polytechnic University, Research School of Chemistry and Applied Biomedical Sciences, Tomsk, Russian Federation*

https://doi.org/10.37904/nanocon.2020.3711

Abstract

The main goal of this work is to create a highly sensitive optical sensor based on the principle of plasmon surface resonance (SPR) for inorganic salts. The experimental concept includes the creation of optical fiber probe with anion capturing agent(ACA) through the diazonium chemistry for selective-entrapping of targeted compounds and their trace amounts detection. The characterization of the obtained structures and their properties were performed using the SERS, AFM and UV-Vis methods. The created hybrid sensor structures were used to measure the presence and concentration of inorganic salts, which often occur in polluted wastewater. The proposed approach has a number of advantages, such as the possibility of real-time detection, high selectivity and sensitivity, and the possibility of miniaturization of the analytical device(s).

Keywords: Fiber optic, sensor, detection, anions, pollution, capturing agents

1. INTRODUCTION

Today, industrial production and agriculture development led to increasing release of inorganic anions in our environment. Released anions formed from toxic organic and inorganic waste products represents a serious ecological risk. [1,2]. These compounds show potential toxic effects even at relatively low concentrations [3,4]. E.g. nitrate anion (NO_3^-) or phosphate compounds (eg $H_2PO_4^-$) from agricultural wastewater can lead to eutrophication of watercourses [5-7]. Nitrate and nitrite anions (NO_2^-) can cause methemoglobinemia in animals or humans organisms [8,9]. Sulphate (SO_4^{2-}) and bisulphate (HSO_4^-) anions are commonly present in radioactive waste and induce a number of problems during water storage and recycling [10,11]. Therefore, it is necessary to control and regulate the concentration of anions in various areas, such as public water mains, river water, various types of drinking water and industrial wastewater.

Effective on-site monitoring of anions requires methods that allow the determination of their low concentrations in the aqueous environment. However, anionic analysis equipment (such as ion chromatography) is very expensive, requires the transport of samples to the laboratory, and the analysis itself takes a lot of time. Recently, fluorescent anionic chemosensors have been developed for this task [12,13]. Other methods of optical detection are also being studied, including the use of chromogenic sensors [14]. However, these methods also have several disadvantages: they require preliminary sample preparation, the production of such sensors is laborious and relatively expensive. The solution to these problems is to become fiber-optic sensors with ligand groups on the surface, selective to anions. Today, fiber optic sensors are an efficient, accurate and cheap tool for the determination of various analytes [15-17].

In this work, we propose an optical approach to the detection of anions. The proposed approach have a number of advantages, such as the possibility of real-time detection, high selectivity and sensitivity, and the possibility of miniaturization of the device. In other words, the main goal of this work is to create a highly sensitive optical sensor based on the principle of plasmon surface resonance (SPR), including a anion-selective layer based on ACA modification for the detection of trace amounts of anions in water in real time. Particular attention will be paid to anions, which often occur in polluted wastewater: NO_3^-, $H_2PO_4^-$, NO_2^-, SO_4^{2-}.

2. EXPERIMENTAL

2.1. Materials

Gold targets for metal deposition (purity of metals, 4 N) were purchased from Safina. Multimode plastic-clad silica optical (PCS) fiber was purchased from CeramOptec (Germany) with core and buffer/cladding diameters of 200 and 230/500 μm, respectively. Deionized water, methanol (reagent grade, ≥99,8%), acetone (97%), zinc nitrate hexahydrate (≥99.0%), sodium dihydrogen phosphate (≥99.0%), sodium nitrite (≥97.0%), sodium sulfate (≥99.0%), were purchased from Sigma-Aldrich and used without further purification.

2.2. Sample preparation.

Preparation of fiber-optical sensor.

The 2 cm of PCS fiber shell was thermally removed, and naked PCS core was purified using washing with deionized water, acetone and methanol. A thin film of Au was deposited on the PCS fiber core by vacuum sputtering (thickness approx. 40 nm). The deposition of Au was accomplished from Au target (DC Ar plasma, gas purity - 99.995 %, pressure 4 Pa, discharge power 7.5 W, sputtering time 400 sec). The fibers were fixed with the replaceable SMA connectors.

Sensor modification.

The obtained optical fibers with gold were electrochemistry modified (4 mM freshly prepared water solutions, −3.0 V applied potential) for 2 min. After modification, fibers were rinsed with water, methanol, and acetone for 20 min, and dried at ambient conditions.

2.3. Measurement Techniques

Raman spectra were measured using ProRaman-L spectrometer (Laser power 40 mW) with 785 nm excitation wavelengths. Spectra were measured 30 times, each of them with 3 s accumulation time.

UV-Vis absorbance spectra of the samples were measured using a HR2000 (Ocean Optics) spectrometer in 400-800 nm wavelengths range using the AvaLight-DHS light source (Avantes). ACA-coated Au fibers were immersed in water solutions of $NaNO_2$, Na_2SO_4, NaH_2PO_4 and $Zn(NO_3)_2$ in different concentrations 10^{-6}, 10^{-4}, 10^{-2} and 1M.

3. RESULTS AND DISCUSSION

The experimental concept is presented in **Figure 1**. An optical fiber covered with an thin layer of Au film was modified with ACA. (Step A) In the next step, the optical fiber was coupled to a light source and with spectrometer. When the sensor is immersed in water, the surface plasmon resonance effect appears on the surface, and an absorption peak as well visible. The position of absorption peak depends on the refractive index of surrounding medium (Step B). Immersion of a modified sensor in an analyte solution leads to pronounced shift of SPR wavelength position, indicating the capture of anions on surface of the sensor. (Step C) The following salts: $NaNO_2$, Na_2SO_4, NaH_2PO_4 and $Zn(NO_3)_2$ were used as analyte solutions.

The modification of the sensor surface was confirmed by Raman spectroscopy (**Figure 2**). The results of Raman spectroscopy show the appearance of characteristic vibration bands of aromatics and $-CH_3$ after modification.

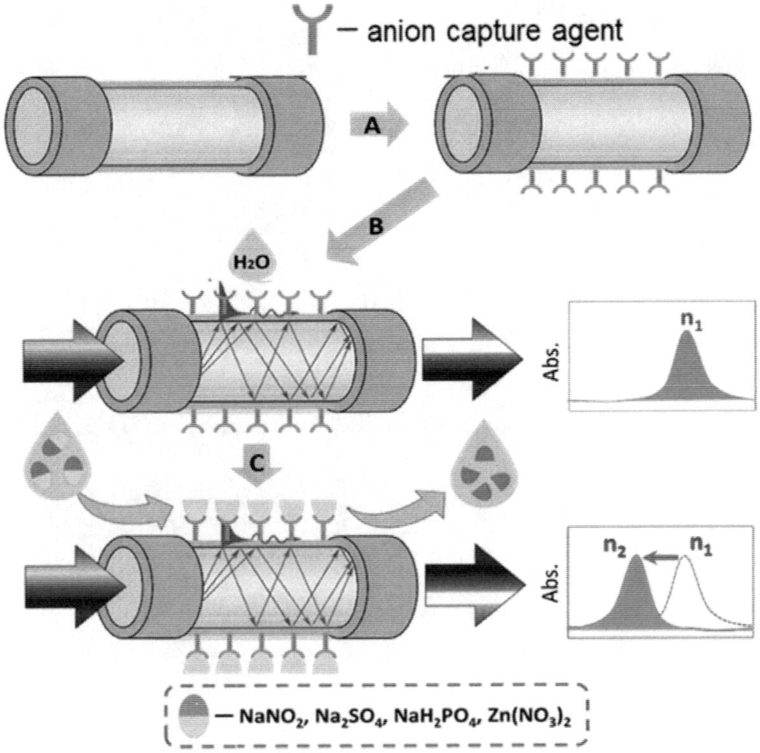

Figure 1 Scheme of preparation and use of an optical sensor. A - pre-modification of the sensor in a freshly prepared aqueous solution of the ACA, B - immersion of the sensor in the aquatic environment and the occurrence of a plasmon absorption band, C - capture of anions and subsequent shift of the absorption band.

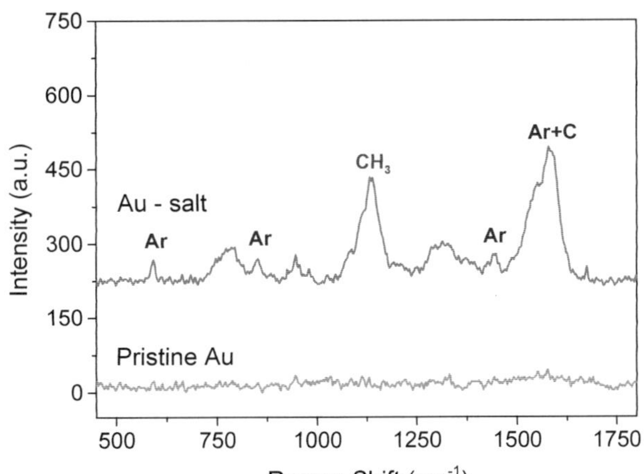

Figure 2 Raman spectra on the surface of: (i) pristine Au, (ii) Au with ACA

During the experiment, the prepared sensors were immersed in solutions of four different anions with different concentrations, which led to a change in the refractive index of the medium surrounding the plasmon-active part of the sensors. The complete sets of absorption spectra are shown in **Figure 3**. As can be seen, entrapping of anions effectively affects the position of the absorption maximum of plasmons.

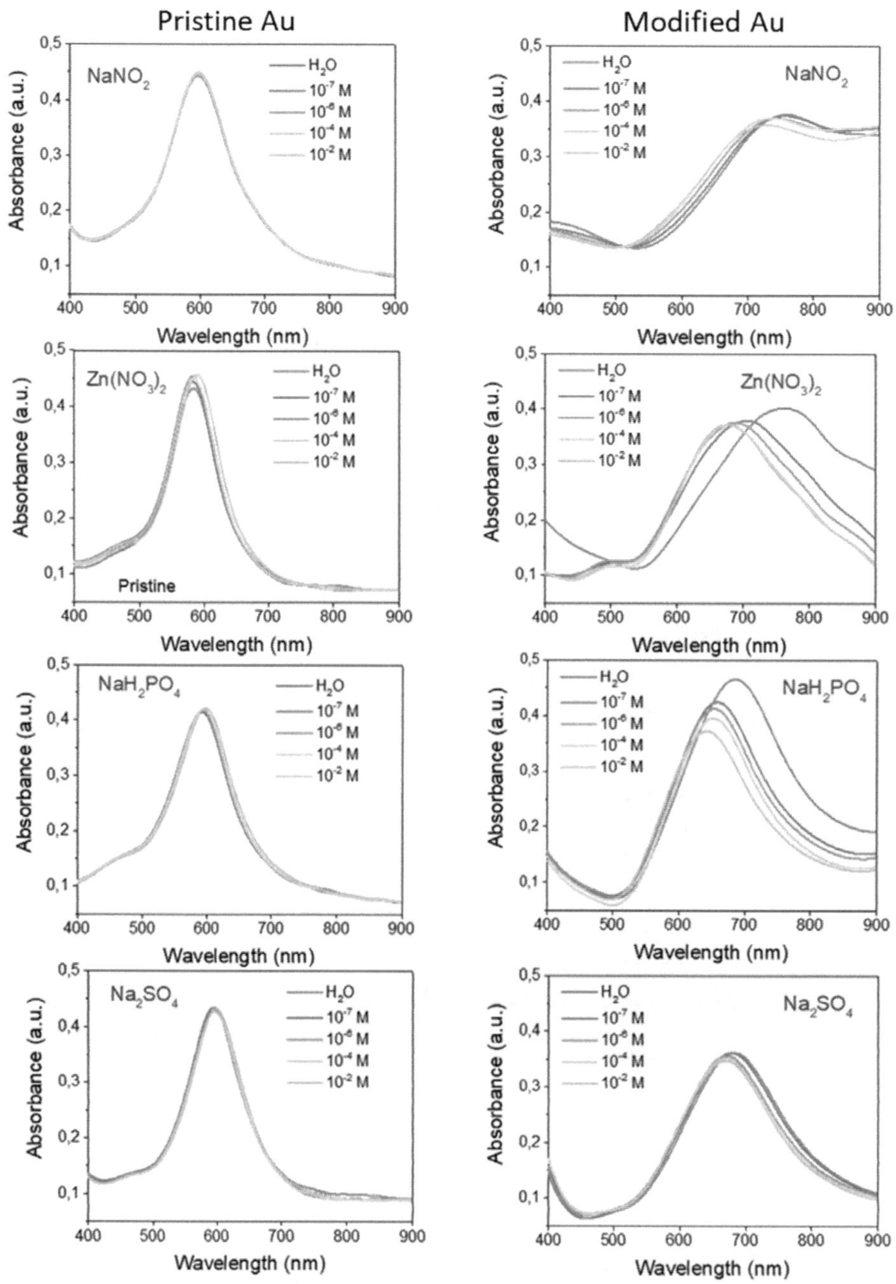

Figure 3 Results of the interaction of pristine and modified sensor with analyte solutions

4. CONCLUSION

In this work, fiber-optic sensors were developed for monitoring of anions and determining their concentrations. Our basic concept uses the functionalization of a plasmon-supported fiber surface modified with an ACA. The salt's layer ensures the extraction of anions from model solutions, which causes a shift in the position of the absorption band. The created system demonstrates high sensitivity to nitrite (NO_2^-), nitrate (NO_3^-), dihydrogen phosphate (eg $H_2PO_4^-$) and sulphate (SO_4^{2-}) anions. It was found that the lower detectable concentration is only 10^{-7} M, which makes the proposed sensors comparable to the conventional analytical approach to the determination of water pollution.

ACKNOWLEDGEMENTS

This work was supported by under the project Internal Grant Agency UCT № 126 88 2005.

REFERENCES

[1] BUSSCHAERT, N., CALTAGIRONE, C., W. VAN ROSSOM, W., GALE, P. Applications of Supramolecular Anion Recognition. *Chem. Rev.* 2015, vol. 115, pp. 8038-8155.

[2] OKESOLA, B., SMITH, D. Applying low-molecular weight supramolecular gelators in an environmental setting - self-assembled gels as smart materials for pollutant removal. *Chem. Soc. Rev.* 2016, vol. 45, pp. 4226-4251.

[3] HAI, F., YAMAMOTO, K., FUKUSHI, K. Hybrid Treatment Systems for Dye Wastewater. *Crit. Rev. Environ. Sci. Technol.* 2007, vol. 37, pp. 315-377.

[4] KIM, H., WATTHANAPHANIT, A., SAITO, N. Simple Solution Plasma Synthesis of Hierarchical Nanoporous MnO2 for Organic Dye Removal. *ACS Sustainable Chem. Eng.* 2017, vol. 5, pp. 5842-5851.

[5] LIU, G., YOU, S., MA, M., HUANG, H., REN, N. Removal of Nitrate by Photocatalytic Denitrification Using Nonlinear Optical Material. *Environ. Sci. Technol.* 2016, vol. 50, pp. 11218-11225.

[6] WANG, X., LÜ, S., GAO, C., FENG, C., XU, X., BAI, X., GAO, N., YANG, J., LIU, M., WU, L. Recovery of Ammonium and Phosphate from Wastewater by Wheat Straw-based Amphoteric Adsorbent and Reusing as a Multifunctional Slow-Release Compound Fertilizer. *ACS Sustainable Chem. Eng.* 2016, vol. 4, pp. 2068-2079.

[7] JI, X., WU, R., LONG, L., GUO, C., KHASHAB, N., HUANG, F., SESSLER, J. Physical Removal of Anions from Aqueous Media by Means of a Macrocycle-Containing Polymeric Network. *J. Am. Chem. Soc.* 2018, vol. 140, no. 8, pp. 2777-2780.

[8] JIAO, S., JIN, J., WANG, L. One-pot preparation of Au-RGO/PDDA nanocomposites and their application for nitrite sensing. *Sens. Actuators B.* 2015, vol. 208, pp. 36-42.

[9] ZHANG, Y., SU, Z., LI, B., ZHANG, L., FAN, D., MA, H. Recyclable Magnetic Mesoporous Nanocomposite with Improved Sensing Performance toward Nitrite. *ACS Appl. Mater. Interfaces.* 2016, vol. 8, pp. 12344-12351.

[10] KIM, S., LEE, J., WILLIAMS, N., LYNCH, V., HAY, B., MOYER, B., SESSLER, J. Bipyrrole-Strapped Calix[4]pyrroles: Strong Anion Receptors That Extract the Sulfate Anion. *Am. Chem. Soc.* 2014, vol. 136, pp. 15079-15085.

[11] KWON, H., JIANG, W., KOOL, E. Pattern-Based Detection of Anion Pollutants in Water with DNA Polyfluorophores. *Chemical Science.* 2015, vol. 6, no. 4, pp. 2575-2583.

[12] TAN, S., KIM, Su J., KOOL, E. Differentiating between fluorescence-quenching metal ions with polyfluorophore sensors built on a DNA backbone. *J. Am. Chem. Soc.* 2011, vol. 133, pp. 2664-2671.

[13] YUEN, L., FRANZINI, R., WANG, S., CRISALLI, P., SINGH, V., JIANG, W., KOOL, E. Pattern-Based Detection of Toxic Metals in Surface Water with DNA Polyfluorophores. *Angew. Chem., Int. Ed.* 2014, vol. 53, pp. 5361-5365.

[14] KOO, C., WANG, S., GAUR, R., SAMAIN, F., BANAEIB, N., KOOL, E. Fluorescent DNA chemosensors: identification of bacterial species by their volatile metabolites. *Chem. Commun.* 2011, vol. 47, pp. 11435-11437.

[15] MILIUTINA, E., GUSELNIKOVA, O., CHUFISTOVA, S., KOLSKA, Z., ELASNIKOV, R., BURTSEV, V., POSTNIKOV, P., ŠVORČÍK, V., LYUTAKOV, O. Fast and All-Optical Hydrogen Sensor Based on Gold-Coated Optical Fiber Functionalized with Metal-Organic Framework Layer. *ACS Sens.* 2019, vol. 4, no. 12, pp. 3133-3140.

[16] MILIUTINA, E., GUSELNIKOVA, O., BURTSEV, V., ELASNIKOV, R., POSTNIKOV, P., ŠVORČÍK, V., LYUTAKOV, O. Plasmon-active optical fiber functionalized by metal organic framework for pesticide detection. *Talanta.* 2020, vol. 208, Article no. 120480.

[17] MILIUTINA, E., GUSELNIKOVA, O., KUSHNARENKO, A., BAINOVA, P., POSTNIKOV, P., HNATOWICZ, V., SVORCIK, V., LYUTAKOV, O. Single Plasmon-Active Optical Fiber Probe for Instantaneous Chiral Detection. *ACS Sens.* 2020, vol. 5, no. 1, pp. 50-56.

NANOPARTICLE-BASED WORLD - ORIGIN OF LIFE THEORY

Lukas NEJDL, Kristyna ZEMANKOVA, Kristyna PAVELICOVA, Eliska SEDLACKOVA, Marketa LUKLOVA, Vojtech ADAM, Marketa VACULOVICOVA

Department of Chemistry and Biochemistry, Mendel University in Brno, Czech Republic, EU, LukasNejdl@gmail.com

https://doi.org/10.37904/nanocon.2020.3723

Abstract

Many theories are currently being accepted as possible explanations for the origins of life on early Earth (e.g. Metabolism-first world, Zinc world, Thioester world, RNA world and others). However, discovered enzyme-mimetic properties of nanoparticles may lead to reconsideration of these theories. Recently, we postulated that one of the stages of chemical evolution could have been associated with nanozymatic activity of different nanoparticles that could form primitive prebiotic photodynamic redox chemical networks with proto-enzymatic activity. Our theory (Nanoparticle-based World) assumes that chemical evolution passed through the nanoparticle-assisted stage and could have led to sustainable metabolism. Formamide-based prebiotic chemistry assumes that formamide could have accumulated in sufficient amounts to serve as a feedstock and reaction medium for the synthesis of the first biogenic molecules. In this work, UV-induced formation (prebiotic scenario) of nanoparticles with xanthine oxidase like activity was demonstrated. All reactants (thiol-containing compounds, metals ions - zinc and cadmium, ammonia and fomamide) were highly probably present on early Earth.

Keywords: Nanoparticles, formamide, Origin of life, UV radiations, metal ions, thiols

1. INTRODUCTION

Many theories like Metabolism-first world [1], Zinc world [2], Thioester world [3], RNA world [4], Lipid world [5] and others, are currently being considered the explanation of the origin of life on Earth. Scientists all around over the world still discuss the physical and chemical conditions on early Earth, sources of energy, the feedstock molecules and transformation of non-living matter (biogenic building blocks) to self-sustaining autocatalytic networks (sustainable life). We believe that all the right places for the emergence of life contained mainly sulfur (especially thiols), metals ions, ammonia, and formamide environment. Formamide-based prebiotic chemistry assumes that formamide could accumulate in high enough amounts to serve as a feedstock and reaction medium for the synthesis of the first biogenic molecules like nucleobases, nucleosides, amino acids, sugars, amino sugars, carboxylic acids and others [6]. In our previous work, we showed that thermal treatment (160 °C, 24 hours) of formamide in presence of various clays (Ni/Fe meteoritic material, Fe_2O_3) caused formation of adenine, guanine, cytosine, thymine, uracil, purine, urea, hypoxanthine, guanidine and glycine [7]. In this work, we proved that formamide (50%) is a great solvent (environment) for UV-induced formation of ZnCd quantum dots (QDs) from very simple mixture of precursors containing thiols (e.g. mercaptosuccinic acid), metals ions (Zn^{2+} and $Cd^{2+)}$ and ammonia (NH_3, in range 0 - 2%). Also it was proved that these ZnCd QDs mimic enzyme xanthine oxidase (XO) under visible light conditions. And that is why we assume that first proto-metabolism pathway could have been associated with purine proto-metabolism catalyzed by nanoparticles (nanozymes). Caetano-Anolles G. et al. strongly suggested that first metabolic pathway in prebiotic chemistry was related to the synthesis of nucleotides for the RNA world, which was linked to the purine metabolic subnetwork [8]. Sun M. et al. showed that CdTe QDs can specifically recognize and cleave the restriction site GATATC in double-stranded DNA, mimicking an enzyme restriction endonuclease

[9]. These findings support the assumption that abiotic artificial materials (nanozymes) were apparently connected to the RNA world. The functions of ribozymes in modern organisms support the hypothesis that life passed through an RNA world before the emergence of proteins or DNA. Moreover, numerous microorganisms are capable of nanoparticle synthesis in order to remove undesired metal species [10-14]. This ability of microorganisms can also support the hypothesis that chemical evolution of life passed through the abiotic artificial material (nanozymes). Nanozymes as alternatives to natural enzymes excel mainly due to their stability, chemical diversity, and functionality in non-aqueous solvents [15]. Currently, nanozymes are prepared mainly from metal or carbon materials [16]. The enzymatic activity of inorganic materials starts to be considered highly important in the context of the new theories about the origin of life [17-19]. In this work, we present and discuss one of the possible scenarios of prebiotic preparation of ZnCd QDs nanozymes (mimic XO under visible light) with connection to first proto-metabolism based on purines catabolism in formamide environment. **Figure 1** represents a graphical summary (timeline) of main events related to the enzymes, ribozymes and nanozymes in origin of life context.

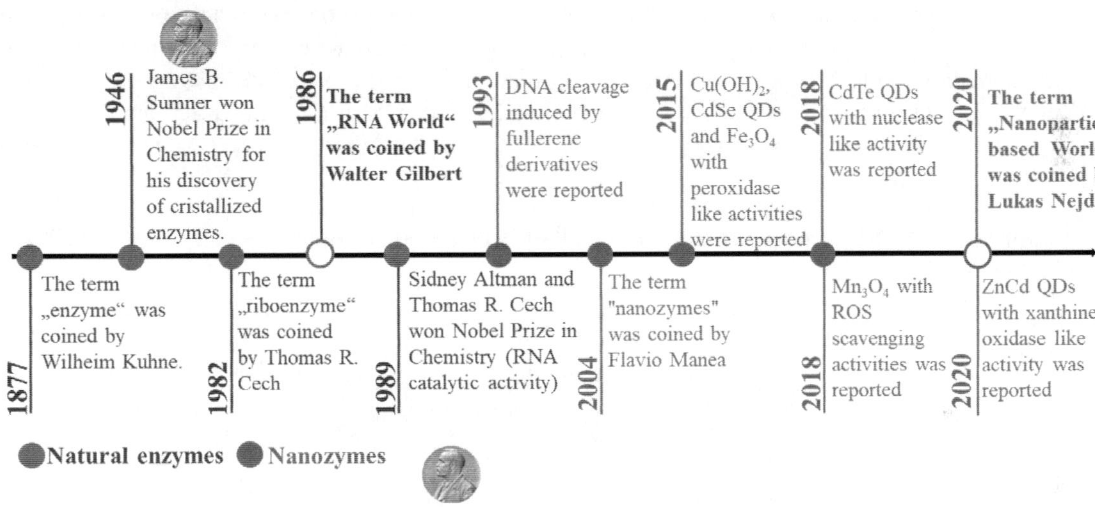

Figure 1 Represents a graphical summary of main events related to the natural enzymes and nanozymes in origin of life context according [9,19,20]

2. MATERIALS AND METODS

2.1. Chemicals

Standards and other chemicals were purchased from Sigma-Aldrich (St. Louis, MO, USA) in ACS purity.

2.2. Precursors preparation, UV- irradiation and fluorescence analysis

Stock solutions of 16 mM mercaptosuccinic acid (MSA), 6 mM zinc(II) acetate, 6 mM cadmium(II) acetate, 15% ammonia (NH_3) were prepared in distilled water and stored at 4 °C. Next, 12.5 µL of zinc(II) acetate, 12.5 µL of cadmium(II) acetate, 12.5 µL of MSA, 12.5 µL of 15%, 7.5%, 3.7%, 1.8% and 0% NH_3 were pipetted into the five neighboring wells of a UV-transparent 96-wellplate with a flat bottom by CoStar (Corning, USA) and subsequently 50 µL of 99.5% formamide was added to each well. A total volume of the samples was 100 µL each. Subsequently, the plate was placed into the UV transilluminator (Vilber Lourmat, Marne-la-Vallee Cedex, France) with λ_{em} = 254 nm and irradiated for 0 and 5 minutes. The sample area of 20 × 20 cm was illuminated by 6 emitting tubes with power of 15 W each. Finally, wavelength of 350 nm was used for fluorescence excitation and the emission scan was measured within the range from 380 to 800 nm by Tecan Infinite 200 M PRO (TECAN, Switzerland).

2.3. Enzymatic reactions

Xanthine oxidase-like activity of ZnCd QDs after visible light irradiation by table 6800K (6W) LED lamp (EMOS, Prerov, Czech Republic) was investigated by highly water-soluble tetrazolium salt that produces a formazan dye upon reduction with a superoxide anion. The reaction was monitored at 440 nm by UV/Vis spectrophotometer Tecan Infinite 200 M PRO (TECAN, Switzerland) using UV-transparent 96 wellplate with a flat bottom by CoStar (Corning, USA). The signal intensity was proportionate to the amount of superoxide anion. Standard enzyme of xanthine oxidase (positive control) was purchased from Sigma-Aldrich.

3. RESULTS AND DISCUSSION

The hydrogen cyanide (HCN) is most abundant three-atoms compound in interstellar environment and together with three-atoms water (H_2O) formed formamide ($CHONH_2$) [6]. Codella C. et al proved according interferometric measurement that formamide (potentially crucial building block of life [21-24]) is efficiently formed in the gas phase around Sun-like protostars [25]. The formamide has been also detected in comets, in the solid phase on grains around the young stellar object, in the galactic center sources Sagittarius and in the interstellar medium [26-30]. This work was focused on one-pot synthesis of the ZnCd QDs in formamide environment and subsequently investigation of their proto-metabolic activity (mimicking enzymes - xanthine oxidases). Photo-chemical processes leading to formation of the ZnCd QDs are described in our previous work [31].

3.1. Synthesis of ZnCd QDs in formamide solution and spectroscopic evaluation of ZnCd QDs xanthine oxidase activity

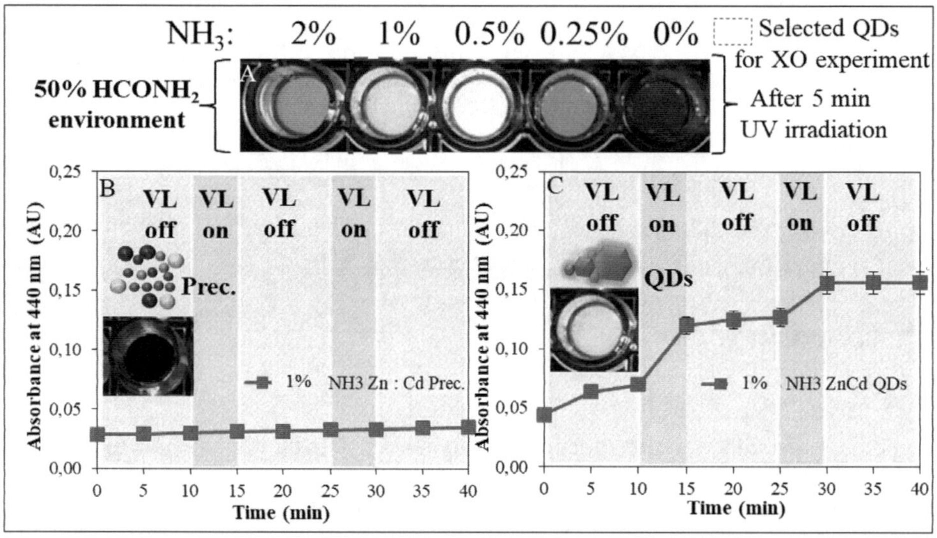

Figure 2 A) Precursors (0.75 mM cadmium acetate, 0.75 mM zinc acetate, 2 mM mercaptosuccinic acid and ammonia solution in range 0 - 2%) were irradiated for 5 minutes by UV and then a real photo was taken. Monitoring of dependence of absorbance at λ = 440 nm on **(B)** precursors and **(C)** ZnCd QDs exposure by visible light in substrate for determination of XO activity.

Several plausible scenarios involve prebiotic reactions in warm mineral and metal rich environment (involving mainly Fe, Cu but also Zn, Cd, Ag, Co, Ni, Pb, Mo etc. [32,33] and their combination with chemistries of sulfide-rich hydrothermal vents [34] or lagoons exposed to UV radiation [35]. Here, the UV-induced reaction was studied in 50% formamide environment. Formamide-based prebiotic chemistry suggests a plausible reaction route for the synthesis of nucleobases and others biogenic molecules [36]. Therefore, we have tested the suitability of formamide environment (50%) for prebiotic formation of ZnCd QDs by evaluation of fluorescence properties of ZnCd QDs formed from the mixture of precursors (0.75 mM cadmium acetate, 0.75 mM zinc acetate, 2 mM mercaptosuccinic acid and 0, 0.25,0.5,1 and 2 % ammonia solution) after 5 minute UV irradiation (λ_{em} = 254 nm). The red shift of ZnCd QDs was observed by increasing of the ammonia concentration as can be seen in **Figure 2 A**. It was proved that formamide is a suitable solvent (environment) for UV-induced synthesis of ZnCd QDs. Subsequently from previous experiment was chosen ZnCd QDs containing 1% ammonia (marked with a red square, **Figure 2 A**) and mixed together with substrate (tetrazolium salt) for monitoring of xanthine oxidase (XO) activity. Also unirradiated precursors of ZnCd QDs were mixed together with substrate. XO-like activity of ZnCd QDs was investigated by tetrazolium salt that produces a formazan dye upon reduction with a superoxide anion generated by XO or ZnCd QDs. The time dependence of the XO-like activity under visible light (VL) is demonstrated in **Figure 2 B** (unirradiated precursors) and **Figure 2 C** (ZnCd QDs). According to the results it is evident, that the VL induces XO activity in case ZnCd QDs. Formamide-based prebiotic chemistry together with formation of ZnCd QDs (mimicking enzyme XO) could be associated with first self-sustaining autocatalytic networks.

4. CONCLUSION

The present work demonstrates that formamide is an excellent solvent (environment) for light (UV)-driven synthesis of ZnCd QDs in the whole spectral range (emission from blue to red). Also, it was proved that ZnCd QDs mimic enzyme xanthine oxidase under visible light irradiation. We believe that all the cellular subsystems could have arisen simultaneously through common formamide-based chemistry and the key reaction steps could have been driven by light. Therefore, we assume that first proto-metabolism pathway could be associated with purine catabolism provided by nanoparticles (nanozymes) like QDs or other types of nanoparticles/nanomaterials. All precursors (metals ions, sulfur-containing compounds and ammonia), together with formamide, are abundantly represented in space environment. We suggest named all these nanoparticle-mediated reactions in the context origin of life as Nanoparticle-based world [36].

ACKNOWLEDGEMENTS

The research was founded by the Internal Grant Agency of Mendel University in Brno IGA MENDELU 2019_TP_009.

REFERENCES

[1] VASAS, V.,SZATHMARY, E.,SANTOS, M. Lack of evolvability in self-sustaining autocatalytic networks constraints metabolism-first scenarios for the origin of life. *Proceedings of the National Academy of Sciences of the United States of America*. 2010, vol. 107. no. 4, pp. 1470-1475.

[2] MULKIDJANIAN, A. Y. On the origin of life in the zinc world: I. Photosynthesizing, porous edifices built of hydrothermally precipitated zinc sulfide as cradles of life on earth. *Biology Direct*. 2009, vol. 4., p. 38.

[3] DEDUVE, C. The thioester world. In: TRANTHANHVAN, J.; TRANTHANHVAN K.; MOUNOLOU J. C.; SCHNEIDER J.; MCKAY C., eds. *Frontiers of life*. Dreux: Editions Frontieres, 1992.

[4] GILBERT, W. Origin of life - the rna world. *Nature*. 1986, vol. 319. no. 6055, pp. 618-618.

[5] SEGRE, D.,BEN-ELI, D.,DEAMER, D. W.,LANCET, D. The lipid world. *Origins of Life and Evolution of the Biosphere*. 2001, vol. 31. no. 1-2, pp. 119-145.

[6] SALADINO, R.,CRESTINI, C.,PINO, S.,COSTANZO, G.,DI MAURO, E. Formamide and the origin of life. *Physics of Life Reviews*. 2012, vol. 9. no. 1, pp. 84-104.

[7] PASTOREK, A.,HRNCIROVA, J., JANKOVIC, L., NEJDL, L., CIVIS, S., IVANEK, O., SHESTIVSKA, V., KNIZEK, A., KUBELIK, P., SPONER, J., PETERA, L., KRIVKOVA, A., CASSONE, G., VACULOVICOVA, M., SPONER, J. E., FERUS, M. Prebiotic synthesis at impact craters: The role of fe-clays and iron meteorites. *Chemical Communications*. 2019, vol. 55. no. 71, pp. 10563-10566.

[8] CAETANO-ANOLLES, G., KIM, H. S., MITTENTHAL, J. E. The origin of modern metabolic networks inferred from phylogenomic analysis of protein architecture. *Proceedings of the National Academy of Sciences of the United States of America*. 2007, vol. 104. no. 22, pp. 9358-9363.

[9] SUN, M. Z., XU, L. G., QU, A. H., ZHAO, P., HAO, T. T., MA, W., HAO, C. L., WEN, X. D., COLOMBARI, F. M., DE MOURA, A. F., KOTOV, N. A., XU, C. L., KUANG, H. Site-selective photoinduced cleavage and profiling of DNA by chiral semiconductor nanoparticles. *Nature Chemistry*. 2018, vol. 10. no. 8, pp. 821-830.

[10] LIU, X., GAO, H., WARD, J. E., LIU, X., YIN, B., FU, T., CHEN, J., LOVLEY, D. R.,YAO, J. Power generation from ambient humidity using protein nanowires. *Nature*. 2020, vol. 578, no. 7796, pp. 550-554.

[11] YAN, Z. Y., QIAN, J., GU, Y. Q., SU, Y. L., AI, X. X., WU, S. M. Green biosynthesis of biocompatible cdse quantum dots in living escherichia coli cells. *Materials Research Express*. 2014, vol. 1., no. 1, p. 14.

[12] SHAO, M., ZHANG, R., WANG, C., HU, B., PANG, D. W., XIE, Z. X. Living cell synthesis of cdse quantum dots: Manipulation based on the transformation mechanism of intracellular se-precursors. *Nano Research*. 2018, vol. 11. no. 5, pp. 2498-2511.

[13] WU, R. R., WANG, C., SHEN, J. S., ZHAO, F. A role for biosynthetic cds quantum dots in extracellular electron transfer of saccharomyces cerevisiae. *Process Biochemistry*. 2015, vol. 50. no. 12, pp. 2061-2065.

[14] TILLEY, R. D.,CHEONG, S. Earthworms lit with quantum dots. *Nature Nanotechnology*. 2013, vol. 8. no. 1, pp. 6-7.

[15] WEI, H., WANG, E. K. Nanomaterials with enzyme-like characteristics (nanozymes): Next-generation artificial enzymes. *Chemical Society Reviews*. 2013, vol. 42. no. 14, pp. 6060-6093.

[16] WU, J. J. X., WANG, X. Y., WANG, Q., LOU, Z. P., LI, S. R., ZHU, Y. Y., QIN, L., WEI, H. Nanomaterials with enzyme-like characteristics (nanozymes): Next-generation artificial enzymes (ii). *Chemical Society Reviews*. 2019, vol. 48. no. 4, pp. 1004-1076.

[17] WALTHER, R., WINTHER, A. K., FRUERGAARD, A. S., VAN DEN AKKER, W., SORENSEN, L., NIELSEN, S. M., OLESEN, M. T. J., DAI, Y. T., JEPPESEN, H. S., LAMAGNI, P., SAVATEEV, A., PEDERSEN, S. E. L., FRICH, C. K., VIGIER-CARRIERE, C., LOCK, N., SINGH, M., BANSAL, V., MEYER, R. L., ZELIKIN, A. N. Identification and directed development of non-organic catalysts with apparent pan-enzymatic mimicry into nanozymes for efficient prodrug conversion. *Angewandte Chemie-International Edition*. 2019, vol. 58. no. 1, pp. 278-282.

[18] HAZEN, R. M., SVERJENSKY, D. A. Mineral surfaces, geochemical complexities, and the origins of life. *Cold Spring Harbor Perspectives in Biology*. 2010, vol. 2. no. 5, p. 21.

[19] NEJDL, L., ZEMANKOVA, K., HAVLIKOVA, M., BURESOVA, M., HYNEK, D., XHAXHIU, K., MRAVEC, F., MATOUSKOVA, M., ADAM, V., FERUS, M., KAPUS, J., VACULOVICOVA, M. Uv-induced nanoparticles-formation, properties and their potential role in origin of life. *Nanomaterials*. 2020, vol. 10. no. 8, pp. 14.

[20] WANG, X. Y., HU, Y. H., WEI, H. Nanozymes in bionanotechnology: From sensing to therapeutics and beyond. *Inorganic Chemistry Frontiers*. 2016, vol. 3. no. 1, pp. 41-60.

[21] SALADINO, R., CAROTA, E., BOTTA, G., KAPRALOV, M., TIMOSHENKO, G. N., ROZANOV, A. Y., KRASAVIN, E., DI MAURO, E. Meteorite-catalyzed syntheses of nucleosides and of other prebiotic compounds from formamide under proton irradiation. *Proceedings of the National Academy of Sciences of the United States of America*. 2015, vol. 112, no. 21, pp. E2746-E2755.

[22] PIETRUCCI, F., SAITTA, A. M. Formamide reaction network in gas phase and solution via a unified theoretical approach: Toward a reconciliation of different prebiotic scenarios. *Proceedings of the National Academy of Sciences of the United States of America*. 2015, vol. 112, no. 49, pp. 15030-15035.

[23] SALADINO, R., DI MAURO, E., GARCIA-RUIZ, J. M. A universal geochemical scenario for formamide condensation and prebiotic chemistry. *Chemistry-a European Journal*. 2019, vol. 25, no. 13, pp. 3181-3189.

[24] SPONER, J. E., SZABLA, R., GORA, R. W., SAITTA, A. M., PIETRUCCI, F., SAIJA, F., DI MAURO, E., SALADINO, R., FERUS, M., CIVIS, S., SPONER, J. Prebiotic synthesis of nucleic acids and their building blocks at the atomic level - merging models and mechanisms from advanced computations and experiments. *Physical Chemistry Chemical Physics*. 2016, vol. 18, no. 30, pp. 20047-20066.

[25] CODELLA, C., CECCARELLI, C., CASELLI, P., BALUCANI, N., BARONE, V., FONTANI, F., LEFLOCH, B., PODIO, L., VITI, S., FENG, S., BACHILLER, R., BIANCHI, E., DULIEU, F., JIMENEZ-SERRA, I., HOLDSHIP, J., NERI, R., PINEDA, J. E., PON, A., SIMS, I., SPEZZANO, S., VASYUNIN, A. I., ALVES, F., BIZZOCCHI, L., BOTTINELLI, S., CAUX, E., CHACON-TANARRO, A., CHOUDHURY, R., COUTENS, A., FAVRE, C., HILY-BLANT, P., KAHANE, C., AL-EDHARI, A. J., LAAS, J., LOPEZ-SEPULCRE, A., OSPINA, J., OYA, Y., PUNANOVA, A., PUZZARINI, C., QUENARD, D., RIMOLA, A., SAKAI, N., SKOUTERIS, D., TAQUET, V., TESTI, L., THEULE, P., UGLIENGO, P., VASTEL, C., VAZART, F., WIESENFELD, L., YAMAMOTO, S. Seeds of life in space (solis) ii. Formamide in protostellar shocks: Evidence for gas-phase formation. *Astronomy & Astrophysics*. 2017, vol. 605, p. 7.

[26] DESPOIS, D., CROVISIER, J., BOCKELEE-MORVAN, D., BIVER, N. Comets and prebiotic chemistry: The volatile component. **In**: LACOSTE, H., ed. Proceedings of the second european workshop on exo-astrobiology. Noordwijk: Esa Publications Division C/O Estec, 2002, vol. 518.

[27] BOCKELEE-MORVAN, D., LIS, D. C., WINK, J. E., DESPOIS, D., CROVISIER, J., BACHILLER, R., BENFORD, D. J., BIVER, N., COLOM, P., DAVIES, J. K., GERARD, E., GERMAIN, B., HOUDE, M., MEHRINGER, D., MORENO, R., PAUBERT, G., PHILLIPS, T. G., RAUER, H. New molecules found in comet c/1995 o1 (hale-bopp) - investigating the link between cometary and interstellar material. *Astronomy & Astrophysics*. 2000, vol. 353. no. 3, pp. 1101-1114.

[28] LIS, D. C., MEHRINGER, D. M., BENFORD, D., GARDNER, M., PHILLIPS, T. G., BOCKELEE-MORVAN, D., BIVER, N., COLOM, P., CROVISIER, J., DESPOIS, D., RAUER, H. New molecular species in comet c/1995 o1 (hale-bopp) observed with the caltech submillimeter observatory. *Earth Moon and Planets*. 1997, vol. 78. no. 1-3, pp. 13-20.

[29] SCHUTTE, W. A., BOOGERT, A. C. A., TIELENS, A., WHITTET, D. C. B., GERAKINES, P. A., CHIAR, J. E., EHRENFREUND, P., GREENBERG, J. M., VAN DISHOECK, E. F., DE GRAAUW, T. Weak ice absorption features at 7.24 and 7.41 mu m in the spectrum of the obscured young stellar object w 33a. *Astronomy & Astrophysics*. 1999, vol. 343, no. 3, pp. 966-976.

[30] SOLOMON, P. M. Interstellar molecules. *Physics Today*. 1973, vol. 26, no. 3, pp. 32-40.

[31] NEJDL, L. Z., K., HAVLIKOVA, M., BURESOVA, M., HYNEK, D., XHAXHIU, K., MRAVEC, F., MATOUSKOVA, M., ADAM, V., FERUS, M., KAPUS, J., VACULOVICOVA, M. Uv-induced nanoparticles-formation, properties and their potential role in origin of life. *Nanomaterials*. 2020, vol. 10, no. 1529.

[32] KUMAR, A., SHARMA, R., KAMALUDDIN. Formamide-based synthesis of nucleobases by metal(ii) octacyanomolybdate(iv): Implication in prebiotic chemistry. *Astrobiology*. 2014, vol. 14, no. 9, pp. 769-779.

[33] BIZZARRI, B. M., BOTTA, L., PEREZ-VALVERDE, M. I., SALADINO, R., DI MAURO, E., GARCIA-RUIZ, J. M. Silica metal oxide vesicles catalyze comprehensive prebiotic chemistry. *Chemistry-a European Journal*. 2018, vol. 24. no. 32, pp. 8126-8132.

[34] KITADAI, N., NAKAMURA, R., YAMAMOTO, M., TAKAI, K., YOSHIDA, N., OONO, Y. Metals likely promoted protometabolism in early ocean alkaline hydrothermal systems. *Science Advances*. 2019, vol. 5. no. 6, p. 9.

[35] PATEL, B. H., PERCIVALLE, C., RITSON, D. J., DUFFY, C. D., SUTHERLAND, J. D. Common origins of rna, protein and lipid precursors in a cyanosulfidic protometabolism. *Nature Chemistry*. 2015, vol. 7. no. 4, pp. 301-307.

[36] SPONER, J. E., MLADEK, A., SPONER, J., FUENTES-CABRERA, M. Formamide-based prebiotic synthesis of nucleobases: A kinetically accessible reaction route. *Journal of Physical Chemistry A*. 2012, vol. 116. no. 1, pp. 720-726

EXTRACTION AND MICRONIZATION OF EDESTIN FROM HEMP SEED

Milos BERAN, Ondrej VLTAVSKY, Josef DRAHORAD

Food Research Institute Prague, Prague, Czech Republic, EU, m.beran@vupp.cz

https://doi.org/10.37904/nanocon.2020.3724

Abstract

Protein edestin extraction from hemp seed press cakes obtained after a cold press oil extraction process has been optimized at laboratory scale and verified in a pilot plant experiment. Subsequent water and brine extraction of the disintegrated hemp seed press cake was used to obtain the water-soluble albumin protein fraction and the brine-soluble globulin fraction - edestin. Isoelectric precipitation was used to obtain the proteins from the extraction solutions. New Carbon Dioxide Assisted Spray Nebulisation Drying (CASND) technology has been used to dry and micronize the protein concentrates and isolates. The protein powders were in form of hollow spheres with average particle diameter about 600 nm. The particles were characterized by the SEM method. The protein microparticulation allows to improve foaming and emulsifying properties and formation of long-term stable water dispersions.

Keywords: Hemp seed, protein concentrates, protein isolates, microparticulation, Carbon Dioxide Assisted Spray Nebulisation Drying

1. INTRODUCTION

Protein in food is an essential nutrient which comes from animal and plant sources. Besides the nutritional value, the functional properties of food proteins affect behavior in food systems and influence the quality attributes, structure, texture, mouth-feel, and flavor of the final product. Plant proteins can differ from animal proteins in terms of digestibility, amino acid composition, and the presence of antinutritional factors [1]. Most evidence suggests that a shift to largely plant-based protein diets would reduce chronic disease risks among industrialized and rapidly-industrializing populations. Filter cakes from canola / rapeseed, sunflower and hemp seeds obtained after oil pressing and extraction, rice, cell fluids obtained from potatoes, or pea seeds belong among the main alternative sources of commercially available plant protein concentrates and isolates for human nutrition. Hemp seed contains the salt-soluble globulin edestin (~ 75%) and the water-soluble albumins (~ 25%) as the main storage proteins. Edestin is a hexameric legumin protein of hemp seed with globular structure of 11S type and molecular weight approximately 300 kDa. Hemp seed proteins have a high level of arginine and a sulfur-rich protein fraction, two unique features that impart high nutritional values [2]. Hemp proteins have a protein digestibility-corrected amino acid score equal to or greater than certain grains, nuts, and some pulses [3]. Hemp seed enzymatic hydrolysates have also proven effective during in vitro and in vivo tests as antioxidant and antihypertensive agents. Therefore, hemp seed proteins and hydrolysates have the potential to be used as ingredients to formulate functional foods [2,4]. Spray drying is usually used to produce powders from the protein rich solutions. Freeze drying is alternative drying technique, which is used less frequently because of higher price and limited capacity. Functional properties of proteins in food matrices are determined by the physicochemical properties of the proteins, degree of denaturation, type of processing, and particle morphology and size, in the case of powdered proteins with limited solubility. The design of protein particles with tailored properties has received an increased attention recently. Control of particle size, morphology, surface and internal properties is crucial for obtaining protein particles with the necessary properties for emerging applications. Singer et al. [5] originally patented the use of whey protein microparticles, formed by thermal aggregation at high shear and low pH. A commercial fat replacer SIMPLESSE®, based on this process, was launched by NutraSweet in 1988 in form of spherical particles in the size range of 0.1-2.5 µm. The initial patent was later extended to other proteins, e.g., bovine serum albumin, egg white albumin and soy protein [6]. SIMPLESSE® has been applied in dressings and mayonnaise, frozen desserts, cheese and other dairy products since that time [7]. The improved creaminess obtained by use of microparticulated protein products was due to particles <5 µm in size, mimicking emulsion droplets [8,9]. The preparation provides emulsion and foam stabilization, heat and pH stability, texture, creaminess and smoothness in a wide range of full-fat and low-fat applications. Two approaches, namely, isoelectro-mechanical and thermo-mechanical processes, are most often used in microparticulation of protein. In these processes, conditions that denature (i.e. heat) or induce a complex or precipitate formation (i.e. isoelectric precipitation) are combined with a strong mechanical treatment, e.g. high share rates or turbulence and cavitation to produce nanoaggregated protein microparticles of desired size and distribution. Several methods, from simple heat treatment in dilute systems to the combination of heat and mechanical treatments in concentrated protein solutions, have been used to obtain protein particles with varying functional properties [10]. Turbulation, cavitation and shear are also the main phenomena encountered in high-pressure homogenizers, such as microfluidizers. The microfluidization technology is an unique type of high-pressure homogenization [11,12]. Alternative processes may also be implemented, such as extrusion cooking at acid pH [13], or two-step emulsification of whey protein isolate in sunflower oil containing polyglycerol polyricinoleate with subsequent heating and oil removal [14]. Supercritical fluid assisted atomization processes are other technologies of choice to produce microparticalated proteins [15]. Carbon Dioxide Assisted Spray Nebulisation Drying (CASND) technology, shortly Spray Nebulisation Drying (SND) is a new emerging technology described recently [16]. The technology combines the spray drying technology, when the liquid to be dried is atomized by a rotary atomizer, with carbon dioxide assisted nebulization process in an original way. A wide range of application forms - low density particles, composite particles, sterically stabilized liposomes, phytosomes, microencapsulated particles or microbial cells, solid dispersions, dried single and multiple emulsions, nano- and microfibers and other - can be produced by this process.

2. MATERIALS AND METHODS

2.1. Material

Hemp seed press cake (Benico variety) was purchased from KONOPRO company (Czech Republic). All other chemicals were purchased from VWR International s.r.o. (Czech Republic).

2.2. Extraction of hemp proteins from the dried filter cake

Laboratory extraction experiment

We have used a modified method according to K. Bailey [17]. Subsequent water and brine extraction of the disintegrated hemp seed press cake was used. Isoelectric precipitation was harnessed to obtain the proteins from the extraction solutions. The dried press cake of hemp seeds was pulverized with a knife blender Catler 800 series (Catler, Australia). Water extraction at 45°C in Series 25 Incubator Shaker (New Brunswick Scinces) at 300 rpm was used to remove albumin fraction and soluble impurities from the pulverized hemp seed press cake. An insoluble sediment was obtained by centrifugation with Rousselet Robatel RA20 Vx centrifuge (Rousselet Robatel, Annonay, France), 4000 rpm. The sediment was extracted two times with surplus of 10% brine solution at 45°C in the shaker at 300 rpm overnight to obtain the globulin edestin fraction. Isoelectric precipitation at pH 4,00 was used to separate edestin from the brine solution. Precipitated edestin was obtained in the sediment fraction after centrifugation in HERMLE Z513 K centrifuge at 5000 rpm (RCF 6 500 x g), resuspended in distilled water and separated by repeated centrifugation. The washed edestin was resuspended in distilled water and micronized and dried simultaneously by Spray Nebulisation Drying (SND) process in Atomizer pilot-plant demonstrator. **Figure 1** shows the process of the isoelectric precipitation of edestin from the brine extraction solution.

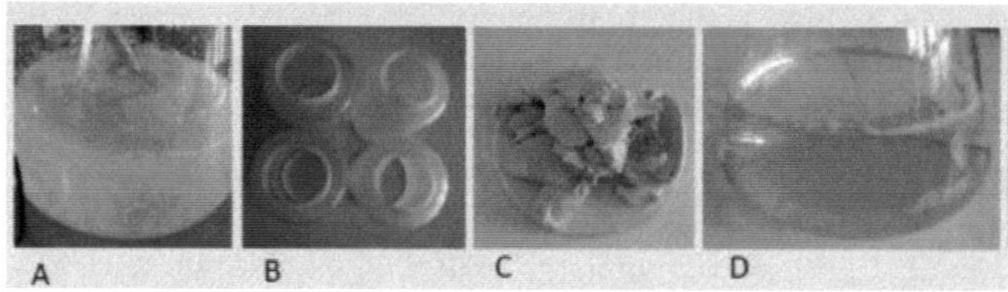

Figure 1 Isoelectric precipitation of edestin from the brine extraction solution

Pilot plant extraction experiment

The extraction process was scaled-up in the The Biotechnological Pilot-Plant of the Institute of Microbiology of the Czech Academy of Sciences. Continuous disk-bowl centrifuge BTPX 205 (Alfa Laval) was used to separate the fibrous sediment after the extraction process and tubular-bowl centrifuge Sharples was used to separate the precipitated edestin.

2.3. Drying and microparticulation of the plant protein extracts

The SND combines the spray drying technology, when the liquid to be dried is atomized by a rotary atomizer, with carbon dioxide assisted nebulization process in an original way. The rotary atomizer used for the SND technology has an unique patented construction allowing to regulate and keep the outlet pressure at an exactly defined level. A solution, emulsion or suspension is saturated by carbon dioxide at pressure 6-8 MPa before the drying process. The atomization process takes place in two steps. In the first step, primary droplets are produced by the centrifugal force at the outlet of the rotary atomizer of special construction. In the second step, the primary droplets are divided into secondary droplets by the CO2 expansion from the inside of primary droplets. The secondary droplets, usually in the form of micro-bubbles, are rapidly dried by warm air stream at temperatures up to 60°C and solid particles are formed in a drying chamber. Electrofilter separator AEROFOG KE1 (Vzduchotechnik, Czech Republic) has been used to separate the powder from the air stream. Simultaneous pressure homogenization and drying of the washed edestin paste resuspended in distilled water was carried out using the nebulization unit of the Atomizer pilot plant demonstrator (DBH Technologies, Czech Republic) under following conditions: Liquid flow rate, 20 $ml.min^{-1}$; Carbon dioxide flow rate, 1.8 $ml.min^{-1}$; Pressure, 6 MPa; Inlet air temperature, 60°C; Outlet air temperature, 48°C; Air flow rate: 1000 $m^3.h^{-1}$.

2.4. Characterisation of the protein microparticles by scanning electron microscopy

Scanning Electron Microscopy (SEM) was used to analyze the particle sizes and morphologies. The samples of the fibres were fixed with a double-faced adhesive tape to the holders and evaluated in a Phenom G2 scanning electron microscope (Phenom-World BV, Eindhoven, Netherlands).

3. RESULTS and DISCUSSION

3.1. Extraction of hemp proteins from the dried filter cake

Laboratory extraction experiment

<u>Material balance of the experiment</u>

Input: 900 g of the disintegrated hemp seed press cake. DM 93.68%, Protein content 33.09% (w/w). Total pure protein input: 297.8 g.

Output:

1) extraction yield: 272,88 g of edestin paste; DM 20.3±1.0%; Protein content: 18.2±5.0%; Protein content 89.66% in DM.

2) extraction yield: 251.90 g of edestin paste; DM 17.2±1.0%; Protein content: 15.0±5.0%; Protein content 87.21% in DM.

Total pure edestin protein yield 87.44 g. Total protein edestin recovery: 29.36 %.

The obtained edestin recovery from the hemp seed press cake has been relatively low, about 30%. There is a significant part of edestin, which can't be extracted under the condition of the technological process. Edestin binding to a water-insoluble polysaccharide fiber is a probable explanation of the limited effectiveness of the extraction process. There are no published studies presenting yields of brine extraction of edestin from hemp seeds to compare with.

Pilot plant extraction experiment

Material balance of the experiment

Input: 10 kg of disintegrated hemp seed press cake. DM 92.1%, Protein content 30,69%. Total pure protein input: 3069 g.

Output:

Total extraction yield was 1.79 kg of a dense edestin sediment after centrifugation; DM 56.1% (w/w); Protein content 90.92% (w/w) of DM. The total pure edestin yield: 0.91 kg from 10 kg of (wet matter) hemp seed press cake.

Total protein edestin recovery: 29,65%.

Using a high-quality industrial centrifuge allows obtaining a dense edestin sediment (DM 56.1%) with high protein content (about 90% of DM). The total yield of the pilot plant extraction experiment was at least comparable with the laboratory experiment yields. The technological process is relatively simple and cheap. Except NaCl, there is no significant consumption of other chemicals.

3.2. Drying and microparticulation of the plant protein extracts

Simultaneous pressure homogenization and drying of the washed edestin paste resuspended in distilled water was successfully demonstrated using the Atomizer pilot plant demonstrator. Our experiments proved high filtration efficiency of the electrofilter with the protein isolate particles produced by the SND process (**Figure 2,C**). Edestin dried and micronized sample is shown in **Figure 2,D**. However, the product yield of the SND process could not be calculated. The reason was that the AEROFOG KE1 electrofilter is not suitable for quantitative recovery of powdered products, because of the small gaps in between the collecting electrodes (**Figure 2,C**). The electrofilter was constructed as an air purifier to remove aerosol particles from air stream. The results inspired a development of a new electrostatic fine powder precipitator which has already been constructed with the aim to facilitate the maximal recovery of the products powdered by the SND technology. The electrostatic fine powder precipitator is tested at present time with hopeful results.

Figure 2 A: washed edestin paste resuspended in DEMI water B: pilot plant demonstrator Atomizer, C: electrofilter ionizing module for powder separation, D: edestin micronized sample

3.3. Characterisation of the protein microparticles by scanning electron microscopy

Comparison of microstructures of the hemp seed protein isolate dried with the ATOMIZER demonstrator and the same sample dried with a conventional spray dryer is shown in **Figure 3.** There is a visible difference between both the samples perceptible in the SEM images. Both the samples consist of hollow nanospheres or microspheres, but the average size of the particles obtained by the SND process is much lower.

Previous experiments [16] showed, that the mean value of the aerosol particle size distribution measured in the drying chamber is about 600 nm. The interval of the particle size distribution is relatively wide. The aerosol inside the drying chamber contains significant amount of nanoparticles smaller than 100 nm, but a small portion of microparticles up to several micrometers, too. The microparticulation of the protein concentrates by the SND process resulted in statistically significant improvement of the foaming capacity and stability, emulsifying activity and emulsion stability [16].

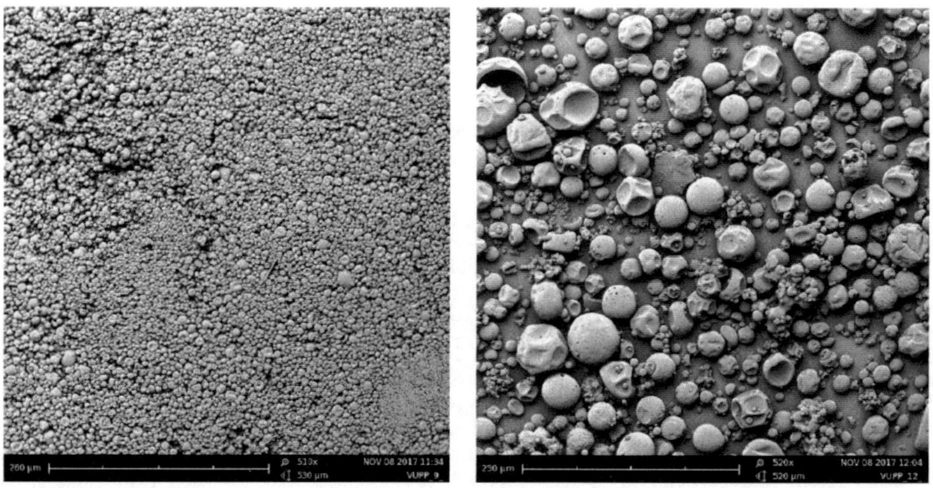

Figure 3 Comparison of SEM images of edestin micronized by the spray nebulisation drying technology (left) and dried by conventional spray drying technology (right), line segment 260 μm

4. CONCLUSIONS

Edestin yields were about 10% (w/w) from the input DM of hemp seed press cake, and edestin recovery was about 30% (w/w). Edestin strong binding to a polysaccharide fiber is a probable explanation of the limited effectiveness of the extraction process. Using a high-quality industrial centrifuge allows obtaining a dense edestin sediment (DM 56,1%) with high protein content (about 90% of DM). The total yield of the pilot plant extraction experiment was at least comparable with the laboratory experiment yields. The technological process is relatively simple and cheap. Except NaCl, there is no significant consumption of other chemicals. The SND technology allows to produce protein concentrates or isolates in a form of submicron hollow spheres with improved functional properties. We have successfully used edestin in several products, including gluten free baguettes and high-protein food products, such as crackers, muffins and protein smoothies. All the products are in compliance with the EFSA nutritional claim for high-protein food products. The products were positively accepted in sensory analysis. No foreign unpleasant taste was noticed.

ACKNOWLEDGEMENTS

This work was supported by the TACR project number TH03010019 and by the Institutional Development Fund RO0320 of FRIP provided by the Ministry of Agriculture of the Czech Republic

REFERENCES

[1] GUEGUEN, J., POPINEAU, Y. *Plant proteins from European crops: food and non-food applications.* Springer-Verlag Berlin Heidelberg, 1998, p. 339.

[2] NADARTHUR, S., WANASUNDARA, J.P.D., SCANLIN, L. *Sustainable protein sources.* Academic Press, 2016, pp: 456.

[3] HOUSE J.D., NEUFEKD, J., LESON, G. Evaluating the quality of protein from hemp seed (Cannabis sativa L.) products through the use of the protein digestibility-corrected amino acid score method. *J Agric Food Chem.* 2010, vol. 58, pp. 11801-11807.

[4] MALOMO, A.S, ALUKO, R.E. Conversion of a low protein hemp seed meal into a functional protein concentrate through enzymatic digestion of fibre coupled with membrane ultrafiltration. *Innov Food Sci Emerg Technol.* 2015, vol 31, pp. 151-159.

[5] SINGER, N.S., YAMMAMOTO, S., LATTELA, J. Protein product base. Patent US 4734287. John LaBatt Limited, London, ON, Canada, 1988.

[6] SINGER, N.S., YAMMAMOTO, S., LATTELA, J. Protein product base. Patent US 4734287. John LaBatt Limited, London, ON, Canada, 1988.

[7] CHEFTEL, J.C., DUMAY, E. Microcoagulation of proteins for development of creaminess. *Food Rev Int.* 1993, vol. 9, pp. 473-502.

[8] SINGER, N.S., DUNN, J.M. Protein microparticulation: the principle and the process. *J Am Coll Nutr.* 1990, vol. 9, pp. 388-397.

[9] IPSEN, R. Microparticulated whey proteins for improving dairy product texture. *Int Dairy.* 2017, vol. J 67, pp. 73-79.

[10] SAĞLAM, D., VENEMA, P., VAN DER LINDEN, E., DE VRIES, R. Design, properties, and applications of protein micro- and nanoparticles. *Curr Opin Colloid Interface Sci.* 2014, vol.19, pp. 428-437.

[11] DAMADORAN, S. *Food proteins and their applications.* Routledge, 2017, p. 694.

[12] DISSANAYAKE, M., VASILJEVIC, T. Functional properties of whey proteins affected by heat treatment and hydrodynamic high-pressure shearing. *J Dairy Sci.* 2009, vol 92, pp. 1387-1397.

[13] VIOQUE, J., SÁNCHEZ-VIOQUE, R., CLAMENTE, A., PEDROCHE, J, MILLÁN, F. Partially hydrolyzed rapeseed protein isolates with improved functional properties. *J Am Oil Chem Soc.* 2000, vol. 77, pp. 447-450.

[14] SAĞLAM D, VENEMA P, DE VRIES R, SAGIS LMC, VAN DER LINDEN E. Preparation of high protein micro-particles using two-step emulsification. *Food Hydrocolloids.* 2011, vol. 25, no. 5, pp. 1139-1148.

[15] YEO, S.D., LIM, G.B., DEBENDETTI, P.G., BERSTEIN, H. Formation of microparticulate protein powder using a supercritical fluid antisolvent. *Biotechnol Bioeng.* 1993, vol. 41, pp. 341-346.

[16] BERAN, M., DRAHORAD, J., VLTAVSKY, O., URBAN, M., LAKNEROVA, I., FRONEK, M., SOVA, J., ONDRACEK, J., ONDRACKOVA, L., KRALOVA, M., FORNANKOVA, S. Pilot-Scale Production and Application of microparticulated Plant Proteins. *J Nutr Food Sci.* 2018, vol. 8, p. 655.

[17] BAILEY, K. The denaturation of edestin by acid: T. B. Osborne's edestan. *Biochem J.* 1942, vol. 36, no 1-2, pp. 140-154.

CARBON MATERIALS PREPARED FROM CIGARETTE FILTERS APPLIED FOR CLOFIBRIC ACID ADORPTION

[1]Susana C. R. MARQUES, [1]Jan FILIP

[1]*Regional Centre of Advanced Technologies and Materials, Palacký University in Olomouc, Czech Republic, EU,* susanacristina.roquemarques@upol.cz

https://doi.org/10.37904/nanocon.2020.3733

Abstract

Chars and carbon membranes were prepared from fresh and smoked cigarette filters, and used as adsorbents for clofibric acid removal. Carbonization of cigarette filters took place at 650, 750 and 900 °C, whereas membranes were synthesized by filter dissolution in acetone, using NaCl (porogen) and glycerol (plasticizer). Acid mediated carbonization (225 and 250 °C) of the membranes was performed. Solution pH was monitored throughout the adsorption experiments. The chars are basic powders with apparent surface areas up to 494 $m^2\ g^{-1}$ and a porosity composed by supermicropores (0.7-2 nm wide) and mesopores (2-50 nm wide), allowing clofibric acid (critical dimension 0.6 nm) to access all adsorption sites. Carbonization of smoked filters promoted higher porosity levels and SEM analysis showed that a more extensive carbonization occurred in the outer surface of the chars particles. The presence of TiO_2 particles was confirmed in all the chars. Pores were homogeneously created at the membranes surface. Acidic carbon membranes ($pH_{PZC} \approx 3.7$) were obtained with different degrees of porosity, proportional to the pyrolysis temperature. Both forms of clofibric acid (protonated and deprotonated) were readily adsorbed onto the carbon materials, with exception of the chars prepared at 900 °C, which adsorbed predominantly the deprotonated form. In equilibrium, an inverse correlation between solution pH and concentration of the pollutant was observed, and higher uptakes were observed for experiments with solution pH values above 5, suggesting that adsorption of the neutral species contributed significantly to the overall removal.

Keywords: Cigarette filters, chars, carbon membranes, adsorption, clofibric acid

1. INTRODUCTION

Cigarette butts (CBs) are among the most prevalent sources of waste litter worldwide [1]. Littered CBs have been found in ecosystems, such as urban areas, beaches and even in the aquatic system, where their presence raises a great level of concern [2]. The main source of contamination in CBs is the cigarette filter (CF), consisting in more than 15000 non-biodegradable cellulose acetate fibers subjected to titanium dioxide (a delustrant), and packed firmly together with triacetin (a binding agent), to produce a single filter. During smoking, a complex mixture of chemical compounds, including toxic heavy metals, polycyclic aromatic hydrocarbons, pesticides, N-nitrosamines and nicotine, is trapped in the CFs [2]. When CBs are littered, these contaminants may leach into the terrestrial and aquatic environments, posing a serious health hazard to humans, animals and even vegetation [2]. CFs have been used, in recent years, as cellulose derivative sources for the development of carbon materials but many questions are still to be answered [3-5]. In this study, chars and carbon membranes were prepared from CFs, and their texture, chemistry and morphology characterized. The materials were applied for clofibric acid adsorption, and the role of solution pH change in the adsorption mechanism was investigated under equilibrium conditions.

2. MATERIALS AND METHODS

2.1. Materials preparation

Fresh (UF) and smoked filters (SF) were carbonized, at 650, 750 and 900 °C for 2 h (N_2 flow 15 cm^3 s^{-1}, heating rate 5 °C min^{-1}), in a tube furnace (model LT 50/300/13). Prior to pyrolysis, the filters were cut into cylinders approximately 0.5 cm thick to increase the surface area exposed to thermal treatment (labelled as UC and SC - fresh and smoked cut filters, respectively). The chars were named according to filter type and carbonization temperature, for example, Ch_UC650.

Membranes were synthesized by dissolving 2 g of filters in approximately 10 cm^3 of acetone (purity ≥ 99 %, Sigma-Aldrich) under stirring. Grounded NaCl (weight ratio of NaCl:filters of 1:7) was used as porogen, and glycerol (3 cm^3, Lach-ner) was added. The mixture was poured onto a petri dish for solvent evaporation, at room temperature. After solidification, the membranes were washed with distilled water, at 80 °C. The membranes were designated according to type of filters (UF or SF) used, for example Memb_SF. Acid mediated carbonization was carried out by soaking the membranes in 50 cm^3 of phosphoric acid (UF soaked in 0.5 mol dm^{-3} and for SF 1 mol dm^{-3} was used) for 2 h, prior to pyrolysis. Carbonization took place at 225 and 250 °C, for 1 h (N_2 flow 15 cm^3 s^{-1}, heating rate 5 °C min^{-1}). The designation of the carbon membranes included type of filter, temperature of carbonization and acid (p) used, for example, Memb_SF250p.

2.2. Characterization of samples

N_2 adsorption-desorption, was carried out in a volumetric gas adsorption analyzer (3Flex, Micromeritics) , at -196 °C. The samples were degassed prior to pyrolysis, under vacuum (0.07 mbar) for 12 hours at 130 °C, and high purity (99.999 %) N_2 and He gases were used for the measurements. The apparent surface area, A_{BET}, was calculated according to recommendations in norm ISO 9277, and the microporosity of the samples was analyzed by applying the α_S method [6,7]. This method allowed the determination of the total micropore volume, V_{micro}, and the specific volumes of ultra, V_{ultra}, and supermicropores, V_{super}.

Scanning Electron Microscopy (SEM) was employed using a field emission gun scanning electron microscope (Hitachi SU6600) with an X-ray energy dispersive system (EDS) (accelerating voltage of 1.0 kV). EDS spectra were acquired using a Thermo Noran System 7 (Thermo Scientific, USA) with Si(Li) detector (accelerating voltage of 15 kV and acquisition time of 300 s).

The pH at the point of zero charge (pH_{PZC}) was determined using 5 cm^3 of NaCl solutions (0.1 mol dm^{-3}), with initial pH values around 2, 4, 6, 8 and 10, adjusted with sodium hydroxide and hydrochloric acid. Amounts of 20 mg of char and 30 mg of membrane were used. The solution pH values obtained after 24 h stirring were measured with a pH/ORP meter (Hanna Instruments, model HI 2211) equipped with a WTW electrode (model SenTix Mic).

X-ray powder diffraction (XRD) patterns were recorded using a PANalytical X'Pert PRO MPD diffractometer (PANalytical, The Netherlands), equipped with an X'Celerator detector and programmable divergence slit and diffracted beam anti-scatter slit. The data was collected using Co-Kα radiation (40 kV, 30 mA, λ = 0.1789 nm), and undesirable Kβ radiation was filtered using an iron filter. Measurements were made in a Bragg-Brentano geometry (angular range 2θ: 5° - 105°, and step size of 0.033°). High Score Plus software (PANalytical), with PDF-4+ database, was used for the identification of the crystalline phases.

2.3. Liquid phase adsorption

Clofibric acid (TCI Chemicals, purity >97.0%) adsorption from aqueous solutions was carried out at the dissolution pH and room temperature. The materials (5 mg of char, 10 mg of membrane) were immersed in 5 cm^3 of solution. Equilibrium adsorption studies were performed by adding 10 mg of chars and 20 mg of membrane to pollutant solutions (initial concentrations ranged from 5 to 200 mg dm^3) in glass vials (30 rpm,

Multi Bio RS-24 programmable rotator). Individual suspensions were prepared and, after equilibrium contact time, the concentration of the filtrated solution (C_e) was determined by UV/Visible spectrophotometry (Biochrom WPA Lightwave II), at wavelength of 280 nm, and the corresponding uptake calculated (q_e) [8].

3. RESULTS AND DISCUSSION

3.1. Chars

The chars are basic powders and have developed wide porosities, composed exclusively by supermicropores and mesopores (**Table 1**). A more significant pore development was achieved at 650 °C, for both fresh and smoked filters. The increase in carbonization temperature had less impact in the porosity of SC-chars, suggesting that the chemical compounds entrapped in the smoked filters prevented the excessive consumption of the fibers matrix while, at the same time, allowing for porosity development. A possible explanation for this is that the pyrolysis of cellulosic fibers leads to the release of water vapor and carbon dioxide, which are commonly used as activating agents in the synthesis of porous materials [9]. Then, tars entrapped in the filters may react with carbon dioxide, forming carbon monoxide and hydrogen [10]. Low yield values between 11 and 17 % were obtained; it can be justified by the high thermal degradability of cellulose acetate, which decomposition onset has been reported to occur at 230 °C leading to a percentage of residue around 13 % [11]. The slightly higher yields obtained for the smoked filters can be easily explained by the incomplete cracking of tars during carbonization.

Table 1 Textural properties, carbonization yields and pH_{PZC} values of the chars. Carbonization yield defined as weight in g of char per 1 g of filters, V_{total} corresponds to the nitrogen volume adsorbed at relative pressure of 0.95, $V_{meso} = V_{total} - V_{micro}$.

Chars	Yield	A_{BET} (m^2 g^{-1})	V_{total} (cm^3 g^{-1})	V_{meso} (cm^3 g^{-1})	V_{micro} (cm^3 g^{-1})	V_{ultra} (cm^3 g^{-1})	V_{super} (cm^3 g^{-1})	pH_{PZC}
Ch_UC650	11	530	0.30	0.10	0.20	0.00	0.20	8.9
Ch_UC750	12	331	0.29	0.18	0.11	0.00	0.11	8.7
Ch_UC900	13	93	0.07	0.04	0.03	0.00	0.03	8.8
Ch_SC650	16	494	0.35	0.17	0.18	0.00	0.18	9.3
Ch_SC750	17	459	0.29	0.12	0.17	0.00	0.17	9.5
Ch_SC900	17	418	0.31	0.16	0.15	0.00	0.15	9.6

Samples Ch_UC650 and Ch_SC650, chosen as representative of the chars, present similar morphology, composed by irregular and sharp-shaped particles (**Figure 1a**). Two textures are visible: smooth surfaces, predominantly on the outside of the particles, and a fibrous texture in surfaces located predominantly inside the particles. The co-existence of these textures suggests different degrees of carbonization: the outer surfaces were more efficiently carbonized, presenting a smooth texture, whereas the inner facets maintained the fibrous texture of the original filters. Elements C, O, Ti and K were detected in Ch_UC650 (**Figure 1b**). Carbon and oxygen originate from the cellulose acetate fibers, and detection of Ti is attributed to titanium dioxide added to the filters during manufacture. The trace amount of K can be explained by contamination from tobacco during the preparation of the filters since potassium is added to tobacco as potassium sorbate. The chars prepared from smoked filters present somewhat similar EDS spectra and a some other metals were detected, attributed to additives typically added to tobacco. X-ray diffraction patterns showed that the chars have an amorphous structure, with an extremely wide peak reflection between $2\Theta \approx 5°$ and 30°, and confirmed the presence of TiO_2 used in the manufacture of the filters (**Figure 1c**).

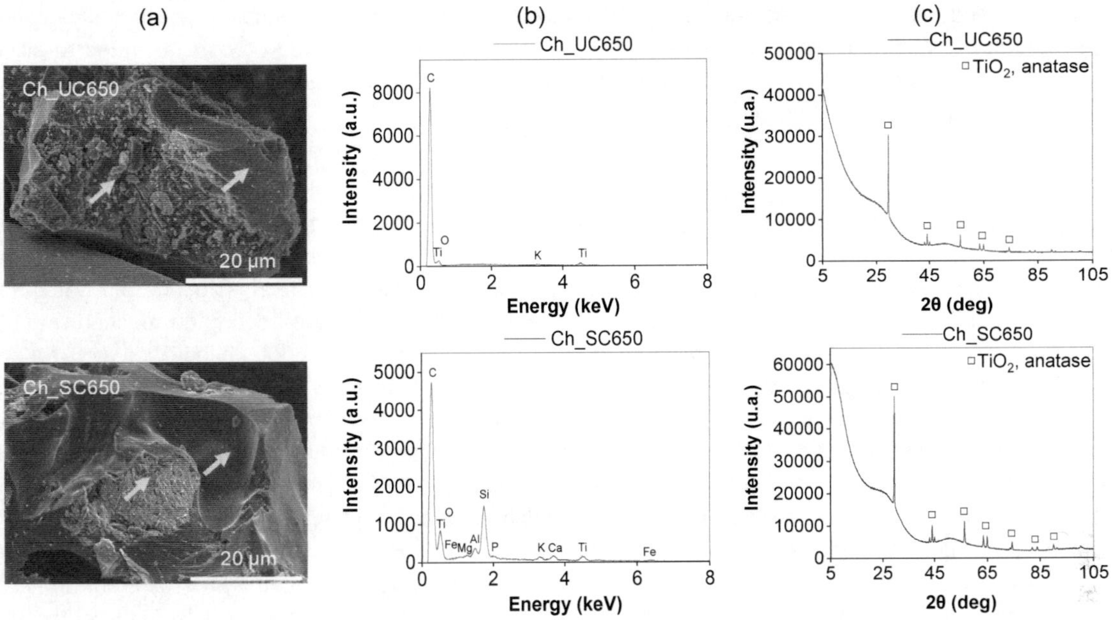

Figure 1 SEM micrographs (a), EDS spectra (b), and X-ray diffractograms (c) of Ch_UC650 and Ch_SC650

3.2. Membranes

The procedure adopted for the synthesis of Memb_SF created pores homogeneously distributed throughout the top surface of the membrane (**Figure 2**). Two types of pores are visible: large pores formed due to acetone evaporation and smaller pores created by NaCl solid (diameters between 25 and 75 µm). Membrane cross-section confirms the predominance of large evaporation pores close to the top surface of the sample. Using phosphoric acid as catalyst allowed for a controlled development of porosity, and membranes Memb_SF225p and Memb_SF250p present distinct morphological features. A more extensive carbonization occurred at higher temperature leading to larger pores at the top surface of Memb_SF250p. Thus, while Memb_SF225p contains pores diameters mostly between 4 and 6 µm, Memb_SF250p presents very wide interconnected surface pores, with diameters generally in the range from 60 to 125 µm.

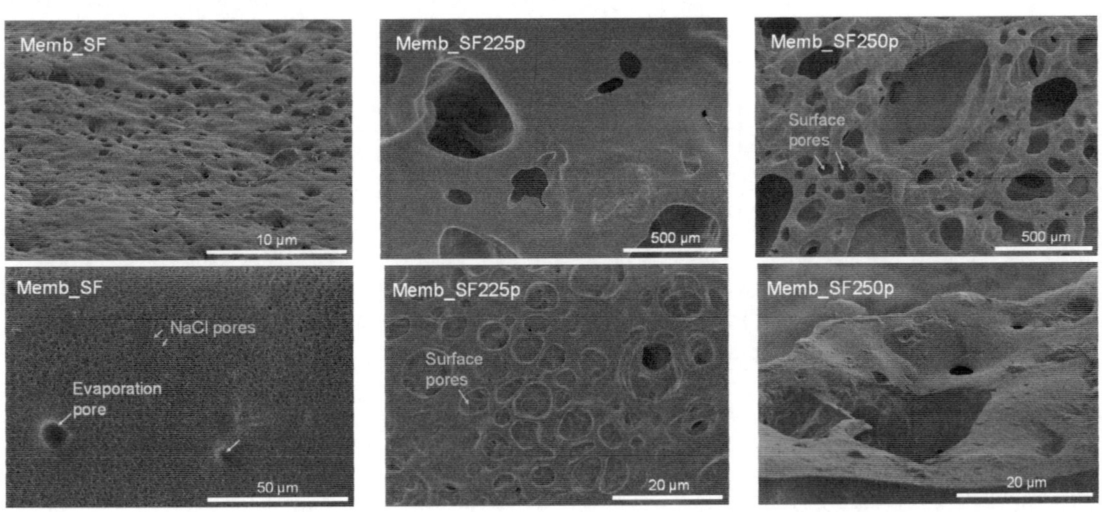

Figure 2 SEM micrographs of Memb_SF, Memb_SF225p and Memb_SF250p

The un-pyrolysed membranes presented a neutral surface chemistry (pH_{PZC} around 7), which makes sense given that the main component of the filters is cellulose acetate. Acid mediated carbonization led to acidic samples (pH_{PZC} values around 3.7), due to the introduction of acidic functionalities during carbonization of the membranes soaked in phosphoric acid.

3.3. Clofibric acid adsorption

The adsorption isotherms of the chars (**Figure 3**) have a profile characteristic of multi-layer adsorption, with more than one saturation plateau. The immersion of the chars caused somewhat similar shifts in solution pH, more pronounced at lower C_e values. The joint analysis of the isotherms, final solutions pH data, and correlation to clofibric acid speciation allowed for a better understanding of the adsorption mechanism [10]. Thus, the isotherms of the chars can be divided into four regions: (1) an initial uptake increase at C_e values around 5 mg dm^{-3}, indicative of cooperative adsorption; (2) a first saturation plateau at solution pH values above 5, relative to the exclusive adsorption of the deprotonated form of clofibric acid; (3) increase in uptake as the solution pH approaches value 5; (4) 2nd saturation plateau achieved at solution pH values below 5 (C_e values higher than 120 mg g^{-1}), when both protonated and deprotonated forms of clofibric acid are present in solution. The pH_{PZC} of the chars affected the solution pH data obtained, that is, Ch_SC650 with a pH_{PZC} of 9.3 caused slightly higher deviations in the solutions than Ch_UC650 (pH_{PZC} of 8.9). Nevertheless, these small deviations influenced the adsorption mechanism of clofibric acid, as demonstrated by the different profile of the isotherms of these materials. However, similar final q_e values were reached around 16.5 mg g^{-1} for both materials, which is in agreement with the similar V_{micro} present in the chars.

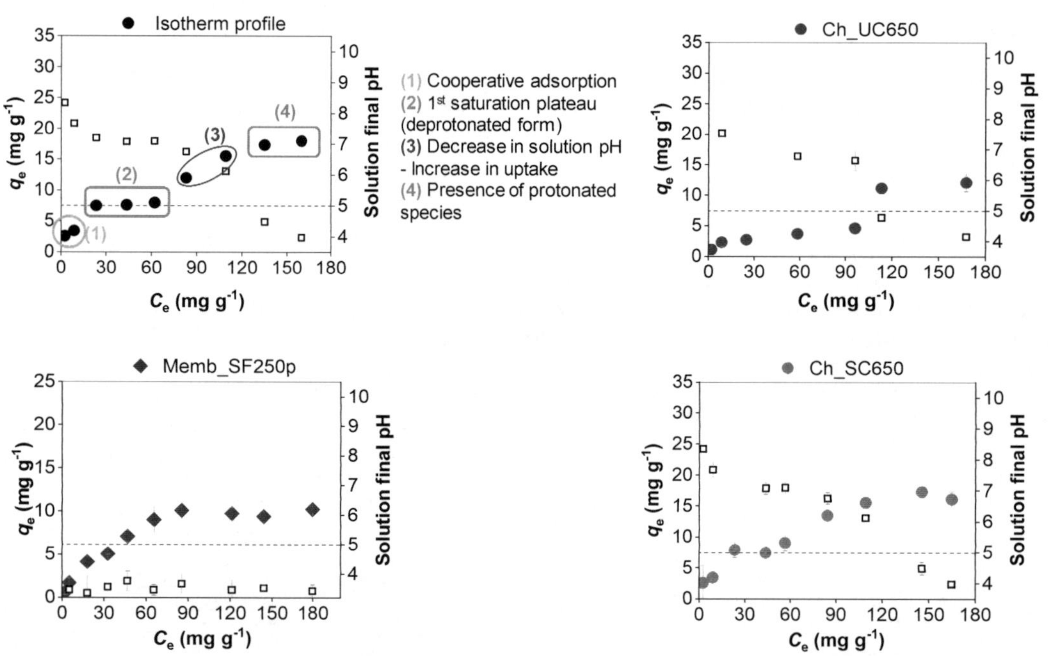

Figure 3 Equilibrium adsorption isotherms profile and data for clofibric adsorption onto the mentioned samples. Solution pH measurements included

Memb_SF250p, representative of the membranes, caused no solution pH shifts, because its pH_{PZC} is around 3.7, similar to the dissolution pH of clofibric acid (3.5). Consequently, the adsorption isotherm of this sample is characteristic of monolayer adsorption with a progressive increase in uptake, until saturation was reached at C_e values higher than 90 mg g^{-1}.

4. CONCLUSION

Carbonization of cigarette filters yielded chars with relatively high degrees of porosity. Tobacco contaminants decreased filters sensitivity to carbonization temperature, while allowing for porosity development. The chars are basic in nature and, as expected, TiO_2 was detected. Membranes were successfully synthesized and phosphoric acid mediated carbonization allowed for a controlled development of porosity and yielded acidic carbon membranes with wide porosity in the range of the micrometers. The materials immersion in water caused, in general, deviations in the solutions pH during the adsorption experiments. Increases in pH had a marked impact in the adsorption mechanism of clofibric acid and in the profile of the adsorption isotherms. Thus, a monolayer characteristic isotherm was obtained for the acidic membrane (no shifts in solution pH), and a more pronounced S-type profile was observed for the most basic char Ch_SC650. Still, the final adsorption capacities achieved appear to have been ruled mainly by the microporous volume of the samples.

ACKNOWLEDGEMENTS

This research was supported by the ERDF projects No. CZ.02.1.01/0.0/0.0/16_019/0000754 and No. CZ.02.1.01/0.0/0.0/17_048/0007323 of the Ministry of Education, Youth and Sports of the Czech Republic, and by the project No. FV20066 from Ministry of Industry and Trade of the Czech Republic. The authors acknowledge the support given by Mgr. Ivo Medřík, Dr. Claudia Aparicio, and Mgr. Lucie Hochvaldová.

REFERENCES

[1] KADIR, A.A., SARANI, N.A. Cigarette Butts Pollution and Environmental Impact - A Review. *Applied Mechanics and Materials*. 2015, vol. 773-774, pp. 1106-1110.

[2] TORKASHVAND, J., FARZADKIA, M', SOBHI, H.R., ESRAFILI, A. Littered cigarette butt as a well-known waste: A comprehensive systematic review. *Journal of Hazardous Materials*. 2020, vol. 383, pp. 1-12.

[3] UBAIDULLAH, M., AHMED, J., AHAMAD, T., SHAIKH, S.F., ALSHEHRI, S.M., AL-ENIZI, A.M. Hydrothermal synthesis of novel nickel oxide@nitrogenous mesoporous carbon nanocomposite using costless smoked cigarette filter for high performance supercapacitor. *Materials Letters*. 2020, vol. 266, pp. 1-4.

[4] LI, S.H., SHI, C.L., WANG, Y.Z., SUN, X.D., QI, D.W., WU, D., WANG, Y., ZHU, J.H. New efficient selective adsorbent of tobacco specific nitrosamines derived from discarded cigarette filters. *Microporous and Mesoporous Materials*. 2019, vol. 284, pp. 393-402.

[5] ZHANG, X., XU, J., LV, Z., WANG, Q., GE, H., WANG, X., HONG, B. Preparation and utilization of cigarette filters based activated carbon for removal CIP and SDS from aqueous solutions. *Chemical Physical Letters*. 2020, vol. 747, pp. 1-9.

[6] ISO 9277. *Determination of the specific surface area of solids by gas adsorption - BET method*. 2010.

[7] RODRIGUEZ-REINOSO, F., MARTIN-MARTINEZ, J.M. A standard adsorption isotherm for the characterization of activated carbons. *Journal of Physical Chemistry - U.S.* 1987, vol. 91, pp. 515-516.

[8] MESTRE, A.S., PINTO, M.L., PIRES, J., NOGUEIRA, J.M.F., CARVALHO, A.P. Effect of solution pH on the removal of clofibric acid by cork-based activated carbons. *Carbon*. 2010, vol. 48, pp. 972-980.

[9] LÉDÉ, J. Cellulose pyrolysis kinetics: An historical review on the existence and role of intermediate active cellulose. *Journal of Analytical and Applied Pyrolysis*. 2012, vol. 94, pp. 17-32.

[10] DE CAPRARIIS, B.D., BASSANO, C., DEIANA, P., PALMA, V., PETRULLO, A., SCARSELLA, M., DE FILIPPIS, P. Carbon dioxide reforming of tar during biomass gasification. *Chemical Engineering Transactions*. 2014, vol. 37, pp. 97-102.

[11] GAAN, S., MAUCLAIRE, L., RUPPER, P., SALIMOVA, V., TRAN, T.-T., HEUBERGER. M. Thermal degradation of cellulose acetate in presence of bis-phosphoramidates. *Journal of Analytical and Applied Pyrolysis*. 2011, vol. 90, pp. 33-41.

COLORIMETRIC HYDROGEN SENSORS

[1]Anna ZABELINA, [1,2]Elena MILIUTINA, [1,2]Olga GUSELNIKOVA, [1]Denis ZABELIN, [1]Vaclav ŠVORČÍK, [1,2]Oleksiy LYUTAKOV

[1]VŠCHT - University of Chemistry and Technology, Prague, Czech Republic, EU, lyutakoo@vscht.cz

[2]Tomsk Polytechnic University, Research School of Chemistry and Applied Biomedical Sciences, Tomsk, Russian Federation

https://doi.org/10.37904/nanocon.2020.3708

Abstract

The area of "green" energy carriers utilization is rapidly developing in the world today. Renewable hydrogen has promising potential as an ecologically safe energy carrier. However, production, storage, transportation and utilization of hydrogen possess certain risks due to the high likelihood of ignition. In this paper, we have demonstrated the design and realization of the colorimetric hydrogen sensor in different liquids. A proposed colorimetric sensor is based on corel-shell Au@Pd nanoparticles, additionally grafted by metal-organic framework IRMOF-20 layer, responsible for hydrogen entrapping. The combination of localized surface plasmon, high affinity of the palladium surface in hydrogen sorption and selectivity of IRMOF-20 towards this gas leads to apparent color change of nanoparticles suspension in hydrogen presence. The proposed approach is favored by high sensitivity, ease of use, low detection limit, and fast response time.

Keywords: Colorimetric hydrogen sensor, hydrogen detection, IRMOF-20, core-shell nanoparticles, gold-palladium nanoparticles, surface plasmon resonance

INTRODUCTION

Under the terms of the Paris Agreement, sustainable energy technological development is an important part of the fight against climate change. After this decision was taken, the demand for "green" energy sources continues to grow [1]. In this regard, renewable hydrogen has promising potential as a green energy carrier [2]. However, the production, storage and utilization of hydrogen is associated with certain risks due to the increased likelihood of inflammation [3-7].

Colorimetric gas sensors may be the best solution to the problems associated with determining the presence of hydrogen in air. In particular, colorimetric sensors based on the principle of localized surface plasmon resonances of silver or gold nanoparticles have a particularly high potential. These sensors change colour in the presence of targeted compounds under room conditions, which is useful in everyday life. Colorimetric sensors can also be made compact and without the presence of electronic components [8,9].

Metal-organic frameworks (MOFs) can improve sensor selectivity and sensitivity through the introduction of additional functionality and surface specificity. MOF is a well-known class of porous materials, the main purpose of which is the capture of gas molecules, including hydrogen molecules (IRMOF-20) [10-19].

1. EXPERIMENTAL

1.1. Materials

Deionized water (EMD MILLIPORE), thieno[3,2-b]thiophene-2,5-dicarboxylic acid (≥99.0%), zinc nitrate (99.999%), dimethylformamide (≥99%), N,N-Diethylformamide (≥99%), acetonitrile (HPLC Plus, ≥99.9%). %), methanol (analytical standard), dimethyl sulfoxide (≥99%), chloroform (analytical standard) dichloromethane (99.8%), hydrochloric acid, trisodium citrate, gold(III) chloride solution, palladium(II) chloride were ordered from Sigma-Aldrich and used without additional purification. 4-carboxybenzenediazonium tosylate (ADT-COOH) was prepared according to [20]. Preparation of IRMOF-20-modified surface was carried out according to previous work [21].

1.2. Sample preparation

Gold nanoparticles were prepared by the Turkevich method [22]. A seed-mediated growth method was used to prepare bimetallic Au@Pd nanoparticles with an Au core and a Pd shell structure [23]. Au@Pd particles were spontaneously modified by diazonium salt by dipping for 2 hours in a freshly prepared aqueous solution of ADT-COOH (concentration 1 mM). After the modification, the nanoparticles were centrifugated and washed by water and methanol.

Later, the modified Au@Pd were immersed for some time in the mother liquid IRMOF-20. To clean the pores of IRMOF-20 from the solvent in which the MOF was prepared, nanoparticles with a layer of a metal-organic framework were immersed in dichloromethane for several days. **Figure 1** schematically shows the preparation route of Au@Pd with IRMOF-20 layer.

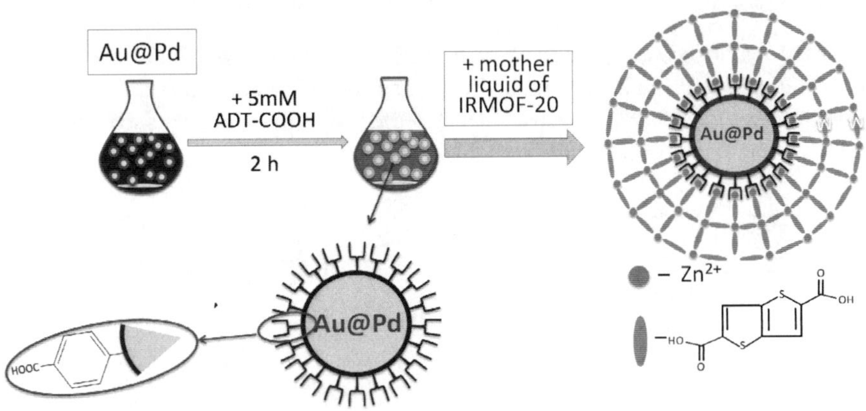

Figure 1 Schematic representation of Au@Pd grafting by -COOH and IRMOF-20

The prepared Au@Pd were dispersed in various solvents of methanol, DMSO, DMF, CH_2Cl_2, H_2O. The hydrogen or carbon dioxide were flown through these solutions for 20 minutes.

1.3. Measurement Techniques

Raman spectra were measured using a ProRaman-L (laser power 30 mW) spectrometer with an excitation wavelength of 785 nm. Ultraviolet-visible spectroscopy (UV-Vis) spectra were measured using Spectrometer Lambda 25 (Perkin-Elmer) in 300-1100 nm wavelength range.

2. RESULTS AND DISCUSSION

Grafting of nanoparticles surface by -COOH and subsequent IRMOF-20 formation were examined using UV-Vis (**Figure 2A**) and SERS (**Figure 2B**) measurements. UV-Vis spectra (**Figure 2A**) indicate the presence of absorbance band near 520 nm. After the -COOH immobilization the band is shifted towards to UV region. Further shifts occur after the formation of IRMOF layer towards to NIR region. As it is evident from the SERS results (**Figure 2B**), after the grafting procedure, the Raman bands, typical for ADT-COOH and IRMOF-20, become apparent. The obtained results confirm grafting during the both stages of surface modification.

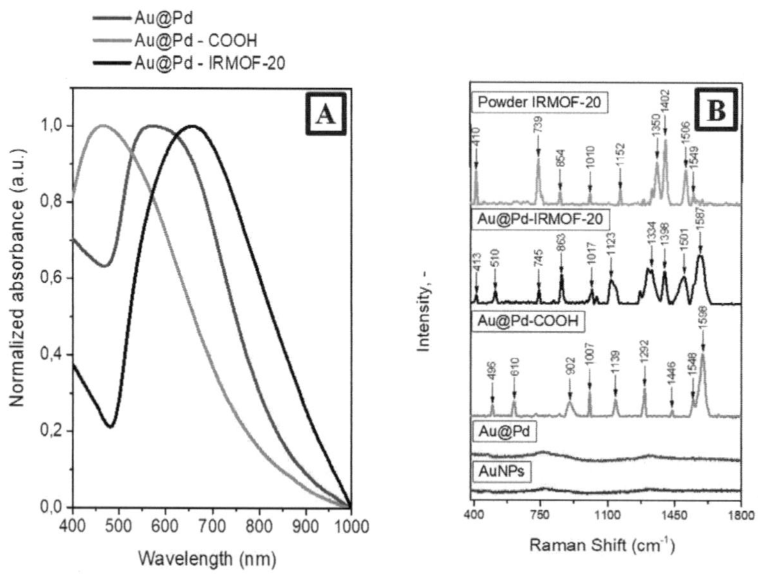

The characteristic peaks of Raman spectroscopy (cm^{-1})	
Au@Pd-COOH	
Pd-C	496
Ar ring mode	902, 1007, 1139
C=O stretch	610
O-H in-plane bending	1292, 1446
Ar ring mode and C=O stretch	1548, 1598
Powder IRMOF-20	
Thio Ring def vib	410
CO def vib	739
C-H def vib	854, 1010
C-O stretch	1152, 1506
C=C in-plane vib, O-H def	1350
O-H def and C-O stretch, C=C in-plane vib	1402
C=O stretch	1549
Au@Pd-IRMOF-20	
Thio Ring def vib	413, 510
CO def vib	745
out-of-plane C-H def vib	863
C-H def vib	1017
C-O stretch	1123
C=C in-plane vib, O-H def vib	1334
O-H def vib, C-O stretch, C=C in-plane vib	1398
C=C in-plane vib	1501
C=O stretch	1587

Figure 2 (A) The UV-Vis absorption spectra of: core-shell Au@Pd nanoparticles, Au@Pd grafted by ADT-COOH, and Au@Pd decorated with IRMOF20 film, (B) Raman spectra of pristine gold nanoparticles Au@Pd grafted by ADT-COOH, and Au@Pd decorated with IRMOF20 film (right part shows the Raman peak affiliation)

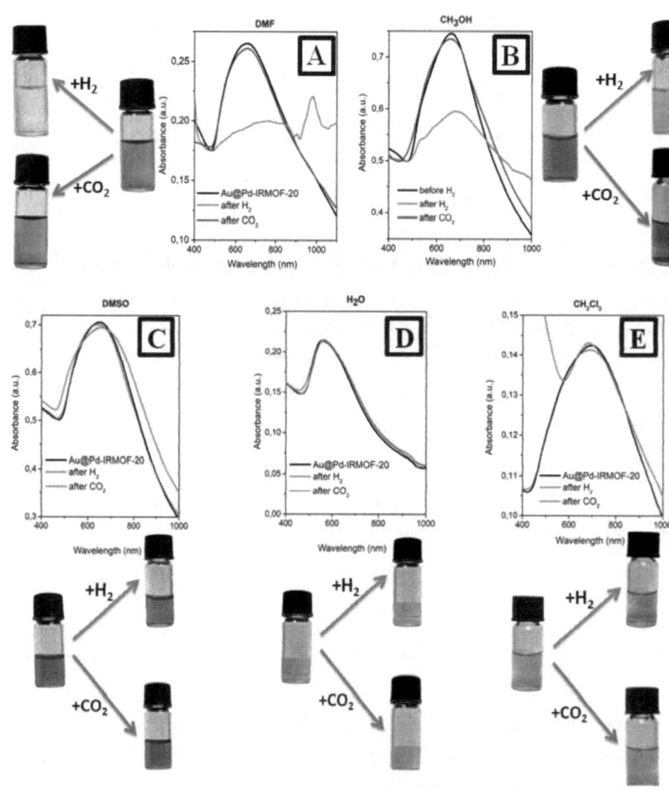

Figure 3 UV-Vis spectra and photos of Au@Pd nanoparticles in different solvents before and after blowing hydrogen and carbon dioxide through: (A) - DMF, (B) - CH3OH, (C) - DMSO, (D) - H2O, (E) - CH2Cl2

The changes of the IRMOF-20 optical properties due to hydrogen and carbon dioxide entrapping were investigated by UV-Vis absorbance spectra. **Figure 3** shows that when carbon dioxide was blown through nanoparticles suspension there were no visible changes in its colour and no displacement of the plasmon absorption peak. However, when hydrogen was bubbled through suspension of nanoparticles in DMF and methanol. The colours were changed. This change was detectable by eyes: In particular, the **Figure 3A** shows the nanoparticles suspension in DMF and colour changing from gray to transparent. In turn, in methanol suspension the hydrogen presence induces the colour shift from blue to transparent.

CONCLUSION

In this article, we propose a new method for preparation of colorimetric sensors based on bimetallic Au@Pd core-shell nanoparticles with an additional layer of organometallic frameworks for fast and selective detection of hydrogen in organic and inorganic solvents (DMF, CH_3OH, DMSO, CH_2Cl_2, and water).

The formation of an IRMOF-20 layer on Au@Pd nanoparticles provides possibility of efficient hydrogen detection, through monitoring of the shift of plasmon resonance wavelength position, and, consequently, changes of the suspension colour. The unique properties of IRMOF-20 ensure the sensitivity and selectivity of the developed sensor to hydrogen even in the presence of other gases.

ACKNOWLEDGEMENTS

This work was supported by under the project Internal Grant Agency UCT №126 88 2008 and the project Russian Science Foundation (RSF-19-73-00238).

REFERENCES

[1] HOSTETTLER, S., GADGIL, A., HAZBOUN, E. *Sustainable access to energy in the global south.* Switzerland: Springer, 2015.

[2] GUSELNIKOVA, O., TRELIN, A., MILIUTINA, E., ELASHNIKOV, R., SAJDL, P., POSTNIKOV, P. S., LYUTAKOV, O. Plasmon-induced water splitting-through flexible hybrid 2D architecture up to hydrogen from seawater under NIR light. *ACS Applied Materials & Interfaces.* 2020, vol. 12, no. 25, pp. 28110-28119

[3] GARCIA, D.A. Analysis of non-economic barriers for the deployment of hydrogen technologies and infrastructures in European countries. *International journal of hydrogen energy.* 2017, vol. 42. No.10, pp.6435-6447.

[4] BARBIR, F. PEM electrolysis for production of hydrogen from renewable energy sources. *Solar energy.* 2005, vol. 78, no. 5, pp.661-669.

[5] ABDEL-AAL, H.K., ZOHDY, K.M., KAREEM, M.A. Hydrogen production using sea water electrolysis. *The Open Fuel Cells Journal.* 2010, vol. 3, no.1.

[6] MORADI, R. AND GROTH, K.M. Hydrogen storage and delivery: Review of the state of the art technologies and risk and reliability analysis. *International Journal of Hydrogen Energy.* 2019. Vol. 44, no. 23, pp.12254-12269.

[7] ELASHNIKOV, R., ZAHORJANOVA, K., MILIUTINA, E., KOLSKA, Z., CIESLAR, M., SVORCIK, V., LYUTAKOV, O. Proton exchange membrane with plasmon-active surface for enhancement of fuel cell effectivity. *Nanoscale.* 2020, vol. 12, pp. 12068-12075.

[8] RIVERO, P.J., IBAÑEZ, E., GOICOECHEA, J., URRUTIA, A., MATIAS, I.R., ARREGUI, F.J. A self-referenced optical colorimetric sensor based on silver and gold nanoparticles for quantitative determination of hydrogen peroxide. *Sensors and Actuators B: Chemical.* 2017, vol. 251, pp. 624-631.

[9] CHAUHAN, P.S. AND BHATTACHARYA, S. Hydrogen gas sensing methods, materials, and approach to achieve parts per billion level detection: A review. *International Journal of Hydrogen Energy.* 2019, vol. 44, no.47, pp. 26076-26099.

[10] MILIUTINA, E., GUSELNIKOVA, O., CHUFISTOVA, S., KOLSKA, Z., ELASHNIKOV, R., BURTSEV, V., LYUTAKOV, O. Fast and All-Optical Hydrogen Sensor Based on Gold-Coated Optical Fiber Functionalized with Metal-Organic Framework Layer. *ACS sensors/.* 2019, vol. 4, no.12, pp. 3133-3140.

[11] COLLINS, D.J. and ZHOU, H.C. Hydrogen storage in metal-organic frameworks. *Journal of materials chemistry*. 2007, vol. 17, no. 30, pp.3154-3160.

[12] WONG-FOY, A.G., MATZGER, A.J. AND YAGHI, O.M. Exceptional H2 saturation uptake in microporous metal–organic frameworks. *Journal of the American Chemical Society*. 2006, vol. 128, no. 11, pp.3494-3495.

[13] FISCHER, M., HOFFMANN, F., FRÖBA, M. Molecular simulation of hydrogen adsorption in metal-organic frameworks. *Colloids and Surfaces A: Physicochemical and Engineering Aspects*. 2010, vol. 357, no. 1-3, pp.35-42.

[14] BECKNER, M. and DAILLY, A. Adsorption enthalpy calculations of hydrogen adsorption at ambient temperature and pressures exceeding 300 bar. *American Journal of Analytical Chemistry*. 2013, Vol. 4, no. 10C, pp.8-16.

[15] LIN, X., JIA, J., HUBBERSTEY, P., SCHRÖDER, M., CHAMPNESS, N.R. Hydrogen storage in metal-organic frameworks. *CrystEngComm*. 2007, vol. 9, no. 6, pp.438-448.

[16] TURNER, M.J., MCKINNON, J.J., JAYATILAKA, D., SPACKMAN, M.A. Visualisation and characterisation of voids in crystalline materials. *CrystEngComm*. 2011, vol. 13, no. 6, pp.1804-1813.

[17] ZHAO, D., YUAN, D., ZHOU, H.C. The current status of hydrogen storage in metal-organic frameworks. *Energy & Environmental Science*. 2008, vol. 1, no. 2, pp.222-235.

[18] BAE, Y.S. AND SNURR, R.Q. Molecular simulations of very high pressure hydrogen storage using metal-organic frameworks. *Microporous and mesoporous materials*. 2010, vol. 135, no. 1-3, pp.178-186.

[19] RAZAVI, S.A.A., MASOOMI, M.Y., MORSALI, A. Stimuli-Responsive Metal-Organic Framework (MOF) with Chemo-Switchable Properties for Colorimetric Detection of CHCl3. *Chemistry-A European Journal*. 2017, vol. 23, no. 51, pp.12559-12564.

[20] FILIMONOV, V.D., TRUSOVA, M., POSTNIKOV, P., KRASNOKUTSKAYA, E.A., LEE, Y.M., HWANG, H.Y., KIM, H. AND CHI, K.W. Unusually stable, versatile, and pure arenediazonium tosylates: their preparation, structures, and synthetic applicability. *Organic letters*. 2008, vol. 10, no. 18, pp.3961-3964.

[21] ROWSELL, J.L., YAGHI, O.M. Effects of functionalization, catenation, and variation of the metal oxide and organic linking units on the low-pressure hydrogen adsorption properties of metal– organic frameworks. *Journal of the American Chemical Society*. 2006, vol. 128, no. 4, pp.1304-1315.

[22] KIMLING, J., MAIER, M., OKENVE, B., KOTAIDIS, V., BALLOT, H. AND PLECH, A. Turkevich method for gold nanoparticle synthesis revisited. *The Journal of Physical Chemistry B*. 2006, vol. 110, no. 32, pp.15700-15707.

[23] ZHENG, Z., XU, H., XU, Z., GE, J. A Monodispersed Spherical Zr-Based Metal-Organic Framework Catalyst, Pt/Au@ Pd@ UIO-66, Comprising an Au@ Pd Core-Shell Encapsulated in a UIO-66 Center and Its Highly Selective CO2 Hydrogenation to Produce CO. *Small*. 2018, vol. 14, no. 5, p.1702812.

LARGE AREA CLEANING AND ACTIVATION OF FLEXIBLE ULTRA-THIN GLASS BY NON-THERMAL ATMOSPHERIC-PRESSURE PLASMA

[1]Slavomír SIHELNÍK, [1]Richard KRUMPOLEC, [1]Monika STUPAVSKÁ, [1]Jianyu FENG, [1]Eva KOSOVÁ, [1]Jakub KELAR, [1,2]Miroslav ZEMÁNEK, [1,2]Dušan KOVÁČIK, [1]Mirko ČERNÁK

[1]Masaryk University, Faculty of Science, CEPLANT, Department of Physical Electronics, Brno, Czech Republic, EU, sihelnik@mail.muni.cz

[2]ROPLASS s. r. o., Kamenice, Brno, Czech Republic, EU

https://doi.org/10.37904/nanocon.2020.3717

Abstract

Flexible ultra-thin glass is used as a substrate or packaging material in microelectronics engineering, where the level of cleanliness determines the quality of the final product. Surface properties of glass are governed by a surface nano-layer. Besides cleaning from coarse impurities, the demand is also for nano-decontamination, where standard cleaning proves insufficient. In microelectronics and printed flexible electronics, the bonding of thin structures deposited using printed conductive inks on glass substrates is of essential importance. The non-thermal, atmospheric-pressure plasma generated by diffuse coplanar surface barrier discharge (DCSBD) was studied as an effective pre-treatment method for cleaning and activation of glass surfaces, implementable into large-scale in-line manufacturing. Two industrial adaptations of DCSBD system were applied on two types of ultra-thin flexible glass to compare the effects of plasma treatment of glass in both relaxed, and bent state. DCSBD "Air-pillow" with a planar discharge unit is designed for contactless treatment of smooth flat large-area surfaces. A roll reactor with a concavely curved DCSBD unit is intended to exemplify its integration into roll-to-roll manufacturing. The effect of plasma treatment and its stability was analyzed with water contact angle measurement and X-ray photoelectron spectroscopy. Significant wettability improvement was achieved with both applied DCSBD geometries, with better effect uniformity and durability after using the DCSBD in the planar configuration.

Keywords: Atmospheric plasma treatment, ultra-thin flexible glass, wetting, large-area, roll-to-roll

1. INTRODUCTION

Naturally, the surface of glass is covered by a water nano-layer adsorbed from air humidity. This layer contains organic contaminants that hinder the quality of various deposition methods. Atmospheric pressure plasma pre-treatment of glass prior to thin film deposition is studied as a unique cleaning and activation technique, which is an environmentally friendly dry alternative to the commonly used wet chemical pre-treatment [1]. Diffuse coplanar surface barrier discharge (DCSBD) operating in ambient air is a plasma source with application potential for surface treatment of various materials. An important advantage of the DCSBD is its high power density of plasma, which ensures fast, effective, and uniformly distributed activation of working gas. This predisposes the DCSBD for involvement in large-area in-line processing [2]. Development of a curved DCSBD geometry improved its applicability on flexible materials and extended its potential as an addition to roll-to-roll systems. Flexible ultra-thin glass is a future material introducing the advantageous properties of glass into the process of miniaturisation. It has found various forward-looking applications in manufacturing of printed flexible electronics like sensors, displays or photovoltaics [3]. In microelectronics and printed flexible electronics, the bonding of thin structures deposited using printed conductive inks on glass substrates is extremely important, and it can be improved by cleaning and chemical activation of the glass surface before deposition. Plasma exposure of glass surface could induce rearrangement of its chemical composition, which could increase its surface free energy and subsequently improve wetting for a limited time [4].

2. EXPERIMENT

A part of experiments to compare the contactless and contact leading of plasma source was also realized on common float glass. Soda-lime glass (SLG) samples with a thickness of 2.1 and 2.8 mm and a size of 20 × 80 mm were manufactured in Polartherm-Flachglas GmbH. Ultra-thin flexible glass (UFG) AF32 and D263T with a thickness of 0.03 and 0.3 mm and a size of 101.6 × 101.6 mm were purchased from Schott AG. Tin is not involved in UFG processing, hence experiments on SLG were also carried out on the air side, which was blown over to eliminate the presence of dust. Atmospheric pressure plasma was generated in air with various DCSBD devices provided by ROPLASS, s. r. o. Sinusoidal high voltage ~10 kV is supplied to comb electrodes embedded in Al2O3 ceramic for actuation of microdischarges that create a 0.3 mm thin plasma layer [2]. Variations of the used DCSBD implementations and their parameters are summarized in **Table 1**. Experiments on standard DCSBD are being realized with samples placed in holders that are guided in contact with the ceramic. DCSBD "Air-pillow" was designed for treatment of flat smooth large-area surfaces applying pneumatic levitation to perform contactless guidance [5]. "Roll" DCSBD reactor works with a concavely curved discharge unit and is intended for treatment of flexible materials that can be bent to the radius of 15 cm of the reactor roll [6]. Tin side detection based on UV light excitation was performed with Commercial Tin Side Detector TS1320 by CRL. The static WCA was measured with See System by Advex Instruments, s. r. o., applying 1 µl drops of DI water. The XPS analysis was realized with ESCALAB 250 Xi analytic platform by Thermo Fisher Scientific, using Al Kα source and Rowland circle monochromator. Spectra calibration, processing and fitting routines were accomplished in Avantage software.

Table 1 Setup of applied devices using DCSBD for atmospheric pressure plasma treatment

Description	Geometry	Dimensions (mm)	Frequency (kHz)	Power (W)	Power density (W/cm^3)
Standard DCSBD	planar	80 x 195	15	400	85.5
DCSBD "Air-pillow"	planar	80 x 80	15	160	83.3
DCSBD "Air-pillow"	planar	80 x 195	15	400	85.5
DCSBD "Air-pillow"	planar	80 x 195	30	600	128.2
"Roll" DCSBD	curved	80 x 195	15	400	85.5

3. RESULTS AND DISCUSSION

Preliminary experiments were aimed at the demonstration of the importance of precise leading of DCSBD unit over the treated surface for achieving large-scale aerial uniformity of the desired effect. The comparative ageing study of contact and contactless treatment was carried out on float SLG samples, due to the fact that the fragile UFG is not suitable for contact leading. **Figure 1** shows the results of WCA measured after plasma exposures with a duration of 1, 3, 5, 7 and 10 s in the chosen sequence during a week.

The reference WCA value (26 ± 1)° was measured on the air side of previously uncleaned samples with visible pollution from dust, grease and cutting oil. In both cases, significant wettability improvement of SLG surface was achieved even after the shortest applied exposure time 1 s; however, the lowest WCA drop was reached after the longest exposure with 10 s duration. In general, immediately after treatment, the values obtained in the experiments with DCSBD "Air-pillow" follow a tendency to decline about 3° lower than the values from the samples modified with standard DCSBD. Furthermore, the lowest WCA of (8.0 ± 0.6)° achieved with standard DCSBD 10 s treatment was a higher value than the highest WCA of (6.4 ± 0.3)° reached with DCSBD "Air-pillow" 1 s treatment. The smallest WCA value shown in the present ageing study on SLG is (4.4 ± 0.9)°, reported after DCSBD "Air-pillow" 10 s treatment. The higher uncertainty of such a low value of WCA is due to the limits of the measuring method.

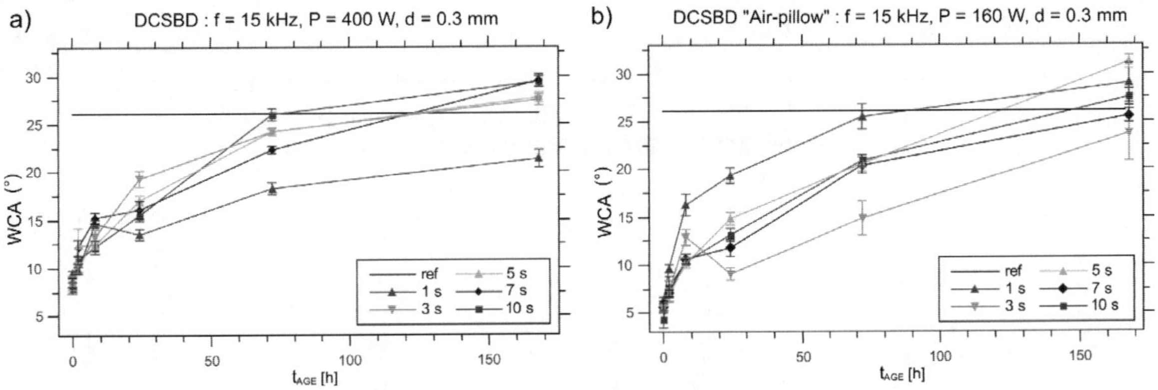

Figure 1 The ageing study of WCA on SLG treated with a) standard DCSBD and b) DCSBD "Air-pillow"

Ageing study of WCA demonstrated a gradually recovering tendency, which resulted in quite similar values for each DCSBD device for longer treatment times 5, 7 and 10 s. WCAs recovered completely to the level of reference value on most of the samples treated with standard DCSBD after 3 days of storage and with DCSBD "Air-pillow" after 7 days. The recovery was more pronounced on the first day of storage when for 5 s treatment with DCSBD "Air-pillow", the WCA has grown only to (10.2 ± 0.6)° during the first 8 hours. Demonstrable stability of hydrophilic effect with a duration of one work shift could be advantageous from the industrial point of view. The measured values and ageing trend are in a quite good accordance with the study on SLG of Homola et al. [7]; however, the results presented here vary in uncertainties that are significantly lower, particularly with the use of longer exposure times 5, 7 and 10 s. Besides better stability, DCSBD "Air-pillow" plasma treatment also showed better reproducibility, which is evident from the similarity of WCAs after longer exposures. Non-uniformity and non-reproducibility of treatment effects could be caused by insufficient removal of organic contamination with very short exposure time to DCSBD plasma [5]. Another possible source of uncertainty is unprecise guidance of treated surface, where 0.3 mm is the advisable distance of the surface from the ceramic of discharge system that is commonly used for DCSBD [2] in order to fully benefit from the diffuse component of its plasma generated in air at atmospheric pressure.

In order to reveal the fundamentals of wetting improvement and its ageing behaviour, the XPS analysis was accomplished on SLG samples that were exposed 1 and 3 s to DCSBD plasma generated on a standard device. The survey spectra registered the presence of oxygen, carbon and silicon (O1s, C1s and Si2p) in an analyzable depth profile (~3 nm), their atomic concentrations are presented in correlation with the results of high-resolution spectra and WCA measurement in **Figure 2**. Atomic concentrations of O, C and Si recorded on a previously uncleaned untreated sample were 40, 39 and 16 %, respectively. Oxygen is present in bulk material which is mostly formed of silicon dioxide. Naturally, it is also included in the water film and organic contaminants originating from air humidity. Another possible source of oxygen on the plasma-treated SLG surface is chemically active functional groups incorporated into it. Applied plasma treatments induced a growth of oxygen concentration that was more significant for longer exposure time 3 s when it increased by 16 %. Ageing of 24 hours resulted in a slight decrease in oxygen content which was simultaneously followed by a more pronounced weakening of hydrophilic effect. The presence of carbon is related to the organic contamination of the surface and also to the occurrence of carbonyl and carboxyl functional groups. After the applied plasma treatments, carbon content markedly decreased, while a more significant relative decline of 27 % was achieved by longer plasma exposure time 3 s. After 24 hours of storage, carbon concentration had a tendency to grow again, which was more pronounced for the treatment of 3 s. Silicon concentration represents the bulk material, and its change is related to the thickness of the nano-layer covering the SLG. In comparison with changes of concentrations of O and C, the concentration of Si increased only slightly, when the change of 4 % was reported for longer plasma exposure time 3 s. This fact supports the expectation that both mechanisms on nano-scale are involved: cleaning effect by removal of pollution and activation by incorporation of oxygen-based groups.

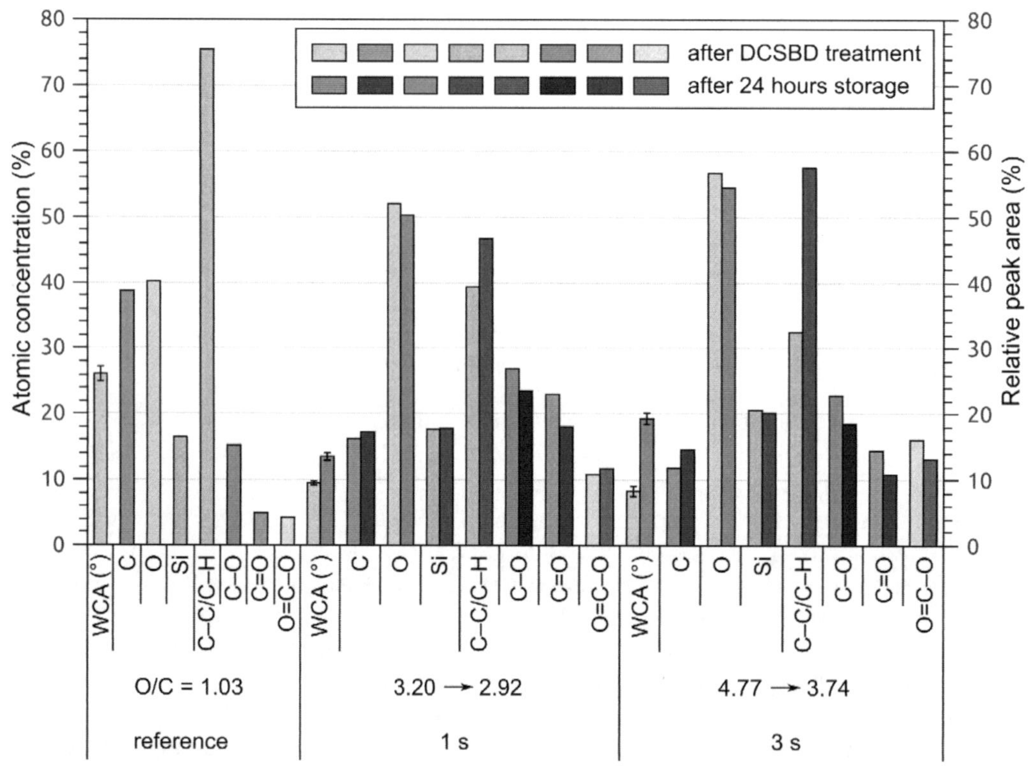

Figure 2 XPS analysis of elemental composition and carbon bonds partition compared with WCA reduction on SLG treated with standard DCSBD

High-resolution spectra aimed to differentiate between the processes during the rearrangement of surface nano-layer. The previously dominating relative peak area of C—C and C—H bonds, representing adsorbents of air contamination, was strongly reduced from 75 % to 39 % by 1 s, and to 32 % by 3 s plasma treatment. Breaking of C—C and C—H bonds is related to an oxidation process resulting in the bonding of highly reactive oxygen to the surface, which was confirmed by a significant increase of relative peak areas of C—O, C=O and O—C=O bonds. The latter is a definite indicator of the formation of carboxyl functional groups that are involved in the corresponding hydrophilic improvement. The highest shown increase of the presence of bonds C-O to 26.9 % and C=O to 23 % was detected 1 s after DCSBD plasma treatment. After 3 s exposure, the relative peak area of C=O was 14 %, while O=C-O, increased to 16.1 %. The essence of this phenomenon consists in a growing quantity of active oxygen, which is generated during plasma interaction proportionally with time. After 24 hours of storage on ambient air, the concentration of C—C and C—H bonds increased markedly to 47 % for 1 s and to 57 % for 3 s treated sample. The noticed reoccurrence of C—C and C—H bonds is related to recovering of the activated surface with air-pollutants attracted to it, with a rate that is proportional to its oxidation. Adsorption of air humidity during storage is coincident with the decrease of relative peak areas of oxygen-containing bonds and hindering of wettability. Ageing of 24 hours after 1 s treatment induced a slight growth of relative peak area of O—C=O bonds, which is in contrast to the more pronounced drop recorded on the samples treated for 3 s. This sign of more evident dissolving of —COOH groups together with significant growth of C—C and C—H bonds supports the interpretation that the impact of adsorbed air humidity is more pronounced on the sample with a highly oxidized surface. This phenomenon limits the applicability of plasma treatment, and as its prolonging does not provide any additional wettability improvement or better stability of the chemical composition of the SLG surface, it is advisable to use the optimal, efficient exposure time. Oxygen and carbon rearrangement induced by cleaning and chemical activation is expressed in O/C ratio that was 1.03 on an untreated sample. Maximum rise of O/C to 4.77 was reached with exposure of 3 s, while DCSBD plasma treatment of 1 s duration showed O/C increase to 3.20. Change of O/C ratio after 24 hours storage was more significant for longer treatment when it dropped more than 3 times compared to 1 s exposure. O, C and Si proportional distribution reported in the study of Homola et al. realized with DCSBD on SLG previously pre-cleaned with 2-propanol showed generally higher values of resulting O/C ratios: initial 3.34 increased to 4.23, and 15 immediately after 1, and 3 s exposure, respectively [7]. The distinction between pre-cleaning methods and proportions of carbon content supports the explanation of its origin in the organic contaminants present on the surface before plasma treatment.

Finally, the optimal DCSBD treatment time 5 s has been estimated for use in experiments on UFG. Results of WCA measurement on two types of flexible glass with two various geometries of DCSBD devices implementing contactless guidance are shown in **Figure 3**. Other investigated parameters having an influence on efficiency, uniformity and stability of surface modification were DCSBD input power and thickness of flexible glass, which were 400 and 600 W and 30 and 300 microns, respectively. Due to various reference WCA values on different types of flexible glass, also a relative graph of WCA reduction is included.

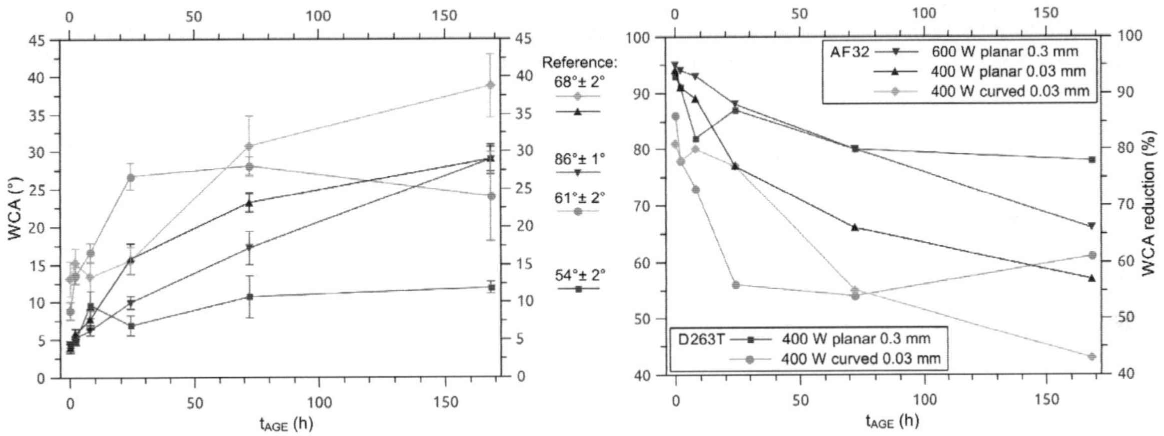

Figure 3 The ageing study of WCA of ultra-thin flexible glass treated 5 s with DCSBD "Air-pillow" and "roll"

The most satisfying WCA values from the view of efficiency and stability were reached with the use of DCSBD "Air-pillow", when resulting angles immediately after treatment were (3.9 ± 0.6)° and (4.0 ± 0.5)° on AF32 thick 30 µm and D263T thick 300 µm. Applying higher input power of discharge (600 W) resulted in WCA of (4.4 ± 0.4)°, which is a value with better accuracy compared to 400 W. Lower uncertainty caused by the increase of power supplied for generation of DCSBD plasma is related to multiplication of its microdischarges, which results in more uniform treatment. Values of WCA measured on 30 µm thick flexible glass treated on "roll" DCSBD were (8.9 ± 1.2)° on AF32 and (13 ± 2)° on D263T, which are doubled and tripled compared to the measured values and uncertainties on the samples treated with DCSBD "Air-pillow". The flexibility of the ultra-thin glass allows for its bending towards the ceramic of DCSBD unit caused by attraction due to electrostatic charge coupled on the glass surface. This might be the cause of weaker uniformity of effect after DCSBD plasma treatment. Another factor affecting the uniformity of the effect is the need for a precise position of the treated surface in the active plasma volume, which is only 0.3 mm thin in the case of DCSBD. Contactless leading implemented in DCSBD "Air-pillow" was more suitable for treatment of samples in the form of wafers from the view of precision, which was also proven by the shown results. Ageing trends shown in the preliminary study on SLG were also confirmed on flexible glass. An additional investigation of increased input power demonstrated lower stability in the observed time range. A satisfying outcome in comparison to the ageing study on SLG is the fact that the measured WCAs did not recover to the level of reference value in the observed time range, neither to 60 % of this value.

4. CONCLUSION

Plasma treatments of soda-lime glass and ultra-thin flexible glass with DCSBD plasma showed fast significant hydrophilic improvement following two mechanisms: cleaning from air-pollutants and simultaneous chemical activation by oxygen-based functional groups. Contactless guidance of planar DCSBD proved more beneficial in order to ensure the best efficiency, stability and uniformity of the treatment. The most significant WCA reduction with DCSBD "Air-pillow" on UFG reached 95 % of the initial value. Nevertheless, the development in handling and packaging of UFG is aiming for an improvement of alignment important for roll-to-roll processing, which should ensure much better precision than in the presented experiments performed on wafer-like samples. Applying curved DCSBD unit in a roll-to-roll system on UFG in the form of a band in a roll could potentially prevent conveying errors and thus improve the achieved effect, supposing the results could be analogous to the present results of the experiments with planar DCSBD.

ACKNOWLEDGEMENTS

This research has been supported by the projects CZ.01.1.02/0.0/0.0/16_053/0007132 funded by the European Regional Development Fund and by the German BMWi under grant No. ZF4028609AG6 and project FV40114 funded by the Ministry of Industry and Trade.

REFERENCES

[1] LISCO, F., SHAW, A., WRIGHT, A., IZA, F., WALLS, J.M. Atmospheric-pressure plasma surface activation for solution processed photovoltaic devices. *Solar Energy*. 2017, vol. 146, pp. 287-297.

[2] ČERNÁK, M., ČERNÁKOVÁ, Ľ., HUDEC, I., KOVÁČIK, D., ZAHORANOVÁ, A. Diffuse coplanar surface barrier discharge and its applications for in-line processing of low-added-value materials. *EPJ Applied Physics*. 2009, vol. 47, no. 2, pp. 22806 (6).

[3] CASTRO-HERMOSA, S., LUCARELLI, G., TOP, M., FAHLAND, M., FAHLTEICH, J., BROWN, T.M. Perovskite Photovoltaics on Roll-To-Roll Coated Ultra-thin Glass as Flexible High-Efficiency Indoor Power Generators. *Cell Reports Physical Science*. 2020, vol. 1, no. 5, pp. 100045 (17).

[4] YAMAMOTO, T., OKUBO, M., IMAI, N., MORI, Y. Improvement on hydrophilic and hydrophobic properties of glass surface treated by nonthermal plasma induced by silent corona discharge. *Plasma Chemistry and Plasma Processing*. 2004, vol. 24, no. 1, pp. 1-12.

[5] SIHELNÍK, S., KELAR, J., ZEMÁNEK, M., BEIER, O., KELAR TUČEKOVÁ, Z., KRUMPOLEC, M., STUPAVSKÁ, M., WITTWER, J., GRÜNLER, B., PFUCH, A. Atmospheric pressure plasma cleaning and activation of float soda-lime glass prior to lamination processing. **In**: *NANOCON 2019: 12th International Conference on Nanomaterials*. Ostrava: TANGER, 2020, pp. 298-303.

[6] SHEKARGOFTAR, M., KRUMPOLEC, R., HOMOLA, T. Enhancement of electrical properties of flexible ITO/PET by atmospheric pressure roll-to-roll plasma. *Materials Science in Semiconductor Processing*. 2018, vol. 75, pp. 95-102.

[7] HOMOLA, T., MATOUŠEK, J., KORMUNDA, M., WU, L.Y.L., ČERNÁK, M. Plasma treatment of glass surfaces using diffuse coplanar surface barrier discharge in ambient air. *Plasma Chemistry and Plasma Processing*. 2013, vol. 33, no. 5, pp. 881-894.

LABORATORY EXPERIMENT OF IRON NANOPARTICLE TRANSPORT IN A ROCK FRACTURE WITH ONLINE CONCENTRATION DETECTION PROBES

[1]Milan HOKR, [1]Petr PARMA, [2]Filip JANKOVSKÝ, [2]Milan ZUNA, [3]Miloslav MRAZÍK

[1]Technical University of Liberec, Liberec, Czech Republic, EU, milan.hokr@tul.cz
[2]ÚJV Řež, a.s., Husinec, Czech Republic, EU, filip.jankovsky@ujv.cz
[3]self-employed, Liberec, Czech Republic, EU, mmrazik@volny.cz

https://doi.org/10.37904/nanocon.2020.3713

Abstract

Principles, design and pilot use of a new probe for zero-valent iron nanoparticles (nZVI) concentration measurement in a micro-borehole are described in the paper. Effect of nZVI on coil inductance is known and used for such measurement before; the presented improvements relate to smaller dimensions, configuration, and electric circuit data accuracy, so that the probe can detect nZVI in small volume of suspension in a narrow fracture. Multichannel apparatus was made for a grid of boreholes. Test experiments were made with nZVI particles breakthrough in an artificial fracture in a granite block. The concentration is measured both by the new probe inside the block and by chemical analyses of samples at the outlet. The spontaneous particle immobilization did not allow saturation with constant concentration necessary for calibration, but within the constraints of input and output concentration and a fully submerged probe test, the quantitative sensitivity of the probe corresponds to theoretical expectations. Probe temperature dependence was also resolved.

Keywords: Nanoparticles, zero-valent iron, electromagnetic, groundwater pollution, measurement

1. INTRODUCTION

Process of nanoparticle transport in rock is important in many applications. In particular the use of nano zero-valent iron (nZVI) is common for in-situ remediation and is a subject of continuing research [1,2]. Although generic physical mechanisms of transport are known, there is still strong interest to improve the understanding by formulation of mathematical models and their fitting to experiments [3-4], including nZVI case [5]. Obtaining spatially and temporally dense data could be very helpful to verify details of the processes.

Compared to solute tracers, it is more complicated to continuously measure the nanoparticles concentration and its spatial distribution. Magnetic properties of nZVI allow such option. One of the earliest uses of magnetic susceptibility sensors to measure the nZVI concentration in soil columns was [6] with own construction and [7] with commercially produced sensor Bartington MS2. The method was then improved by either more sophisticated magnetic field evaluation around the sensor coils [8], sensor movement [9] or by more accurate sensing of the coil inductance through extended discrete counting of resonance frequency and sensor movement and calibration automation [10]. The measuring coil in the cited cases was either placed outside the cylindric column, or buried in the cohesionless soil [11].

The advantage of susceptibility measurement is almost linear dependence on the zero-valent iron concentration, which is contrary to other options for spatial distribution capturing like e.g. image processing from a transparent column photos (the attempt [12] did not lead to concentration values).

Study of nZVI in rock fractures is important as they can be dominant for the transport contrary to pores and these conditions bring new challenges for experimental configuration, nZVI sensing, and evaluation. Only few studies have been made compared to soil materials. Experiment in [13,14] injected nZVI into a chalk core with a single fracture in longitudinal direction, detecting the concentration commonly at the output by discrete sampling and analyses.

The use of magnetic susceptibility sensor is compromised by the access to the measured suspension volume, sensor/coil size, and sensitivity to an eventually small amount of iron. For laboratory single-fracture experiment, it means the probe packer diameter similar to common electric conductivity sensors (i.e. below 20 mm) and detection of less than 1 mm layer of nZVI water suspension. As such, it could be used as a next step of granite block experiments with solute tracers and hydraulic behaviour [15].

2. MEASURING PROBE

2.1. Physical principle

Inductance L of a coil is controlled by the magnetic susceptibility χ (or permeability) of the environment inside and around the coil. Iron is a ferromagnetic material, having the susceptibility by orders of magnitude larger than common rock/soil components, so controlling a coil inductance in its neighborhood. Measuring of susceptibility can be practically done by two ways: (1) mutual induction between two coaxial coils in a constant-frequency alternating current and sensing the voltage on the secondary coil by an A/D converter (this is the approach of [6] and its followers and suffer from the voltage and frequency stability and A/D conversion noise), (2) establishing a LC circuit with a fixed capacitor and measuring its resonant frequency f, which can be done directly in a digital form without additional conversion inaccuracy (approach of [10] and of this work).

While the $L(\chi)$ dependence is linear (for homogeneous "infinite" environment), $f(L)$ and consequently $f(\chi)$ are nonlinear but can be linearized for a reasonable range of nZVI concentrations - the iron in the suspension fills relatively small volume and the relative variations of frequency can be below 10^{-3}. As the magnetic field is non-uniform, the contribution of χ from different places in/around coil is different. It can be partly concentrated to a defined volume using a ferrite core in the coil.

In case of fracture, the geometry of the space filled with iron suspension is irregular (unknown fracture aperture and coil relative position to the coarse surface) so the probe sensitivity on concentration would be place-specific. Similar situation has been shown and solved during calibration of electric conductivity sensors in a fracture, with unknown volume and geometric distribution of the electrolyte at the sensor electrodes [16].

2.2. Technical construction

The measuring system is composed of individual probes connected by cables to a multichannel control electronic panel (**Figure 2** right), which is then connected to a PC by the serial port. The probe is a plexiglass tube adapted as a packer to 18 mm diameter micro-borehole. The scheme in **Figure 1** shows the dimensions and the assembly from two parts glued together after installing the coil and a small printed circuit board. The plastic material is necessary to avoid influence to the measurement.

The coil has 250 turns of one lacquered wire of maximum cross-section, which fits into one chamber of the two-chamber skeleton. The coil on the skeleton is vacuum encapsulated in a ferrite half-core P14x8, H12, Al 1500 (**Figure 2** lower left). Each terminal passes through one hole in the core, the length of the terminals is 50 mm.

Based on experience [10], the entire LC circuit (**Figure 2** upper left) is integrated directly into the probe. The shaped signal is measured using a single-chip microcomputer whose clock frequency is controlled by a crystal oscillator. Time measurement resolution between signal leading edges is 10^{-6} s.

The measuring control panel was equipped with a crystal oscillator thermostat, whose stability has key importance for the measurement accuracy. One thermometer with high resolution and stability is included, which can be attached inside or on a face of the block (with insulation from the air by e.g. foam). It provides a "central" temperature compensation of the magnetic susceptibility measurement. It is designed for a very narrow temperature range (24-26 °C) with a high resolution of 0.001 °C.

The probes and cabling were designed so that measurements could be performed on all probes simultaneously without interfering with each other, as convenient for the borehole grid. Mutual interference is prevented, among other things, by slightly different operating frequencies of the individual probes.

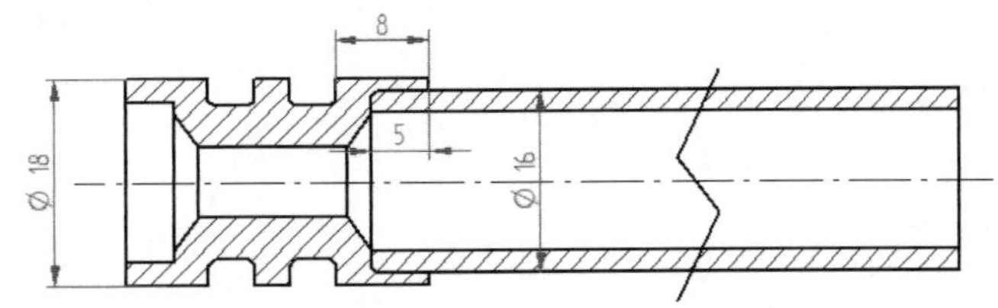

Figure 1 Drawing of the probe housing of two attached parts: The left part contains the ferrite cup (14 mm diameter) and the coil inside and rubber rings around. The right part is for electronics emplacement and cabling. Dimensions in mm.

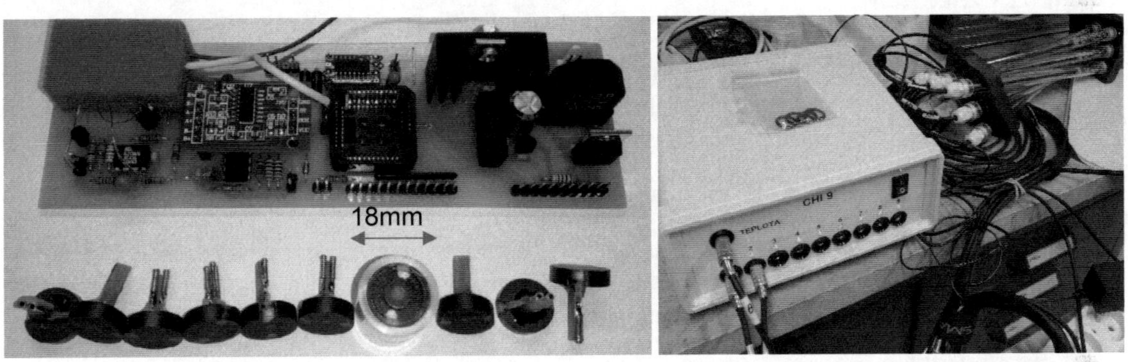

Figure 2 Printed circuit board of the analogue processing inside the probe, measuring coils in ferrite cups (one of them inside the plexiglass housing), and the completed multichannel apparatus

2.3. Calibration tests

Preliminary verifications included the temperature dependence for application of a correction and the dependence on nZVI concentration for a fully submerged probe (calibration). The temperature dependence was tested in a beaker with water freely placed in a room, i.e. with uncontrolled temperature change during gradual equilibration. The beaker is moderately stirred to enhance equilibration of the water and the probe. The evolution of temperature and frequency is plotted in **Figure 3** (left), together with evolution of frequency processed by a linear correction.

The desired relation of nZVI concentration and resonant frequency change was verified as follows: A beaker with 100 ml of demineralized water was immersed in about 5 liters of water in a PUR foam container. After the temperature and the probe signal had stabilized, 0.1 mL of a source suspension (100 g/L) was injected into the beaker 10 times, making the steps of 0.1 g/L in the measured concentration. The storage vessel was shaken before each injection. The injection time interval was chosen so that the signal always stabilized after injection. The beaker was permanently stirred moderately. The result is in **Figure 3** (right).

I can be seen, that the effect of temperature in about 1 °C range is of similar magnitude as the intended measuring range for 1 g/L concentration. Therefore, either a very good temperature stabilization is needed for the experiment (variation in hundredths of Kelvin) or a compensation must be made, for which the system is equipped.

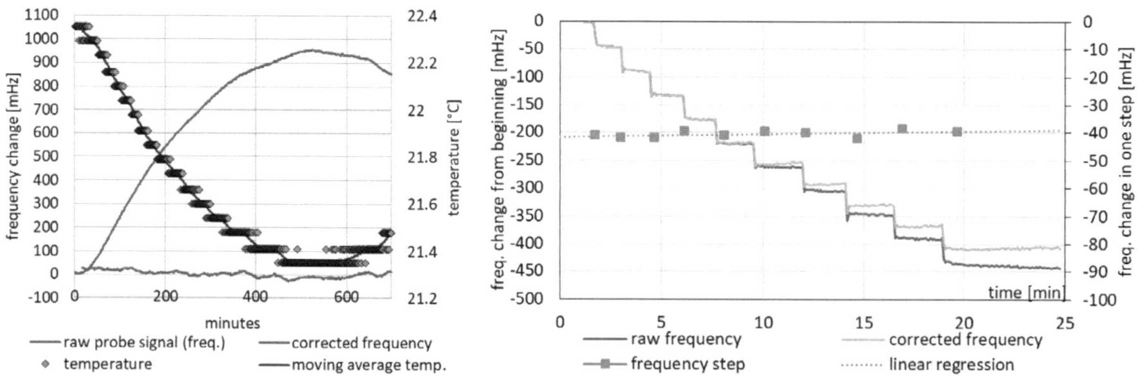

Figure 3 Verification of sensor operation and properties: Left is the temperature dependence of the probe output in pure water with linear compensation. Right is the dependence of probe output on the nZVI concentration in the beaker demonstrating the linearity between concentration and frequency.

3. PILOT EXPERIMENT

3.1. Materials: iron nanoparticles and granite block

Nanoparticles manufactured by Nanoiron (Rajhrad, Czech R.) and sold under the trade name Nanofer 25S [17] were used for pilot experiments. This product contains 20 % (w/w) elemental iron nanoparticles and an organic modifier to prevent particle aggregation.

Before the actual application, the product was diluted with tempered water to a final concentration of 10 g/L and carboxy methyl cellulose (CMC) as a final modifier added so that its concentration was 5 g/L in the suspension. The diluted suspension was dispersed using an IKA T 18 digital ULTRA-TURRAX disperser with a S 18 N - 19 G dispersing attachment for about 5 minutes at 20,000 rpm.

The granite block 40 cm × 25 cm × 20 cm (L-W-H) was artificially split and reassembled. The generated approximately horizontal fracture was sealed around the perimeter (epoxy and tape). Two boreholes were drilled through the upper part (centered with respect to the width and 10 cm from sides in the longitudinal direction) and inlet and outlet tubes installed on the smaller vertical sides into the fracture. This granite block was also used prior to the study [15], so that the hydraulic and conservative tracer properties were known. The average aperture is approx. 0.4 mm, i.e. 40 mL total void volume.

3.2. Test procedure

The whole laboratory was tempered several days in advance, including the experimental block and water storage tank. The dispersed suspension (necessarily heated) was equilibrated for one hour before the application. Before the nZVI injection, the whole volume of the fracture was flooded and washed with water. Because the signal of the probes is partly dependent on the pressure of the liquid at the front of the probe, stabilization and zeroing (autozero) was performed at a constant flow of wash water of the same value as the flow of test suspension was subsequently selected during the experiment.

During the application, the nZVI suspension was subsequently kept in buoyancy using an IKA EUROSTAR 20 digital shaft stirrer set with an R 1312 Turbine stirrer at 350 rpm. The dosing was performed using a precision laboratory peristaltic pump Ismatec IPC8 (**Figure 4** left). The flow rate for the experiment was 10 mL/min. Three-way valve was used to switch between sources of pure water and nZVI suspension.

Samples were periodically taken at the outlet of the block throughout the experiment in 1 or 2 minute intervals. In these samples, the total iron content was determined (includes both the remaining suspension and Fe ions formed by reaction with water during migration). This determines the Fe balance during the experiment.

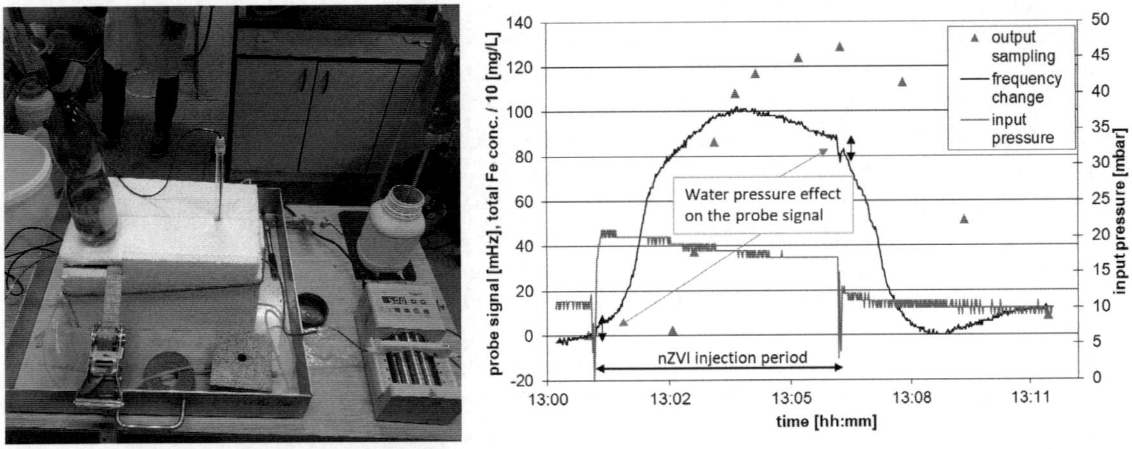

Figure 4 Experimental granite block with the measuring probe and thermal insulation. Measurement result: evolution of probe signal (10 cm from injection) and output total Fe samples (40 cm from injection). For reference, the input pressure is shown, with effect of either water or nZVI suspension injection.

3.3. Results discussion

An example of results for one of the transport tests with one probe in the borehole closer to the injection is shown in **Figure 4** (right). Qualitatively, the presence of nZVI in the fracture was well detected with the probe. We did not succeed to reach fully stable probe signal with continuous injection, which can be explained by irregular effect of sedimentation or other tracer retention. Therefore we could not determine the calibration factor for defined concentration below the probe. A constraint is given from output iron concentration, whose peak is 1.2 g/L, eight times less than the injection. So the concentration at the probe is somewhere in between. Considering the sensitivity of 400 mHz per 1 g/L for submerged probe (a guess of 1 mL affected volume), the sensitivity at the fracture could be 20 mHz per 1 g/L (the affected volume of about 0.5 mL), which would mean the peak measured concentration of 5 g/L. The calculated mass balance between input and output is approx. 15 %, i.e. shows a strong iron immobilization.

4. CONCLUSION

Based on the previous work with magnetic susceptibility measurement for nano zero-valent iron concentration determination, we designed a probe suitable for local measurement in a microborehole arrangement. The manufactured prototype was successfully tested on the granite fracture nZVI migration experiment, although the calibration with determined concentration at the probe was not possible. Even with known limitations and technical problems, this new measuring method can contribute to understanding of transport processes. At the moment, full interpretation of the test results was not subject of this paper and will continue in the following work with large block of meter scale with a grid of 9 probes.

ACKNOWLEDGEMENTS

The work has been supported by Czech Technological Agency (TACR) under Project No. TH02030543.

REFERENCES

[1] CRANE, R. A. and SCOTT, T. B.. Nanoscale zero-valent iron: Future prospects for an emerging water treatment technology. *Journal of hazardous materials*. 2012, vol. 211-212, pp. 112-125.

[2] TOSCO, T., PAPINI, M. P., VIGGI, C. C. & SETHI, R. Nanoscale zerovalent iron particles for groundwater remediation: a review. *Journal of Cleaner Production*. 2014, vol. 77, pp. 10-21.

[3] JAMES, S. C. & CHRYSIKOPOULOS, C. V. Effective velocity and effective dispersion coefficient for finite-sized particles flowing in a uniform fracture. *Journal of Colloid and Interface Science*. 2003, vol. 263, pp. 288-295.

[4] SALAMA, A., NEGARA A., EL AMIN M., SUN S., Numerical investigation of nanoparticles transport in anisotropic porous media. *Journal of Contaminant Hydrology*. 2015, vol 181, p. 114-130.

[5] MACCARI, F. *Effect of suspension properties of NANOFER STAR nZVI particles on transport behavior and modeling of transport using MNMs*. 2018. Master's Thesis. Universität Stuttgart - VEGAS.

[6] BUCHAU, A., DE BOER, C., KLAAS, N. & RUCKER, W. Inductive detection and concentration measurement of nano sized zero valent iron in the subsurface. *IET Science, Measurement & Technology*. 2010, vol. 4, pp. 289-297.

[7] DALLA VECCHIA, E., LUNA, M. & SETHI, R. Transport in Porous Media of Highly Concentrated Iron Micro- and Nanoparticles in the Presence of Xanthan Gum. *Environmental Science & Technology*. 2009, vol. 43, pp. 8942-8947.

[8] LI, H., BUCHAU, A., RUCKER, W. M., KLAAS, N. & BANUCU, R. Optimisation of a concentration measurement sensor for nano sized zero valent iron using numerical simulation. *IET Science, Measurement & Technology*. 2015, vol. 9, pp. 636-643

[9] TOSCO, T., GASTONE, F. & SETHI, R. Guar gum solutions for improved delivery of iron particles in porous media (Part 2): Iron transport tests and modeling in radial geometry. *Journal of Contaminant Hydrology*. 2014, vol. 166, pp. 34-51.

[10] PARMA, P. *Studium migrace modifikovaných nanočástic na bázi elementárního železa (Study of migration of modified nanoparticles based on elemental iron)*. Czech Republic, 2018. Ph.D. Thesis. Technical University of Liberec.

[11] PEŠKOVÁ K., MIYAJIMA K., BRAUN J., ČERNÍK M. Study of the migration of nanoiron particles in the 2- and 3-D homogeneous artifical aquifer. **In**: *NANOCON 2016 International Conference on Nanomaterials*. Ostrava: Tanger, 2016, pp. 240-245.

[12] NOSEK, J. *Laboratorní výzkum a modelování transportních vlastností nanoželeza (Laboratory research and modeling of nanoiron transport properties)*. Czech Republic, 2009. Ph.D. Thesis. Technical University of Liberec.

[13] COHEN, M., WEISBROD, N. Transport of iron nanoparticles through natural discrete fractures. *Water Research, Elsevier BV*. 2018, vol. 129, pp. 375-383.

[14] COHEN, M., YAKIREVICH, A. & WEISBROD, N. The Role of Stabilizer Concentration in the Mobility of Carbon-Supported Nanozerovalent Iron (nZVI) in Fractured Media. *Water Resources Research*. 2019, vol. 55, pp. 8164-8177.

[15] JANKOVSKÝ F., ZUNA M., HAVLOVÁ V., KOTOWSKI J., JANKOVEC J., HOKR M. Contaminant migration experiments in an artificial block-scale granite fracture. **In**: *Goldschmidt 2019 conference (talk)*. Barcelona, 2019.

[16] KOTOWSKI J., ČERNOUŠEK T., JANKOVSKÝ F., KŮS P., POLÍVKA P., SKALA M., KOVÁŘOVÁ H., ZUNA M. Development of Experimental Instrumentation for Measurement of Advection in Narrow Aperture in Granite Block. *Journal of Nuclear Engineering and Radiation Science*. 2019, vol. 5, no. 3, pp. 1-4.

[17] NANOIRON Ltd. *NANOFER 25S*. [online], [viewed 2020-10-19] Available from: https://nanoiron.cz/en/products/zero-valent-iron-nanoparticles/nanofer-25s.

SESSION C
BIONANOTECHNOLOGY, NANOMATERIALS IN MEDICINE

Chairmen

Prof. Dr. Anton FOJTIK	Czech Technical University in Prague, Czech Republic, EU
Prof. Dr. Jiri HOMOLA	Institute of Photonics and Electronics of the CAS, Prague, Czech Republic, EU

STUDY OF THE EFFECT OF PARACETAMOL BINDED IN POLYMERIC NANOPARTICLES ON DAFNIA MAGNA

[1]Barbora HAVELKOVA, [1,2,3]Karel SEHNAL, [4]Dominik BANAS, [5]Marta KEPINSKA, [2,6]Branislav RUTTKAY-NEDECKY, [2]Martina STANKOVA, [7]Carlos FERNANDEZ, [1]Miroslava BEKLOVA, [2,3,5]Rene KIZEK

[1]Department of Ecology and Diseases of Zooanimals, Game, Fish and Bees, Faculty of Veterinary Hygiene and Ecology, University of veterinary and pharmaceutical sciences, Brno, Czech Republic, EU, havelkovab@vfu.cz, beklovam@vfu.cz

[2]Department of Research and Development, ECO-ENVI-NANOLIFE, Prague, Czech Republic, EU

[3]Department of Pharmacology and Toxicology, Faculty of Pharmacy, Masaryk University, Brno, Czech Republic, EU, karelsehnal15@gmail.com, kizek@sci.muni.cz

[4]Department of Biochemistry, Faculty of Science, Masaryk University, Brno-Bohunice, Czech Republic, EU, dominik.banass@gmail.com

[5]Department of Biomedical and Enviromental Analyses, Faculty of Pharmacy, Wroclaw Medical University, Wroclaw, Poland, EU, marta.kepinska@umed.wroc.pl

[6]Department of Molecular Pharmacy, Faculty of Pharmacy, Masaryk University, Brno, Czech Republic, EU, ruttkay-nedeckyb@pharm.muni.cz

[7]School of Pharmacy and Life Sciences, Robert Gordon University, Garthdee Road, Aberdeen, United Kingdom, c.fernandez@rgu.ac.uk

https://doi.org/10.37904/nanocon.2020.3747

Abstract

Drugs are important xenobiotics in the environment. Their use increases with the growth of the human population, but also in agricultural primary production. Paracetamol (PAR) is a widely used analgesic and antipyretic and its production is still growing. Commonly available drug production technologies are being developed very intensively with nanotechnological modifications for their gradual and targeted release. Nanoparticles (ST/PAR) from starch were prepared: PAR (0, 1, 2, 3, 5 and 10 mg/L) was mixed with citric acid ester in a 1:8 v/v ratio for 30 min at 25 °C. By the centrifugation (16.000 g, 30 min) ST/PAR were obtained in the pellet. The effect of PAR was studied on *Daphnia magna* Straus (Cladocera, Crustacea). Adult females (70-400 mg) were used for self-evaluation. The EC50 was 3.749 mg/L after 48 h of PAR treatment. Total protein values determined by Lowry method were between 0.5-2.2 mg/mL and by Bradford method between 190-676 mg/L. Antioxidant activity values determined by CUPRAC method were between 4-15 µg/mL GAE and by ABTS method ranged between 40-103 µg/mL GAE. PAR values were between 9-40 µM. Subsequently, the biological activity of the prepared nanoparticles was tested.

Keywords: Ecotoxicology; chemical and biochemical analysis; nanomedicine

1. INTRODUCTION

Drugs are important xenobiotics in the environment. Their use increases with the growth of the human population, but also in primary agricultural production. Paracetamol (PAR) is a non-steroidal anti-inflammatory drug widely used [1]. PAR enters the aquatic environment with wastewater and thus affects aquatic organisms

[2,3]. There is little information on the effect of PAR on detoxification processes. PAR induces oxidative stress, can manifest in endocrine disruption [3,4] and affect the expression of selected genes [1].

The increase in their environmental concentrations in individual components of the environment is obvious, and with the use of modern analytical techniques, residues are detected in soil, surface water, sediments, groundwater, and marine ecosystems [5]. It is highly probable that increasing concentrations of PAR in the aquatic environment and its transformation by the food chain may affect a number of biochemical and physiological processes determining the growth and development of aquatic biocenosis [6]. The importance of PAR monitoring stems from the results of monitoring studies that have shown its high concentrations in wastewater [7,8]. Wastewater treated plants cannot effectively eliminate most medicines, so they are a particularly significant environmental risk for aquatic ecosystems [9]. Little relevant information is available, in particular on the sublethal effects of PAR on aquatic organisms, in addition, the effects of nanoparticle-bound drugs (NPs) are completely unknown. Cladocera *Daphnia magna* Straus (Cladocera, Crustacea) is not only an important model species in ecotoxicology, but also a planktonic crustacean, which is a key consumer of algae and cyanobacteria, as well as food for many fish [10]. It thus serves as a link between primary phytoplankton production and higher trophic levels in the aquatic ecosystem. Commonly available drug manufacturing technologies are being developed very intensively by nanotechnological modifications for their gradual and targeted release [11,12]. Nanotechnological modification of PAR could find application in the treatment of cancer [13]. The aim of this project is to extend existing knowledge about the toxicity of PAR and its nanoform (NPs-PAR) to aquatic organisms. The determined values of acute and chronic toxicity of the monitored substances will allow the estimation of the risk to the aquatic environment.

2. MATERIAL AND METHODS

Biological experiments

The solution and elaboration of the topic presupposes the mastery of selected standard ecotoxicological tests on aquatic crustaceans - Cladocera *Daphnia magna*. Tests according to ČSN EN ISO 6341 (75 7751) was used to evaluate ecotoxicity. Immobilization test for *Daphnia magna* Straus (Cladocera, Crustacea) - Acute toxicity test and ČSN ISO 10706 (75 7752 - Determination of chronic toxicity of substances for *Daphnia magna* Straus (Cladocera, Crustacea). The acute test on Clacodera *D. magna* pearls consists in monitoring their immobilization in a selected range of test substance concentrations at exposure for 24 and 48 hours.

Chemical analysis

Amount of 150 µL LOWRY solution I (7 mM Na-K tartrate, 0.81 M sodium carbonate, 0.5 M NaOH) was pipetted into cuvettes and then in 9th period (81 s) 9 µL of barley extract was added. Afterwards, LOWRY solution II (70 mM Na-K tartrate, 40 mM $CuSO_4$ and 0.1 M NaOH) was added in 42nd period (378 s) in volume of 20 µL and finally 172 µL of LOWRY solution III (1:15 Folin-Ciocalteu reagent: H_2O) in 90th period (810 s) was added. Reaction was evaluated as a response in miliabsorbance units between period 93 to 96 (837 seconds to 864 seconds from pipetting of LOWRY I solution). Wavelength: 660 nm. Quality of reagents were controlled via regulation diagram for 188 mg/L bovine serum albumin standard with good reproducibility of reaction (8400 ± 258 mAU, RSD 3.07 %, 8 days).

PARACETAMOL methodology. Measurement in stems - Approximately 1 g of sample for each concentrations was crushed with sea sand and 2 mL of PBS, pH = 7 was added. Crushed stems and buffer were quantitatively transferred to 2 mL eppendorf microtubes and centrifuged for 30 minutes for 16.900 g. Supernatant was pipetted into clear microtubes and concentration of paracetamol was measured. Amount of 320 µL of Paracetamol solution I (17.9 mM sodium nitroprusside and 13.4 mM $K_3Fe(CN)_6$) was pipetted into cuvettes and then) 40 µL of barley extract was added. Afterwards, 40 µL of Paracetamol solution II (2 M NaOH) was added in 43nd period (559 seconds). Reaction was evaluated as a response in absorbance units in period 146 (1898 s from pipetting of Paracetamol solution 1). Wavelength: 700 nm. 270 µL CUPRAC solution 1 (10 mM $CuSO_4$; 7.5 mM neocuproine in 99% ethanol and 1 M ammonium acetate in 1:1:1 ratio) was pipetted into cuvettes and then 9th period (81 s) 30 µL of sample was added. Reaction was evaluated as a response in miliabsorbance units between period 75 to 79 (675 s to 711 s from pipetting of PBM solution 1). Wavelength: 450 nm. Quality of reagents were controlled via regulation diagram for two concentrations of gallic acid; 25 µg/mL and 12.5 µg/mL. Based on 7 separate days of measurements, responses for concentration 25 µg/mL are in range of 58804 ± 1964 mAU, RSD 3.34 % and for concentrations 12.5 µg/mL are in range of 34461 ± 2360 mAU, RSD 6.85 %, which shows good reproducibility of reaction. 200 µl ABTS solution 1 (0.7 mM ABTS and 495 µM potassium persulfate) was pipetted into cuvettes and then in 9th period (81 s) 45 µL of sample was added. Reaction was evaluated as a response in miliabsorbance units between period 75 to 79 (675 seconds to 711 s from pipetting of PBM solution 1). Wavelength: 660 nm. Quality of reagents were controlled via regulation diagram for two concentrations of gallic acid; 11.5 µg/mL and 5.75 µg/mL. Based on 4 separate days of measurements, responses for concentration 11.5 µg/mL are in range of 11149 ± 2790 mAU, RSD 25.03 % and for concentrations 5.75 µg/mL are in range of 29636 ± 4209 mAU, RSD 14.20 %. Precision is lowered, because ABTS is based on decolourization of the reaction mixture, which is always connected with lower precision. 190 µl of Bradford solution I (0.1 g/L Coomassie Brilliant Blue; 8.5 % H_3PO_4; 3.4 % ethanol) was pipetted into cuvettes and then 10 µL of sample was added. Reaction was evaluated as a response in absorbance units in period 45 (598 s from pipetting of Bradford solution 1). Wavelength: 700 nm. 150 µL GST solution 1 (2 mM CDNB in 20 % methanol) was pipetted into cuvettes and then in 9th period (81 s) 45 µL of sample was added. Afterwards, GST solution II (12.5 mM GSH) was added in 42nd period (378 s) in volume of 20 µL. Reaction was evaluated as a response in miliabsorbance units in 80th (end of the reaction) and 42nd period (when GST solution II was added) and activity of GST was calculated via formula. PAR (0, 1, 2, 3, 5,10 mg/L) were used for acute toxicity testing. At the end of the test, *D.magna* was washed in distilled water and frozen at -20°C. Homogenized in 1 ml of water. PAR concentrations were determined photometrically at 700 nm. Total SH groups (Ellman's method at 405 nm), GSH, GSSG (at 450 nm), GST (at 480 nm) and metallothionein electrochemically by the Brdička method. Total protein levels were determined by pyrogallol, biuret and Bradford methods. In our experimental model, the acute toxicity of PAR was performed in three independent experiments (n = 3).

3. RESULTS AND DISUSSION

A photometric method based on a colour reaction was designed and tested for rapid analysis of PAR content in samples [14-17]. The method showed very good reproducibility and stability of the reaction, RSD ranged up to 5% (**Figure 1**). Subsequently, the method was applied to the determination of PAR in water and in cell homogenates of *D.magna*.

To date, very little attention has been paid to the evaluation of PAR toxicity to *D. magna*. Some selected summary information can be found in the work of Grung et al. [18]. Kim et al. found that after 21 days of NOEC exposure (5.72 mg/mL) no effects on reproduction were observed [10]. In a study by Daniel et al., no effect on reproduction was demonstrated in *D. magna* [19]. Even in the detailed assessment of wastewater no significant effects on biological assessment were found [20]. In a study, Ding et al observed chronic effects on reproduction at a concentration of 50 mg/mL [1]. In the case of acute exposure, an effect on the up-regulation of the HRP96, CYP360A8, CYP314, MRP4 and P-gp genes was observed. However, after 96 h, the expression was already reduced [1]. A detailed study of the effect of PAR was performed by Castro et al. In addition, he recommends assessing the reproduction of the offspring of the F-1 generation. There was an effect on maternal reproduction after PAR (F-1) exposure, although these effects were not very pronounced [21]. In our acute toxicity tests, we observed an EC50 of about 3.749 mg PAR/L (**Figure 2**).

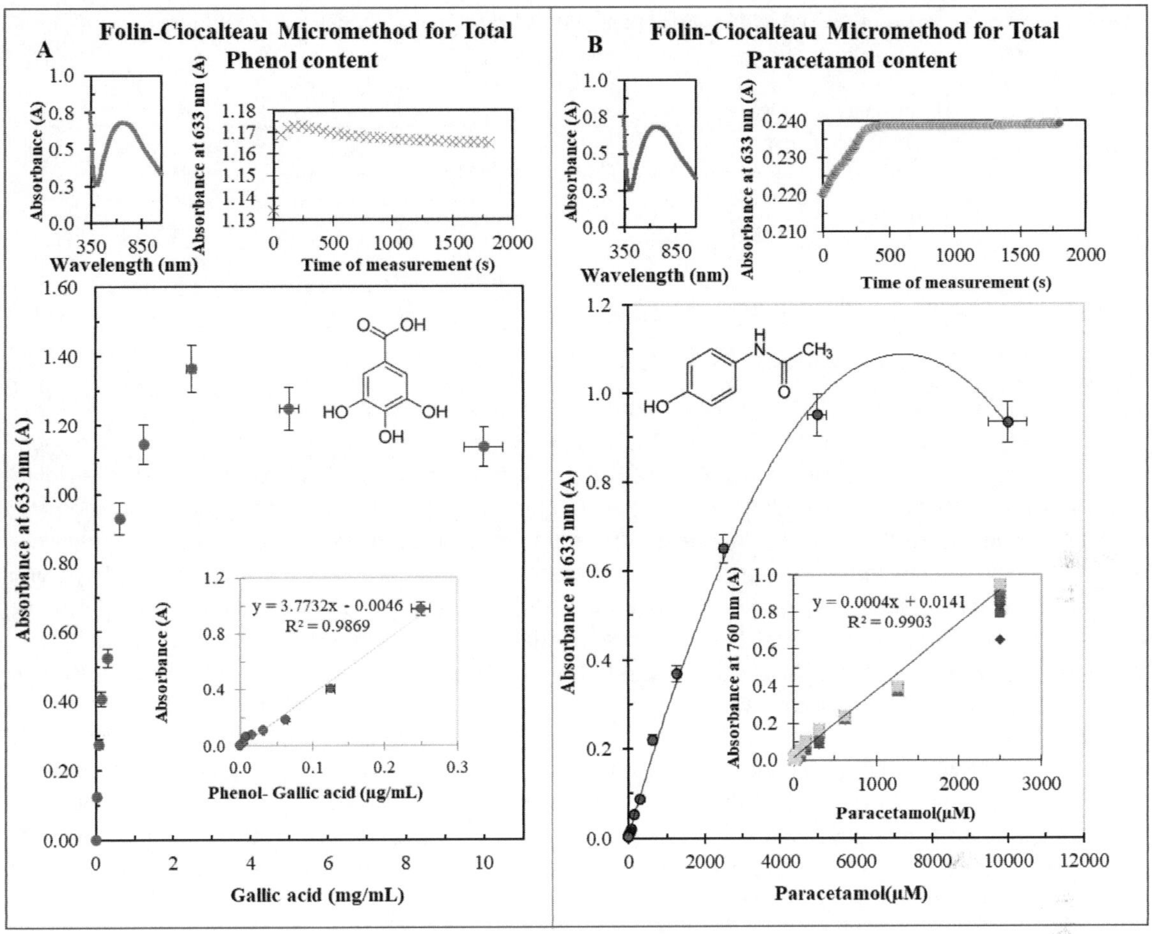

Figure 1 Typical dependence of absorbance on the concentration of gallic acid (GA) - A, and paracetamol (PAR) - B, determined by the Folin-Ciocalteau Micromethod. Typical VIS spectra of GA (5 mg/mL) and PAR (5 mM PAR). Stability of the reaction in time 0-2.000 s. Dependence of absorbance on the concentration 0-10 mg/mL GA and in the insert 0-0.3 µg/ml. Dependence of absorbance on the concentration of 0- 2.000 µM PAR in the insert 0-3.000 µM.

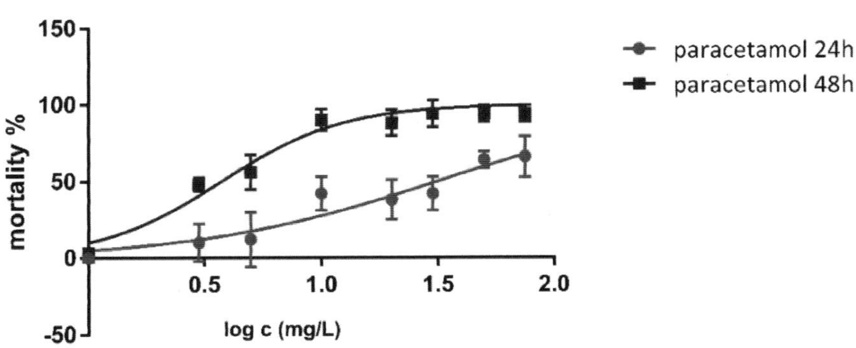

Figure 2 The EC50 for PAR in *D. magna* were determined at 24 and 48 h 21.48 (24.34 to 40.70) and 3.749 (3.283 to 4.282) mg/L, respectively

Table1 Chemical analysis of culture water after application of PAR. Each measurement was performed 5 times

Sample name	Protein	sodium	potassium	chloride	pH	conductivity	density	redox potential	ammonia	electrochemical index	nitrates
PAR (1mg)	8.3	4.1	33.9	7.3	7.8	726.8	1.00028	19.7	415.4	16.2	1.4
PAR (2mg)	13.0	10.1	24.5	4.9	7.8	699.0	1.0003	21.9	314.6	14.2	1.3
PAR (5mg)	14.5	21.6	34.7	6.0	7.8	755.6	1.0003	22.1	480.7	14.5	4.9

Preparation of SPION starch nanoparticles

Starch (100 mg) was dissolved in 20 ml of distilled and deionized water at 80 °C under magnetic stirring. A 5 mL portion of solution containing 0.1 M Fe^{2+} and 0.2 M Fe^{3+} was poured into a prepared starch solution under vigorous stirring. The starch and iron ion mixture (25 mL) was then added dropwise into 250 mL of 0.1 M NaOH under vigorous mechanical stirring (2000 rpm/min) at 60 °C for 2 h. Around 50 wt % of water was evaporated, and the remaining solution was cooled to room temperature and allowed to stand 12 h. The gels formed were washed with deionized water until the pH became less than 8.5. Excess salt and ions were removed by using dialysis at 37 °C for 2-3 days against 5 L of distilled water. To cleave glycosidic bond and reduce the polymeric chain to an average molecular weight, the influence of oxidizing agent, used for cleavage of the polymeric starch chains, was investigated. H_2O_2 (5 mL of 0.46 M) was mixed with 20 mL (10 mg/mL) of starch-coated SPION. Starch citrate (0.8 mg/mL) was mixed with paracetamol. The concentration of paracetamol in the reaction mixture was 3205 mM. The reaction volume was 1.6 mL. The 2 mL tube was left on the rotator for 2 hours. Subsequently, it was centrifuged (5 min, 14.000 g) and the paracetamol concentration was measured. Subsequently, 1.6 mL of water were added, and the mixture was allowed to stir (40 rpm), after which the concentration of the supernatant was measured again. Samples were taken according to 0, 30, 60, 90, 120 and 150 min. The binding of 99% paracetamol to starch citrate was demonstrated, paracetamol was not released from the binding during the experiment [11,12].

4. CONCLUSION

The acute toxicity of PAR to *D. magna* was monitored and subsequently starch nanoparticles were prepared. These nanoparticles were modified with PAR. We found the binding of PAR to the surface of the prepared nanoparticles and PAR was gradually released from the nanoparticles.

ACKNOWLEDGEMENTS

Supported by the grant FVHE/Pikula/ITA2020

REFERENCES

[1] DING, R., LIU, S. J., HE, C. P., NIE, X. P. Paracetamol affects the expression of detoxification- and reproduction-related genes and alters the life traits of Daphnia magna. *Ecotoxicology.* 2020, vol. 29, no. 4, pp. 398-406.

[2] MACKULAK, T., SKULCOVA, A., BELISOVA, N., HORAKOVA, I., ZABKA, D., SEMERAD, M., STANOVA, A. V., BRANDEBUROVA, P. Medicines and Drugs: an Environmental Problem? *Chemicke Listy.* 2019, vol. 113, no. 11, pp. 654-661.

[3] MA, R. X., WANG, B., YIN, L. N., ZHANG, Y. Z., DENG, S. B., HUANG, J., WANG, Y. J., YU, G. Characterization of pharmaceutically active compounds in Beijing, China: Occurrence pattern, spatiotemporal distribution and its environmental implication. *Journal of Hazardous Materials.* 2017, vol. 323, pp. 147-155.

[4] PAROLINI, M. Toxicity of the Non-Steroidal Anti-Inflammatory Drugs (NSAIDs) acetylsalicylic acid, paracetamol, diclofenac, ibuprofen and naproxen towards freshwater invertebrates: A review. *Science of the Total Environment.* 2020, vol. 740, p. 13.

[5] HENSCHEL, K. P., WENZEL, A., DIEDRICH, M., FLIEDNER, A. Environmental Hazard Assessment of Pharmaceuticals. *Regulatory Toxicology and Pharmacology.* 1997, vol. 25, no. 3, pp. 220-225.

[6] NUNES, B., ANTUNES, S. C., SANTOS, J., MARTINS, L., CASTRO, B. B. Toxic potential of paracetamol to freshwater organisms: A headache to environmental regulators? *Ecotoxicology and Environmental Safety.* 2014, vol. 107, pp. 178-185.

[7] PIEDADE, F., BIO, S., NUNES, B. Effects of common pharmaceutical drugs (paracetamol and acetylsalicylic acid) short term exposure on biomarkers of the mussel Mytilus spp. *Environmental Toxicology and Pharmacology.* 2020, vol. 73, p. 10.

[8] GIMENEZ, V., NUNES, B. Effects of commonly used therapeutic drugs, paracetamol, and acetylsalicylic acid, on key physiological traits of the sea snail Gibbula umbilicalis. *Environmental Science and Pollution Research.* 2019, vol. 26, no. 21, pp. 21858-21870.

[9] AKAY, C., TEZEL, U. Biotransformation of Acetaminophen by intact cells and crude enzymes of bacteria: A comparative study and modelling. *Science of the Total Environment.* 2020, vol. 703, p. 11.

[10] KIM, P., PARK, Y., JI, K., SEO, J., LEE, S., CHOI, K., KHO, Y., PARK, J., CHOI, K. Effect of chronic exposure to acetaminophen and lincomycin on Japanese medaka (Oryzias latipes) and freshwater cladocerans Daphnia magna and Moina macrocopa, and potential mechanisms of endocrine disruption. *Chemosphere* 2012, vol. 89, no. 1, pp. 10-18.

[11] MIOTKE, M., STRANKOWSKA, J., KWELA, J., STRANKOWSKI, M., JOZEFOWICZ, M. Transport of paracetamol in swellable and relaxing polyurethane nanocomposite hydrogels. *Polymer Bulletin.* 2020, vol. 77, no. 1, pp. 483-499.

[12] CHIN, S. F., ROMAINOR, A. N. B., PANG, S. C., LEE, B. K., HWANG, S. S. pH-Responsive Starch-Citrate Nanoparticles for Controlled Release of Paracetamol. *Starch-Starke.* 2019, vol. 71, no. 9-10, p. 9.

[13] WU, Y. J. J., NEUWELT, A. J., MULDOON, L. L., NEUWELT, E. A. Acetaminophen Enhances Cisplatin- and Paclitaxel-mediated Cytotoxicity to SKOV3 Human Ovarian Carcinoma. *Anticancer Research.* 2013, vol. 33, no. 6, pp. 2391-2400.

[14] AL-SHWAIYAT, M. K. E. Spectrophotometric Determination of Paracetamol by Reduction of 18-Molybdo-2-Phosphate Heteropoly Anion. *Jordan Journal of Chemistry.* 2013, vol. 146, no. 896, pp. 1-11.

[15] NAGENDRA, P. Spectrophotometric estimation of paracetamol in bulk and pharmaceutical formulations. *Journal of Chemistry.* 2011, vol. 8, no. 1, pp. 149-152.

[16] SHRESTHA, B. R., PRADHANANGA, R. R. Spectrophotometric method for the determination of paracetamol. *Journal of Nepal Chemical Society.* 2009, vol. 24, pp. 39-44.

[17] NAGARAJA, P., SRINIVASA MURTHY, K. C., RANGAPPA, K. S. Spectrophotometric method for the determination of paracetamol and phenacetin. *Journal of Pharmaceutical and Biomedical Analysis.* 1998, vol. 17, no. 3, pp. 501-506.

[18] GRUNG, M., KALLQVIST, T., SAKSHAUG, S., SKURTVEIT, S., THOMAS, K. V. Environmental assessment of Norwegian priority pharmaceuticals based on the EMEA guideline. *Ecotoxicology and Environmental Safety.* 2008, vol. 71, no. 2, pp. 328-340.

[19] DANIEL, D., DIONISIO, R., DE ALKIMIN, G. D., NUNES, B. Acute and chronic effects of paracetamol exposure on Daphnia magna: how oxidative effects may modulate responses at distinct levels of organization in a model species. *Environmental Science and Pollution Research.* 2019, vol. 26, no. 4, pp. 3320-3329.

[20] HAN, G. H., HUR, H. G., KIM, S. D. Ecotoxicological risk of pharmaceuticals from wastewater treatment plants in Korea: Occurrence and toxicity to Daphnia magna. *Environmental Toxicology and Chemistry.* 2006, vol. 25, no. 1, pp. 265-271.

[21] CASTRO, B. B., FRECHES, A. R., RODRIGUES, M., NUNES, B., ANTUNES, S. C. Transgenerational Effects of Toxicants: An Extension of the Daphnia 21-day Chronic Assay? *Archives of Environmental Contamination and Toxicology.* 2018, vol. 74, no. 4, pp. 616-626.

OPTIMIZATION OF NUCLEIC ACID BINDING TO MAGNETIC PARTICLES WITH THE AIM OF DETECTION OF DANGEROUS VIRUSES

[1,2]Dominik BANÁŠ, [2]Ondřej RYCHLÝ, [3]Stefano SALMISTRARO, [2,4,5]Ahmet Davut AKSU, [6]Miroslava KRZYŽÁNKOVÁ, [2,4]Rene KIZEK

[1]*Department of Biochemistry, Masaryk University, Brno, Czech Republic, EU, dominik.banass@gmail.com*

[2]*Department of Research and Development, ENVI-ECO-NANOLIFE, s.r.o., Prague, Czech Republic, EU*

[3]*University of Bologna, Ozzano dell' Emilia - Bologna, Italy, EU*

[4]*Department of Pharmacology and Toxicology, Faculty of Pharmacy, Masaryk University, Brno, Czech Republic, EU*

[5]*Bezmialem Vak*[illegible] *Üniversites, Istanbul, Turkey*

[6]*Veterinary Research Institute, Brno, Czech Republic, EU, krzyzankova@vri.cz*

https://doi.org/10.37904/nanocon.2020.3748

Abstract

African Swine Fever Virus (ASFV) is a DNA virus of the Asfivirus genus of the Asfarviridae family that is found in blood, body fluids, and internal organs. ASFV was described more than 40 years ago. This virus spreads pandemically and the mortality rate of the virus-related disease ranges from 90 to 100 %. The aim of this study was to propose the detection of specific nucleic acid of ASFV using electrochemical hybridization biosensor. Determination of DNA was conducted by AdTSV DPV a CV (potential 0 V, end potential -1.8 V, step potential 5 mV, modulation amplitude 25 mV, 0.2 M acetate buffer pH 5.0). The volume of analysed sample was 10 µL. CV signals CA (log -0.0373x, r 0.99, Ep -1.30 V) and P peak (log -0.0801x, r 0.99, Ep -1.52 V) were observed. To increase the sensitivity, a modification of ODN with CdTe was proposed. The CdTe signal was observed around the potential of -0.56 V and for modified ODNs the signal was -0.58 V. SPION were prepared to capture DNA. The interaction of DNA (PCR fragment, 280 bp) with SPION was very fast within 30 s. The technique will be further used for a microfluidic system.

Keywords: Emergency biosensor, nucleic acid, oligonucleotide, quantum dots, super paramagnetic nanoparticle

1. INTRODUCTION

Viruses (Ebola virus, flu virus etc.) cause a variety of dangerous diseases which can be life-threatening for animals and humans. Highly infectious coronavirus pandemic is an obvious evidence of this fact [1]. For purpose of development of suitable curative and diagnostic approaches, new experimental model systems are searched. African swine fever (ASF) is very serious disease which affects wild and domestic pigs (*Suidae*) [2,3]. ASF firstly appeared in Sub-Saharan area of Africa [4] and afterwards spread via the Transcaucasian area to Russia, China and states of European Union [5-8]. ASF has not been confirmed in Pacific area yet. Not only local people are concerned that this disease will soon penetrate to this area because of people travelling and beef import from countries with ASF occurrence. Epidemiologic situation of transfer of ASF virus (ASFV) shows that, in 2019, there were 1894 infection outbreaks among domestic pigs in European states. The most serious situation was in Romania (1728 outbreaks). Small breeding were affected the most. In 2020, big breeding in Romania and Bulgaria were also endangered. The situation is completely out of control in several states in terms of wild pigs (Poland and Balkan states are most affected). Besides Europe, the epidemic gains strength in Southwest Asia (China, Bali, Indonesia, Laos, The Philippines, Vietnam and Cambodia) [9].

As it is seen from previous knowledge, the instruments for reliable and fast detection of ASFV are necessary. For the fast diagnostics directly in a place of infection outbreak, the portable detectors based on biomolecules (enzyme, protein, peptide, antibody, nucleic acid etc.) can be very helpful. Biosensors can use a plethora of methods based on selective and specific bonds with searched analyse (in our case - a virus or a part of virus). The huge advantage of suggested devices is their relatively small operating and acquisition price [10,11]. Biosensors can be differently organised based on the type of biorecognition element and transducer (piezoelectric, thermal, optical, electrical, and electrochemical). Electrochemical detection of nucleic acid is based on redox abilities of their nucleic bases [10]. In 1986 Irena Postbielgová with Emil Paleček suggested a technique of adsorptive transfer (AdTSV), when nucleic acid, in a form of small drop (3-10 µl) is transferred and accumulated on electrode surface [12-14]. The cornerstone of design of biosensor for rapid analysis of ASFV was suggested. The described AdTSV DPV was used for studying of oligonucleotides KING R and KING F, which are complementary to viral DNA and their interaction with CdTe quantum dots as well [15]. The aim of this project is to receive information about detection of nucleic acid bound on surface of magnetic nanoparticles with use of electrochemistry (**Figure 1**).

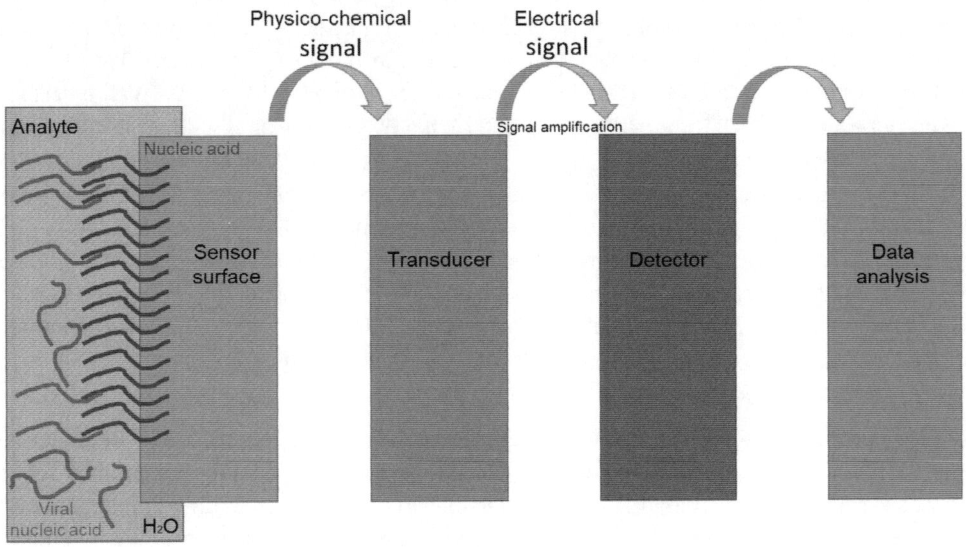

Figure 1 Simplified scheme of biosensor for detection of nucleic acids. Analysed sample reacts with the surface of biosensor (biorecognition element). On the biosensor´s surface a specific probe is bound (for example short chain of oligonucleotide). Reaction surface is necessary to modify to avoid non-specific bond of nucleic acid. After hybridisation of nucleic acid, signal (physical or chemical) is transferred via transducer to detector. Measured signal is then mathematically processed.

2. MATERIAL AND METHODS

Chemicals. All chemicals used in this study such as $Cd(CH_3COO)_2 \cdot 2H_2O$, Na_2TeO_3, mercaptosuccinic acid (MSA), Trizma base, trisodium citrate, hydrogen tetrachloroaurate(III) ($HAuCl_4$), DMSO, 3,3′,5,5′-tetramethylbenzidine (TMB), hydrogen peroxide (H_2O_2), acetic acid (HAc), sodium acetate (NaOAc), tris(2-carboxyethyl)phosphine hydrochloride (TCEP), ethylenediaminetetraacetic acid (EDTA), disodium hydrogen phosphate (Na_2HPO_4), potassium dihydrogen phosphate (KH_2PO_4), sodium chloride (NaCl), potassium chloride (KCl), tris(hydroxymethyl)aminomethane (Tris), hydrogen chloride (HCl), KING F: 5'-CTGCTCATGGTATCAATCTTATCGA-3', KING R: 5'-GATACCACAAGATCAGCCGT-3' and HCl were purchased from Sigma-Aldrich (St. Louis, MO, USA), in ACS purity. Propanol and $NaBH_4$ were purchased from Merck (Darmstadt, Germany). All plastic materials used (tubes, tips) in this study were purchased from

Eppendorf (Hamburg, Germany). Deionised water was prepared by using the reverse osmosis equipment Aqual 25 (Brno, Czech Republic), and was further purified by using an ELGA apparatus equipped with a UV lamp (Lane End, United Kingdom). The resistance was 18 MΩ and the pH was measured using the pH meter (WTW).

Instruments. For absorption spectra, the wavelength was in the range from 200 to 800 nm. For fluorescence spectra, there were an excitation wavelength of 250 nm and an emission wavelength in the range from 350 to 800 nm (Varioskan, Thermo Fisher Scientific, USA). The optical properties of nanoparticles were studied by spectral analysis. The absorbance spectra of nanoparticles were recorded within the range of 400 to 800 nm using a UV-3100PC UV-VIS spectrophotometer (VWR, Germany). Electrochemical measurements were performed with AUTOLAB Analyser connected to VA-Stand 663, using a standard cell with three electrodes. The working electrode was a hanging mercury drop electrode (HMDE) with a drop area of 0.4 mm^2. The reference electrode was an Ag/AgCl/3M KCl electrode and the auxiliary electrode was a graphite electrode. The supporting electrolyte containing 0.2 M acetate buffer (pH 5.0) was used. AdTSV DPV was conducted via two independent methods for measuring a.) Oligonucleotides/DNA and b.) Cadmium. AdTSV DPV parameters were set as follows: method a.) an initial potential of 0 V, an end potential -1,7 V, a modulation time 0.05 s, a time interval 1 s, a step -5 mV/s, a modulation amplitude of 25 mV, Eads = 0 V.; method b.) an initial potential of -1,7 V, an end potential 0,05 V, a modulation time 0.05 s, a time interval 0.5 s, a step 50 mV/s, a modulation amplitude of 25 mV, Eads = -1.2 V. Scan rate in CV was changed from 0.05 V/s to 0.6 V/s, an initial potential of 0 V, an end potential -1.85 V. The size distribution (i.e., the hydrodynamic diameter, DH) was determined by dynamic light scattering (DLS) using the Zetasizer Nano ZS ZEN3600 (Malvern Instruments, Malvern, UK) with the detection angle of 173° in optically homogeneous square polystyrene cells. The samples were diluted hundredfold with deionized water. All measurements were performed at 25 °C. Each value was obtained as an average of 5 runs with at least 10 measurements. Version 7.10 of the Zetasizer Software was applied for data evaluation. The particle charge (ζ-potential) was measured by the microelectrophoretic method using a Malvern Zetasizer Nano ZS ZEN3600 (Malvern Instruments, Malvern, UK). All the measurements were performed at 25 °C in polycarbonate cuvettes. Each value was obtained as an average of 5 subsequent runs of the instrument with at least 20 measurements.

Synthesis of SPION/Au/NPs. 1.3 g of $Fe(NO_3)_3 \cdot 9H_2O$ was dissolved in 80 mL of water (18 MΩ). A quantity of 1.4 mL 25% NH_3 was diluted in 8.6 mL water and 0.2 g $NaBH_4$ was dissolved in this mixture and, subsequently, the mixture was stirred (300 rpm, 10 min at 22 °C). The solution colour turned to dark brown. The mixture was heated to 100 °C for 2 h and stirred (300 rpm, stirring overnight at room temperature). The magnetic particles were separated from the solution via magnet and washed several times in water. The solution of $HAuCl_4$ (20 mL, 1 mM) was added to the magnetic particles and stirred (300 rpm 3 h at 22 °C). Subsequently, the solution of $C_6H_5Na_3O_7 \cdot 2H_2O$ (0.5 mL, 0.265 g/10 mL) was added to the mixture and stirred overnight. Finally, the gold SPIONs were separated via magnet and dried (40 °C).

Statistical analysis of data. Experimental work was performed in at least three independent experiments. Each sample in the experiments was analysed at least five times. The obtained data presented in this paper are the average values. No experimental points were excluded from the proposed experimental study. All the obtained data were stored in the Qinslab database. If possible, data were processed and evaluated mathematically and statistically in the Qinslab database. The results were expressed as mean ± standard deviation (SD).

3. RESULTS AND DISCUSSION

In our suggested biosensor for detection of ASFV, the hybridisation between nucleic acids with oligonucleotide probe labelled with electroactive mark (metals, metal oxides, enzymes, quantum dots, nanoparticles) is used [16-19]. Quantum dots (QDs) have very good properties for electrochemical detection. Their surface can be modified with different molecules and thus it is possible to use them as biosensors. Furthermore, it is possible to prepare different types of QDs, which can provide several measurable signals. Each signal can be used for recognition of specific sequence of nucleic acids (details are published in paper Banáš et. al.) [15]. Whole detection system can be enclosed into 3D-print prepared simple electronic microchip. Sample is injected into microchip. In reservoir inside the chip, DNA of ASFV virus is hybridised with QDs-labelled oligonucleotide probe. Electrochemical signal, which is responsible for the confirmation or the rejection of the presence of searched DNA, is perceived by connected electrode [20].

Oligonucleotide probes KING R and KING F complementary to PCR fragment (280 bp) were analysed. The calibration curves from 0.4 to 1.7 µg/mL for KING F and from 0.1 to 0.6 µg/mL for KING R and from 1 to 10 µg/mL for PCR fragment were measured. When the intensities of signals for oligonucleotides and PCR fragment are compared, the best sensitivity was calculated for PCR fragment (50 nA/amol molecules/min) then KING R (25 nA/amol molecules/min) and finally KING F (14 nA/amol molecules/min). When only ODNs were accumulated on Hg electrode, the signals of cytosine and adenine (CA signal) in potential about -1.3 V [3] (Hg against Ag/AgCl/3 M KCl) were 33 ± 8 nA for King F and 22 ± 3 nA for KING R (3 minutes; 1.0 µg/mL King F and 0.3 µg/mL King R; 10 measurements). For interaction ODNs and CdTe, CA signals were detected as follows: KING F/QDs 15 ± 8 nA, KING R/QDs 16 ± 5 nA and cadmium ions signals were detected as follows: KING F/QDs 61 ± 15 nA and KING R/QDs 89 ± 18 nA. Successful verification of interaction was proved by measurement of signal of cadmium ion and lower signals of oligonucleotides in interaction complex, because of lowered sensitivity of nucleotides when bound with CdTe QDs.

To evaluate, how ASFV PCR fragment is accumulated on electrode surface, dependences of signal of CA peak and P peak on time of accumulation (30; 60; 120; 240; 480 a 720 s) were measured. Scan rate was 0.25 V/s. Dependence for CA peak was linear (23.6525 + 0,1687 x; r = 0.99509), dependence for P peak was slightly hyperbolic (-229.2775 + 7.1954 x - 0.0048 x^2; r = 0.99433) and therefore 2nd degree polynomic curve was calculated for characterisation of behaviour of peak. Dependence of peak height on time of accumulation of DNA on Au-SPION nanoparticles was measured. Accumulation was conducted in standard conditions in phosphate buffer (c = 0.1 M, pH = 7). Times of accumulation were 15, 30, 60, 90 and 120 s. Strongest signal was 504 nA in 30 s. With increasing time of accumulation, the signal was slightly reduced (around 400 nA), when time was only 15 seconds, only 10 nA signal was measured.

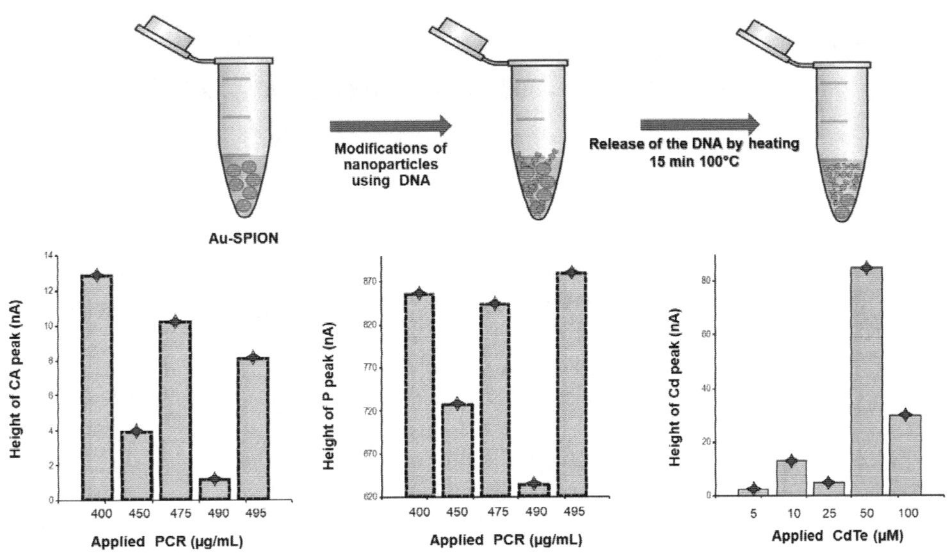

Figure 2 Comparison of CA, P a Cd signals after binding of nucleic acid on SPION (30 min interaction) and CdTe. After interaction, 3 wash steps were conducted with PBS. Measurement was conducted in acetate buffer, 0,2 M, pH 5, tA 120 s. AdTSV DPV: scan rate 5 mV/s, starting potential 0 V, terminating potential -1.8 V, n = 2. Data are statistically showed as box plots for current response and potential of signal.

SPION nanoparticles are used, because of the two properties for their surface (separation and detection). The ability of SPION nanoparticles to catch PCR/DNA, especially ASFV PCR fragment (DPV AdTSV 25 mV/s, drop 10 µL, 120 s) was tested (**Figure 2**). RSD of detection of DNA was 16.25 % (n = 44), concentration dependence (0 - 6 µg/mL) was linear (y = 8.63x). PCR/DNA (100 µg/mL) was mixed with SPION nanoparticles (1 mg/mL). Interaction was conducted 30 minutes, 300 rpm, 25 °C, phosphate buffer pH 7. Non-specific bound PCR/DNA was washed (3 times, 500 µl of phosphate buffer, pH 7, 300 rpm, 25° C). Specific bound PCR/DNA was thermally released from SPION (50 µL, phosphate pH 7, 350 rpm, 99 °C, 15 min). Average CA signals (-1.30 V) of caught PCR/DNA were 7.2 ± 5.8 CI nA (n = 5) with the DNA recovery about 10 %. Sensitivity and selectivity of determination was quite good, but our aim was to improve sensitivity more. Therefore, P peak as a catalytic signal was studied. Using P peak instead of CA peak make the sensitivity 15 times higher than using CA peak. Furthermore, variability of analysis was lowered to 16%. Besides above-mentioned analysis, different types of modification in the term of reaction volume were tested for the maximization of electrochemical response. Steps of hybridisation on SPION nanoparticles were conducted with effectiveness about 5 %. Different shapes and sizes of 3D chips were suggested, and their properties were tested.

4. CONCLUSION

Many experimental manuscripts were published about electrochemical behaviour of nucleic acids [19]. However, about interactions of oligonucleotides with quantum dots, there is a lack of available data [21]. This work was based on basic electrochemical behaviour of ODN and ODN/QDs. Different behaviour of oligonucleotides King F and King R was found out on HDME. Furthermore, we prove differences in signals of ODN (*Ip*, Ep) when interact with QDs. From these results, it can be concluded that these changes in structure can significantly influence electrochemical behaviour and must be accounted, when experimental data are interpreted. Besides this fact, this knowledge can be useful for suggestion of new types of biosensors [22,23]. Isolation of DNA from biological material is necessary for its detection. Early diagnosis of highly infectious pathogens is key to taking anti-epidemic measures. Modified SPION nanoparticles are suitable surface for detection and separation.

ACKNOWLEDGEMENTS

The study was supported by the EU programme for education, training, youth, and sport Erasmus+, NANOVIR JCMM 277/2020 and project AMOR QK1920113.

REFERENCES

[1] YORK, A. Novel coronavirus takes flight from bats? *Nature Reviews Microbiology.* 2020, vol. 18, p. 191.

[2] WANG, N., ZHAO, D. M., WANG, J. L., ZHANG, Y. L., WANG, M., GAO, Y., LI, F., WANG, J. F., BU, Z. G., RAO, Z. H.,WANG, X. X. Architecture of African swine fever virus and implications for viral assembly. *Science.* 2019, vol. 366, no. 6465, pp. 640-644.

[3] WANG, N., ZHAO, D., WANG, J., ZHANG, Y., WANG, M., GAO, Y., LI, F., WANG, J., BU, Z., RAO, Z.,WANG, X. Architecture of African swine fever virus and implications for viral assembly. *Science.* 2019, vol. 366, no. 6465, pp. 640-644.

[4] KRZYZANKOVA, M., KRASNA, M., BENA, M.,VASICKOVA, P. Virus afrického moru prasat a možnosti jeho šíření masem a masnými výrobky. *Maso.* 2020, vol. 1, no. 2020, pp. 32-38.

[5] GOGIN, A., GERASIMOV, V., MALOGOLOVKIN, A.,KOLBASOV, D. African swine fever in the North Caucasus region and the Russian Federation in years 2007-2012. *Virus Res.* 2013, vol. 173, no. 1, pp. 198-203.

[6] ZHOU, X. T., LI, N., LUO, Y. Z., LIU, Y., MIAO, F. M., CHEN, T., ZHANG, S. F., CAO, P. L., LI, X. D., TIAN, K. G., QIU, H. J.,HU, R. L. Emergence of African Swine Fever in China, 2018. *Transbound. Emerg. Dis.* 2018, vol. 65, no. 6, pp. 1482-1484.

[7] CAPUA, I.,MONTI, M. African swine fever could splinter the EU. *Nature.* 2019, vol. 566, no. 7744, pp. 326-326.

[8] GARIGLIANY, M., DESMECHT, D., TIGNON, M., CASSART, D., LESENFANT, C., PATERNOSTRE, J., VOLPE, R., CAY, A. B., VAN DEN BERG, T.,LINDEN, A. Phylogeographic Analysis of African Swine Fever Virus, Western Europe, 2018. *Emerg. Infect. Dis.* 2019, vol. 25, no. 1, pp. 184-186.

[9] KUCINSKY, P. Aficky mor prasat. *Veterinarstvi.* 2020, vol. 70, no. 8, pp. 475-478.

[10] PALECEK, E., JELEN, F. Electrochemistry of nucleic acids and development of DNA sensors. *Critical Reviews in Analytical Chemistry.* 2002, vol. 32, no. 3, pp. 261-270.

[11] THEVENOT, D. R., TOTH, K., DURST, R. A.,WILSON, G. S. Electrochemical biosensors: recommended definitions and classification. *Biosensors & Bioelectronics.* 2001, vol. 16, no. 1-2, pp. 121-131.

[12] PALECEK, E., POSTBIEGLOVA, I. Adsorptive stripping voltammetry of biomacromolecules with transfer of the adsorbed layer. *Journal of Electroanalytical Chemistry.* 1986, vol. 214, no. 1-2, pp. 359-371.

[13] PALECEK, E. New trends in electrochemical analysis of nucleic-acids. *Bioelectrochemistry and Bioenergetics.* 1988, vol. 20, no. 1-3, pp. 179-194.

[14] PALECEK, E., FOJTA, M. Detecting DNA hybridization and damage. *Analytical Chemistry.* 2001, vol. 73, no. 3, pp. 74A-83A.

[15] BANAS, D., AKSU, D. A., NOGUERA, V. M., MERT, P., HOSNEDLOVA, B.,KIZEK, R. Elektrochemická studie oligonukletidových sond značených kvantovými tečkami pro detekci nukleové kyseliny viru afrického moru prasat. *Chem. Listy.* 2020, vol. 101, pp. 1-6.

[16] MILLS, D. M., FOGUEL, M. V., MARTIN, C. P., TRIEU, T. T., KAMAR, O., CALVO-MARZAL, P., KOLPASHCHIKOV, D. M.,CHUMBIMUNI-TORRES, K. Y. Rapid detection of different DNA analytes using a single electrochemical sensor. *Sens. Actuator B-Chem.* 2019, vol. 293, pp. 11-15.

[17] KOKKINOS, C. T., GIOKAS, D. L., ECONOMOU, A. S., PETROU, P. S.,KAKABAKOS, S. E. Paper-Based Microfluidic Device with Integrated Sputtered Electrodes for Stripping Voltammetric Determination of DNA via Quantum Dot Labeling. *Anal. Chem.* 2018, vol. 90, no. 2, pp. 1092-1097.

[18] POLSKY, R., HARPER, J. C.,BROZIK, S. M. Nanomaterial-Based Electrochemical DNA Detection. In: *Electrochemical DNA Biosensors*. Singapore: Pan Stanford Publishing Pte Ltd., 2012, pp. 427-465.

[19] DRUMMOND, T. G., HILL, M. G.,BARTON, J. K. Electrochemical DNA sensors. *Nat. Biotechnol.* 2003, vol. 21, no. 10, pp. 1192-1199.

[20] GARGULAK, M., SEHNAL, K., HOSNDLOVA, B., HOAI, N., DOCEKALOVA, M., OFOMAJA, A., STANKOVA, M., UHLIROVA, D., KEPINSKA, M., MILNEROWICZ, H., FERNANDEZ, C., VACIKOVA, P.,KIZEK, R. 3D-printed CdTe QDs-based sensor for sensitive electrochemical detection of viral particles. **In:** *IEEE International Conference on Sensors and Nanotechnology.* Penang, Malaysia, 2019, pp. 1-6.

[21] BOUSSICAULT, F., ROBERT, M. Electron transfer in DNA and in DNA-related biological processes. Electrochemical insights. *Chem. Rev.* 2008, vol. 108, no. 7, pp. 2622-2645.

[22] SIRIWONG, K.,VOITYUK, A. A. Electron transfer in DNA. *Wiley Interdiscip. Rev.-Comput. Mol. Sci.* 2012, vol. 2, no. 5, pp. 780-794.

[23] KELLEY, S. O.,BARTON, J. K. Electron transfer between bases in double helical DNA. *Science.* 1999, vol. 283, no. 5400, pp. 375-381.

MOLECULARLY IMPRINTED POLYMER NANOPARTICLES AS POTENTIAL TOOL FOR IMMUNOHISTOCHEMISTRY

Jaroslava BEZDEKOVA, Kristyna TOMECKOVA, Kristyna PAVELICOVA, Kristyna ZEMANKOVA, Marketa VACULOVICOVA

Department of Chemistry and Biochemistry, Mendel University in Brno, Brno, Czech Republic, EU, bezdekovajar@gmail.com

https://doi.org/10.37904/nanocon.2020.3751

Abstract

Immunohistochemistry (IHC) is a powerful technique enabling visualization/detection of cellular components (e.g. overexpressed proteins) in tissue samples and thus ensuring timely recognition of a wide range of diseases. Nowadays, antibodies labelled by different kinds of sensing probes are routinely used for selective recognition of IHC markers. However, antibodies as bio-macromolecules have a number of drawbacks including physical and (bio) chemical instability or large production cost. Therefore, the design and synthesis of artificial antibodies that are able to bind a target molecule with similar affinity and specificity have become a long-term goal in a range of scientific branches. In this work, molecularly imprinted polymer nanoparticles (MIPs), as antibody mimics, were used as IHC agents. Specifically, polydopamine MIP nanoparticles doped with metal ions and selective for metallothionein as potential IHC marker were developed and combined with laser ablation ICP-MS. This novel approach can significantly enhance the abilities of IHC analysis and solve issues connected with the low stability of antibodies.

Keywords: Molecularly imprinted polymers, immunohistochemistry, metallothionein

1. INTRODUCTION

Immunohistochemistry (IHC) is a laboratory method, indispensable in clinical diagnostics for identification and classification of various diseases. Very important role IHC plays also in research where is utilized to the investigation of many biological processes e.g. visualization of proteins expressed on the cell surface, characterization of protein interactions, observe the distribution and localization of specific cell structures etc. [1].

Among the most common methods for tissue samples visualization belongs fluorescence microscopy based on visualization of the fluorescent probes or light microscopy based on visualization of chromogenic substrate created by enzymatic probes [2]. However, these methods have limited sensitivity and do not allow visualizing high number of analytes in the same tissue section. Recently, visualization through LA-ICP-MS (Laser Ablation Inductively Coupled Plasma Mass Spectrometry) based on conjugation with elemental tags have become a promising alternative [3,4].

In contrast to the above mention methods, LA-ICP-MS can be used for the multiplex analysis. By this method, it is possible to determine several tissue antigens simultaneously using recognition elements containing various metal ions or rare elements [5]. Moreover, LA-ICP-MS enables measurement of trace naive elements in tissues which also play a significant role in cancer diagnostics. Because it was demonstrated that the levels of some trace elements are significantly elevated in cancer tissue [6].

Ordinarily, analyte within the tissue is specifically recognized by a primary antibody labelled with an appropriate probe (fluorescent, enzyme, metal). However, antibodies have several disadvantages e.g. they have limited physical and (bio)chemical stability, sometimes it is difficult to obtain antibodies against chosen targets, and their production in large quantities is demanding and expensive. Therefore, design and synthesis of chemical alternatives of antibodies are extensively studied. One possible way is the use of molecularly imprinted polymers (MIPs) [7]. MIPs are synthetic materials with a defined spatial arrangement of the free functional groups of the polymer chains which enable them to specifically recognize target molecule. The process of MIP synthesis is quite simple. Initially, template (imprinted molecule) and functional monomers form a complex through either covalent or noncovalent interactions. Subsequently, the copolymerization process with cross-linking monomers is initiated which leads to the creation of polymer. Removal of the template molecules from the three-dimensional polymer network enable to the creation of imprinted binding sites complementary to the template in terms of size, shape, and positioning of functional groups.

In this work, polydopamine MIP nanoparticles, doped with copper ions, selective for metallothionein (MT) were prepared. MT is usually expressed in human cells at low concentration levels however its expression is increased during oxidative stress to protect the cells against cytotoxicity, radiation and/or DNA damage. In various human tumors (e.g. breast, colon, kidney, liver, lung, etc.) an increased expression of MT was determined and therefore nowadays many studies are focused on the application of MT as potential IHC marker. Synthetized MIP particles were subsequently combined with LA-ICP-MS as a visualization method for IHC. This completely novel approach enables solve issues connected with the poor stability and high production-cost of antibodies and significantly enhance the abilities of IHC analysis. For better imagination, the idea of the suggested approach is shown in **Figure 1**.

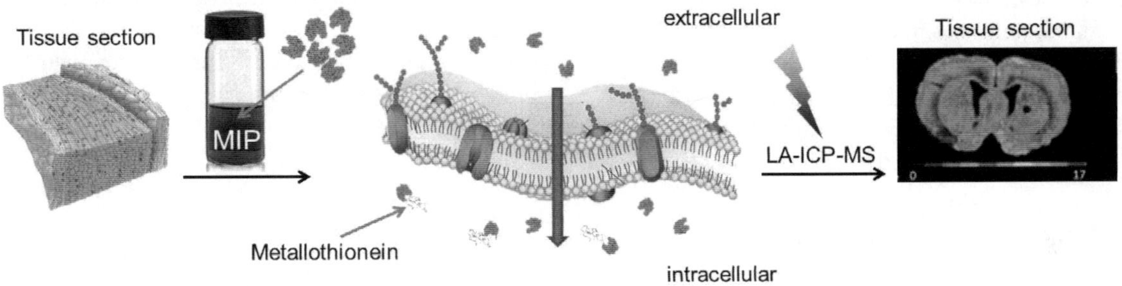

Figure 1 The tissue section is incubated with prepared MIP particles. Follows penetration of MIP particles into the cell where they selectively recognize and bind MT. Unbound MIP particles are washed out and subsequent LA-ICP-MS enables to detect copper ions in MIP particles which leads to highlighted area of tissue with increased metallothionein concentration

2. MATERIALS AND METHODS

2.1. Materials

Dopamine hydrochloride, Trizma base (TRIS), sodium dodecyl sulfate (SDS), sodium tetraborate decahydrate, copper(II)sulfate pentahydrate ($CuSO_4 \cdot 5H_2O$) and acetic acid (HAc) were purchased from Sigma-Aldrich (St. Louis, MO, USA). Ammonia solution 25% and ethanol absolute were obtained from Merck (Darmstadt, Germany). Metallothionein-2 from rabbit liver (MT-2) was purchased from Enzo Life Sciences (Farmingdale, NY, USA). Deionized water was obtained from a Millipore (Milli-Q) purification system at a resistivity of 18.2 MΩ·cm. All chemicals and solvents were of analytical or HPLC grade and used without further purification.

2.2. Preparation of MIPs and non-imprinted polymers (NIPs)

MIP particles are synthetized in parallel with NIP particles which are chemically identical but are synthesized without the presence of the template molecule and therefore, they lack affinity to MT. These particles are used for the monitoring of non-selective interactions. In both cases, dopamine was used as a functional monomer because of its ability to undergo fast self-polymerization in the presence of oxygen and alkaline environment.

The MIPs were synthesized through the oxidation and self-polymerization of dopamine molecules in a solution consisting of water, ethanol and ammonia at room temperature in the presence of template molecules (MT-2) and Cu(II) ions. 1, 2 or 4 mg of Cu(II) ions were dissolved in solution consisting of 900 µl of deionized water, 400 µl of absolute ethanol and 30 µl of ammonia aqueous solution (25%) and stirring at 30 °C for 45 min. A 100 µl of an aqueous solution of dopamine hydrochloride (5 mg/ml) and MT-2 (1 mg/ml) was quickly injected into this solution. It was observed that the solution color turned to pale yellow immediately and then gradually changed to black after 1 h. After 24 h, the created MIPs were separated by centrifugation (13,500 rpm, 25 °C, 30 min) and washed with 3% HAc twice and once with 10 mM TRIS pH 7.4. NIPs were prepared by the same protocol but without the presence of template (MT-2).

2.3. Isolation of MT-2 from by MIPs

50 µl MIP or NIP particles suspended in 10 mM TRIS pH 7.4 were mixed with 50 µl MT-2 (0.04, 0.08, 0.16 or 0.33 mg/ml) and incubated with constant stirring (30 °C, 500 rpm) for (10, 20, 30, 40 or 50 min). Then the mixture was centrifuged (13,500 rpm, 25 °C, 5 min) and the supernatant was measured by MEKC (micellar electrokinetic chromatography) with UV-vis detection or MIP/NIP particles were washed with MilliQ water and sonicated by (5, 10, 15, 20 min) which led to release of bound analyte followed by analysis by MECK with UV-vis detection.

Quantification of MT-2 was performed by capillary electrophoresis (CE) instrument 7100 (Agilent Technologies, Germany) with absorbance detection at a wavelength of 200 nm. Fused silica capillary with an internal diameter of 75 µm, with a total length of 64.5 cm and an effective length of 56 cm was used. The sample was introduced hydrodynamically at 50 mbar for 5 s and a separation voltage of 30 kV was applied. A background electrolyte (BGE) was composed of 40 mM sodium borate buffer, 60 mM SDS at pH 9.8. Before the analysis, the capillary was washed for 60 seconds using BGE.

3. RESULTS AND DISCUSSION

3.1. Characterization of obtained MIP/NIP particles

MIP particles were synthesized by the oxidation and self-polymerization of dopamine in a mixture containing water, ethanol, and ammonia, which led to the creation of spherical nanoparticles. Their size could be easily controlled by tuning the molar ratio of ammonia and dopamine. The size of MIP and NIP particles was determined by dynamic light scattering using a Zetasizer Nano from Malvern Instruments Ltd (Malvern, UK). Average hydrodynamic size in 10 mM TRIS buffer pH 7.4 was: 175 nm for MIP and 170 nm for NIP. The homogeneity of prepared particles is demonstrated by relatively low polydispersity: in case of MIP 0.22 and 0.21 in case of NIP.

3.2. Optimization of Cu ions concentration

The LA-ICP-MS is technique capable of quantitative determination of elements. In this work, the copper contained in MIP/NIP particles was determined. However, firstly, it was necessary to carry out the experiment that reveals the amount of copper ions which can be added to the polymeric mixture without the loss of efficiency of resulting MIPs. Three different concentrations of $CuSO_4 \cdot 5\,H_2O$ were added into the polymeric mixture, specifically 1, 2 and 4 mg/ml. Subsequently, the ability of obtained particles to selectively recognize MT-2 was studied. It was found out that MIP particles prepared with a concentration of 2 mg/ml of Cu(II) ions have the best efficiency and simultaneously is this concentration sufficient for LA-ICP-MS determination. Measured data are shown in **Figure 2 A**.

3.3. Optimization of binding time

Further, adsorption kinetics of MIP/NIP particles was investigated in the time range from 10 to 50 min in 10 min intervals. The curve of adsorption kinetics is shown in **Figure 2 B**. From obtained data, it is seen that initially the binding capability is high due to a large number of empty binding sites available to the target protein. Saturation of all binding sites of MIP was achieved after 20 min of incubation and therefore this incubation time was selected as optimal.

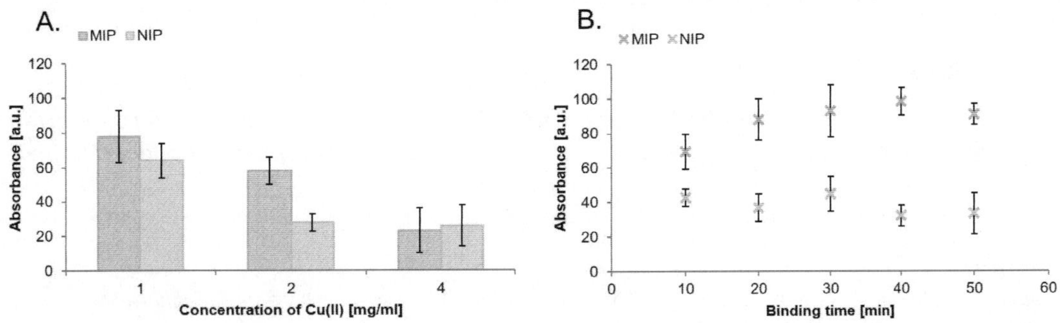

Figure 2 A. Optimization of copper ions concentration; **B**. The curve of absorption kinetic; *Error bars represent a deviation of three repeated measurements

3.4. Optimization of sonication time

In the above mention experiments, the MT-2 concentration was determined indirectly by measuring of unbound MT-2 in the supernatant. However, for measuring the calibration curve, it was necessary to release the bound MT-2 from MIP binding sites. The release of MT-2 was carried out by sonication of prepared MIPs. It this experiment, the optimal sonication time was investigated. As shown in **Figure 3 A**, 10 minutes of sonication enabled to release the majority of bound protein but did not cause their destruction therefore 10 minute sonication was chosen as optimal.

3.5. Calibration curve

To evaluate the binding properties of MIP/NIP particles, an experiment based on incubation of MIP/NIP particles in different initial concentrations of MT-2 (0.33, 0.165, 0.083, 0.041 mg/ml) was carried out. Obtained data are shown in **Figure 3 B**. All experiments focused on the optimization of MIP particles preparation were performed by using CE with UV-vis detection because this method provides more detailed information about the interaction of the analyte with MIP/NIP particles. Optimized MIP particles can be subsequently applied in IHC and detected by LA-ICP-MS which ensures a lower detection limit in comparison with CE and provides closer information about the study tissue section.

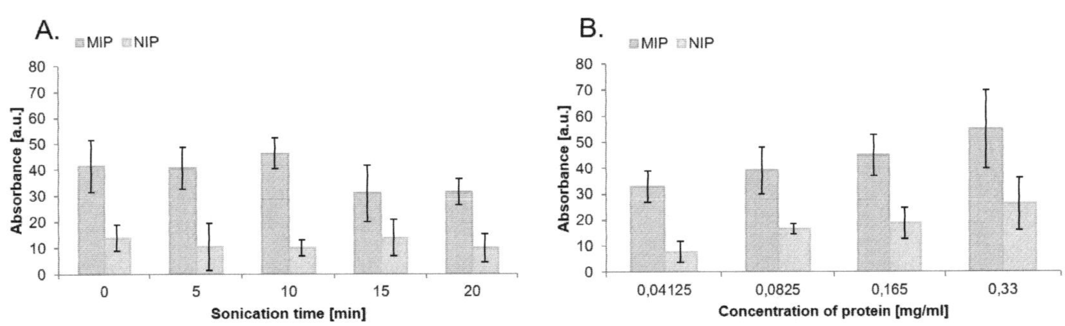

Figure 3 A. Optimization of sonication time necessary for the release of bind analyte; **B**. The calibration curve. *Error bars represent a deviation of three repeated measurements

4. CONCLUSION

In this work, MIP particles were prepared for the first time to be used as an artificial recognition element for IHC. The technique of non-covalent molecular imprinting was used in the preparation process. Dopamine was used as a functional monomer. The experiments focused on the binding time and adsorption efficiency of created MIP particles was carried out by using CE with UV-vis detection because this method provides more detail information about the interaction between MIP particles and MT (e.g. nonspecific sorption). Thus, optimized MIP particles can be applied in IHC with detection by LA-ICP-MS.

ACKNOWLEDGEMENTS

This research was carried out under the project CEITEC 2020 (LQ1601) with financial support from the Ministry of Education, Youth and Sports of the Czech Republic under the National Sustainability Programme II.

REFERENCES

[1] AZIZ, S. A., MEHTA, R. *Immunohistochemistry: Overview, its potential, and challenges. Technical aspects of toxicological immunohistochemistry.* In: Aziz S., Mehta R. (eds) *Technical Aspects of Toxicological Immunohistochemistry.* New York: Springer, 2016, pp. 1-4.

[2] DURAIYAN, J., GOVINDARAJAN, R., KALIYAPPAN, K., PALANISAMY, M. Applications of immunohistochemistry. *Journal of pharmacy & bioallied sciences.* 2012, vol. 4. no. Suppl 2, p. S307.

[3] SEUMA, J., BUNCH, J., COX, A., MCLEOD, C., BELL, J., MURRAY, C. Combination of immunohistochemistry and laser ablation icp mass spectrometry for imaging of cancer biomarkers. *Proteomics.* 2008, vol. 8. no. 18, pp. 3775-3784.

[4] PUGH, J., COX, A., MCLEOD, C., BUNCH, J., WHITBY, B., GORDON, B., KALBER, T., WHITE, E. A novel calibration strategy for analysis and imaging of biological thin sections by laser ablation inductively coupled plasma mass spectrometry. *Journal of Analytical Atomic Spectrometry.* 2011, vol. 26. no. 8, pp. 1667-1673.

[5] GIESEN, C., MAIRINGER, T., KHOURY, L., WAENTIG, L., JAKUBOWSKI, N., PANNE, U. Multiplexed immunohistochemical detection of tumor markers in breast cancer tissue using laser ablation inductively coupled plasma mass spectrometry. *Analytical chemistry.* 2011, vol. 83. no. 21, pp. 8177-8183.

[6] RIZK, S. L., SKY-PECK, H. H. Comparison between concentrations of trace elements in normal and neoplastic human breast tissue. *Cancer research.* 1984, vol. 44. no. 11, pp. 5390-5394.

[7] HAUPT, K., MEDINA RANGEL, P. X., BUI, B. T. S. Molecularly imprinted polymers: Antibody mimics for bioimaging and therapy. *Chemical Reviews.* 2020, vol. 120 no. 17, pp. 9554-9582.

SPECIAL NANOFIBER SCAFFOLD DESIGNED FOR CELLULAR PRODUCTS IN THE TREATMENT OF CHRONIC WOUNDS

[1]Petr BRAŤKA, [2]Matej BUZGO, [3]Hana WALASKÁ, [4]Josef ROSINA, [1]Martin ČERVEŇÁK, [1]Matěj LOUDA

[1]Grade Medical s.r.o., Řevnice, Czech Republic, EU

[2]InoCure s.r.o., Čelákovice, Czech Republic, EU

[3]ING MEDICAL s.r.o., Prague, Czech Republic, EU

[4]Faculty of Biomedical Engineering, Czech Technical University in Prague, Kladno, Czech Republic, EU

https://doi.org/10.37904/nanocon.2020.3753

Abstract

In this work we have prepared and characterized several types of nanofibers to create unique nanofiber substrates as a medical device for long-term non-healing wound treating using cellular products. Our nanofibers are based on biodegradable polymers such as polycaprolactone (PCL), poly(lactide-co-caprolactone) (PLCL), poly(vinyl)alcohol (PVA), polyethyleneimine (PEI) and hyaluronic acid. Prepared nanofiber carriers were specifically adjusted for the autologous MSCs (mesenchymal stromal cells) applications on the chronic wound. In addition, the nanofiber sheets were constructed as a biodegradable material to guarantee proper timing of its resorption in a chronic wound during the healing process. Furthermore, the effect of growth factors on MSC proliferation was tested. The release of bFGF from adsorbed lipid particles was tested. The results show increased proliferation of MSCs. Despite fast increasing advanced technologies in healthcare, chronic wound treating tends to be still very difficult and challenging. Our developed nanofiber-based dressings are very promising for poorly healing wound therapy using MSCs. The main goal is to make chronic wound healing more effective and decrease a time of healing process.

1. INTRODUCTION

In the recent years, there has been a growing interest in nanofiber materials for biomedical use including wound healing [1]. Nanofibers due to their properties (huge surface area, persistent diameter, high aspect ratio, and tailorability) provide multiple advantages for wound healing applications. Nanofibrous structures are most often prepared by electrospinning process [2,3]. During this process polymer nanofibers are prepared by electrospinning from a polymeric solution and trapped on base material (e.g. nonwoven textile). The resulting nanofibrous membranes show high porosity, uniform pore distribution, high pore interconnection and the overall structure mimics extracellular matrix [4]. Electrospinning was shown to enable processing wide range of polymers including synthetic biodegradable (i.e. polylactic acids, polyglycolic acid, polycaprolactone, polyvinyl alcohol, polyethylene oxide), natural biodegradable polymers (i.e. gelatine, collagen, hyaluronic acid, alginate, chitosan) and also synthetic polymers (i.e. polyamide, polyacrylonitrile, polyvinyl difluoride) [5].

As a part of this research several mentioned polymers were used for the preparation of the nanofiber scaffolds. Polycaprolactone (PCL) is biodegradable polyester widely used on biomedical industry. The nanofibers prepared from polycaprolactone show biodegradation depending on molecular weight [6]. PCL nanofibers were shown to support adhesion and proliferation of keratinocytes, melanocytes, and fibroblasts [7]. Recently, we have reported nanofibers from PCL in form of wound dressing [8]. The system showed optimal healing by utilization as integrative wound dressing with low exchange rates. Adhesive properties of fibers upon exchange showed slower regeneration by removing of newly formed tissue upon removal. The PCL nanofibers were also shown to stimulate the healing upon functionalization with blood derivatives [9,10]. Polycaprolacton-co-lactic acids (PLCL) are biodegradable polyester which shows higher elasticity then PCL [11], but this material is much less explored for electrospinning compered to PCL. Nevertheless, PLCL was shown to produce scaffolds in combination with natural polymers (i.e. collagen and heparin) [12]. Another fiber-forming polymer is poly(vinyl)alcohol (PVA), which is a biodegradable polymer with hydrophilic properties. PVA was shown to produce nanofiber scaffolds for wound dressings with potential for non-adhesive dressings [8]. Polyethyleneimine (PEI), and its derivatives, are polycationic polymers also widely used for electrospinning biocompatible scaffolds fabrication [e.g. 13]. Khanam et al. has developed and standardized the PEI-based scaffold, which promotes the direct formation of new tissue.

Moreover, described biopolymers are utilized for increase of cell adhesion and biocompatibility of natural fibers. The nanofiber-based wound dressings were shown to be further functionalized by blending with hyaluronic acid [14]. Hyaluronic acid, that has unique capacity in retaining water, is neutral skin component involved in its moisturizing process [15]. Hussein et al. [16] has reported nanofiber based wound dressings formed by blend electrospinning of PVA and hyaluronic acid with L-arginine. The system showed increased wound healing potential *in vitro*.

2. METHODS

2.1. Electrospinning of polycaprolactone (PCL)

Polycaprolactone (MW 45,000; Sigma Aldrich) was dissolved in chloroform: ethanol (9:1). The concentration of PCL was set 28% (w/v) and solution was stirred overnight at 50 °C. The formed solution was electrospun on InoSPIN MINI (InoCure) device using G10 needle electrode at 100 ml/h dosing rate. The voltage was set at +45kV, -35 kV and distance of 200 mm. The resulting nanofibers were collected on rotating drum collector (500 rpm). Each batch of fibers was spun from 30 ml of solution with deposition area of 1100 cm^2.

2.2. Electrospinning of polycaprolacton-co-lactic acids (PLCL)

PLCL (Corbion) was dissolved in DMF. The concentration of PLCL was set 15% (w/v) and solution was stirred overnight at 50 °C. The formed solution was electrospun on InoSPIN MINI (InoCure) device using G20 needle electrode at 30 ml/h dosing rate. The voltage was set at +42kV, -30 kV and distance of 200 mm. The resulting nanofibers were collected on rotating drum collector (500 rpm). Each batch of fibers was spun from 30 ml of solution with deposition area of 1100 cm^2.

2.3. Electrospinning of poly(vinyl)alcohol (PVA)

10% (w/v) PVA (40-88; Merck) was dissolved in distilled water with addition of 40,000 ppm glyoxal and 30,000 ppm H_3PO_4. The solution was prepared overnight using stirring and heating (80 °C). The formed solution was electrospun on InoSPIN MINI (InoCure) device using linear slit needleless electrode at 100 ml/h dosing rate. The voltage was set at +45kV, -30 kV and distance of 200 mm. The resulting nanofibers were collected on rotating drum collector (500 rpm). Each batch of fibers was spun from 30 ml of solution with deposition area of 1100 cm^2. The formed scaffolds were crosslinked at 90 °C for 5 min.

2.4. Electrospinning of polyethyleneimine (PEI)

PCL-PEI scaffolds were prepared by blend electrospinning. Polycaprolactone (MW 45,000; Sigma Aldrich) was dissolved in chloroform: ethanol (9:1). The concentration of PCL was set 28% (w/v) and solution was stirred overnight at 50 °C. PEI (Alpha Aesar) was added to the solution in ratio 9:1 (w/v). The formed solution was electrospun on InoSPIN MINI (InoCure) device using G10 needle electrode at 100 ml/h dosing rate. The voltage was set at +45kV, -35 kV and distance of 200 mm. The resulting nanofibers were collected on rotating drum collector (500 rpm). Each batch of fibers was spun from 30 ml of solution with deposition area of 1100 cm^2.

2.5. Electrospinning of PVA-HA

8% (w/v) PVA (40-88; Merck) was dissolved in distilled water with addition of 40,000 ppm glyoxal and 30,000 ppm H_3PO_4. The solution was prepared overnight using stirring and heating (80 °C). After dissolution 1% (w/v) of hyaluronic acid (Hyalgan) was added to the solution and left for additional 5 hours to stir at room temperature. The formed solution was electrospun on InoSPIN MINI (InoCure) device using linear slit needleless electrode at 100 ml/h dosing rate. The voltage was set at +45kV, -30 kV and distance of 200 mm. The resulting nanofibers were collected on rotating drum collector (500 rpm). Each batch of fibers was spun from 30 ml of solution with deposition area of 1100 cm^2. The formed scaffolds were crosslinked at 90 °C for 5 min.

2.6. Characterization by SEM

Samples were cut to discs (5 mm diameter) and coated with layer of platinum (sput-coater Quorum). The samples were analysed using Tescan Vega electron microscope.

2.7. MSC cell culture

Blood marrow was aspirated from the iliac wing of a minipig into a 5 mL-syringe containing 1 mL PBS and 25 IU heparin under general anesthesia. The mononuclear cells were isolated using gradient separation with the plasma substitute Gelofusine®. Briefly, blood marrow was mixed with 1.25 mL Gelofusine®. After 30 min, the upper and medium layers containing plasma, mononuclear cells, and erythrocytes were aspirated, and centrifuged at 270 × g for 15 min. Subsequently, the medium layer with mononuclear cells was aspirated and seeded in tissue culture flasks. Adherent cells were cultured in Minimum Essential Medium (MEM) (with L-glutamine, PAA) containing 10% fetal bovine serum (Mycoplex, PAA), 100 IU/mL penicillin, and 100 µg/mL streptomycin. The cells were passaged using the trypsin-EDTA method before confluence was reached. The cells from the third passage were used for the cell culture study.

2.8. Platelet functionalization

The PCL-based nanofiber scaffolds, selected as most satisfactory carriers, were tested in combination with thrombocytes to support the MSCs activity and/or viability. Platelets were adsorbed on the surface of the support using the vacuum functionalization device (Grade Medical). The MSCs were seeded in density 40,000 cells/cm^2 on the surface of platelet functionalized PCL nanofibers and PCL nanofibers without platelets. The samples were analysed on day 7 using propidium iodide (Sigma Aldrich) and $DiOC_6$ (Sigma Aldrich) according to Knotek et al [17]. Samples were visualized using confocal microscope (Leica).

2.9. Doping of nanofiber carriers with growth factors

The release of basic fibroblast growth factor (bFGF) from lipid particles based on 1-tetradecanol (Sigma Aldrich) drug delivery system was tested subsequently. The solid lipid particles (SLP) based drug delivery system were produced by the functionalization device (Grade Medical) using nano- or micro-emulsification process under the controlled condition (dose, temperature, rotation speed, pressure).

3. RESULTS AND DISCUSSION

Electrospinning process showed proper formation of nanofibers using multijet technology. The nanofibers from PCL showed highest production rate with formation up to 10 jets per emitter. In case of PLCL, the electrospinning process was slower and resulted in lower production capacity. PVA and PVA-HA were spun from needleless electrode enabling formation of > 50 jets. Due to lower production capacity caused by increased surface tension and lower polymer concentration the process was slower and despite increased numbers of jets, the overall productivity was lower than in case of PCL.

The process for all samples resulted in formulation of well solidified scaffolds enabling mechanical handling. The samples from PLCL showed shrinkage of scaffolds due to relaxing of mechanical tension in stretched PCLC polymeric chains. PCL showed highest mechanical stability.

The analysis using electron microscopy showed proper fibrous morphology (**Figures 1, A-D**). PCL showed morphology with bimodal distribution of nanofibers (221 ± 48 nm - nanofibrous fraction, 536 ± 52 nm submicrofiber fraction). The morphology also showed minor population of microfibers. In case of PLCL the morphology of nanofibers was 750 ± 120 nm and showed partially beaded structure. In case of PVA the fibers showed size 250 ± 32 nm with low fiber deviation and homogenous structure. In case of PVA-HA combination was observed fibers with a diameter 270 ± 45 nm. PCL-PEI electrospinning resulted in formation of fibers with bimodal distribution of nanofibers (240 ± 65 nm - nanofibrous fraction, 420 ± 84 nm submicrofiber fractions).

The overall structure of the fibers corresponds to macroscopic properties of nanofibrous layer. The low presence of defects improves mechanical properties of fibers.

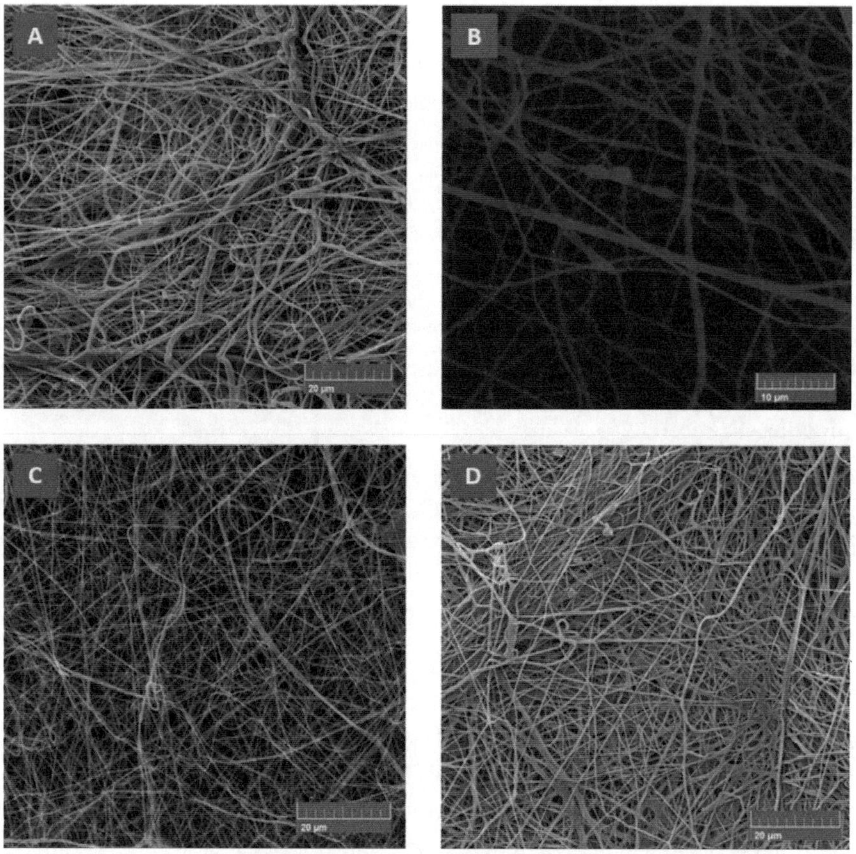

Figure 1 SEM images of electrospun nanofiber scaffolds based on PCL (**A**), PLCL (**B**), PVA (**C**) and PVA-HA (**D**)

The initial results of *in vitro* testing of PCL with adhered thrombocytes have shown increased cell proliferation on platelet carriers compared to PCL nanofibers (see **Figure 2**). The results indicate bioactivity retention of thrombocytes after vacuum deposition.

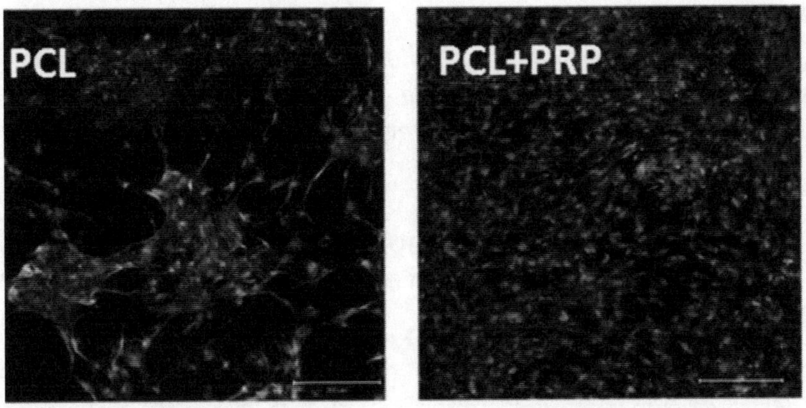

Figure 2 Confocal microscope images of MSC proliferation on non-doped PCL carrier (left) and carrier with platelet-rich plasma (PRP) (right)

Furthermore, we gave showed that vacuum deposition enables adsorption of solid lipid particles on the surface of nanofibers. The scaffold morphology shows microparticles attached on the surface of fibrous structure (**Figure 3**). The preliminary cell culture study indicates MSC survival on the scaffold with adsorbed SLPs (**Figure 4**).

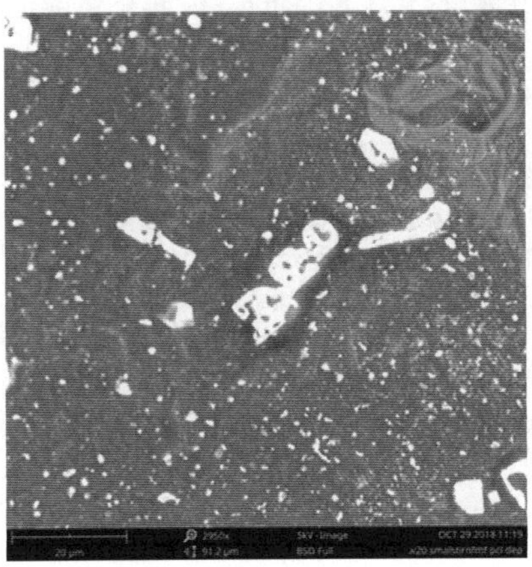

Figure 3 SEM image of SLP adsorbed on PCL nanofibers

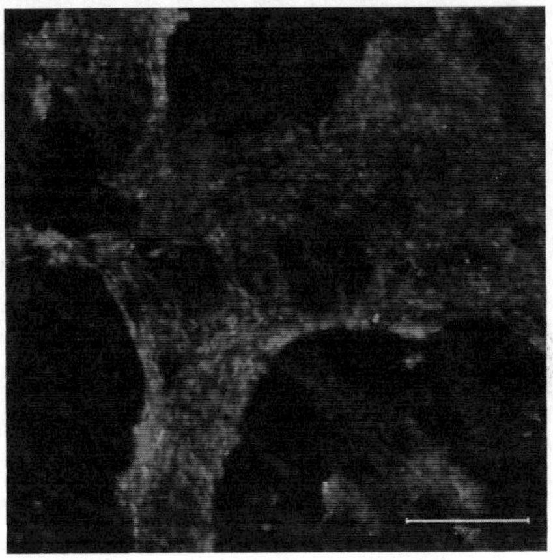

Figure 4 Confocal image of MSC on PCL nanofibers with SLP containing bFGF on day 7 of culture

4. CONCLUSION

The electrospinning technology was showed to enable processing of PCL, PLCL, PVA, PEI and PVA-HA for wound dressing applications. The fibers showed beadles structure with different properties of nanofibers which were subsequently tested using MSCs. The samples with both platelets and SLPs showed cell adhesion properties and enabled cellular growth after 7 days in culture. The results suggest that vacuum deposition is a suitable method for functionalization of nanofiber scaffolds. However the potential of the formed scaffolds will be further evaluated in long-term cell culture and *in vivo* conditions, results obtained indicate these nanofibrous scaffolds as suitable carrier for MSCs themselves as well as carriers of drug delivery system for controlled release of supportive substances, such as soluble pro-regenerative factors, used during the MSCs therapy. Such a nanofiber-based dressings are then very promising for poorly healing wound therapy using MSCs with the main goal to make chronic wound healing more effective and decrease a time of healing process.

ACKNOWLEDGEMENTS

This work was performed as part of the project FV20422 "Development of nanofibrous scaffolds ensuring application of cellular products, including physical stimulation effect, with the intended purpose of the treatment of chronic wounds".

REFERENCES

[1] STOCCO, T.D., BASSOUS, N.J., ZHAO, S., GRANATO, A.E.C., WEBSTER, T.J., LOBO, A.O. Nanofibrous scaffolds for biomedical applications. *Nanoscale.* [online]. 2018, vol. 10, pp. 12228-12255. Available from: https://doi.org/10.1039/c8nr02002g.

[2] TAHALYANI, J., RAHANGDALE, K.K., AEPURU, R., KANDASUBRAMANIAN, B., DATAR, S. Dielectric investigation of a conducting fibrous nonwoven porous mat fabricated by a one-step facile electrospinning process. *RSC Adv.* [online]. 2016, vol. 6, pp. 36588-36598. Available from: https://doi.org/10.1039/c5ra23012h.

[3] ARUCHAMY, K., MAHTO, A., NATARAJ, S.K. Electrospun nanofibers, nanocomposites and characterization of art: insight on establishing fibers as product. *Nano-Struct Nano-Objects.* [online]. 2018, vol. 16, pp. 45-58. Available from: https://doi.org/10.1016/j.nanoso.2018.03.013.

[4] SILL, T.J., VON RECUM, H.A. Electrospinning: applications in drug delivery and tissue engineering. *Biomaterials.* [online]. 2008, vol. 29, no. 13, pp. 1989-2006. Available from: https://doi.org/10.1016/j.biomaterials.2008.01.011.

[5] MEIRELES, A.B., CORREA, D.K., SILVEIRA, J.V.W., MILLÁS, A.L.G., BITTENCOURT, E., DE BRITO-MĚLO, G.E.A., GONZÁLEZ-TORRES, L.A. Trends in polymeric electrospun fibers and their use as oral biomaterials. *Experimental biology and medicine (Maywood, N.J.).* [online]. 2018, vol. 243, no. 8, pp. 665-676. Available from: https://doi.org/10.1177/1535370218770404.

[6] GOLDBERG, D. A review of the biodegradability and utility of poly(caprolactone). *Journal of environmental polymer degradation.* [online]. 1995, vol. 3, pp. 61-67. Available from: https://doi.org/10.1007/BF02067481.

[7] VOCETKOVA, K., BUZGO, M., SOVKOVA, V., BEZDEKOVA, D., KNEPPO, P., AMLER, E. Nanofibrous polycaprolactone scaffolds with adhered platelets stimulate proliferation of skin cells. *Cell proliferation.* [online]. 2016, vol. 49, no. 5, pp. 568-578. Available from: https://doi.org/10.1111/cpr.12276.

[8] BUZGO, M., PLENCNER, M., RAMPICHOVA, M., LITVINEC, A., PROSECKA, E., STAFFA, A., KRALOVIC, M., FILOVA, E., DOUPNIK, M., LUKASOVA, V., VOCETKOVA, K., ANDEROVA, J., KUBIKOVA, T., ZAJICEK, R., LOPOT, F., JELEN, K., TONAR, Z., AMLER, E., DIVIN, R., FIORI, F. Poly-ε-caprolactone and polyvinyl alcohol electrospun wound dressings: adhesion properties and wound management of skin defects in rabbits. *Regen Med.* [online]. 2019 May, vol. 14, no. 5, pp. 423-445. Available from: https://doi.org/10.2217/rme-2018-0072.

[9] SOVKOVA, V., VOCETKOVA, K., RAMPICHOVA, M., MICKOVA, A., BUZGO, M., LUKASOVA, V., DANKOVA, J., FILOVA, E., NECAS, A., AMLER, E. Platelet lysate as a serum replacement for skin cell culture on biomimetic PCL nanofibers. *Platelets.* [online]. 2018, vol. 29, no. 4, pp. 395-405. Available from: https://doi.org/10.1080/09537104.2017.1316838.

[10] LUKÁŠOVÁ, V., BUZGO, M., VOCETKOVÁ, K., SOVKOVÁ, V., DOUPNÍK, M., HIMAWAN, E., STAFFA, A., SEDLÁČEK, R., CHLUP, H., RUSTICHELLI, F., AMLER, E., RAMPICHOVÁ, M. Needleless electrospun and centrifugal spun poly-ε-caprolactone scaffolds as a carrier for platelets in tissue engineering applications: A comparative study with hMSCs. *Mater Sci Eng C Mater Biol Appl.* [online]. 2019, vol. 97, pp. 567-575. Available from: https://doi.org/10.1016/j.msec.2018.12.069.

[11] JEONG, S.I., KIM, S.H., KIM, Y.H., JUNG, Y., KWON, J.H., KIM, B-S., LEE, Y.M. Manufacture of elastic biodegradable PLCL scaffolds for mechano-active vascular tissue engineering. *Journal of biomaterials science. Polymer edition.* [online]. 2004, vol. 15, pp. 645-660. Available from: https://doi.org/10.1163/156856204323046906.

[12] KWON, I.K., MATSUDA, T. Co-Electrospun Nanofiber Fabrics of Poly(l-lactide-co-ε-caprolactone) with Type I Collagen or Heparin. *Biomacromolecules.* [online]. 2005, vol. 6, no. 4, pp. 2096-2105. Available from: https://doi.org/10.1021/bm050086u.

[13] KHANAM, N., MIKORYAK, C., DRAPER, R.K., BALKUS, K.J. Electrospun linear polyethyleneimine scaffolds for cell growth. *Acta Biomaterialia.* [online]. 2007, vol. 3, no. 6, pp. 1050-1059. Available from: https://doi.org/10.1016/j.actbio.2007.06.005.

[14] SNETKOV, P., MOROZKINA, S., USPENSKAYA, M., OLEKHNOVICH, R. Hyaluronan-Based Nanofibers: Fabrication, Characterization and Application. *Polymers.* [online]. 2019, vol. 11, p. 2036 (1-25). Available from: https://doi.org/10.3390/polym11122036.

[15] PAPAKONSTANTINOU, E., ROTH, M., KARAKIULAKIS, G. Hyaluronic acid: A key molecule in skin aging. *Dermato-endocrinology.* [online]. 2012, vol. 4, no. 3, pp. 253-258. Available from: https://doi.org/10.4161/derm.21923.

[16] HUSSEIN, Y., E EL-FAKHARANY. M., KAMOUN, E. A., LOUTFY, S. A., AMIN, R., TAHA, T. H., SALIM, S.A., AMER, M. Electrospun PVA/hyaluronic acid/L-arginine nanofibers for wound healing applications: Nanofibers optimization and in vitro bioevaluation. *International Journal of Biological Macromolecules.* [online]. 2020, Available from: https://doi.org/10.1016/j.ijbiomac.2020.07.126.

[17] KNOTEK, P., POUZAR, M., BUZGO, M., KRIZKOVA, B., VLCEK, M., MICKOVA, A., PLENCNER, M., NAVESNIK, J., AMLER, E., BELINA, P. Cryogenic grinding of electrospun poly-ε-caprolactone mesh submerged in liquid media. *Materials Science & engineering. C, Materials for Biological Applications.* [online]. 2012, vol. 32, no. 6, pp. 1366-1374. Available from: https://doi.org/10.1016/j.msec.2012.04.012.

TEST OF COMPLEX NANOSTRUCTURES AS GENE DELIVERY SYSTEM TO CARDIAC CELLS

Josef SKOPALIK[1,2], Jaroslav PRUCHA[3,4], Jiri SEKORA[2], Vratislav CMIEL[2], Tomas PARAK[1], Josef MASEK[5,6]

[1]*Department of Pharmacology and Toxicology, Faculty of Pharmacy, Masaryk University, Brno, Czech Republic, EU, j.skopalik@gmail.com*

[2]*Department of Biomedical Engineering, Faculty of Electrical Engineering and Communication, Brno University of Technology, Brno, Czech Republic, EU*

[3]*Department of Health Care Disciplines and Population Protection, Faculty of Biomedical Engineering, Czech Technical University in Prague, Czech Republic, EU*

[4]*Department of Information and Communication Technologies in Medicine, Faculty of Biomedical Engineering, Czech Technical University, Prague, Czech Republic, EU*

[5]*Centre of Experimental Medicine, Slovak Academy of Sciences, Bratislava, Slovakia, EU*

[6]*Department of Pharmacology and Toxicology, Veterinary Research Institute, Brno, Czech Republic, EU*

https://doi.org/10.37904/nanocon.2020.3757

Abstract

Various nanostructures, including liposomes, dendrimers, polymers, carbon or silicon materials, and metal nanoparticles seems to be evaluated as carriers in different gene delivery systems. Muscle cells are target of modern gene medicine, due to of the much pathology (arrhythmias, channels pathological mutation, abnormal apoptosis) with limited curability by traditional drugs. The zeta potential of the muscle cells were identified by non-traditional method of DLS. This was starting point to setting of parameters for experimental liposome, the liposome surface charge have been tested and modified by cationic plasmid and final complex was evaluated as delivery system of DNA into the muscle cardiac cells.

Keywords: Nanoliposom, nanoparticle, transfection, zeta potential, cell engineering, regenerative medicine

1. INTRODUCTION

The zeta potential of the cells and the zeta potentials of the modern „Trojan horse particles“ (liposomes, exosomes, nanoparticles) are two key parameters, which must be tested to ideal compatibility, if there is the aim of the maximal effectivity of „Trojan soldiers“ homing into the living cells. The DLS technique was previously applied primarily in order to study microorganisms, cancer cells or blood cells [1,2]. We used a Zetasizer Nano ZS analyser to analyse the zeta potential of cardiomyocytes and also for characterisation of nanoparticles/nanoliposomes conjugated with GFP vector, which can be used s delivery system into the muscle and another type of mammalian cells. The analysis was correlated also with tests based on electrophoresis methods. Transfection of the cells and gen/protein delivery is the modern direction of the experimental medicine, however precise description of this phenomenon and developing of new „nano-entities“ need precise analysis of the surface charge and precise analysis of the interaction between cells and selected "Trojan particles“.

2. METHODS

2.1. Preparation of two types of cardiac cells

Neonatal rat cardiomyocytes were isolated from Wistar 2-5 days old Neonatal rats. Hearts were removed and dissociated in a balanced salt solution containing 20 mM HEPES, 120 mM NaCl, 1 mM NaH_2PO_4, 5.5 mM glucose, 5.4 mM KCl, and 0.8 mM $MgSO_4$ (pH 7.3-7.4). Cardiomyocytes from the tissue homogenates were isolated by trypsin digestion, selection of cardiomyocytes were done using adhesive affinity to collagen bottom described in our previous experiments [3]. The cardiomyocytes cultures were suspended in DMEM and transferred (1000 cells/ 100 µL) to 96 well culture chamber plates, which was rewarmed to 37°C. The first part of the cell culture was resuspendend and immediately taken from the bottom of plastic chamber and used for Zetasizer measurement of surface charge (chapter 2.2). The second part of the cells was incubated in DMEM medium and used for transfection tests (chapter 2.4) on microscopic unit.

Adult rat cardiomyocytes were obtained from young adult Wistar rats (250 ± 50 g). The cardiomyocytes were isolated using the method of enzymatic dissociation via [4] (the heart was perfused with Ca^{2+} free Tyrode's solution containing collagenase, the final dissociated cardiomyocytes were collected in Ca^{2+} free Tyrode's solution and gently mixed with standard Tyrode's solution (0.09 mmol/l $CaCl_2$) and diluted 1:1 byDMEM medium in 96 well chamber in following 30 minutes. The first part of the cell culture were resuspendend from the bottom of plastic chamber after 10 minutes and used for Zetasizer measurement of surface charge (chapter 2.2). The second part of the cells was used for transfection tests (chapter 2.4). All experiments underwent under improvement of ethics committee.

2.2. The cell surface charge identification by Zetasizer

The zeta potential of the cells was recorded in a suspension (0.3×10^{6} cells/ml) using the electrophoretic light scattering technique on a Zetasizer Nano ZS analyser (Malvern Instruments, Great Britain). The measurements were performed in a U-shaped cell with gold-plated electrodes at 25°C or 37°C.

2.3. The nanoparticle and lipid vesicle selection and their surface charge identification

Nano-liposomes (NL) were prepared by hydration of phospholipid film method composed of N-[1-(2, 3-Dioleoyloxy)propyl]-N,N,N-trimethylammonium methyl-sulphate (DOTAP) and 1,2-Dioleoyl-sn-Glycero-3-Phosphoethanolamine (DOPE) [1]. The suspension was extruded through polycarbonate filters (pore size of 100 nm). Resultant liposomes were mixed with plasmid pcDNA4/TO-bio-myc-NES-EGFP to form lipid-DNA complexes, three variants of concentration were used (details in Results, **Figure 2**).

Maghemite nanoparticles (FeNP) were synthesized by borohydride reduction (53 mmol in liquid ammonia) of ferric chloride $FeCl_3{\cdot}6H_2O$ (37 mmol), both purchased from Sigma-Aldrich Co. (St Louis, MO, USA), at room temperature. After the reduction reaction (indicated by change of colour to black), the temperature of the mixture was increased to 100°C and held constant for 2 hours. After cooling the mixture to room temperature, the magnetic fraction was separated using an external magnet and washed several times with water. Details in [5].

The surface of the liposomes or nanoparticles was modified by addition of plasmid pcDNA4/TO-bio-myc-NES-EGFP to form final DNA-particle of DNA-liposome complexes. Conjugation was tested with three different concentration of plasmid (10 µg/µL, 20 µg/µL, 40 µg/µL) in conjugation solution (timing and temperature described in Results) and after the conjugation step the electrophoresis was used for quantitative detection of amount of free (non bound) plasmid and relative effectivity of plasmid binding (details in Results).

3. RESULTS

3.1. The cell surface charge identification by Zetasizer

The zeta potential of cardiomyocytes in DMEM medium was measured under 25°C or 37°C respectively; all variants are reprinted in the following **Table 1**.

Table 1 Cell samples measurement by Zetasizer

Sample variant	Temperature 25°C	Temperature 37°C
Neonatal cardiomyocytes	−9.60 mV	−9.1 mV
Adult cardiomyocytes	−10.77 mV	−14.24 mV

3.2. The nano-complexes surface charge identification by Zetasizer and selection of the optimal concentration of solution for conjugation

The positive surface charge was detected by Zetasizer and also by electrophoresis method on prepared NL and FeNP (on pure entities, non-conjugated with any plasmid). The addition of the different amount of the DNA plasmid to the conjugation solution underwent in 0.5 ml plastic microtube in thermostatic shaker (37°C, 120 rpm), the mixture of different concentration of plasmid versus constant concentration of nano-entities caused different adhesivity of plasmid NL or FeNP, all variants of concentration (10, 20, 40 ng/µL of plasmid and 5 µg/µL of FeNP respectively 0.5 µg/µL of NL) displayed that the final state of conjugation is almost stable formed in all variants of solution during the first 10 minutes. This fact gives possibility to apply plasmid and remodify the originally nano-entities to complexes covered by significant amount of plasmids in very short time. The most important information from electrophoresis data is quantification of relative and absolute amount of effectively binding plasmid versus resting non-bound plasmid, the data are represented on **Figure 1** (conjugation with liposomes) and **Figure 2** (conjugation with nanoparticles).

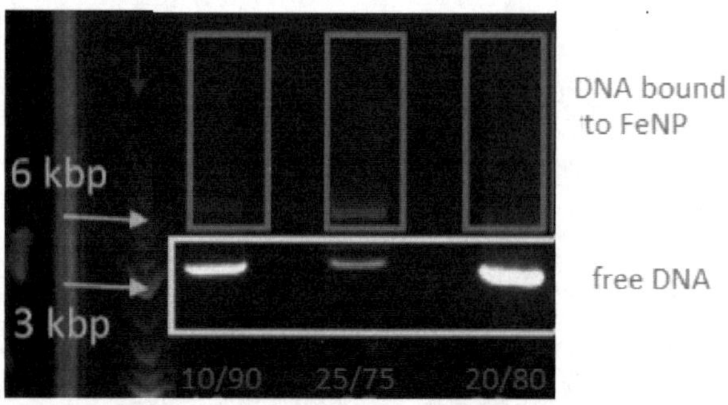

Figure 1 Effectivity of plasmid-FeNP complex creation in mixture tube. Mixed samples (from left to right variant 10, 20 or 40 ng/µL of plasmid in conjugation solution) were transpippeted to gel and fractions were measured after 30 min of migration on gel electrophoresis (110V, arrow means direction of field to anode). UV scan and Kodak software visualized bound / free fraction of DNA plasmid.

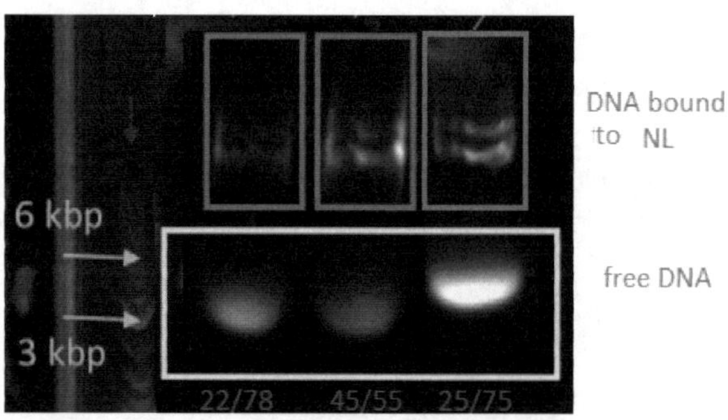

Figure 2 Effectivity of plasmid-NL complex creation in mixture tube. Mixed samples (from left to right variant 10, 20 or 40 ng/µL of plasmid in conjugation solution) were transpippeted to gel and fractions were measured after 30 min of migration on gel electrophoresis (110V, arrow means direction of field to anode). UV scan and Kodak software visualized bound / free fraction of DNA plasmid.

The surface charge detected in DMEM medium by Zetasizer was -5.3 mV for plasmid-FeNP complex (variant 20ng/µL) and -1.1 mV for plasmid-NL complex (the variant 20 ng/µL)

3.3. The test of the final transfection effectivity on the live cells

Both types of optimized "Trojan horses" (complex based on liposomes or nanoparticles) were tested on cell cultures (addition of previously prepared plasmid-particle complex to DMEM at 37°C and 5% CO2 atmosphere of the lab incubator, absolute plasmid-particle concentration in solution was adjusted to 0,8 ng/µL in all finally comprised variant). The final GFP positive cells (48 hours after transfection) are describe in **Table 2**, the representative microscopically scans of cells are on **Figure 3**.

Table 2 Transfection variants and effectivity on live cells

Transfection variant	Plasmid-NL complex	Plasmid-FeNP
Neonatal cardiomyocytes	5.5 ± 3.1 %	11.7 ± 5.5 %
Adult cardiomyocytes	21.5 ± 8.5 %	12.2 ± 9.5 %

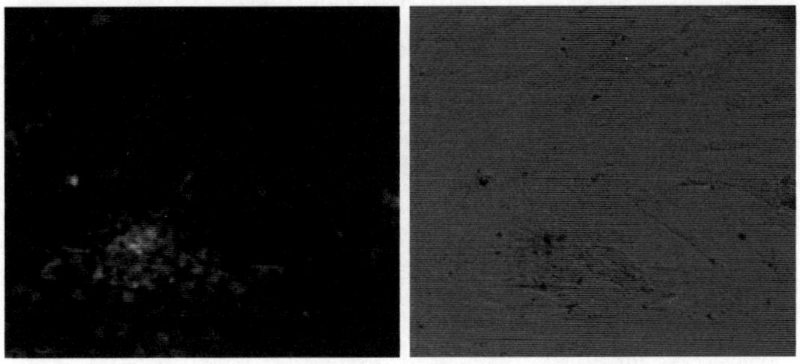

Figure 3 Illustration of microscopically evaluation of neonatal cardiomyocytes transfection and visibility of GFP (variant plasmid-NL). Fluorescence mode exc.490/ em. 520nm (left), the same field of view visualized by phase contrast mode (right).

The very actual preliminary data also illustrated the possibility of higher effectivity of invasion NL or FeNP complexes to the cardiac cells, if the altering electromagnetic field is applied on the cell samples (data not shown), optimizing of the electromagnetic field and its biocompatibility with muscle cells and covering tissue was stared in our parallel project [1].

4. CONCLUSION

Our investigation has two basic outputs. The complex zeta potential analysis of cells and entities for gene delivery (cardiomyocytes and nanoparticles or nanolyposomes) has been identified using zetapotential mode of standard DLS machine. The amount of the bound DNA on final „Trojan nanosystems" and charge profile of these nano-systems was adjusted and the optimised variant was used for pilot transfection experiments on cardiac cells. Transfection effectivity was 5-20%, however the methods have potential to be upgraded by additive electromagnetic field which accelerate invasion of charged complex into the cells.

ACKNOWLEDGEMENTS

The project was supported by Ministry of Education, Youth and Sports of Czech Rep. (project "FIT" CZ.02.1.01/0.0/0.0/15003/0000495) and by Ministry of Industry of Czech Rep. - project FV20422 and project TACR FW01010106 respectively.

REFERENCES

[1] HANAKOVA, L., PRUCHA, J., SOCHA, V., ŠTENGL, M., VAN BERGH, S. Effect of High-Induction Magnetic Stimulation on Complex Heart Rate Variability of Sus Scrofa Domesticus under General Anesthesia. *Appl. Sci.* [online]. 2020, vol. 10, p. 589. Available from: https://doi.org/10.3390/app10020589

[2] BONDAR, O. V., SAIFULLINA, D.V, SHAKHMAEVA, I. I., MAVLYUTOVA, I.I., ABDULLIN, T.I. "Monitoring of the zeta potential of human cells upon reduction in their viability and interaction with polymers." *Acta Naturae (англоязычная версия).* 2012, vol. 4, no. 1, pp. 80-83

[3] SKOPALIK, J., PASEK, M., RYCHTARIK, M., KORISTEK, Z., GABRIELOVA, E., SCHEER, P., KLABUSAY, M. Formation of cell-to-cell connection between bone marrow cells and isolated rat cardiomyocytes in a cocultivation model. *Journal of Cell Science & Therapy*. 2014, vol. 5, no. 5, pp. 1-8.

[4] BÉBAROVÁ, M., MATEJOVIČ, P., PÁSEK, M., HOŘÁKOVÁ, Z., HOŠEK, J., ŠIMURDOVÁ, M., ŠIMURDA, J., 2016. Effect of ethanol at clinically relevant concentrations on atrial inward rectifier potassium current sensitive to acetylcholine. *Naunyn-Schmiedeberg's archives of pharmacology*. 2016, vol. 389, no.10, pp.1049-1058.

[5] SKOPALIK, J., POLAKOVA, K., HAVRDOVA, M., JUSTAN, I., MAGRO, M., MILDE, D., KNOPFOVA, L., SMARDA, J., POLAKOVA, H., GABRIELOVA, E., VIANELLO, F. Mesenchymal stromal cell labeling by new uncoated superparamagnetic maghemite nanoparticles in comparison with commercial Resovist-an initial in vitro study. *International journal of nanomedicine*. 2014, vol. 9, p.5355.

BIO-APPLICABLE METAL NANOPARTICLES

[1]Vít VYKOUKAL, [1]Radka DOPITOVÁ, [1]Martin POLÁK, [1]Jiří NOVÁČEK

[1]*Ceitec MU - Central European Institute of Technology Masaryk University, Brno, Czech Republic, EU*
jiri.novacek@ceitec.muni.cz

https://doi.org/10.37904/nanocon.2020.3736

Abstract

Metal nanoparticles find wide application potential in the biological research due to their unique optical, magnetic, electrical properties. Utilization of the nanoparticles prepared by chemical synthesis for biological research is limited by its solubility in water and toxicity. One potential solution to overcome this limitation is encapsulation of metal nanoparticles into protein or lipidic shell.

Apoferritin is highly symmetric 12 nm protein cage composed of 24 apoferritin monomers which forms hollow structure with 8 nm cavity. Protein shell specifically interacts with the receptor on the cell membrane which facilitates uptake of the apoferritin from the extra-cellular environment into the cell. Due to the high stability of the protein cage and inherent capacity to encompass metal nanoparticles, apoferritin is widely focused as a potentionally optimal and general system for delivery of the metal nanoparticles into the organism.

In addition, apoferritin can be also used as a nanoreactor for the nanoparticle production. We have generated a set of different nanoparticles encapsulated in apoferritin cage which we have intended to use as a label for structural and cellular biology research by cryo-electron microscopy. Here, we show that despite the 8 nm cavity, single 6-8 nm nanoparticle is not formed inside apoferritin cage. Instead, larger number of 2 nm or smaller nanoparticles is present inside apoferritin reducing overall number of atoms which can be incorporated into the molecule and thus the attainable contrast during electron microscopy imaging. Despite its wide utilization in life-science research, we conclude, that apoferritin derived nanoparticle system is not an optimal labeling probe for cryo-electron microscopy.

Keywords: Apoferritin, metal nanoparticles, cryo-electron microscopy

1. INTRODUCTION

Chemical synthesis of metal nanoparticles (NPs) is nowadays progressive field of science. Metal nanoparticles can be produced in miligram-to-gram scale by various methods e. g. reduction of metal salts solution in presence of a surfactant [1-4], thermal decomposition of metal precursors [5-7], or ball milling [8,9]. They have found wide range of applications in electronics [10,11], optics [12], catalysis [13] etc. Furthermore, metal NPs are ideal candidates as contrast agent for life-science electron microscopy research due to the significantly higher electron density in comparison to biological samples. NPs bound to antibody or affinity tag are widely used in imuno-electron microscopy studies for localization of molecules of interest [14,15]. However, a robust system which would allow targeting molecules of interest inside living cell is nowadays not available because NPs are, in general, not taken by a cell and are, in most cases, toxic for cells. Even gold NPs which are declared as bio-compatible and non-toxic are not taken up by cells which limit their application as markers for research on viable biological specimen. Integration of the NP into the cell own shell is one potential approach to overcome this issue. Apoferritin was proposed as an ideal candidate for production of hybrid NPs due to its unique structural and functional properties [16].

Apoferritin is a 12 nm hollow protein complex with 8 nm in diameter cavity. It forms a tetrahedral cage composed of 24 subunits connected through 14 pores. The structure has six twofold symmetry axes, four threefold symmetry axes, and three fourfold symmetry axes. Apoferritin monomers can withstand exposure to temperatures above 70 °C and wide pH range 2.0-10.0. The native protein is composed of two kinds of subunits, heavy and light (H and L). Apoferritin shell exhibits reversible self-assembling ability. The assembly can be destabilized or even disassociated into monomers under specific conditions which can subsequently be reassembled back to the apoferritin structure. It naturally binds iron, serves as iron storage, and functions in distribution of iron to areas where it is required. The inner cavity is able to absorb around 4500 atoms of Fe(III) to form ferritin [17].

Previous studies showed possibility to synthesize metal nanoparticles inside of apoferritin cavity. Various works declared monodispersive metal nanoparticles embedded in apoferritin shell [17-19]. Metal nanoparticles in apoferritin cavity can be prepared by two approaches: (A) the apoferritin shell is disassociated into monomers. This monomer solution is combined with metal source solution followed by apoferritin shell reconstruction, dialysis or gel filtration to remove excess metal ions outside of apoferritin cavities. Metal ions trapped into cavity are reduced to form metal nanoparticles; (B) Metal ions enter into the apoferritin cavity through channels, where they are trapped, and the excess of ions outside the apoferritin cage is subsequently removed followed by ion reduction inside the cavities. Herein, we have tested both approaches in order to generate hybrid NP where the apoferritin cage is completely filled with single large nanoparticle made of a defined metal. We have synthesized various types of metal nanoparticles and studied the role of pH and urea concentration on NP size and localization. We have found out that single large NP is not formed inside the apoferritin cage and instead large number of smaller NPs are present which is probably due to the presence of multiple sites for NP nucleation [20]

2. EXPERIMENTAL

2.1. Characterization and sample preparation

Transmission electron microscopy (TEM) was performed on Tecnai F20 (FEI, Eindhoven) operating at 200 kV equipped with 4kx4k CCD camera. 4 μl of the sample was applied on a 3 mm TEM copper grid containing 12 nm continual carbon film. The sample was incubated for 1 min on the grid and subsequently wicked away with a filter paper. Sample preparation for negative staining electron microscopy comprised 1 min incubation of 4 μl sample drop on the TEM copper grid supplemented with 12 nm home-made continual carbon film followed by two round of rinsing the grid in 16 μl of 2 % solution of uranyl acetate, and removal of the residual amount of the mixture by filter paper. Finally, the sample was allowed to dry under ambient conditions.

2.2. Preparation of the apoferritin sample

Apoferritin was expressed from LF2422 plasmid which contains human H ferritin chain cloned into pGEX2T with a TEV site instead of a thrombin site (gift from Christos Savva). The plasmid was transformed into chemically competent E.coli BL21(DE3)pLYSS. Cells were plated on plates containing Ampicilin and incubated at 37 °C overnight. Few colonies were used as starter culture followed inoculation bigger volume of LB Amp medium. Cells were growing at 37 °C until A600nm = 0.1 then IPTG (0.5mM) was added to start apoferritin production overnight at 20 °C. Cells were harvested by centrifugation (4 °C, 5000 g, 20 min) and the cell pellets were resuspended in lysis buffer (1x PBS, Roche Complete Tablet, 0.5% Triton X-100, 0.5 mM TCEP, pH = 7.4), lysed by sonication and the residual cellular debris were removed by centrifugation. Supernatant was incubated at 4 °C for 30 min with GST resin. The mixture was centrifuged and the pellet was washed four times with the wash buffer (1x PBS, 0.5% Triton X-100, 0.5 mM TCEP) followed by three washes with cleavage buffer (50 mM Tris pH = 7.5, 100 mM NaCl, 0.5 mM TCEP). The GST-tag was removed by incubation with 1:100 w/w TEV protease overnight. Subsequently, the sample was purified by size exclusion chromatography (Superdex S200). The fractions of central peak were analyzed by SDS PAGE and cryo-electron microscopy.

2.3. Metal nanoparticles in apoferritin cavity synthesis and characterization

Apoferritin was separately mixed with various metal precursors ($HAuCl_4 \cdot xH_2O$, $CuSO_4 \cdot 5H_2O$, K_2PdCl_4 or $NiCl_2 \cdot 6H_2O$) in molar ratio 1 : 20000 at pH 8.5 in buffer (0.1 mol·dm^{-3}, TRIS and 0.15 mol·dm^{-3}). Reaction mixtures were incubated at laboratory temperature for 24 h with agitation, and then dialyzed against same buffer pH 7.5 for additional 24 hours. Solution of $NaBH_4$ (5 equivalent to metal salt) was added to the reaction mixtures which resulted in immediate change of color to ruby, reddish-brown, dark brown, and black for Au, Cu, Pd, and Ni, respectively. The reaction scheme is summarized in the **Figure 1**.

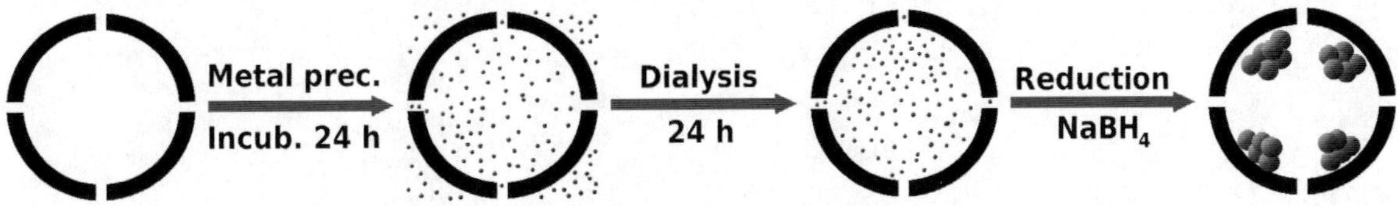

Figure 1 Scheme of apoferritin incubation with metal precursors with subsequent procedures

In case of $HAuCl_4$, the reaction was monitored by TEM during the incubation period which preceded sample reduction. The results of the negative staining EM (TEM-NS) are shown in **Figure 2**. Apoferritin cavities are primarily without observable metal nanoparticles prior reduction (**Figure 2-A**). Only few apoferritin particles reveal small seeding gold NPs (Au-NPs, 3-85 Å). In addition, irregular gold particles (50-90 Å diameters) are presents despite the absence of the reducing agent. This phenomenon is probably caused by reduction of $HAuCl_4$ by residual light during sample manipulation although the mixture was kept in dark during the whole reaction.

Addition of reducing agent ($NaBH_4$) caused color change of the reaction mixture from original pale yellow to ruby which indicated Au-NPs formation in accordance with TEM observation (**Figure 2-B)**. Au-NPs are primarily located on the outside of the apoferritin cavity and are not removed during dialysis. Nanoparticles are irregular in shape with wide size distribution (20-320 Å). As the inner part of the apoferritin is primarily void of NPs, we speculate that the Au atom seeding the NP formation localizes close to the apoferritin pores and blocks the entry of other Au atoms into the cavity in these cases.

In parallel, we have tested whether the accumulation of gold ions inside the cavity increases with the incubation time. We have prolonged the interaction time three times but we have not observed any effect with respect to number or size of the NPs present in apoferritin cavity (**Figure 2-C**). On the other hand, we have observed increased aggregation of apoferritin in this case.

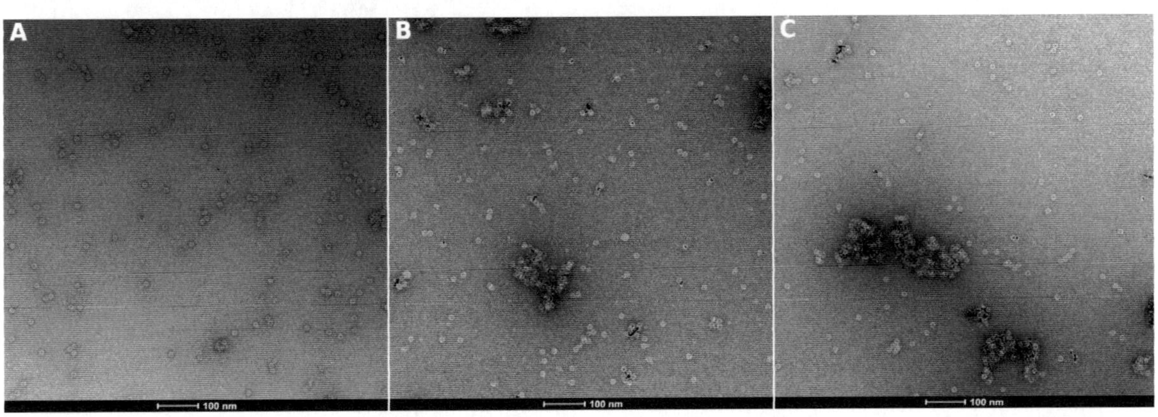

Figure 2 TEM-NS analysis of apoferritin incubation with $HAuCl_4$ for 24 h after dialysis and before reduction (A), after reduction (B) and 72 h incubation (C)

The reactions of apoferritin with copper, palladium and nickel precursors are summarized in **Figure 3**.

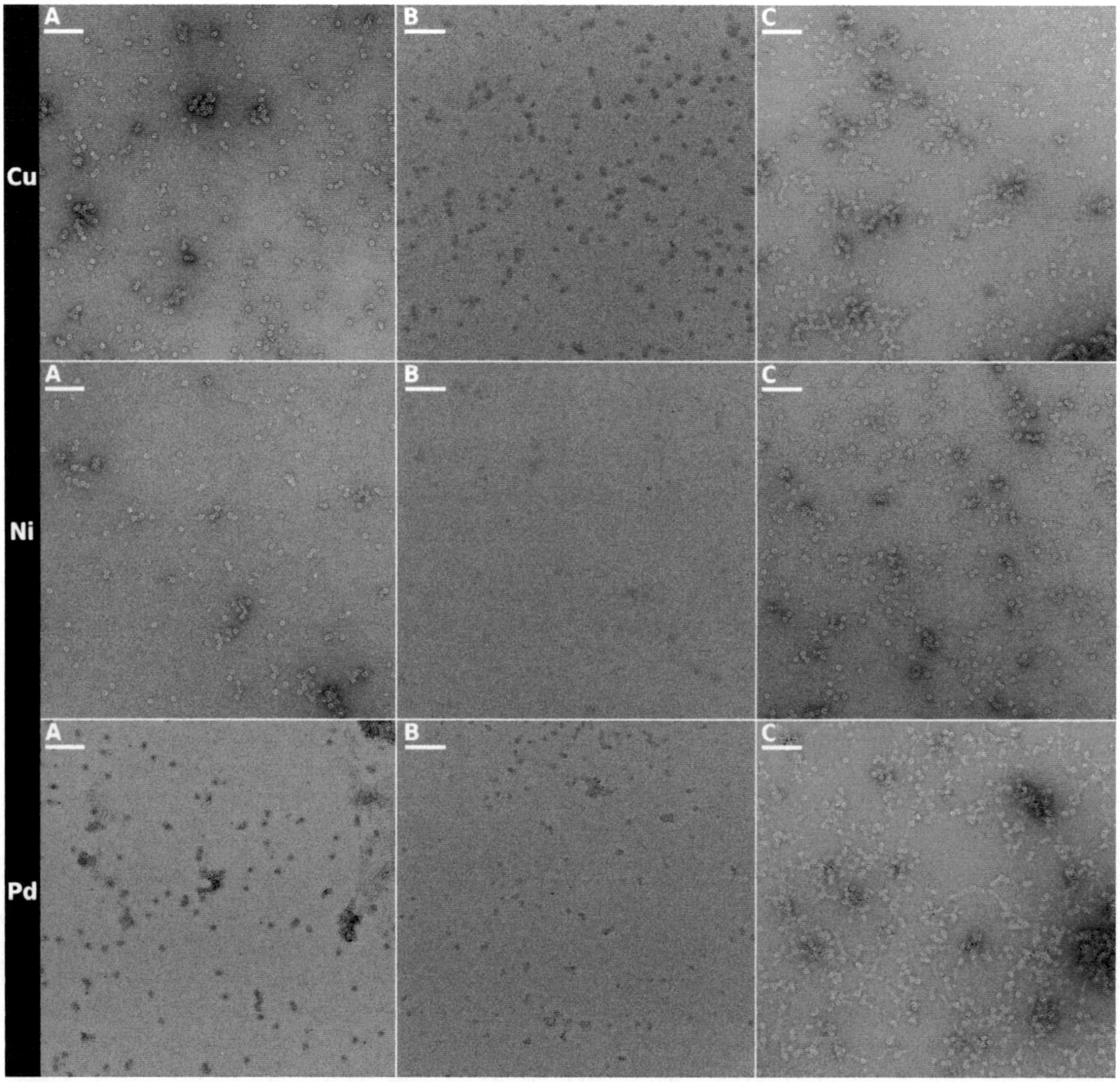

Figure 3 Summary of TEM analysis of apoferritin reacted with copper, nickel and palladium precursors from top to down. Columns A and B display negative and positive stained samples, respectively. Column C displays samples which were incubated 72 h.

The reaction with copper (Cu-NP, **Figure 3**) reveals negligible amount of copper ions trapped by apoferritin cavities. Reaction mixture changed color from blue to reddish brown after adding of reducing agent. Negative stained sample characterized by TEM did not exhibit any visible metal signals located in apoferritin cavities. Positive staining EM data of the same sample showed small amount of metal nanoparticles which are intricately distinguishable from background. Long time incubation has not led to encapsulation of copper ions inside of apoferritin as shown in **Figure 3-C**.

Reaction mixture of apoferritin and nickel chloride changed color from blue-green to black after $NaBH_4$ addition. Nickel nanoparticles (Ni-NPs) are present in larger quantities inside apoferritin cavity in comparison to Cu-NPs. We have observed very few Ni-NPs located inside of the apoferritin cavity, while the major part was detected outside of the apoferritin shell in concert with the observation we have made earlier for Au-NPs. Presence of Ni-NPs was further confirmed by positive staining EM (**Figure 3-B**) where nanoparticles with diameters ranging 13 to 53 Å were observed. Prolonger incubation time has neither increased the portion of the nanoparticles present inside the apoferritin cavity, nor the diameter of the observed nanoparticles.

The results of the palladium nanoparticle (Pd-NP) preparation were similar to Ni-NPs. Reaction mixture changed color from original orange to dark brown or black after addition of $NaBH_4$. TEM analysis showed the highest tendency for interaction between metal ions and apoferritin among the metals we have used. Similarly to previous cases, Pd-NPs were observed both on the outside and inside the apoferritin cavity. Longer incubation time probably led to denaturation of apoferritin (**Figure 3-C**). In addition to the apoferritin cage molecules, various small protein species and higher amount of palladium nanoparticles were present. Small protein particles probably aroused from apoferritin disassociation. These mono- or higher units interacted with palladium ions and formed various palladium-protein composites.

We have also performed apoferritin reaction with $HAuCl_4$ in molar ratio 1 : 20000 at various pH values to understand its role in trapping of Au^{3+} ions in apoferritin cavity. **Figure 4** summarizes reactions carried out at pH = 4.19 (A), 5.97 (B), 7.88 (C), 9.39 (D) 10.28 (E), and incubation reaction at pH = 10.28 carried out for 72 hours (F). Reaction mixtures were reduced by $NaBH_4$ (in molar ratio to $HAuCl_4$ 5 : 1) which was added after 24 h of incubation. Dialyses were not performed. Reduction was accompanied by typical color change from original light yellow to final ruby. Reaction mixture carried out at pH 10.28 (**Figure 4-F**) spontaneously changed color from original light yellow to final ruby before $NaBH_4$ addition.

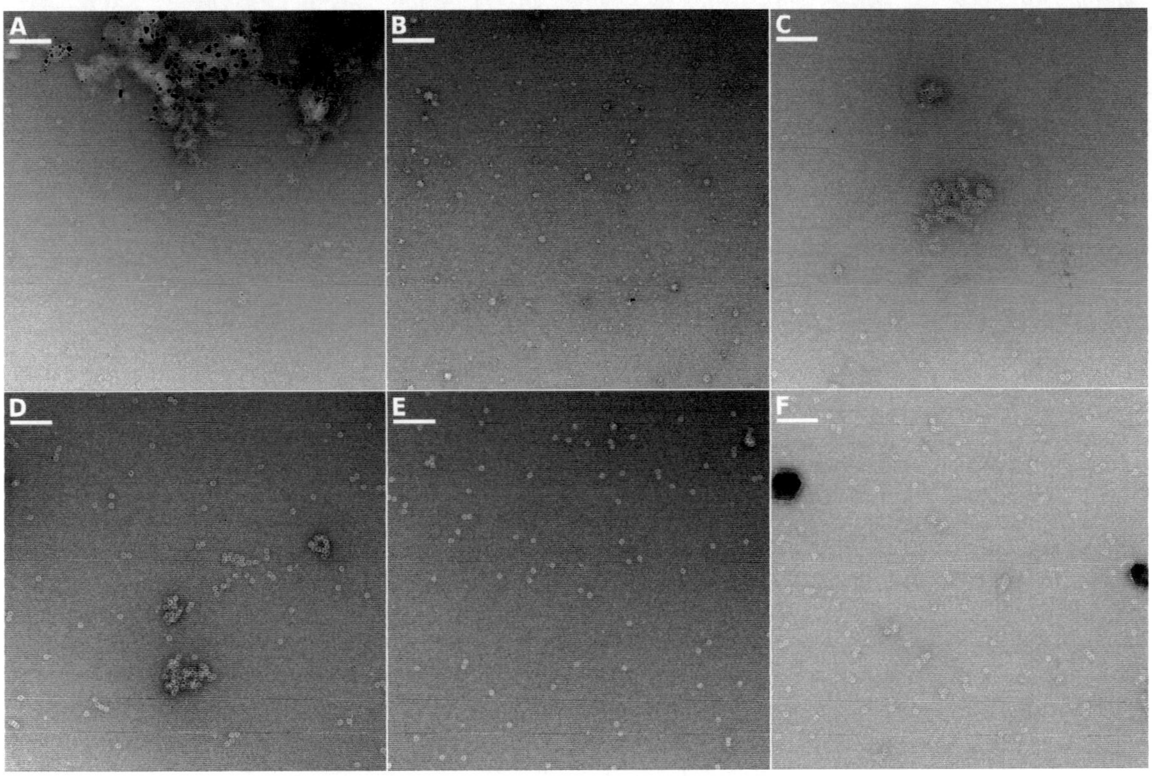

Figure 4 Summary of TEM analysis of apoferritin reacted with $HAuCl_4$ at various pH. A = 4.19, B = 5.97, C = 7.88, D = 9.39 and E = 10.28. Figure F displays reaction under pH = 10.28 with incubation time 72 h

The role of pH in nanoparticle formation was further monitored by TEM-NS (**Figure 4**). The reaction carried out at the lowest pH led to destabilization of apoferritin and formation of Au nanoparticles with broad size distribution. Nanoparticles were not located inside apoferritin cavities similarly as in the case of the reaction carried out at pH 6 (**Figure 4-B).** However, the apoferritin degradation was observed to a lesser extent at pH 6 (**Figure 4-B**) with respect to reaction carried out at pH 4 (**Figure 4-A**). Almost none of the intact apoferritin molecules were occupied by Au nanoparticles which were primarily concentrated on the apoferritin degradation products. Size distribution of gold nanoparticles was noticeably narrower at pH 6 than at pH 4. The most promising results were obtained when the reaction was carried out at pH 8 (**Figures 4-C,D)**. Au-NPs embedded in apoferritin shell form agglomerates in this case, but the apoferritin molecules remain intact. Reaction performed at pH 9 led to similar results but apoferritin cavity is occupied by nanoparticles to lesser extent. In addition, small nanoparticle seeds were also observable outside of the apoferritin shell in this case. Increasing pH above 9 prevents uptake of the Au^{3+} ions into apoferritin cavities even for prolonged incubation time (**Figures 4-E,F)** [21]. On the contrary, large irregular Au-NPs were formed on the outside of the apoferritin cage in this case (**Figure 4-F**).

3. CONCLUSION

We have carried out a systematic study of the nanoparticle formation inside apoferritin cage using four different metal precursors (gold, copper, nickel and palladium). TEM analysis showed palladium nanoparticles which were formed in apoferritin cavities in the highest yield from all studied metals. The role of pH was described by TEM analysis when apoferritin was incubated with gold ions under different pH (in range of 4-10). Apoferritin was desaturated, disassociated and re-assembled into irregular species under the low pH. Increasing of the pH led to accumulation of Au^{3+} ions in the apoferritin cavities. The reactions carried out at pH 7-9 provided the largest content of metal ions inside the apoferritin cavity. None of the tested approaches resulted in homogeneously sized nanoparticles incorporated into the apofferitin cavity at high-yield and purity. Therefore, we conclude that this system for preparation of apoferritin-based nanoparticles is not suitable for production of biocompatible markers for electron microscopy.

ACKNOWLEDGEMENTS

We acknowledge Cryo-Electron Microscopy and Tomography Core Facility of CIISB, Instruct-CZ Centre, supported by MEYS CR (LM2018127).

This work is financially supported by TA ČR (project TN01000008)

We kindly thank to the Protex facility at the University of Leicester, Louise Fairall and Christos Savva for using their plasmid LF2422

REFERENCES

[1] ZOU, Chang-dong, GAO, Yu-lai, YANG, Bin, ZHAI, Qi-jie. Size-dependent melting properties of Sn nanoparticles by chemical reduction synthesis. *Transactions of Nonferrous Metals Society of China.* [online]. 2010, vol. 20, no. 2, pp. 248-253. ISSN 10036326. Available from: https://doi.org/10.1016/S1003-6326(09)60130-8.

[2] WANG, Hongshui, QIAO, Xueliang, CHEN, Jianguo, WANG, Xiaojian, DING Shiyuan. Mechanisms of PVP in the preparation of silver nanoparticles. *Materials Chemistry and Physics.* [online]. 2005, vol. 94, no. 2-3, pp. 449-453. ISSN 02540584. Available from: https://doi.org/10.1016/j.matchemphys.2005.05.005.

[3] ROSHANGHIAS, Ali, VRESTAL, Jan, YAKYMOVYCH, Andriy, RICHTER, W. Klaus, IPSER, Herbert. Sn-Ag-Cu nanosolders: Melting behavior and phase diagram prediction in the Sn-rich corner of the ternary system. *Calphad.* [online]. 2015, vol. 49, pp. 101-109 [cit. 2015-09-30]. ISSN 03645916. Available from: https://doi.org/10.1016/j.calphad.2015.04.003.

[4] KIMLING, J., MAIER, M., OKENVE, B., KOTAIDIS, V., BALLOT, H., PLECH, A.. Turkevich Method for Gold Nanoparticle Synthesis Revisited. *The Journal of Physical Chemistry B.* [online]. 2006, vol. 110, no 3, pp. 15700-15707. ISSN 1520-6106. Available from: https://doi.org/10.1021/jp061667w.

[5] VYKOUKAL, Vit, HALASTA, Vitezslav, BABIAK, Michal, BURSIK, Jiri, PINKAS, Jiri. Morphology Control in AgCu Nanoalloy Synthesis by Molecular Cu(I) Precursors. *Inorganic Chemistry*. 2019, vol. 58, no. 22, pp. 15246-15254. ISSN 0020-1669. Available from: https://doi.org/10.1021/acs.inorgchem.9b02172.

[6] ZHANG, Yawen, HUANG, Wenyu, HABAS, Susan E., KUHN, John N., GRASS, Michael E., YAMADA, Yusuke, YANG, Peidong, SOMORJAI, Gabor A.. Near-Monodisperse Ni−Cu Bimetallic Nanocrystals of Variable Composition: Controlled Synthesis and Catalytic Activity for H_2 Generation. *The Journal of Physical Chemistry C*. [online]. 2008, vol. 112, no. 32, pp. 12092-12095. ISSN 1932-7447. Available from: https://doi.org/10.1021/jp805788x.

[7] WAKUDA, D, KIM, KEUN-SOO, SUGANUMA, K. Room-Temperature Sintering Process of Ag Nanoparticle Paste. *IEEE Transactions on Components and Packaging Technologies*. [online]. 2009, vol. 32, no. 3, pp. 627-632 [cit. 2015-04-18]. ISSN 1521-3331. Available from: https://doi.org/10.1109/TCAPT.2009.2015874.

[8] GINGU, Oana, ROTARU, P., MILEA, A., MARIN, A., NICOLICESCU, C., SIMA, Gabriela, TANASESCU, Speranta. In-situ synthesis of AgCu/Cu_2O nanocomposite by mechanical alloying: The effect of the processing on the thermal behavior. *Thermochimica Acta*. [online]. 2015, vol. 606, pp. 1-11. ISSN 00406031. Available from: https://doi.org/10.1016/j.tca.2015.03.002.

[9] GÎNGU, Oana, NICOLICESCU, Claudiu, SIMA, Gabriela. Research of the Milling Time Influence on Ag-Cu Powder Particles Size Processed by Mechanical Alloying Route. *Solid State Phenomena*. [online]. 2012, vol. 188, pp. 382-387. ISSN 1662-9779. Available from: https://doi.org/10.4028/www.scientific.net/SSP.188.382.

[10] KIM, Chang Kyu, LEE, Gyoung-Ja, LEE, Min Ku and RHEE, Chang Kyu. A novel method to prepare Cu@Ag core-shell nanoparticles for printed flexible electronics. *Powder Technology*. [online]. 2014, vol. 263, pp. 1-6. ISSN 00325910. Available from: https://doi.org/10.1016/j.powtec.2014.04.064.

[11] JUNG, Inyu, JO, Yun Hwan, KIM, Inyoung and LEE, Hyuck Mo. A Simple Process for Synthesis of Ag Nanoparticles and Sintering of Conductive Ink for Use in Printed Electronics. *Journal of Electronic Materials*. [online]. 2012, vol. 41, no. 1, pp. 115-121. ISSN 0361-5235. Available from: https://doi.org/10.1007/s11664-011-1761-3.

[12] KELLY, K. Lance, CORONADO, Eduardo, ZHAO, Lin Lin and SCHATZ, George C. The Optical Properties of Metal Nanoparticles: The Influence of Size, Shape, and Dielectric Environment. *The Journal of Physical Chemistry B*. [online]. 2003, vol. 107, no. 3, pp. 668-677. ISSN 1520-6106. Available from: https://doi.org/10.1021/jp026731y.

[13] BROZ, Pavel, HEJDUKOVA, Martina, VYKOUKAL, Vii, ZELENKA, Frantidek, SOPOUSEK, Jiri, BURSIK, Jiri and ZOBAC, Ondrej. Study of surface effects and catalytic properties of selected Ni-based bimetallic nanoparticles by Knudsen effusion mass spectrometry. *Calphad*. [online]. 2019, vol. 64, pp. 334-341. ISSN 03645916. Available from: https://doi.org/10.1016/j.calphad.2019.01.013.

[14] PAGE FAULK, W a MALCOLM TAYLOR, G. Communication to the editors. *Immunochemistry*. [online]. 1971, vol. 8, no. 11, pp. 1081-1083. ISSN 00192791. Available from: https://doi.org/10.1016/0019-2791(71)90496-4.

[15] ZHONG, Ling, BROWN, Joshua C., WELLS, Clive a GERGES, Nashaat Z. Post-embedding Immunogold Labeling of Synaptic Proteins in Hippocampal Slice Cultures. *Journal of Visualized Experiments*. [online]. 2013, no. 74. ISSN 1940-087X. Available from: https://doi.org/10.3791/50273.

[16] MAITY, Basudev, HISHIKAWA, Yuki, LU, Diannan and UENO, Takafumi. Recent progresses in the accumulation of metal ions into the apo-ferritin cage: Experimental and theoretical perspectives. *Polyhedron*. [online]. 2019. ISSN 02775387. Available from: https://doi.org/10.1016/j.poly.2019.03.048.

[17] JUTZ, Günther, VAN RIJN, Patrick, SANTOS MIRANDA, Barbara and BÖKER, Alexander. Ferritin: A Versatile Building Block for Bionanotechnology. *Chemical Reviews*. [online]. 2015, vol. 115, no. 4, pp. 1653-1701. ISSN 0009-2665. Available from: https://doi.org/10.1021/cr400011b.

[18] GÁLVEZ, Natividad, FERNANDEZ, Belen, VALERO, Elsa, SÁNCHEZ, Purificación, CUESTA, Rafael and DOMÍNGUEZ-VERA, José M. Apoferritin as a nanoreactor for preparing metallic nanoparticles. *Comptes Rendus Chimie*. [online]. 2008, vol. 11, no. 10, pp. 1207-1212. ISSN 16310748. Available from: https://doi.org/10.1016/j.crci.2008.09.003.

[19] DOMÍNGUEZ-VERA, José M., GÁLVEZ, Natividad, SÁNCHEZ, Purificación, MOTA, Antonio J., TRASOBARES, Susana, HERNÁNDEZ, Juan C. a CALVINO, Jose J. Size-Controlled Water-Soluble Ag Nanoparticles. *European Journal of Inorganic Chemistry.* [online]. 2007, no. 30, pp. 4823-4826. ISSN 14341948. Available from: https://doi.org/10.1002/ejic.200700606.

[20] MAITY, Basudev, HISHIKAWA, Yuki, LU, Diannan and UENO, Takafumi. Recent progresses in the accumulation of metal ions into the apo-ferritin cage: Experimental and theoretical perspectives. *Polyhedron.* [online]. 2019, vol. 172, pp. 104-111. ISSN 02775387. Available from: https://doi.org/10.1016/j.poly.2019.03.048.

[21] KONG, Bo, HUANG, He-Qing, LIN, Qing-Mei, CAI, Zong-Wei and CHEN, Ping. Effect of pH and Phosphate on Trapping Capacity of Various Heavy Metal Ions With Ferritin Reactor in Flowing Seawater. *Applied Biochemistry and Biotechnology.* [online]. 2005, vol. 126, no. 2, pp. 133-148. ISSN 0273-2289. Available from: https://doi.org/10.1385/ABAB:126:2:133.

ANTIBACTERIAL ELECTROSPUN MEMBRANE PREPARED FROM POLY (VINYLIDENE FLUORIDE)-CO-HEXAFLUOROPROPYLENE WITH LAURIC ACID MONOACYLGLYCEROL

[1]Jana ZELENKOVA, [1]Petra PEER, [2]Pavel PLEVA, [2]Magda JANALIKOVA, [3]Jana SEDLARIKOVA, [1]Petr FILIP

[1]Institute of Hydrodynamics of the Czech Academy of Sciences, v. v. i., Prague, Czech Republic, EU, zelenkova@ih.cas.cz, peer@ih.cas.cz, filip@ih.cas.cz

[2]Faculty of Engineering, Tomas Bata University in Zlin, Department of Environmental Protection Engineering, Zlin, Czech Republic, EU, ppleva@utb.cz, mjanalikova@utb.cz

[3]Faculty of Engineering, Tomas Bata University in Zlin, Department of Fat, Surfactant and Cosmetics Technology, Zlin, Czech Republic, EU, sedlarikova@utb.cz

https://doi.org/10.37904/nanocon.2020.3741

Abstract

The aim of this study was to prepare an antibacterial nanofibrous membrane using electrospinning technique. The nanofibrous membranes were spun from polymer solution of poly(vinylidne fluoride)-*co*-hexafluoropropylene (PVDF-*co*-HFP) dissolved in N,N´-dimethylformamide. Monoacylglycerol of lauric acid (MAG C12) was used as an antimicrobial agent at the concentrations ranging from 1 to 3 wt%. The impact of MAG C12 incorporation on the rheological, structural and antibacterial properties was investigated. The rheological tests of polymer solutions, as steady shear and oscillatory shear, proved that addition of MAG C12 changed marginally rheological quantities such as viscosity, elastic (storage) and viscous (loss) moduli. Measurement of mean nanofibres diameter indicated a slight decrease with increasing MAG C12 concentration. Antimicrobial activity of PVDF-*co*-HFP nanofibre membranes with incorporated MAG C12 against Gram-positive bacteria *Staphylococcus aureus* and Gram-negative *Escherichia coli* was studied. An antibacterial activity was revealed for the samples containing MAG C12 at all concentrations against Gram-positive bacteria *Staphylococcus aureus* by the disk diffusion method.

Keywords: Nanofibres, electrospinning, antibacterial membrane, rheology, polymer solution

1. INTRODUCTION

Usage of membrane technology is very common in many industrial fields as electro-technology [1,2], water treatment [3-5] or fluids separation [6]. At present, the fabrication of nanofibrous membranes by an electrospinning method is the common approach. Nanofibres are created in an electric field between polymer drop and a collector under optimized conditions. Fluorinated polymers as poly (vinylidene fluoride) (PVDF) or polytetrafluorethylene (PTFE) [7] are suitable for membrane fabrication, among other things also due to their high resistance to chemical and mechanical impact of environment. In recent years, the copolymer of PVDF with hexafluoropropylene (HFP) proved its potential due to better mechanical properties, lower crystallinity, better solubility and higher hydrophobicity compared with pure PVDF [3,4]. The modification of characteristics of electrospun nanofibers, e.g. hydrophobicity, is achieved by blending the polymer with such ingredients like monoacylglycerols to control wettability and obtain antimicrobial activity. Monoacylglycerols (MAGs) are organic compounds consisted of glycerol linked to fatty acid via an ester bond. The antibacterial (bacteriostatic and bactericidal) properties of saturated fatty acids and their derivatives, such as lauric acid monoacylglycerol with 12 carbon atoms, have been investigated by many researches [8-11]. Although the mechanism of inhibition is not completely known, Yoon et al. [12] present that the antimicrobial activity is given by three cells processes based on cell lysis, disruption of electron transport in oxidative phosphorylation process and inhibition of membrane enzymes.

The aim of this contribution was to prepare the electrospun antibacterial membranes based on PVDF-*co*-HFP dissolved in N,N´-dimethylformamide. Different concentrations of MAG C12 and solvent were used and rheological characteristics were investigated with an emphasis paid to correlation with nanofibres quality.

2. EXPERIMENTAL

PVDF-*co*-HFP Kynar® 2801 was purchased from Arkema (Arkema Inc. France). N, N´- dimethylformamide p.a. (DMF) used as a solvent was purchased form P-LAB (Czech Republic). Both chemicals were used without further purification. 1-monocaprin (MAG C12) was prepared by direct addition of decanoic acid into glycidol by the epoxide ring opening in a double skin reactor at the temperature of 90 °C [13]. The product was then recrystallized from ethanol to the purity of 99 %.

2.1. Sample preparation

Four samples differing in concentration of MAG C12 were prepared. Each sample contained 23 wt.% of PVDF-*co*-HFP, the remaining 77 wt.% were shared by DMF and MAG C12 with the ratios 77-0, 76-1, 75-2, and 74-3 wt.%. All samples were mixed at 25 °C using a magnetic stirrer Heidolph MR Hei-Tec (Heidolph, Germany) for 24 hours.

2.2. Rheological characterization of samples

The steady shear and oscillatory tests were applied for the sample characterization. The measurements were carried out using a rotational rheometer Physica MCR 501 (Anton Paar, Austria) equipped with concentric cylinders geometry (the inner and outer diameters were 26.6 and 28.9 mm, respectively) at temperature 25 °C. Strain sweep measurement was carried out in the range 0.1 - 100 % and frequency sweep measurement was carried out in the range 0.1 - 100 Hz at 1 % strain. The phase angle δ was determined by means of the definitoric relation, $\tan \delta = G''/G'$, where G'' is the loss (viscous) modulus and G' is the storage (elastic) modulus. Consequently, the viscosity was measured in the range 0.1 - 300 s^{-1} and shear rate value 0.12 s^{-1} (in linear viscoelastic (LVE) region) was chosen as the reference point.

2.3. Electrospinning process

Nanofibrous mats were electrospun using a laboratory device (details are introduced in [14]) with the tip-to-collector distance 10 cm under voltage 18 kV (a high voltage power supply Spellman SL70PN150, USA). The volume of the processed polymer sample attained approximately 0.2 mL. The experiments were carried out under ambient conditions (temperature 23 ± 1 °C, relative humidity 34 ± 1 %).

2.4. Scanning electron microscopy

The scanning electron microscopy measurement was used for characterization of electrospun fibres. The analysed samples were sputtered by a conductive coating (gold) layer using a sputter Quorum Q150R (Quorum Technologies Ltd., UK) and fibres quality was evaluated by a scanning electron microscope Vega 3 Tescan (Tescan, Czech Republic). The mean fibres diameter was determined using Adobe Creative Suite software by means of which 300 fibres were analysed from 3 different samples.

2.5. Wettability

The wettability of the nanofibrous membranes was analysed by gauging contact angles according to the sessile drop method using the Surface Energy Evaluation System by the Advex Instruments (Czech Republic) at laboratory temperature. The mean values were calculated as an average from five independent measurements. Demineralized water was employed as the reference liquid; the volume of each deposited droplet attained 3 μL.

2.6. Antibacterial tests - agar disk diffusion method

In order to observe the antibacterial activity, the agar disk diffusion method was carried out: circular samples (9 mm in diameter) of nanofibres from neat PVDF-*co*-HFP or PVDF-*co*-HFP enriched with MAG C12 (1, 2, 3 wt.%) were placed on agar plates previously inoculated with 1 mL of 0.5 McF turbid bacterial suspension (*Escherichia coli* CCM 3954, *Staphylococcus aureus* CCM 3953) in sterile saline solution. Moreover, sterile paper disks (9 mm in diameter) were loaded by 10 μl MAG C12 (5 wt.% in ethanol) and tested in the same way as nanofibres. The plates were incubated at 37 °C for 24 hours and the whole experiment was repeated three times. The inhibition zones as well as growth under the samples were evaluated.

3. RESULTS AND DISCUSSION

Proper electrospinnability of polymeric materials is closely related to their viscoelasticity. The following rheological measurements were carried out for four polymeric materials differing in MAG C12 content (0, 1, 2, and 3 wt.%). First, oscillatory strain and frequency sweep measurements describing a degree of elasticity of the studied materials are depicted in **Figure 1**. Based on these measurements, the phase angle δ relating a mutual ratio of viscous and elastic moduli was determined, see **Figure 2** (left). The values of shear viscosity obtained for the value of shear rate 0.12 s^{-1} in the linear LVE region are presented in **Figure 2** (right) jointly with the mean fibres diameters. **Figure 3** provides visual evaluation of all four nanofibrous mats. Unlike e.g. dodecyltrimethyl ammonium bromide used as antibacterial agent in [15], monoacylglycerol MAG C12 does not change the structure of the fibres.

Apparently, monoacylglycerol MAG C12 had a negligible impact to the storage and loss moduli and mean nanofibre diameter contrasting to its influence on hydrophobicity (hydrophilicity) of nanofibrous membranes. Their wettability was evaluated by the sessile drop method as presented in **Table 1**. The mean contact angles document hydrophilic behaviour for the MAG C12-modified nanofibrous membranes while the pure PVDF-*co*-HFP membrane exhibits hydrophobic behaviour.

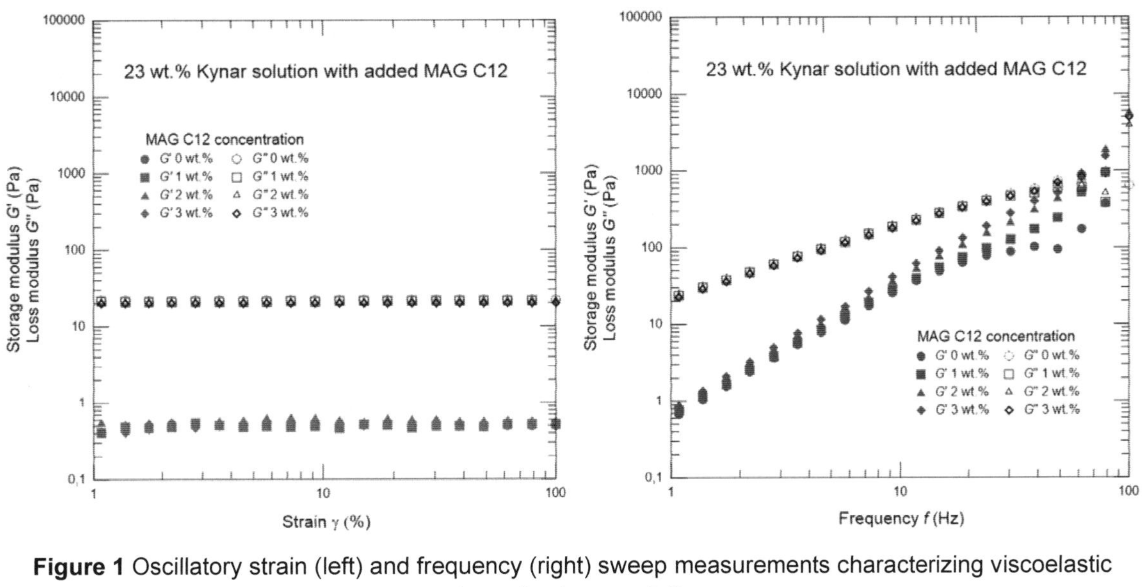

Figure 1 Oscillatory strain (left) and frequency (right) sweep measurements characterizing viscoelastic nature of polymer solutions

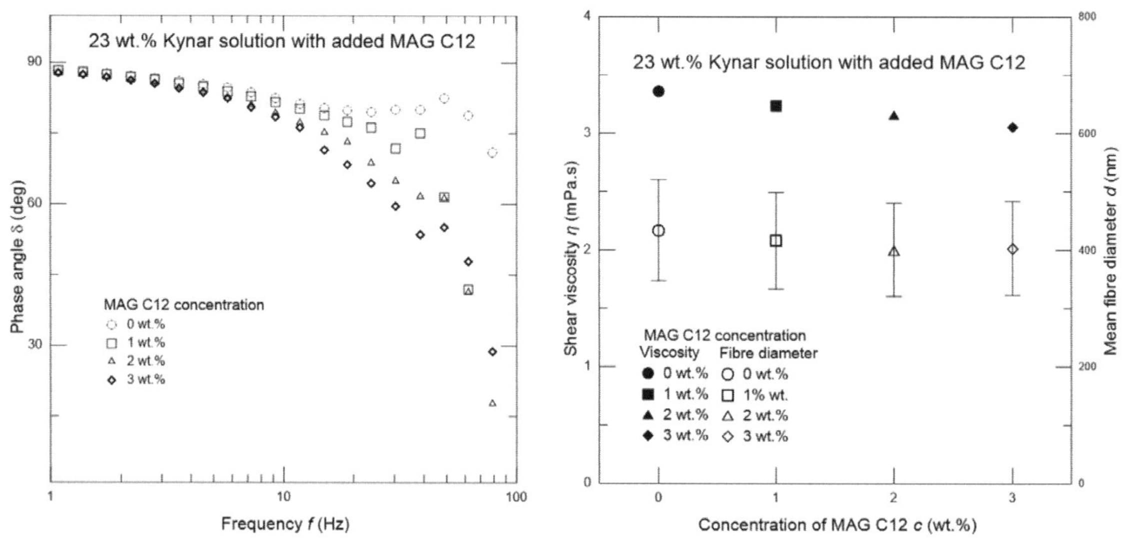

Figure 2 Phase angle (left), shear viscosity of polymer solutions (right) and mean fibre diameter of electrospun nanofibres (right)

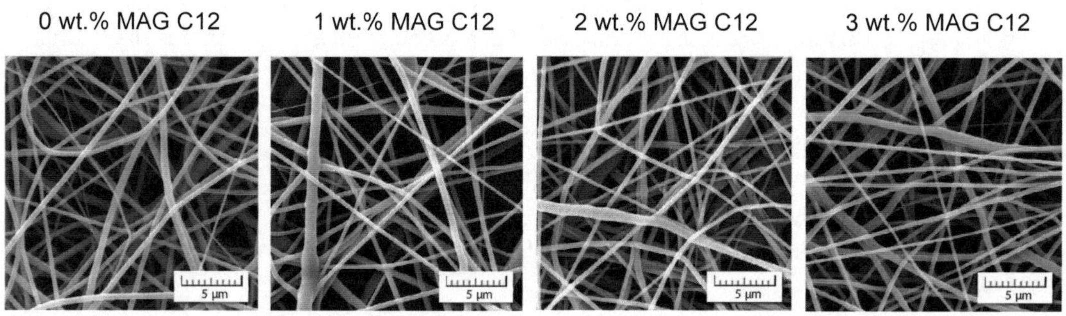

Figure 3 The quality of nanofibrous mats without/with added MAG C12

Table 1 Contact angle for PVDF-*co*-HFP nanofibrous membranes in dependence on MAG C12 content

MAG C12 concentration (wt.%)	0	1	2	3
Contact angle (deg)	128	19	25	26

The antibacterial activity of MAG C12, neat PVDF-*co*-HFP and PVDF-*co*-HFP/MAG C12 nanofibrous membranes against *Escherichia coli* and *Staphylococcus aureus* was performed by the agar disk diffusion method. MAGs were previously reported to be effective against various Gram-positive and Gram-negative bacteria [12]. In this work, it was found that MAG C12 (5 wt.%) against *E. coli* is effective and against *S. aureus* has antibacterial activity, see **Table 2**. Neat PVDF-*co*-HFP nanofibrous membranes exhibited no growth inhibition using the disk diffusion method, on the other hand MAG-modified membranes proved antibacterial activity against *Staphylococcus aureus,* see **Figure 4**. Antibacterial activity of MAG C12 incorporated into nanofibrous membranes was higher with increasing concentration, however the effect of 2 wt.% and 3 wt.% PVDF-*co*-HFP/MAG C12 nanofibrous membranes seemed to be comparable. PVDF-*co*-HFP/MAG C12 nanofibrous membranes did not prove to be inhibitory against *Escherichia coli.* Nevertheless, it is possible to expect antifouling activity against all bacteria as it was proved for the similar system of PVB/MAG C10 nanofibrous membranes [16].

Smaller inhibition zones observed in the case of PVDF-*co*-HFP/MAG C12 nanofibrous membranes in comparison with MAG C12 can be explained either by lower concentration of applied MAG C12 or/and by lower amount of MAG C12 diffused from membranes. Monocaprin (MAG C10) have been reported to exhibit very similar antibacterial activity as monolaurin (MAG C12). It was recently published that MAG C10 from PVB/MAG C10 nanofibrous membranes was not diffused almost at all [16]. On the other hand, this work proves a release of MAG C12 from PVDF-*co*-HFP/MAG C12 nanofibrous membranes.

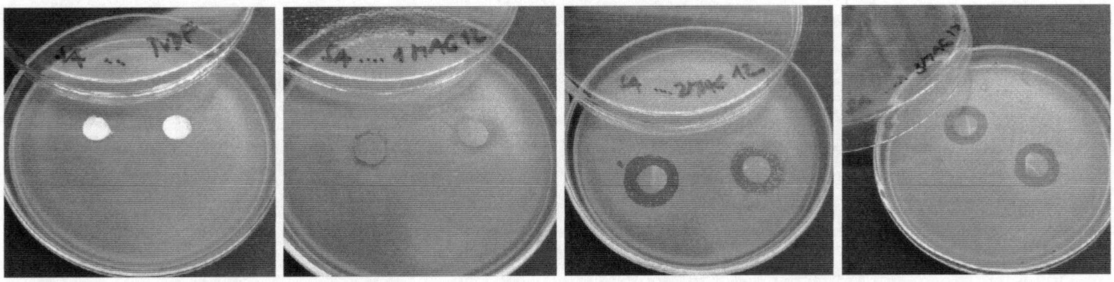

Figure 4 The inhibition zones of *S. aureus* (SA) nanofibrous membranes without/with added MAG C12 (from left to right: 0 wt.%, 1 wt.%, 2 wt.%, 3 wt.%)

Table 2 The inhibition zones of nanofibrous membranes PVDF-*co*-HFP/MAG C12 (disk diameter 9 mm)

	SA (mm)	EC (mm)
MAG C12 (5 wt.%)	27	11
PVDF-*co*-HFP / 0 wt.% MAG C12	9	9
PVDF-*co*-HFP / 1 wt.% MAG C12	13	9
PVDF-*co*-HFP / 2 wt.% MAG C12	19	9
PVDF-*co*-HFP / 3 wt.% MAG C12	18	9

4. CONCLUSION

The application of MAG C12 as an antimicrobial agent exhibited non-negligible advantages. As documented above, no changes in rheological characterization of primary solutions were evoked by adding this agent in units of percentage. The courses of loss and storage moduli, and shear viscosity were practically unchanged as well as the mean nanofibre diameters. The addition of MAG C12 had other positive aspects. First, a purely hydrophobic behaviour of neat PVDF-*co*-HFP membranes was abruptly converted to hydrophilic character with adding as low as 1% of MAG C12, which is suitable for filtration applications. Moreover, the antimicrobial efficiency of PVDF-*co*-HFP/MAG C12 membranes against *Staphylococcus aureus* was proved.

ACKNOWLEDGEMENTS

This research was supported by the Ministry of Education, Youth and Sports of the Czech Republic (Project LTC 19034), and within Program NPU I (LO1504). Institutional support was provided by the Czech Academy of Sciences, Czech Republic (RVO: 67985874).

REFERENCES

[1] CAO, J-H., ZHU, B-K., XU, Y-Y. Structure and ionic conductivity of porous polymer electrolytes based on PVDF - HFP copolymer membranes. *Journal of Membrane Science*. 2006, vol. 281, no. 1- 2, pp. 446 - 453.

[2] STEPHAN, A. M., NAHM, K. S., KULANDAINATHAN, M. A., RAVI, G., WILSON, J. Poly(vinylidenefluoride - hexafluoripropylene((PVdF-HFP) based composite electrolytes for lithium batteries. *European Polymer Journal*. 2006, vol. 42, no. 8, pp. 1728-1734.

[3] TIAN, X., JIANG, X. Poly(vinylidene fluoride-co-hexafluoropropylene) (PVDF-co-HFP) membranes for ethyl acetate removal from water. *Journal of Hazardous Materials*. 2008, vol. 153, no. 1 - 2, pp. 128 - 135.

[4] GARCÍA-PAYO, M. C., ESSALHI, M., KHAYET, M. Effects of PVDF-HFP concentration on membrane distillation performance and structural morphology of hollow fiber membranes. *Journal of Membrane Science*. 2010, vol. 347, no. 1-2, pp. 209-219.

[5] LALIA, B. S., GUILLEN-BURRIEZA, E., ARAFAT, A. H., HASHAIKEH, R. Fabrication and characterization of polyvinylidenefluoride-co-hexafluoropropylene (PVDF-HFP) electrospun membranes for direct contact membrane distillation. *Journal of Membrane Science*. 2013, vol. 428, no. 1, pp. 104-115.

[6] WANG, X., XIAO, C., LIU, H., HUANG, Q., HAO, J., FU, H. Poly(vinylidene fluoride-hexafluorpropylene) porous membrane with controllable structure and applications in efficient oil/water separation. *Materials*. 2018, vol. 11, no. 3, p. 443.

[7] KANG, G-D., CAO, Y-M. Application and modification of poly(vinylidene fluoride) (PVDF) membranes - A review. *Journal of Membrane Science*. 2014, vol. 463, no. 1, pp. 145-165.

[8] KODICEK, E., WORDEN, A. N. The effect of unsaturated fatty acids on Lactobacillus helveticus and other Gram-positive Micro-organisms. *Biochemical Journal*. 1945, vol. 39, pp. 78-85.

[9] KABARA, J. J., SWIECZOWSKI, D. M., CONLEY, J. A., TRUANT, J. P. Fatty acids and derivatives as antimicrobial agents. *Antimicrobial Agents and Chemotherapy*. 1972, vol. 2, no. 1, pp. 23-28.

[10] SCHLIEVERT, P. M., DERINGER, R. J., KIM, M. H., PROJAN, S. J., NOVICK, R. P. Effect of glycerol on bacterial growth and toxin production. *Antimicrobial Agents and Chemotherapy*. 1992, vol. 36, no. 3, pp. 626-631.

[11] OH, D. H., MARSHALL, D. L. Antimicrobial activity of ethanol, glycerol monolaurate or lactic acid against Lysteria Monocytogenes. *International Journal of Food Microbiology*. 1993, vol. 20, no. 4, pp. 239-246.

[12] YOON, B. K., JACKMANN, J. A., VALLE-GONZÁLES, E. R., CHO, N-J. Antibacterial free fatty acids and monoglycerides: Biological activities, Experimental Testing and Therapeutic Applications. *International Journal of Molecular Sciences*. 2018, vol. 19, no. 4, pp. 1-40.

[13] JANIS, R., KLASEK, A., KREJCI, J., BOBALOVA, J. Influence of some chromium complexes on the conversion rate of glycidol - fatty acid reaction. *Tenside Surfactants Detergents*. 2005, vol. 42, no. 1, pp. 44-48.

[14] PEER, P., STENICKA, M., PAVLINEK, V., FILIP, P. The storage stability of polyvinylbutyral solutions from an electrospinnability standpoint. *Polymer Degradation and Stability*. 2014, vol. 105, no., pp. 134-139.

[15] CAPKOVA, P., KORMUNDA, M., KOLSKA, Z., TROGL, J., MUNZAROVA, M., RYSANEK, P. Electrospun antimicrobial PVDF-DTAB nanofibrous membrane for air filtration: Effect of DTAB on structure, morphology, adhesion, and antibacterial properties. *Macromolecular Materials and Engineering*. 2018, vol. 303, no. 3, 1700415.

[16] PEER, P., SEDLARIKOVA, J, JANALIKOVA, M., KUCEROVA, L., PLEVA, P. Novel polyvinyl butyral/monoacyl-glycerol nanofibrous membrane with antifouling activity. *Materials*. 2020, vol. 13, p. 3662.

COMBINATION OF LABEL-FREE SURFACE-ENHACED RAMAN SPECTROSCOPY WITH CONVOLUTIONAL NEURAL NETWORK FOR DNA RECOGNITION

[1]Anastasia SKVORTSOVA, [1]Andrei TRELIN, [1]Vaclav SVORCIK, [1]Olga GUSELNIKOVA, [1]Oleksyi LYUTAKOV

[1]*UCT - University of Chemistry and Technology, Prague, Czech Republic, EU*
skvortss@vscht.cz

https://doi.org/10.37904/nanocon.2020.3742

Abstract

Nowadays, the rapid identification of bacterial antibiotic resistance is one of the major biomedical challenges. Classical methods of detection (culture and sensitivity testing, microbial whole-genome sequencing) fail in the context of time requirements. In this work, we propose the express method for the detection of gene encoding enzyme responsible for bacterial antibiotic resistance. Proposed analytical approach is based on a combination of unique advantages provided by surface enhanced Raman spectroscopy (SERS) and artificially created convolutional neural network (CNN). SERS is known for the extremely high sensitivity and fast analysis, while CNN seems to be a promising alternative to find even ambiguous spectral properties produced by the Raman signal.

Keywords: SERS, DNA, neural networks, CNN, antibiotic resistance

1. INTRODUCTION

The culture-based approach for diagnosis of antibiotic-resistive bacteria development is currently used. However, culturing of the bacteria takes more than 24 hours and together with further species identification and evaluation can prolong time of analysis up to several days [1], which is crucial in need of urgent treatment. On the other hand, such methods as multiplex PCR, [2] electrochemical detection [3], and mass spectrometry [4] can achieve high accuracy for recognition of specific DNA, responsible for antibiotic resistence. Nevertheless, these techniques require expensive instruments, sophisticated sample preparation, and trained staff for obtained data analysis [5].

Recently, Surface-enhanced Raman scattering (SERS) analysis became a promising analytical tool in the field of sensing of DNA oligomers, with especial focus on the presence of antibiotic-resistant genes [6;7;8]. The main advantages of this method are related to the possibility to provide rich spectral information obtained through direct analysis of biomedical samples [9]. However, poor reproducibility and possible interferences of SERS bands due to the complex structure of biological samples restrict the direct SERS application. As an overcoming solution the machine-learning spectral data analysis was recently proposed [10,11]. It is well known, that typical post-processing statistical tools, such as PCA, linear discriminant analysis or 2D correlation fail in the need to find non-linear spectral correlations [12], when machine learning algorithms are characterized by a capability to found complex relationships in data analysis, making the overall analytical procedure highly reliable.

In our previous work [10,11], combination of SERS and artificial neural networks for relevant DNA oligomers recognition and its promising applications were demonstrated for the first time, and now we have focused on the optimization of the biosensor to increase the reproducibility, accuracy and usefulness of the measurements.

2. EXPERIMENTAL

2.1. Reagents

Acetic acid (reagent grade, ≥99 %), diethyl ether, deionized water, 4-aminobenzoic acid (≥99.0 %), p-Toluenesulfonic acid monohydrate (ACS reagent, ≥98.5 %), high-purity water (EMD MILLIPORE) were purchased from Sigma-Aldrich and used without further purification. The oligonucleotides (ONDs) were obtained from Thermofisher. The OND sequences used in this study are presented in Table S1. DVD+R disks (Verbatim) were purchased from local shop (Alza).

2.2. Preparation of samples

For preparation of plasmon-active substrate the polymer grating was used. The Au thin film was deposited onto a patterned polymer surface by vacuum sputtering (discharge power of 7.5 W, sputtering time 350 s, resulted in thickness 25 nm).

The obtained gratings were spontaneously modified by soaking in 1 mM freshly prepared aqueous solution of 4-carboxybenzenediazonium tosylate (ADT-COOH) and rinsed with water and ethanol twice.

0.5 nmol of Au-C (NH2-terminated) was grafted to surface through EDC/sulfo-NHS activation. For DNA hybridization experiments the 10 mM Tris buffer was used. All samples were kept in a refrigerator at 5 °C

2.3. Characterization techniques

For characterization of the sample surface and nanomechanical properties the peak force AFM technique was used. AFM scratch tests were carried out on control sample on glass substrate by profiling across a scratch at an angle of 90° relative to the surface. SERS spectra were measured On ProRaman-L spectrometer with 785 nm excitation wavelengths. The spectra were recorded at a resolution of 2 cm^{-1} in the 3000-200 cm^{-1} wavenumber range. UV-Vis spectra were measured using Spectrometer Lambda 25 (Perkin-Elmer) in 300-1100 nm wavelength range.

2.4. CNN data processing

All SERS spectra were evaluated using home-made CNN design with implementation of TensorFlow 2 framework [13]. The collected data set consisted of individual spectra marked with corresponding categories. Spectra preprocessing involved their normalization and noise removing. The training was continued until manually observed convergence, which took 50 epochs in total, training and validation losses were converged to 0.1299 and 0.1291 respectively.

3. RESULT AND DISCUSSION

Recent advances in achieving low limits of detection and possibility to get massive spectral data in a short period of time make surface-enhanced Raman scattering a useful tool for the detection of DNA oligomers [10]. However, spectral differences are easily masked by background noise in complex biomolecules; thereby peak interference reduces universality of the method. On the other hand, artificially created convolutional neural network (CNN) is characterized by the ability to split the interfered peaks and reveal the most important regions of the spectrum [14] for the more accessible data interpretation.

To get rid of the long sample preparation, polymer grating as a cost-effective and commercially available alternative for the biosensor platform was used. After sputtering of the plasmonic metal (Au), periodical structure of the grating provided the SERS effectivity. The thickness of gold was optimized to get the highest enhancement factor (**Figure 1**). Optimization have demonstrated that the value of EF reach $2.3*10^6$ in the case of 25 nm thick gold layer (350 s of sputtering).

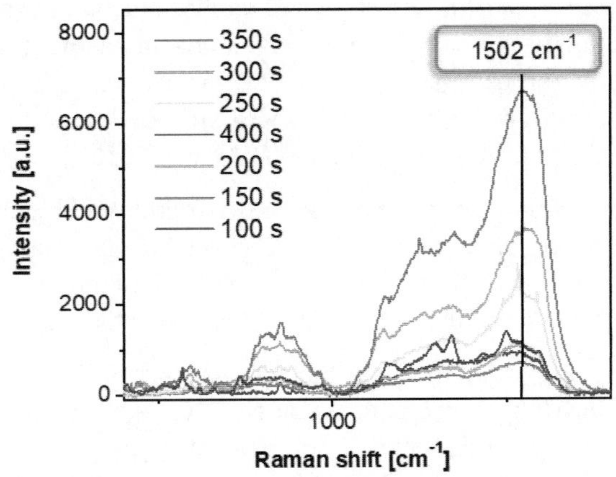

Figure 1 Calculation of EF of gold grating: SERS spectra of R6G on Au grating with various thicknesses

Activation of the low-reactive surface of the substrate was achieved by diazonium modification for 4-carboxyphenyl groups grafting, which are then able to covalently bond with the amino-terminated OND (C-OND) (**Figure 2**).

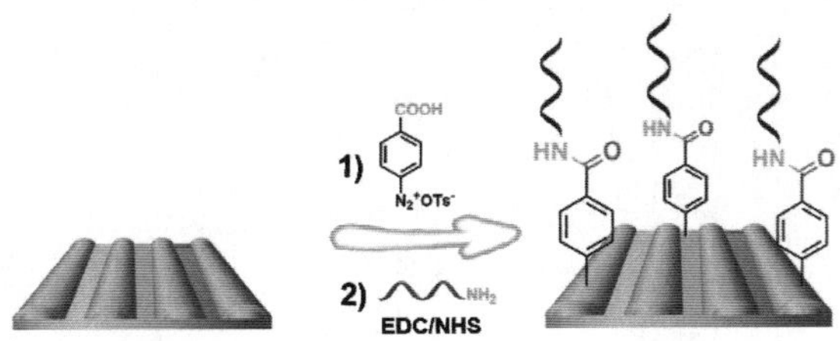

Figure 2 Scheme of preparation of gold grating with grafted capture oligonucleotide (Au-C)

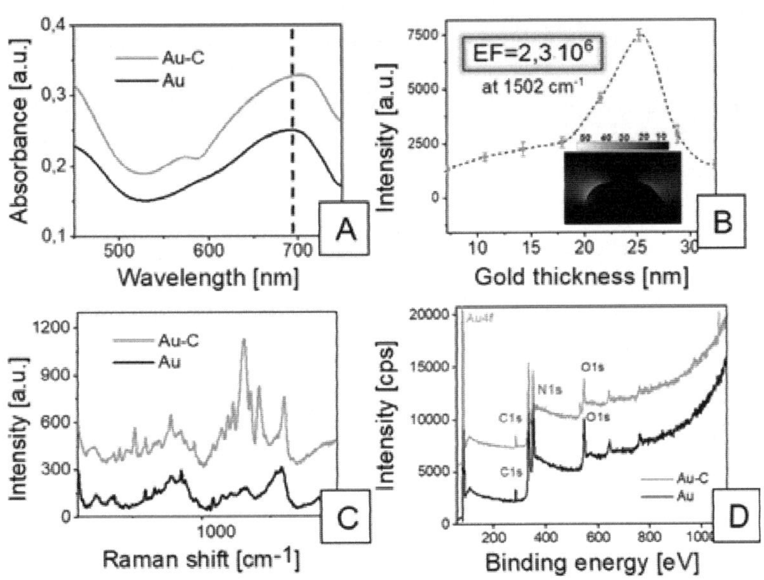

Figure 3 Characterization of Au and Au-C: (a) UV-Vis spectroscopy, (b) Calculation of enhancement factor of Au using R6G (insert is simulation of EM field distribution); (c) SERS spectra; (c) survey XPS spectra

SERS spectra of Au-C confirm the successfulness of C-OND grafting via the appearance of new characteristic bands typical for the oligonucleotide structure. (**Figure 3C**). The attachment of 4-carboxyphenyl groups leads to the appearance of carboxyl group related peaks (1596 cm^{-1}) and aromatic ring (786, 852, 1086, 1214 cm^{-1}). After the coupling with amino-terminated OND-C, there are new peaks in the region 780-1600 cm^{-1}, which are typical for the oligonucleotide structure (bands at 778 cm^{-1}, 1310 cm^{-1}, 1359 cm^{-1}, and 1422 cm^{-1}).

Also, the simulation of plasmon intensity across the grating was performed by finite-difference-time-domain method (FDTD). Numerical simulation of the electric field (EF) distribution on gold grating was performed for excitation with 785 nm light (**Figure 3 A**). Cross sections of one period of the structure yielded the distribution of the localized EF, suggesting that the energy is indeed concentrated in the slopes of the grating (**Figure 3B**).

According to SEM and AFM images, morphology of the resulting substrate consisted of parallel wave-like patterns, with a height of about 168±3 nm and a period of about 710±7 nm (as measured from a cross-section profile, **Figure 4**). After the diazonium modification and covalent grafting of amino-terminated C-OND the pristine grating structure was conserved.

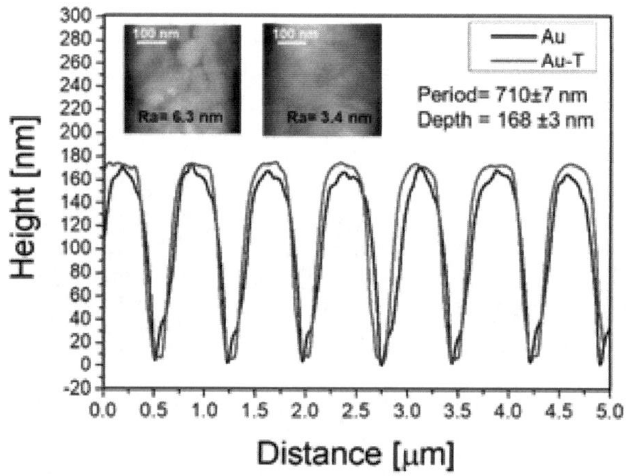

Figure 4 profiles of Au and Au-C, inserts are magnified scans (0.4×0.4 µm2)

To get spectral information about the presence of NDM-encoding gene (T-OND), samples already grafted with the first OND (Au-C) were immersed in a buffer solution to capture the second one. Massive SERS spectra collected prepared samples from were used as a NN input for the deep learning to identify the presence of NDM-encoding gene.

The validation data were utilized for convolutional NN training to automated multiclass classification of the corresponding ONDs using a trained neural network for differentiation between various DNA. The deep convolutional neural network implemented within Keras was used for classification [15]. The network was trained on 75% of randomly selected data and verified on 25% of data. After verifying the convergence, the accuracy reached 99.92% with a level of confidence exceeding 95%.

Also it should be noted that the total time from the beginning of the measurement to obtaining the results is 1-1.5 hours with a preset program of the neural network that is a huge advantage compared to gold-standard cultural-based methods taking more than 24 hours.

4. CONCLUSION

Here we demonstrated the proof-of-concept performance of sensor by the analysis of ONDs related to specific genes responsible for antibiotic resistance. We utilized grafted SERS substrates for DNA capturing. Prepared sensor was involved in the hybridization with T-OND and other mutated ONDs. Further collected SERS spectra measured by Raman spectrometer were utilized as a learning dataset for CNN. Several types of ONDs were detected with accuracy higher than 99,9% with a level of confidence exceeding 95%.

As developed sensor is operated by the ONDs in the similar way as PCR methods does, it is applicable not only for bacterial resistivity but also for tumors, diseases, food and toxicants. This entitles our method to be a universal easy-to-performed platform for the detection of DNA oligomers.

ACKNOWLEDGEMENTS

The work was supported by GACR under the project 20-03913S.

REFERENCES

[1] LEE, A., MIRRET, S., RELLER, L.B., WEINSTEIN, M.P. Detection of bloodstream infections in adults: how many blood cultures are needed? *J Clin Microbiol*. 2007, vol. 45, pp. 3546-3548.

[2] STROMMENGER, B., KETTLITZ, C., WERNER, G., WITTE, W. Staphylococcus aureus antibiotic resistance genes in detection of nine clinically relevant multiplex PCR assay for simultaneous. *J Clin Microbiol.* 2003, vol. 41, pp. 4089-4094.

[3] TSUI-MING-KUO, MO-YUAN SHEN, SHIH-YING HUANG. Facile Fabrication of a Sensor with a Bifunctional Interface for Logic Analysis of the New Delhi Metallo-β-Lactamase (NDM)-Coding Gene. *ACS Sens.* 2016, vol. 1, no. 2, pp. 124-130.

[4] CHARRETIER, Y., SCHRENZEL, J. Mass spectrometry methods for predicting antibiotic resistence. *Proteomics Clinical Applications*. 2016, vol. 10, pp. 964-981.

[5] DANIEL, D., GALVAN, Y. Surface-Enhanced Raman Scattering for Rapid Detection and Characterization of Antibiotic-Resistant Bacteria. *Advanced Helthcare materials*. 2018, vol. 7.

[6] WOOD, R., JENSEN, T., WADSWORTH, C., CLEMENT, M., NAGPAL, P., PITT, P. Analysis of Identification Method for Bacterial Species and Antibiotic Resistance Genes Using Optical Data From DNA Oligomers. *Front. Microbiol.* 2020.

[7] GALVAN, D., YU, Q. Surface-Enhanced Raman Scattering for Rapid Detection and Characterization of Antibiotic-Resistant Bacteria. *Advanced healthcare materials*. 2018, vol. 7, no. 13.

[8] GUSELNIKOVA, O., POSTNIKOV, P., KOLSKA, Z., ZARUBA, K., KOHOUT, K., ELASHNIKOV, R., SVORCIK, V., LYUTAKOV, O. Homochiral metal-organic frameworks functionalized SERS substrate for atto-molar enantio-selective detection. *Applied Materials Today*. 2020, vol. 20.

[9] NOVELLI-ROUSSEAU, A., ESPAGNON, I., FILIPUTTI, D. Culture-free antibiotic-susceptibility determination from single-bacterium Raman spectra. *Scientific reports*. 2018.

[10] GUSELNIKOVA, O., TRELIN, A., SKVORTSOVA, A., ULBRICH, P. Label-free surface-enhanced Raman spectroscopy with artificial neural network technique for recognition photoinduced DNA damage. *Biosensors and Bioelectronics*. 2019, vol.145.

[11] ERZINA, M., TRELIN, A., GUSELNIKOVA, O. Precise cancer detection via the combination of functionalized SERS surfaces and convolutional neural network with independent inputs. *Sensors and Actuators B: Chemical.* 2020, vol. 308.

[12] MADRY, A., MAKELOV, A., SCHMIDT, L., TSIPRAS, D., VLADU, A. Towards deep learning models resistant to adversarial attacks. 2017.

[13] CHOLLET F. Keras. 2015.

[14] VIRTANEN P. et al. SciPy 1.0: Fundamental Algorithms for Scientific Computing in Python. *Nature Methods.* 2020, vol. 17, pp. 261-272.

[15] HO, C., JEAN, N., HOGAN C., BLACKMON, L. Rapid identification of pathogenic bacteria using Raman spectroscopy and deep learning. *Nature.* 2019, vol. 10, no. 4927.

COVALENTLY CROSS-LINKED HYALURONIC ACID/BSA/GELATINE HYDROGELS AS BETTER SURFACE FOR CELL CULTURE

[1]Simon KLIMOVIC, [1]Jan PRIBYL, [2,3]Vladimir ROTREKL, [2,3]Šárka JELINKOVA, Hana VICAROVA

[1]CEITEC, Masaryk University, Brno, Czech Republic, EU, simon.klimovic@ceitec.muni.cz, jan.pribyl@ceitec.muni.cz

[2]Department of Biology, Faculty of Medicine, Masaryk University, Brno, Czech Republic, EU, vrotrekl@med.muni.cz, sarka.jelinkova89@gmail.com

[3]International Clinical Research Center (ICRC), St.Anne's University Hospital, Brno, Czech Republic, EU

https://doi.org/10.37904/nanocon.2020.3739

Abstract

The mechanical and biomechanical properties of the cell's extracellular matrix is a factor in their later development. In this regard, elastic biocompatible materials as a surface for cultivating cells are in recent years, becoming an exciting field of study. Hydrogels are a hydrophilic 3D network of synthetic polymers or biopolymers. They can have tunable mechanical properties, controllable degradability, or they can be designed for long-time release of treatments. Here, hydrogels from Hyaluronic acid (HA), Bovine serum albumin (BSA) and gelatin was prepared, via carbodiimide chemistry. Morphology and mechanical properties of these hydrogels was characterized via Atomic Force Microscopy (AFM). Young's modulus of HA/BSA and HA/BSA/gel were 124.7 ± 15.9 and 20.3 ± 0.5 kPa, respectively. Mouse embryonic fibroblasts were then cultivated on hydrogels and on the glass surface as a reference. Mechanical and morphological properties of fibroblasts were examined by AFM and via phalloidin-TRITC staying. Relationship between the structure of cells and the type of surface was seen. Cells grown on glass were more flattened with an evenly linear actin structure. On hydrogels, fibroblasts were more star-shaped with non-linear actin structures and many filopodia. Furthermore, height of cells was higher was lower compared to cells on both types of hydrogels (0.36 µm vs. 0.56 µm vs. 1.03 µm). Young's modulus of cells on fibroblast was highest, which relates to the whole range of structural changes linked with surface stiffness. In conclusion, this type of hydrogel might be utilized in the future as a better surface material for cell cultivation.

Keywords: AFM, Hydrogel, Actin structure, hyaluronic acid

1. INTRODUCTION

Cells can recognize various cues by extracellular matrix (ECM), starting from various chemical signals and proteins interactions to ECM's mechanical properties. Each cell type favors a different set of these cues to work correctly. A classical approach consists *in vitro* cell culturing on plastic or glass surfaces. Although it is universally accepted as a standard cultivating surface, it does not mimic ECM in any way. Moreover, it has been reported that cells cultivating on flat surfaces can demonstrate the abnormal distribution of integrins or forced cell polarity [1]. It has also been shown that different mechanical properties of the growth surface affect morphology and differentiation, organelle organization, cell migration, or resistance to chemotherapy [1-4]. In recent years, there is an increasing need for a biocompatible scaffold for cell cultures with tunable mechanical properties and bioactivity. Hydrogels, 3D networks of synthetic or biopolymers with high water retention has proven useful in that regard [1, 5-7]. To mimic ECM mechanical properties and high-water retention, it is ideal to synthesize hydrogels from biopolymers. As a major component of the extracellular matrix in various tissues, Hyaluronic acid (HA) comes to mind [8]. HA is anionic biopolymer, consisting of its structure N-acetylglucosamine and D-glucoronic acid repeating units. In the cell, HA forms long chains, partially stabilized by weaker bonds between them. To modulate mechanical properties such as stiffness and elasticity, HA must be further stabilized by cross-linking. Chemical modification of hyaluronic acid by carbodiimides (EDAC) has been often used to stabilized HA [5,9]. EDAC modify side-groups of HA and mediate ester bond formation between hydroxyl and carboxyl groups of HA. Other types of biopolymers or molecules can be mixed with HA and EDAC to get different mechanical properties, such as collagen [5] or gelatin [7]. Bovine serum albumin (BSA) by its similarity with human variant, is an interesting candidate as material for a hydrogel, with the capability to bind, retain and release a variety of molecules in a defined manner [10,11].

In this study, the hydrogel matrix from HA and BSA was prepared and characterized. For improved mechanical stability, 1-ethyl-3-(3-dimethylaminopropyl)-carbodiimide (EDAC), together with N-hydroxysuccimid (NHS) was used as a cross-linking agent. Resulting hydrogels were characterized by Atomic Force Microscopy for topography and mechanical properties in various conditions (temperature, medium). Resulting hydrogels showed desirable mechanical properties; however, Young's Modulus (YM) was further modulated by the addition of gelatin into hydrogel mixture. To demonstrate different morphology of cells on softer substrates, mouse embryonic fibroblasts (MEF) were then cultured on hydrogels. Finally, the actin structures of cells by Phalloidin-TRITC staining was analyzed.

2. METHODS

2.1. Materials

BSA, EDAC, NHS, Gelatin and Phalloidin-TRITC were purchased from Sigma-Aldrich (St. Louis, MO, USA). Trimethylamine (TEA) and (3-Aminopropyl)triethoxysilane (APTES) used for silanization were purchased from Honeywell research chemicals (Charlotte, NC, USA). Hyaluronic acid (M_W=550 kDa) was kindly provided by Jan Víteček. HEPES was purchased from ROTH (Carl, Germany). Mitotically inactivated mouse embryonic fibroblasts (mEF) for cultivation were kindly provided to us by Vladimir Rotrekl research group, LF Masaryk University.

2.2. Silanization of glass cover slips

To immobilize hydrogels for AFM measurement, alkoxysilane molecules were introduced on glass slips surface. Firstly, glass slip was attached on the bottom of the petri dish (TPP, Trasadingen, Switzerland) and cleaned with chromic acid, deionized water, and ethanol. After that, dry and clean petri dish with a glass slip attached was put to a vacuum desiccator together with 50 µl of TEA and 50 µl of APTES. Vacuum was applied for 10 minutes, and then samples were left in desiccator for 2 hours.

2.3. Fabrication and cross-linking of HA/BSA hydrogels

Hydrogel mixture was prepared from HA and BSA, with a weight ratio of 2:8, respectively. For 100 µl of mixture, 50 µl of HA (32 mg/ml) and 50 µl of BSA (128 mg/ml) was added. Alternatively, 10 µl of gelatin (50 mg/ml) was added at BSA's expense. After thorough mixing, 6 mg of EDAC and 1 mg NHS was put into a mixture. Resulted slurry was poured on a silanized glass coverslip. After two hours of polymerization at room temperature, 2 ml of HEPES (50 mM) was added and hydrogels were left to swell overnight in 5 °C.

2.4. Characterization of topography and mechanical properties by AFM

For topography measurements, "Imaging in contact" mode on Atomic Force Microscope (JPK NanoWizard 3, Bruker, Billerica, MA, USA) was used with HYDRA-2N-100N cantilever (AppNano, Mountain View, CA, USA). Imaged area was 10x10 µm with setpoint: 100 pN, iGain: 50, PGain: 0.006, Z range: 15 µm, and Scan rate: 1 Hz. For the measurement of mechanical properties, "Force Mapping" mode with setpoint 0.5 nN, relative setpoint: 1 nN, IGain: 70 Hz, PGain: 0.002 and extended time: 0.5 s, was used. Lastly we

"Quantitative imaging" mode for topography images was used. The temperature of samples was maintained at 37 °C by Petri Dish Heater (Bruker, Billerica, MA, USA).

Force maps acquired were processed in JPK Data Processing 5 software using the Sneddon-Hertz model. All other processing of AFM images was done in Gwydion software [12].

2.5. Cultivation of cells on hydrogels and phalloidin staining

Frozen mitotically inactivated mouse embryonic cells were thawed in a water bath (37 °C) and then transferred into 15 ml tube. After that 12 ml of cold mEF medium (86 % KnockOut Dulbecco modified eagle medium, 10 % fetal bovine serum, 1 % L-glutamine, 1 % penicillin/streptomycin, 1 % nonessential amino acids, 0,1 mM 2-mercaptoethanol) was poured into a tube, which was then centrifuge 200g/5 min. Medium above the cell pellet was removed and warm mEF medium (37°C) was added. The resulting cell suspension was divided between hydrogels samples.

Cells were stained after two days of cultivation. Firstly, mEF medium was removed, cells were washed with PBS buffer and then fixated with 3.7% paraformaldehyde in PBS for 5 minutes at room temperature. Samples were washed with PBS 3x times and incubated with 0.1% Triton-X in PBS for 10 minutes and washed with PBS again. After that 200 µl of phalloidin-TRITC was added for 60 minutes, washed in PBS, and 200 µl of 0.1 % DAPI were added. Finally, samples were washed 2x in PBS, dried and stored for further measurement.

The confocal microscope (LSM 700, Zeiss, Oberkochen, Germany) was used for imaging phalloidin and DAPI staining. Images were further processed in ImageJ software [13].

3. RESULTS AND DISCUSSION

3.1. Optimization and characterization of hydrogels by AFM In the process of optimization HA/BSA hydrogel system, two sources of HA - Hyaluronic acid sodium salt and high molecular crosslinked Hyalobarrier gel, was tried. Latter mentioned source could not be sufficiently polymerized. Ester bond formation during EDC/NHS reaction occurs on hydroxyl and carboxyl groups of HA and BSA.

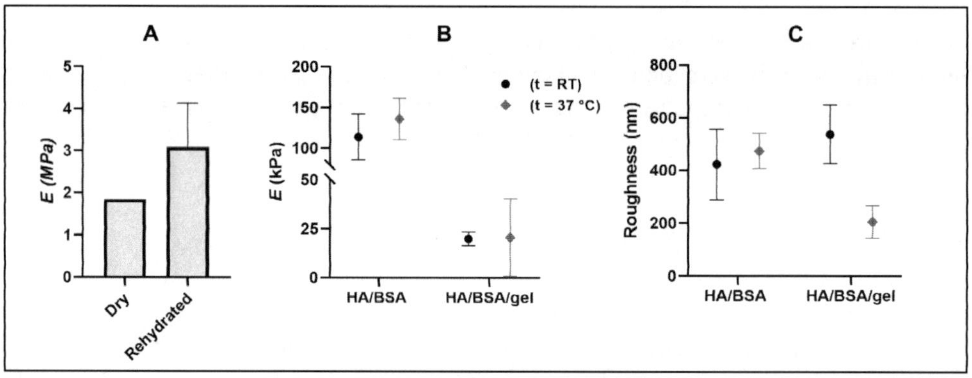

Figure 1 - Results from optimization of hydrogel preparation process. A - Difference between dry and rehydrated hydrogel, where we can see elevated YM of latter mentioned. B, C - Results of YM and Roughness of HA/BSA and HA/BSA/Gelatine hydrogels in room temperature (RT) and 37 °C.

3.2. Hyalobarrier gel comes from production already partially polymerized and It probably either lacks active groups, or they are not available for the reaction. For further experiments, HA sodium salt was used. Mechanical properties of hydrogels without gelatin were tried first. During Force mapping, the cantilever frequently lost contact with the surface, and stiffness values were in units of MPa (**Figure1A** - Dry). High stiffness might have been caused by collapsing of hydrogel structure under AFM cantilever, which was previously shown [14,15]. Findings in previous study with alginate hydrogels suggested, that drying out and rehydrating of hydrogels can stabilize the structure. [16]. Therefore, same approach was utilized, which a partial success. While the cantilever was no longer losing contact with hydrogel, the stiffness was even more elevated. In **Figure 1A** we can see YM for both dry and rehydrated hydrogels. It was concluded that hydrogel, after drying out, could not be rehydrated well enough, which on the one hand, might have caused better strength, but on the other hand, higher stiffness. Therefore, preparation process was optimized by letting hydrogels polymerized at room temperature with addition of HEPES buffer after two hours. **Figure 1B** shows YM of HA/BSA and HA/BSA/Gelatin hydrogels in room temperature and in 37 °C. In previous studies, it has been stated that rotation around linkages in structure of HA are easier, with increasing temperature [17], causing better flexibility and, therefore, lower stiffness. Yet, this effect was not seen in our experiments. The addition of gelatin into a hydrogel mixture had an effect on YM (124.7 vs. 20.32, $P < 0,0001$). Roughness values did not differ significantly (**Figure 1C**). **Figure 2** shows representative topography and YM AFM maps of HA/BSA and HA/BSA/Gelatin hydrogels. For cell cultivation, both HA/BSA and HA/BSA/gelatin hydrogels were chosen.

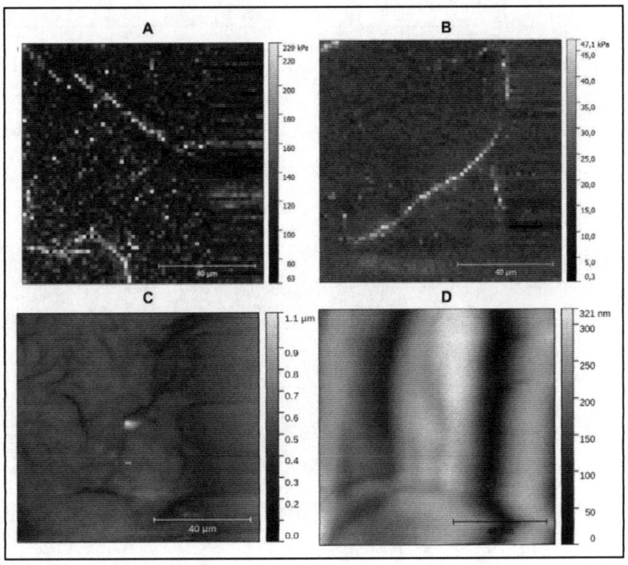

Figure 2 - Representative AFM maps of Young's Modulus and topography of HA/BSA hydrogel in RT (1A, 1B), respectively and HA/BSA/gelatine hydrogel in RT (1B,1D).

3.3. Cultivation of cells and actin structures

The primary aim of this experiment was to determine if and how cells will grow on hydrogels. Thus, Mouse embryonic fibroblast on HA/BSA, HA/BSA/gelatin hydrogels, and on glass for reference, were cultivated. The structure of cells was evaluated via actin staining. Topography and mechanical properties were measured by AFM. In **Figure 4**, pictures from confocal microscopy, actin structures via phalloidin-TRITC staining, and topography via AFM for the sample with reference surface, can be seen. Fibroblasts were most evenly grown on the glass. Actin structures and filopodia were mostly linear. On the other hand, cells on hydrogels were more irregular, often star-shaped, with more prominent filopodia and lamellipodia (arrows in 4E, H). Atomic Force microscopy was used to obtain topography images and mechanical properties of cells. **Figure 3A** shows that cell stiffness was highest on glass surface and dropped on hydrogels surfaces. This results suggests that there is influence of cultivating surface on cell stiffness, firstly in the sense that the object with the same stiffness would appear softer on softer surfaces and vice versa, but secondly, due to changes in cellular structure, due stiffness of the surface. These changes in cellular structure are visible from topography images and actin structures, where cells are growing in a different manner, which is changing mechanical properties. Fibroblasts on glass were flatter (**Figure 4C**), and height was increasing with decreasing stiffness of surface. This trend is visible in **Figure 3B**.

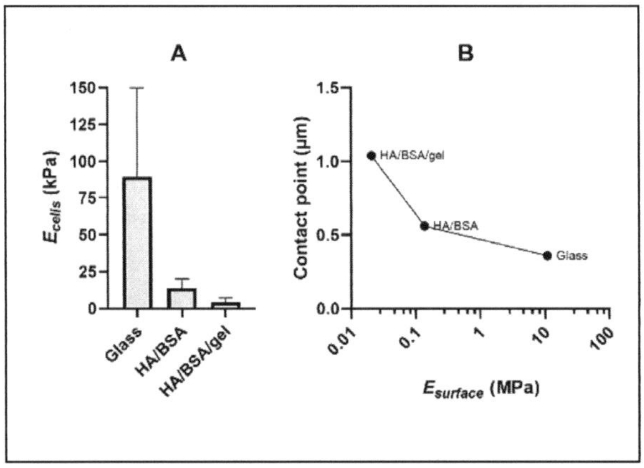

Figure 3 - A - Young's Modulus of cells was highest in glass sample and lowest in both hydrogels (89.3 ± 60.7 vs. 14.0 ± 5.9 vs 4.3 ± 3.7). **B -** Relationship between contact point of AFM cantilever in μm and Young's Modulus of surface. In other words, cells are more likely to flattened on stiff surfaces then on soft surfaces.

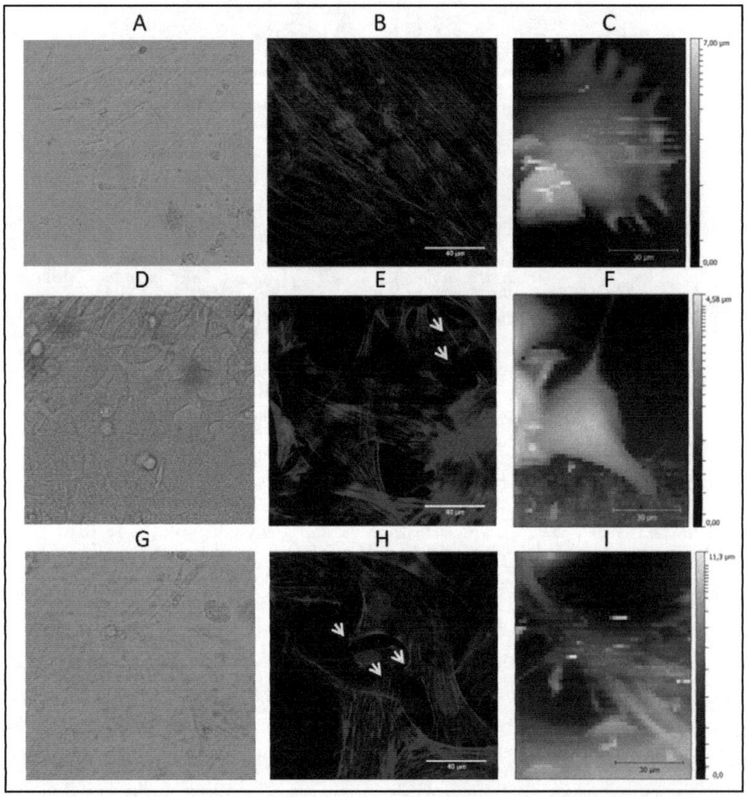

Figure 4 - Representative images of cells in confocal microscopy, actin structures and AFM topography. **A-C** - cells on glass; **D-F** - cells on HA/BSA hydrogel; **G-I** - cells on HA/BSA/gel hydrogel. (arrows represents filopodia and lamellipodia)

4. CONCLUSION

In this study, hydrogels from hyaluronan, bovine serum albumin, and gelatin was prepared, using carbodiimide chemistry for cross-linking. Hydrogels were characterized by Atomic Force Microscopy, and stiffness values were calculated via the Hertz-Sneddon model from force curves. Values of Young's modulus were 124.7 ± 15.9 and 20.3 ± 0.5 kPa, for hydrogels with and without gelatin, respectively. Mouse embryonic fibroblasts were cultivated on both types of prepared scaffolds and on glass surface as a reference. The structure of cells was examined via confocal microscopy, Atomic Force Microscopy and actin structure was shown via staying with phalloidin conjugated with tetramethylrhodamine. Results showed great differences in cellular structure and morphology depending on surface type. Gupta et al. showed a connection between the stiffness of the surface and structure of actin filaments in a cell [18]. Cells on rigid surfaces tend to grow bigger are with linear actin structures and vice versa. Our findings correspond with the results of this study. In conclusion, we showed that this type of hydrogel can be used as a cultivation surface. Moreover, cells on these hydrogels are growing in a more physiologically manner than ones on standard surfaces such as glass.

ACKNOWLEDGEMENTS

CIISB, Instruct-CZ Centre of Instruct-ERIC EU consortium, funded by MEYS CR infrastructure project LM2018127, is gratefully acknowledged for the financial support of the measurements at the CF Nanobiotechnology. The work was also supported by the European Regional Development Fund - Project ENOCH (No. CZ.02.1.01/0.0/0.0/16_019/0000868)

REFERENCES

[1] CALIARI, S.R., BURDICK, J.A.. A practical guide to hydrogels for cell culture. *Nature Methods*. 2016, vol. 13, no. 5, pp. 405-414.

[2] BALESTRINI, J.L., CHAUDHRY, S., SARRAZY, V., et al. The mechanical memory of lung myofibroblasts. *Integrative Biology*. 2012, vol. 4, no. 4, pp. 410-421.

[3] EVEN-RAM, S., YAMADA, K.M. Cell migration in 3D matrix. *Current Opinion in Cell Biology*. 2005, vol. 17, no. 5, pp. 524-532.

[4] NGUYEN, T.V., SLEIMAN, M., MORIARTY, T., et al. Sorafenib resistance and JNK signaling in carcinoma during extracellular matrix stiffening. *Biomaterials*. 2014, vol. 35, no. 22, pp. 5749-5759.

[5] PARK, S.-N., PARK, J.-C., KIM, H.O., et al. Characterization of porous collagen/hyaluronic acid scaffold modified by 1-ethyl-3-(3-dimethylaminopropyl)carbodiimide cross-linking. *Biomaterials*. 2002, vol. 23, no. 4, pp. 1205-1212.

[6] CAMCI-UNAL, G., CUTTICA, D., ANNABI, N., et al. Synthesis and characterization of hybrid hyaluronic acid-gelatin hydrogels. *Biomacromolecules*. 2013, vol. 14, no. 4, pp. 1085-1092.

[7] VANDERHOOFT JL, ALCOUTLABI M, MAGDA JJ, PRESTWICH GD. Rheological Properties of Cross-Linked Hyaluronan-Gelatin Hydrogels for Tissue Engineering. [onlne]. 2009, vol.9, no. 1, pp. 20-8. [Accessed in October 2020] .Available from: https://www.ncbi.nlm.nih.gov/pmc/articles/PMC2711643/.

[8] FRASER, J.R., LAURENT, T.C., LAURENT, U.B. Hyaluronan: its nature, distribution, functions and turnover. *Journal of Internal Medicine*. 1997, vol. 242, no. 1, pp. 27-33.

[9] KUO, J.W., SWANN, D.A., PRESTWICH, G.D. Chemical modification of hyaluronic acid by carbodiimides. *Bioconjugate Chemistry*. 1991, vol. 2, no. 4, pp. 232-241.

[10] ARABI, S.H., AGHELNEJAD, B., SCHWIEGER, C., et al. Serum albumin hydrogels in broad pH and temperature ranges: characterization of their self-assembled structures and nanoscopic and macroscopic properties. *Biomaterials Science*. 2018, vol. 6, no. 3, pp. 478-492.

[11] AKDOGAN, Y., REICHENWALLNER, J., HINDERBERGER, D. Evidence for Water-Tuned Structural Differences in Proteins: An Approach Emphasizing Variations in Local Hydrophilicity. *PLOS ONE*. 2012, vol. 7, no. 9, p. e45681.

[12] NEČAS, D., KLAPETEK, P. Gwyddion: an open-source software for SPM data analysis. *Open Physics*. 2012, vol. 10, no. 1, pp. 181-188.

[13] SCHNEIDER, C.A., RASBAND, W.S., ELICEIRI, K.W. NIH Image to ImageJ: 25 years of image analysis. *Nature Methods*. 2012, vol. 9, no. 7, pp. 671-675.

[14] HARICH, R., BLYTHE, T.W., HERMES, M., et al. Gravitational collapse of depletion-induced colloidal gels. *Soft Matter*. 2016, vol. 12, no. 19, pp. 4300-4308.

[15] JPK Instruments. *JPK Application Note: Determining the elastic modulus of biological samples using atomic force microscopy*.

[16] VREEKER, R., LI, L., FANG, Y., et al. Drying and Rehydration of Calcium Alginate Gels. *Food Biophysics*. 2008, vol. 3, no. 4, pp. 361-369.

[17] COWMAN, M.K., SCHMIDT, T.A., RAGHAVAN, P., et al. Viscoelastic Properties of Hyaluronan in Physiological Conditions. *F1000Research*. 2015, vol. 4, p. 622.

[18] GUPTA, M., SARANGI, B.R., DESCHAMPS, J., et al. Adaptive rheology and ordering of cell cytoskeleton govern matrix rigidity sensing. *Nature Communications*. 2015, vol. 6, no. 1, p. 7525.

THE INTERACTION BETWEEN SELECTED ANTIDEPRESSANTS AND ZINC OXIDE NANOPARTICLES

[1]Roman MARŠÁLEK, [1]Martin ŠVIDRNOCH

[1]*University of Ostrava, Ostrava, Czech Republic, EU, roman.marsalek@osu.cz*

https://doi.org/10.37904/nanocon.2020.3737

Abstract

Interactions between tricyclic antidepressants and zinc oxide nanoparticles have been studied. Amitriptyline and nortriptyline, which were immobilized from buffer medium at 37 °C, were selected as models. The key factor influencing the adsorption of these substances on zinc oxide is pH. During the adsorption, an acid-base equilibrium was established between the buffer, zinc oxide and the antidepressant. These pH changes were also reflected in the surface charge of the adsorbent and the values of the zeta potential, which was also monitored. Both substances have a similar structure, yet they differ in their acid-base properties and also in their ability to form micelles. These different properties caused different values of the amount adsorbed on the surface of the zinc oxide. Adsorption isotherms show a sigmoidal course. The highest adsorbed amount of amitriptyline on ZnO is 6.38 mmol g^{-1}, in the case of nortriptyline it is 3.68 mmol g^{-1}. The adsorption is directed in accordance with the pseudo-second-order kinetic equation. The values from the kinetic equations, as well as the changes in the zeta potential, indicate different mechanisms of immobilization of amitriptyline and nortriptyline on the surface of zinc oxide nanoparticles. In the case of both substances, due to the interaction with zinc oxide, they were significantly removed from the liquid medium; in the case of amitriptyline, the residual concentration was less than 10% at an initial concentration of 5 mmol L^{-1}.

Keywords: Antidepressants, ZnO nanoparticles, adsorption, zeta potential

1. INTRODUCTION

With the growing production and use of pharmaceuticals, their release into the environment increases. In Western civilizations, the use of medicines is steadily growing. This increase applies to all classes of drugs, including significant antibiotics, analgesics, antidepressants and many others. In the United States of America, or in some Scandinavian countries, up to 100 people in every 1,000 people use antidepressants. Tricyclic antidepressants are partially trapped by activated sludge in wastewater treatment plants. However, some of these substances enter the watercourses; they are not readily hydrolysed and are also not biodegraded [1]. In addition to the environmental burden mentioned above, there is another risk associated with the use of antidepressants. The risk of poisoning can be very critical especially in the case of children [2]. Possibilities to remove antidepressants from the body in case of overdose are being studied. An example may be a study using a mixture of liposomes, proteins and serum [3]. The aim is therefore to remove pharmaceutical substances from the environment in which they are harmful. One possibility that is widely examined is adsorption. Adsorption can be used to remove toxic substances from water sources, but also from human digestive tract.

In the case of adsorption reviews, scientists are mainly concerned with adsorption materials, adsorption conditions and the mechanism of adsorption. A variety of adsorbents are investigated for pharmaceuticals adsorption, such as: carbonaceous materials, clay minerals, polymers, silica based materials, and other various adsorbents. In addition to synthetic adsorbents, so-called cheap adsorbents are studied for economic reasons [4,5]. These review articles summarize the adsorption capacity of sorbents for individual drugs. The authors also discuss in detail the factors that influence the adsorption process, the kinetics and thermodynamics of adsorption. Another review article deals with the flow adsorption of pharmaceuticals contaminants on various materials [6].

One group of adsorbents are metal oxides, in which photocatalytic properties are studied in addition to adsorption activity. A mixture of titanium oxide and silicon oxide was used to remove paracetamol and ibuprofen from the liquid medium [7]. Heterojunction zinc tin oxide (ZnO/SnO_2) was used for photodegradation of amytriptyline. The material was prepared as nanoparticles [8]. Core-shell nanoparticles of the type Fe_3O_4@ZrO_2@N- cetylpyridinium were used for solid phase extraction of antidepressant drugs amitriptyline and nortriptyline from plasma [9]. The nanoparticles of magnetic surface molecular imprinted polymer mesoparticles (Fe_3O_4@SiO_2-MIP) were studied as a selective adsorbent for amitriptyline in biological samples [10]. Six antidepressants were adsorbed on silver nanoparticles and the mechanism of adsorption was compared with the interaction between antidepressants and receptors [11].

The aim of this work is to characterize the adsorption of amitriptyline and nortriptyline on zinc oxide nanoparticles. The kinetics of adsorption, adsorption capacity of materials, change of surface charge and mainly influence of pH were studied. The possible mechanism of the adsorption of amitriptyline and nortriptyline has been suggested.

2. EXPERIMENTAL PART

2.1. Materials and methods

The amitryptiline (AMIT) and the nortriptyline (NORT) used were in an HCl forms which are freely soluble in water, a pKa value of AMIT is 9.4 and 9.7 for NORT, respectively. They were purchased from Sigma Aldrich, USA. Nanoparticle oxide ZnO was used as the commercial product purchased from Sigma Aldrich, USA. The size of particles was under 100nm. Phosphate buffered saline tablets (Sigma Aldrich, USA) were used for solution preparation of pH 7.4. All other used chemicals were of the highest purity grade available from commercial sources. The zeta potential of all suspensions was measured using the Zetasizer Nano ZS (Malvern Instruments Ltd., GB). Before zeta potential was measured all samples were sonicated for 5 minutes

2.2. Adsorption experiments

The basic design, which was the same for all adsorption experiments, was as follows: solution volume 5 ml, pH 7.4, adsorbent weight 5 mg, shaken in a bath at 37 ° C. The contact time was 24 hours, except for the measurement of adsorption kinetics. After the contact time, the solutions were centrifuged and filtered through a syringe filter. The resulting antidepressants concentration was determined by UV-VIS spectrophotometry. Amitriptyline and nortriptyline as well as exhibit a maximum absorbance at 239 nm. All experiments were performed at least three times.

In the case of kinetic experiments, it was performed as follows. The initial antidepressants concentration was 10 mmol/L. Samples were taken and analysed at specified time intervals. A total of 7 samples were prepared in flasks, one for each time sampling. Thus, samples were not taken sequentially from a single flask, thus reducing the volume in the flask and changing the ratio between the liquid and solid phases. The pseudo-first-order and pseudo-second-order kinetic models are most commonly used to describe the rate of adsorption [12,13].

The maximum of adsorption capacity for our adsorption materials was evaluated from adsorption isotherms. Isotherms show how the adsorbed amount depends on the equilibrium concentration. The initial concentration of AMIT and NORT ranged from 0.1 mmol L^{-1} to 10 mmol L^{-1}. After the contact time (24 hours), the samples were analysed as described above. The amount of antidepressant adsorbed (*a*) was determined from the change in the solution concentration before and after equilibrium, according to:

$$a = \frac{(c_0 - c_e).V}{m} \qquad (1)$$

where:

a - the adsorbed amount (mmol g^{-1})

c_0 - the initial concentration of AMIT (NORT) solution (mmol L^{-1})

c_0 - the concentration of AMIT (NORT) solution at the adsorption equilibrium (mmol L^{-1})

V - the volume of solution (ml)

m - the mass of ZnO (mg)

3. RESULTS AND DISSCUSIONS

The key factor that will affect the interactions between zinc oxide nanoparticles and the antidepressant will be pH. PBS buffer was chosen from previous studies and according to literature sources. It is a commonly used buffer simulating a physiological environment with a pH value around 7.4. The traditional composition of PBS buffer is: NaCl, KCl, NaH_2PO_4 and KH_2PO_4. The material chosen for the immobilization of amitriptyline and nortriptyline is zinc oxide. Its solubility in water is relatively low, yet studies are known to document the effect of zinc oxide on pH [14]. This effect is further supported by possible reactions between ZnO dissociation products and compounds contained in the buffer, especially with phosphates. The following reactions can take place in the system:

$$ZnO + H_2O \leftrightarrow Zn^{2+} + 2\ OH^- \qquad (2)$$

The formation of hydroxide anions alone will lead to an increase in pH. However, in the presence of a buffer, this effect should be suppressed. Zinc cations then react with phosphates to form various forms of complex particles.

$$ZnO + H_2PO_4^- \leftrightarrow ZnHPO_4 + OH^- \qquad (3)$$

$$Zn^{2+} + H_2PO_4^- \leftrightarrow Zn(H_2PO_4)_2 \qquad (4)$$

In addition to raising the pH, phosphates will also precipitate, forming flakes that are larger in size than the original zinc oxide. These agglomerates will also include antidepressant molecules, which are also present in solution. The instability of zinc oxide in an aqueous environment is also described by other authors [15]. To understand the interactions between the solid phase and the antidepressant molecules, the charge of these substances at a given pH is important. The pH dependence of zinc oxide is shown in **Figure 1**.

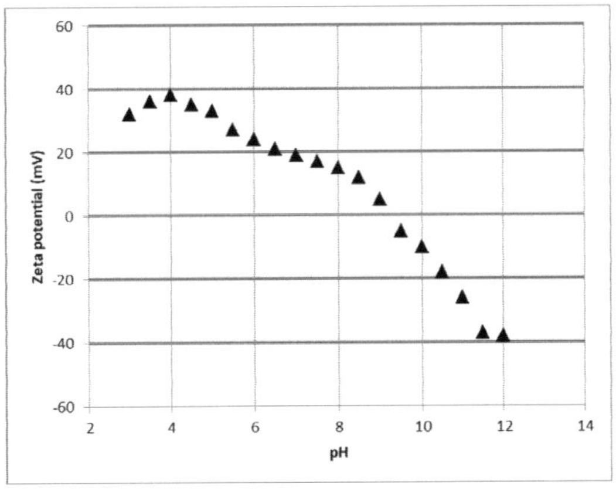

Figure 1 The influence of pH on zeta potential of ZnO

On the curve of the dependence of the zeta potential on pH, the point at which the value of the zeta potential is zero is particularly important. This is the so-called isoelectric point. The pH value at which the zeta potential of the zinc oxide particles is zero is around pH 9. In the case of zinc oxide, the isoelectric point value depends on the form in which it is present, the amount of impurities, etc. In general, two pH values are given for zinc oxide, in which the charge is zero. One pH is around pH 4-5, the other around pH 9-10 [16-18]. Due to the fact that the immobilization took place at a pH higher than seven, this weakly basic environment is especially important.

When nano-sized zinc oxide was added to the buffer, the pH shifted to about pH 10 in accordance with the above equations (2-4). According to **Figure 1**, at this pH, the zeta value of the zinc oxide potential is about -15 mV. Thus, the surface of the particles is negatively charged and should preferably attract positively charged particles. The antidepressants used, i.e. amitriptyline and nortriptyline, are tricyclic compounds which have a nitrogen atom in their aliphatic part of the molecule. The only difference in their molecules is on this nitrogen. In the case of amitryptyline, two methyl groups are attached, in the case of nortryptyline, there is one methyl group and one hydrogen. The pK_A values found in the literature are for amitriptyline 9.4 and for nortryptyline 9.7 [19]. According to this criterion, amitriptyline is a slightly stronger acid. However, both of these substances will be in solution in different forms according to the actual pH. In **Figure 2**, these forms are shown for nortryptyline.

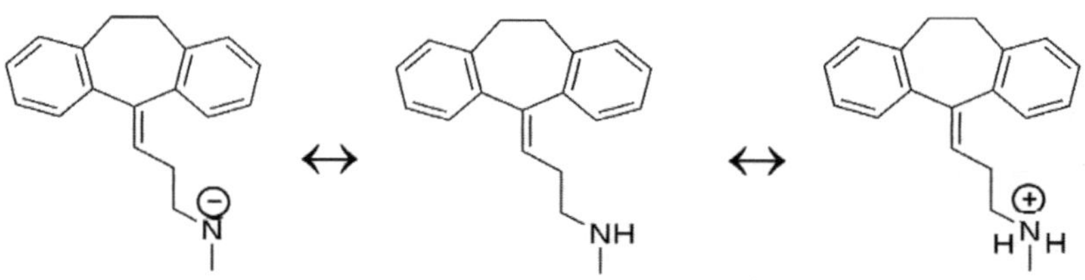

Figure 2 Forms of neutral molecule and ions of nortryptyline

Although both antidepressants can be considered as weak acids, their pH dropped after their addition to the solution, depending on their concentration. In summary, it can be recalled that the initial pH of the PBS buffer was 7.4, increased to 10 after the addition of zinc oxide and then decreased again in the presence of antidepressants. Next **Figure 3** shows the dependence of the adsorbed amount of antidepressant on the equilibrium concentration.

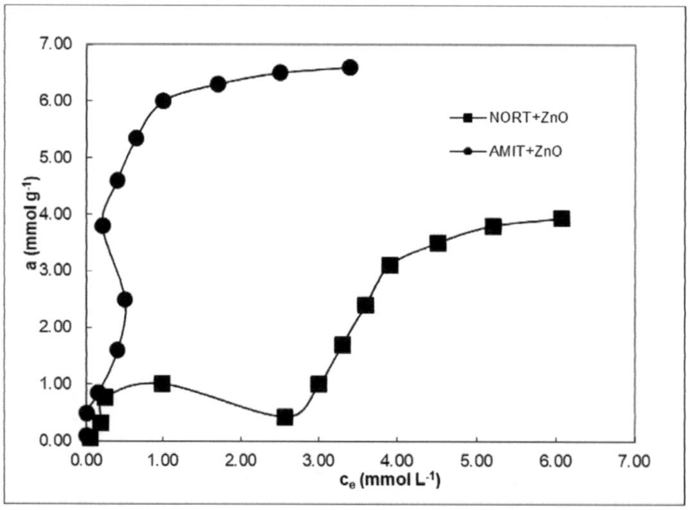

Figure 3 Adsorption isotherms of nortryptyline and amitryptyline on ZnO

The adsorption isotherms of amitriptyline and nortriptyline have a sigmoidal character, which is evident especially in the adsorption of nortryptyline. At an initial nortriptyline concentration of up to 2 mmol L^{-1}, the amount adsorbed increases. The pH was measured continuously and for these low concentrations of nortriptyline the pH was about 10. At this pH, the zeta potential of zinc oxide is negative and, conversely, nortriptyline occurs in solution in the form of a cation. From an initial concentration of 3 mmol L^{-1}, the pH decreases due to deprotonation of the nortriptyline molecule. The pH takes values around 9, which is the value of the isoelectric point of the zinc oxide used. The nortriptyline molecule has a neutral character; there is a relative decrease in the amount adsorbed. As the antidepressant concentration is further increased, the pH of the solution continues to decrease. The zeta potential of zinc oxide becomes positive, the nortriptyline molecule is negatively charged and adsorption increases again. The maximum adsorbed amount of nortriptyline is about 6.4 mmol g^{-1}, in the case of nortriptyline this value is about 3.9 mmol g^{-1}. These are relatively high values, which are probably caused not only by adsorption, but also by the precipitation of zinc oxide with the buffer components and the subsequent immobilization of antidepressants inside the formed precipitates. The almost double adsorption capacity for amitriptyline compared to nortriptyline can be explained by micelle formation. Both substances form micelles in a high ionic strength environment. The critical micellar concentration is lower in the case of nortriptyline, in other words the substance also occurs in solution in the form of micelles, the ability of which is less trapped on the surface of zinc oxide.

A comparison of linearized shapes of kinetic models shows that the adsorption of antidepressants on zinc oxide nanoparticles corresponds better to the second-order pseudo-kinetic equation. The estimated values of the adsorption amount correspond to the conclusions from the adsorption isotherms. The rate of equilibrium was approximately the same for both substances. Different kinetic parameters were found only in extreme cases of concentrations. By this is meant the concentration of substances which has led to a change in the pH of the solution, to the reaching of an isoelectric point and thus to a decrease in the amount adsorbed.

4. CONCLUSION

The oxide nanoparticles have a high affinity for tricyclic antidepressants. Adsorption on the surface of zinc oxide nanoparticles together with precipitation led to the removal of amitriptyline and nortriptyline from the PBS buffer medium. The most important factor that affects the adsorption process is pH. The removal of antidepressants from solution is not only controlled by simple adsorption, but is a complex of chemical-physical processes. However, the adsorption capacities found suggest the possible use of zinc oxide nanoparticles for the removal of tricyclic anti-depressants from liquid media. These properties could be used in wastewater treatment, but also in the removal of these substances from the body during unwanted poisoning.

ACKNOWLEDGEMENTS

This study was supported by the project of Faculty of Science, University of Ostrava, No. SGS08/PřF/2020. Authors thank bc. Jakub Malota (Department of chemistry, Faculty of Science, University of Ostrava) for the measurement of antidepressants concentration.

REFERENCES

[1] CHOI, J.-W., YUFENG, Z., BEDIAKO, J.K., CHO, Ch.-W, YUN, Y.-S. Estimating environmental fate of tricyclic antidepressants in wastewater treatment plant. *Science of The Total Environment.* 2018, vol. 634, pp. 52-58.

[2] KERR, G., MCGUFFIE, A. WILKIE, S. Tricyclic antidepressant overdose: a review. *Emergency Medicine Journal: EMJ.* 2001, vol. 18, no. 4, pp. 236-241.

[3] HOWELL, B.,CHAUHAN, A.. Uptake of amitriptyline and nortriptyline with liposomes, proteins, and serum: Implications for drug detoxification. *Journal of Colloid and Interface Science.* 2008, vol. 319, no. 1, pp. 81-93.

[4] AKHTAR, J., AMIN, N.A.S., SHAHZAD, K. A review on removal of pharmaceuticals from water by adsorption. *Desalination and Water Treatment.* 2016, vol. 57, no. 27, pp. 12842-12860.

[5] DE ANDRADE, J.M., OLIVEIRA, F., DA SILVA, M.G.C., VIEIRA, M.G.A. Adsorption of Pharmaceuticals from Water and Wastewater Using Nonconventional Low-Cost Materials: A Review. *Industrial & Engineering Chemistry Research*. 2018, vol. 57, no. 9, pp.3103-3127.

[6] AHMED, M.J., HAMEED, B.H. Removal of emerging pharmaceutical contaminants by adsorption in a fixed-bed column: A review. *Ecotoxicology and Environmental Safety*. 2018, vol. 149, pp. 257-266.

[7] CIESIELCZYK, F., GOSCIANSKA, J., ZDARTA,J., JESIONOWSKI, T. The development of zirconia/silica hybrids for the adsorption and controlled release of active pharmaceutical ingredients. *Colloids and Surfaces A: Physicochemical and Engineering Aspects*. 2018, vol. 545, pp. 39-50.

[8] IVETIĆ, T.B., FINČUR, N.L., ABRAMOVIĆ, B.F, DIMITRIEVSKA, M., ŠTRBAC, G.R., ČAJKO, K.O., MILJEVIĆ, B.B., ĐAČANIN, Lj.R., LUKIĆ-PETROVIĆ, S.R. Environmentally friendly photoactive heterojunction zinc tin oxide nanoparticles. *Ceramics International*. 2016, vol. 42, no. 2, pp. 3575-3583.

[9] ZARE, F., GHAEDI, M. DANESHFAR, A.. Solid phase extraction of antidepressant drugs amitriptyline and nortriptyline from plasma samples using core-shell nanoparticles of the type Fe3O4@ZrO2@N- cetylpyridinium, and their subsequent determination by HPLC with UV detection. *Microchimica Acta*. 2015, vol. 182, no. 1-12, pp. 1893-1902.

[10] KAMARI, K., TAHERI, A.. Preparation and evaluation of magnetic core-shell mesoporous molecularly imprinted polymers for selective adsorption of amitriptyline in biological samples. *Journal of the Taiwan Institute of Chemical Engineers*. 2018, vol. 86, pp. 230-239.

[11] JAWORSKA, A., MALEK, K. A comparison between adsorption mechanism of tricyclic antidepressants on silver nanoparticles and binding modes on receptors. Surface-enhanced Raman spectroscopy studies. *Journal of Colloid and Interface Science*. 2014, vol. 431, pp. 117-124.

[12] LAGERGREN, S. Y. Zur Theorie der sogenannten Adsorption gelöster Stoffe. *Kungliga Svenska Vetenskapsakademiens*. Handlingar 1898, vol. 24, pp. 1−39.

[13] HO, Y. S., MCKAY, G. A comparison of chemisorption kinetic models applied to pollutant removal on various sorbents. *Process Safety and Environmental Protection*. 1998, pp. 332-340.

[14] MEISSNER, T., OELSCHLÄGEL, K. POTTHOFF, A.. Implications of the stability behavior of zinc oxide nanoparticles for toxicological studies. *International Nano Letters*. 2014, vol. 4, no. 3, pp 116.

[15] TSO, Ch., ZHUNG, Ch., SHIH, Y., TSENG, Y.-M., WU, S., DOONG, R. Stability of metal oxide nanoparticles in aqueous solutions. *Water Science and Technology*. 2010, vol. 61, no. 1, pp. 127-133.

[16] MOHD OMAR, F., ABDUL AZIZ, H., STOLL, S. Aggregation and disaggregation of ZnO nanoparticles: Influence of pH and adsorption of Suwannee River humic acid. *Science of The Total Environment*. 2014, vol. 468-469, pp. 195-201.

[17] MARSALEK, R. Particle Size and Zeta Potential of ZnO. *APCBEE Procedia*. 2014, vol. 9.

[18] GUSTAFSSON, J., NORDENSWAN, E., ROSENHOLM, J.B. Effect of pH on the sedimentation, z-potential, and rheology of anatase suspensions. *Colloids and Surfaces A: Physicochemical and Engineering Aspects*. 2003, vol. 212, pp 235-247.

[19] FLORENCE, A., ATTWOOD, D. *Physicochemical principles of pharmacy*. 4. ed., reprinted. London: Pharmaceutical Press, 2007, pp. 56-91.

DIFFUSION OF DYES IN BIOPOLYMERIC HYDROGELS

[1]David VYROUBAL, [1]Martina KLUČÁKOVÁ

[1]*Brno University of Technology, Faculty of Chemistry, Materials Research Centre, Brno, Czech Republic, EU, David.Vyroubal@vut.cz*

https://doi.org/10.37904/nanocon.2020.3755

Abstract

This study is focused on diffusion of dyes in biopolymer-based hydrogels. These hydrogels are based on interaction between biopolymer-like electrolytes with oppositely charged surfactants. When polyelectrolytes interact with oppositely charged surfactants, micelle-like nano-containers can be formed. These nano-containers are able of binding hydrophobic compounds. In this study, combination of modified dextran (diethylaminoethyl dextran) with positive charge and oppositely charged sodium dodecyl sulfate as surfactant was used for preparation of hydrogels. Next type of hydrogel was based on hyaluronan and positive charged surfactant Septonex (carbethoxypendecinium bromide). As a diffusion probes in hydrogels dyes Nile red and ATTO 488 were used. The diffusion of these dyes from aqueous solutions of NaCl or surfactants into hydrogels was monitored in time. Transport of dyes into structure of hydrogels was characterized by diffusion coefficients and structural parameters of hydrogels.

Keywords: Diffusion, hydrogel, polyelectrolyte, dye, surfactant

1. INTRODUCTION

Hydrogels are widely used in many disciplines for their unique characteristics. Hydrogels are very similar to biological tissues therefore they are often used for drug delivery systems in medicine [1,2,3]. They are biocompatible and biodegradable. Their advantages are reduced side effects, prolonged drug action and low frequency with which drugs need to be administered [4,5]. Because hydrogels contain a large amount of water one of the main problems is that they are not capable of solubilizing hydrophobic compounds. Incompatibility between hydrogels and hydrophobic solutes can be solved by the incorporation of some hydrophobic domains into the hydrogel structure. Hydrophilic network and aqueous internal phase of the hydrogel still provide its biocompatibility while hydrophobic domains enable solubilisation of hydrophobic compounds in the structure of the hydrogel. These hydrogels with the hydrophobic domains can be prepared by the interaction between biopolymer-like electrolytes with oppositely charged surfactants [6,7,8]. In this study, cationized dextran and sodium form of hyaluronan were used as polyelectrolytes. Sodium dodecyl sulfate (SDS) and Septonex were used as oppositely charged surfactants. Dextran and hyaluronan are both naturally occurring carbohydrate-based biopolymers. Hyaluronan is a linear polysaccharide formed by alternating units of β-1,3 and β-1,4-linked N-acetylglucosamine and glucuronic acid [9]. Dextran is bacterial-derived non-linear polysaccharide made up from α-1,6-linked D-glucopyranose residues. Appearance and frequency of α-1,2; α-1,3 and α-1,4-linked side chains depends on the production process or the production organism [10]. These biopolymers are non-toxic, biocompatible, high water soluble, biodegradable and offer high content of functional groups usable in cross-linking [11].

In this study, the incorporation of two different dyes into hydrogels based on dextran with SDS and hyaluronan with Septonex was studied. Nile red was chosen as a model of hydrophobic diffusion probe and Atto 488 was chosen as a model of hydrophilic diffusion probe. The aim of this work is to describe absorption capacity and capability of hydrogel to absorb dyes by the diffusion from their solutions into prepared hydrogel. The dyes were used for the incorporation into domains prepared in the hydrogels. Diffusion coefficients and structural parameters of these hydrogels were studied to assess the potential for use in the development of drug-carrier systems.

2. MATERIALS AND METHODS

In this study, hyaluronan and cationized dextran was used as polyelectrolytes. Diethylaminoethyl-dextran hydrochloride (Sigma-Aldrich, Czech Republic; DEAED) was used in molecular weight 500 kDa. Sodium dodecyl sulfate (SDS, ≥ 98,5 %) was purchased from Sigma Aldrich (Czech Republic) and used as surfactant for dextran. Sodium form of hyaluronan was purchased from Contipro (Czech Republic). Hyaluronan was used in two different molecular weights as 340 kDa (LMW) and 1540 kDa (HMW). Carbethoxypendecinium bromide (Septonex, Czech Pharmacopoeia quality) was obtained from GBNchem Company (Czech Republic) and used as surfactant for hyaluronan.

All stock solutions were prepared in 0.15M NaCl solution using purified water (Purelab ELGA system). Salt solution was used because preliminary experiments showed that a non-zero ionic strength on the aqueous medium is important for obtaining gel-like materials [12,13]. Samples of hydrogels was prepared by mixing polyelectrolyte and surfactant stock solutions in a 1:1 volume ratio. The concentrations of initial stock solutions of polyelectrolytes and surfactants are given in **Table 1.**

Table 1 Concentrations of initial stock solutions used to prepare hydrogels

Hydrogel	Polyelectrolyte	Concentration of polyelectrolyte (% w/v)	Surfactant	Concentration of surfactant (mM)
D-I	Cationized dextran	4	SDS	400
D-II	Cationized dextran	4	SDS	100
H-I	HMW hyaluronan	2	Septonex	200
H-II	HMW hyaluronan	2	Septonex	100
L-I	LMW hyaluronan	2	Septonex	200
L-II	LMW hyaluronan	2	Septonex	100

Atto 488 and Nile red were both purchased from Sigma Aldrich. Nile red was dissolved in Septonex (200mM for H-I, L-I and 100mM for H-II, L-II) and in SDS (400mM for D-I and 100mM for D-II). Atto 488 was dissolved in Septonex (200mM for H-I, L-I and 100mM for H-II, L-II) or physiological saline (0.15M NaCl). The dyes were used in ten different initial concentrations which are given in **Table 2.** Hydrogels were equilibrated for 24 hours after preparation and separated from the liquid residue. After that hydrogels were covered by 5 cm^3 of SDS, Septonex or NaCl solution with dissolved dye. The concentration decrease of dyes in solution was monitored by means of UV/VIS spectrometry (Hitachi U-3900). The data were used for the determination of dye absorption in hydrogels distribution coefficient and their diffusivity.

Table 2 Initial concentrations of dyes in the solutions of SDS, Septonex and NaCl used for diffusion experiments

Solution	a	b	c	d	e	f	g	h	i	j
Dye (μM)	0.1	0.3	0.5	0.7	0.8	0.9	1.0	3.0	5.0	7.0

3. RESULTS AND DISCUSSION

In this work, several different approaches for the investigation of transport of model dyes into hydrogels were applied. Dyes were prepared in various solutions. Nile red was prepared as its solution in 100mM and 400mM SDS for measurements in dextran-based hydrogels and in 100mM and 200mM Septonex for hyaluronan-based hydrogels. Atto 488 was prepared as its water solution in 0.15M NaCl for both types of hydrogels and in 100mM and 200mM Septonex for hyaluronan-based hydrogels. Used concentrations of both surfactants SDS and Septonex were much higher than its critical micellar concentration (CMC). Critical micellar concentration of SDS is around ~8mM [14,15,16] and CMC of Septonex is ~0.8mM [15,17,18]. Therefore, dyes should be completely distributed in the micelles of both surfactants due to concentrations of their solutions high above CMC. On the contrary, Atto 488 was dissolved in 0.15 water solution of NaCl and therefore we assumed that it diffused in hydrogels in the form of simple (partially dissolved) molecules. The differences between hydrogels based on chemically identical raw materials were probably connected with the use of different concentrations of surfactants on cross-linking, which means different ratios between functional groups in biopolymers and surfactant ions. The theoretical ratio of charges between biopolymer (hyaluronan, cationized dextran) and surfactant (Septonex, SDS) are ~1 for D-II; ~2 for H-II and L-II; and ~4 for D-I, H-I, L-I. We assumed that a part of surfactant can be exhausted for the formation of hydrogel networks. In the case of D-II, H-II and L-II, the large amount of surfactant is consumed for cross-linking of hydrogel and the content of surfactant in pores is low. In contrast for hydrogels D-I, H-I and L-I, this part is relatively small, therefore the pore structure in hydrogel contains solution with surfactant micelles. If we take account of these differences in the dextran-based hydrogels, we can assume the faster diffusion into hydrogel D-II with low theoretical ratio of charges. However, the results of the diffusion coefficients for hyaluronan-based hydrogels are opposite. Diffusion into hyaluronan-based hydrogels with higher theoretical ratio of charges (H-I, L-I) is faster. The probable theory for hyaluronan-based hydrogels is that higher excess of Septonex surfactant non-consumed for cross-linking actively participates in the diffusion and binds dye into its micelles. The examples of the diffusive flux in the dependence on initial dye concentration for dextran-based hydrogels are shown in **Figure 1.** The rate of diffusion was strongly influenced by initial concentration of dye solution used as the source of diffusion particles. We can see that the diffusive flux is much higher in D-II hydrogels with lower theoretical ratio of charges (~1). A summary of all diffusion coefficients obtained is then shown in **Table 3.**

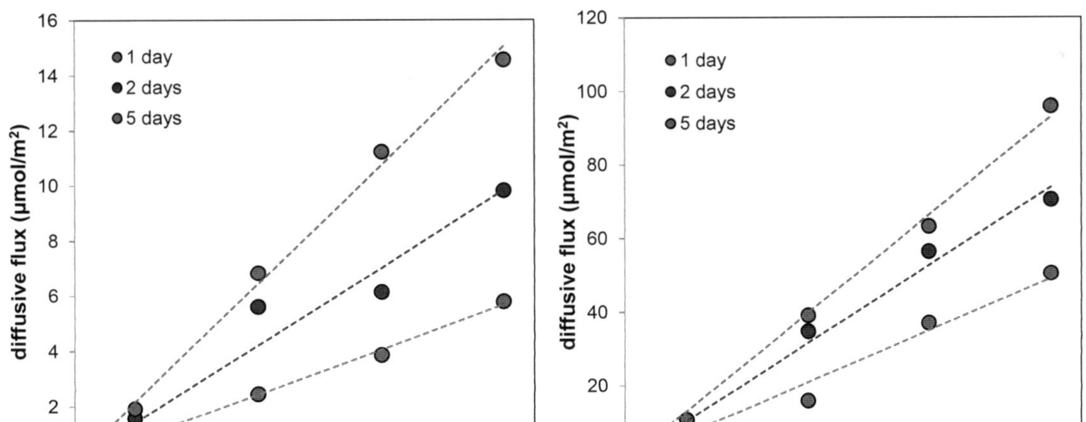

Figure 1 Examples of the diffusive flux in the dependence on initial dye concentration for hydrogels D-I (left) and D-II (right) with Atto 488

The diffusion into hydrogels are more difficult as a result of their intrinstic structure constituted by the hydrogel network and pore structure. Due to various curvatures of pores, the diffusion is strongly influenced not only by the porosity (volume of pores) but also by tortuosity given by their shapes. Hydrogel D-II contains much less free SDS than D-I and its structure should be less cross-linked, therefore the diffusion into the hydrogel D-II is less difficult and the properties of hydrogel has the strong influence. The situation about less or more cross-linked hydrogel is the same with hyaluronan-based hydrogels. Hydrogels H-I and L-I contains much more Septonex than H-II and L-II and its structure should be more cross-linked. However the diffusion rate is opposite to dextran-based hydrogels. Which means that the diffusion coefficients are higher in more cross-linked hyaluronan-based hydrogels (H-I, L-I). As already mentioned, this difference is probably due to higher excess of Septonex surfactant non-consumed for cross-linking which actively binds and pulls in dyes from solution into its micelles. Next difference between two studied hydrogels which could affect diffusion coefficients is in the structure of the used biopolymers. Dextran is non-linear bioppolymer with many side chains which depends on production organism and productional process whereas hyaluronan is linear biopolymer. Branching of the dextran chains could affect porosity, volume, size and curvature of the pores and also their tortuozity.

The examples of kinetic data are shown in **Figure 2.** We can see that the amount of dye diffused into more cross-linked hyaluronan-based hydrogel H-I is higher than in less cross-linked H-II. On the other hand, the amount of dye diffused into less cross-linked dextran-based hydrogel D-II is higher than in more cross-linked D-I. The dye content in hydrogels increased strongly mainly in first days.

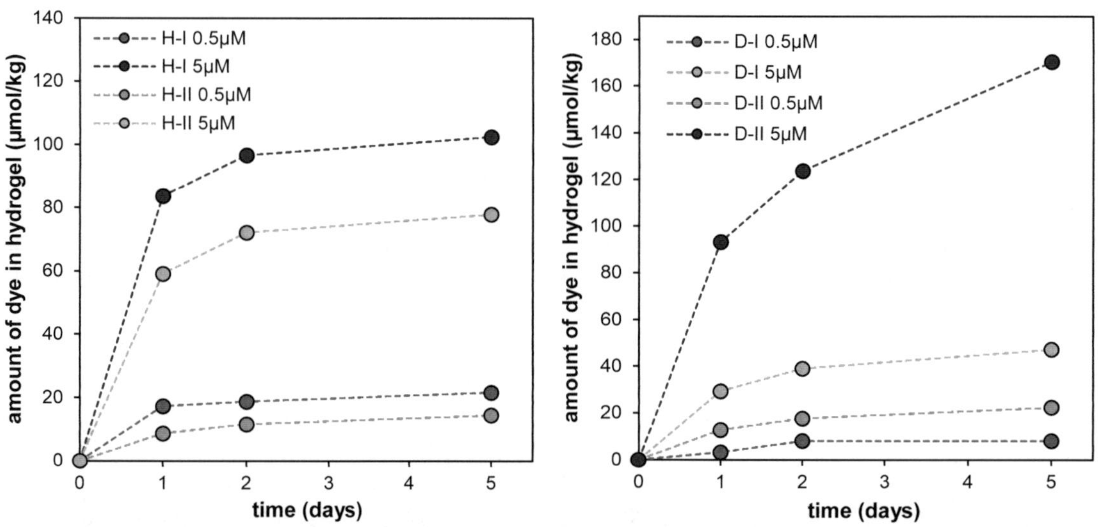

Figure 2 The amount of dyes diffused into hydrogels in the dependence on time: Hyaluronan-based hydrogels with Atto 488 (left) and dextran-based hydrogels with Nile red (right)

Table 3 Effective diffusion coefficients of dyes in hydrogels

	Diffusion coefficients (m^2/s)			
Hydrogel	**Atto 488 in NaCl solution**	**Atto 488 in Septonex**	**Nile red in Septonex**	**Nile red in SDS**
D-I	1.55×10^{-10}	nd	nd	4.22×10^{-10}
D-II	3.92×10^{-10}	nd	nd	4.63×10^{-10}
H-I	1.21×10^{-9}	5.93×10^{-10}	7.86×10^{-10}	nd
H-II	4.14×10^{-10}	5.69×10^{-10}	7.40×10^{-10}	nd
L-I	7.17×10^{-10}	4.78×10^{-10}	5.53×10^{-10}	nd
L-II	5.26×10^{-10}	4.42×10^{-10}	4.28×10^{-10}	nd

The values of effective diffusion coefficients listed in **Table 3.** were obtained on the basis of mathematical model developed by Klučáková et al. [19]. This model was developed for the diffusion couple with phase interface. In this work, the couple is comprised by the hydrogel (acceptor part) and the solution of dye above hydrogel (donor part). Both parts are placed in cylindrical vessel. Results published by Zhang et al. showed that the diffusion coefficient of Atto 488 in water is 4.0 x 10^{-10} m^2/s [16,20]. The diffusion coefficient of Nile red in water is 3.3 x 10^{-10} m^2/s [20]. We can see that diffusion coefficients of Atto 488 and Nile red in water are lower (except D-I and D-II hydrogels with Atto 488 in NaCl solution) in comparison with our obtained results of diffusion coefficients in hydrogels. If we compare our measured diffusion coefficients of dyes in hydrogels with their diffusion coefficients in aqueous solution, then the coefficients in hydrogels have higher values and the diffusion of dyes in hydrogels is faster than in aqueous medium. Thus, higher diffusion coefficients of the dyes in the hydrogels may support the theory that free micelles of surfactants non-consumed for cross-linking located in the pores of hydrogel could accelerate diffusion.

4. CONCLUSION

In this work, the diffusion of two different dyes into hydrogels based on a combination of polyelectrolyte and opposite charged surfactant was studied. Hydrogels was based on the combination of cationized dextran with sodium dodecyl sulfate as surfactant and sodium form of hyaluronan with Septonex as surfactant. It was found that the diffusion of dyes into hydrogels is influenced by several factors. One of the factors is amount of surfactant non-consumed for cross-linking located in the pores of hydrogel. Another of the possible factors is difference in branching between linear hyaluronan and non-linear dextran. Diffusion coefficients of Nile red and Atto 488 in the dextran based hydrogel D-II (due to smaller amount of SDS non-consumed for the cross-linking) was much faster than in hydrogel D-I. Diffusion coefficients of Nile red and Atto 488 in hyaluronan based hydrogels H-I and L-I (which contains higher amount of Septonex non-consumed for the cross-linking) was faster than in hydrogels H-II and L-II.

ACKNOWLEDGEMENTS

This work was supported by the Czech Science Foundation, project No. 16-12477S and by the project LO1211 from National Programme for Sustainability I (Ministry of Education, Youth and Sports, Czech Republic).

REFERENCES

[1] LIU, H., WANG, C., LI, C., QIN, Y., WANG, Z., YANG, F., LI, Z. and WANG, J. A functional chitosan-based hydrogel as a wound dressing and drug delivery system in the treatment of wound healing. *RSC* Advances. 2018, vol. 8, no. 14, pp. 7533-7549.

[2] KONG, B. J., KIM, A., and PARK, S. N. Properties and in vitro drug release of hyaluronic acid-hydroxyethyl cellulose hydrogels for transdermal delivery of isoliquiritigenin. *Carbohydrate Polymers*. 2016, vol. 147, pp. 473-481.

[3] ZHANG, S., ERMANN, J., SUCCI, M. D., ZHOU, A., HAMILTON, M. J., LANGER R. and KARP J. M. An inflammation-targeting hydrogel for local drug delivery in inflammatory bowel disease. *Science Translational Medicine*. 2015, vol. 7, no. 300.

[4] HUYNH, C. T., NGUYEN, M. K. and LEE, D. S. Injectable block copolymer hydrogels: achievements and future challenges for biomedical applications. *Macromolecules*. 2011, vol. 44, pp. 6629-6636.

[5] ULLAH F., OTHMAN, M. B. H., JAVED, F., AHMAD, Z. and AKIL, H. M. Classification, processing and application of hydrogels: A review. *Materials Science and Engineering: C*. 2015, vol. 57, pp. 414-433.

[6] PEKAŘ, M. Hydrogels with micellar hydrophobic (nano)domains. *Frontiers in Materials*. 2015, vol. 1, no. 35, pp. 1-14.

[7] PICULELL, L. Understanding and exploiting the phase behavior of mixtures of oppositely charged polymers and surfactants in water. *Langmuir*. 2013, vol. 29, no. 33, pp. 10313-10329.

[8] LI, D. and WAGNER, N. J. Universal binding behavior for ionic alkyl surfactants with oppositely charged polyelectrolytes. *Journal of the American Chemical Society*. 2013, vol. 135, no. 46, pp. 17547-17555.

[9] ZHANG, W., JIN, X., LI, H., ZHANG, R. R. and WU, C. W. Injectable and body temperature sensitive hydrogels based on chitosan and hyaluronic acid for pH sensitive drug release. *Carbohydrate Polymers*. 2018, vol. 186, pp. 82-90.

[10] MARY HELEN, K.C.B., VETTORIA, P. B., CORTEZIA, M., CRISTIAN J.C. and DE LIMAB, J. B. Dextran: effect of process parameters on production, purification and molecular weight and recent applications. *Dialogos & Ciencia*. 2012, vol. 31, pp. 171-186.

[11] OH, J. K., DRUMRUGHT, R., SIEGWART, D. J. and MATYJASZEWSKI, K. The development of microgels /nanogels for drug delivery applications. *Progress in Polymer Science*. 2008, vol. 33, pp. 448-477.

[12] KROUSKÁ, J., PEKAŘ, M., KLUČÁKOVÁ, M., ŠARAC, B. and BEŠTER-ROGAČ, M. Study of interactions between hyaluronan and cationic surfactants by means of calorimetry, turbidimetry, potentiometry and conductometry. *Carbohydrate Polymers*. 2017, vol. 157, pp. 1837-1843.

[13] VENEROVÁ, T. and PEKAŘ., M. Rheological properties of gels formed by physical interactions between hyaluronan and cationic surfactants. *Carbohydrate Polymers*. 2017, vol. 170, pp. 176-181.

[14] UMLONG, I. M. and ISMAIL, K. Micellization behaviour of sodium dodecyl sulfate in different electrolyte media. *Colloids and Surfaces, A: Physicochemical Engineering Aspects*. 2007, vol. 299, no. 1-3, pp. 8-14.

[15] DUTKIEWICZ, E. and JAKUBOWSKA, A. Effect of electrolytes on the physicochemical behaviour of sodium dodecyl sulphate micelles. *Colloid and Polymer Science*. 2002, vol. 280, pp. 1009-1014.

[16] ZHANG, X., PONIEWIERSKI, A., JELINSKA, A., ZAGOZDZON, A., WISNIEWSKA, A., HOU, S. and HOLYST, R. Determination of equilibrium and rate constants for complex formation by fluorescence correlation spectroscopy supplemented by dynamic light scattering and Taylor dispersion analysis. *Soft Matter*. 2016, vol. 12, no. 39, pp. 8186-8194.

[17] KARGEROVÁ, A. and PEKAŘ, M. Ultrasonic study of hyaluronan interactions with Septonex - a pharmaceutical cationic surfactant. *Carbohydrate Polymers*. 2019, vol. 204, pp. 17-23.

[18] FISCHER, J. and JANDERA, P. Chromatographic behaviour in reversed-phase high-performance liquid chromatography with micellar and submicellar mobile phases effects of the organic modifier. *Journal of Chromatography B*. 1996, vol. 681, pp. 3-19.

[19] KLUČÁKOVÁ, M. and PEKAŘ, M. Transport of copper(II) ions in humic gel - new results from diffusion couple. *Colloids and Surfaces, A: Physicochemical and Engineering Aspects*. 2007, vol. 349, no. 1-3, pp. 96-101.

[20] ZHANG, L. X., CAO, X. H., CAI, W. P. and LI, Y. Q. Observations of the effect of confined space on fluorescence and diffusion properties of molecules in single conical nanopore channels. *Journal of Fluorescence*. 2011, vol. 21, no. 5, pp. 1865-1870.

METTALOTHIONEIN SENSING USING MOLECULARLY IMPRINTED POLYMERS COUPLED LASER ABLATION INDUCTIVELY COUPLED PLASMA-MASS SPECTROMETRY

[1]Kristyna ZEMANKOVA, [1]Kristyna PAVELICOVA, [1]Jaroslava BEZDEKOVA, [1,2]Lukas NEJDL, [3]Marketa VEJVODOVA, [3]Tomas VACULOVIC, [1,2]Marketa VACULOVICOVA

[1]Department of Chemistry and Biochemistry, Mendel University in Brno, Czech Republic, EU, zemankova.kristyna@seznam.cz

[2]Central European Institute of Technology, Brno University of Technology, Czech Republic, EU

[3]Department of Chemistry, Faculty of Science, Masaryk University, Brno, Czech Republic, EU

https://doi.org/10.37904/nanocon.2020.3749

Abstract

In this work, we report a facile method for a detection of mettalothionein (MT) - potential biomarker of tumor diseases. Combination of laser ablation inductively coupled plasma coupled to mass spectrometric detection (LA-ICP-MS) with sample pretreatment by magnetic particles modified by molecularly imprinted polymers (Mag-MIP) enables selective and sensitive protein detection and quantification. After Mag-MIP MT extraction, elements specific for the protein (S, Zn and Cd) were detected in healthy pig skin and pig melanoma tissue using MeLiM (Melanoma-bearing-Libechov-Minipig) model. It was found that levels of detected elements were significantly elevated in melanoma tissue compared to healthy skin. Currently, the investigation of MT dimerization in cancer progression is carried out taking advantage from easily controllable *in vitro* MT dimerization which is used for simple preparation of selective MIP extraction phase. Unlike other recognition elements, which are not always available for target analyte (e.g. antibodies), MIPs can be easily prepared as required. Moreover, magnetic particles as a MIP substrate enable elegant extraction approach and LA-ICP-MS provides extremely sensitive detection. Therefore, Mag-MIP-LA-ICP-MS is a unique cross-border combination of molecular and elemental analysis.

Keywords: Metallothionein, Molecularly imprinted polymers, Magnetic particles, LA-ICP-MS

1. INTRODUCTION

Metallothioneins (MTs) are a class of low molecular-weight (6 to 7 kDa) and cysteine-rich proteins. MTs are intracellular and ubiquitous in eukaryotes, and have specific structural characteristics giving them potent metal-binding and redox capabilities [1], due their high affinity to metals, MTs participate in the regulation of cellular metabolism of metals like zinc and copper, in detoxification of toxic metals like copper, cadmium and mercury, and in protection of cells against reactive oxygen species and alkylating agents [2]. MTs participate in the carcinogenic process, which include the generation of reactive oxygen species, oxidative DNA damage, genomic instability and others [3].

Malignant melanoma is one of the most dangerous and deadly forms of cancer, being responsible for 1.2 % of all cancer deaths in the European Union. Malignant melanomas often go unnoticed, it is characterized by early metastasis and poor prognosis, and its incidence is increasing each year [4,5]. For immediate therapy and increase of survivors of melanoma, evaluation of histopathological and clinical parameters is important and mainly, the identification of potential biomarkers plays a critical role [6].

Molecularly imprinted polymers (MIPs) are synthetic materials with artificially generated recognition sites able to selectively interact with target molecules. Currently, MIPs are attracting widespread attention due to their properties such as flexibility, variability, high chemical and mechanical stability, relatively low cost and simplicity in preparation [7,8]. The use of nanomaterials - magnetic nanoparticles - in combination with MIPs provides large surface-to-volume ratio and well defined shape; moreover possibility of rapid separation of magnetic particles by the aid of an external magnet is favorable [9].

In this work, a method combining laser ablation inductively coupled plasma mass spectrometric detection (LA-ICP-MS) with sample pretreatment by magnetic particles modified by molecularly imprinted polymers (Mag-MIP) was developed. The suggested approach enables selective and sensitive protein detection and quantification, especially detection of MT. After Mag-MIP MT extraction, elements specific for the protein (S, Zn and Cd) were detected as this information is essential for further development of effective and timely diagnostic tools for melanoma.

2. MATERIALS AND METHODS

2.1. Materials and reagents

Dopamine hydrochloride, Trizma® base and acetic acid were purchased from Sigma-Aldrich (MO, USA) in ACS purity. MT from rabbit liver was obtained from Enzo Life Science (NY, USA). Dynabeads™ MyOne™ Silane magnetic particles and sodium tetraborate decahydrate were purchased from Thermo Fisher Scientific (MA, USA).

2.2. Preparation of magnetic MIPs

Briefly, 50 µl of magnetic nanoparticles (MPs) (40 $mg \cdot mL^{-1}$) were washed by 200 µL of 20 mM TRIS (pH 8.5) for three times. MT (1 $mg \cdot mL^{-1}$) was dissolved in 20 mM TRIS (pH 8.5) and 400 µL of solution was added to the washed MPs for preparation of Mag-MIPs. To prepare non-imprinted polymers (NIPs) used as a control, only 400 µL of 20 mM TRIS (pH 8.5) was added to the washed MPs. The mixtures were stirred for 1 hour and then 100 µL of dopamine (17.5 $mg \cdot mL^{-1}$) dissolved in 20 mM TRIS (pH 8.5) was added and the reaction was continued overnight at room temperature. The product was collected using external magnetic field, supernatant was removed and discarded. The template was washed out three times by 200 µL of 10 % acetic acid and once by 200 µL of MilliQ.

2.3. Sample preparation

After washing of Mag-MIPs and Mag-NIPs by 20 mM TRIS (pH 8.5), 200 µL of sample was added and mixture was left shaking for 2 hours. After supernatant removal, Mag-MIPs and Mag-NIPs were washed three times with 200 µL of 20 mM TRIS (pH 8.5) and samples were analyzed by LA-ICP-MS.

2.4. LA-ICP-MS analysis

LA-ICP-MS experiments were performed using a setup consisting of the laser ablation system UP213 (NewWave Research, USA) emitting laser radiation with a wavelength of 213 nm. The ablated material was washed away using He (1.0 $L \cdot min^{-1}$) from the ablation chamber (Supercell). Ar flow (0.6 $L \cdot min^{-1}$) was admixed into a flow of helium with the sample aerosol behind the ablation cell. Hence, the total gas flow was 1.6 $L \cdot min^{-1}$. This mixture was fed into a quadrupole ICP-(Q)MS spectrometer Agilent 7500CE (Agilent Technologies, Japan) equipped with a collision-reaction cell for suppressing possible polyatomic interferences. The CRC was utilized in collision mode with a He (99.000%) flow rate of 2$mL \cdot min^{-1}$.

3. RESULTS AND DISCUSSION

The MIP-based separation procedure using MPs and following LA-ICP-MS analysis is schematically shown in **Figure 1.**

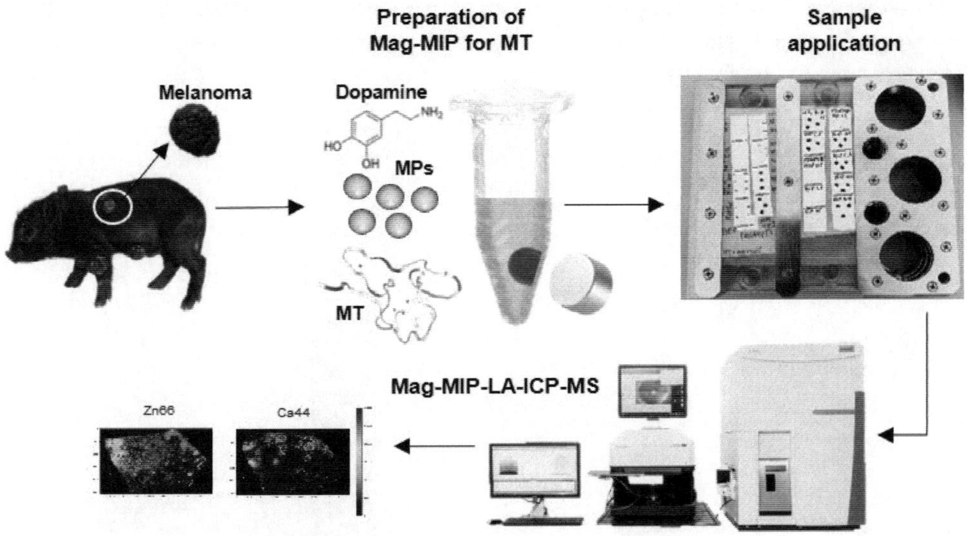

Figure 1 Schematic experimental workflow of Mag-MIP-LA-ICP-MS.

3.1. Metal detection in MT by LA-ICP-MS

Current analytical methods for MT detection include capillary electrophoresis, immunoassays, liquid chromatography, matrix-assisted laser desorption/ionization time-of-flight mass spectrometry and electrochemistry [10]. LA-ICP-MS is suitable for quantitative analysis of very low concentrations therefore; it was employed for quantitation of levels of metal ions present in MT.

In **Figure 2**, determined Zn levels are shown. The nonspecific sorption on polymeric layer without presence of cavities (NIP) was reasonably low and this background signal can be subtracted for quantification purposes.

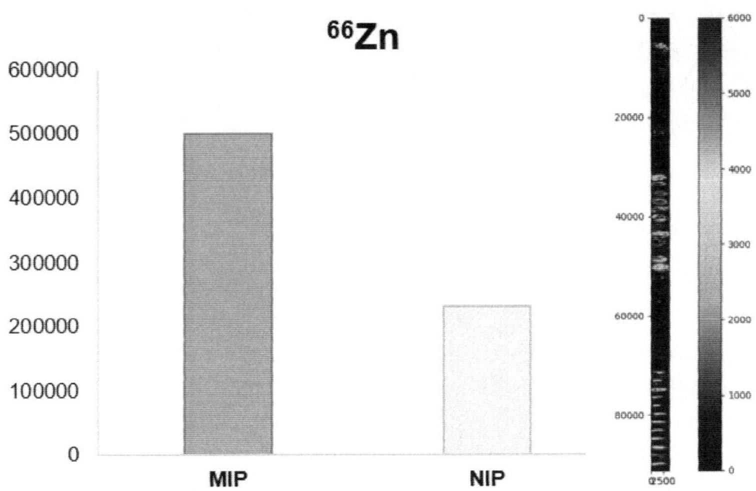

Figure 2 LA-ICP-MS analysis of ^{66}Zn levels after extraction of MT by Mag-MIP

3.2. Recognition of melanomas

For evaluation of melanoma, analysis of clinical parameters is important as well as identification of potential biomarkers. MT is highly probably one of such markers.

In this study, the melanomas and healthy skin of melanoma-bearing minipigs (MeLiMs) were tested using the magnetic MIPs specific for MT and it was found that levels of detected elements were significantly elevated in melanoma tissue compared to healthy skin (**Figure 3**).

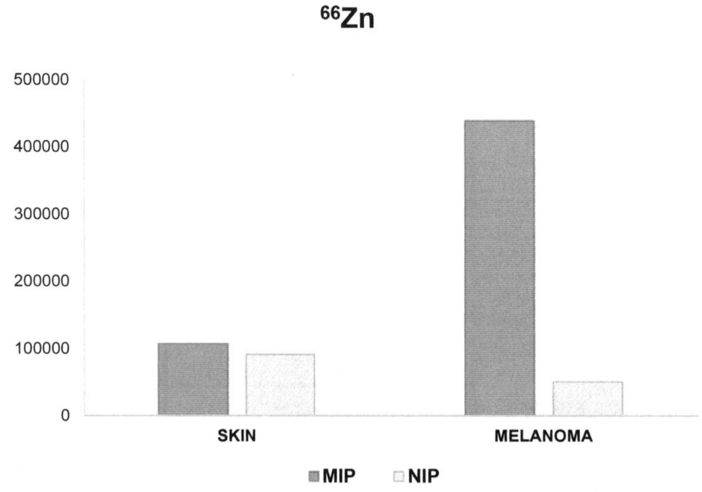

Figure 3 Levels of ^{66}Zn detected in MT isolated by Mag-MIP from healthy skin and melanoma of MeLiMs

4. CONCLUSION

In this work, power and variability of molecular imprinting technology in combination with high surface area of nanomaterials and magnetic properties of iron oxide creates an extremely effective tool for bioanalytical applications. Mag-MIP-LA-ICP-MS is a unique cross-border combination of molecular and elemental analysis. Mainly, the ^{66}Zn level was elevated in the majority of melanomas in comparison with healthy skin. This new approach enables the get information which is essential for further development of effective and timely diagnostic tools for melanoma detection.

ACKNOWLEDGEMENTS

The research was financially supported by AF-IGA20120-IP059.

REFERENCES

[1] GAD, S.C. Metallothionein. In: P. Wexler. *Encyclopedia of Toxicology.* Third Edition. Oxford: Academic Press, 2014, pp. 230.

[2] PALUMAA, P., et al. Metal binding of metallothionein-3 versus metallothionein-2: lower affinity and higher plasticity. *Biochimica et Biophysica Acta (BBA) - Proteins and Proteomics.* 2005, vol. 1747, no. 2, pp. 205-211.

[3] SLUSSER, A., et al. Metallothionein isoform 3 expression in human skin, related cancers and human skin derived cell cultures. *Toxicology Letters.* 2015, vol. 232, no. 1, pp. 141-148.

[4] FALLER, W.J., et al. Metallothionein 1E is methylated in malignant melanoma and increases sensitivity to cisplatin induced apoptosis. *Melanoma Research.* 2010, vol. 20, no. 5, pp. 392-400.

[5] KOPF, A.W., BART, R.S., RODRÍGUEZ-SAINS, R.S. Malignant Melanoma: A Review. *ImmunoTargets and Therapy.* 1977, vol. 3, no. 1, pp. 41-117.

[6] KRIZKOVA, S., et al. Microarray analysis of metallothioneins in human diseases-A review. *Journal of Pharmaceutical and Biomedical Analysis.* 2016, vol.117, pp. 464-473.

[7] SAMAH, N.A., et al. Molecularly imprinted polymer for the removal of diclofenac from water: Synthesis and characterization. *Sci Total Environ*. 2018, vol. 631-632, pp. 1534-1543.

[8] UZURIAGA-SÁNCHEZ, R.J., et al. Magnetically separable polymer (Mag-MIP) for selective analysis of biotin in food samples. *Food Chem.* 2016, vol. 190, pp. 460-467.

[9] ZHAO, Y., et al. Surface imprinted polymers based on amino-hyperbranched magnetic nanoparticles for selective extraction and detection of chlorogenic acid in Honeysuckle tea. *Talanta*. 2018, vol. 181, pp. 271-277.

[10] MERLOS RODRIGO, M.A., et al. Fully automated two-step assay for detection of metallothionein through magnetic isolation using functionalized γ-Fe2O3 particles. *Journal of chromatography. B, Analytical technologies in the biomedical and life sciences*. 2016, vol. 1039, pp. 17-27.

USING QD-FRET BASED METHOD TO INVESTIGATE PROTEIN-PROTEIN INTERACTIONS

[1]Kristyna PAVELICOVA, [1]Kristyna ZEMANKOVA, [1]Jaroslava BEZDEKOVA, [1,2]Marketa VACULOVICOVA

[1]*Department of Chemistry and Biochemistry, Mendel University in Brno, Czech Republic, EU,* *k.pavelicova@seznam.cz*

[2]*Central European Institute of Technology, Brno University of Technology, Brno, Czech Republic, EU*

https://doi.org/10.37904/nanocon.2020.3750

Abstract

Förster resonance energy transfer (FRET) is an energy transfer process between a pair of light-sensitive molecules, where the donor fluorophore (initially in its electronic excited state) transfers energy to an acceptor chromophore. In this study, FRET was used to investigate the dimerization of metallothionein isoform MT-1A. The FRET system was developed based on a fluorescent quantum dots (QDs) and cyanine dye 3.5 (Cy3.5) as a versatile tool to probe small distance changes between acceptor and donor fluorophores in nanometer range. Herein, the water-soluble 450-nm emitting QDs as the donor and 590-nm Cy3.5 as the acceptor were covalently conjugated with MT-1 according to the protocol. Previous studies suggest that MTs may form oligomers under certain conditions. Therefore, further studies of this phenomenon, which has been studied here using capillary electrophoresis (CE) coupled with fluorescence detection.

Keywords: Förster resonance energy transfer (FRET), quantum dots (QDs), Oligomerization, Capillary electrophoresis, Metallothionein

1. INTRODUCTION

Optical biosensors often take advantage of fluorescence resonance energy transfer (FRET) which has been used in carefully designed sensing systems for proteins, peptides, nucleic acids and small molecules. FRET is a photophysical mechanism particularly useful to probe the dynamics of the formation of recognition complexes. This phenomenon involves dipole−dipole interactions between a donor−acceptor pair (**Figure 1**). The process is sensitive to the distance between the FRET partners, and thus provides a versatile spectroscopic tool to monitor events occurring between moieties at intimate contact [1,2]. QDs and organic fluorophores such as cyanine dyes are widely exploited as FRET probes for numerous chemical and biological applications such as protein folding investigation or for sensing and imaging of macromolecular interactions. Quantum dots (QDs) with the exceptional fluorescent properties are excellent FRET donors. In other words, wavelengths optimal for excitation of QDs are far apart from the excitation maxima of acceptors, thereby avoiding their direct excitation [3-5]. Metallothioneins (MTs) are a family of small (6-7 kDa) proteins with cysteine-rich (30%) structure and high affinity for metal ions [6,7]. Due to this reason MTs are involved in the metabolism of heavy metals and they serve as an intracellular reservoir of essential trace elements. Moreover, due to the high amount of disulphide bonds, MTs can create dimers or higher

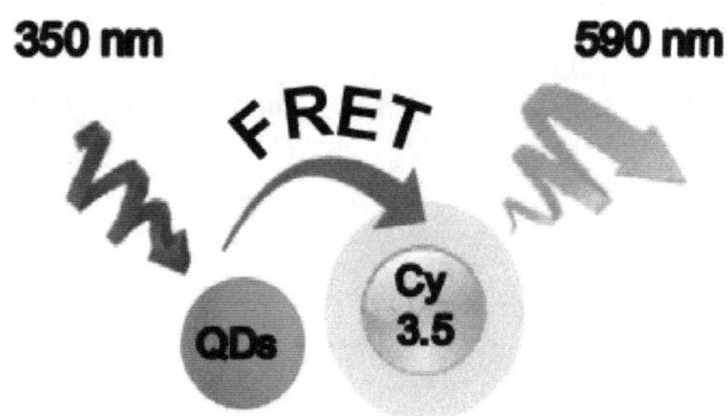

Figure 1 The theoretical scheme of the FRET system

oligomers, which can be formed either in oxidative (e.g. presence of NO or hydrogen peroxide) or non-oxidative conditions (addition of excess of Cd^{2+}). Investigation of their structural arrangement can help understand the development of oxidative stress and the mechanism of transport of toxic metals. Moreover, the oligomer formation (as well as their structures) may play an important role in a number of neurological disorders such as Alzheimer disease and amyotrophic lateral sclerosis [7].

In the present work, the interactions between metallothioneins covalently conjugated with QDs and Cy 3.5 were investigated using CE coupled with fluorescence detector and fluorescence spectroscopy as well.

2. MATERIALS AND METHODS

2.1. Materials and reagents

MT isoform (MT-1) from rabbit liver was obtained from Enzo Life Science, USA. Sodium borate, zinc acetate, cadmium acetate, sodium phosphate, mercaptosuccinic acid (MSA), isopropanol, *N*-Ethyl-*N'*-(3-dimethylaminopropyl)carbodiimide hydrochloride (EDC), *N*-Hydroxysulfosuccinimide sodium salt (Sulfo-NHS) and commercial Cyanine 3.5 dye (Cy3.5) labelling kit were purchased from Sigma-Aldrich in ACS quality. The stock solution of MT (1 mg/mL) was prepared in ultrapure water and stored in the dark at -20 °C. Ultrapure water purified by Milli-Q system was used for preparation of all solutions.

2.2. Preparation of QDs

Suspension of ZnCd QDs was prepared by mixing stock solutions of the 6 mM zinc acetate, 6 mM cadmium acetate, 20 mM sodium phosphate buffer (PB) pH 7 and 16 mM mercaptosuccinic acid (MSA). The resulting mixture with the typical molar ratio of 1:4:4:6 (Cd^{2+}:MSA:PB:Zn^{2+}) was exposed to UV irradiation for 5 minutes. The ZnCd QDs were precipitated by isopropanol and then isolated by centrifugation. Finally, ZnCd QDs were suspended in sodium phosphate buffer (PB, pH 7.2) and sonicated for 2 minutes before use.

2.3. QDs and cyanine dye bioconjugation

At first, conjugation of ZnCd QDs with 0.1 mM MT-1 was carried out by a method using coupling agents EDC and Sulfo-NHS according to the protocol published elsewhere [8]. Conjugation of Cy3.5 with MT-1 was carried out according to the manufacturer's protocol.

2.4. MT dimerization

Dimers (or higher oligomers) of MTs were obtained by storing MT-1 (0.1 mM) in 20 mM PB (pH 9.2) in presence of 0.5 mM Cd^{2+} at 8 °C under aerobic conditions for 1 week.

2.5. Capillary electrophoresis

Monitoring of FRET signal between MTs conjugates was performed using a Beckman Coulter CE instrument (P/ACE MDQ, USA) equipped with a light emitting diode (375 nm) as an excitation source and a long pass emission filter (550 nm). Separations were performed in an uncoated fused-silica capillary (Polymicro Technologies, USA) with an internal diameter of 75 µm and external diameter of 375 µm. The total length of the capillary was 48 cm and the effective length to the detection window was 37.5 cm. The capillary was flushed with 0.1 M NaOH for 5 min and with background electrolyte (sodium borate buffer, pH 9) for 15 min prior to the first use. Before each run, the capillary was rinsed for 120 s with background electrolyte (BGE). Sample was injected hydrodynamically by pressure of 1 psi for 4 s. Separation voltage was 20 kV.

2.6. Fluorescence analysis

Samples of MTs conjugates were pipetted (100 µL) in to the well plate and emission spectra were recorded (λ_{Ex} = 375 nm and λ_{Em} = 405 - 800 nm). Fluorescence signal was acquired by multifunctional microplate reader

Tecan Infinite 200 M PRO (TECAN, Switzerland). The samples (100 µL) were placed in UV-transparent 96 well plate with flat bottom by CoStar (Corning, USA). Then excitation or emission spectra were recorded using 2-nm steps and gain 100.

3. RESULTS AND DISCUSSION

Fluorescence-based detection techniques are highly selective and very sensitive with high potential for multiplexing. Moreover, FRET enables the measurements of distances at the molecular level. Thus, this technique was selected for detection of protein-protein interactions. The selection of molecules with optimal optical properties for the FRET pair is crucial. Therefore, firstly, the selection of the FRET probes (donor and acceptor fluorophores) was optimized. Resonance energy transfer is highly dependent on several factors and one of the most important of them is the spectral overlap of the donor emission spectrum and the acceptor absorption spectrum. The combination of cyanine dye (Cy3.5) and quantum dots (QDs) was tested and as can be seen in **Figure 2,** the optimal combination providing the satisfying spectral overlap was selected. Metallothionein isoform MT-1 was used as a model biomolecule for protein interaction.

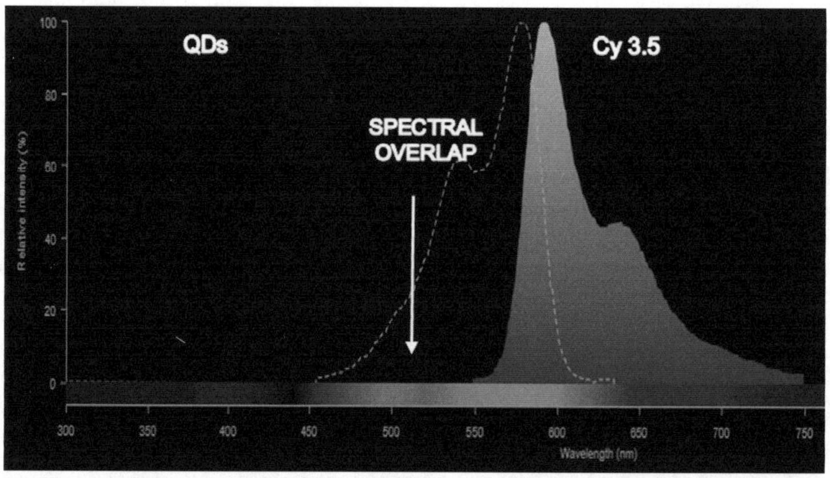

Figure 2 Spectral overlap between donor (QDs) and acceptor (Cy3.5) which is crucial for the FRET

The capillary electrophoresis method was used to demonstrate the FRET signal which was observed after interactions of MTs. The aliquots of MT-1 protein were fluorescently labelled (each with one member of the FRET pair - Cy3.5 and QDs). In case of MTs interactions (dimerization or oligomerization), the FRET occurred due to the proximity of fluorophores. On the other hand, if there are no interactions between MT-1, the distance of the fluorophores is larger than required and therefore, the FRET signal is not observed. QDs nanoparticles developed in our laboratory were tested as a suitable donor fluorophore for the FRET pair. The emission wavelength could be easily tuned by duration of irradiation.

Conjugates of Cy3.5MT-1, QDsMT-1 and Cy3.5MT-1QDsMT-1 were studied by capillary electrophoresis and their electropherograms are shown in **Figure 3**. It can be seen clearly that Cy3.5MT-1 provides a weak signal (green trace), which is due to the excitation source 375 nm (Cy3.5 optimal excitation wavelength is 570 nm). The conjugate of QDsMT-1 provides a weak signal as well (red trace), even though the instrumental setting (emission filter 550 longpass) should disable the detection of the QDs fluorescence (emission maximum of QDs is 450 nm). Probably, these weak signals were caused by broad emission spectra of QDs and Cy3.5 and were considered as background signal. After interaction between the conjugates Cy3.5MT-1 and QDsMT-1 took place, a FRET signal occurred between Cy3.5 and QD and therefore, a FRET signal was obtained (beige trace).

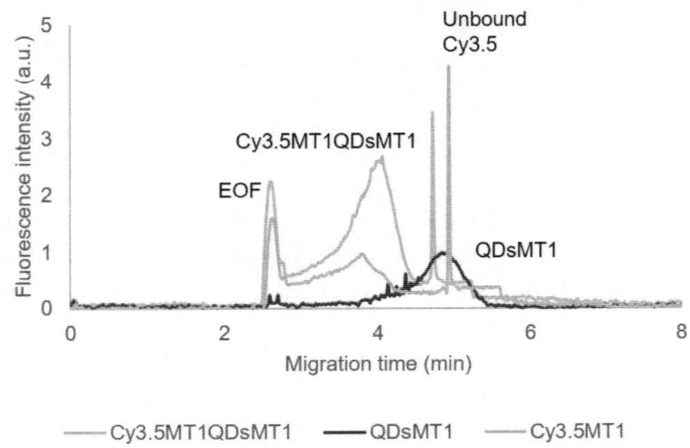

Figure 3 Electropherogram of QDsMT-1, Cy3.5MT-1 conjugates and their conjugate

In addition, regarding to previous research, metallothioneins can create oligomers under specific conditions (temperature, addition of Cd^{2+} etc.). A solution of MT-1 was stored under aerobic conditions at 8 °C for 1 week with addition of Cd^{2+}. By this we confirmed that the MTs oligomerization was increased after Cd^{2+} addition and metal bridges between MTs were formed. Because of metal bridges cause a tighter connection between metallothioneins, stronger FRET signal was observed. This fact was verified by fluorescence spectroscopy (**Figure 4A**) and CE (**Figure 4B**).

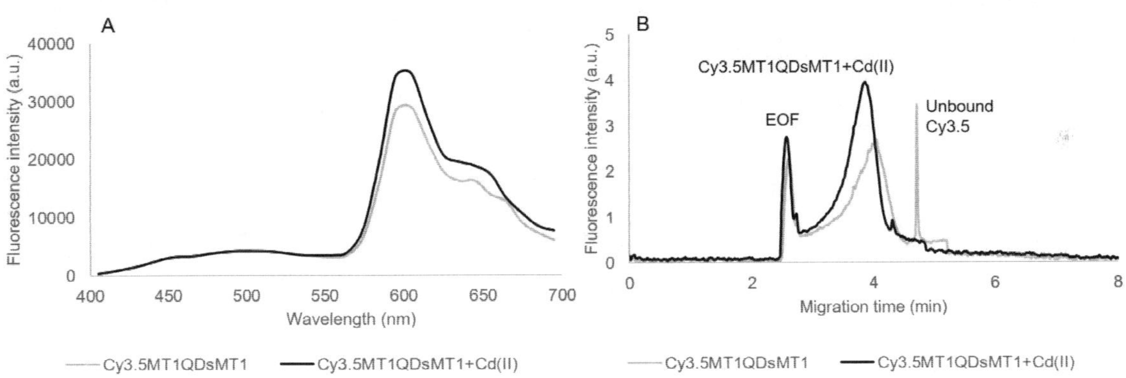

Figure 4 (A) Emission spectra of Cy3.5MT-1QDsMT-1 without and with the addition of Cd(II) and (B) electropherograms of these conjugates

4. CONCLUSION

In conclusion, we optimized a method to study protein interactions based on QDs and Cy3.5 FRET pair. Metallothionein isoform MT-1 was used as a model protein. The FRET signal was studied not only by fluorescence spectrometry, but also by CE with fluorescence detection. The main benefit of CE over fluorescence spectrometry is the fact, that in CE only complexes exhibiting stronger interaction are visualized. In during fluorescence spectroscopic analysis, FRET occurring between fluorophores in close proximity even without any chemical interaction can be detected.

In case of MT oligomerization it should be highlighted that the role of MTs oligomerization in organism is unclear and it is important to note that insufficient literature records are available. However, oligomerization of MTs might play an important role in signal pathways. Therefore, further investigation is needed.

ACKNOWLEDGEMENTS

The research was financially supported by Internal Grant Agency MENDELU IGA grant, no. IP_025/2019.

REFERENCES

[1] FREEMAN, R., GIRSH, J. and WILLNER I. Nucleic Acid/Quantum Dots (QDs) Hybrid Systems for Optical and Photoelectrochemical Sensing. *ACS Applied Materials & Interfaces*. 2013, vol. 5, no. 8, pp. 2815-2834.

[2] MEDINTZ, I.L., et al. Self-assembled nanoscale biosensors based on quantum dot FRET donors. *Nature Materials*. 2003, vol. 2, no. 9, pp. 630-638.

[3] ZHANG, Y. and WANG T.-H. Quantum Dot Enabled Molecular Sensing and Diagnostics. *Theranostics*. 2012, vol. 2, no. 7, pp. 631-654.

[4] BUCKHOUT-WHITE, S., et al. Assembling programmable FRET-based photonic networks using designer DNA scaffolds. *Nature communications*. 2014, vol. 5, p. 5615.

[5] LI, Y.-Q., et al. High-sensitivity quantum dot-based fluorescence resonance energy transfer bioanalysis by capillary electrophoresis. *Biosensors and Bioelectronics*. 2010, vol.25, no. 6, pp. 1283-1289.

[6] SANZ-NEBOT, V., ANDÓN, B. and BARBOSA, J. Characterization of metallothionein isoforms from rabbit liver by liquid chromatography coupled to electrospray mass spectrometry. *Journal of Chromatography B*. 2003, vol.796, no. 2, pp. 379-393.

[7] ZANGGER, K., et al. Oxidative dimerization in metallothionein is a result of intermolecular disulphide bonds between cysteines in the alpha-domain. *Biochemical Journal*. 2001, vol. 359, pp. 353-360.

[8] PEREIRA, M. and LAI, E. Capillary Electrophoresis for the Characterization of Quantum Dots After Non-Selective or Selective Bioconjugation with Antibodies for Immunoassay. *Journal of nanobiotechnology*. 2008, vol. 6, p. 10.

ELEGANT, RAPID AND SIMPLE PROCEDURE FOR LABELING OF ANTIBODIES WITH FLUORESCENT ZnCd/S QUANTUM DOTS FOR LASER ABLATION ICP-MS DETECTION

[1,2]Navid ASSI, [1,2]Kristyna PAVELICOVA, [1,2]Marketa VACULOVICOVA, [3]Tomas VACULOVIC

[1]Department of Chemistry and Biochemistry, Mendel University in Brno, Brno, Czech Republic, EU, navid.assi@vutbr.cz, marketa.ryvolova@seznam.cz, k.pavelicova@seznam.cz

[2]Central European Institute of Technology, Brno University of Technology, Brno, Czech Republic, EU, navid.assi@vutbr.cz, marketa.ryvolova@seznam.cz

[3]Department of Chemistry, Masaryk University in Brno, Brno, Czech Republic, EU, tomas.vaculovic@ceitec.muni.cz

https://doi.org/10.37904/nanocon.2020.3752

Abstract

Antibody labeling with a signal-providing tag (e.g. an enzyme, chromophore, fluorophore, metal chelate, radioisotope, etc.) is a key procedure in bioanalytical techniques such an enzyme-linked immunosorbent assay, western blot, or immunohistochemical analysis. The process may be laborious, impair the activity, and time-consuming. Concisely, in this work, an elegant method of rapid and effective antibody labeling by quantum dots was developed taking advantage of partial reduction of antibody structure and UV-induced quantum dot formation. Zinc and cadmium with the thiol group of the antibody as capping agents stabilizing the fluorescent nanoparticle while the biorecognition capabilities were maintained. The ZnCd/S quantum dots creation has to prosper detected with capillary electrophoresis (CE) and laser ablation ICP- MS (LA- ICP- MS).

Keywords: Antibody, antigen, quantum dots, cleavage disulfide bonds, fluorescent

1. INTRODUCTION

Antibody labeling techniques are extremely an important tool for protein detection and it can be done by direct or indirect labeling. The disadvantage of the process may impair antibody activity with excessive labeling, steric hindrance, and alter activity for high molecular weight such as enzymes, discontinuity conjugation for multiple fluorophores and enzymes, laborious and time-consuming [1,2].

Quantum dots (QDs) are described as the most popular fluorescent inorganic nanoparticles (FINPs) which have properties such as good biocompatibility, stable photoluminescence, and narrow emission band. These materials attract attention in recent years and play a key role in a different field such as ion detection, bio-labeling or bioimaging [3,4]. Antibodies are widely used as targeting moieties with QDs for specific cell labeling. They interact with the host cell and remain adhered to the surface or internalized by endocytosis [5]. The labeled antibody with quantum dots has been detected with laser ablation ICP-MS (LA-ICP-MS) for trace element determination [6] and capillary electrophoresis to verified the formation of QDs-antibody [7].

In this research work, for the first time, ZnCd/S quantum dots prepared by UV-induced synthesis with partially reduced antibody as a capping agent were used for immunoanalysis with elemental analysis. UV irradiation duraion and metal ratio were optimized to achieve a high fluorescent intensity. To explore ZnCd/S formation, LA-ICP-MS, and CE were used as superior instruments for quantum dots characterization.

2. MATERIALS AND METHODS

2.1. Materials

Anti-mouse IgG H&L (ab6708) was purchased from Abcam (Cambridge, UK). All chemicals and solutions used in this study provisioned daily without further purification were purchased from Sigma-Aldrich (St. Louis, MO, USA) in ACS purity. Millipore water was used throughout the experiment.

2.2. Simultaneous QDs Synthesis and Antibody Conjugation Process

Quantum dots-antibody (QDs-Ab) probe was prepared according to the simple modus operandi. In order to reduction of 1 mg/mL of the anti-mouse IgG, tris(2-carboxyethyl) phosphine (TCEP) was used in the concentration of 25 mM at 37 °C for 90 min with sodium phosphate buffer (Na_2HPO_4/NaH_2PO_4) pH=7 in a total volume of 10 µL. Precursors containing zinc acetate (4×10^{-5} mM) and cadmium acetate (6×10^{-6} mM) were mixed with reduced anti-mouse IgG in 100 µL sodium phosphate buffer pH=7. The prepared solution was pipetted into the UV-transparent 96-well plate (Corning, USA) and placed into the UV transilluminator (Vilber Lourmat, Marne-la-Vallee Cedex, France) with wavelength of 254 nm. Resulting solution was analyzed by fluorescence spectrometry. Fluorescent intensity was measured in the range of 230 to 700 nm with Synergy H1 (BioTek, USA). **Scheme 1** is illustrating the overall procedure.

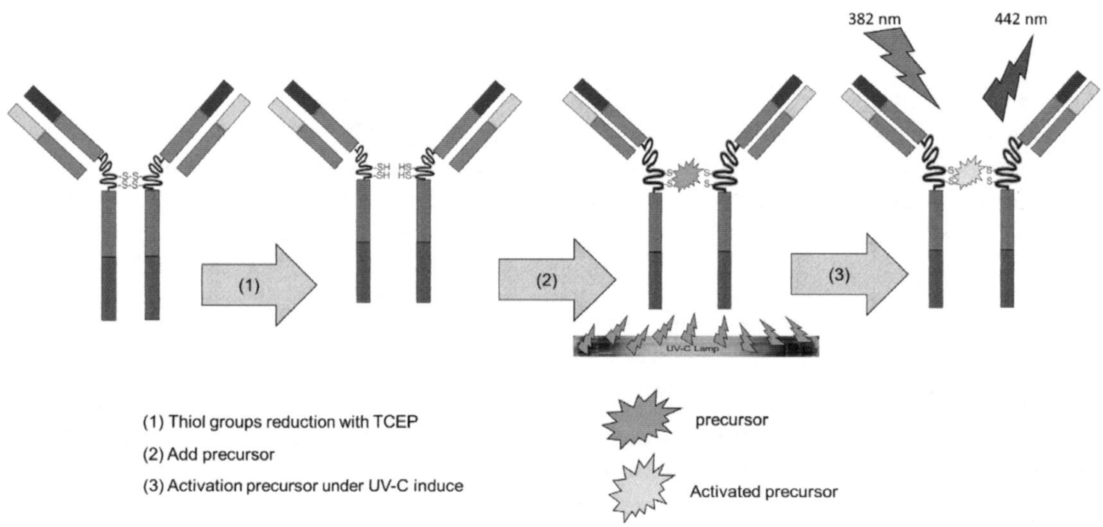

Scheme 1 Anti-mouse IgG reduction and creation of ZnCd/S quantum dots with antibody conjugation

2.3. Capillary electrophoresis (CE)

Prepared QDs-Ab was analyzed by CE instrument 7100 (Agilent Technologies, Germany) with absorbance detection at a wavelength of 254 nm. Fused silica capillary with an internal diameter of 75 µm, with a total length of 64.5 cm, and an effective length of 56 cm was used. The samples were injected hydrodynamically by 50 mbar applied for 6 s and the separation voltage was 20 kV. The background electrolyte (BGE) was composed with 20 mM sodium borate buffer pH 9 for 120 s. Between the injections, the capillary column was washed for 60 s using BGE.

2.4. LA- ICP- MS Quantitative Mapping

Qds-Ab formation was evaluated as describer earlier [8] by LA-ICP-MS setup consisting, LA system UP213 (NewWave Research, USA), emitting laser radiation with a wavelength of 213 nm, the pulse width of 4.2 ns, ablation flow of a He (1.0 l/min) into ICP-MS Agilent 7500CE (Agilent Technologies, Japan).

3. RESULT AND DISCUSSION

3.1. Effect of UV irradiation time and Zn/Cd molar ratio

It is comprehended that increasing the UV irradiation time and Zn/Cd molar ratio would increase the yield of prepared QDs-Ab. Therefore, these parameters were evaluated. UV irradiation time had an important effect on the preparation ZnCd/S quantum dots [9] which is illustrated in **Figure 1 (A)**, the maximum fluorescent intensity was achieved at 442 nm under 382 nm excitation. The composition of ZnCd/S quantum dots for obtaining higher fluorescent intensity was mainly dependent on the initial concentration of Zn, Cd, and the intrinsic reactivity of Zn and Cd toward S [10]. The QDs-Ab solution was prepared with the different molar ratios of Zn/Cd (4, 16, 32, and 64) and the maximum emission was obtained in molar ratio 32 as shown in **Figure 1 (B)**.

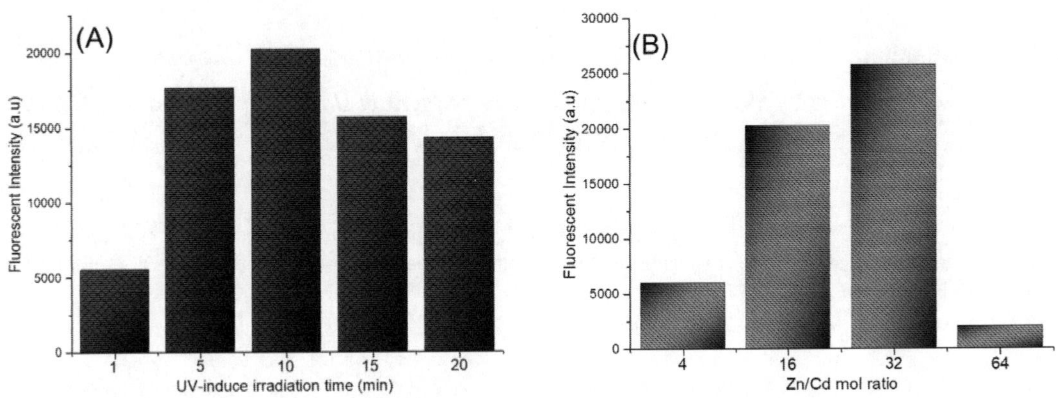

Figure 1 Effect of UV-induces irradiation time (A) and Zn/Cd molar ratio on fluorescent intensity (B)

3.2. CE and LA-ICP-MS analysis

To reveal that QDs-Ab was formed, CE is a valuable instrument [11]. **Figure 2 (A)** shows the electropherograms of anti-mouse IgG before and after reduction and anti-mouse IgG labeled by in situ synthesized QDs (QDs-Ab). In general, a peak in migration time 4.17 min belongs to electroosmotic flow (EOF). Firstly, the anti-mouse IgG was analyzed (blue trace) and a sharp peak appeared in the migration time of 6.65 min. Next, anti-mouse IgG after reduction exhibited slightly distorted peak (red trace) with migration time of 6.79 min. Eventually, the peak (green trace) with migration time, 6.96 min demonstrates that anti-mouse IgG was labeled ZnCd/S. The increased migration time suggests not only increasing size but also increasing negative charge of the QDs-Ab.

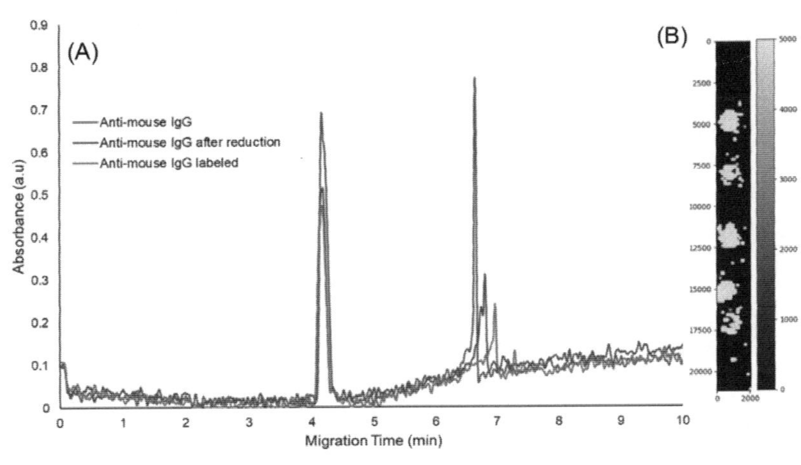

Figure 2 Electropherograms of anti-mouse IgG before and after reduction and anti-mouse IgG labeled with ZnCd/S (A) and Cd analysis of QDs-Ab by LA-ICP-MS (B)

LA-ICP-MS has been used for the determination of metals in purified QDs-Ab samples. As is illustrated in **Figure 2 (B)**, five dots of QDs-Ab were detected in polyvinylidene difluoride (PVDF) membrane, with comparable intensity of Cd.

4. CONCLUSION

Labeling anti-mouse IgG with in situ prepared ZnCd/S quantum dots by utilizing antibody thiol groups as a stabilizer was accomplished for the first time. Simplicity, convenience and time-effectivness are the main benefits of this procedure for antibody labeling. Fluorescent intensity is the main sign of preparation quantum dots optimized based on UV irradiation time and precursor metals ratio. Antibodies labeled with quantum dots were analyzed by LA-ICP-MS and CE and will be used in the near future for immuno-based analysis (e.g. dot blot or ELISA).

ACKNOWLEDGEMENTS

The research was founded by the Internal Grant Agency of Mendel University in Brno IGA MENDELU 2019_TP_009.

REFERENCES

[1] ELLISMAN, M. H., DEERINCK, T. J., SHU, X., SOSINSKY, G. E. Chapter 8 - picking faces out of a crowd: Genetic labels for identification of proteins in correlated light and electron microscopy imaging. In: MÜLLER-REICHERT, T.; VERKADE P., eds. *Methods in cell biology*. Academic Press, 2012, vol 111.

[2] EKINS, R. Merits and disadvantages of different labels and methods of immunoassay. In: *Immunoassays for the 80s*. Springer, 1981.

[3] LIN, T.-Y., LIAN, Z.-J., YAO, C.-X., SUN, X.-Y., LIU, X.-Y., YAN, Z.-Y., WU, S.-M. Cdse quantum dots labeled staphylococcus aureus for research studies of thp-1 derived macrophage phagocytic behavior. *RSC Advances*. 2020, vol. 10. no. 1, pp. 260-270.

[4] NG, S. M., KONESWARAN, M., NARAYANASWAMY, R. A review on fluorescent inorganic nanoparticles for optical sensing applications. *RSC Advances*. 2016, vol. 6, no. 26, pp. 21624-21661.

[5] SAHOO, S. L., LIU, C.-H., KUMARI, M., WU, W.-C., WANG, C.-C. Biocompatible quantum dot-antibody conjugate for cell imaging, targeting and fluorometric immunoassay: Crosslinking, characterization and applications. *RSC Advances*. 2019, vol. 9, no. 56, pp. 32791-32803.

[6] HUTCHINSON, R. W., COX, A. G., MCLEOD, C. W., MARSHALL, P. S., HARPER, A., DAWSON, E. L., HOWLETT, D. R. Imaging and spatial distribution of β-amyloid peptide and metal ions in alzheimer's plaques by laser ablation-inductively coupled plasma-mass spectrometry. *Analytical Biochemistry*. 2005, vol. 346. no. 2, pp. 225-233.

[7] STANISAVLJEVIC, M., VACULOVICOVA, M., KIZEK, R., ADAM, V. Capillary electrophoresis of quantum dots: Minireview. *Electrophoresis*. 2014, vol. 35. no. 14, pp. 1929-1937.

[8] VANECKOVA, T., BEZDEKOVA, J., TVRDONOVA, M., VLCNOVSKA, M., NOVOTNA, V., NEUMAN, J., STOSSOVA, A., KANICKY, V., ADAM, V., VACULOVICOVA, M. Cds quantum dots-based immunoassay combined with particle imprinted polymer technology and laser ablation icp-ms as a versatile tool for protein detection. *Scientific reports*. 2019, vol. 9. no. 1, pp. 1-9.

[9] NEJDL, L., ZEMANKOVA, K., HAVLIKOVA, M., BURESOVA, M., HYNEK, D., XHAXHIU, K., MRAVEC, F., MATOUSKOVA, M., ADAM, V., FERUS, M. Uv-induced nanoparticles-formation, properties and their potential role in origin of life. *Nanomaterials*. 2020, vol. 10. no. 8, pp. 1529.

[10] WANG, N.-X., WANG, Y.-Q., HE, X.-W., LI, W.-Y. One-step and rapid synthesis of composition-tunable and water-soluble zncds quantum dots. *Journal of nanoscience and nanotechnology*. 2011, vol. 11. no. 5, pp. 4039-4045.

[11] KLEPÁRNÍK, K., DATINSKÁ, V., VORÁČOVÁ, I., LIŠKOVÁ, M. Analysis of quantum dots and their conjugates by capillary electrophoresis with detection of laser-induced luminescence. *Quantum dots: Applications in biology*. Springer, 2014.

[12] MÜLLER, S. D., DIAZ-BONE, R. A., FELIX, J., GOEDECKE, W. Detection of specific proteins by laser ablation inductively coupled plasma mass spectrometry (la-icp-ms) using gold cluster labelled antibodies. *Journal of Analytical Atomic Spectrometry*. 2005, vol. 20. no. 9, pp. 907-911.

HIGHLY SENSITIVE MICROFLUIDIC SENSOR ARCHITECTURE FOR SERS MEASUREMENTS OF HORMONES

[1]Vasilii BURTSEV, [1,2]Elena MILIUTINA, [1,2]Mariia ERZINA, [1]Vaclav ŠVORČÍK, [1,2]Oleksiy LYUTAKOV

[1]VŠCHT - University of Chemistry and Technology, Prague, Czech Republic, EU, lyutakoo@vscht.cz

[2]Tomsk Polytechnic University, Research School of Chemistry and Applied Biomedical Sciences, Tomsk, Russia

https://doi.org/10.37904/nanocon.2020.3743

Abstract

Today, there is considerable interest in the development of microfluidic chips that can be integrated into various analytical devices and further used for chemical or biological research. The microfluidic approach can reduce the size of all types of analytical laboratory equipment's and improve their technological performances. In addition, in combination with Surface Enhanced Raman Scattering (SERS), microfluidic devices can detect unprecedentedly low concentrations of targeted analytes. SERS provides a significant amplification of the nonlinear optical response of a molecule adsorbed on a suitable plasmon-active (most often silver or gold) surface (for example nanograting, nanoparticles, etc.). On the other hand, microfluidics allows a substantial reduction in the volume of sample required for analysis. In this work, an approach based on a combination of SERS and microfluidics was implemented and enables the detection of low concentrations of the target analyte - hormones. Proposed preparation of microfluidic chip comprises several subsequent steps: (i) preparation of microfluidic platform using 3D printing; (ii) laser assisted creation of patterned surface, further covered by a thin Au layer, ensuring the excitation of surface plasmon polariton in the microfluidic canal, (iii) subsequent grafting of $-NH_2$ groups, and their activation for hormones entrapping. The rapid, reproducible, and ultrasensitive detection of hormones - Bisphenol, Estradiol, Estriol ($< 10^{-6}$ M) was achieved.

Keywords: Lab-on-a-chip, SERS, 3D printing, microfluidics system, hormones

1. INTRODUCTION

Sensors that determine the concentration of hormones, especially estrogens, are of particular interest for medical and environmental research [1]. Even a small, uncontrolled use of hormones by a person can cause adverse health effects, since certain types of hormones have been shown to cause cancer, heart disease and stroke [2]. Thus, there is a need for the determination of hormones to control their concentration in water and other biological fluids [3,4].

Today, there are several approaches to detecting hormones such as liquid chromatography and mass spectrometry [5,6]. However, they are quite complex, expensive, and time-consuming to analyse and results interpretation. Also, in recent years, sensors operating on the principle of surface plasmon resonance have become popular [7], but they have low selectivity and detection limit, which restricts their practical utilization. Therefore, the development of a plasmon-based (bio)sensor that will make it possible to carry out analysis quickly and reliably even with a small sample volume remains unsolved task.

The microfluidic approach makes it possible to reduce the size of all types of analytical laboratory equipment and improve their technological properties [8,9]. In addition, when combined with surface enhanced Raman scattering (SERS), microfluidic devices can detect unprecedented low concentrations of target analytes even with a small sample volume [10-13]. SERS provides a significant enhancement of the nonlinear optical response of a molecule adsorbed on a suitable metal (most often silver or gold) surface, while microfluidics can significantly reduce the sample requirements for analysis. In this work, we propose an approach based on a combination of SERS and microfluidics, which made it possible to identify low concentrations of the target analytes - hormones.

2. EXPERIMENTAL

2.1. Materials

The 3D printable polymer, Clear resin, was purchased from Formlabs, USA. The solution of photoresist, Su-8, was obtained from Microchem, Germany, Isopropyl alcohol (≥98.5%), deionized water, tert-Butyl nitrite (90%), methanol (reagent grade, ≥ 99,8 %), p-Toluenesulfonic acid monohydrate (ACS reagent, ≥98.5%), Bisphenol A (≥99%), β-Estradiol (≥98%) and Estriol (≥97%) were purchased from Sigma-Aldrich and used without further purification. The Au target (purity 4 N) was purchased from Safina. 4-aminobenzenediazonium tosylate (ADT-NH_2) was prepared according to published procedure [14].

2.2. Samples preparation

Microfluidic chip preparation

The microfluidic chip was made using 3D printing. The model for printing was designed in the program COMSOL Multiphysics. After fabrication, the microfluidic micromixer was washed with isopropyl, dried at 40° C for 24 h and additionally irradiated by UV-source for 30 min.

Su-8 film (10 µm) were spin-coated on the surfaced of microfluidic chip (1000 rpm, 10 min), dried at 60 °C for 24 h, irradiated by UV-source for 30 min, and annealed at 90 °C for 2 h. Pattering of Su-8 surface was performed using linearly polarized excimer laser beam from COMPexPro 50F KrF (emission wavelength 248 nm, laser fluence 10 mJ × cm^{-2}, 3500 total number of pulses, beam incident angle 40°).

The Au thin films were deposited onto the patterned surface by vacuum sputtering (thickness 30 nm).

Diazonium modification and diazotization

Au grating was electrochemically modified in 3 mM fresh water solutions of ADT-NH_2 without addition of any electrolytes, under the potential −5 V for 6 min. After modification, chips were rinsed under sonication sequentially with deionized water, ethanol, and acetone for 15 min, and dried in desiccator for 3 h.

The sample was immersed in a 15 ml methanol solution of p-Toluenesulfonic acid monohydrate and 0.3 ml of tert-Butyl nitrite was added. After activation chips were rinsed under sonication with MeOH for 15 min and dried in desiccator for 3 h.

2.3. Measurement Techniques

Raman Spectroscopy Investigations-Concentration Dependence

For microfluidic SERS measurements, the chips were pumped with water solutions of Bisphenol, Estradiol and Estriol. Raman spectra were collected on portable ProRaman-L spectrometer (Laser power 35 mW) with 785 nm excitation wavelengths. Spectra were measured in the 2000-400 cm^{-1} wavenumber range with 60 s accumulation time and averaged 3 times.

3. RESULTS AND DISCUSSION

The preparation of the proposed SERS microfluidic chips consists of several stages, as schematically shown in **Figure 1**. First, a 3D microchannel was made using 3D printing technology and covered with a thin layer of Su-8. In the second stage, the periodic structure was created on the Su-8 by irradiation with excimer laser and covered with a thin layer of gold. Further the chip surface was grafted with -NH_2 groups and activated to obtain a $N{=}N^+$ reactive sites, that allows hormones capturing.

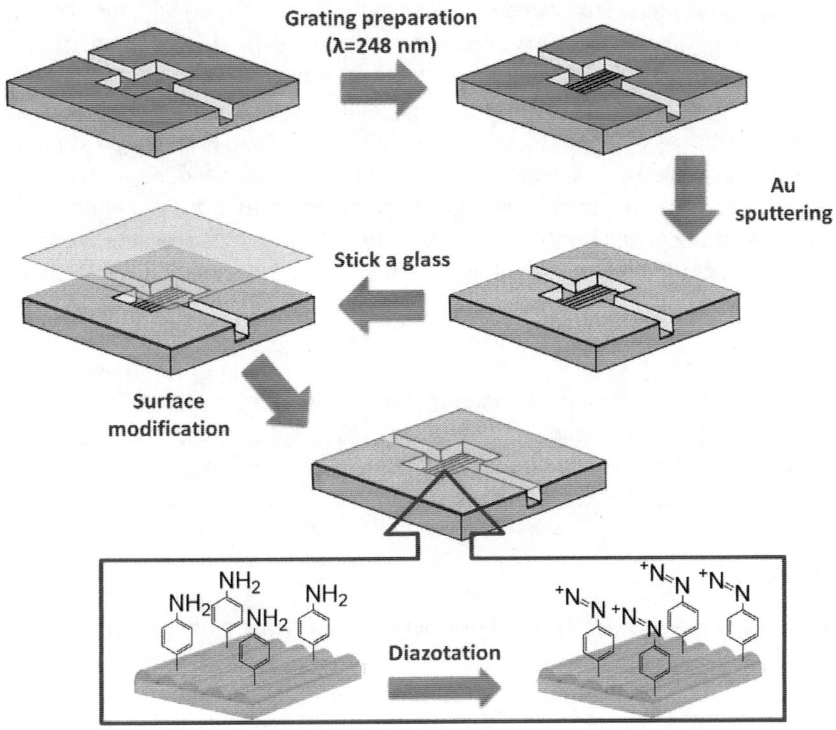

Figure 1 Schematic representation of the preparation of hybrid microfluidic sensor

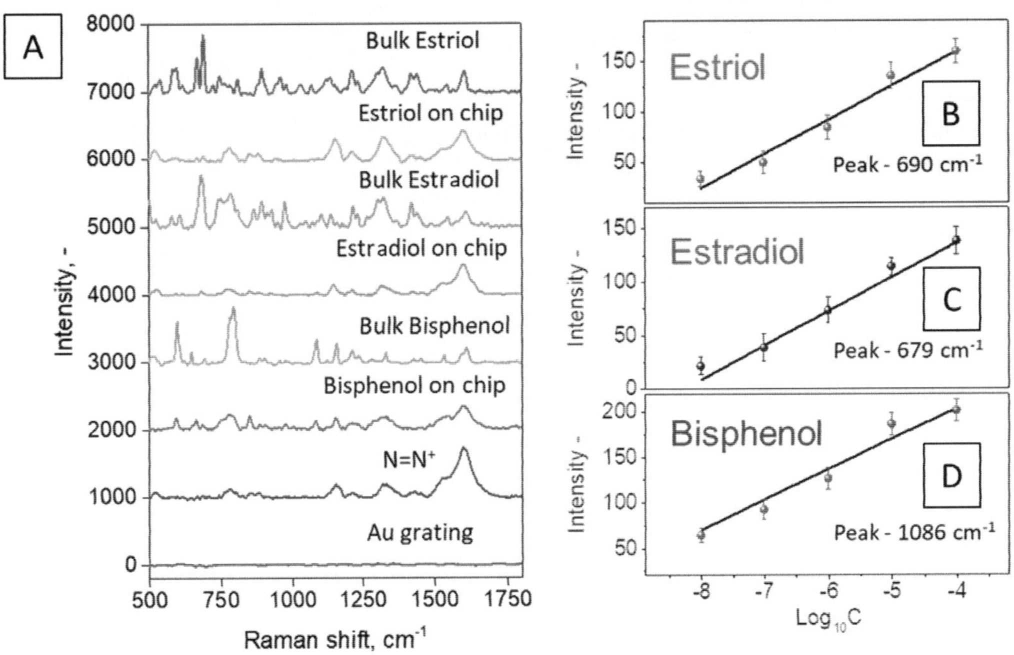

Figure 2 (A) SERS spectra measured on bulk hormones and hormones, entrapped on chip (10^{-6} M) in microfluidic regime. (B) dependency of characteristic Estriol peak intensity on it initial concentration in water; (C) dependency of characteristic Estradiol peak intensity on it initial concentration in water; (D) dependency of characteristic Bisphenol peak intensity on it initial concentration in water.

In the next step, we used two natural steroidal estrogens (estradiol and estriol) and one non-steroidal estrogen (bisphenol A) as model analytes for the study. We compare the SERS spectra, measured on SERS active substrate after hormones capturing in microfluidic regime with Raman spectra of targeted analyte in bulk. In all cases, the perfect coincidence of peak position and relative intensities (after spectra subtraction) was observed, indicating the success of proposed experimental route. In turn, **Figures 2B-D** show the calibration curves, prepared with more intensive, characteristic hormones SERS band. From calibration curves it is evident, that all used hormones were successfully entrapped detected up to 10^{-8} M concentration. Comparison of obtained measurements uncertainty with typical errors from **Figures 2B-D** allows us to claim that by the proposed method it is possible to determine investigated hormones concentration with high precision.

4. CONCLUSION

In this work, we present the novel design of microfluidic-based chip for SERS detection of Bisphenol A, β-Estradiol and Estriol. The microfluidic chip was designed in Comsol and fabricated using 3D printing. The proposed detection approach is simple, fast, sensitive, and versatile, with great potential in hormone detection applications to monitor the safety of water and environment.

ACKNOWLEDGEMENTS

This work was supported by the project Internal Grant Agency 126 88 2007.

REFERENCES

[1] HAN, X.X., PIENPINIJTHAM, P., ZHAO, B., and OZAKI, Y. Coupling Reaction-Based Ultrasensitive Detection of Phenolic Estrogens Using Surface-Enhanced Resonance Raman Scattering. *Analytical Chemistry*. 2011, vol. 83, no. 22, pp. 8582-8588.

[2] TAYLOR, A.E., KHOURY, R.H., and CROWLEY, W.F. A comparison of 13 different immunometric assay kits for gonadotropins: implications for clinical investigation. *The Journal of Clinical Endocrinology & Metabolism*. 1994, vol. 79, no. 1, pp. 240-247.

[3] GJERGJIZI, B., ÇOĞUN, F., YILDIRIM, E., ERYILMAZ, M., SELBES, Y., SAĞLAM, N., and TAMER, U. SERS-based ultrafast and sensitive detection of luteinizing hormone in human serum using a passive microchip. *Sensors and Actuators B: Chemical*. 2018, vol. 269, pp. 314-321.

[4] WANG, R., CHON, H., LEE, S., CHENG, Z., HONG, S.H., YOON, Y.H., and CHOO, J. Highly Sensitive Detection of Hormone Estradiol E2 Using Surface-Enhanced Raman Scattering Based Immunoassays for the Clinical Diagnosis of Precocious Puberty. *ACS Applied Materials & Interfaces*. 2016, vol. 8, no. 17, pp. 10665-10672.

[5] STOPFORTH, A., BURGER, B.V., CROUCH, A.M., and SANDRA, P. The analysis of estrone and 17β-estradiol by stir bar sorptive extraction-thermal desorption-gas chromatography/mass spectrometry: Application to urine samples after oral administration of conjugated equine estrogens. *Journal of Chromatography B*. 2007, vol. 856, no. 1, pp. 156-164.

[6] STANCZYK, F.Z., CLARKE, N.J. Advantages and challenges of mass spectrometry assays for steroid hormones. *The Journal of Steroid Biochemistry and Molecular Biology*. 2010, vol. 121, no. 3, pp. 491-495.

[7] MUDA, N.E., ABU BAKAR, MOHD.A. and MAJLIS, B.Y. The Use of Electronic Sensor in Hormone Analysis. *The Malaysian Journal of Medical Sciences : MJMS*. 1999, vol. 6, no. 2, pp. 12-16.

[8] CASTILLO-LEÓN, J. Microfluidics and Lab-on-a-Chip Devices: History and Challenges. In: J. CASTILLO-León and W.E. SVENDSEN, eds. *Lab-on-a-Chip Devices and Micro-Total Analysis Systems: A Practical Guide*. 2015, pp. 1-15.

[9] JEON, J., CHOI, N., CHEN, H., MOON, J.-I., CHEN, L., and CHOO, J. SERS-based droplet microfluidics for high-throughput gradient analysis. *Lab on a Chip*. 2019, vol. 19, no. 4, pp. 674-681.

[10] BURTSEV, V., MILIUTINA, E., ERZINA, M., KALACHYOVA, Y., ELASHNIKOV, R., SVORCIK, V., and LYUTAKOV, O. Advanced Design of Microfluidic Chip Based on SPP-LSP Plasmonic Coupling for SERS Detection with High Sensitivity and Reliability. *The Journal of Physical Chemistry C*, 2019, vol. 123, no. 50, pp. 30492-30498.

[11] PU, H., XIAO, W., and SUN, D.-W. SERS-microfluidic systems: A potential platform for rapid analysis of food contaminants. *Trends in Food Science & Technology*. 2017, vol. 70, pp. 114-126.

[12] MILIUTINA, E., GUSELNIKOVA, O., CHUFISTOVA, S., KOLSKA, Z., ELASHNIKOV, R., BURTSEV, V., POSTNIKOV, P., SVORCIK, V., and LYUTAKOV, O. Fast and All-Optical Hydrogen Sensor Based on Gold-Coated Optical Fiber Functionalized with Metal-Organic Framework Layer. *ACS Sensors*. 2019, vol. 4, no. 12, pp. 3133-3140.

[13] GAO, R., KO, J., CHA, K., HO JEON, J., RHIE, G., CHOI, J., DEMELLO, A.J., and CHOO, J. Fast and sensitive detection of an anthrax biomarker using SERS-based solenoid microfluidic sensor. *Biosensors and Bioelectronics*, 2015, vol. 72, pp. 230-236.

[14] GUSELNIKOVA, O., POSTNIKOV, P., ELASHNIKOV, R., TRUSOVA, M., KALACHYOVA, Y., LIBANSKY, M., BAREK, J., KOLSKA, Z., ŠVORČÍK, V., and LYUTAKOV, O. Surface modification of Au and Ag plasmonic thin films via diazonium chemistry: Evaluation of structure and properties. *Colloids and Surfaces A: Physicochemical and Engineering Aspects*. 2017, vol. 516, pp. 274-285.

CELL BASED AFM BIOSENSENSING FOR SCREENING OF PULMONARY-DRUG RELATED ARRHYTMIC EFFECTS

[1,2,3] Martin PESL, [4]Jan PRIBYL, [4]Simon KLIMOVIC, [5]Martin SCUREK, [1,2]Deborah BECKEROVÁ, [5]Kristian BRAT, [4,6]Petr SKLADAL, [1,2]Vladimir ROTREKL

[1]ICRC, St. Anna University Hospital, Czech Republic, EU

[2]Department of Biology, Medical faculty, Masaryk University, Czech Republic, EU

[3]1st Internal medicine clinic-Cardio-angiology, St. Anna University Hospital/Masaryk University, Czech Republic, EU

[4]Nanobiotechnology, CEITEC MU, Czech Republic, EU

[5]Dept. of Respiratory Diseases, University Hospital Brno and Faculty of Medicine, Masaryk University, Czech Republic, EU

[6]Dept. of Biochemistry, Faculty of Science, Masaryk University, Czech Republic, EU

https://doi.org/10.37904/nanocon.2020.3745

Abstract

Atomic force microscopy (AFM) combined with stem cell derived human cardiomyocytes (CM) enables dynamic follow-up of cardiac contractions (e.g. beating rate, contraction and relaxation times), simultaneously with other CM biomechanical properties. Today, majority of drugs entering clinical usage needs to be tested for adverse arrhythmic effects; nevertheless, the effects on cardiomyocyte contraction are not routinely employed, only when related to cardiac pathologies. AFM-based biosensor allows in-vitro disease modeling, but also enables to monitor the effect of CM-contraction affecting drugs. Until today only few selected drugs modulating contractility and spontaneous pacing were described in animal models. This work for the first time demonstrates that basic biomechanical parameters, such as average value of contraction force and the beat rate, represent valuable pharmacological indicators of different phenotypic effects on cells without genetic burden. The presented method is robust and has low computational requirements, while keeping optimal spatial sensitivity (force detection limit 200 pN, corresponding to 20 nm displacement). The cardiac stimulating activities of drugs utilized in pneumology as aminophylline, ipratropium, and salbutamol were tested. Stimulating drugs, e.g. methylxanthines and caffeine, presented aberrant cardiomyocyte response, confirming arrhythmogenic potential, and force related fluctuations. Quantification of spontaneous contraction irregularities and related contractility changes allow precise scaling of potential negative effects adding new safety level to clinically relevant drug testing. AFM combined with human CMs serve as robust real-time screening platform for effects of pulmonary drugs. Here we describe changes in CM contractility, which is hard to describe by other screening methods and was never tested with described medication.

Keywords: Cardiomyocyte, contraction, arrhythmia, in vitro modeling, drug adverse events, pulmonary drugs

1. INTRODUCTION

There is large group of patients with chronic obstructive pulmonary disease (COPD) and bronchial asthma (AB), receiving long-term/lifelong and combined bronchodilator (BD) treatment. Majority of commonly used drugs in this combination has certain influence on heart contractility and rhythm. The most prevalent drugs include methylxanthines, beta-2-sympathomimetics (β2-SM), parasympatholytics, and inhaled or oral/intravenous corticosteroids [1,2].

Salbutamol, a β2-SM, provides relief of shortness of breath and other symptoms for relatively short period of about six hours. Nevertheless, a number of cases of abuse was, reported due to its supposed anabolic effects and muscle performance enhancement [3-8]. Nowadays, there is a number of case studies and experimental body of evidence that during long-term BD treatment by β2-SM, parasympatholytics and methylxanthines, some patients [or the substance abusers) develop cardiomyopathy (CMP), chronic heart failure (CHF), cardiac arrhythmia (CA) and even sudden cardiac death (as the first cardiac manifestation of CMP) [9-17].

Cellular and even cardiomyocyte (CM) interactions with BD drugs were studied and are well-known from animal models and primary CMs mixtures (homogenized animal hearts) [18,19]. Despite wide array of phenotypic assays available [20] human CMs have not yet been studied and it remains to be disclosed, how BD substances affect their physiological functions, especially contractility and rhythmicity.

Unique application of atomic force microscopy (AFM) as nanomechanical transducer combined with stem cell derived human CMs enables dynamic monitoring of cardiac contractions [21-23]. CMs beating rate, contraction and relaxation times and absolute force values can be recorded simultaneously with other relevant biomechanical properties [24]. Human CMs gain role in drug development, improving attrition rates [25], especially cardiotoxicity assays [26-29]. Adult human CMs, are not readily accessible from obvious reasons, still CMs can be differentiated from either human embryonic or induced pluripotent stem cells (hES and iPS, respectively) [30]. In this pilot work, we present an electromechanical in vitro system of 3D cardiac models and AFM together for drug testing in the format of an (organ) heart-on-a-chip. For this reason, we have used clinically relevant concentrations of selected drugs aminophylline (methylxanthine), salbutamol (β2-SM) and ipratropium (parasympatholytic).

2. METHODS

The hES line CCTL14 derived and characterized at Masaryk University, Brno [31] was used. Cardiac differentiation was performed as previously described [30,32,33] with minor modifications, resulting in 3D spheroids of regular size and shape, called embryonic bodies (EB). AFM setup (JPK NanoWizard 3, JPK, Berlin, Germany), together with an inverted light microscope (IX-81S1F-3, Olympus, Tokyo, Japan), was employed to record mechanocardiograms of spontaneously contracting EBs as previously described [21-23]. The tested drugs were diluted to clinically relevant concentrations [19,34] and the resulting response curves were recoded after initial equilibration in Tyrode's solution, followed by sequenced exchanges of media with increasing drug concentrations.

Each measurement consisted of 10 min stabilization and 10 min measurement. The mechanical properties of beating EBs were expressed as force of contraction in nN (R-S) as previously described [30]; however, the values were relativized for final comparison. Rhythmical properties were described as contractions/beats per minute (BPM). Statistical evaluation was carried out in GraphPad Prism 8.4.3 software (GraphPad Software, Inc., La Jolla, CA, USA). All data were tested for outliers by ROUT (Q = 1 %) method, and available normality tests were performed. Contraction and force of EBs with different concentration of aminophylline was cross-compared by Brown-Forsythe ANOVA test, with Dunnett's T3 multiple comparison test. Due to single measured entity, statistics were not applied to salbutamol and ipratropium.

3. RESULTS

Pilot sets were measured for 12 clusters of CMs derived from hES cell line CCTL14. Total of 10 clusters were measured in four subsequent concentrations of aminophylline, nevertheless 3 of those exhibited aberrant behavior, previously described as stop-and go effect [23]. These were excluded from the pilot evaluation. Only pilot sets were measured for Salbutamol and Ipratropium (so far).

Force (RS) and BPMs were not significantly differing, probably due to small sample size; nevertheless, the observed trend has shown increased force and frequency for high concentrations (10 mM) of Aminophylline.

Moreover, the initially compact set of contractions became highly variable. On the contrary, small Aminophylline concentrations (10 μM) led to insignificant decrease of contractility and force. Details are depicted in **Figure 1**.

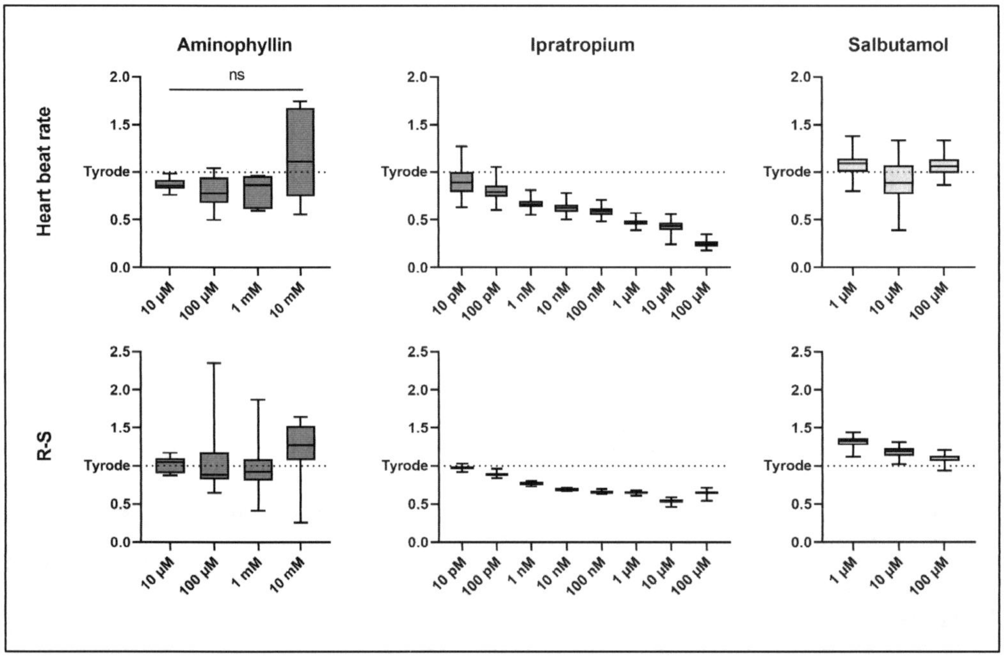

Figure 1 relativized force of contraction in nN (R-S) contractions/beats per minute (BPM)

Salbutamol in pilot trial did not exhibit change in contraction rate, nevertheless small concentration of Salbutamol resulted in 1.5 fold increase in contractility, which negatively correlated with increasing concentration of the substance up to 100 μM.

Ipratropium showed sustained negative trend through all concentrations, in both contraction rate and force.

4. DISCUSSION

This pilot set of data has for the first time shown consistent trend in CMs behavior influenced by pulmonary drugs. The Aminophylline end-point function is a phosphodiesterase inhibitor; thus an increase of intracellular calcium levels should be present, contributing to positive inotropy [35]. Nevertheless, those changes can be also ascribed to direct catecholamine effect [36]. This limited set of data would support opinion, that Aminophylline does not significantly contribute to myocardial contractility [37]; however, it may have some role in increasing contraction rate and the effect on the regularity of contraction has to be further studied.

Salbutamol on the other hand has shown negative trend for inotropic response, which is in contrast with positive inotropic effect in animals (guinea pig and dog), despite describing lower-than-Isoprenaline effect [38]. Difference may be attributed to lower concentrations used in animal experiments (less than 10 μM), which may correspond to the first (ascending) part of contractility curve. Here may be shown the same, but descending part of curve, after reaching maximal inotropic effect of the substance. Chronotropic effect of Salbutamol was ascribed to atrioventricular (AV) nodal increased conduction [39,40], rather than sinoatrial node (SA). Increase of the beating frequency in the whole organ can also relate to lower refractory period in the large piece of tissue, enabling easier arrhythmia occurrence and spreading [40]. Nevertheless, its direct effect on SA node is very small compared to AV node and this seems to be also irrelevant to the 3D CM model of small scale, where the spontaneous contractions are independent of conductive system. Increase in rhythm of contraction cannot be traced in the pilot Salbutamol dataset.

Positive chronotropic effect of ipratropium is attributed to decrease of parasympathetic vagal stimulation, typical for anticholinergic drugs [41,42]. One work described a small decrease of contraction frequency due to other muscarinic agonist (Tiotropium), Although no significant change was traced directly to ipratropium [43] Contrary to this, we have observed sustained decreased chronotropic and inotropic effects of the substance; further investigation has to expand the number of samples and provide more data beyond the pilot experiment.

5. CONCLUSION

This pilot set confirmed that AFM-based nanomechanical system combined with cardiomyocytes can serve as a robust screening platform for direct drug effects, especially myocardial contractility, which is hard to describe by other screening methods. Pulmonary drugs with stimulating properties such as aminophylline, presented aberrant cardiomyocyte response in this context. This is a clear sign of arrhythmogenic potential of distinct compounds. Moreover, force related fluctuations were present in pilot data *in vitro*. Spontaneous contraction irregularities quantification and related contractility changes allow precise scaling of potential negative effects, adding new safety level to subsequent clinically relevant drug testing.

ACKNOWLEDGEMENTS

Supported by Ministry of Health of the Czech Republic, grant AZV NU20-06-00156, we acknowledge CF Nanobiotechnology supported by MEYS CR (LM2018127).

Supported by the project no. LQ1605 from the National Program of Sustainability II (MEYS CR) project FNUSA-ICRC and Supported by the European Regional Development Fund - Project ENOCH (No. CZ.02.1.01/0.0/0.0/16_019/0000868). Supported by Ministry of Health of the Czech Republic (MH CZ-DRO FNBr 65269705). Martin Pesl was supported by "Junior researcher 2020" scheme, Medical faculty, Masaryk University.

REFERENCES

[1] POLVERINO, F., SAM, A., GUERRA, S. COPD: To Be or Not to Be, That is the Question. *Am J Med*. 2019, vol. 132, no. 11, pp.1271-8.

[2] ZINELLU, E., PIRAS, B., RUZITTU, G.G.M., FOIS, S.S., FOIS, A.G., PIRINA, P. Recent Advances in Inflammation and Treatment of Small Airways in Asthma. *Int J Mol Sci*. 2019, vol. 20, no. 11, p. 2617.

[3] COLLOMP, K., CANDAU, R., LASNE, F., LABSY, Z., PRÉFAUT, C., DE CEAURRIZ, J. Effects of short-term oral salbutamol administration on exercise endurance and metabolism. *J Appl Physiol*. 2000, vol. 89, no. 2, pp.430-6.

[4] VAN BAAK, M.A., MAYER, L.H., KEMPINSKI, R.E., HARTGENS, F. Effect of salbutamol on muscle strength and endurance performance in nonasthmatic men. *Med Sci Sports Exerc*. 2000 Jul, vol. 32, no. 7, pp. 1300-6.

[5] LE PANSE, B., ARLETTAZ, A., PORTIER, H., LECOQ, A-M., DE CEAURRIZ, J., COLLOMP, K. Short term salbutamol ingestion and supramaximal exercise in healthy women. *Br J Sports Med*. 2006 Jul, vol. 40, no. 7, pp. 627-31.

[6] MARTINEAU, L., HORAN, M.A., ROTHWELL, N.J., LITTLE, R.A. Salbutamol, a beta 2-adrenoceptor agonist, increases skeletal muscle strength in young men. *Clin Sci (Lond)*. 1992, vol. 83, no. 5, pp. 615-21.

[7] BAILEY, J., COLAHAN, P., KUBILIS, P., PABLO, L. Effect of inhaled beta 2 adrenoceptor agonist, albuterol sulphate, on performance of horses. *Equine Vet J Suppl*. 1999, no. 30, pp. 575-80.

[8] BOUCHER, A., PAYEN, C., GARAYT, C., IBANEZ, H., DIENY, A., DOCHE, C., et al. Salbutamol misuse or abuse with fatal outcome: a case-report. *Hum Exp Toxicol*. 2011 Nov, vol. 30, no. 11, pp. 1869-71.

[9] COUGHLIN, S.S., METAYER, C., MCCARTHY, E.P., MATHER, F.J., WALDHORN, R.E., GERSH, B.J., et al. Respiratory illness, beta-agonists, and risk of idiopathic dilated cardiomyopathy. The Washington, DC, Dilated Cardiomyopathy Study. *Am J Epidemiol.* 1995 Aug 15, vol. 142, no. 4, pp. 395-403.

[10] BOUVY, M.L., HEERDINK, E.R., DE BRUIN, M.L., HERINGS, R.M., LEUFKENS, H.G., HOES, A.W. Use of sympathomimetic drugs leads to increased risk of hospitalization for arrhythmias in patients with congestive heart failure. *Arch Intern Med.* 2000 Sep 11, vol. 160, no. 16, pp. 2477-80.

[11] CAZZOLA, M., SANTUS, P., D'ADDA, A., PIZZOLATO, S., DI MARCO, F., CENTANNI, S. Acute effects of higher than standard doses of salbutamol and ipratropium on tiotropium-induced bronchodilation in patients with stable COPD. *Pulm Pharmacol Ther.* 2009 Jun, vol. 22, no. 3, pp. 177-82.

[12] MAAK, C.A., TABAS, J.A., MCCLINTOCK, D.E. Should acute treatment with inhaled beta agonists be withheld from patients with dyspnea who may have heart failure? *J Emerg Med.* 2011 Feb, vol. 40, no.2, pp. 135-45.

[13] ABRAMSON, M.J., WALTERS, J., WALTERS, E.H. Adverse effects of beta-agonists: are they clinically relevant? *Am J Respir Med.* 2003, vol. 2, no. 4, pp. 287-97.

[14] MEYER, M.F., HOPKINS, W.E., KAMINSKY, D.A. Cardiovascular collapse in a 77-year-old-woman with an asthma exacerbation following bronchodilator treatment. *Chest.* 2003 Sep, vol. 124, no. 3, pp. 1160-3.

[15] JENNE, J.W. Can oral beta2 agonists cause heart failure? *Lancet.* 1998, vol. 352, no.9134, pp. 1081-2.

[16] TOMLIN, A.M., WOODS, D.J., LLOYD, H.S., STEWART, R.A.H., TILYARD, M.W. Understanding medicines with a propensity to increase the risk of heart failure: Combining existing knowledge with targeted population assessment. *Pharmacoepidemiol Drug Saf.* 2018, vol. 27, no. 9, pp. 1019-28.

[17] SAY, B., DEGIRMENCIOGLU, H., GOZDE KANMAZ KUTMAN, H., URAS, N., DILMEN, U. Supraventricular tachycardia after nebulized salbutamol therapy in a neonate: case report. *Arch Argent Pediatr.* 2015 Apr, vol. 113, no. 2, pp. e98-100.

[18] WANG, Y., YUAN, J., QIAN, Z., ZHANG, X., CHEN, Y., HOU, X., et al. β2 adrenergic receptor activation governs cardiac repolarization and arrhythmogenesis in a guinea pig model of heart failure. *Sci Rep.* 2015 Jan 8, vol.5, p. 7681.

[19] SIEDLECKA, U., ARORA, M., KOLETTIS, T., SOPPA, G.K..R, LEE, J., STAGG, M.A., et al. Effects of clenbuterol on contractility and Ca2+ homeostasis of isolated rat ventricular myocytes. *Am J Physiol Heart Circ Physiol.* 2008 Nov, vol. 295, no. 5, pp. H1917-1926.

[20] PESL, M., PRIBYL, J., CALUORI, G., CMIEL, V., ACIMOVIC, I., JELINKOVA, S., et al. Phenotypic assays for analyses of pluripotent stem cell-derived cardiomyocytes. *Journal of Molecular Recognition.* 2017, vol. 30, no. 6.

[21] PRIBYL, J., PEŠL, M., CALUORI, G., ACIMOVIC, I., JELINKOVA, S., DVORAK, P., et al. Biomechanical Characterization of Human Pluripotent Stem Cell-Derived Cardiomyocytes by Use of Atomic Force Microscopy. *Methods Mol Biol.* 2019, vol. 1886, pp. 343-53.

[22] CALUORI, G., PRIBYL, J., CMIEL, V., PESL, M., POTOCNAK, T., PROVAZNIK, I., et al. Simultaneous study of mechanobiology and calcium dynamics on hESC-derived cardiomyocytes clusters. *J Mol Recognit.* 2019 Feb, vol. 32, no. 2, p. e2760.

[23] PESL, M., PRIBYL, J., ACIMOVIC, I., VILOTIC, A., JELINKOVA, S., SALYKIN, A., et al. Atomic force microscopy combined with human pluripotent stem cell derived cardiomyocytes for biomechanical sensing. *Biosensors and Bioelectronics.* 2016, vol. 85, pp. 751-7.

[24] CHEN, A.T., ZOU, S. Evaluation of drug-mediated arrhythmic changes in spontaneous beating cardiomyocytes by AFM. *Analyst.* 2016 Nov 21, vol. 141, no. 22, pp. 6303-13.

[25] SINNECKER, D., LAUGWITZ, K-L., MORETTI, A. Induced pluripotent stem cell-derived cardiomyocytes for drug development and toxicity testing. *Pharmacology & Therapeutics.* 2014 Aug, vol. 143, no. 2, pp. 246-52.

[26] TAKEDA, M., MIYAGAWA, S., FUKUSHIMA, S., SAITO, A., ITO, E., HARADA, A., et al. Development of In Vitro Drug-Induced Cardiotoxicity Assay by Using Three-Dimensional Cardiac Tissues Derived from Human Induced Pluripotent Stem Cells. *Tissue Engineering Part C: Methods.* 2017 Oct 1, vol. 24, no. 1, pp. 56-67.

[27] ACIMOVIC, I., VILOTIC, A., PESL, M., LACAMPAGNE, A., DVORAK, P., ROTREKL, V., et al. Human pluripotent stem cell-derived cardiomyocytes as research and therapeutic tools. *Biomed Res Int.* 2014, vol. 2014, p. 512831.

[28] BRAAM, S.R., TERTOOLEN, L., VAN DE STOLPE, A., MEYER, T., PASSIER, R., MUMMERY, C.L. Prediction of drug-induced cardiotoxicity using human embryonic stem cell-derived cardiomyocytes. *Stem Cell Research*. 2010 Mar 1, vol. 4, no. 2, pp. 107-16.

[29] CONG, Y., HAN, X., WANG, Y., CHEN, Z., LU, Y., LIU, T., et al. Drug Toxicity Evaluation Based on Organ-on-a-chip Technology: A Review. *Micromachines (Basel)*. 2020 Apr 3, vol. 11, no. 4.

[30] PESL, M., ACIMOVIC, I., PRIBYL, J., HEZOVA, R., VILOTIC, A., FAUCONNIER, J., et al. Forced aggregation and defined factors allow highly uniform-sized embryoid bodies and functional cardiomyocytes from human embryonic and induced pluripotent stem cells. *Heart Vessels*. 2014 Nov, vol. 29, no. 6, pp. 834-46.

[31] ADEWUMI, O., AFLATOONIAN, B., AHRLUND-RICHTER, .L, AMIT, M., ANDREWS ,P.W., et al. Characterization of human embryonic stem cell lines by the International Stem Cell Initiative. *Nat Biotechnol*. 2007 Jul, vol. 25, no. 7, pp. 803-16.

[32] KRUTÁ, M., ŠENEKLOVÁ, M., RAŠKA, J., SALYKIN, A., ZERZÁNKOVÁ, L., PEŠL, M., et al. Mutation frequency dynamics in HPRT locus in culture-adapted human embryonic stem cells and induced pluripotent stem cells correspond to their differentiated counterparts. *Stem Cells Dev*. 2014 Oct 15, vol. 23, no. 20, pp. 2443-54.

[33] JELINKOVA S, VILOTIC A, PRIBYL J, AIMOND F, SALYKIN A, ACIMOVIC I, et al. DMD Pluripotent Stem Cell Derived Cardiac Cells Recapitulate in vitro Human Cardiac Pathophysiology. *Front Bioeng Biotechnol*. [online]. 2020. Available from: https://doi.org/10.3389/fbioe.2020.00535.

[34] HARVEY, K.L., HUSSAIN, A., MADDOCK, H.L. Ipratropium bromide-mediated myocardial injury in in vitro models of myocardial ischaemia/reperfusion. *Toxicol Sci*. 2014 Apr, vol. 138, no. 2, pp. 457-67.

[35] COLUCCI, W.S., WRIGHT, R.F., BRAUNWALD, E. New positive inotropic agents in the treatment of congestive heart failure. Mechanisms of action and recent clinical developments. *2. N Engl J Med*. 1986 Feb 6, vol. 314, no. 6, pp. 349-58.

[36] SPALDING, M. *The hemodynamic effects of aminophylline, adenosine, losartan and nitric oxide administered shortly after right heart infarct in a porcine model*. [online]. Oulu; 2001 [cited 2020 Oct 20]. Available from: http://jultika.oulu.fi/files/isbn9514264010.pdf

[37] ELLIOTT, C.G., NIETRZEBA, R.M., ADAMS, T.D., CRAPO, R.O., JENSEN, R.L., YANOWITZ, F.G.. Effect of intravenous aminophylline upon the incremental exercise performance of healthy men. *Respiration*. 1985, vol. 47, no. 4, pp. 260-6.

[38] HUGHSON, R.L., LEDSOME, J.R. The Inotropic and Chronotropic Responses of the Guinea Pig and Dog Myocardium to Isoprenaline and Salbutamol. *Can J Physiol Pharmacol*. 1975 Apr 1, vol. 53, no. 2, pp. 231-8.

[39] KALLERGIS, E.M., MANIOS, E.G., KANOUPAKIS, E.M., SCHIZA, S.E., MAVRAKIS, H.E., KLAPSINOS, N.K., et al. Acute Electrophysiologic Effects of Inhaled Salbutamol in Humans. *CHEST*. 2005 Jun 1, vol. 127, no. 6, pp. 2057-63.

[40] INSULANDER, P., JUHLIN-DANNFELT, A., FREYSCHUSS, U., VALLIN, H.. Electrophysiologic effects of salbutamol, a beta2-selective agonist. *J Cardiovasc Electrophysiol*. 2004 Mar, vol. 15, no. 3, pp.316-22.

[41] VAN VLYMEN, J.M., PARLOW, J.L. The effects of reversal of neuromuscular blockade on autonomic control in the perioperative period. *Anesth Analg*. 1997 Jan, vol. 84, no. 1, pp. 148-54.

[42] SINGH, S., LOKE, Y.K., ENRIGHT, P., FURBERG, C.D. Pro-arrhythmic and pro-ischaemic effects of inhaled anticholinergic medications. *Thorax*. 2013 Jan, vol. 68, no. 1, pp.114-6.

[43] SUBE R, ERTEL EA. Cardiomyocytes Derived from Human Induced Pluripotent Stem Cells: An In-Vitro Model to Predict Cardiac Effects of Drugs. *JBiSE*. 2017, vol. 10, no. 11, pp. 527-49.

THE USE OF GOLD NANOPARTICLE-ANTIBODY CONJUGATES IN IMMUNE TEST FOR MICROCYSTIN-LR DETECTION

[1]Elena A. ZVEREVA, [1]Olga D. HENDRICKSON, [1]Anatoly V. ZHERDEV, [1]Boris B. DZANTIEV, [1,2]Sergey A. EREMIN

[1]A.N. Bach Institute of Biochemistry, Research Center of Biotechnology of the Russian Academy of Sciences, Moscow, Russia, zverevaea@yandex.ru
[2] M.V. Lomonosov Moscow State University, Moscow, Russia, saeremin@gmail.com

https://doi.org/10.37904/nanocon.2020.3738

Abstract

Because of unique optical properties and easy complexation with biopolymers, gold nanoparticles (GNPs) are actively used as markers in various analytical systems, in particular, as components of conjugates with antibodies in rapid immunochromatographic test systems (ICTSs). However, the choice of the most effective conjugates is often empirical. We compared the possibilities of direct sorption immobilization of antibodies on the surface of GNPs and indirect immobilization through the binding of native-specific antibodies to immobilized antispecies antibodies. The work was performed using the example of ICTS for the detection of microcystin-LR (MC-LR), an extremely dangerous phycotoxin produced by microalgae that contaminates drinking water, fish, and seafood. The formats of ICTS with direct and indirect labeling of specific antibodies were compared. It has been shown that indirect labeling provides a lower limit of detection (LOD) for MC-LR than the direct one (the LODs for visual assessment of the results were 0.2 ng/mL and 1 ng/mL, respectively). The duration of the assay was 20 min. The advantages of ICTSs were shown by comparison with a homogeneous MC-LR immunoassay based on fluorescence polarization detection. It was found that the limit of detection of MC-LR for the last assay is 7.5 ng/mL despite the equilibrium of immune interactions. The data obtained confirm the advantages of using indirect immobilization of antibodies on the surface of GNPs, which preserves the functional properties of bound molecules.

Keywords: Gold nanoparticles, lateral flow immunoassay microcystin, food safety

1. INTRODUCTION

Nanoparticles are actively used in a wide range of bioanalytical systems [1]. Their advantages as markers and carriers are due to the large total surface area of suspensions, the possibilities of various methods of conjugation with molecules of different natures, varying sizes and shapes, and the implementation of various highly sensitive detection methods. Among the nanoparticles, gold nanoparticles (GNPs) are especially popular because of their unique optical properties determined by the effect of surface plasmon resonance, simple adsorption and covalent immobilization of various biopolymers, and high stability of the obtained conjugates. In particular, because of this, gold nanoparticles have become the most widely used marker in immunochromatographic test systems (ICTSs)-effective means for out-of-laboratory diagnostics and control [2]. However, despite the large number of developments focused on GNPs and their conjugates, their choice for analytical use is usually made on the basis of empirical recommendations. Thus, in the production of reagents for ICTSs, adsorption immobilization dominates, although in recent years data have been obtained that demonstrate a significant-up to 87%-inactivation of adsorbed antibodies [3].

To overcome these problems, eliminate the loss of specific reagents, and achieve high sensitivity of ICTSs, we consider indirect immobilization of antibodies [4]. Namely, the conjugate of specific antibodies with GNPs is replaced by a combination of native-specific antibodies and a universal reagent-a conjugate of antispecies antibodies with GNPs. In some cases, such a replacement allows for reduction of the consumption of specific antibodies and the detection limit of ICTSs by two orders of magnitude; however, this gain varies considerably when passing from one system to another [5,6]. Various explanations have been proposed for the mechanisms that provide the benefits of indirect immobilization [7-9]. In this situation, further characterization of new ICTSs with indirect immobilization of antibodies is required, including a comparison of reagents based on GNPs obtained by direct and indirect immobilization.

In the presented work, such a comparative analysis of two methods of immobilization and ICTSs implemented with their use, as well as an alternative rapid immunoassay format based on the registration of fluorescence polarization, was carried out using the example of the microcystin-LR (MC-LR) immunoassay. MC-LR is a heptacyclic peptide toxin synthesized by cyanobacteria. Anthropogenic impacts on the marine ecosystems have led to a significant increase in eutrophication and the risk of contamination of water resources [10]. The subsequent movement of toxins along the food chains leads to risk of consuming contaminated fish and seafood. The negative consequences of consuming contaminated water and foods include toxic effects (hepato- and nephrotoxicity), endocrine and skin diseases [10,11]. Therefore, there are regulatory requirements for permissible levels of MC-LR. Thus, for drinking water, the World Health Organization states that the total MC-LRs levels should be < 1 μg/L. Monitoring of water and food for compliance with these requirements necessitates the need for rapid and sensitive analytical methods. For these purposes, various immunoanalytical methods, including ICTSs [12,13], are being actively developed.

The aim of this study was to compare the capabilities of different rapid immunoanalytical systems for detecting MC-LR, including systems with different conjugates of nanoparticles.

2. MATERIALS AND METHODS

2.1. Preparation and characterization of GNPs

GNPs with an average diameter of 30 nm were obtained via citrate reduction of chloroauric acid as described in [14]. Their size was estimated by transmission electron microscopy on a JEM-100C microscope (JEOL, Tokyo, Japan). The obtained images were processed using the Image Tool program.

2.2. Antibodies immobilization on the GNPs

Monoclonal antibodies against MC-LR from Eximio Biotec (Hangzhou, Zhejiang, China) and antimouse polyclonal antibodies from Arista Biologicals (Allentown, PA, USA) were used in the study. First, the antibodies were dialyzed against Tris buffer (0.01 M, pH 8.5). Then the antibodies were added to the GNP solution adjusted to the same pH. The reactants' ratios were 8.5 μg of monoclonal antibodies per 1 mL of the GNP solution, or 6 μg of polyclonal antibodies per 1 mL of the GNP solution. The mixture was incubated at room temperature for 45 min and stabilized by bovine serum albumin (BSA) with its final 0.25% concentration for an additional 15-min incubation. The conjugates were separated by centrifugation (4°C, 13,400 g, 15 min) and stored at 4°C.

2.3. Preparation of immunochromatographic tests

Reagents were immobilized on nitrocellulose membrane CNPC-15 (Advanced Microdevices, Ambala Cantt, India) using an Iso-Flow dispenser (Imagene Technology, Hanover, NH, USA). The load of the MC-LR-BSA conjugate (the analytical zone) and anti-mouse polyclonal antibodies (the control zone) was 0.75 mg/mL. The GNP-antibody conjugate was applied onto a glass fiber membrane at D_{520} = 0.5 (direct ICTS) and 2.0 (indirect ICTS). The volumes of the loading solutions were 32 μL per 1 cm of the test strip. The assembled membranes were cut into strips and stored in sealed bags at low humidity and room temperature.

2.4. Immunochromatographic assay

For direct format: solutions of MC-LR or tested samples were added to wells, test strips were immersed, and 15-min incubation was performed. For indirect format: solutions of MC-LR or tested samples were mixed with the anti-MC-LR antibodies (200 ng/mL) at equal volumes and incubated 3 min, test strips were immersed, and 17-min incubation was performed. Images of the test strips were registered using a flatbed scanner, and the GNPs-caused coloration was accessed using the TotalLab software and compared with the calibration curve.

2.5. Modification of MC-LR by fluorescein derivative

N,N′-Dicyclohexylcarbodiimide (DCC) and N-hydroxysuccinimide (NHS) were dissolved in N,N-dimethylformamide (0.5 mL) and added to MC-LR under nitrogen. The molar ratio of reagents MC-LR/NHS/DCC=1:16:16. The mixture was stirred for 3 h and ethylenediamine fluorescein thiocarbamyl (EDF) was added (MC-LR/EDF=1:1) for the following 1-h incubation. The reaction mixture was separated by thin-layer chromatography (TLC) in a mixture of $CHCl_3$ and CH_3OH (v:v=4:1). The band with Rf 0.1 was extracted with CH_3OH and purified again by the TLC. The final preparation was stored as methanol solution at 4°C.

2.6. Polarization fluorescent immunoassay (PFIA)

The reactions were carried out in borate buffer, pH 8.0. For the assays, MC-LR solutions (tested samples), MC-LR conjugate with EDF, and antibodies were mixed at equal volumes, incubated for 2-3 min at room temperature, and fluorescence polarization and intensity were measured.

3. RESULTS AND DISCUSSION

3.1. Preparation and characterization of immunoreagents for ICTSs

The GNPs were synthesized via the most commonly used gold salt reduction by citrate. The obtained preparations were characterized by transmission electron microscopy. The GNPs images and data of their processing demonstrate the absence of aggregates and similar shape of the particles, close to spherical (**Figure 1**). The average diameter of the GNPs preparation was 31.7 nm. The GNPs demonstrated low variability of size; the RSD value for the diameter was 5.6 nm. Stability of the preparations under storage demonstrates the possibility of using them for conjugation with antibodies.

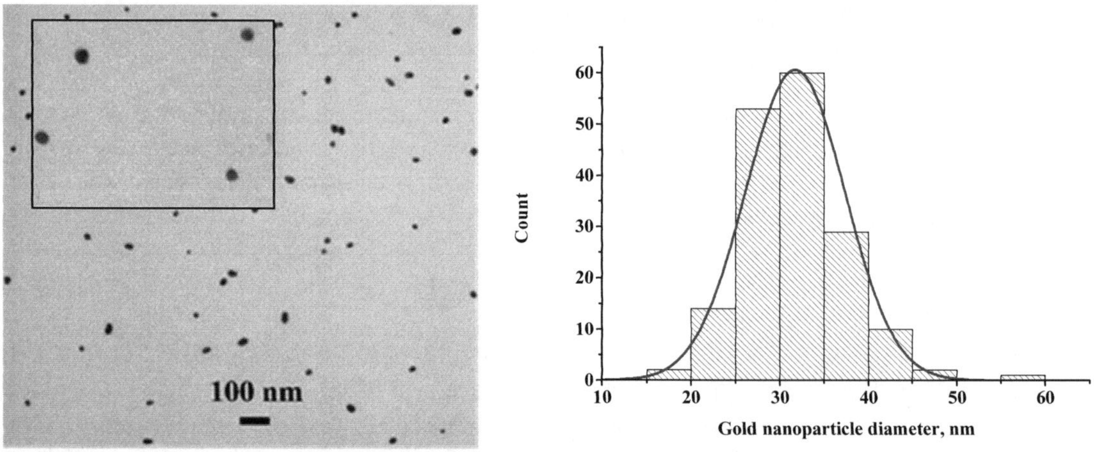

Figure 1 Fragment of GNP microphotograph (including zoom for individual particles) and histogram of particle diameter distribution

GNPs conjugates with specific and antispecies antibodies were obtained. To find the necessary concentrations of the antibodies, their adsorption isotherms were obtained. Namely, the dependence of D580 from the antibodies concentration was registered after the reactants were mixed and 10% NaCl solution was added. An example of the obtained dependence for the anti-MC-LR antibodies is given in **Figure 2**. The point of plateau reaching was interpreted as saturation for binding sites for the adsorption immobilization providing stability of the GNPs colloidal solution. At the plateau point, only half of the GNPs surface is covered, but further increase of the loading does not lead to growth of binding capacity for the antibodies after immobilization, as was demonstrated by our previous studies. Based on the data from these experiments, we have chosen the concentration of anti-MC-LR antibodies equal to 8.5 µg/mL and the concentration of antispecies antibodies equal to 6 µg/mL as optimal for further preparative syntheses.

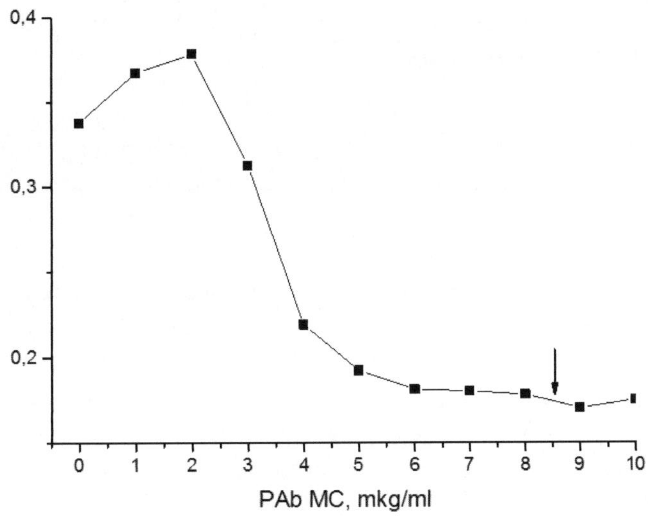

Figure 2 Choice of the concentration of specific antibodies used for conjugation with GNPs (D520 = 1.0). The selected antibody concentration (8.5 µg/mL) is marked by arrow

3.2. The development and characterization of direct format of ICTS for MC-LR detection

In this ICTS, the MC-LR molecules potentially contained in the tested sample and the MC-LR-protein conjugate applied on the analytical zone competed for binding with the GNPs-labeled specific antibody applied on a fiberglass membrane. When choosing the reagents concentrations, we considered two demands: intense coloration of binding zones and low limit of detection. Thus, the chosen concentrations were the following: 0.75 mg/mL for MC-LR-BSA conjugate and D520 = 0.5 for the antibody-GNP conjugate.

The resulting ICTS demonstrated a visual limit of detection equal to 10 ng/mL and instrumental limit of detection equal to 5 ng/mL. Duration of the assay was 15 min. It should be noted that the time of liquid movement along the test strip was much shorter (about 7-8 min), but for better reproducibility, additional time was necessary to reach higher coloration of the bound GNPs.

3.3. The development and characterization of indirect format of ICTS for MC-LR detection

The approach of indirect labeling in the ICTSs is based on the competition of the MC-LR molecules in the sample and the applied MC-LR-protein conjugate for binding with native-specific antibodies. The formed complexes are then labeled by the GNP-antispecies antibodies conjugate. In this way, all specific antibodies are involved in the competition, and their quantity may be reduced without loss of the detected signal. Moreover, each antigen molecule in the tested sample decreases the detected optical signal (exclusion of nonproductive binding with several antibody molecules immobilized at the same GNP without decrease of the registered coloration). The assay format was optimized based on the same rules as in the previous case. Thus, **Figure 3** demonstrates variations of the concentrations of specific antibodies in the range of 1.8-0.1 µg/mL, with the corresponding decreases of coloration intensity. The chosen optimal parameters for the test strip preparation were the following: immobilization of antispecies antibodies at a concentration of 0.5 mg/mL, MC-LR-BSA conjugate applying at a concentration of 0.75 mg/mL, and the use of GNPs conjugated with the antispecies antibodies in a concentration that accords with D520 = 2.0.

The assay under the chosen conditions demonstrated the visual detection limit of 1 ng/mL, whereas the instrumental detection limit was 0.2 ng/mL. Thus, a five- to tenfold improvement of the analytical parameters was reached. The assay time was equal to 20 min (including 3 min of starting incubation i).

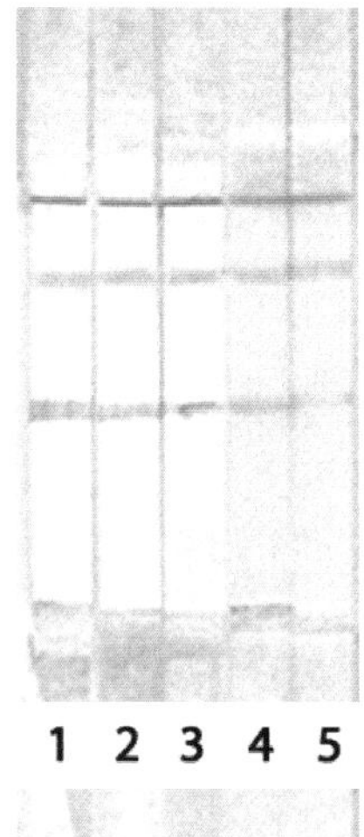

Figure 3 ICTSs (indirect format) after the assay. Test strips 1-5 correspond to concentrations of specific antibodies: 1.8 µg/mL; 0.9 µg/mL; 0.4 µg/mL; 0.2 µg/mL; and 0.1 µg/mL, respectively

3.4. PFIA of MC-LR

The PFIA is a homogeneous analytical technique (without separation and washing) that is based on the competitive binding of controlled and fluorophore-labeled analyte molecules with specific antibodies and the measurement of fluorescence polarization value that depends on the analyte content in the sample.

Optimization of the competitive FPIA conditions included the choice of antibody concentration and the content of the reaction media. It was demonstrated that the antibody dilution of 1:600 provided a stable analytical signal and maximum assay sensitivity. Increased dilution of antibodies resulted in a significant decrease in signal stability. Two tested sets of prepared reactants demonstrated limits of detection equal to 20 and 7.5 ng/mL. Linearity ranges for these completions were 58-470 ng/mL and 15-125 ng/mL, respectively. Thus, even the best completion of reactants for PFIA demonstrated worse sensitivity compared to ICTSs (instrumental detection), despite the equilibrium conditions of immune interactions. This difference confirms preference GNPs as efficient optical labels for immunoanalytical techniques.

4. CONCLUSION

Results of the implemented comparative study (summarized in Table 1) confirm advantages of ICTSs as efficient tools for rapid sensitive testing. However, common immunochromatographic protocol is associated with the inactivation of some part of specific antibodies after their immobilization. The use of the indirect format of ICTSs precludes this problem and provides oriented immobilization of the specific antibodies and the possibility of reducing their quantity used per assay. Therefore, the further application of this approach to other ICTSs seems reasonable.

Table 1 Comparison of analytical parameters for the developed immunoassays of MC-LR.

Analysis	Instrumental limit of detection, ng/mL	Visual limit of detection, ng/mL	Analysis time, min
Direct format of ICTSs	5.0	10.0	15
Indirect format of ICTSs	0.2	1.0	20
PFIA	7.5	-	20

ACKNOWLEDGEMENTS

This study was supported by the Russian Scientific Foundation (project 20-43-07001). The authors are grateful to S.M. Pridvorova (Research Center of Biotechnology) for TEM experiments.

REFERENCES

[1] NOAH, N.M., NDANGILI, P.M. Current trends of nanobiosensors for point-of-care diagnostics. *Journal of Analytical Methods in Chemistry*. 2019, pp. 2179718.

[2] HUANG, X., AGUILAR, Z.P., XU, H., LAI, W., XIONG, Y. Membrane-based lateral flow immunochromatographic strip with nanoparticles as reporters for detection: A review. *Biosensors & Bioelectronics*. 2016, vol. 75, pp. 166-180.

[3] TRIPATHI, K., DRISKELL, J.D. Quantifying bound and active antibodies conjugated to gold nanoparticles: A comprehensive and robust approach to evaluate immobilization chemistry. *ACS Omega*. 2018, vol. 3, no. 7, pp. 8253-8259.

[4] URUSOV, A.E., ZHERDEV, A.V., DZANTIEV, B.B. Use of gold nanoparticle-labeled secondary antibodies to improve the sensitivity of an immunochromatographic assay for aflatoxin B1. *Microchimica Acta*. 2014. vol. 181, pp. 1939-1946.

[5] PETRAKOVA, A.V., URUSOV, A.E., GUBAYDULLINA, M.K., BARTOSH, A.V., ZHERDEV, A.V., DZANTIEV, B.B. "External" antibodies as the simplest tool for sensitive immunochromatographic tests. *Talanta*. 2017, vol. 175, pp. 77-81.

[6] HENDRICKSON, O.D., ZVEREVA, E.A., POPRAVKO, D.S., ZHERDEV, A.V., XU, C., DZANTIEV, B.B. An immunochromatographic test system for the determination of lincomycin in foodstuffs of animal origin. *Journal of Chromatography B*. 2020, vol. 1141, article 122014.

[7] BERLINA, A.N., BARTOSH, A.V., SOTNIKOV, D.V., ZHERDEV, A.V., XU, C., DZANTIEV, B.B. Complexes of gold nanoparticles with antibodies in immunochromatography: comparison of direct and indirect immobilization of antibodies for the detection of antibiotics. *Nanotechnologies in Russia*. 2018, vol. 13, pp. 430-438.

[8] DI NARDO, F., CAVALERA, S., BAGGIANI, C., GIOVANNOLI, C., ANFOSSI, L. Direct vs mediated coupling of antibodies to gold nanoparticles: the case of salivary cortisol detection by lateral flow immunoassay. *ACS Applied Materials & Interfaces*. 2019, vol. 11, no. 36, pp. 32758-32768.

[9] URUSOV, A.E., PETRAKOVA, A.V., ZHERDEV, A.V., ZVEREVA, E.A. Indirect labeling of antibodies as a universal approach to increase sensitivity of lateral flow tests: A case study for mycotoxins detection. *The Open Biotechnology Journal*. 2019, vol. 13, pp. 113-121.

[10] PREECE, E.P., HARDY, F.J., MOORE, B.C., BRYAN, M. A review of microcystin detections in Estuarine and Marine waters: Environmental implications and human health risk. *Harmful Algae*. 2017, vol. 61, pp. 31-45.

[11] GURBUZ, F., UZUNMEHMETOĞLU, O.Y., DILER, Ö., METCALF, J.S., CODD, G.A. Occurrence of microcystins in water, bloom, sediment and fish from a public water supply. *Science of the Total Environment*. 2016, vol. 562, pp. 860-868.

[12] LIU, Y., JI, J., CUI, F., SUN, J., WU, H., PI, F., ZHANG, Y., SUN, X. Development of a two-step immunochromatographic assay for microcystin-LR based on fluorescent microspheres. *Food Control*. 2019, vol. 95, pp. 34-40.

[13] AKTER, S., KUSTILA, T., LEIVO, J., MURALITHARAN, G., VEHNIAINEN, M., LAMMINMAKI, U. Noncompetitive chromogenic lateral-flow immunoassay for simultaneous detection of microcystins and nodularin. *Biosensors*. 2019, vol. 9, no. 2, pp. 14672-14685.

[14] FRENS, G. Controlled nucleation for the regulation of the particle size in monodisperse gold suspensions. *Nature Physical Science*. 1973, vol. 241, pp. 20-23.

TIME-LAPSE MONITORING OF CELL MECHANICAL PROPERTIES

[1]Jan PŘIBYL, [2]Vladimir ROTREKL, [2]Martin PEŠL, [2]Šárka JELÍNKOVÁ, [3]Irena KRATOCHVÍLOVÁ

[1]CEITEC MU, CF Nanobiotechnology, Masaryk University, Brno, Czech Republic, EU, jan.pribyl@ceitec.muni.cz

[2]Department of Biology, Faculty of Medicine, Masaryk University, Brno, Czech Republic, EU, vrotrekl@med.muni.cz

[3]Institute of Physics, Academy of Sciences Czech Republic v.v.i, Prague, Czech Republic, EU, krat@fzu.cz

https://doi.org/10.37904/nanocon.2020.3740

Abstract

Atomic force microscopy (AFM) is a highly sensitive non-invasive surface method able to provide insight into cells' mechanical parameters. Membrane and sub-membrane development, as well as internal cellular properties, can be monitored. The stiffness of cells is a fundamental phenomenon that reflects changes in cell physiology. More importantly, changes in cell mechanical properties are also often found to be closely associated with various disease conditions. Cell mechanics are mainly dependent on cytoskeletal architecture. The development of cryopreserved cells' mechanical properties (stiffness) after thawing was studied using AFM. Cell stiffness was mapped and thus monitored in time and space under nearly physiological conditions (i.e., in culture medium and at elevated temperature). In AFM force spectroscopy mode, cells are indented at many sites, and their complete elastic responses are recorded, enabling them to reconstruct a stiffness map. We measured the frozen cell surface stiffness immediately after thawing; they, when the dynamics of development of the cell stiffness were monitored in time up to 24 hours. Moreover, the AFM spectroscopy was combined with fluorescence-based staining of the cytoskeleton, thus enabling to directly correlate cytoskeleton development with stiffness mapping.

Keywords: Atomic Force Microscopy, Mechanical Mapping, Cell stiffness, Cryopreservation

1. INTRODUCTION

Characterization of cell mechanical properties [1] help to understand many biological process, including cell cytoskeleton development [2] and remodeling [3], cell membrane structure, overall cell development and cell death [4]. Cell stiffness is regarded to the development of cytoskeleton assembly, myosin activity, nucleus state and processes [5, 6]. Actin filaments structure is a basic indicator of cell development and adhesion properties. Many critical cellular properties, such tumor formation and development, are mirrored in the changes of mechanical properties [7]. Similarly, the cytoskeleton mechanical properties can be used for sensing of cell apoptosis, moreover, actin filaments organization was shown as relevant to breast cell phenotype [8].

There is a limited number of methods available for the investigation of the cell stiffness under physiological conditions, such as Brillouin microscopy [9], holographic microscopy [4], micropipette aspiration [10] or microwave propagation [11]. Atomic Force Microscopy (AFM) presents a method, which can be easily applied to the mechanical characterization of living cells adhered on solid surface under so called nearly physiological conditions. Moreover, high resolution mapping with the AFM probe is easily offered, maps of Young's modulus are reconstructed, when the force-distance curve measured within the network of the points are fitted with the appropriate mathematical model [6].

In this work, we studied stiffness of cryopreserved frozen/thawed cells and process of these cell mechanical properties/cytoskeleton regeneration after freezing/thawing. Ability of the AFM based nano-indentation technology for time lapsed monitoring of the cell mechanical properties, thus served as tool for mechano-related cellular processes. Overall description of the whole experimental concept can be inspected in the **Figure 1**.

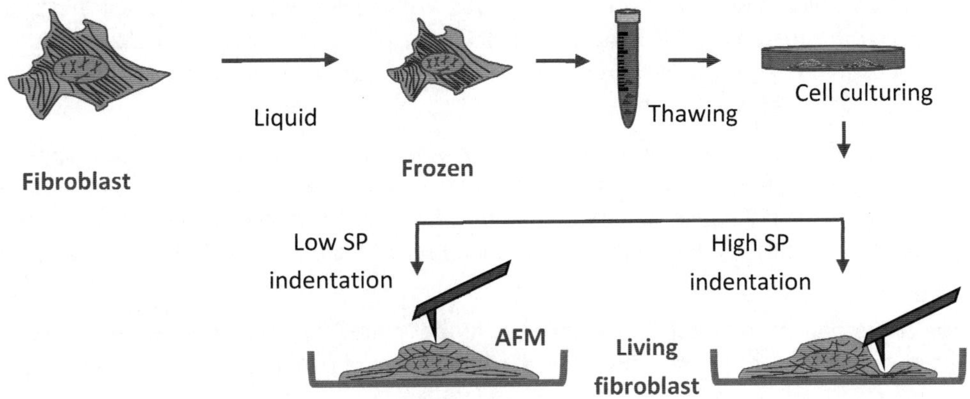

Figure 1 Overall schematic of the experiments. The mouse fibroblast cells are frozen in a liquid nitrogen after the standard incubation. Then the cells are thawed and the process of the cell development immediately after this is followed by the AFM nanoindentation method. High and low force

2. EXPERIMENTAL PART

2.1. Freezing and thawing of the cells

Fibroblasts from mouse embryos (mouse strain CF-1, MEFs) were cultured to 3rd passage (P3). Cell suspension was frozen, 10^6 cells / 2 ml cryo tube (TPP, Trasadingen, Switzerland). Drop by drop addition of 800 μl of cold freezing medium into the same amount of cell suspension in MEF medium initiated the freezing process. MEF medium was composed of the following components: Knockout Dulbecco's modified Eagle's medium (KO-DMEM; Gibco), 10% heat-inactivated fetal bovine serum (FBS; Invitrogen), 1% non-essential amino acids (PAA), 1% L-glutamine (Gibco), 1% penicillin-streptomycin (PAA), and 0.1 mM β-mercaptoethanol (Sigma). Freezing medium was composed of KO-DMEM : FBS : DMSO in the following ratio: 3 : 1 : 1 (v/v/v).

The cell thawing process was started, when the cryo tube with the frozen cells (MEFs P3) was taken out from liquid nitrogen. The tube was transported to the place of thawing on ice. Solid cell suspension was quickly thawed in the hot water until the moment, when a few last crystals could be visible in the tube. The whole content of the tube was then transferred to the standard Falcon tube, cold MEF medium (12 ml) was drop wised by Pasteur pipette. After a short and gentle centrifugation of the tube (200 g, 4°C, 5 minutes), the MEF medium excess was removed from the above of the cell pellet. Cells were then re-suspended in 1000 μl of preheated MEF medium (37°C). Thus, prepared suspension of fibroblast cells was seeded into the 3 plastic 34 mm plastic Petri dishes 93040 (TPP). Adhesion process was started in the standard CO_2 incubator for about 20 minutes, then the dish was transferred to the JPK Petri Dish Heater (JPK, Berlin, Germany), where the nanoindentation process was started.

2.2. Mechanical mapping of cells

Silicon nitride cantilever Hydra 2R-100N (AppNano, Mountain View, CA, USA) with pyramidal silicon tip was used to characterize the cell mechanical properties. Cantilever stiffness and sensitivity was calibrated before each experiment, when the measurement setup was preheated to 37°C for at least half an hour (Petri Dish

Heater, PDH, JPK). The laser reflection to the photodiode was optimized by the standard procedure described in the instrument manual. The AFM setup sensitivity was calculated as a slope of the force-distance curve (FDC) - length (Z-height) 450 nm, curve was recorded at speed of 0.9 µm/s. The sensitivity of the setup was typically in the range from 15.07 to 15.37 nm/V, stiffness of the cantilever was calculated by analysis of the thermal noise, and was found to be between 0.0173 and 0.0192 N/m.

JPK NanoWizard3 bioAFM microscope (JPK) was employed to characterize the cell mechanical properties in a real time following the thawing. AFM head for scanning by probe was placed on the inverted optical microscope Olympus IX-81. The optical microscope was used to find appropriate area containing a single fibroblast cell, which already started to adhere on a plastic bottom of the dish.

Mechanical properties of the cells were investigated by nano-indentation process, mode Force Mapping (JPK). Following experimental parameters were used: maximal loading force (Set Point) 1.0 nN (relative to baseline value), curve recording speed 30 µm/s, Z- length 15.0 µm. Force-distance curves were recorded with data sample rate of 2000 Hz. Network of 64x64 points, so called Force Maps, were captured when area 55x55 to 75x75 µm was investigated.

Reproducibility of the nanomechanical measurement was performed by 5 times repeated force mapping process on identical place (scanning over the identical cell) with use of parameters mentioned above.

Place to place reproducibility was studied, when the identical force mapping experiments was subsequently performed on two different places found randomly on the Petri dish surface covered with fibroblasts. Effect of set point value on measured stiffness of the cells was studied, too.

Long term monitoring of cell mechanical properties during its development started 20 minutes after the cell thawing. When first cells started to adhere, culturing medium in the dish was completely exchanged and force mapping process was started. Nanomechanical measurement was performed for 12 hours of continuous experiment, when the Force Maps were recorded repeatably on the identical cell. The experimental parameters described above were employed, MEF medium preheated in the CO2 incubator was periodically exchanged every 60 minutes.

Networks of force distance curves (Force Maps) were processed by fitting the FDCs with Hertzian Sneddon equation (Eq. 1) thus providing value of Young's modulus. Data processing module of the JPK software was employed here, resulted Young's modulus maps were post-processed by Gwyddion software ver. 2.44X.

$$F(\delta) = (2E \tan\alpha) / (\pi (1-\upsilon^2))\ \delta \qquad (1)$$

Where F is the measured force, E - Young's modulus, v - Poisson ration (0.5 for incompressible materials), δ is tip sample separation (obtained by correction of the cantilever height to its bending) and α is half angle to face of pyramidal tip (reflects the tip geometry).

Data post processing was initiated by threshold defined masking of the cell surrounding area presented by plastic material of high stiffness. The process of masking was finished by manual correction of mask by mask editor in Gwyddion software. Resulted Young's modulus maps contained only data points related to the area covered by cell. Average value of the cell stiffness was afterwards calculated by Statistical quantities module of the Gwyddion software.

3. RESULTS AND DISCUSSION

Mechanical properties of cell in the time period after the thawing were monitored. Storing cells in liquid nitrogen is a common method of storing them. The process of their thawing is relatively little studied, and the properties of the cells may be different from their normal behavior, which may We observed the mechanical properties of the cells in the time period after their thawing. The overall description of the freezing-thawing process combined with nanomechanical study is schematically described in the **Figure 1**.

The value of the maximum loading force (so called set-point) plays a critical role in the indentation process, higher value of the set-point leads to deeper indentation. Cell compartments located inside can be inspected by this way, on the other hand, sub-membrane structures can be selectively studied, when low forces are applied. Effect of the applied set-point value on measured values of the Young's modulus is shown in **Figure 2**. Measured cell stiffness increase with increased force value, however, only the lowest set-point leads to increased Young's modulus values, as only the membrane and close sub-membrane structure were investigated in this case.

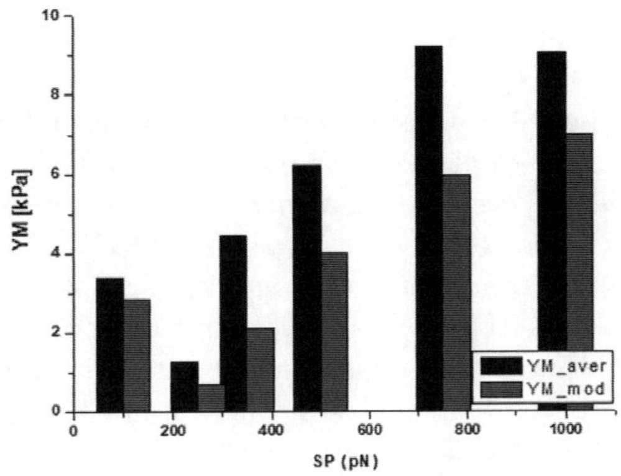

Figure 2 Effect of the loading force (set-point, SP) on the measured stiffness of the cell (YM, Young's modulus). Black columns show average values, red columns values modified values according to the substrate effect.

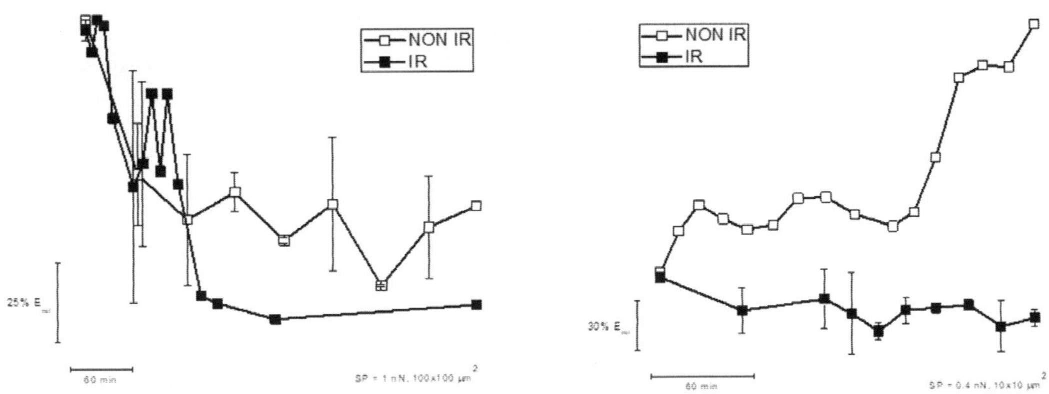

Figure 3 Time-lapsed progress of the average stiffness in the time, monitored in the time period immediately after the thawing process. Indentation set-point 1.0 nN and 0.4 nN was used for left and right graph, respectively. Area of 10x10 and 100x100 μm^2 was monitored - graphs on the left- and right-hand side, respectively. Wild type (NON-IR) and mitotically inhibited (IR) by gamma irradiation were characterized in both cases.

Time lapsed monitoring of the Young's modulus of the freshly thawed cells is shown on the graphs (**Figure 3**). Deep indentation process with the set-point value of 1 nN monitors the intracellular process. Cell stiffness decreases during the time period of 2 hours after the thawing, then the cell elasticity stabilize on stable level, which is about 25% higher in case of mitotically inhibited cells (gamma-irradiated), when this is compared with wild type non-treated cells.

Low force indentation (set-point value 400 pN) describes the cell development after the thawing procedure. Such a force leads to monitoring of membrane and sub-membrane structures. The indentation depth is only about 6% of the total cell height (approx. 550 nm), comparing to the indentation depth of 2.5 μm (approx. 30% of the total cell height), when the higher set-point is used. Totally different view of the cell status can be seen when the low indentation method is used. Sub-membrane structures of the WT cells are rapidly stiffening for the whole time period of the monitoring, as the cells can normally develop. On the other hand, the mitotically inhibited fibroblast cells cannot process the regular cell cycle, thus keeping the stiffness of the sub-membrane structures on a constant level.

4. CONCLUSION

Mechanic and elastic properties of a cell are closely related to its function. Some aspects of cell's internal working and interactions with its surroundings are based upon mechanical as well as biochemical principles. In this work, we showed the ability of the AFM-based nano-indentation method to study the overall cell mechanical properties in a real time. The biological example of the cell regeneration after the thawing was chosen to illustrate the method ability to monitor cell membrane, sub-membrane and internal content changes. Low and high force indentation was applied to study sub-membrane and intracellular cellular structures. Moreover, time-lapsed monitoring of the cellular stiffness has led to an interesting view of the cell development during the post thawing period. Presented work offers an interesting methodological approach for various biological experiments dealing with changes of the cell stiffness.

ACKNOWLEDGEMENTS

Supported by Ministry of Health of the Czech Republic, grant AZV NU20-06-00156, we acknowledge CF Nanobiotechnology supported by MEYS CR (LM2018127).

Supported by the project no. LQ1605 from the National Program of Sustainability II (MEYS CR) project FNUSA-ICRC and Supported by the European Regional Development Fund - Project ENOCH (No. CZ.02.1.01/0.0/0.0/16_019/0000868). Martin Pesl was supported by "Junior researcher 2020" scheme, Medical faculty, Masaryk University.

REFERENCES

[1] NARDONE, G., CRUZ, J.O.-D.L., VRBSKY, J., et al. YAP regulates cell mechanics by controlling focal adhesion assembly. *Nature Communications*. 2017, vol. 8, article no. 15321.

[2] GOLAN, M., JELINKOVA, S., KRATOCHVÍLOVÁ, I., et al. AFM Monitoring the Influence of Selected Cryoprotectants on Regeneration of Cryopreserved Cells Mechanical Properties. *Frontiers in Physiology*. 2018, vol. 9, p. 804.

[3] GOLAN, M., PŘIBYL, J., PESL, M., et al. Cryopreserved Cells Regeneration Monitored by Atomic Force Microscopy and Correlated With State of Cytoskeleton and Nuclear Membrane. *IEEE Transactions on NanoBioscience*. 2018, vol. 17, no. 4, pp. 485-497.

[4] RAUDENSKA, M., KRATOCHVILOVA, M., VICAR, T., et al. Cisplatin enhances cell stiffness and decreases invasiveness rate in prostate cancer cells by actin accumulation. *Scientific Reports*. 2019, vol. 9, no. 1, pp. 1-11.

[5] PERESTRELO, A.R., SILVA, A.C., OLIVER-DE LA CRUZ, J., et al. Multiscale Analysis of Extracellular Matrix Remodeling in the Failing Heart. *Circulation Research*. 2020.

[6] CALUORI, G., PRIBYL, J., PESL, M., et al. Advanced and Rationalized Atomic Force Microscopy Analysis Unveils Specific Properties of Controlled Cell Mechanics. *Frontiers in Physiology*. 2018, vol. 9, p. 1121.

[7] DENG, X., XIONG, F., LI, X., et al. Application of atomic force microscopy in cancer research. *Journal of Nanobiotechnology*. 2018, vol. 16, article no. 102.

[8] PARK, S., LEE, Y.J. AFM-based dual nano-mechanical phenotypes for cancer metastasis. *Journal of Biological Physics*. 2014, vol. 40, no. 4, pp. 413-419.

[9] ELSAYAD, K., POLAKOVA, S., GREGAN, J. Probing Mechanical Properties in Biology Using Brillouin Microscopy. *Trends in Cell Biology*. 2019, vol. 29, no. 8, pp. 608-611.

[10] GONZÁLEZ-BERMÚDEZ, B., GUINEA, G.V., PLAZA, G.R. Advances in Micropipette Aspiration: Applications in Cell Biomechanics, Models, and Extended Studies. *Biophysical Journal*. 2019, vol. 116, no. 4, pp. 587-594.

[11] WU, P.H., AROUSH, D.R., ASNACIOS, A., et al. A comparison of methods to assess cell mechanical properties. *Nature Methods*. 2018, vol. 15, no. 7, pp. 491-498.

PREPARATION OF SILVER NANOPARTICLES BY GREEN SYNTHESIS OF VINE SEEDS - ANTIBACTERIAL EFFECT

[1,2]Branislav RUTTKAY-NEDECKÝ, [1,3,4]Karel SEHNAL, [5]Dominik BANAS, [1,3]Martina STANKOVA, [6]Marta KEPINSKA, [7]Duong Ngonc BACH, [1]Jiri SOCHOR, [1]Mojmir BARON, [8]Awais FARID, [7]Hoai Viet NGUYEN, [1,3,4,6]René KIZEK

[1]*Faculty of Horticulture, Department of Viticulture and Enology, Mendel University in Brno, Lednice, Czech Republic, EU, karelsehnal15@gmail.com, jiri.sochor@mendelu.cz*

[2]*Department of Molecular Pharmacy, Faculty of Pharmacy, Masaryk University, Brno, Czech Republic, EU, ruttkay-nedeckyb@pharm.muni.cz*

[3]*Department of Research and Development, ECO-ENVI-NANOLIFE, Prague, Czech Republic, EU*

[4]*Department of Pharmacology and Toxicology, Faculty of Pharmacy, Masaryk University, Brno, Czech Republic, EU, kizek@sci.muni.cz*

[5]*Department of Biochemistry, Faculty of Science, Masaryk University, Kamenice, Brno-Bohunice, Czech Republic, EU, dominik.banass@gmail.com*

[6]*Department of Biomedical and Enviromental Analyses, Faculty of Pharmacy, Wroclaw Medical University, Wroclaw, Poland, EU marta.kepinska@umed.wroc.p l*

[7]*Research Center for Environmental Monitoring and Modeling, VNU University of Science, Hanoi, Vietnam, nguyenviethoai@hus.edu.vn*

[8]*Divison of Environment and Sustainability, Hong Kong University of Science and Technology, Kowloon, Hong Kong, awais@ust.hk*

https://doi.org/10.37904/nanocon.2020.3746

Abstract

Several silver nanoparticles (AgNPs) with biological effect were prepared by green synthesis. AgNPs were prepared from *Vitis vinifera* seeds (Merlos variety) used as wine production waste. Green synthesis brings intensive surface modifications of nanoparticles. The seeds were lyophilized and then homogeneously ground. Purified extracts (0.5, 2.5, 5 and 10 g / 100 mL water) were added to $AgNO_3$ solution(1 M) in a 1:1(v/v) ratio and stirred for 24 h. The formed nanoparticles were precipitated with methanol (1:1) (v/v) and lyophilized. Secondary metabolites were analyzed by various methods. The preparation yield of AgNPs ranged between 3 - 25 %. The total protein values determined by the Lowry method ranged between 1.8-3.6 mg/mL. Antioxidant activity values determined by the CUPRAC method ranged between 76 - 157 µg/mL GAE. Total phenols values determined by Folin-Ciocalteu ranged between 88 - 160 µg/mL GAE, by 4-aminoantipyrine method (TAAP) ranged between 728 - 1,299 µg/mL GAE, by Price Butler method (PBM) ranged between 57 - 108 µg / mL GAE. AgNPs prepared from *Vitis vinifera* seeds (AgNPs-VV) showed also antibacterial activity. Minimal inhibition concentration (MIC) of AgNPs-VV in *S.aureus* was 31 µg/mL and MIC in *E. coli* was 55 µg/mL.

Keywords: Green synthesis, phenolic compounds, analytical methods, antibacterial effects; traditional medicine, ethnobotany

1. INTRODUCTION

Chemotherapeutics based on natural sources are very intensively searched and studied [1,2]. Secondary plant metabolites involve a number of groups of substances [3]. At the beginning of the 21st century there is still a major concern of infections arising from improper use of antibiotics, disinfectants in hospitals and still not well-understood mechanisms [4]. Preventing these infections is not easy [4]. According to statistics, more people die from bacterial infections than from injuries and cancer [5,6]. The observed rapid rise in bacterial resistance requires the search for new strategies [6]. One of the possible solutions seems to be the use of nanotechnologies [7]. Some types of nanoparticles, including silver nanoparticles (AgNPs), show antimicrobial, antiviral and antifungal effects [8]. In addition, green synthesis of AgNPs uses enzymes and plant extracts [8]. It has lower costs, is environmentally friendly and does not require the use of high pressure and temperature [8]. In addition, important groups are represented by phenolic structures, which have antitumor, antiviral and antibacterial properties [9]. Stilbenes are very important in this area [10]. Stilbenes are part of foods and beverages such as blueberries, peanuts, grapes and red wine [11]. Vine is one of the most important sources of phenolic compounds (including stilbenes). These phenols are present in the skins and seeds [12] and they are shown in **Figure 1**. Resveratrol is the most studied stilbene, which has positive health effects [10]. The wine industry produces a number of wastes (wood, cane, and root) in the production of wine. Modification of the nanoparticle surface with these secondary metabolites can bring a number of completely new properties that can be used in biological applications [13].

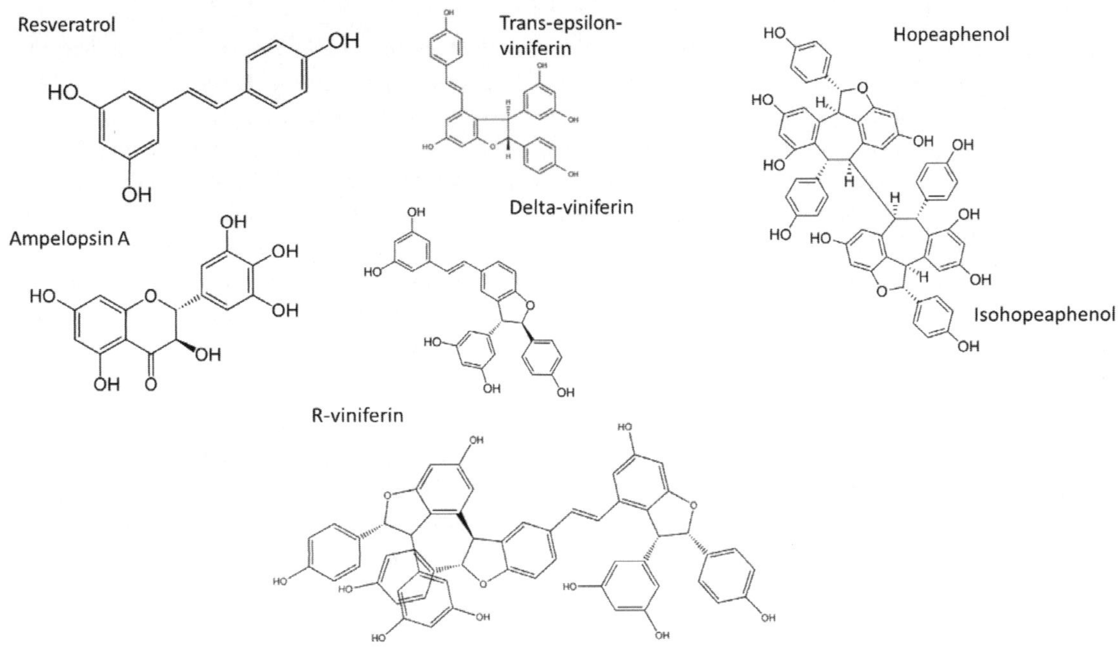

Figure 1 Oligostilbens are a major component of stilbenes extracted from these wastes. An important group of stilbenes in wine are: resveratrol, ampelopsin A, trans-epsilon-viniferin, delta-viniferin, hopeaphenol, isohopeaphenol, and r-viniferin [14,15].

The aim of this work was to design new types of AgNPs from the waste product of *Vitis vinifera* seeds and to test their antibacterial activity.

2. MATERIAL AND METHODS

AgNPs from Vitis vinifera AgNPs-VV. Short description of nanoparticle preparation: Immediately after collection, the plants were washed in distilled water and divided into smaller parts. Seeds of grape Merlot (Lednice, Czechia) were obtained during processing of the grapes into wine. The seeds were washed and lyophilized (48 h, -80 °C, 1 mbar), then homogenized by grinding, using a laboratory grinder (Retsch, GM 200, Germany) (3 min, 10,000 rpm). The material thus prepared was used to prepare the plant extract. Plant extracts were prepared from various amounts of plant material (0.5; 2.5; 5.0; 10.0 g / 100 mL ultrapure water). The extracts were stirred at 25 °C, on a magnetic stirrer (600 rpm, 60 min). They were then centrifuged (20 min, 14,000 g). Each plant extract was filtered and allowed to cool to room temperature. After filtration, the plant extracts were mixed with 0.1 M $AgNO_3$ in a 1:1(v/v) ratio and allowed to stir with a magnetic stirrer (IKA RH basic, Malaysia) at room temperature (23 °C) for 18 hours. The purified nanoparticles were centrifuged (14,000 g, 30 min) and the pellet was lyophilized (24 h, -77 °C, 0.6 mbar). The yield of the reaction was determined.

Photometric characterization of the extract. VIS absorption spectra were measured in the 400–750 nm range. During the formation of nanoparticles, the colour of the resulting solution gradually changed (increasing the absorbance in the area of 450 nm due to the formation of nanoparticles). (Biochemical analysis of AgNPs surface was performed on BS-300 automatic analyzer (Mindray, China). DPPH (2,2-diphenyl-1-picrylhydrazyl), ABTS (2,2'-azino-bis(3-ethylbenzothiazoline-6-sulfonic acid) and FRAP (ferric reducing ability of plasma) methods were used for sample analysis [16,17]. The extracts were characterized by spectrophotometric methods for the content of phenolic substances (Folin Ciocalteau, 4-aminoantipyrine method - TAAP, Price Butler method - PMB) and proteins (Lowry method, pyrogallol red).

Antibacterial activity of AgNPs-VV. Escherichia coli a *Staphylococcus aureus* were obtained from the Collection of Microorganisms of Masaryk University Brno (cultivation of stock culture LB medium, 37 °C, 24 h). Infinite F50 (Tecan, Switzerland) was used for measurements. The antibacterial activity of the AgNPs-VV prepared by green synthesis was determined by the microdilution method, with some modifications. Different volumes of the stock solution AgNPs-VV and broth media were added to 96-well microtiter plates to obtain tested concentrations with a final volume of 250 µL. Then a 1-10 µL of the microbial inoculums were inoculated in microtiter plate wells to obtain a final concentration of 10^4 cells/mL. The plates were incubated for 24 h at 30 ºC and after incubation, viable cell numbers were enumerated, and the CFU/mL were determined. The growth curves were determined for 24 h at 30 °C in a sterile microtiter plate (0.3 ml, shaking 5 s, 150 rpm). Measurements were performed on an Infinite 50 (Tecan, Switzerland) at 620 nm. Absorbances were recorded every 15 min.

Mathematical and statistical analysis. Experimental work was performed in at least three independent experiments. Each sample in the experiments was analysed at least five times. The obtained data presented in this paper are the average values. No experimental points were excluded from the proposed experimental study. All the obtained data were stored in the Qinslab database. If possible, data were processed and evaluated mathematically and statistically in the Qinslab database. The results were expressed as mean ± standard deviation (SD). Positive and negative controls were included in all assays. Probit analysis used to determine the minimum inhibitory concentration (MIC).

3. RESULTS AND DISUSSION:

3.1. Preparation of new AgNPs-VV from Vitis vinifera seed (Merlos variety)

In our previous experimental work, approaches for the synthesis and characterization of AgNPs were optimized [18]. The effect of obtaining dry and dispersed nanoparticles on the time of sonication was studied in detail on AgNPs prepared with extracts of tea, wormwood and sage (the effect was studied as an increase in the A450 absorbance signal). Elevated temperature drying (60 °C, 24 h) and lyophilization (-80 °C, 0.1 mbar, 48 h) were used to dry the nanoparticles. After the drying process, the nanoparticles were prepared at a concentration of 10 mg / mL. They were then dispersed in a conventional ultrasonic bath (4 W for a maximum of 300 minutes). For AgNPs prepared using extracts of Vietnamese tea, wormwood, sage after drying and dispersion, the absorbance ranged 0.1 - 1.4; 0.05 - 1.0; 0.05 - 0.6 ($y = -0.0934 + 0.0124\ x + 0.00001\ x^2$, $R^2 = 0.988$; $y = -0.0114 + 0.0030\ x$, $R^2 = 0.976$; $y = 0.0143 + 0.0009\ x + 0{,}00001\ x^2$, $R^2 = 0{,}953$), respectively and after lyophilization, the absorbance ranged 0.6 -1.60; 0.1 - 1.2; 0.2 - 1.0 ($y = 0.4600 + 0.0077\ x + 0.00001x^2$, $R^2 =$

0.991; y = 0.1683 + 0.0032 x, R^2 = 0.976; y = 0.1475 + 0.0058 x + 0.00001x^2, R^2 = 0.993), respectively. The results clearly showed that the lyophilization process improves the dispersibility of the nanoparticles and the process further depends on the type of extract used. We applied these conditions for the preparation of new AgNPs-VV. Extracted from lyophilized seeds in amounts (0.5; 2.5; 5.0; 10.0 g / 100 mL) were prepared. The prepared extracts were characterized by visual coloration. The yield increased (from 3 to 25 %) linearly depending on the amount used (y = 2.339x + 1.771, r = 0.999). According to the optimized procedure, AgNPs-VV were prepared, in which we focused on the introduction of new methods for the evaluation of flavonoids present in grapevine seeds.

3.2. Automated analysis of phenolic compounds in *V. vinifera* extracts

New methods have been introduced for the characterization of plant extracts and silver nanoparticles in terms of quantification of phenolic substances, proteins, antioxidant activity and flavonones. CUPRAC method, which is based on the principle of reduction of Cu^{2+} -neocuproine complex to Cu^{+} -neocuproine due to antioxidants present in the sample (**Figure 2**). The measurement of the resulting complex was at 450 nm. In addition, it was possible to fully automate the method. As a control for the stability of the method, a control chart was created for the gallic acid concentration of 25 µg / mL and 12.5 µg / mL, where the average value of the control chart for 7 days (58804 ± 1964 mAU and 34461 ± 2360 mAU).

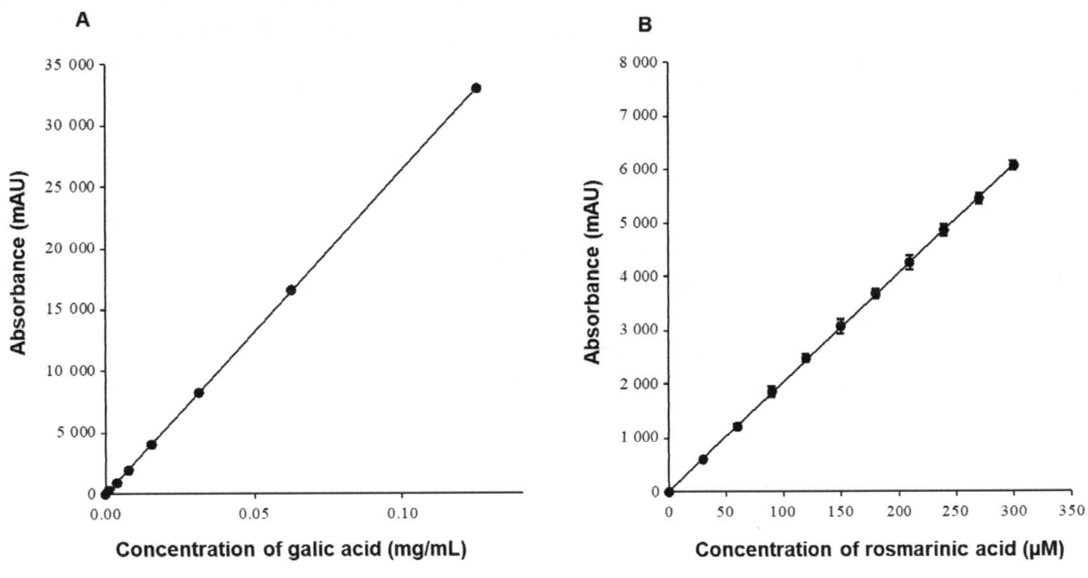

Figure 2 Evaluation of antioxidant activity using the CUPRAC method. The activity is expressed as the equivalent of gallic acid (A). Typical dependence of absorbance on rosmarinic acid concentration (B).

The FLAVANONES method, which is based on the reaction of flavanones of plant extracts with 2,4-DNPH and after subsequent alkalization, results in a quantitative black-blue coloration of the solution. The measurement of the resulting complex was at 505 nm and the method could be fully automated. As a control for the stability of the method, a control chart was created for the concentration of hesperetin 6 µg / mL, where the average value of the control chart for 7 days (4012 ± 323 mAU). The Price Butler method (PBM), which is based on the reaction of a mixture of ferric chloride and potassium ferrocyanide with phenolic substances in a slightly acidic medium. The measurement of the color complex was at 740 nm and the method could be fully automated. As a control for the stability of the method, a control diagram for the concentration of gallic acid 13 µg / mL was created, where the average value of the control diagram for 7 days (58068 ± 3573 mAU). TAAP method, which is based on the reaction of a mixture of potassium ferricyanide and 4-aminoantipyrine in an alkaline medium.

The measurement of the resulting complex was at 450 nm and the method could be fully automated. As a control for the stability of the method, a control diagram for the gallic acid concentration of 53 µg / mL was created, where the average value of the control diagram for 7 days (3947 ± 368 mAU). The methods used showed very good reproducibility and stability during the analysis of the obtained samples. Individual analyzes were performed in the used plant extracts. We found that the content of total phenols determined by the Folin-Ciocalteu method ranged from 0.2 to 1.4 mg / mL GAE, by TAAP method ranged between 0.1-1.2 mg/mL GAE, by Price Butler method (PMB) ranged between 0.1 - 0.8 mg/mL GAE. We paid special attention to the analysis of flavanones. Their content ranged from 0.07 to 0.47 mg / mL hesperetin, 0.06 to 1.17 mg / mL silimarin and by CUPRAC method from 0.13 to 0.95 mg / mL GAE. The amount of total protein ranged from 1 to 6 mg / mL of extract. Analyzes were also performed in AgNPs-VV. Total phenols values determined by Folin-Ciocalteu ranged between 88 - 160 µg/mL GAE, by TAAP method ranged between 728 - 1,299 µg/mL GAE, by PBM method ranged between 57 - 108 µg / mL GAE. The total protein values determined by the Lowry method ranged between 1.8-3.6 mg/mL.

3.3. AgNPs-VV antibacterial activity

Developing bactericidal surfaces using simple chemical methods can be a very promising way to many applications. Antibacterial activity was determined on model organisms (*S. aureus, E. coli*). Growth curves were measured for individual bacterial strains (24 h). We found that AgNPs-VV showed 35-50% inhibitory activity of the control (*S.aureus* or *E.coli* without AgNPs-VV). AgNPs-VV showed higher antibacterial activity against *S. aureus* and lower antibacterial activity against *E. coli*. Based on the calculation of the IC_{50}, the MIC of AgNPs-VV in *S.aureus* was determined to be 31 µg/mL and MIC of AgNPs-VV in *E.coli* was 55 µg/mL.

4. CONCLUSION

There is still very little information on the behavior of nanoparticles in the environment. In addition to chemical synthesis, green synthesis is an alternative that can improve the degradability of nanoparticles from the environment. AgNPs-VV were prepared from several extracts from *V. vinifera* seeds. Total phenols were determined by different methods in both seed extracts and AgNPs-VV. It was shown, that AgNPs-VV contained phenols and had antioxidant activity. AgNPs-VV also showed antibacterial activity against both *S.aureus* and *E.coli*. Our results show that the application of green chemistry processes improves the synthesis of AgNPs and probably improves their potential use in biological applications.

ACKNOWLEDGEMENTS

The work was carried out with the support of the H2020 CA COST Action CA18, NAKI_ID1902015 and Liga proti Rakovině Praha.

REFERENCES

[1] LI, F. S., WENG, J. K. Demystifying traditional herbal medicine with modern approaches. *Nature Plants.* 2017, vol. 3, no. 8, p. 7.

[2] TEIXIDOR-TONEU, I., JORDAN, F. M., HAWKINS, J. A. Comparative phylogenetic methods and the cultural evolution of medicinal plant use. *Nature Plants.* 2018, vol. 4, no. 10, pp. 754-761.

[3] CHONG, J. L., POUTARAUD, A., HUGUENEY, P. Metabolism and roles of stilbenes in plants. *Plant Science.* 2009, vol. 177, no. 3, pp. 143-155.

[4] LIBERTUCCI, J., YOUNG, V. B. The role of the microbiota in infectious diseases. *Nature Microbiology.* 2019, vol. 4, no. 1, pp. 35-45.

[5] DABBAGH, A., LAWS, R. L., STEULET, C., DUMOLARD, L., MULDERS, M. N., KRETSINGER, K., ALEXANDER, J. P., ROTA, P. A., GOODSON, J. L. Progress Toward Regional Measles Elimination - Worldwide, 2000-2017. *Mmwr-Morbidity and Mortality Weekly Report.* 2018, vol. 67, no. 47, pp. 1323-1329.

[6] LI, M., DU, X., VILLARUZ, A. E., DIEP, B. A., WANG, D. C., SONG, Y., TIAN, Y. R., HU, J. H., YU, F. Y., LU, Y., OTTO, M. MRSA epidemic linked to a quickly spreading colonization and virulence determinant. *Nature Medicine.* 2012, vol. 18, no. 5, pp. 816-U217.

[7] MURA, S., NICOLAS, J., COUVREUR, P. Stimuli-responsive nanocarriers for drug delivery. *Nature Materials.* 2013, vol. 12, no. 11, pp. 991-1003.

[8] KUMAR, A., VEMULA, P. K., AJAYAN, P. M., JOHN, G. Silver-nanoparticle-embedded antimicrobial paints based on vegetable oil. *Nature Materials.* 2008, vol. 7, no. 3, pp. 236-241.

[9] MATTIO, L. M., CATINELLA, G., DALLAVALLE, S., PINTO, A. Stilbenoids: A Natural Arsenal against Bacterial Pathogens. *Antibiotics-Basel.* 2020, vol. 9, no. 6, pp. 40.

[10] AJA, I., RUIZ-LARREA, M. B., COURTOIS, A., KRISA, S., RICHARD, T., RUIZ-SANZ, J.-I. Screening of Natural Stilbene Oligomers from Vitis vinifera for Anticancer Activity on Human Hepatocellular Carcinoma Cells. *Antioxidants.* 2020, vol. 9, no. 6, p. 469.

[11] SNOPEK, L., MLCEK, J., SOCHOROVA, L., BARON, M., HLAVACOVA, I., JURIKOVA, T., KIZEK, R., SEDLACKOVA, E., SOCHOR, J. Contribution of Red Wine Consumption to Human Health Protection. *Molecules.* 2018, vol. 23, no. 7, p. 16.

[12] GOUFO, P., SINGH, R. K., CORTEZ, I. A Reference List of Phenolic Compounds (Including Stilbenes) in Grapevine (Vitis vinifera L.) Roots, Woods, Canes, Stems, and Leaves. *Antioxidants.* 2020, vol. 9, no. 5, p. 33.

[13] HOSNEDLOVA, B., SOCHOR, J., BARON, M., BJORKLUND, G., KIZEK, R. Application of nanotechnology based-biosensors in analysis of wine compounds and control of wine quality and safety: A critical review. *Critical Reviews in Food Science and Nutrition.* 2020, vol. 60, no. 19, pp. 3271-3289.

[14] TAKAYA, Y., YAN, K.-X., TERASHIMA, K., HE, Y.-H., NIWA, M. Biogenetic reactions on stilbenetetramers from Vitaceaeous plants. *Tetrahedron.* 2002, vol. 58, no. 45, pp. 9265-9271.

[15] ZACHOVÁ, Z., TŘÍSKA, J., VRCHOTOVÁ, N., BALÍK, J., SAJFRTOVÁ, M., SOVOVÁ, H. Combining high-pressure methods for extraction of stilbenes from grape cane. *The Journal of Supercritical Fluids.* 2018, vol. 142, pp. 38-44.

[16] OU, B. X., HUANG, D. J., HAMPSCH-WOODILL, M., FLANAGAN, J. A., DEEMER, E. K. Analysis of antioxidant activities of common vegetables employing oxygen radical absorbance capacity (ORAC) and ferric reducing antioxidant power (FRAP) assays: A comparative study. *Journal of Agricultural and Food Chemistry.* 2002, vol. 50, no. 11, pp. 3122-3128.

[17] RE, R., PELLEGRINI, N., PROTEGGENTE, A., PANNALA, A., YANG, M., RICE-EVANS, C. Antioxidant activity applying an improved ABTS radical cation decolorization assay. *Free Radical Biology and Medicine.* 1999, vol. 26, no. 9-10, pp. 1231-1237.

[18] SEHNAL, K., LY, P. T., UHLIROVA, D., DUNG, M. L., STANKOVA, M., XUAN, T. T., VSETICKOVA, M., ANH, N. N., HOSNEDLOVA, B., KEPNSKA, M., RUTTKY-NEDECKY, B., BACH, D. N., MILNEROWICZ, H., PRAKASH, T., HUNG, N. T., NGUYEN, H. V., KIZEK, R. Green synthesis of silver nanoparticles using plants originating in tropical areas of vietnam for biological applications. **In:** *11th International Conference on Nanomaterials - Research & Application - NANOCON 2019.* Brno: Tanger, 2019, pp. 463-468.

SILVER NANOPARTICLES SYNTHESIZED USING CANNABIS SATIVA EXTRACT AND THEIR ANTIBACTERIAL ACTIVITY

[1]Jana MICHAILIDU, [1]Alena ČEJKOVÁ

[1]*UCT, University of Chemistry and Technology, Prague, Czech Republic, EU,* jana.michailidu@vscht.cz

https://doi.org/10.37904/nanocon.2020.3744

Abstract

With growing pressure for wide application of silver nanoparticles, the methods of their production have become increasingly important. Moreover, repurposing waste has been a globally acknowledged trend in the context of circular economy approaches in recent decades. Combining the two, this study presents a facile method of silver nanoparticle production with the help of *Cannabis sativa* extract originating from a waste product originating from industrial hemp processing. The presence of produced nanoparticles was confirmed using UV-VIS spectrophotometry and TEM. After that, the antimicrobial activity against planktonic cells of an opportunistic pathogenic bacterium, *Pseudomonas aeruginosa,* was tested using a microcultivation device, Bioscreen C. Our results show *Cannabis sativa* extract is capable of mediating silver nanoparticle synthesis and stabilization and the produced nanoparticles are able of effectively inhibiting the planktonic cells of all *P. aeruginosa* strains tested. These results suggest there is an economically and environmentally friendly method of silver nanoparticle synthesis for antimicrobial applications.

Keywords: Silver nanoparticles, antimicrobial activity, plant extract

1. INTRODUCTION

Nanotechnology is a prosperous industry with new potential applications surfacing every year. With nanoparticles being incorporated in mass produced commodities (e.g. clothes [1]) the methods of their production have become a very important topic. As physico-chemical methods of nanoparticle production come with indisputable advantages (e. g. uniform morphology), they definitely also bring about some major setbacks: Physical methods of production often consume great amounts of energy therefore making these approaches expensive, while chemical methods usually require the use of toxic solvents which can sometimes contaminate the product making these nanoparticles unusable in some areas of application [2].

In recent decades, many studies were performed exploring alternative ways of nanoparticle production, some of which take advantage of living organisms or their parts as a mediator for the reduction and stabilization [3]. A successful synthesis of metal nanoparticle was already described not only using microorganisms such as *Shewanela algae, Rhodopseudomonas capsulata* or *Pseudomonas stutzeri* [4] but also using extracts from plants, some of which are *Pelargonium graveolens, Coriandrum sativum* and *Eucalyptus hybrida* [5].

However, when the materials used for metal ion reduction and nanoparticle stabilization are being chosen, the ecological relevance and sustainability of the approach should be considered. Adhering to the emerging trend of circular economy, considered a priority in a European Commission document "A new Circular Economy Action Plan For a cleaner and more competitive Europe" [6], in various domains of human activity, waste valorization is a key mechanism which needs to be assessed as a desirable approach in as many areas as possible [7]. This is why, in this study, agricultural waste from industrial hemp processing was used for the mediation of nanoparticle production.

2. MATERIALS AND METHODS

2.1. Materials for nanoparticle synthesis

Industrial hemp (*Cannabis sativa*) waste, silver nitrate (Sigma aldrich), ethanol solution (96%), distilled water.

2.2. Hemp extract production

Industrial hemp waste was homogenized using a blender. 150 mg of homogenized hemp were mixed with 600 ml of 40% ethanol solution. This mixture was macerated in the dark for 24h. After that, the extract was filtered through an average laboratory filter (0.8 µm) and subsequently through a filter with 0.2 µm porosity. The finished extract was stored in dark and cold.

2.3. Nanoparticle synthesis and detection

A mixture of 10 % hemp extract and 10 mM of silver nitrate was created and was left to react in dark for 24h. After that, UV-VIS spectrophotometry was performed to detect the characteristic peaks in a spectral plot (250-700 nm). After that a sample of produced nanoparticles was photographed using TEM.

2.4. Microbial strains and growth media

Pseudomonas aeruginosa (DBM 3081, DBM 3777, ATCC 10145) glycerol cryopreserves of the microorganisms were stored at -70° C. Before the experiment, all *P. aeruginosa* strains were precultivated in Luria-Bertani (LB) liquid medium at 37° C and 150 rpm for 24h to achieve the exponential phase of growth.

2.5. Inhibition of planktonic cells of *P. aeruginosa*

The inhibition of planktonic cells of *P. aeruginosa* strains was determined using a microcultivation device (Bioscreen C, Finland). The cells were cultivated for 24h in a microtiter plate in the presence of different % v/v of silver nanoparticles (0, 0.31, 0.63, 1.25, 1.88, 2.5, 3.13, and 4.69 % v/v); each experiment was done in 10 parallels. After that, the growth inhibition was evaluated by plotting the growth intensity for each experiment.

3. RESULTS AND DISCUSSION

3.1. Nanoparticle synthesis and characterization

During the 24h after mixing the silver nitrate solution and hemp extract, the mixture undergone a change of colour; it gradually went from slightly tinted to dark brown. After nanoparticle production was finished, their presence was confirmed using a UV-VIS spectral analysis. This method showed a peak between 400 and 450 nm which is characteristic of silver nanoparticles according to literature [8]. Subsequently, TEM was performed (**Figure 1**) and it revealed the nanoparticles produced are characterized by high polydispersity, varying morphology and sizes between 5 to 80 nm. In a study by Ahmed et al. (2015) silver nanoparticles were produced using *Azadirachta indica* leaf extract; the nanoparticles also exhibited high polydispersity and the diameters ranged between 8 and 100 nm [9]. In another study, silver nanoparticle production was mediated by *Chenopodium murale* leaf extract and the nanoparticle size varied between 30 and 50 nm [10].

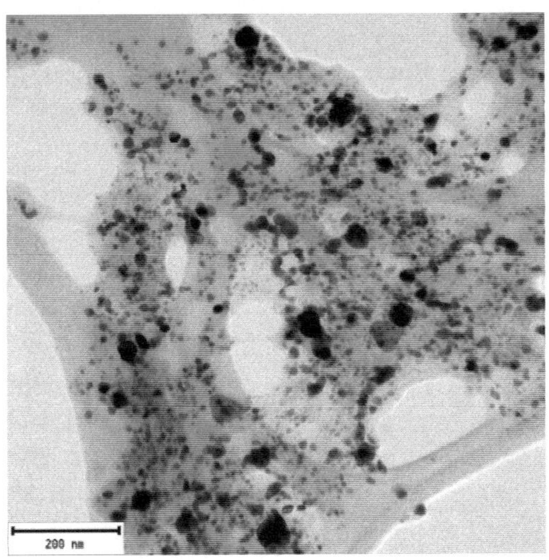

Figure 1 TEM photograph of nanoparticles formed using *Cannabis sativa* extract

3.2. Planktonic cell inhibition

When observing the antibacterial activity of produced nanoparticles against planktonic cells of *P. aeruginosa* (DBM 3081) and *P. aeruginosa* (DBM 3777), more than 90 % inhibition was achieved in the presence of 0.31 % v/v (**Figure 2** and **Figure 3**).

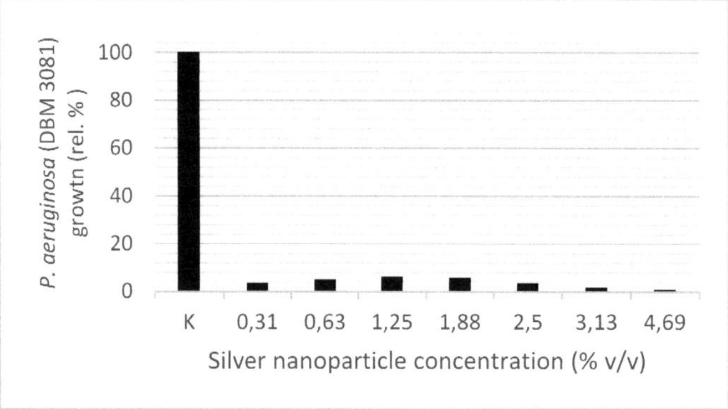

Figure 2 Growth inhibition of *P. aeruginosa* (DBM 3081) planktonic cells mediated by silver nanoparticles; K - control experiment (0 % v/v of nanoparticles)

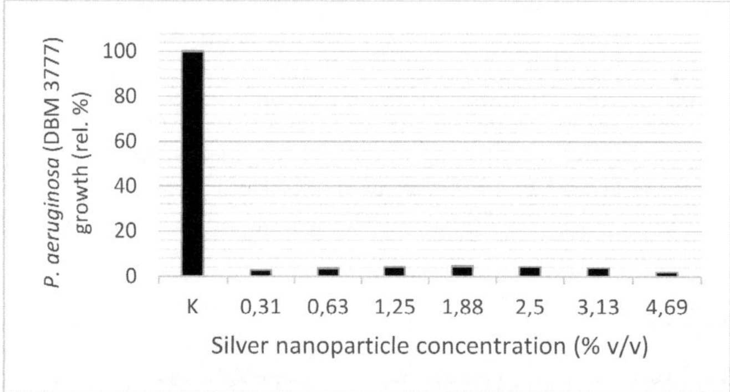

Figure 3 Growth inhibition of *P. aeruginosa* (DBM 3777) planktonic cells mediated by silver nanoparticles; K - control experiment (0 % v/v of nanoparticles)

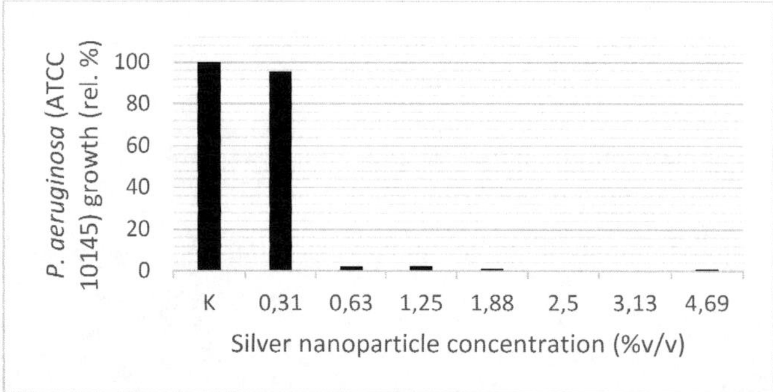

Figure 4 Growth inhibition of *P. aeruginosa* (ATCC 10145) planktonic cells mediated by silver nanoparticles; K - control experiment (0 % v/v of nanoparticles)

In the case of *P. aeruginosa* (ATCC 10145), 90 % inhibition of planktonic cell growth was achieved when 0.63 % v/v of produced nanoparticles was used (**Figure 4**).

Our results showed the nanoparticles produced were very effective at the inhibition of planktonic cells of a gram-negative bacterium *P. aeruginosa*. This corresponds with the scientific understanding of the interaction of a microbial cell and silver nanoparticles. All silver nanoparticles interfere with the microbial cell predominantly by the mechanism of *in situ* silver ion release. However, with nanoparticles of a diameter smaller than 10 nm, the disruption of intracellular processes is mediated by the nanoparticle itself [11].

Antimicrobial activity of silver nanoparticles produced by "green" syntheses was already described in literature. A study was conducted where silver nanoparticles were produced using a culture supernatant of *Nocardiopsis* sp. MBRC-1 and their antimicrobial activity against clinically relevant strains of pathogenic microorganisms such as *Bacillus subtilis* and *Candida albicans* was demonstrated [12]. In another study, silver nanoparticles were produced using *Salvia spinosa* extract with their antimicrobial activity being proved against *Bacillus subtilis* and *Escherichia coli* [13].

4. CONCLUSION

In this study, it was found that agricultural waste originating from *Cannabis sativa* plants can be used for the production of an extract capable of mediating "green" synthesis of silver nanoparticles. Moreover, these nanoparticles were able to inhibit the planktonic cell growth of an opportunistic human pathogen, *P. aeruginosa*. This approach to silver nanoparticle production could be used in the context of various applications (e. g. antimicrobial coating of surfaces) in order to adhere to the principles of circular economy.

ACKNOWLEDGEMENTS

This work was supported from the grant of Specific university research - grant No A2_FPBT_2020_006

REFERENCES

[1] MITRANO, D.M., RIMMELE, E., WICHSER, A., ERNI, R., HEIGHT, M., NOWACK, B. Presence of Nanoparticles in Wash Water from Conventional Silver and Nano-silver Textiles. *ACS Nano.* 2014, vol. 8, no. 7, pp. 7208-7219.

[2] SINGH, J., DUTTA, T., KIM, K.-H., RAWAT, M., SAMDDAR, P., KUMAR, P. 'Green' synthesis of metals and their oxide nanoparticles: applications for environmental remediation. *Journal of Nanobiotechnology.* 2018, vol. 16, no. 84, pp. 1-24.

[3] SRIKAR, S.K., GIRI, D.D., PAL, D.B., MISHRA, P.K., UPADHYAY, S.N. Green Synthesis of Silver Nanoparticles: A Review. *Green and Sustainable Chemistry.* 2016, vol. 6, no. 1, pp. 34-56.

[4] PARK, T.J., LEE, K.G., LEE, S.Y. Advances in microbial biosynthesis of metal nanoparticles. *Applied Microbiology and Biotechnology.* 2016, vol. 100, pp. 521-534.

[5] IRAVANI, S. Green synthesis of metal nanoparticles using plants. *Green Chemistry.* 2011, vol. 13, pp. 2638-2650.

[6] EUR-LEX. *Communication from the Commission to the European Parliament, the Council, the European Economic and Social Committee and the Committee of the Regions. A new Circular Economy Action Plan for a cleaner and more competitive Europe.* [online]. Brussels, 2020. [viewed 2020-10-09]. Available from: https://eur-lex.europa.eu/resource.html?uri=cellar:9903b325-6388-11ea-b735-01aa75ed71a1.0017.02/DOC_1&format=PDF.

[7] PATWA, N., SIVARAJAH, U., SEETHARAMAN, A., SARKAR, S., MAITI, K., HINGORANI, K. Towards a circular economy: An emerging economies context. *Journal of Business Research.* [online]. 2020, vol. 122, pp 725-735. Available from: https://doi.org/10.1016/j.jbusres.2020.05.015.

[8] BHUI, D.K., BAR, H., SARKAR, P., SAHOO, G.P., DE, S.P., MISRA, A. Synthesis and UV-vis spectroscopic study of silver nanoparticles in aqueous SDS solution. *Journal of Molecular Liquids.* 2009, vol. 145, no. 1, pp. 33-37.

[9] AHMED, S., SAIFULLAH, AHMAD, M., SWAMI, B.L., IKRAM, S. Green synthesis of silver nanoparticles using *Azadirachta indica* aqueous leaf extract. *Journal of Radiation Research and Applied Sciences.* 2016, vol. 9, no. 1, pp. 1-7.

[10] ABDEL-AZIZ, M.S., SHAHEEN, M.S., EL-NEKEETY, A.A., ABDEL-WAHHAB, M.A. Antioxidant and antibacterial activity of silver nanoparticles biosynthesized using *Chenopodium murale* leaf extract. *Journal of Saudi Chemical Society.* 2014, vol. 18, no. 4, pp. 356-363.

[11] DURÁN, N., DUÁN, M., DE JESUS, M.B., SEABRA, A.B., FÁVARO, W.J., NAKAZATO, G. Silver nanoparticles: A new view on mechanistic aspects on antimicrobial activity. *Nanomedicine: Nanotechnology, Biology and Medicine.* 2016, vol. 12, no. 3, pp. 787-799.

[12] MANIVASAGANM P., VENKATESAN, J., SENTHILKUMAR, K., SIVAKUMAR, K., KIM, S.-K. Biosynthesis, Antimicrobial and Cytotoxic Effect of Silver Nanoparticles Using a Novel *Nocardiopsis* sp. MBRC-1. *BioMed Research International. Biotechnology and Green Chemistry.* 2013, vol. 2013, article no: 287638.

[13] PIRTARIGHAT, S., GHANNADNIA, M., BAGHSHAHI, S. Green synthesis of silver nanoparticles using the plant extract of Salvia spinosa grown in vitro and their antibacterial activity assessment. *Journal of nanostructure Chemistry.* 2019, vol. 9, pp. 1-9.

GREEN SYNTHESIS AND THE STABILIZATION OF SELENIUM NANOPARTICLES USING CARBOXYMETHYL STARCH

Vishakha VISHAKHA, A. M. ABDEL-MOHSEN, J. JANCAR

Central European Institute of Technology, Brno University of Technology, Brno, Czech Republic, EU,
vishakha.vishakha@ceitec.vutbr.cz

https://doi.org/10.37904/nanocon.2020.3754

Abstract

The growing interest in biodegradable products paves the way for the safest sustainable earth. Starch is an extensively studied, cost-effective, easily accessible, and highly trusted resource to produce biodegradable products in the present and future. However, the exploitation of these starch in several fields requires substantial changes in its chemical functionalities and related properties. Here, we investigated the conditions (pH, temperature, the concentration of starch, concentration of chloroacetate, time, the ratio between starch/sodium hydroxide, etc.) that affect the preparation of carboxymethyl starch (CMS). The chemical structure and degree of substitution of native starch and CMS were confirmed by Fourier transform infrared (FTIR), X-ray powder diffraction (XRD), Thermogravimetric analysis (TGA), potentiometric titration, Scanning electron microscope (SEM), and Nuclear magnetic resonance spectroscopy (NMR). CMS's rheological properties show that CMS's intrinsic viscosity increased with increased degrees of substitutions (DS) from CMS (0.05 to 0.45). The CMS with different DS (0.05 to 0.45) was used for the first time to stabilize selenium nanoparticles (Se-NPs), showing spherical shape with a high homogenous size of Se-NPs (approx. 50 nm). The NPs shape and size stability were investigated and confirmed by different techniques like Dynamic light scanning (DLS), SEM, and Transmission electron microscope (TEM).

Keywords: Selenium nanoparticles, carboxymethyl starch, starch

1. INTRODUCTION

Sodium carboxymethyl starch was first prepared in 1924. Since then, many derivatives have been prepared using the starch's different sources such that potato, amaranth, rice, mungbean, etc. These starches have variations in their amylose content, which is the primary cause of the different substitution degrees. Chemical modification of starch in this way could be useful for the textile, pharmaceutical industries, food industries, absorbents, and adhesives, etc. Nowadays, researchers try to make the material from the CMS for the cell carrier using inorganic material insertion. The carboxymethyl starch (CMS) is prepared by starch's reaction with the sodium monochloroacetate (SMCA) or monochloroacetate (MCA) in the presence of NaOH. Generally, this reaction occurs using a heterogeneous medium such as (ethanol/water, isopropyl alcohol/ water, benzene/ water), etc. This is because the response between starch and SMCA follows the Williamson ether synthesis and is based on the SN^2 mechanism. The polar aprotic solvent is required to do etherification efficiently. The substitution factor is solvent, the concentration of the NaOH, SMCA, temperature, and time [2,3].

The solvent medium is mostly partially water because Carboxymethyl starch's solubility in water starts from 0.1 DS. Many researchers have claimed that using isopropanol as the organic solvent with water is the most prominent solvent for the higher degree of substitution (DS) in CMS. They have used many combinations of the organic solvent and water such as methanol/water, ethanol/water, isopropyl alcohol/water for the reaction. They have claimed that isopropyl alcohol/water mixture is one of the best heterogeneous solvents for the carboxymethyl starch with an intact granule size. It is easy to remove unreactive and impurities from CMS [1].

The temperature is also the primary cause of changing the starch's properties because gelatinization occurs in starch at higher temperatures. Still, the conditions may vary according to the percentage of the amylose content in the source. Potato starch is an abundant source with 28% amylose content, and its gelatinized at ~65°-80°C in the water. Choosing a suitable solvent also plays a crucial role in the reaction because it needs to dissolve the reactants.

The solvent's concentration affects the solubility of the NaOH during the reaction because it is completely soluble in water but does not soluble in isopropyl alcohol at room temperature. The alkylation of the starch needs to be dissolved in the solvent. Otherwise, the separation of the two layers becomes broader in the reaction mixture. Moreover, penetration of the NaOH in the starch is impossible, leading only to surface annealing. Therefore 10% of isopropyl alcohol is recommended for the highest DS. Concerning the amylose content present in the starch, the NaOH concentration has also demonstrated the primary factor for increasing the DS because the complete substitution of the SMCA is based on the catalyst (NaOH). As many researchers reported, changing the ratio of the SMCA: NaOH shows a significant effect on the DS. There is more chance to do side reaction rather than the primary reaction during the CMS's preparation. The side reaction may compete with the immediate response and leads to a decrease of DS.

Researchers have used the synthesis of Se-NPs by ascorbic acid at room temperature in the past few years, as it is a convenient and eco-friendly method [6,8] and for the stabilization of the nanoparticles used polysaccharides such as cellulose and its derivatives [7]. This study's main aim was to stabilize the Se-NPs by using synthesized CMS as polysaccharides act as stabilizers, facilitated by inter-and intra-hydrogen bonding and resulting in a template that binds the nanoparticles and avoids them to aggregate [4,5]. Moreover. In the synthesis of selenium nanoparticles (Se-NPs), the capping agent has a crucial role in influencing the nanoparticle characteristics. Starches are abundant natural biopolymers, inexpensive, and renewable. Starches are composed of polymers that contain amylose and amylopectin. Amylose and amylopectin have the functional molecules before and after modification, acting as a selenium nanoparticles template [4].

2. EXPERIMENTAL SECTION

2.1. Material and Reagent

All chemicals were purchased from the Sigma Aldrich, Penta chemicals and used as received. Potato starch is purchased from the Czech Republic. The Bruker FT-IR was used for the Fourier transformation infrared in attenuated total internal reflectance 400 cm^{-1} to 4000 cm^{-1} at room temperature. Thermogravimetry analysis was carried out on the Trios instrument using N_2 as carrier gas with a temperature ramp is 10 degrees /min from room temperature to 700 degrees.

2.2. Carboxymethylation of the Potato Starch

1g of starch (6 mmol) was added to the 250 ml dried round bottom flask and mixed with 45 ml isopropyl alcohol and 5 ml distilled water (9:1). Followed by the dropwise addition of the 10% NaOH (2.5 M) solution (w/v) for 60 min by noticing the pH (8-12) with stirring at (500 rpm - 900 rpm) at room temperature, continuing the stirring for 6h. After 6h, the addition of an aqueous solution of SMCA (6 mmol to18 mmol) (w/v) for 120 min at 50 degrees Celcius. Once the addition of the SMCA was done, then the reaction was continued for 1 hour at the above temperature. Followed by the Neutralization with 6M HCl (5.5to 6 pH), and the filtration was done by cold 90% ethanol /85% ethanol for several times filtration to remove the chlorides. The degree of substitution was calculated by the back titration followed by the complexometric titration. The morphology of the CMS and their shape after a modification has been confirmed by SEM analysis, and the XRD analysis was used to confirm the loss of crystallinity after carboxymethyl group substitution on the potato starch.

2.3. Preparation of the Selenium Nanoparticles

The addition (5-12ml) of 12.5mM ascorbic acid into the 25ml round bottom flask containing (1-2ml) 25mM sodium selenite solution, which was stirred at room temperature for an hour, until the color changed colorless to orange radish. The appearance of color was due to the reduction of selenium ions into the atoms and for the stability of the nanoparticles, added 0.2% of CMS. It was stirred for 5 hours until the solution got homogenized. **Figure 1** is to illustrate the presence of Se-NPs. The SEM images confirmed the size and shape of the Se-NPs.

Figure 1 Visibility comparison of CMS with high, low DS, and with Se-NP

2.4. Back titration

CMS samples should be acidic and taken 0.02 g of sample for each measurement and dissolved in 6 ml of 0.1 M NaOH and titrated the solution with 0.1 M HCl. The average of the readings has been included for the calculation of the DS.

$$W_{CH2COO} = \frac{(V_b - V_s)M_{Hcl}\, m_{CH2COO}}{m_s} \times 100$$

$$DS = \frac{162 \times W_{CH2COO}}{(100 - W_{CH2COO})m_{CH2COO}}$$

Where:

V_b - blank volume,

$V_{s\cdot}$ - sample volume

m_s- Mass of the sample in milligram

2.5. Complexometric titration

In this titration, 0.02 g of each sample of CMS were taken in the vials and dissolved in the minimum amount of water, and after the dissolution, precipitation occurs by the addition of the excess of $CuSO_4.5H_2O$ solution and titrated against the EDTA (Ethylene diamine tetraacetate)

$$n_{CH2COONa} = \frac{(V_b - V_s) \times 2 \times C}{1000}$$

$$DS = \frac{162 \times n_{CH2COONa}}{\mathrm{W} - 80 \times n_{CH2COONa}}$$

2- Mole ratio of the CH_2COONa/ Initial moles of the EDTA, C is the EDTA concentration (0.01 M), and W signifies the weight of the sample in gram.

3. RESULTS

3.1. Overview of the result

Percentage yield, reaction efficiency, and substitution were analyzed by the experiment performed under the constant temperature and with the definite pH. The reaction's efficiency decreased as we exceed the ratio of SMCA over the 1:1 molar ratio because of the concentration of sodium glycolate and the unreactive SMCA increases. The molar ratios: 1:0.5, 1:1, 1:1.5, 1:2, 1:3 and their percentage yields are 57.55%, 49.8%, 42.01%, 37.3%, and 30% respectively and their DS is 0.10, 0.13, 0.47, 0.50 and 0.62 by back titration. These all ratios are soluble in water at room temperature except the 1:0.5 molar ratio.

3.2. Analysis of the carboxymethyl starch

FT-IR analysis of CMS is illustrated in **Figure 2**. The sharp band comes around 1600 cm^{-1}, and the 1400 cm^{-1} shows a carboxylic group where an unsymmetric stretching peak comes at 1600cm^{-1}, and the symmetric stretching peak is visible at about 1400 cm^{-1}. (COO^-) Moreover, the unmodified portion was shown under the range of the 1200 cm^{-1} to 500 cm^{-1}. **Figure 3** is presenting the effect of pH on the DS. When the pH increases up to some level, DS also increases. **Figure 4** illustrates the effect of the concentration of (starch: SMCA) on the %yield of the CMS, and **Figure 5** defines the impact of SMCA on the carboxymethyl percentage on the starch.

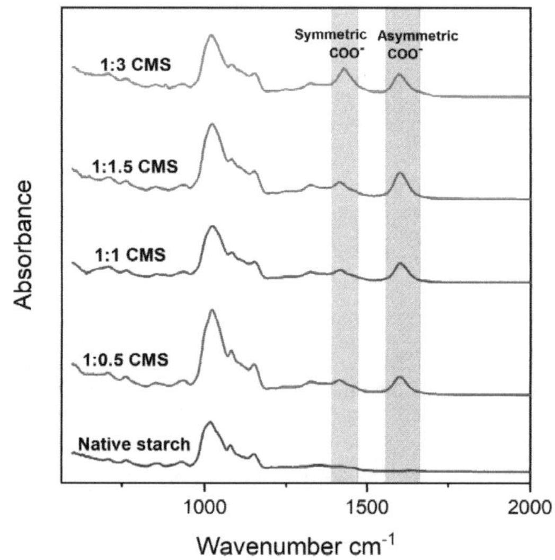

Figure 2 FT-IR spectra demonstrating the presence of carbonyl peaks

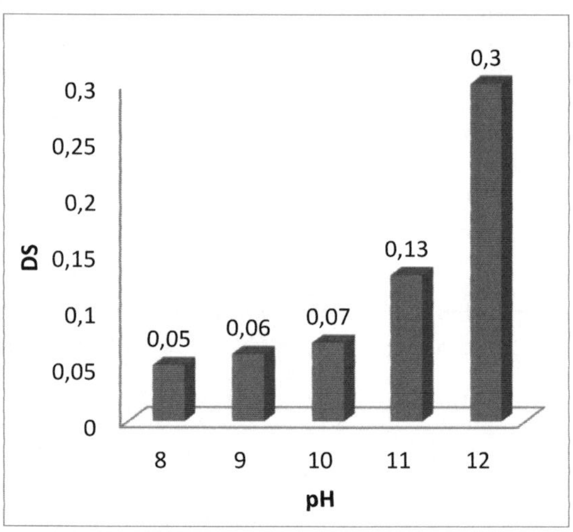

Figure 3 Bar graph is demonstrating the effect of pH on the degree of substitution

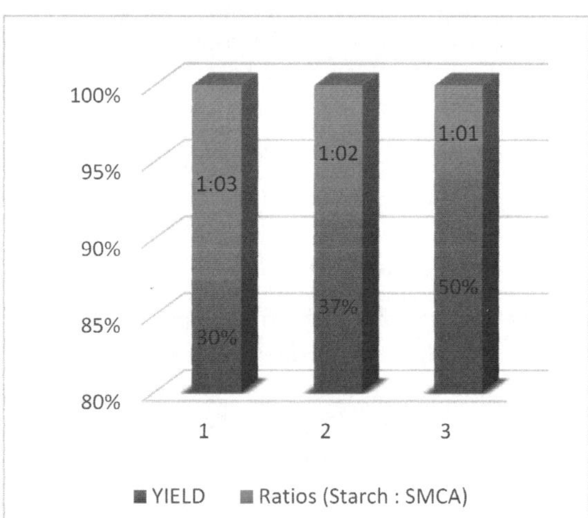

Figure 4 Bar graph is demonstrating the effect of the starch: SMCA ratio on the %yield of CMS

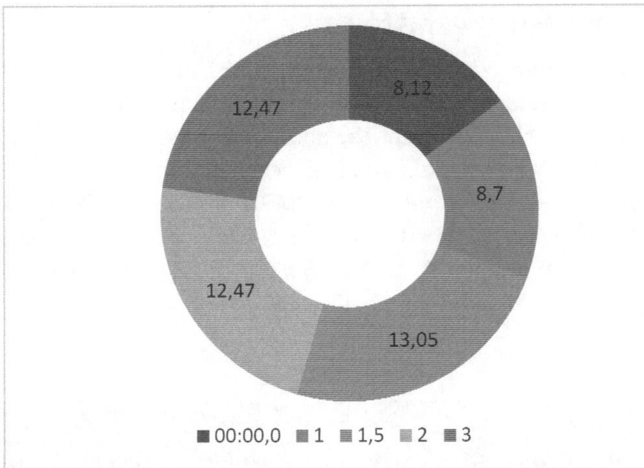

Figure 5 Pie-chart is demonstrating the effect of the amount of SMCA on the carboxymethyl substitution

3.3. X-Ray Diffraction Analysis

X-ray powder diffractometer rigaku smart lab 3kw was used with automatic X-ray powder diffractometer with ϴ/ϴ goniometer. The brag-Brentano and parallel beam modes are complemented by the use of additional asseries. Diffractometer measurement has been taken at 40 kilovolts, current 30 milliamperes. In **Figure 6**, all samples' showed no sharp peak, which illustrates the loss of crystallinity after the chemical modification, which indicates that substituted carboxymethyl groups deform the crystallinity during the chemical modification. The small sharp peak that appeared in one of the ratios should be of impurity. The degree of crystallinity decreases as the substitution degree increases. **Figure 7** depicts crystalline peaks at 28.6 and 42.9 degrees, which confirm the presence of Se-NPs embedded with CMS; in this figure, the XRD pattern shows some characteristics peaks of Se-NPs that confirm the presence of Se(0). The reason for having low-intensity peaks and less due to the CMS's high viscosity might hide the minimal peaks.

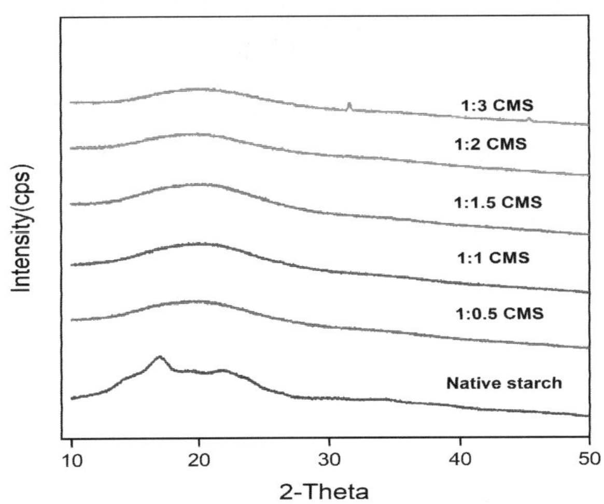

Figure 6 XRD spectra demonstrating the loss of crystallinity of the CMS ratios with respect to the native starch

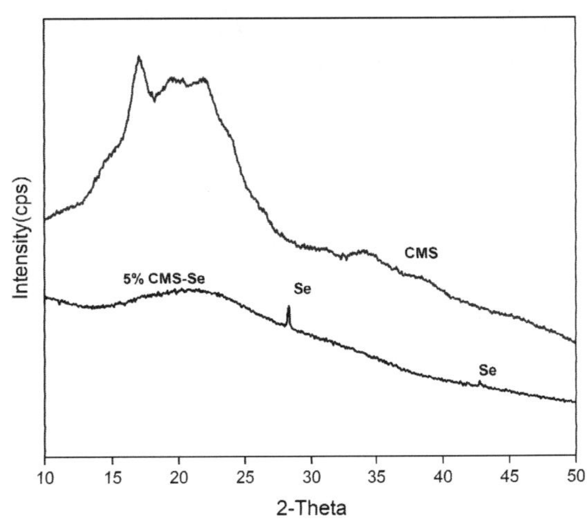

Figure 7 XRD spectra demonstrating the characteristic peaks of Se-NPs embedded in CMS

3.4. Investigating the Surface Morphology (SEM)

Figure 8 illustrates the surface morphology of native starch, CMS, and Se-NPs capped with CMS.which was studied using a scanning electron Microscope. **Figure (a)** shows the shape of the potato starch granules, spherical, and almost all regular in shape. **Figure (b)** shows the change in the shape of the potato starch granule after modification by carboxymethylation, size has increased, and shape has distorted**. Figure (c)** and (d) show the spherical shape of the Se-NPs present on CMS's surface. We have used, The Thermo Fisher (VARIOS) 460 L Field -emission scanning electron microscope (FESEM), which offers sub-nanometer resolution over a wide energy range (0.7 nm @ 1keV, 0.6 nm @ 2-30 keV) with excellent materials contrast. The microscope was equipped with a wide array of imaging and analytical detectors for structural and compositional analysis.

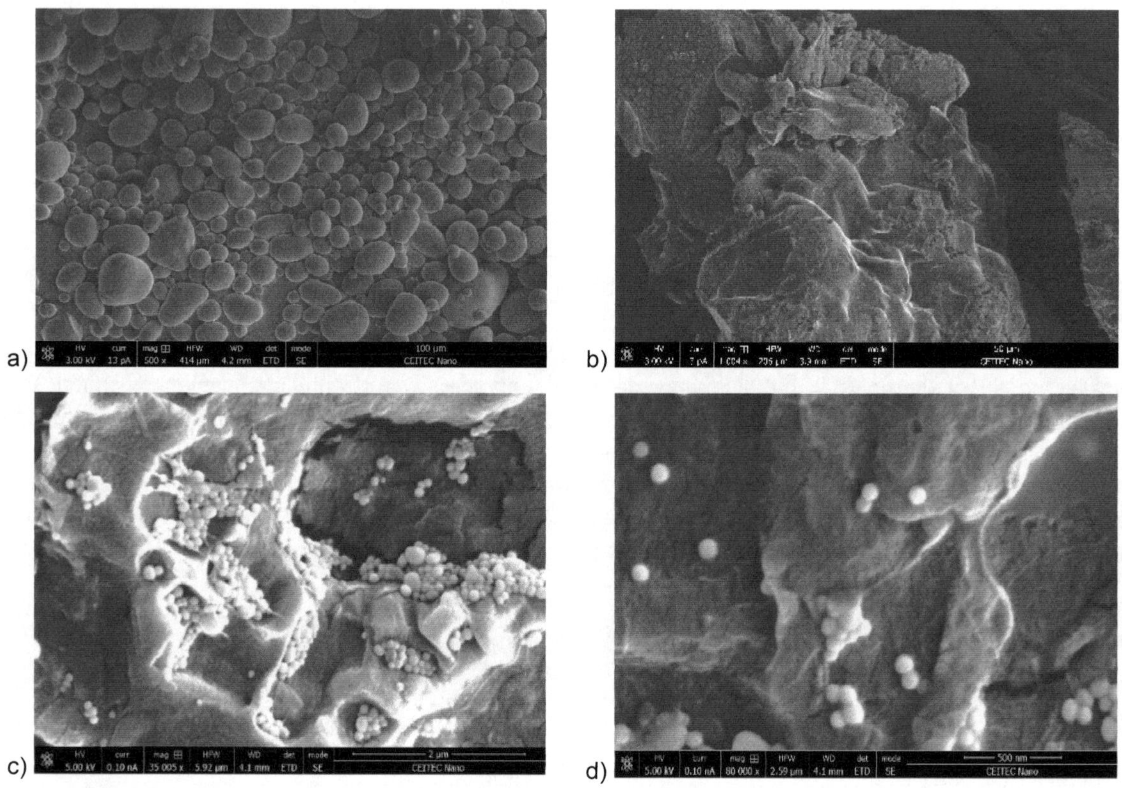

Figure 8 SEM image is demonstrating the shape of Potato starch granules; (a). SEM image is demonstrating the shape of Carboxy;(b). SEM images demonstrate the presence of Se-NPs synthesized by ascorbic acid and capped with CMS;(c) and (d).

4. DISCUSSION

In the past, nanoparticles were stabilized by different stabilizers; some are synthetic, and some are biocompatible [7,8]. In this study, we have used the CMS as a capping agent for the Se-NPs, which has a higher capability to stabilize the Se-NPs at room temperature due to the carboxymethyl group, which introduces the chargeable group. Additionally, the charge group's presence makes it best to bind with Se-NPs and hold them firmly for a long without destroying the Se-NPs original size and shape. The SEM technique confirmed the size and shape.

5. CONCLUSION

Various degree of carboxymethyl moiety substitution was successfully carried out using the less harmful solvent, which acted as a heterogeneous medium for the reaction. Our study confirmed that the amount of SMCA played an essential role in CMS's efficiency and yield. We have confirmed the substitution of the OH group by CH2COONa in the potato starch by titration, FTIR, and XRD. The best pH for each substitution of CMS has been found and would be used in our subsequent studies. The low substituted CMS and higher DS were used as a capping agent for the Se-NPs and analyzed the stability of Se-NPs and confirmation of the size and shape by SEM and XRD.

ACKNOWLEDGEMENTS

This research was carried out under the project CEITEC 2020 (LQ1601) with financial support from the Ministry of Education, Youth, and Sports of the Czechia under the National Sustainability Programme II.

REFERENCES

[1] HEINZE, T., LIEBERT, T., HEINZE, U., SCHWIKAL, K. Starch derivatives of a high degree of functionalization 9: carboxymethyl starches. *Cellulose*. 2004, vol. 11, no. 2, pp. 239-245.

[2] HEINZE, T., KOSCHELLA, A. Carboxymethyl ethers of cellulose and starch-a review. *Macromolecular Symposia*. 2005, vol. 223, no. 1, pp. 13-40.

[3] MASINA, N., CHOONARA, Y. E., KUMAR, P., DU TOIT, L. C., GOVENDER, M., INDERMUN, S., PILLAY, V. A review of the chemical modification techniques of starch. *Carbohydrate polymers*. 2017, vol. 157, pp. 1226-1236.

[4] WONGMANEE, Kittiyaporn, SUREEPORN, Khuanamkam and SANOE, Chairam. "Gold nanoparticles stabilized by starch polymer and their use as catalyst in homocoupling of phenylboronic acid." *Journal of King Saud University-Science*. 2017, pp. 547-552.

[5] CHANG, Peter R., et al. "Polysaccharides as stabilizers for the synthesis of magnetic nanoparticles." *Carbohydrate polymer*. 2011, vol. 83, no.2, pp. 640-644.

[6] VAHDATI, Mahsa and TAHEREH, Tohidi Moghadam. "Synthesis and characterization of Selenium nanoparticles-Lysozyme nanohybrid System with Synergistic Antibacterial properties." *Scientific reports*. 2020, vol. 10, no. 1, pp. 1-10.

[7] SHIN, Yongsoon, et al. "Synthesis and stabilization of selenium nanoparticles on cellulose nanocrystal." *Materials Letters*. 2007, vol. 61, no. 21, pp. 4297-4300.

[8] MALHOTRA, Sonam, NEETU, Jha, and KRUTIKA, Desai. "A superficial synthesis of selenium nanospheres using wet chemical approach." *Int J Nanotechnol Appl*. 2014, vol. 3, pp. 7-14.

THE STUDY OF THE HYDROGEL SYSTEMS WITH MICELLAR NANODOMAINS AND THE EFFECT OF THE PH CHANGES ON THEIR PROPERTIES

[1]Richard HEGER, [1]Filip MRAVEC, [1]Miloslav PEKAŘ

[1]*Brno University of Technology, Faculty of Chemistry, Brno, Czech Republic, EU,* xchegerr@fch.vutbr.cz

https://doi.org/10.37904/nanocon.2020.3734

Abstract

Interaction between polyelectrolyte and oppositely charged surfactant leads to a formation of a hydrogel with micellar nanodomains. The main focus of this work was to monitor and study how pH and its changes affect mainly mechanical properties of phase-separated hydrogels with micellar nanodomains. This work focuses on interaction of hyaluronan and Septonex (carbethoxypendecinium bromide). The studied pH range was 4-9. Rheology was the main technique to study the mechanical properties of the hydrogels. The rheology results were obtained for all prepared hydrogels at the pH range and as well for hydrogels that had changed pH after their preparation. The pH values were always changed to the limit values of the selected range, i.e. four and nine. The results show that the mechanical properties and partly the internal structure of hydrogels vary according to the pH of their dispersion medium. By changing the pH to limit values, it was possible to strengthen or soften the bonds within the hydrogel.

Keywords: Hydrogel, pH, rheology, hyaluronan, Septonex

1. INTRODUCTION

Interaction polyelectrolyte-surfactant is widely researched topic especially for its application potential. The phase separation method makes it possible to prepare physical hydrogels by the interaction of these substances. Hydrogels are known for their ability to absorb a huge amount of water into its structure and thus increase its volume. This fact is used especially in medical applications [1] and for example hydrogels are ideal candidates for use as a drug carrier. This carrier should guarantee a prolonged circulation of the drug and due to its specific structure release the drug slowly and gradually. Its structure also guarantees the passage of oxygen and others nutrients [2].

When working with hydrogels focused on medical applications that could come into contact with the human body, then the conditions that change in this way must be taken into account. One of these conditions is the pH value, which is a significant factor for all physical interactions. Whether it is the isoelectric point of amino acids, peptides or proteins at which they have total zero charge. It is also the maintenance of a constant pH that is one of the basic tasks of the internal environment [3].

The application of the hydrogel determines what pH value the hydrogel will be exposed to. The pH values of the human body varies considerably. When applied to the skin, the hydrogel may be exposed to pH in the range of 4 - 7.4 [4]. Upon ingestion, the hydrogel is immediately exposed to the pH of saliva (6.2 - 7.6) [5], then proceeds up to the stomach where it is exposed to a significantly more acidic pH (1.7 - 6.7) [6] and then the undigested residue would theoretically be exposed to pH 4 - 7 [7]. In case of vaginal application, it would get in contact with pH 3.5 - 4.3 [8].

The aim of this work was to monitor and describe changes in phase-separated hydrogels caused by a change of the pH value. The range of studied pH values correlates with the pH values that the hydrogel could encounter in the human body. As starting materials for formation of hydrogels by polyelectrolyte-surfactant interactions, a negatively charged polyelectrolyte was selected hyaluronan and the positively charged surfactant Septonex.

Characterization of the mechanical properties of the prepared hydrogels was performed using rheological methods. All the characteristics were compared between individual gels prepared at different pH values and as well for hydrogels that had changed pH after preparation. The pH values were always changed to the limit values of the selected range, i.e. four and nine.

2. MATERIALS AND METHODS

Hydrogels were prepared by mixing the powder substances and then adding the dispersion environment. As a negatively charged polyelectrolyte was used the sodium form of hyaluronan (HyA). In this study the hyaluronan was used at high molecular weight (1540 kDa). As a positively charged surfactant was used carbethopendecinium bromide (Septonex). Both of these substances were mixed together in the clear vial and dissolved in desired buffer. The contents of the vial were for thorough mixing placed on the Vortex shaker and mixed for a brief moment. Thus prepared hydrogel was left to stand for at least 24 hours. The ionic strength of all prepared hydrogels was adjusted to the same value with sodium chloride. Final concentrations of substances were 1 wt% for HyA and 100 mM for Septonex. Hydrogels were prepared at different pH values (4, 5, 6, 7, 8 and 9). The pH values were adjusted with buffers. Specifically these buffers were citrate-phosphate buffer and borax-hydrochloric acid buffer.

Rheology was the main technique to study the mechanical properties of these hydrogels. The rheology results were obtained for all prepared hydrogels at the pH range and as well for hydrogels that had changed pH after their preparation (i.e. 4 and 9). These gels were measured on the AR-G2 rheometer from TA Instruments. The measurement was performed using plate-plate geometry (a diameter of 8 mm, gap size 500 μm). After dosing the sample onto the instrument plate, few drops of silicone oil were added to the sample to prevent it from drying for the duration of the measurement. Before each measurement, a relaxation step was introduced, which allowed the sample to relax for five minutes at the set temperature of 25 °C. For the purposes of this work, strain sweep and frequency sweep tests were performed.

3. RESULTS AND DISCUSSION

3.1. Strain sweep tests

The first test that was performed was strain sweep test. This test makes possible to detect linear viscoelastic region (LVR). This area tells us where the moduli are independent on the amplitude of deformation. The dependence of the viscous and elastic moduli was determined at a constant frequency value and varying amplitude deformations. With this test we detected the LVR in the range of 0.01-32%. During the whole test the elastic modulus (G') prevailed, which indicates that it is a gel. This course and predominance of the elastic modulus were identical for all measured samples. From this range the value of the appropriate amplitude of deformation was chosen. The chosen value was 1% and this value falls into LVR of all samples. This value was used when setting up the instrument for the oscillation tests for all the samples.

From the value of the end of LVR it is possible to draw conclusions about the mechanical properties of the prepared hydrogels, more specifically the bond strength. These results are summarized in **Table 1**. The bigger the value of the end of LVR, the stronger bonds should be and longer resist the compression of the sensor. From the table below it is clear that the strongest gel was a sample prepared at pH 9. On the contrary, the softest was the gel prepared at pH 4, which, however, had very close results as other samples. The end of LVR for the other samples occurred at very similar values of amplitude of deformation, from which it can be deduced that these hydrogels are very similar and only the samples prepared at pH 9 differs significantly. Other values that we can find in the **Table 1** are the average values of the elastic (G') and viscous (G'') moduli in the LVR. The values of these moduli describe the amount of formed gel. Samples with higher moduli values produce more gel and vice versa. Samples with lower values of moduli absorb a larger amount of dispersion medium. According to the **Table 1,** the most of a gel should form in the sample prepared at pH 9 and gel prepared at pH7 should absorb the most dispersive medium.

Table 1 Data acquired from the strain sweep tests for all the gels prepared at different pH (end of LVR, G', G")

pH	End of LVR (%)	G' (Pa)	G" (Pa)
4	9.99	2370 ± 39	925 ± 45
5	14.69	2951 ± 48	1205 ± 30
6	10.03	1871 ± 18	792 ± 16
7	10.01	1145 ± 15	503 ± 7
8	14.69	3333 ± 29	1379 ± 17
9	31.84	4886 ± 57	701 ± 22

In **Table 2** we can find the end of LVR values for the samples with changed pH values. The values of the end of LVR were the highest in the samples that had changed pH to 9. All samples had almost the same LVR end, which means they all should have equally strong bonds. However these bonds should be weaker than the sample prepared at pH 9. Samples with the pH value changed to 4 had almost an identical LVR end value as a sample prepared at pH 4. The strange sample is the sample originally prepared at pH 7. According to the measured values it should have softer bonds than the original sample prepared at pH 4, because its LVR end value is the smallest. It can be explained that the sample, from which this hydrogel was derived before the pH change, had weaker bonds than other samples, which were based on hydrogels with stronger bonds. Comparison of the above mentioned can be seen in **Figure 1**.

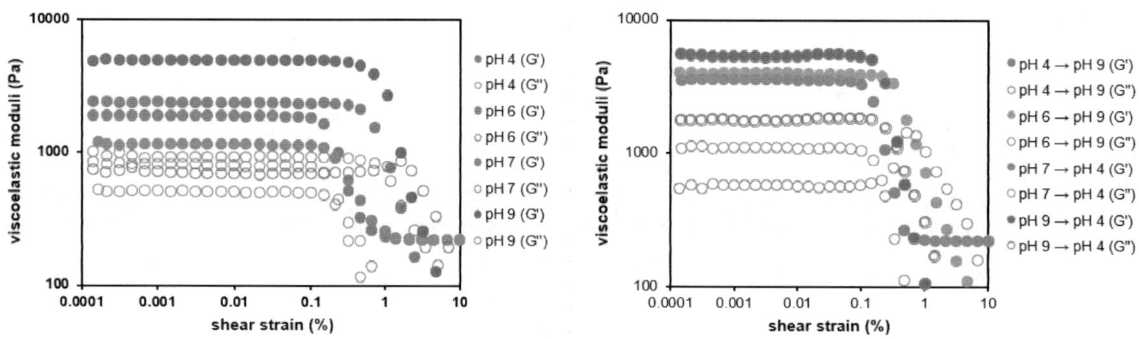

Figure 1 Dependence of viscoelastic moduli on amplitude of deformation for samples prepared at different pH value (left) and samples with changed pH environment (right)

Table 2 Data acquired from the strain sweep tests for all the gels witch exchanged pH (end of LVR, G', G")

pH	End of LVR (%)	G' (Pa)	G" (Pa)
4 → 9	14.71	3525 ± 44	511 ± 21
5 → 9	14.69	4369 ± 20	700 ± 12
6 → 9	14.67	3948 ± 45	570 ± 12
7 → 4	6.84	3559 ± 33	1110 ± 15
8 → 4	10.02	4203 ± 72	1297 ± 31
9 → 4	10.05	5320 ± 80	1778 ± 35

3.2. Frequency sweep tests

This test is another oscillatory test which measures the dependency of elastic and viscous moduli on the frequency of oscillations. These measurements take place at a constant value of the amplitude deformation and varying frequency of sensor oscillations. In the **Figure 2**, which is describing the course of dependence of viscoelastic moduli on the increasing frequency of oscillation for samples prepared at different values of pH and as well samples prepared with changed pH environment, can be observed gel behaviour. At the beginning of the measurement, the component of the viscous modulus prevailed and increasing the frequency of oscillation led to the point of intersection of the curves, so called cross-over point. Where the values of viscous (G'') and elastic (G') moduli are equal. In the beginning, the measurement deforms weak bonds and increasing frequency of oscillation deforms the strong bonds as well. This is indicated in the **Figure 2** by the steep rise of elastic modulus. Since the amplitude of deformation from the LVR was chosen for this measurement, it is elastic deformation and after stopping the oscillation, the sample would return to its original state.

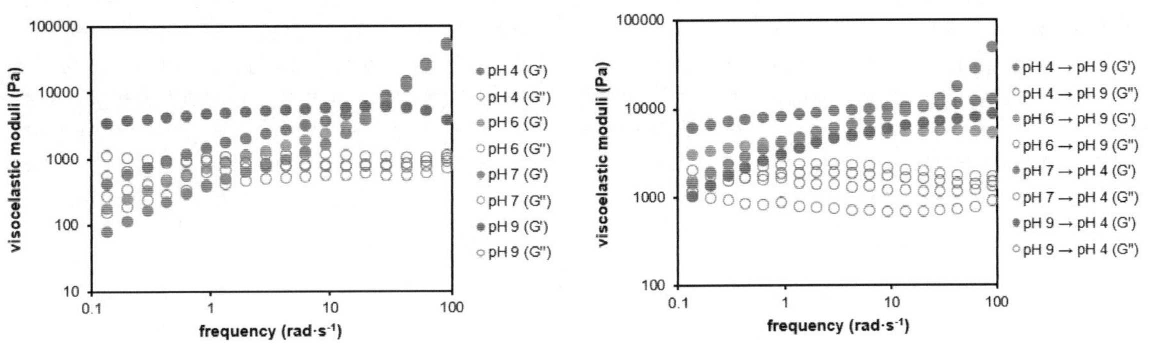

Figure 2 Dependence of viscoelastic moduli on frequency of oscillation for samples prepared at different pH values (left) and samples with changed pH environment (right)

Using the Rheology Advantage Data Analysis software, it was possible to record the frequency of oscillation and values of viscoelastic moduli at the cross-over point for all measured samples. These values are summarized in **Table 3**.

Table 3 Data acquired from frequency sweep test for all gels at different pH at cross-over point (frequency, viscoelastic moduli)

pH	Frequency (rad·s^{-1})	Viscoelastic moduli (Pa)
4	0.296	808
5	0.395	709
6	0.545	581
7	0.843	336
8	0.394	664
9	No cross-over point	

It can be seen from the **Table 3** that the modulus value, which corresponds with cross-over point that it was highest for the sample prepared at pH 4. The oscillation frequency value for this sample is on the contrary the smallest. This means that the elastic modulus (G') starts to prevail in the sample sooner than at the other samples. What can be further observed from the table is that the value of the modulus is gradually decreasing with increasing pH up to the sample prepared at pH 7. In this sample the lowest value of the module and highest value of the oscillation frequency were measured. That indicates that this sample should have the greatest distances between the individual nodes, which stabilize the structure. This is supported by the visual characterisation of this sample itself and the thermogravimetric tests, from which it was found that this sample is able to accept the largest amount of water. On the contrary it was with the sample prepared at pH 9. In this case the moduli G' and G" did not intersect in the measured range of the sample (**Figure 2**). Thus, in this sample predominates the elastic modulus. Unlike hydrogel prepared at pH 7, this hydrogel should have much smaller distances between individual nodes, which should indicate its impaired permeability. That was again supported by thermogravimetric measurements, from which it turned out that the sample was able to absorb the smallest amount of water.

In **Table 4**, the cross-over point values for the samples with exchanged pH values were recorded. Samples prepared at pH 4, 5 and 6 had their pH adjusted to 9. Samples prepared at pH 7, 8 and 9 had their pH changed to 4. Immediately it can be noted that the samples, which were changed to pH 9, did not have the cross-over point. This means that samples prepared at pH 4, 5 and 6, which had the cross-over point in their initial measured range, had their structure changed simply by changing the pH value of their environment. The fact that there is no cross-over point means that these samples are very similar to samples already prepared at pH 9. Conversely, at samples prepared at pH 7, 8 and 9, which had the pH of their environment changed to 4, we could observe increase of the viscoelastic moduli in the cross-over point above the values of original samples. The frequency of oscillation were lower than at the sample prepared at pH 4. This indicates that changing the pH will not convert the sample to a perfect copy of the sample prepared at pH 4, but that the structure retains some of the original bonds.

Table 4 Data acquired from the frequency sweep test for all the gels with exchanged pH at cross-over point (frequency, viscoelastic moduli)

pH	Frequency (rad·s^{-1})	Viscoelastic moduli (Pa)
4 → 9	No cross-over point	
5 → 9	No cross-over point	
6 → 9	No cross-over point	
7 → 4	0.179	1444
8 → 4	0.174	1045
9 → 4	0.199	1199

4. CONCLUSION

Twelve hydrogel samples were prepared to study the mechanical properties of hydrogels prepared by phase-separation. Six samples were prepared at the pH range 4-9 and the next six samples were prepared at the same pH values but they had their pH values of their environment changed before the measurement. In this work was presented detailed comparison of mechanical properties by rheological tests. First of all, the gels were studied by strain sweep tests which demonstrated that the softest hydrogel was prepared at pH 4 with very close values to gel at pH 5 and 6. The hardest gel was prepared at pH 9. From the results we could draw conclusion about the amount of prepared gel. According to the results the gel formed at pH 9 consisted of the largest amount of gel and conversely the smallest amount of absorbed water. In contrast the gel prepared at pH 7 consisted of the largest amount of absorbed water. Results for the altered pH values showed that the samples which changed to pH 9 all had the same strong bonds, but these bonds were weaker than the bonds of the sample originally prepared at pH 9. In contrast, the samples which had the pH changed to 4 all had equally strong bonds as sample prepared at pH 4.

Complementary results were obtained from frequency sweep tests. After comparing all the values of the cross-over points we found that the sample prepared at pH 7 had the greatest distances between individual nodes which stabilize the structure. This predestines it for the best and easiest water absorption. On the contrary for the hydrogel prepared at pH 9, the elastic and viscous moduli did not intersect. In this hydrogel the elastic modulus predominated and the distance between individual nodes is much smaller than for other gels. That's why this hydrogel has very low water permeability. In this direction, the hydrogel prepared at pH 9 appears to be an ideal candidate as s drug carrier with sustained release. For the altered results we recorded that all of cross-over point values were shifted by just the pH change. However these values were not identical to the values obtained for original hydrogels. This proves that a change in the pH after preparation can change the mechanical properties of hydrogels but at the same time, we do not create exact copies of original hydrogels. These result can be transferred to custom preparation of hydrogel depending on the application.

REFERENCES

[1] KIZILAY, E., KAYITMAZER, A.B., DUBIN, P.L. Complexation and coacervation of polyelectrolytes with oppositely charged colloids. *Advances in Colloid and Interface Science*. 2011, vol. 167, no. 1-2, pp 24-37.

[2] AMIN, S., RAJABNEZHAD, S., KOHLI, K. Hydrogels as potential drug delivery systems. *Scientific Research and Essay*. 2009, vol. 3, no. 11, pp 1175-1183.

[3] AHMED, E.M. Hydrogel: Preparation, characterization, and applications. *Journal of Advanced Research*. 2015, vol. 6, no. 2, pp. 105-121.

[4] DARGAVILLE, T.R., FARRUGIA, B.L., BROADBENT, J.A., PACE, S., UPTON, Z., VOELCKER, N.H. Sensors and imaging for wound healing: A review. *Biosensors and Bioelectronics*. 2013, vol. 41, pp. 30-42.

[5] BALIGA, S., MUGLIKAR, S., KALE, R. Salivary pH: A diagnostic biomarker. *Journal of Indian Society of Periodontology*. 2013, vol. 17, no. 4.

[6] DRESSMAN, J.B., BERARDI, R.R., DERMENTZOGLOU, L.C., RUSSEL, TL., SCHMALTZ, S.P., BARNETT, J.L., JARVENPAA, K.M. Upper Gastrointestinal (GI) pH in Young, Healthy Men and Women. *Pharmaceutical Research*.1990, vol. 7, no. 7, pp. 756-761.

[7] KOZIOLEK, M., GRIMM, M., BECKER, D., IORDANOV, V., ZOU, H., SHIMIZU, J., WANKE, C., GARBACZ, G., WEITSCHIES, W. Investigation of pH and Temperature Profiles in the GI Tract of Fasted Human Subjects Using the Intellicap® System. *Journal of Pharmaceutical Sciences*. 2015, vol. 104, no. 9, pp. 2855-2863.

[8] O'HANLON, D.E., COME, R.A., MOENCH, T.R. Vaginal pH measured in vivo: lactobacilli determine pH and lactic acid concentration. *BMC Microbiology*. 2019, vol. 19, no. 1.

SULPHUR PARTICLES IMMOBILIZED ON ACTIVATED POLYSTYRENE SURFACE

[1]Simona LUPÍNKOVÁ, [1]Jaroslava JAROLÍMKOVÁ, [1]Martin KORMUNDA, [1]Zdeňka KOLSKÁ

[1]J. E. Purkinje University in Usti nad Labem, Faculty of Science, Usti nad Labem, Czech Republic, EU, simona.lupinkova@email.cz

https://doi.org/10.37904/nanocon.2020.3735

Abstract

Materials with immobilized or entrapped nanoparticles are of considerable interest. Sulphur as one of the abundant elements on earth is cheap and environmentally friendly. In this work, we have studied the surface properties of polystyrene foil and changes of its surface properties after (i) activation by ultraviolet radiation and (ii) subsequent grafting with sulphur particles (SPs). We have also investigated the effect of surface pre-grafting with cysteamine on subsequent SPs grafting. SPs have been prepared by an acid catalyzed precipitation of sodium thiosulphate in the presence of sodium dodecyl sulphate as capping agent. The changes in surface properties of modified foils were characterized by contact angle measurement, electrokinetic analysis and X-ray photoelectron spectroscopy (XPS). The contact angle decreased after UV activation due to the formation of oxygen polar groups. The presence of sulphur and sodium on the polystyrene surface, revealed by XPS, showed that SPs were bound to this surface. The surface morphology of samples and grafted SPs size were examined by scanning electron microscopy. The significant changes in SPs agglomeration after grafting on surface were observed.

Keywords: Polystyrene, sulphur particles, surface modification, UV treatment, surface properties

1. INTRODUCTION

The modification of polymer surfaces by the covalent attachment of molecules, nanoparticles or microspheres has been an active topic of investigation in the field of surface sciences and has provided an opportunity to fabricate novel heterostructures with desired properties [1-3].

Sulphur is a widely used element in different applications such as fertilizers, pharmaceuticals, antimicrobial agents, insecticides and fumigants. Sulphur nano- and micro- particles have been examined for modification of metal and carbon nanotubes, synthesis of composites for lithium batteries, anti-cancer agent, antibacterial agent and as adsorbent for the extraction of metal ions [4,5].

The aim of our research was to bring an insight and understanding into the mechanism of UV activation of polymer surface and its subsequent functionalization with molecules and particles.

In this study, the sulphur particles (SPs) have been synthesized by quick precipitation method in the presence of sodium dodecyl sulphate (SDS) that was used as a stabilizer to control the SPs size. We have investigated size, size distribution and zeta potential of prepared particles by dynamic light scattering (DLS). We have also focused on the modification of polystyrene foil by UV radiation and subsequent grafting with stabilized sulphur particles (SDS-SPs). The surface properties (polarity, surface chemistry and structure) of polystyrene before and after modification were studied by various techniques (goniometry, electrokinetic analysis and X-ray photoelectron spectroscopy). Scanning electron microscopy was employed for imaging the microstructure and morphology of surface.

2. EXPERIMENTAL

2.1. Chemicals and materials

The chemicals used for this study were taken from the following companies: sodium thiosulfate pentahydrate ($Na_2S_2O_3 \cdot 5H_2O$, Lach:Ner, CZ), oxalic acid ($H_2C_2O_4 \cdot 2H_2O$, Lach:Ner, CZ), sodium dodecyl sulphate (SDS, Sigma-Aldrich, USA), cysteamine (cys, $HS(CH)_2)_2NH_2$, 98%, Sigma Aldrich, USA).

Polystyrene foil (PS, thickness 50 µm, biaxially oriented, GoodFellow Ltd., UK) was used for the experiments.

2.2. Particle synthesis

SPs were synthesized according to the method described in the work [3], with slight modifications. A mixture of sodium thiosulfate and SDS was prepared by combining 45 ml of 0.05 M $Na_2S_2O_3$ with 1 ml of 0.05 M SDS. The mixture was stirred mechanically at 350 rpm at room temperature (25°C). Then an appropriate amount of 0.3 Macid solution was added to the mixture under continuous stirring. A white precipitate was observed after a while; the reaction was stopped after 40 min. The particles suspension was centrifuged and washed with distilled water. The obtained precipitate was dispersed in distilled water for subsequent modification of PS samples.

2.3. Surface modification of polystyrene

PS foil was activated by UV radiation for 15, 30, 45 or 60 minutes using UV lamp with wavelength 254 nm. Immediately after activation the samples were inserted into 1% aqueous solution of cysteamine. After 24 hours the samples were rinsed with distilled water and inserted to the SPs solution for 24 hours. After this time, samples were rinsed with distilled water and allowed to air dry.

2.4. Samples characterization

The zeta potential and the particle size of prepared SPs were determined by dynamic light scattering using LitesizerTM 500 (Anton Paar, AUT). Values were determined at room temperature, with a semiconductor laser, 40 mW, 658 nm, at constant pH with repeatability of 10 %. The particles were analyzed immediately after being prepared.

Surface properties of the PS samples (pristine, activated, or grafted) were studied using the following methods:

Tensile strength test was used to evaluate mechanical properties of PS samples before and after UV activation using testing machine LabTest 6.050 (Labortech, CZ). Samples were cut in the longitudinal and transverse direction. The tensile strength was calculated from the maximum stretching force at break divided by the original cross-sectional area of the sample (width × thickness).

The surface morphology was investigated using scanning electron microscopy (SEM, VEGA, Tescan, CZ). Measurements were carried out using secondary electron imaging mode with acceleration voltage 20 kV. The samples were sputtered by a 20 nm thick gold layer to eliminate surface charging.

The contact angle characterizing surface wettability was determined by the sessile drop technique employing a goniometer DSA30 (KRÜSS GmbH, DE). Droplets of volume (2.00 ± 0.05) µl were positioned at the centre of the surface of samples. The values of contact angle were evaluated automatically by ADVANCE software.

Zeta potential of pristine and modified PS samples was accomplished on SurPASS Instrument (Anton Paar, AUT). Samples were fixed on two sample holders (size 2 × 1 cm^2 and gap between 100 µm) and placed inside the adjustable gap cell in contact with the electrolyte (0.001 mol·dm^3 KCl). All samples were measured four times at constant pH value (6.5) with the relative error of 10 %. The streaming current method was applied for the determination of the zeta potential.

For surface elemental analysis there was used X-ray photoelectron spectroscopy. The high vacuum chamber was equipped with source SPECS X-Ray XR50, where Al cathode (1486.6 eV) was used, and with a hemispherical analyzer SPECS PHOIBOS 100 with 5-channels detector.

3. RESULTS AND DISCUSSION

SPs were synthesized by redox reaction of $Na_2S_2O_3 \cdot 5H_2O$ in oxalic acid and using sodium dodecyl sulphate (SDS) as stabilizer. Sample preparation for DLS analysis was carried out by diluting 100 µl of the colloidal solution containing SPs to 1 ml with distilled water. **Figure 1A** shows size distribution of SPs. SPs are distributed homogeneously within the solution, the mean size of 188.6 nm with the standard deviation of 26.7 nm. **Figure 1B** shows the zeta-potential distribution for SPs at their natural pH. The SDS-SPs appear to be negatively charged with the mean value of (-66.7 ± 2.1) eV, SDS is an anionic surfactant with carbon chain structure [6].

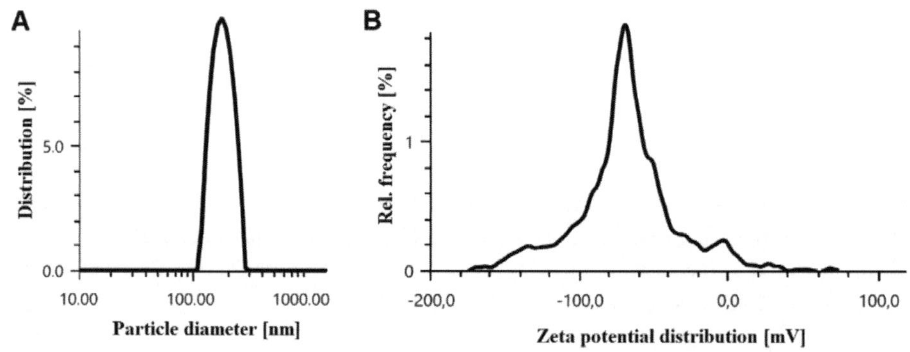

Figure 1 Particle size distribution (A) and zeta potential (B) of freshly prepared SDS-SPs

The tensile test was conducted to evaluate the effect of UV radiation on the mechanical properties of PS foil. The results presented in **Figure 2** show the tensile properties of unmodified PS foil are the same in both directions. It is assumed that UV radiation can destroy the polymeric chains [7] and can decrease the tensile strength of polymer foils. The results demonstrated that the tensile strength in transverse direction was not significantly affected by UV radiation. Contrary to longitudinal direction, where the decrease of tensile strength after 30 min of exposure is noticeable.

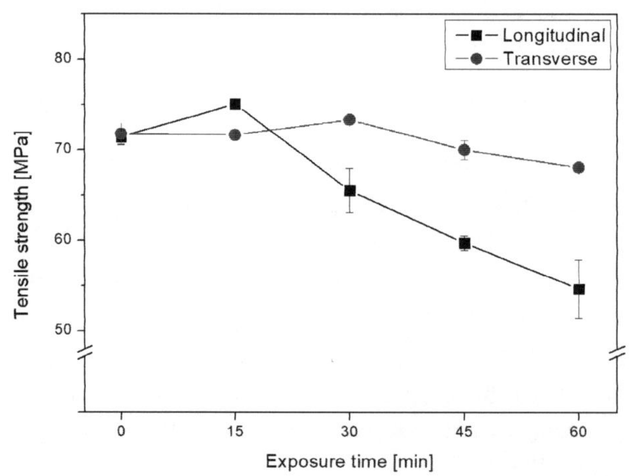

Figure 2 Effect of UV irradiation on tensile strength of PS samples

The morphology and the size of SDS-SPs after grafting on UV treated PS were characterized using scanning electron microscopy (SEM). The SEM micrographs, presented in **Figure 3**, show that grafting of SPs on polymer surface results in SPs aggregation with a size of a few micrometers. This effect is probably caused by high surface free energy of PS after UV treatment [8]. However, it is apparent that cysteamine pre-grafting reduces the SDS-SPs aggregation and lead to more homogenous distribution over the polymer surface. It was also found that the amount and change in aggregation of SPs grafted on the polymer surface strongly depends on the UV exposure time. Substrates exposed to UV light by shorter time (15 min) resulted in small number of grafted SPs than substrates modified with times 30-60 min. Otherwise, significant changes in SPs aggregation was observed for substrates modified for a longer time (60 min).

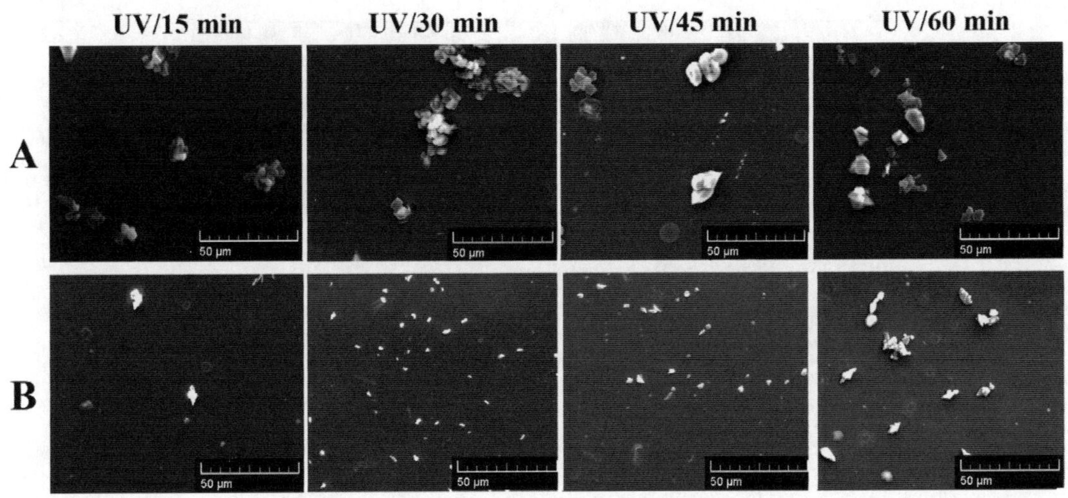

Figure 3 Scanning electron microscopy (SEM) images of SDS-SPs grafted on UV-activated PS surface (A), UV-activated PS surface pre-grafted with cysteamine (B)

UV treatment is a very clean and effective method for activation of inert polymer surface inducing chemical and structural changes, cleavage of bonds and creation of oxygen-containing and reactive groups [7]. All these processes have a significant effect on contact angle.

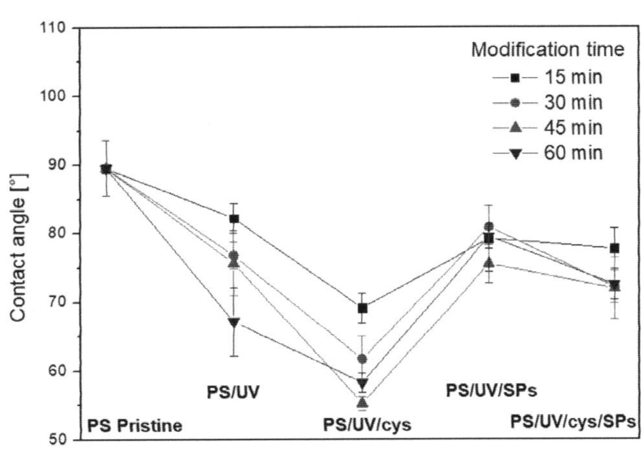

Figure 4 Contact angles of unmodified PS foil (PS Pristine) and after individual steps of modification, after UV exposure (PS/UV) and after subsequent grafting of either cysteamine (PS/UV/cys) or SDS-SPs (PS/UV/SPs) or both (PS/UV/cys/SPs)

Figure 4 presents the results of the contact angle measurement of PS foil before and after individual modification steps. All samples after UV exposure exhibit decrease of contact angle caused by creation of oxygen-containing groups on activated surface [9]. The presence of oxygen groups has also been confirmed by XPS determination discussed below. Samples modified by UV for longer time (60 min) had significantly lower values of contact angle (CA = 67°) compared with samples exposed for a shorter time (15 min, CA = 82°). Contact angle of all samples decreased with increasing UV exposure time. The subsequent cysteamine grafting led to even more hydrophilic surface, on the other hand SDS-SPs grafting caused an increase of contact angle. In comparison with unmodified PS (CA = 90°), all modification steps led to more hydrophilic surface.

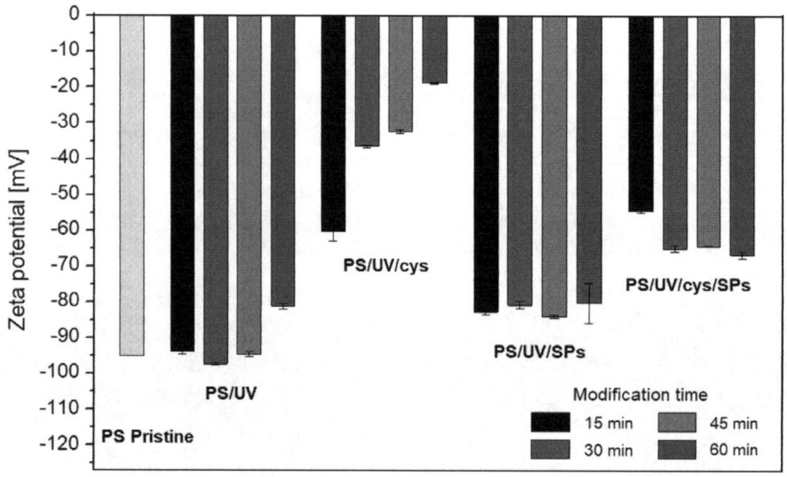

Figure 5 Zeta potential of unmodified PS foil (PS Pristine) and after individual steps of modification, after UV exposure (PS/UV) and after subsequent grafting of either cysteamine (PS/UV/cys) or SDS-SPs (PS/UV/SPs) or both (PS/UV/cys/SPs)

The zeta potential values before and after individual modification steps are presented in **Figure 5**. As it is evident, the polymer surface properties affect the value of zeta potential and the zeta potential changes after UV treatment and after cysteamine and SDS-SPs grafting. UV radiation causes mild changes of zeta potential due to creation of new polar groups and reactive sites on the surface, most significant change was observed at sample exposed for a longer time (60 min). The grafting of cysteamine results in a less negative zeta potential, due to the presence of amino- groups, which creates a positive charge on the polymer surface in the presence of electrolyte. Significant differences in values, depending on UV exposure time (increasing zeta potential of PS/UV/cys with increasing time) may be caused by different amount of grafted cysteamine and/or different way of cysteamine bonding to surface (via -SH or $-NH_2$ group) [10]. All these changes in zeta potential values indicate reliably the successful grafting of cysteamine and SDS-SPs on PS surface.

Table 1 Elemental concentration in at.% for PS foils as measured by XPS

Sample	C 1s	O 1s	N 1s	S 2p	Na 1s
PS Pristine	100.0	-	-	-	-
PS/UV (30 min)	93.1	6.9	-	-	-
PS/UV/cys	89.8	7.3	1.9	1.0	-
PS/UV/SPs	92.3	7.2	-	0.4	0.1
PS/UV/cys/SPs	87.6	9.0	2.0	1.3	0.1

The elemental composition of the surface of pristine, UV-activated PS for 30 min, and subsequently grafted with cysteamine and/or with SDS-SPs was determined from XPS spectra. The resulting concentrations (in at.%) are shown in **Table 1**. UV treatment results in cleavage of bonds in polymer chains and production of free radicals. This causes the oxidation of polymer surface and incorporation of oxygen polar groups, which is detected as an increase of oxygen concentration (from 0 % to 6.9 %) in XPS spectra. This result was also confirmed by goniometry and electrokinetic analysis. Grafting of cysteamine leads to increase of nitrogen and sulphur on the polymer surface, in the case of SDS-SPs, sulphur and small amount of sodium is observed.

4. CONCLUSION

New nanocomposite consisting of polymer (PS) and SDS-capped sulfur particles was prepared. The SPs were synthesized using oxalic acid and sodium thiosulfate in the presence of SDS. A mean particles size was 188.6 ± 26.7 nm as determined by DLS. UV treatment, cysteamine and SPs grafting cause changes in surface charge, chemistry and polarity of PS. UV radiation leads to decrease of contact angle and higher hydrophilicity of polymer. The SEM results showed that significant agglomeration of grafting SPs takes place during the process. Cysteamine pre-grafting significantly reduced SPs agglomeration and led to more homogenous distribution over the polystyrene surface. UV exposure time strongly affects the amount and agglomeration of grafted SPs. These findings may be of importance for advance research and development of new composite materials composed of polymers and nanoparticles.

ACKNOWLEDGEMENTS

This work was supported by GACR under Project 20-01768S, by the Grant Agency of J. E. Purkyně University in Usti nad Labem under project UJEP-SGS-2020-53-007-2, by ERDF/ESF Project „UniQSurf - Centre of biointerfaces and hybrid functional materials" (No. CZ.02.1.01/0.0/0.0/17_048/0007411) and the Research Infrastructure NanoEnviCz, supported by the Ministry of Education, Youth and Sports of the Czech Republic under Project No. LM2015073.

REFERENCES

[1] HETEMI, D., PINSON, J. Surface functionalisation of polymers. *Chem. Soc. Rev.* 2017, vol. 46, p. 5701.

[2] KVITEK, O., REZNICKOVA, A., ZELENAKOVA, A., ZELENAK, V., ORENDAC, M., SVORCIK, V. Immobilization of Fe@Au superparamagnetic nanoparticles on polyethylene. *Eur. Polym. J.* 2019, vol. 110, p. 56.

[3] GODDARD, J.M., HOTCHKISS, J.H. Polymer surface modification for the attachment of bioactive compounds. *Prog. Polym. Sci.* 2007, vol. 32, p. 698.

[4] CHAUDHURI, R.G., PARIA, S. Synthesis of sulfur nanoparticles in aqueous surfactant solutions. *J. Colloid Interface Sci.* 2010, vol. 343, p. 439.

[5] XIE, X., DENG, R., PANG, Y., BAI, Y., ZHENG, W., ZHOU, Y. Adsorption of copper(II) by sulfur microparticles. *Chem. Eng. J.* 2017, vol. 314, p. 434.

[6] SULEIMAN, M., AL-MASRI, M., AL ALI, A., AREF, D., HUSSEIN, A., SAADEDDIN, I., WARAD, I. Synthesis of nano-sized sulfur nanoparticles and their antibacterial activities. *J. Mater. Environ. Sci.* 2015, vol. 6, p. 513.

[7] EVE, S., MOHR, J. Study of the surface modification of the PMMA by UV-radiation. *Procedia Eng.* 2009, vol. 1, p. 237.

[8] LUPÍNKOVÁ, S., KAIMLOVÁ, M., KORMUNDA, M., KOLSKÁ, Z. Chitosan-capped sulfur microparticles grafted on UV-treated PET surface. *Surf. Interface Anal.* 2021, vol. 53, p. 108.

[9] KASAHARA, T., SHOJI, S., MIZUNO, J., Surface Modification of Polyethylene Terephthalate (PET) by 172-nm Excimer Lamp. *J. Japan Inst. Electron. Packag.* 2012, vol. 5, pp. 47.

[10] KNAPOVA, T., MATOUSEK, J., KOLAROVA, K., SLEPICKA, P., SICHA, V., TROGL, J., KOLSKÁ, Z. Nanostructured Surface and Antimicrobial Properties of Chemically Modified Polymer Foils. *ChemistrySelect.* 2019, vol. 4, pp. 4382-4391.

SESSION D
MONITORING AND TOXICITY OF NANOMATERIALS

Chairman

Dr. Jan TOPINKA Institute of Experimental Medicine of the CAS, Prague, Czech Republic, EU

TOXIC RESPONSES IN HUMAN LUNG EPITHELIAL CELLS (BEAS-2B) EXPOSED TO PARTICULATE MATTER EXHAUST EMISSIONS FROM GASOLINE AND BIOGASOLINE

[1]Táňa ZÁVODNÁ, [2]Helena LÍBALOVÁ, [1]Kristýna VRBOVÁ, [1]Jitka SIKOROVÁ, [3]Michal VOJTÍŠEK-LOM, [3]Vít BERÁNEK, [3]Martin PECHOUT, [4]Jiří KLÉMA, [5]Miroslav CIGANEK, [5]Miroslav MACHALA, [5]Jiří NEČA, [2]Pavel RÖSSNER Jr., [1]Jan TOPINKA

[1]Department of Nanotoxicology and Molecular Epidemiology, Institute of Experimental Medicine AS CR, Prague, Czech Republic, EU,
helena.libalova@iem.cas.cz, kristyna.vrbova@iem.cas.cz, pavel.rossner@iem.cas.cz

[2]Department of Genetic toxicology and Epigenetics, Institute of Experimental Medicine AS CR, Prague, Czech Republic, EU, tana.brzicova@iem.cas.cz, jitkastolcpartova@seznam.cz, jan.topinka@iem.cas.cz

[3]Center of Vehicles for Sustainable Mobility, Faculty of Mechanical Engineering, Czech Technical University in Prague, Prague, Czech Republic, EU,
michal.vojtisek@fs.cvut.cz, vit.beranek@fs.cvut.cz, pechout@tf.czu.cz

[4]Department of Cybernetics, Faculty of Electrical Engineering, Czech Technical University in Prague, Prague, Czech Republic, EU, klema@fel.cvut.cz

[5]Department of Chemistry and Toxicology, Veterinary Research Institute, Brno, Czech Republic, EU,
ciganek@vri.cz, machala@vri.ca, neca@vri.cz

https://doi.org/10.37904/nanocon.2020.3763

Abstract

Motor vehicle emissions substantially contribute to air pollution worldwide and cause serious health problems. While the deleterious effects of diesel exhaust particulate matter (PM) have been widely studied, much less attention is paid to toxicity of PM emitted by gasoline engines although they also produce considerable amount of PM. The primary objective of this research was to assess toxic potencies of exhaust PM released by conventional gasoline engine fueled with neat gasoline (E0) or gasoline-ethanol blend (15% ethanol, v/v, E15). Despite a similar particle mass (µg PM/kg fuel) produced by both fuels, PM emitted by E15 contained higher amount of harmful polycyclic aromatic hydrocarbons (PAH) as suggested by chemical analysis. To examine the toxicity of organic PM constituents, human lung BEAS-2B cells were exposed for 4h and 24h to a subtoxic dose of E0 and E15 PM organic extracts. We used genome scale transcriptomic analysis to characterize the toxic response and to identify modulated biological process and pathways. Whereas 4h exposure to both PM extracts resulted in modulation of similar genes and pathways related to lipid and steroid metabolism, activation of PPARα, oxidative stress and immune response, 24h exposure was more specific for each extract; although both induced expression of PAH-metabolic enzymes, modulated metabolism of lipids or activated PPARα, E15 additionally deregulated variety of other pathways. Overall, the PM mass produced by both fuels was similar, however, higher PAH content in E15 PM organic extract may have contributed to more extensive toxic response particularly after 24h exposure in BEAS-2B cells.

Keywords: Particulate matter emissions, gasoline, biofuels, toxicity, gene expression profiling

1. INTRODUCTION

Motor vehicle emissions substantially contribute to air pollution worldwide. They represent an important source of particulate matter (PM). Numerous scientific studies have linked PM exposure to various health effects including pulmonary and cardiovascular disorders or cancer [1]. Combustion-related PM consists of relatively high concentrations of toxic substances bound on the particle surface. Among them, polycyclic aromatic hydrocarbons (PAHs) play an important role in PM toxicity [2]. Of special concern are ultrafine particles (<100 nm) because they can deposit deep into the lungs, enter the bloodstream and reach other organs [3]. Compared to coarse (>2,5 µm) or fine (100 nm-2,5 µm) PM, ultrafine particles exhibit a large surface area that allows them to carry a relatively large load of toxic compounds. For many years, diesel engines dominated among the mobile sources responsible for negative environmental issues and adverse health effects associated with PM exposure. However, modern gasoline engines recently emerged as important contributors to traffic related particulate pollution [4]. Increasing demands for the replacement of conventional fossil fuels with alternatives produced from renewable sources have raised an interest in numerous biofuels and their blends. Ethanol is the most commonly used bio additive for gasoline. Despite this fact, studies on the comparative toxicity of particulate emissions or their organic extracts from fossil gasoline and gasoline-ethanol blends are still scarce. The present study aimed to compare the toxic effects of organic complex mixtures extracted from particulate emissions produced by a passenger car fueled with neat gasoline (E0) or ethanol-gasoline blend (E15). To achieve this, we employed genome-scale mRNA expression profiling as a sensitive method to monitor the complex molecular response and thus reveal deregulated genes, processes and pathways.

2. METHODS

2.1. PM collection, extraction of organic compounds and chemical analysis

A 2011 Skoda Fabia 1.4 16V, 5MT, MPI was driven on four-wheel chassis dynamometer MAHA AIP-ECDM 48L-4mot along basic driving cycle the Common Artemis Driving Cycle (motorway variant 130 km.h-1). The exhaust has been routed into a fullflow dilution tunnel with a constant volume sampler (CVS) operating at 10.8 m3.min-1. Particles were sampled on teflon-coated glass fiber filters (Pall TX40HI20-WW), at 67.8 m3.h-1 sampling rate. Organic compounds were extracted with dichloromethane and both E0 and E15 extracts were subjected to chemical analysis and PAH contaminants were quantified. The procedure is described elsewhere [5].

2.2. Cell cultures, exposure conditions, RNA isolation and microarray analysis

BEAS-2B cells were exposed to 50 µg/mL of each extract for 4 and 24h. Cell viability was assessed using WST-1 and LDH assays. RNA from cell lysates was extracted and the integrity of RNA was analyzed using Agilent 2100 Bioanalyzer. RNA was then transcribed into biotinylated complementary DNA and hybridized onto Human-HT12 v4 Expression BeadChips (Illumina). The detailed protocol is presented in [5].

3. RESULTS

3.1. Characteristics of collected gasoline PM and chemical analysis of organic extracts

Total particulate mass emissions (expressed in µg per kg of fuel) produced by the tested vehicle was comparable for both E0 and E15 fuels. However, the number of particles > 20 nm was app. 40 times higher for E15 than for E0 and also chemical analysis revealed that the sum of all analyzed PAHs and their derivatives such as oxy-, nitro- or dinitro-PAHs in E15 extract was several fold higher than in E0 extract (**Table 1**).

Table 1 PM characteristics and PAH content in fuel extracts

	E0	**E15**
PM (µg/kg of fuel)	112.2	110.3
Particle number (per driving cycle)	6.23×10^5	2.56×10^7
Sum of PAHs (ng/mg PM)	579.0	1944.2
Sum of cPAHs (ng/mg PM)	203.5	887.6
Sum of oxygenated PAHs (ng/mg PM)	368.4	477.9
Sum of nitrated PAHs (pg/mg PM)	1117.8	684.0
Sum of dinitrated PAHs (pg/mg PM)	21.1	14.7

3.2. Gene expression profiling

3.2.1. Differential expression of individual genes

Four-hour incubation of BEAS-2B cells with both extracts resulted in deregulation of 13 common genes while 5 deregulated genes were specific for E0 and 22 genes for E15 treatment (**Figure 1A**). After 24h exposure, we found 42 common significantly deregulated genes, 29 genes specific for E15 and 77 genes for E0 treatment (**Figure 1B**).

A)

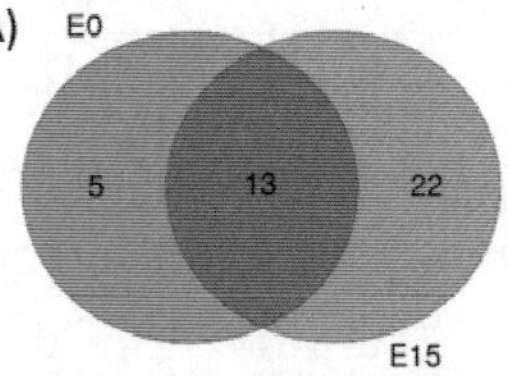

Numbers of deregulated genes (4h)

	E0	E15	E0+E15
Total	5	22	13
Up↑	3	4	5
Down↓	2	18	8

B)

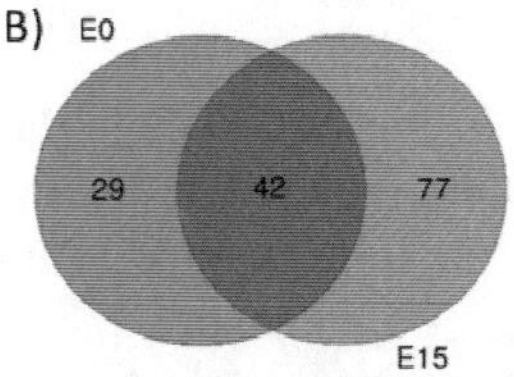

Numbers of deregulated genes (24h)

	E0	E15	E0+E15
Total	29	77	42
Up↑	11	30	22
Down↓	18	47	20

Figure 1 Venn diagrams illustrating the number of significantly deregulated genes for E0 and E15 and their overlap after A) 4h and b) 24h exposure (p-value < 0.05, fold change > 1.5 and < 0.67)

3.2.2. Pathway analysis

In order to reveal modulated biological processes and signaling pathways, we analyzed differentially expressed genes using ToppFun, a tool providing transcriptome, ontology, phenotype, proteome and pharmacome annotations based gene list functional enrichment analysis (https://toppgene.cchmc.org/). After 4h exposure, both extracts deregulated a variety of pathways related to cellular lipid metabolism and homeostasis, steroid hormone biosynthesis or Sterol Regulatory Element Binding Protein (SREBP) signaling. We further identified modulated pathways associated with Peroxisome proliferator-activated receptor alpha (PPARα) signaling or pathways indicating oxidative stress response and alterations in immune functions (**Table 2**). Each individual extract treatment also affected a range of specific pathways (**Table 3** and **Table 4**).

Table 2 Top 5 common deregulated pathways with contributing genes after 4h exposure to both extracts

Pathway	Source (Biosystem)	E0	E15
Metabolism of lipids and lipoproteins	REACTOME	↑*TXNRD1, AKR1C2* ↓*LDLR, CTGF, COQ5, HMGCS1, INSIG1*	↑*TXNRD1, AKR1C2* ↓*LPIN1, CTGF, HMGCR, HMGCS1, IDH1, SC5DL, LDLR, INSIG1, SQLE, NSDHL*
Regulation of cholesterol biosynthesis by SREBP (SREBF)	REACTOME	↓*HMGCS1, INSIG1*	↓*HMGCR, HMGCS1, SC5DL, INSIG1, SQLE*
NFkB activation by Nontypeable Hemophilus influenzae	MSigDB C2 BIOCARTA (v6.0)	↓*IL8, NFKBIA*	↓*TGFBR2, IL8, NFKBIA*
Validated transcriptional targets of AP1 family members Fra1 and Fra2	Pathway Interaction Database	↑*TXNRD1* ↓*CTGF, HMGCS1*	↑*HMOX1, FOSL1* ↓*IL8*
PPARA activates gene expression	REACTOME	↑*HMOX1* ↓*IL8*	↑*TXNRD1* ↓*CTGF, HMGCR, HMGCS1*

Table 3 Top five specific deregulated pathways with contributing genes after 4h exposure to E15 extract

Pathway	Source (Biosystem)	E15
cholesterol biosynthetic	Pathway Ontology	↓*HMGCR, HMGCS1, SC5DL, SQLE, NSDHL*
mevalonate pathway	BIOCYC	↓*HMGCR, HMGCS1*
IL-17 signaling pathway	KEGG	↑*FOSL1* ↓*IL8, NFKBIA*
NADPH regeneration	REACTOME	↓*IDH1*
Fluid shear stress and atherosclerosis	KEGG	↑*HMOX1, CTSL1* ↓*KLF2*

Table 4 Top five specific deregulated pathways with contributing genes after 4h exposure to E0 extract

Pathway	Source (Biosystem)	E0
Ferroptosis	KEGG	↑*GCLM, HMOX1*
Fas Signaling Pathway	MSigDB C2 BIOCARTA (v6.0)	↓*IL8, NFKBIA*
LPA receptor mediated events	Pathway Interaction Database	↓*IL8, NFKBIA*
Glutathione biosynthesis, glutamate => glutathione	KEGG	↑*GCLM*
Atherosclerosis	Pathway Ontology	↓*LDLR*

Twenty-four hour exposure resulted in more distinct expression profiles. Whereas several pathways deregulated by both extracts were similar to those modulated after 4h exposure (lipid metabolism, SREBP signaling, PPARα signaling), others (allopregnanolone biosynthesis, interleukin-1 processing) were specific for 24h exposure only (**Table 5**). E0 specifically modulated pathways related to metabolism of steroids and xenobiotics (**Table 6**) while E15 rather affected a large variety of pathways linked to lipid and sterol metabolism, extracellular matrix assembly and organization, cell junction and communication or MAPK signaling associated with cellular stress (**Table 7**).

Table 5 Top 5 common deregulated pathways with contributing genes after 24h exposure to both extracts

Pathway	Source (Biosystem)	E0	E15
Steroid hormone biosynthesis	KEGG	↑*CYP1A1, CYP1B1, AKR1C4, AKR1C2*	↑*CYP1B1, AKR1C4, AKR1C2* ↓*HSD17B8*
Metabolism of lipids and lipoproteins	REACTOME	↑*TXNRD1, MED24, CYP1A1, CYP1B1, AKR1C4, AKR1C2, ANGPTL4* ↓*PPARGC1A, TM7SF2, FADS2, LSS, COL4A3BP*	↑*AKR1C4, AKR1C2, MED24, ANGPTL4, CYP1B1* ↓*TECR, HMGCR, HMGCS1, NSDHL, LPIN1, PPARGC1A, FDFT1, SLC25A1, EBP, TM7SF2, LSS, MVD, DBI, HSD17B8, PCSK9*
PPARA activates gene expression	REACTOME	↑*TXNRD1, MED24, CYP1A1, ANGPTL4* ↓*PPARGC1A*	↑*MED24, ANGPTL4* ↓*HMGCR, HMGCS1, PPARGC1A, FDFT1*
allopregnanolone biosynthesis	BIOCYC	↑*AKR1C4, AKR1C2*	↑*AKR1C4, AKR1C2*
Interleukin-1 processing	REACTOME	↑*IL1A, IL1B*	↑*IL1A, IL1B*

Table 6 Top specific deregulated pathways with contributing genes after 24h exposure to E15 extract

Pathway	Source (Biosystem)	E15
Fatty acid, triacylglycerol, and ketone body metabolism	REACTOME	↑*MED24, ANGPTL4* ↓*TECR, HMGCR, HMGCS1, LPIN1, PPARGC1A, FDFT1, SLC25A1, DBI, HSD17B8*
Assembly of collagen fibrils and other multimeric structures	REACTOME	↑*LAMA3, LAMB3, LAMC2, CTSL1* ↓*COL8A1*
Laminin interactions	REACTOME	↑*LAMA3, LAMB3, LAMC2*
Degradation of the extracellular matrix	REACTOME	↑*LAMA3, LAMB3, LAMC2, CTSL1* ↓*CDH1*
MAPK signaling pathway	KEGG	↑*MYC, RPS6KA2, DUSP6, IL1A, IL1B* ↓*STMN1, FGFR3*

Table 7 Top specific deregulated pathways with contributing genes after 24h exposure to E0 extract

Pathway	Source	E0
bioactivation via cytochrome P450	Pathway Ontology	↑*CYP1A1, CYP1B1*
Synthesis of epoxy (EET) and dihydroxyeicosatrienoic acids (DHET)	BioSystems: REACTOME	↑*CYP1A1, CYP1B1*
Synthesis of (16-20)-hydroxyeicosatetraenoic acids (HETE)	BioSystems: REACTOME	↑*CYP1A1, CYP1B1*
gamma-hexachlorocyclohexane degradation	Pathway Ontology	↑*CYP1A1, CYP1B1*

4. DISCUSSION

Our results demonstrated that the mass of particulate emissions was not substantially affected by the supplementation of gasoline fuel with 15% ethanol. This is in line with our previous study [5] where we observed similar PM mass emitted by E0 and E15 although different engine technology (GDI) was used. On the other hand, in the recent study [6], authors reported that ethanol rather reduced the mass of PM. Such inconsistency might be caused by many factors including differences among engine design, calibration, settings and operating conditions. Importantly, despite similar particle mass, E15 produced much higher particle number comparing to E0 indicating generation of harmful ultrafine particles (<100 nm). This finding correlates with the higher concentration of PAHs in E15 organic extract as revealed by chemical analysis. Gene expression profiling revealed numerous processes similarly deregulated processes after 4h exposure to both E0 and E15 extract. Suppression of lipid metabolism and cholesterol synthesis was evident due to the downregulation of key contributing genes HMGCR, HMGCS1 and others. It has been demonstrated that PAHs repress genes involved in cholesterol biosynthesis and disrupt lipid homeostasis through an activated aryl hydrocarbon receptor (AhR) [7]. Both extracts further triggered oxidative stress response, possibly due high amount of ROS released during metabolism of PAHs or by other redox-active organic compounds. HMOX1 and TXNRD1 are key redox-sensitive enzymes that neutralize ROS and help to maintain redox homeostasis. Both enzymes are regulated by NRF2 transcription factor that controls a variety of processes responsible for cellular defense against xenobiotic and oxidative stress [8]. Oxidative stress and antioxidant response may also negatively regulate expression and activity of PPARα [9] as also indicated by our results. Specific effects of E15 extract treatment involve downregulation of IDH1, one of the key enzymes in NADPH regeneration with the citrate cycle. It has been shown that PAHs also involve alterations of mitochondrial functions and decrease gene expression of mitochondrial enzymes including IDH1 in multiple organs [10]. Twenty four hour exposure was characterized by metabolism of PAHs and activation of AhR. Upregulation of CYP1B1, AKR1C2 and AKR1C4 was common for both extracts while expression of CYP1A1 was elevated after E0 extract treatment only. CYP1 enzymes participate in the metabolic activation of PAHs and formation of reactive intermediates which form stable DNA adducts. Other enzymes, such as AKRs, are also implicated in PAH activation and generate redox-active PAH *o*-quinones accompanied with formation of ROS [11]. Similarly as for 4h exposure, suppressed metabolism of lipids and cholesterol as well as PPARα signaling was observed. Increased expression of IL1A and IL1B indicated immune response associated with genotoxic and oxidative stress [12]. In contrast to E0, E15 extract modulated a variety of pathways related to extracellular matrix. The role of PAHs in extracellular matrix remodeling has been proposed [13]. E15 further activated MAPK signaling which is known to regulate various cell functions such as proliferation, gene expression, differentiation, mitosis, cell survival, and apoptosis in response to diverse stimuli including oxidative and genotoxic stress. It has been suggested that PAHs in nanomolar levels are able to induce MAPKs [14].

5. CONCLUSIONS

Although E0 produced similar mass of PM as E15, the number of particles was much higher for E15 than for E0 indicating generation of particularly toxic ultrafine particles. Accordingly, chemical analysis revealed a higher content of PAHs in E15 extract. The toxic effects of E0 and E15 extracts in BEAS-2B cells were mostly associated with the action of PAHs and activated AhR. Four-hour incubation with both extracts resulted in many identically deregulated processes, such as suppression of lipid metabolism and PPARα signaling or oxidative stress response. On the other hand, response to 24h exposure was more diverse, besides common processes, such as activation of AhR and metabolism of PAHs, suppressed lipid metabolism, activation of PPARα- or IL1-dependent immune response, E15 extract specifically induced a large variety of pathways related to extracellular matrix assembly or MAPK signaling. In contrast, only few specific pathways were found after 24h treatment with E0 extract. Taken together, E15 extract elicited a more extensive toxic response particularly after 24h treatment than E0 extract, possibly due to the higher content of PAHs. These findings may help to explore the impact of PM emissions generated by alternative gasoline fuels on human health.

ACKNOWLEDGEMENTS

This work was supported by Czech Science Foundation (project no. 18-06548Y) and MEYS CR (project no. LM2015073).

REFERENCES

[1] ENGLERT N. Fine particles and human health--a review of epidemiological studies. *Toxicology Letters*. 2004, vol. 149, no. 1-3, pp. 235-42.

[2] REKELLY, F. J., FUSSELL, J. C. Size, source and chemical composition as determinants of toxicity attributable to ambient particulate matter. *Atmospheric Environment*. 2012, vol. 60, no. 0, pp. 504-526.

[3] SCHRAUFNAGEL, D.E. The health effects of ultrafine particles. *Experimental & Molecular Medicine*. 2020, vol. 52, pp. 311-317.

[4] BAHREINI, R., MIDDLEBROOK, A. M., DE GOUW, J. A., WARNEKE, C., TRAINER, M., BROCK, C. A., STARK, H., BROWN, S. S., DUBE, W. P., GILMAN, J. B., HALL, K., HOLLOWAY, J. S., KUSTER, W. C., PERRING, A. E., PREVOT, A. S. H., SCHWARZ, J. P., SPACKMAN, J. R., SZIDAT, S., WAGNER, N. L., WEBER, R. J., ZOTTER, P., PARRISH, D. D. Gasoline emissions dominate over diesel in formation of secondary organic aerosol mass. *Geophysical Research Letters*. 2012, vol. 39, no. 6, pp. 0094-8276

[5] LIBALOVA, H., ROSSNER, P. JR., VRBOVA, K., BRZICOVA, T., SIKOROVA, J., VOJTISEK-LOM, M., BERANEK, V., KLEMA, J., CIGANEK, M., NECA, J., MACHALA, M., TOPINKA, J. Transcriptional response to organic compounds from diverse gasoline and biogasoline fuel emissions in human lung cells. *Toxicology In Vitro*. 2018, vol. 48, pp 329-341.

[6] KARAVALAKIS, G., SHORT, D., CHEN, V., ESPINOZA, C., BERTE, T., T. DURBIN, T., ASA-AWUKU, A., JUNG, H., NTZIACHRISTOS, L., AMANATIDIS, S., BERGMANN, A. Evaluating Particulate Emissions from a Flexible Fuel Vehicle with Direct Injection when Operated on Ethanol and Iso-butanol Blends, *SAE Technical Paper*. 2014-01-2768.

[7] TANOS, R., PATEL, R.D., MURRAY, I.A., SMITH, P.B., PATTERSON, A.D., PERDEW, G.H. Aryl hydrocarbon receptor regulates the cholesterol biosynthetic pathway in a dioxin response element-independent manner. *Hepatology*. 2012, vol. 55, no. 6, pp. 1994-2004.

[8] TONELLI, C., CHIO, I.I.C., TUVESON, D.A. Transcriptional Regulation by Nrf2. *Antioxidants & Redox Signaling*. 2018, vol. 29, no. 17, pp. 1727-1745.

[9] LIU, G.H., QU, J., SHEN, X. Thioredoxin-mediated negative autoregulation of peroxisome proliferator-activated receptor alpha transcriptional activity. *Molecular Biology of the Cell*. 2006, vol. 17, no. 4, pp.1822-33.

[10] JI, X., LI, Y., HE, J., SHAH, W., XUE, X., FENG, G., ZHANG, H., GAO, M. Depletion of mitochondrial enzyme system in liver, lung, brain, stomach and kidney induced by benzo(a)pyrene. *Environmental Toxicology and Pharmacology*. 2016, vol. 43, pp. 83-93.

[11] XUE, W., WARSHAWSKY, D. Metabolic activation of polycyclic and heterocyclic aromatic hydrocarbons and DNA damage: a review. *Toxicology and Applied Pharmacology*. 2005, vol. 206, no. 1, pp.73-93.

[12] COHEN, I. DNA damage talks to inflammation. *Cytokine & Growth Factors Reviews*. 2017, vol. 33, pp. 35-39

[13] TOMOKIYO, A., MAEDA, H., FUJII, S., MONNOUCHI, S., WADA, N., HORI, K., KOORI, K., YAMAMOTO, N., TERAMATSU, Y., AKAMINE, A. Alternation of extracellular matrix remodeling and apoptosis by activation of the aryl hydrocarbon receptor pathway in human periodontal ligament cells. *Journal of Cellular Biochemistry*. 2012, vol. 113, no. 10, pp. 3093-103.

[14] JARVIS, I.W., BERGVALL, C., MORALES, D.A., KUMMROW, F., UMBUZEIRO, G.A., WESTERHOLM, R., STENIUS, U., DREIJ, K. Nanomolar levels of PAHs in extracts from urban air induce MAPK signaling in HepG2 cells. *Toxicology Letters*. 2014, vol. 229, no. 1, pp. 25-32.

FINE AND ULTRAFINE PARTICULATE MATTER IN THE WORK ENVIRONMENT AND THEIR POTENTIAL IMPACT ON MENTAL STATE OF WORKERS

[1]Michal URBÁNEK, [1]Klaudia KÖBÖLOVÁ, [1]Vladimír ADAMEC, [2]Kateřina WOLFOVÁ, [3]Kristina ČABANOVÁ, [1]Jana Victoria MARTINCOVÁ

[1]Brno University of Technology, Institute of Forensic Engineering, Brno, Czech Republic, EU, michal.urbanek@usi.vutbr.cz

[2]Masaryk University, Faculty of Arts, Brno, Czech Republic, EU

[3]VSB - Technical University of Ostrava, Ostrava, Czech Republic, EU

https://doi.org/10.37904/nanocon.2020.3762

Abstract

This study presents the results of pilot measurement, where the exposure of fine and ultrafine particulate matter was monitored. The measurement was performed in different workplaces, where these particles are produced unintentionally. These were mainly engineering operations of welding shops, paint shops, but laboratory workplace was also observed. The measurement consisted of collecting information and measuring the concentration of particles in the workplace. Data collection was primarily focused on inhalation exposure. Particle samples were also obtained during the measurement to determine the morphology and chemical composition of the particles. An approach was also proposed to observe the selected psychological aspects (e.g. employee well-being) and occupational health and safety in an environment with the presence of fine and ultrafine particles.

Keywords: Work environment, fine and ultrafine particles, risk assessment, industrial and organizational psychology

1. INTRODUCTION

Fine particles (FP) and ultrafine particles (UFP) as a part of everyday life can have potential unacceptable impact on workers, as they are first to be exposed to the potential risk. It is necessary to set safety and health criteria at work that define the responsible development of nanotechnologies. Schulte et al. [1] presents five critical actions that should make a decisive impact on responsible development: the identification and monitoring of hazardous particles in the workplace, assess exposure and report potential hazards to workers, manage risks to safety and health at work, and support the safe development of nanotechnology.

Three basic group of origin of FP and UFP can be used in relation to work environment [2]:

- processes in which particles/materials are intentionally produced,
- processes related to the use of nanomaterials,
- particles created unintentionally during work processes.

Effects of nanoparticles on human health are currently in place with fast development of technologies. The toxic effect of inhaled nanoparticles has been proven many times in the last years, however, there is still discussion concerning the exact mechanism of this impact on living organisms [3-5].

The toxicity of nanoparticles is affected by many factors. These factors include their physical and chemical properties, size, shape, specific surface area, surface charge, catalytic activity, and the presence or absence of the shell and active groups on the surface [6]. Exposure time and concentration are part of the key indicators for setting standards of health assessment risks [7]. Inorganic nanoparticles can enter the body in four main ways: ingestion, inhalation, dermal penetration, blood circulation [8].

Song et al. [9] suggest that there is an association between long-term nanoparticles exposure without protective measures and serious damage to human lungs. Effective and protective methods should be used to in terms of prevention.

Castillo [10] emphasizes that an important factor is the involvement of employees in determining appropriate precautionary measures to eliminate or reduce the possibility of exposure to nanoparticles, where technically possible. Castillo [10] states as an example of good practice an independent government agency (Safe work Australia), which developed a tool to evaluate and identify safe ways of working with nanomaterials for industries. The knowledge of processes and procedures at the workplace is evaluated in the following areas:

- equipment design,
- modification / substitution of nanoparticles,
- closed system works,
- local ventilation,
- high efficiency particulate air filters (HEPA).

In comparison, European legislation states the following hierarchy of measures related to exposure to nanomaterials in the workplace [11]:

- technical control measures at the source,
- organizational measures,
- personal protection equipment, as the last resort.

In addition, there is a lack of legislative regulations on nanosafety [12]. For this reason, a relative comparison of background concentration values and actual measured values is used. In this paper the background value of the concentrations then corresponds to the minimum measured value. This was measured before the shift before processes at workplaces were initiated. The highest concentrations of nanoparticles are usually recorded in facilities where metals are treated under very high temperatures such as iron and steel works or welding shops [13,14].

There is evidence that an individual's experience in the physical, emotional, mental or social sphere affects a person in and out of the workplace [15]. In this regard workplace well-being is considered to be related to all aspects of working life, including how workers feel about their work, work environment and climate, work organization and quality and safety of the physical environment. Measures should be adjusted to complement the occupational health and safety to ensure that workers are safe, healthy, satisfied and engaged at work [16].

In the present work, the exposure to the particles in multiple workplaces with different conditions was estimated. Several measurement metrics were used to determine exposure e.g., concentration, size distribution, morphology, elemental analysis and saliva analysis. This study presents basic approach for measuring exposure in workplaces.

2. MATERIALS AND METHODS

For monitoring nanoparticles in atmosphere of the working environment were selected working processes, where these particles are created unintentionally. Multiple workplaces were monitored, these were mainly welding shops, paint shops and laboratory. Tungsten Inert Gas (TIG) and Metal Active Gas (MAG) welding methods were used in welding shops as well as grinding and cleaning with compressed air. In paint shops multilayer painting of stainless steel with sealing was used. Atomic absorption spectroscopy with multiple elements was used in laboratory. The selection of these workplaces is based on workplace measurements review [13], where highest concentration of FP and UFP can be observed. The working environment of the laboratory was chosen due to the process of atomization of heavy metals.

Four mobile devices were used in this study to measure concentrations of fine and ultrafine particles in the air, namely Condensation Particle Counter (TSI CPC 3007), TSI AM520 SidePak, Optical Particle Sampler (TSI OPS 3330), AirChek Touch (SKC, Inc.). CPC operates on the principle of particle condensation counting, which allows high measurement accuracy over the particle size range of 0.01-1 µm. SidePak is a personal air aerosol meter. It uses photometry to determine the mass concentration of particles in the atmosphere. The basic instrument range is 0.1-10 µm. The OPS works on a principle of optical spectrometry, it measures not only the concentration but also the number of particles in 16 channels of fractions. The total range of this instrument is 0.3-10 µm. The Airchek Touch does not belong to the measuring instruments category, but to the sampling devices. It is a sampling pump with adjustable air flow, which is connected to the sampling cassette. A round-shaped polycarbonate filter with porosity of 0.4 µm was placed in the cassette. The total particle size range that can be captured by the instrument is 0.01-10 µm. Thanks to the overlap of the fraction range it is possible to compare the results from individual instruments with each other.

At each workplace, the devices were placed close to the working area and possible source of UFP. It was about 1.5 meters from the work area to avoid damaging the devices and at the same time not to restrict the activities of the worker. One of the AirChek was placed in same area as other devices, second one was attached to the worker clothes. Cassette was placed in breathing zone of worker. Worker's saliva was collected into autoclavable centrifuge microtubes Eppendorf-type (5 ml) before and after work shift. At the beginning of the work shift, workers filled out a simple questionnaire that will be used to create a comprehensive test battery.

Collected filter samples were analysed by scanning electron microscope (SEM MIRA3, Tescan) with using of elemental analysis energy dispersive X-ray analysis (EDAX). Samples of workers saliva (1 ml) were applied in three coats to a slide. Each layer was dried in flowbox under germicidal radiation. Prepared samples were sprayed using an SC7620 sprayer and covered with a thin layer of metal. Subsequently, they were analysed by SEM (Quanta FEG 450, FEI), with EDAX to determine morphology and elemental particle analysis.

3. RESULTS AND DISCUSION

The measured data from the CPC, OPS and SidePak show the same trends of obtained results. Data values for comparison from CPC measurement are listed in **Table 1**. As expected, the lowest values of average concentrations were measured in the laboratory, on the contrary the highest values of concentrations could be observed in welding shops.

Table 1 Comparison of concentrations according to the working environment

Particles concentration (#/cm^3)	**Welding shops**	**Paint shops**	**Laboratory (AAS)**
Minimum	32,061	1,189	1,013
Maximum	551,582	24,199	2,091
Mean	119,981	5,219	1,530

Minimum values in welding shops were measured before the work shift, maximum values appeared during the cleaning of the weld with compressed air, when the particles were agitated. Other peaks were caused by grinding or welding itself. An example of the concentration course with description is shown in **Figure 1.** The values in some time periods exceed the maximum value of the measurable concentration by the instrument more than five times. The accuracy of above-limit measurements is reduced, so significantly high values can be taken as random measurement errors. The concentration measured in paint shops is significantly lower due to strong ventilation of entire space. The maximum value was shown when the worker sanded the sealant before the ventilation was turned on. Despite the fact that heavy metals (arsenic, cadmium) were atomized in the laboratory, the concentration values were around 1500 particles/cm^3, due to local suction directly above the atomization cuvette.

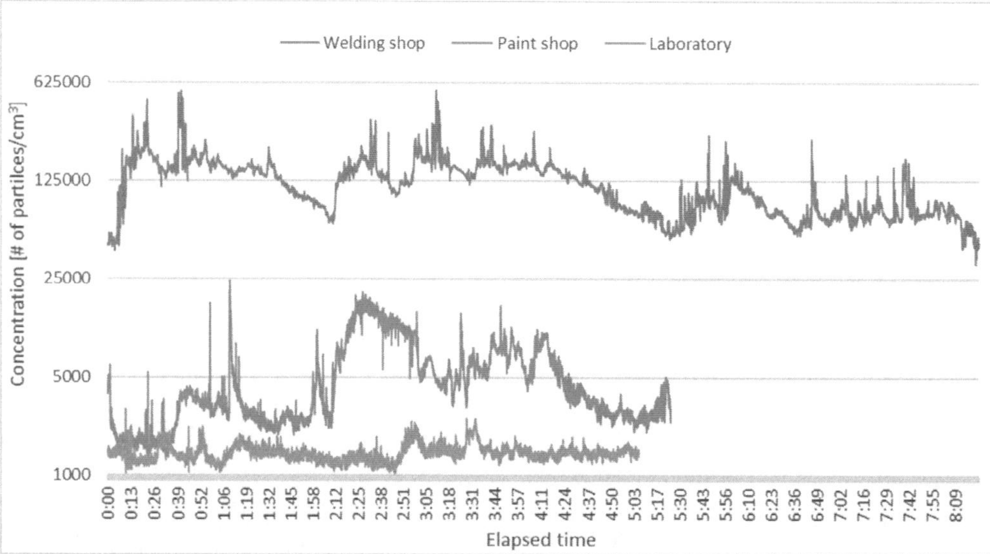

Figure 1 Example of fine and ultrafine concentration courses during the work shift measured with TSI CPC 3007 in different workplaces

From the results of OPS measurements performed at the workplace it can be concluded that particles larger than 0.8 µm are formed only in a minimal amount. The highest concentrations were measured for particles 0.3 µm and smaller, which are due to their size able to penetrate through the respiratory system deep into the human organism, where they may have an adverse effect on the worker's health [17].

The results of analyses of saliva and exposed filters of the worker by SEM methods showed the occurrence of elements that were used in the processes. In welding, it was mostly iron, silicon and manganese. Organic elements appeared in the paint shop. Heavy metal elements and relatively larger amounts of radon were captured in the laboratory. The presence of radon in laboratories could be caused by other laboratory devices using this element. In terms of particle morphology, the shape is mostly irregular, flat with sharp edges. The representation of particle morphology is shown in **Figure 2**. With a larger number of particles, these merges into larger units. This reduces the risk of the particle being directly inhaled into the lungs [17].

The processes, protective equipment and exposure times used at individual workplaces are very different. Due to the very short exposure (only during the painting itself) and a number of protective equipment (general ventilation of the closed room, respirator, fresh air supply) in combination with relatively small concentrations of particles, paint shops are much safer than welding shops. Although there are central ventilation systems in welding shops, they are very often not sufficient for ventilation of complex hall spaces of machine shops. This can be observed at the minimum measured values, which reached 30,000 particles/cm^3. These values were measured before and after the shift when no processes were taking place. Here comes the problem with exposure: workers in welding shops are, apart from lunch breaks, constantly in the hall with a concentration of particles higher than the highest values in paint shops. Therefore, exposure times are much higher than for painters. Very low values were measured in the laboratory and the exposure time is also very low. The worker turns on the process and leaves the room. The worker returns to the room only after the completion of the process, when the values of particle concentrations are significantly reduced by ventilation.

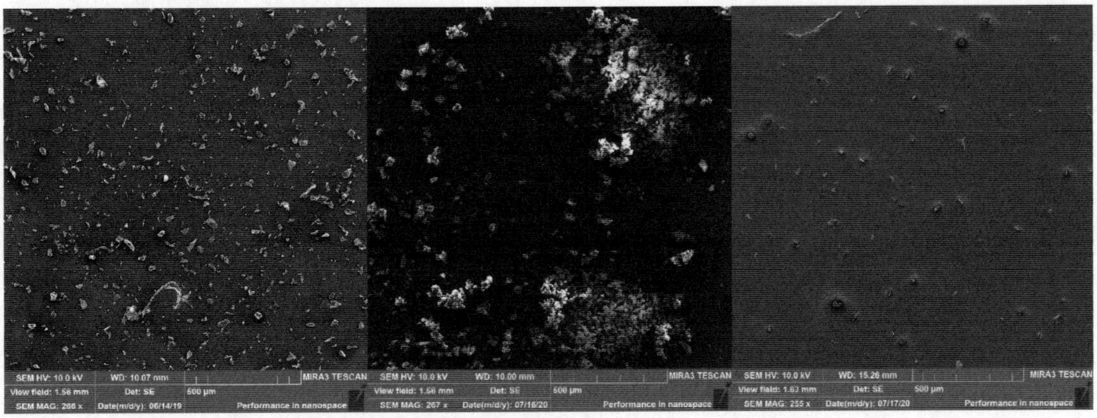

Figure 2 Example of SEM scan: left - welding shop; middle - paint shop; right - laboratory

In terms of evaluation work-related well-being should be considered: assessment and management of health risks, surveillance of employees' health; introduction of measures at workplace for the protection and promotion of workers health, contributing to wellbeing at work; and a special focus on workers fulfilment [18]. Workplace health and nanosafety questionnaire for workers is currently being constructed with regard to the legislation of the European Agency for Safety and Health at Work (OSHA). The aim of the questionnaire is to determine the level of knowledge and risks associated with nanoparticles, general knowledge of occupational safety and procedures, rights and obligations related to occupational safety and employee participation in safety issues. Despite the increasing use of nanotechnologies, employees who work with and are exposed to nanoparticles are often not educated in this area [19].

4. CONCLUSION

This study deals with exposure to fine and ultrafine particles in work environment. Their shape and composition depend on the examined process. The measured results of the concentration of particles in the air of the workplace show that, mainly particles with a size of about 0.3 µm are produced. The shape of these particles on the filter is mainly irregular. In terms of elemental composition, the analysed particles contained mainly iron, manganese, silicon, organic materials and heavy metals. Nanoscale concentration of these elements, according to various studies, can have toxic effects. In comparison of samples from saliva and from respiratory tract we can see very similar exposure, so oral exposure should be tested as well.

ACKNOWLEDGEMENTS

This paper is supported by TA ČR within the TL02000240 project of Increasing the Level of OSH Management in Workspace with Occurrence of Fine and Ultrafine particles.

REFERENCES

[1] SCHULTE, P. A., GERACI, C. L., MURASHOV, V., et al. Occupational safety and health criteria for responsible development of nanotechnology. *Journal of Nanoparticle Research.* [online]. 2014, vol. 16, no. 1. Available from: https://doi.org/10.1007/s11051-013-2153-9. ISSN 1388-0764.

[2] VAN BROEKHUIZEN, P., VAN BROEKHUIZEN, F., CORNELISSEN, R., REIJNDERS, L. Workplace exposure to nanoparticles and the application of provisional nanoreference values in times of uncertain risks. *Journal of Nanoparticle Research* [online]. 2012, vol. 14, no.4. Available from: https://doi.org/10.1007/s11051-012-0770-3. ISSN 1388-0764.

[3] BUNDSCHUH, M., FILSER, J., LÜDERWALD, S., et al. Nanoparticles in the environment: where do we come from, where do we go to? *Environmental Sciences Europe.* [online]. 2018, vol. 30, no. 1, p. 6. Available from: https://doi.org/10.1186/s12302-018-0132-6.

[4] PANDEY, R. K., PRAJAPATI, V. K. Molecular and immunological toxic effects of nanoparticles. *International Journal of Biological Macromolecules.* [online]. 2018, vol. 107, pp. 1278-1293. Available from: https://doi.org/10.1016/J.IJBIOMAC.2017.09.110.

[5] ROY, R., KUMAR, S., TRIPATHI, A., DAS, M., AND DWIVEDI, P. D. Interactive threats of nanoparticles to the biological system. *Immunology Letters.* [online]. 2014, vol. 158, no. 1-2, pp. 79-87. Available from: https://doi.org/10.1016/J.IMLET.2013.11.019.

[6] SUKHANOVA, A., BOZROVA, S., SOKOLOV, P., BERESTOVOY, M., KARAULOV, A., NABIEV, I. Dependence of nanoparticle toxicity on their physical and chemical properties. *Nanoscale research letters.* [online]. 2018, vol. 13.1, no. 44, pp. 1-21. Available from: https://doi.org/10.1186/s11671-018-2457-x.

[7] CONNELL, Des W., QIMING, J. Y., VERMA, V. Influence of exposure time on toxicity-An overview. *Toxicology.* [online]. 2016, vol. 355, pp. 49-53. Available from: https://doi.org/10.1016/j.tox.2016.05.015.

[8] DE MATTEIS, V. Exposure to inorganic nanoparticles: routes of entry, immune response, biodistribution and in vitro/in vivo toxicity evaluation. *Toxics.* [online]. 2017, vol. 5, no. 4, p. 29. Available from: https://doi.org/10.3390/toxics5040029.

[9] SONG, Y., LI, X., DU, X. Exposure to nanoparticles is related to pleural effusion, pulmonary fibrosis and granuloma. *European respiratory journal.* [online]. 2009, vol. 34, no. 3, pp. 559-567. Available from: https://doi.org/10.1183/09031936.00178308.

[10] PONCE DEL CASTILLO, A. M. Nanomaterials And Workplace Health & Safety. What Are The Issues For Workers?. *European Trade Union Institute.* [online]. 2013. [viewed 2020-09-29]. Available from: https://www.etui.org/sites/default/files/ez_import/Guide_Nanos_EN.pdf

[11] European Agency for Safety and Health at Work. *Managing nanomaterial in the workplace.* [online]. Brussels, Belgium [viewed 2020-09-29]. Available from: https://osha.europa.eu/cs/themes/nanomaterials.

[12] Regulation (EC) No 1907/2006 of the European Parliament and of the Council of 18 December 2006 concerning the Registration, Evaluation, Authorisation and Restriction of Chemicals (REACH).

[13] VIITANEN, A.-K., UUKSULAINEN, S., KOIVISTO, A. J., HÄMERI, K., KAUPPINEN, T. Workplace Measurements of Ultrafine Particles-A Literature Review. *Annals of Work Exposures and Health.* [online]. 2017, vol. 61, no. 7, pp. 749-758. Available from: https://doi.org/10.1093/annweh/wxx049.

[14] NOWACK, B., BROUWER, C., GEERTSMA, R. E., HEUGENS, E. H. W., ROSS, B. L., TOUFEKTSIAN, M.-C., WIJNHOVEN, S. W. P., AITKEN, R. J. Analysis of the occupational, consumer and environmental exposure to engineered nanomaterials used in 10 technology sectors, *Nanotoxicology.* [online]. 2012, vol. 7, no. 6, pp. 1152-1156. Available from: https://doi.org/10.3109/17435390.2012.711863.

[15] DANNA, K.; GRIFFIN, R., W. Health and well-being in the workplace: A review and synthesis of the literature. *Journal of management.* [online]. 1999, vol. 25, no. 3, pp. 357-384. Available from: https://doi.org/10.1016/S0149-2063(99)00006-9.

[16] International Labour Organization: Workplace well-being [online]. Geneve, Switzerland [viewed 2020-09-29]. Available from: https://www.ilo.org/safework/areasofwork/workplace-health-promotion-and-well-being/WCMS_118396/lang--en/index.htm

[17] THOMAS, R. J. Particle size and pathogenicity in the respiratory tract. *Virulence* [online]. 2014, vol. 4, no. 8, pp. 847-858 [viewed 2020-07-13]. DOI: 10.4161/viru.27172. ISSN 2150-5594. Available from: http://www.tandfonline.com/doi/abs/10.4161/viru.27172

[18] BUFFET, M., A., GERVAIS, R., L., LIDDLE, M., EECKELAERT, L. Well-being at work: creating a positive work environment. *Publications Office of the European Union.* [online]. 2013. ISSN: 1831-9351, 76, DOI: 10.2802/52064. Available from: https://osha.europa.eu/en/publications/well-being-work-creating-positive-work-environment

[19] PONCE DEL CASTILLO, A. Training for workers and safety representatives on manufactured nanomaterials. *NEW SOLUTIONS: A Journal of Environmental and Occupational Health Policy.* [online]. 2019, vol. 29, no. 1, pp. 36-52. Available from: https://doi.org/10.1177/1048291119830085.

SCENTED CANDLES AS A SOURCE OF NANOPARTICLES IN THE WORKSPACE

[1]Petra ROUPCOVÁ, [2]Hana KUBÁTOVÁ, [1,3]Karel KLOUDA, [1]Ondřej CHROMEČKA

[1]*VSB - Technical University of Ostrava, Ostrava, Czech Republic, EU,*
petra.roupcova@vsb.cz; karel.klouda@vsb.cz; ondrej.chromecka@vsb.cz
[2]*State Office for Nuclear Safety, Prague, Czech Republic, EU, hana.kubatova@sujb.cz*
[3]*Research Institute for Occupational Health and Safety, Prague, EU, klouda@vubp-praha.cz*

https://doi.org/10.37904/nanocon.2020.3759

Abstract

Scented candles are used in many professions. Both gaseous and solid emissions are generated in the workplace by their combustion. In our pilot experiment, we focused on determining the concentration of nanoparticles in the environment, their mean diameter, and lung deposited surface area (LSDA). The article presents the results obtained during the measurement in areas simulating a dry environment (shop, restaurant) and a humid environment (spa, rehabilitation). The concentrations of nanoparticles in the area of the simulation workplace (area 5.3 m^2, volume 12.7 m^3) during the burning of a single candle were measured to be ca. 1600 thousand particles in cm^3 in the atmosphere. Such values are comparable to a foundry, engineering plant or glassworks. Measured concentrations can pose a risk primarily to both employees and clients. While in industrial plants the risks arising from the presence of dust and nanoparticles are taken into account and workers are provided protective equipment, in shops, spas or beauty salons, where scented candles are burned, they are often neglected.

Keywords: Scented candles, emissions, nanoparticles, measurements, precaution

1. INTRODUCTION

Scented candles are a very popular item. They are used not only in households but also in stores, beauty salons, relaxation centers, cafes and restaurants, where their scent contributes to creating a pleasant atmosphere and the sense of well-being and relaxation which accompany the services offered. Burning scented candles releases a large amount of emissions into the environment, both gaseous and solid (particles). The composition of the emissions depends on the composition of the individual components of candles. The main components of candles are wax and wick; others components include aromatic substances (scents) and dyes or pigments. [1,2] Wax is the fuel that burns in candles. The origin of the wax used, the method of production and its chemical composition influence the composition of emissions. The most common types of wax from which candles are made are paraffin and stearin, or mixtures thereof. Beeswax and vegetable waxes are used less mainly because of their cost. Paraffin is a mixture of paraffinic hydrocarbons obtained by processing petroleum and may contain residues of aliphatic and aromatic hydrocarbons, and a variety of other substances. Stearin (tristearin) is a triglyceride derived from three units of stearic acid, and it is produced by processing animal fats and vegetable oils [3]. In addition to the fuel (wax), the composition of emissions is also affected by volatile substances which give scented candles their aroma. Synthetic scents in particular cause problems. Laboratory analyses carried out in studies on the composition of emissions from the burning of scented candles have shown that the emissions include volatile organic compounds (VOCs), such as toluene, benzene or ethylbenzene, polycyclic aromatic hydrocarbons (PAH) and aldehydes. These are often toxic substances that can have a negative impact on the health of exposed persons [1,2], and thus on the quality of the working environment where candles are used. Particulate matter (PM) is also a significant part of the emissions that can affect health. When burning candles, a wide range of respirable particles is formed, from coarse particles (PM_{10}) and fine particles ($PM_{2.5}$) to ultrafine particles (UFP $PM_{0.1}$), resp. nanoparticles [3-5,7].

Dr. Anne Steinemann, a leading environmental scientist, has presented her studies on aromatic products (perfume fragrances) in a number of publications. Even a small amount of a fragrance component can have demonstrably negative effects on human health [6]. Candles made from natural oils and waxes - beeswax, soy, rapeseed, olive, sunflower or coconut oil - can be friendlier for the environment (work and living). However, even in these more ecological variants, the presence of synthetic additives can negatively affect the health safety of the candles.

2. EXPERIMENTAL PART

2.1. Materials and methods

The Yankee Candle Company and Woodwick scented candles, namely WoodWick (Rose), WoodWick (Warm Wool, Petite candle) and Yankee candle (A Calm & Quiet Place), were selected for measurement. Not only the authors of the article selected the candles for measuring the nanoparticle concentrations, but the choice of candles was consulted with the sellers in the stone candle shop to make them generally popular scents that are often sold. WoodWick candles are made of a mixture of soy wax and paraffin which according to the manufacturer ensures a cleaner burning without smoke. Their wick is wooden [8]. The Yankee candle is made of paraffin wax of first-class quality, and the wick is 100% cotton, lead-free [9].

The workplaces where employees can come into contact with emissions from burning scented candles were simulated in our experiments by a bathroom - a room with two windows, an area of 5.28 m^2 and a volume of 12.672 m^3. Open windows provided natural ventilation during all measurements (similar to small shops and massage rooms). The experiments were performed in dry and humid environments. The arrangement of the experiments and positions for the placement of candles and measuring techniques are shown in **Figure 1**.

For the measurement, we used a portable Testo DiSCmini (Testo Ltd.) designed to measure the number of nanoparticles and the average size of nanoparticles with a time resolution of 1 second. At the same time, the device determined the surface area of nanoparticles present in the measured space (LDSA). As part of the measurement, we compared the change in the number of particles (measured for particles in the range of 10 to 700 nm) and the size of nanoparticles before and after ignition of the selected scented candles in specified measuring positions, and the total surface area of settled particles in the alveoli. The obtained results are presented graphically as change in the number of particles in a volume unit of the atmosphere over time, change in the size of particles over time, and change in the area of particles over time.

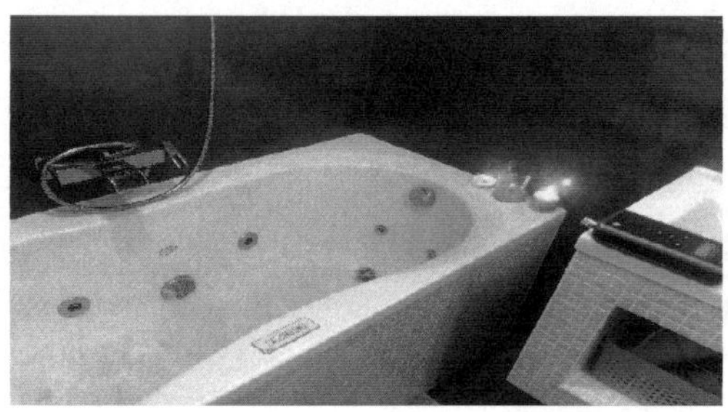

Figure 1 Arrangement of the experimental room, position of the candles and measuring technique (experiment with three burning candles in a humid environment).

The measurement always took place for a total of 11 min, with a distance of 20-30 cm from the candle and consisted of three parts: phase No. 1 (measurement length 2 min before lighting the candle), phase No. 2 (measurement length 6 min when a scented candle was burning) and phase No. 3 (measurement duration 3 min after extinguishing the candle).

2.2. Arrangement of the experiment for a dry (normal) working environment

For the purpose of simulating exposure in a dry working environment, a background measurement was first performed in the space reserved for the experiment without burning candles. No person was present in the room during the measurement. Measurement conditions: pressure 985.5 hPa, temperature 26.1 °C, and relative humidity 53.2 %. Subsequently, measurements were performed with individual scented candles placed on the edge of the bath. The final 4th measurement in a dry environment was to verify the synergistic effect. Three candles were lit during the measurement to simulate the realistic effect they would have in wellness facilities. The measuring device was placed at a distance of about 20-30 cm from the burning medium (see **Figure 1**). During the measurement, the operator of the device was present in the room.

2.3. Arrangement of the experiment for a humid working environment

To simulate exposure in a humid working environment, a bath was filled with water in an experimental room and background measurements were performed. A person was present in the room during the measurement. Measurement conditions: pressure 985.1 hPa, temperature 25.2-26.3 °C, and relative humidity in the range of 55.3-80 %. A total of 2 measurements were performed with a Yankee candle (A Calm & Quiet Place), and with 3 candles lit simultaneously placed on the edge of the tub.

3. RESULTS AND DISCUSSION

The measurement results of individual candles are presented graphically as the change in the number of particles (measured for particles with a size of 10 to 700 nm) in a volume unit of atmosphere over time, the change in particle size over time, and the change in particle area over time. The graphs (see **Figures 2-6**) are divided into 3 phases: phase No. 1 (measurement length 2 min without candle burning), phase No. 2 (measurement length 6 min with scented candle burning), and phase No. 3 (measurement length 3 min after extinguishing the candle). All measurements of nanoparticle concentrations (**Figures 2, 4**) showed an increase in the concentration of nanoparticles after lighting the candle in phase 2. The largest increase in concentration was recorded during the measurement of Woodwick Rose candle with up to 350,000 particles/cm^3. The increase in the concentration of nanoparticles during the measurement was reflected in a decrease in their mean size (**Figures 3, 5**). A difference between dry and humid environments can be observed. In the humid environment there was almost a 3x increase in nanoparticle concentrations (**Figures 2, 4**). Burning the Yankee candle (A Calm & Quiet Place) increased the concentration from 14,000 particles/cm^3 (dry medium) to 58,000 particles/cm^3 (humid medium), while three candles burning simultaneously increased the average concentration from 170,000 particles/cm^3 (dry medium) to 550,000 particles / cm^3 (humid medium). The Lung-Deposited Surface Area (LDSA) measured during the burning of 3 candles in a dry environment was 117 μm^2/cm^3, and in a humid environment 312 μm^2/cm^3 **(Figure 6)**.

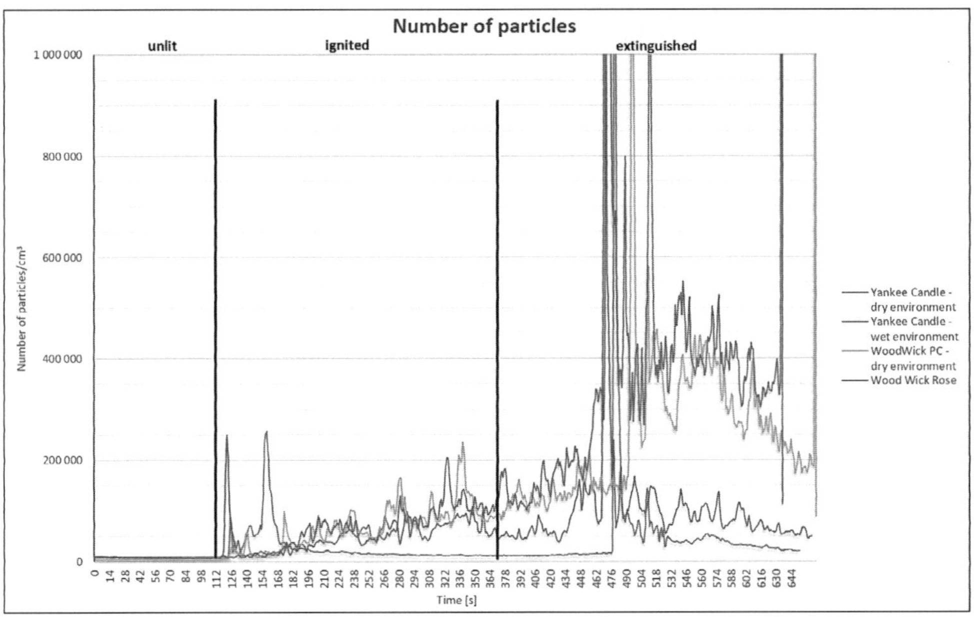

Figure 2 Nanoparticle concentration in dry and humid working environments with a burning candle during experiments (four experiments)

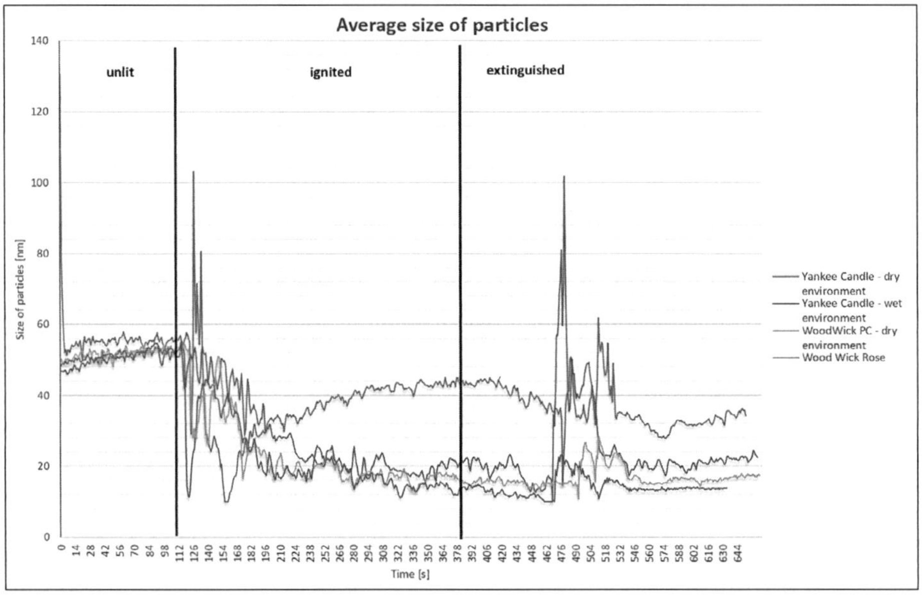

Figure 3 The average diameter of nanoparticles in dry and humid working environments with a burning candle during the experiment - Yankee candle (four experiments)

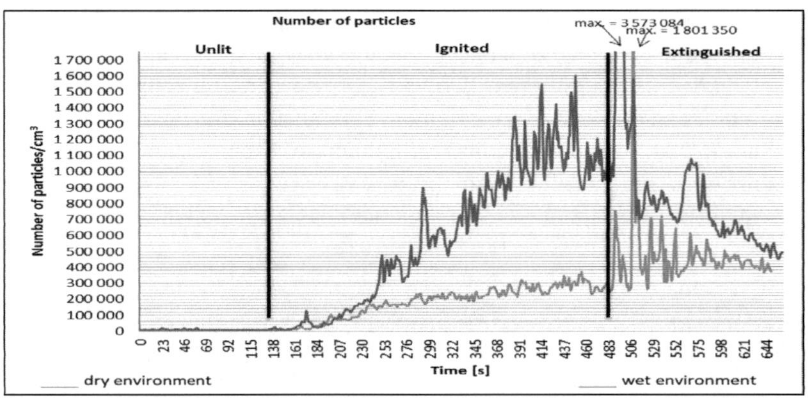

Figure 4 Nanoparticle concentration in dry and humid environments where 3 scented candles burn simultaneously (Yankee candle (A calm and quiet place), WoodWick Rose, Woodwick Petite candle)

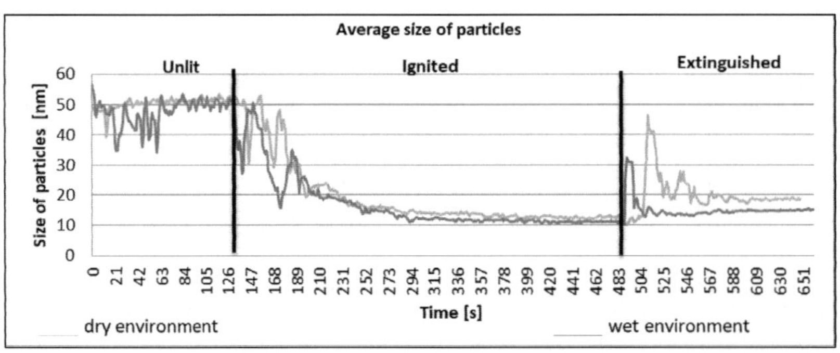

Figure 5 The average size of nanoparticles in dry and humid environments where 3 scented candles burn simultaneously (Yankee candle (A calm and quiet place), WoodWick Rose, Woodwick Petite candle)

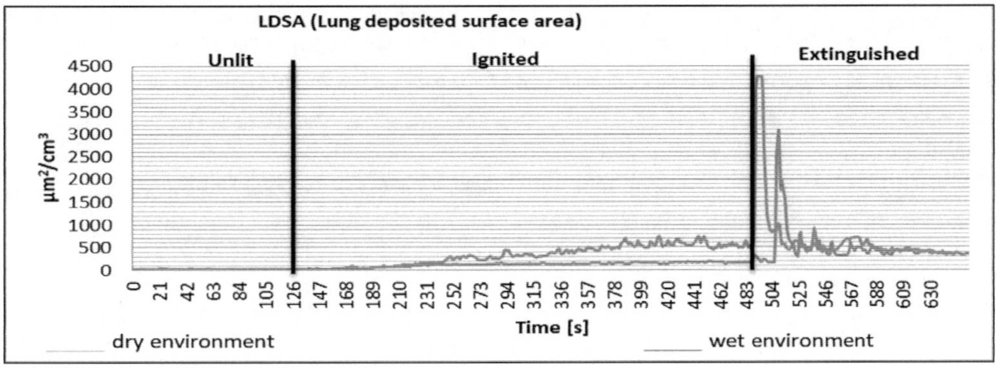

Figure 6 LDSA in dry and humid environments where 3 scented candles burn simultaneously (Yankee candle (A calm and quiet place), WoodWick Rose, Woodwick Petite candle).

4. CONCLUSION

The measurement of a set of three types of scented candles took place first in a bathroom with an empty bathtub and then with a proband and a bathtub full of water. In all measurements of nanoparticle concentrations there was an increase in the concentration of nanoparticles after lighting the candle in phase 2. The largest increase in the concentration of nanoparticles was measured when burning a WoodWick scented candle - a scented rose in a dry environment. Further, most of all measurements showed an increase in the concentration of nanoparticles formed during the burning of scented candles in a humid environment compared to a dry environment. A detailed assessment of the influence of the type of wax and wick on burning scented candles has not been investigated in more detail during the experiments. From the measured data it is evident that the concentration of measured nanoparticles was higher in two performed experiments for humid environment compared to dry environment. Combustion products were formed during the burning of scented candle. The reaction conditions were changed (humid and dry environment) subsequently different combustion products were formed. These products might have a hydrophilic or hydrophobic character that could explain the differences between measured concentrations of nanoparticles. As the concentration of nanoparticles increased, the mean diameter of the nanoparticles decreased. These results show that the measured concentrations of nanoparticles in the bathroom atmosphere when burning a scented candle have values even higher than in engineering companies, foundries and glassworks during the manual processing of glass.

REFERENCES

[1] PETRY, T., VITALE D., JOACHIM F. J., SMITH B., CRUSE L., MACHARENHAS R., SCHNEIDER S., SIGAL M. Human health risk evaluation of selected VOC, SVOC and particulate emissions from scented candles. *Regulatory Toxicology and Pharmacology*. 2014, vol. 69, no.1, pp. 55-70.

[2] DERUDI M., GELOSA S., SLIEPCEVICH A., CATTANEO A., ROTA R., CAVALLO D., NANO G. Emissions of air pollutants from scented candles burning in a test chambre. *Atmospheric Environment.* 2012, vol. 55, pp. 257-262.

[3] SOPPA, V. J., SCHINS, R. P., HENNING, F., HELLACK, B., QUASS, U., KAMINSKI, H., KUHLBUSCH, T. A., HOFFMAN, B., WEINMAYR, G. Respiratory effects of fine and ultrafine particles from indoor sources--a randomized sham-controlled exposure study of healthy volunteers. *International journal of environmental research and public health.* 2014, vol. 11, no. 7, pp. 6871-6889.

[4] THE DANISH ENVIRONMENTAL PROTECTION AGENCY. Environmentally friendly candles with reduced particle emissions [online]. [Viewed 2019-11-20]. Available from: https://www2.mst.dk/Udgiv/publications/2018/11/978-87-7038-009-6.pdf.

[5] ANEC position paper. *ANEC recommendations on the emissions to the indoor air.* [Viewed 2020-04-20]. Available from: https://www.anec.eu/images/Publications/position-papers/Chemicals/ANEC-PT-2015-CEG-016.pdf.

[6] STEINEMANN, A., GOODMAN. N. Fragranced consumer products and effects on asthmatics: an international population-based study. *Air Quality, Atmosphere & Health.* 2019, vol. 12, no. 6, pp. 643-649.

[7] CSN EN15426/2019 (650122) Candles - Specification for the determination of the smokyness of candles.

[8] WOODWICK SVICKY. [Viewed 2019-12-02]. Available from: https://woodwick.svicky.cz/woodwick-rose-vaza-stredni.html.

[9] VERYBERRY. [Viewed 2019-11-04]. Available from: https://veryberry.cz/vonne-a-klasicke-svicky/8798-yc-sklo-1-a-calm-quiet-place-5038581033327.html.

IMMOBILIZATION OF PHARMACEUTICALS IN SOILS

[1]Martina KLUČÁKOVÁ

[1]Brno University of Technology, Faculty of Chemistry, Brno, Czech Republic, EU, klucakova@fch.vutbr.cz

https://doi.org/10.37904/nanocon.2020.3758

Abstract

Worldwide production and consumption of pharmaceuticals increases every year. Due to the fact that these substances are not always completely eliminated in the human or animal body, subsequently get into the environment, which leads to a negative effect of certain constituents of natural ecosystems. Knowledge of contaminant behaviour is essential for their mobility and toxicity in the soils and surface- and ground-water environments. In this study, interactions of pharmaceuticals with soils and humic substances as the most important constituents of soil organic matter are investigated. Humic substances contain more types of active sites (hydrophilic functional groups and hydrophobic structures) able to bind different drugs and form relatively stable complexes with them. The complexation of drugs with soil organic matter thus can reduce their mobility and toxicity in natural systems. This study deals with interactions of soils and humic substances with drugs. the aim is to determine their binding capacity and stability of formed complexes with respect to the possible immobilization of drugs in the humic structure.

Keywords: Humic acids, soil, ibuprofen, stability

1. INTRODUCTION

In the European Union about three thousands different substances are used in human and veterinary medicine [1-3]. The persistence of these pharmaceuticals makes them "emerging pollutants" and stresses the need to advance waste and wastewater treatment technologies in addition to studying their potential effects in aquatic environments [1,4]. These substances are not completely eliminated in the body. It has been reported that 80 % of all consumed drugs are eliminated from the body unchanged, due their high stability against biological degradation [5-7]. These pharmaceuticals can therefore enter the environment. Some drug residuals were detected in surface and underground water [8-10] as well as in sediments and soils [12-16]. Because of their physical and chemical properties, many of these substances or their bioactive metabolites end up in soils and sediments, where they can accumulate and induce adverse effects in terrestrial or aquatic organisms [5,10,11]. Some pharmaceuticals may be removed by degradation. Laboratory studies show that degradation rates of pharmaceutical compounds in soils vary widely, with half-lives ranging from days to years. Within the same therapeutic class, half-lives can still be significantly different as a result of differences in soil properties [16-17]. Knowledge of contaminant behaviour is essential for their mobility and toxicity in the soils and surface- and ground-water environments.

The behaviour of pharmaceuticals in nature can be affected by their interactions with organic matter and humic substances as their most important constituents. Klavins et al. [1] determined the binding constants between humic acids and selected pharmaceuticals using a fluorescence quenching technique. Their findings suggest that an electrostatic interaction plays a dominant role in the complex formation between humic acids and pharmaceuticals, which was also confirmed by a salt effect and pH dependence of the fluorescence quenching effect. Khil´ko and Semenova [17] studied interactions of salts of humic acids with drug preparations. Their results were indicative mainly of binding between the charged groups of the macro-anions of humic acid salts and the positively charged centres of drug molecules (supplemented obviously by hydrogen bonds and hydrophobic interactions). They stated that the number of moles of drug preparations capable of interacting with a natural humic macro-molecule was determined by their molecular structure peculiarities and charges. Margon et al. [18] investigated interactions of diclofenac with soil humic acids and resulted that they may led to the formation of diclofenac-humic supramolecules and micelles which can migrate through the coarse soil profile.

Kodešová et al. [19] measured sorption isotherms of several pharmaceutical substances on different soils. The simultaneous sorption experiments showed that the sorption affinity decreased with soil depth, i.e. with the content of soil organic matter. Lin and Gan [20] studied the sorption of diclofenac, ibuprofen, naproxen, sulfamethoxazole and trimethoprim in soils. They concluded that the poor sorption and relative persistence of diclofenac and ibuprofen under anaerobic conditions suggest that they may pose a high leaching risk when using recycled for irrigation or ground water replenishment. Martínez Mejía et al. [21] studied sorption mechanism of enrofloxacin on humic acids extracted from three Brazilian soils. They stated that the sorption of humic acids was higher in magnitude comparing soils from which they were isolated. The primary interactions were ionic and cation binding due to abundant carboxylic groups and H-bond moieties with carbohydrate-like structures. Liu et al. [22] studied adsorption behaviour and mechanism of ciprofloxacin and sulfamethoxazole. Their kinetics results indicated that the adsorption process included the fast-adsorption stage first and the slow-adsorption stage thereafter. Földényi et al. [23] dealt with adsorption of diclofenac on activated carbon in the presence of organic matter. They confirmed that the adsorption was enhanced by humic substances. Similarly, Kohay et al. [24] investigated the influence of humic acids on diclofenac binding on polycation-clay sorbents. Antilen et al. [25] proved that soil organic matter was capable of generating interactions with antibiotics, which resulted in a decrease in their availability.

Above-described high reactivity of soil organic matter is well-known and widely studied [26-29]. The sorption of pharmaceuticals to organic matter is an important mechanism related to their immobilization. The majority of studies dealing with interactions of drugs with organic matter were focused to the adsorption isotherms described by empirical Freundlich model used mainly for the physical character of binding, e.g. [19,25]. Some authors used also Langmuir model characterizing chemical adsorption in mono-molecular layer [24] or their combination [25]. The pollutants can be bound to soil organic matter by different strengths and three main fractions of them can be defined. First is the mobile fraction which is extractable by water, second fraction is ion-exchangeable and third is strongly bound [30,31].

2. MATERIALS AND METHODS

In this work, one of the most used drugs, Ibuprofen, and its interactions with three types of soil sampled in the Czech Republic were studied. Ibuprofen was purchased from Sigma-Aldrich. Soil A (phaeozem) was sampled in the region Jablůnka (closed to river Bečva), soil B (regosol) was sampled in the Hodonín (locality Pánov), and soil C (chernozem) was sampled in Brno (locality Slatina, closed to protected area Stránská skála). Samples A and B are arable soils with periodically changed arable crops as wheat and corn. Sample B is soil with grass vegetation included in the project of Technology Agency of the Czech Republic no. TH02030073. Basic characteristics of soil samples are in **Table 1** (elemental analysic was realised by means of EuroEA Elemental Analyzer EA 3000, Euro Vector; contents of moisture and organic fraction by means of thermogravimetric analyzer TGA Q50, TA Instruments).

Soil samples were mixed with the solution of ibuprofen (1 - 10 mg/dm^3), stirred (48 h) and centrifuged (Hettich ROTINA 46 R; 5000 rpm, 10 minutes). The ratio between the solid powder sample and solution was 0.5 g : 25 cm^3. Supernatants were filtered (0.22 μm) in order to remove solid particles and analysed by means of UV/VIS spectrometry (HITACHI U-3900H) in order to determine the residual amount of ibuprofen in solution after adsorption.

The stability of formed complexes were investigated by means of desorption experiments. Ibuprofen-soil complexes were mixed with 25 cm^3 of deionized water, stirred, centrifuged, filtered and analysed by the same methods as in the case of adsorption experiments.

Table 1 Elemental composition, moisture, and organic fraction of soil samples

Sample	C (wt.%)	H (wt. %)	N (wt. %)	O (wt. %)	moisture (wt. %)	org. fraction (wt. %)
Soil A	1.44	0.76	0.14	3.41	1.57	5.75
Soil B	0.45	0.12	0.03	0.57	0.22	1.17
Soil C	1.84	1.00	0.14	3.88	3.24	6.86

3. RESULTS AND DISCUSSION

In this work, the interactions between ibuprofen as a frequently used drug and three types of soils were investigated. Ibuprofen was prepared as its solution in deionized water. Soils were used in the form of solid powders. In **Figure 1**, the efficiency of adsorption for studied soil samples and adsorbed amount divided into mobile and residual bound fractions are shown. We can see, that the efficiency of adsorption is closely conned with the content of organic fraction in soil. The efficiency ranges between 49 and 83 % for soil A and between 42 and 89 % for soil C. These soils contain much higher amount of organic matter in comparison with sandy soil B. The efficiency is influenced not only by the amount of organic matter but also by its quality (composition, structure and properties). As mentioned above, electrostatic interactions can be considered as one of the major pharmaceutical binding mechanisms therefore the content of charged functional groups play crucial role in the immobilization of drugs in soils [1,21,23,35]. Klavins et al. [1]. correlated positively the binding of several pharmaceuticals with the content of carboxyl groups in humic acids (as the most important constituents of soil organic matter). On the other hand, hydrophobic interactions can play an important role in the adsorption of some drugs in dependence on their structure [1,35]. Földényi et al. [18] obtained isotherms with a breaking point resulting in the hypothesis of two adsorption steps: the first step related to the charge transfer interaction and the second one related to hydrogen bond formation.

The stability of complexes formed by adsorption was investigated by means of desorption of ibuprofen from humic acids and soil into deionized water. The fraction leached into water was regarded as the mobile fraction. The residual amount of ibuprofen was bound by ionic or covalent binds. In comparison with previous works [30,31], ibuprofen was divided only into two fractions in this study: the mobile fraction extractable by water, and residual bound fraction comprised of ion-exchangeable and strongly bound fractions.

We can see that the amounts of free mobile fractions are higher than residual bound fraction of ibuprofen in the case of sandy soil B with low content of organic matter. This type of coil is not able to bind strongly pollutants and the majority of them is bound only by means of weak physical forces. As expected, the amounts leachable into water were much lower for soil samples rich in organic matter (A and C). The efficiency of adsorption gradually decreased with the increasing concentration of ibuprofen for soil samples A and C. In the case of soil B the efficiency slightly increased for more concentrated solutions of ibuprofen (> 6 mg/dm^3). The increase did not influence the amount of bound fraction because the binding capacity of soil organic matter was exhausted. The binding sites (functional groups) are occupied and ibuprofen cannot be adsorbed by chemical or ion-exchange mechanisms. In contrast, the binding sites in soils rich in organic matter are covered gradually and no striking increase in physically bound ibuprofen was observed.

In spite of the fact that ibuprofen is adsorbed on soil surface by chemical and physical bonds, the well-known Langmuir adsorption isotherm [24,25,37] was applied on the experimental data and apparent adsorption capacity of soil samples was determined. Their values are stated **Figure 2** where the dependence of adsorption capacity on the content of organic matter in soils is shown. We can see that the capacity can be positively correlated with the content of organic matter. It surprising, that the dependence is strongly linear. In my opinion, it is partially caused by coincidence. The adsorption capacity is strongly influenced by many other factors as soil composition, structure, micro-organization and many other physical-chemical properties. However, it was confirmed that the higher contents organic matter in soils can improve their adsorption abilities and supported chemical interactions between ibuprofen and soil resulting in its stronger immobilization. The ratio between contents of mobile and residual bound fractions increased generally with increasing concentration of ibuprofen. Its value strongly increased in the case of soil B as a result of higher physically bound drug. Soils rich in organic matter (A and C) had maximum of its value around 1 and no noticeable increase was observed in more concentrated systems.

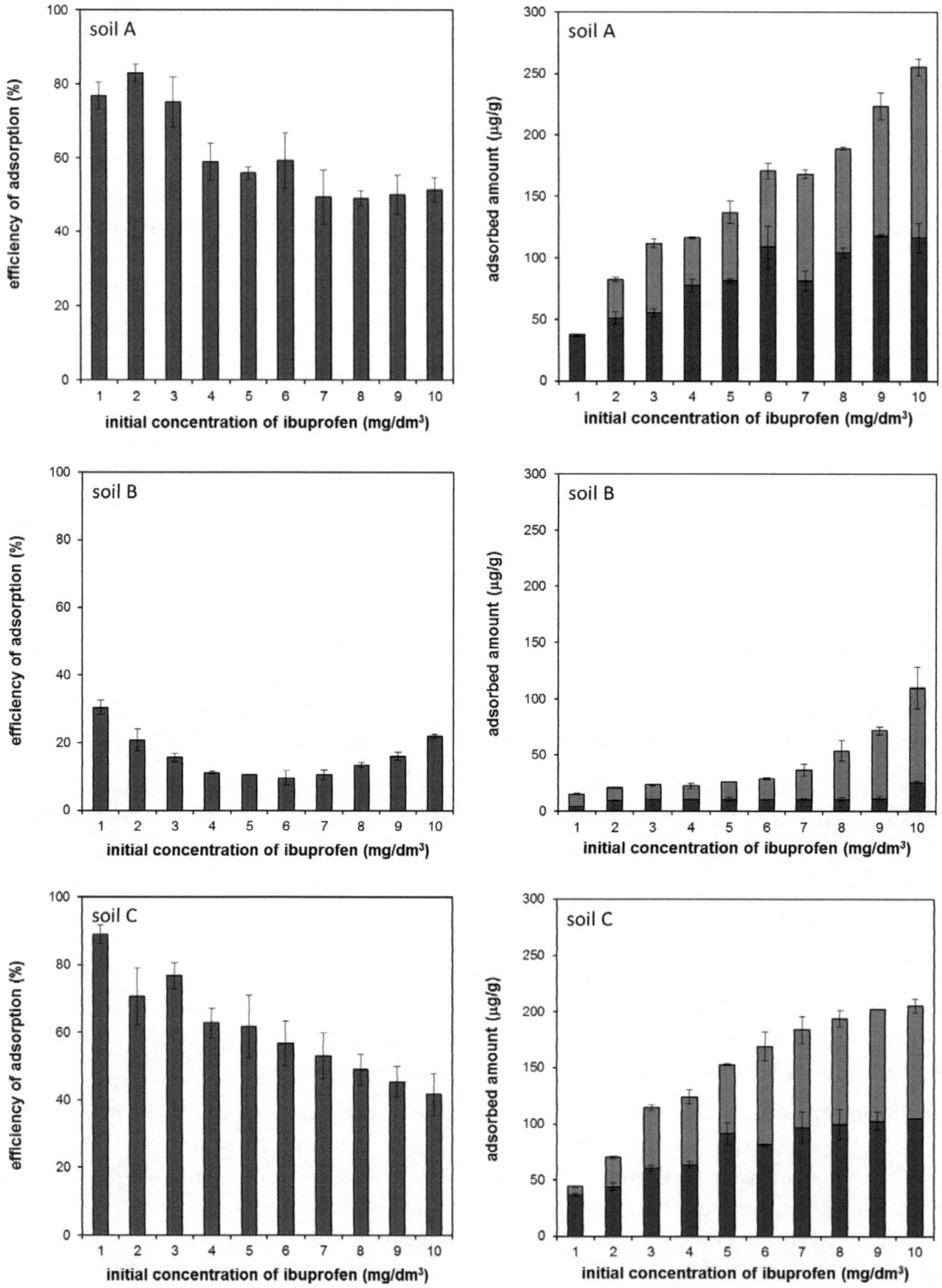

Figure 1 The efficiency of adsorption of ibuprofen on soils (left) and adsorbed amount of ibuprofen (right) divided into mobile fraction (green) and residual bond fraction (red): Soil A - up, B- amid, C -down

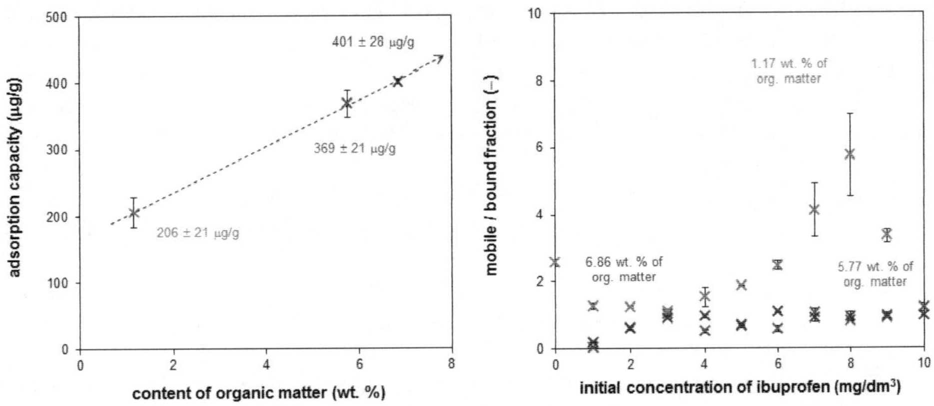

Figure 2 The dependence of adsorption capacity on content of organic matter in soils (left); ratio between mobile fraction of ibuprofen and its residual bound fraction (right):; soil A - blue, soil B - green and soil C - red

4. CONCLUSION

In this work, the interactions of soils with ibuprofen were investigated. It was found that the immobilization ability of soils was strongly influenced by the content of organic matter. The stability of formed complexes determined on the basis of leaching experiments confirmed that the binds between ibuprofen and organic matter are relatively strong. The mobility of ibuprofen in soils rich in organic matter can be effectively supressed by its immobilization.

REFERENCES

[1] KLAVINS, M., ANSONE, L., PURMALIS, O., ZICMANIS, A. Characterization of interaction between tricyclic structures containing pharmaceuticals, their model and humic substances. *Water Science & Technology.* 2011, vol. 63, no. 5, pp. 845-852.

[2] FENT, K., WESTON, A.A., CAMINADA, D. Ecotoxicology of human pharmaceuticals. *Aquatic Toxicology.* 2006, vol. 76, no. 2, pp. 122.159.

[3] CUNNINGHAM, V.L., BINKS, S.P., OLSON, M.J. Human health risk assessment from a presence of human pharmaceuticals in the aquatic environment. *Regulatory Toxicology and Pharmacology.* 2009, vol. 53, no. 1, pp. 39-45.

[4] RICHARDSON, S.D., TERNES, T.A. Water analysis: emerging contaminants and current issues. *Analytical Chemistry.* 2005, vol. 77, no. 12, pp. 3807-3838.

[5] COOPER, E.R., SIEWICKI, T.C., PHIPPIPS, K. Preliminary risk assessment database and risk ranking of pharmaceuticals in the environment. *Science of Total Environment.* 2008, vol. 398, no. 1-3, pp. 26-33.

[6] TOGOLA, A., BUDZINSKI, H. Analytical development for analysis of pharmaceuticals in water samples by SPE and GC-MS. *Analytical and Bioanalytical Chemistry.* 2007, vol. 388, iss. 3, pp. 627-635.

[7] AHRER, W., SCHERWENK, E., BUCHBERGER, W. Determination of drug residues in water by the combination of liquid chromatography or capillary electrophoresis with electrospray mass spectrometry. *Journal of Chromatography A.* 2001, vol. 910, no. 1, pp. 69-78.

[8] JUX, U., BAGINSKI, R., ARNOLD, H.G., KRÖNKE, M., SENG P.N. Detection of pharmaceutical contaminations of river, pond, and tap water from Cologne (Germany) and surroundings. *International Journal of Hygiene and Environmental Health.* 2002, vol. 205, no. 5, pp. 393-398.

[9] SACHER, F., LANGE, F., BRAUCH, H., BLANKENHORN, I. Pharmaceuticals in groundwaters: Analytical methods and results of a monitoring program in Baden-Württemberg, Germany. *Journal of Chromatography A.* 2001, vol. 938, no. 1-2, pp. 199-210.

[10] SIM, W., LEE, J., OH, J. Occurrence and fate of pharmaceuticals in wastewater treatment plants and rivers in Korea. *Environmental Pollution.* 2010, vol. 158, no. 5, pp. 1938-1947.

[11] KIM, S.C., CRLSON, K. LC-MS2 for quantifying trace amounts of pharmaceutical compounds in soil and sediment matrices. *Trends in Analytical Chemistry.* 2005, vol. 24, no. 7, pp. 635-644.

[12] PÉREZ-CARRERA, E., HANSEN, M., LEÓN, V.M., BJÖRKLUND, E., KROGH, K.A., HALLING-SØRENSEN, B., GONZÁLEZ-MAZO, E. Multiresidue method for the determination of 32 human and veterinary pharmaceuticals in soil and sediment by pressurized-liquid extraction and LC-MS/MS. *Analytical and Bioanalytical Chemistry.* 2010, vol. 398, no. 3, pp.1173-1184.

[13] ÁLVAREZ-RUIZ, R., ANDRÉS-COSTA, J.M., ANDREU, V., PICÓ, Y. Simultaneous determination of traditional and emerging illicit drugs in sediments, sludges and particulate matter. *Journal of Chromatography A.* 2015, vol. 1405, no. 1, pp. 103-115.

[14] KOBA, O., GOLOVKO, O., KODEŠOVÁ, R., FÉR, M., GRABIC, R. Antibiotics degradation in soil: A case of clindamycin, trimethoprim, sulfamethoxazole and their transformation products. *Environmental Pollution.* 2017, vol. 220, no. B, pp. 1251-1263.

[15] MONTEIRO, S.C., BOXALL, A.B.A. Factors affecting the degradation of pharmaceuticalsin agricultural soils. *Environmental Toxicology and Chemistry.* 2009, vol. 28, no. 12, pp. 2546-2554.

[16] SCHLÜSENER, M.P., BESTER, K. Persistence of antibiotics such as macrolides, tiamulin and salinomycin in soil. *Environmental Pollution.* 2006, vol. 143, no. 3, pp. 565-571.

[17] KHIL´KO, S.L., SEMENOVA, R.G. Interaction of humic acid salts with drug preparations. *Solid Fuel Chemistry.* 2016, vol. 50, no. 6, pp. 60-64.

[18] MARGON, A., PASTRELLO, A., MOSETTI, D., CANTONE, P., LEITA, L. Interaction between diclofenac and soil humic acids. *Soil and Sediment Contamination.* 2009, vol. 18, no. 4, pp. 489-496.

[19] KODEŠOVÁ, R., GRABIC, R., KOČÁREK, M., KLEMENT, A., GOLOVKO, O., FÉR, M., NIKODEM, A., JAKŠÍK, O. Pharmaceuticals' sorptions relative to properties of thirteen different soils. *Science of the Total Environment.* 2015, vol. 511, no. 1, pp. 435-443.

[20] LIN, K., GAN, J. Sorption and degradation of wastewater-associated non-steroidal anti-inflammatory drugs and antibiotics in soils. *Chemosphere.* 2011, vol. 83, no. 3, pp. 240-246.

[21] MARTÍNEZ-MEJÍA, M. J., SATO, I., RATH, S. Sorption mechanism of enrofloxacin on humic acids extracted from Brazilian soils. *Environmental Science and Pollution Research.* 2017, vol. 24, no. 19, pp. 15995-16006.

[22] LIU, X., LU, S., LIU, Y., MENG, W., ZHENG, B. Adsorption of sulfamethoxazole (SMZ) and ciprofloxacin (CIP) by humic acid (HA): characteristics and mechanism. *RCS Advances.* 2017, vol. 7, no. 81, pp. 50449-50458.

[23] FÖLDÉNYI, R., JOÓ, S., TÓTH, J. Adsorption of diclofenac on activated carbon and its hypochlorination in the presence of dissolved organic matter. *International Journal of Environmental Science and Technology.* 2017, vol. 14, no. 5, pp. 1071-1080.

[24] KOHAY, H., IZBITZBITSKI, A., MISHAEL, Y.G. Developing polycation-clay sorbents for efficient filtration of diclofenac: Effect of dissolved organic matter and comparison to activated carbon. *Environmental Science & Technology.* 2015, vol. 49, no. 1, pp. 9280-9288.

[25] ANTILEN, M., BUSTOS, O., RAMIREZ, G., CANALES, C., FAUNDEZ M., ESCUDEY, M., PIZARRO, C. Electrochemical evaluation of ciprofloxacin adsorption on soil organic matter. *New Journal of Chemistry.* 2016, vol. 40, no. 1, pp. 7132-7139.

[26] GHABBOUR, E.A., DAVIES, G. Environmental insights from Langmuir adsorption site capacities. *Colloids and Surfaces A.* 2011, vol. 381, no. 1-3, pp. 37-40.

[27] KLUČÁKOVÁ, M., PEKAŘ, M. New model for equilibrium sorption of metal ions on solid humic acids. *Colloids and Surfaces A.* 2006, vol. 286, no. 1-3, pp. 126-133.

[28] PARK, J., CHO, K.H., LEE, E., LEE, S., CHO, J. Sorption of pharmaceuticals to soil organic matter in a constructed wetland by electrostatic interaction. *Science of the Total Environment.* 2018, vol. 435, no. 1, pp. 1345-1350.

[29] KLUČÁKOVÁ, M. Complexation of metal ions with solid humic acids, humic colloidal solutions, and humic hydrogel. *Environmental Engineering Science.* 2014, vol. 31, no. 11, pp. 612-620.

[30] KLUČÁKOVÁ, M., KALINA, M. Diffusivity of Cu(II) ions in humic gels - influence of reactive functional groups of humic acids. *Colloids and Surfaces A.* 2015, vol. 483, no. 1, pp. 162-170.

[31] KLUČÁKOVÁ, M., KALINA, M., SEDLÁČEK, P., GRASSET, L. Reactivity and transport mapping of Cu(II) Ions in humic hydrogels. *Journal of Soils and Sediments.* 2014, vol. 14, no. 2, pp. 368-376.

RNA EXTRACTION FROM SOIL BACTERIUM PSEUDOMONAS PUTIDA AND GREEN ALGA RAPHIDOCELIS SUBCAPITATA AFTER EXPOSURE TO NANOSCALE ZERO VALENT IRON

[1,2]Cheryl S.Y. YEAP, [1]Nhung H.A. NGUYEN, [3]Olga Blifernez-KLASSEN, [3]Jan H. MUSSGNUG, [4]Tobias BUSCHE, [3]Olaf KRUSE, [1]Alena SEVCU

[1]Institute for Nanomaterials Advanced Technologies and Innovation, Technical University of Liberec, Liberec, Czech Republic, EU, alena.sevcu@tul.cz

[2]Faculty of Mechatronics, Informatics and Interdisciplinary Studies, Technical University of Liberec, Liberec, Czech Republic, EU, cheryl.yeap@tul.cz

[3]Algae Biotechnology and Bioenergy, Faculty of Biology, Center for Biotechnology (CeBiTec), Bielefeld University, Bielefeld, Germany, EU, jan.mussgnug@uni-bielefeld.de

[4]Microbial Genomics and Biotechnology, Faculty of Biology, Center for Biotechnology (CeBiTec), Bielefeld University, Bielefeld, Germany, EU, tbusche@cebitec.uni-bielefeld.de

https://doi.org/10.37904/nanocon.2020.3764

Abstract

Soil bacterium *Pseudomonas putida* and green alga *Raphidocelis subcapitata* are often used in ecotoxicology studies, including assessment of nanomaterials. Exposure of these microorganisms to reactive nZVI, however, reduce the quality of extracted RNA for further transcriptomic analysis. In this study, we compare RNA extraction using eight extraction protocols. The extraction using the commercial column kits was often unable to elute both the RNA species in a single elution, whereas phenol-chloroform method using RNAzol recovered both small RNA and large RNA from *P. putida*. On the other hand, the column based RNA extraction kit from ISOLATE II RNA Mini gave the best yield approximately of 1 µg/µl of RNA and RIN 9.0. RNA extraction from *R. subcapitata* was more complicated when we used a similar column based RNA extraction system, it required additional and thorough cell lysis steps that included cell lyophilisation and ribolization prior to phenol-chloroform extraction method. Then the yield of an effective RNA concentration ranged from 300 ng/µl to 980 ng/µl, giving the RIN 5.5-7.8. The final protocols solved most of the extraction problems, and allow experiments involving RNA gene expression analysis of microorganisms exposed to reactive nZVI.

Keywords: Metal oxides nanoparticles, Iron, Bacteria, Green algae, RNA integrity assessment

1. INTRODUCTION

The nanoscale zero-valent iron (nZVI) is well known as a powerful reductant in transforming many hazardous pollutants into safer by-products [1,2]. Ever since the introduction of nZVI into aquifers, studies of its effect on the aquatic microbial consortia were largely based on phenotypic analysis, cell physiology or mechanisms of contaminant sequestration complianced to the OECD guidelines [3]. In contrast to these studies, little is known about the response of the microorganisms on the transcriptomic level. Isolation of high quality RNA is often not easy, when there are compounds that bind to and/or co-precipitate with RNA or experimental conditions that need special attention to preserve the intergirty of RNA such as the addition of reactive nZVI. Hence, our focus in this study was to optimize the RNA extraction protocol from cells after exposure to nZVI and iron cations released from oxidized nZVI (nZVI Fe ions) or nFe_3O_4 as a control that may interfere with RNA. We used common environmental soil bacterium, *Pseudomonas putida* NCTC 10936 and freshwater microalga, *Raphidocelis subcapitata* ATCC 22662. The effectiveness of several RNA extraction methods were compared, including different cell lysis protocols in the case of microalga.

2. MATERIALS AND METHODS

2.1. Preparation of nZVI and its ions

The supplied NANOFER STAR powder (nZVI) (CAS no: 7439-89-6, size 10-150 nm) and nano Fe_3O_4 (nFe_3O_4) (CAS No: 1317-61-9, size 50-100 nm) were obtained from NANOIRON s.r.o, Czech Republic, and Sigma Aldrich, Merck, Germany, respectively. Activation of 20% nZVI suspension was done according to producer guidelines for 48 h [4]. Simultaneously, the aqueous phase of nZVI slurry containing iron cations (44.5 µg L^{-1}) released from oxidized nZVI was prepared by high speed centrifugation twice at 14, 000 *x g* for 20 min per cycle separating the supernatant from nZVI and served as one of the exposure condition (nZVI Fe ions).

2.2. Culture condition and experimental setup

2.2.1. *P. putida*

Pseudomonas putida NCTC 10936, was obtained from CCM Czech Collection of Microorganisms, Brno, Czech Republic. The cells were grown in tryptone soy medium at 30 °C and when reaching its mid-log phase, 10 ml of *P. putida* (3.3 x 10^8 cells/ml) was harvested and transferred immediately to the nanoparticle exposure medium. Three different experimental conditions were prepared: i) unexposed *P. putida* (control), ii) *P. putida* with 44.5 µg L^{-1} nZVI Fe ions and, iii) *P. putida* with 100 mg L^{-1} nZVI. Whole experiment was performed at room temperature in 250 mL Erlenmeyer flasks containing 50 mL of exposure medium consisting of carbonate buffer (1,5 mg L^{-1} Na_2CO_3 and 167,16 mg L^{-1} $NaHCO_3$, pH 8.0), cells and treatments, shaken at 120 rpm and immediately sampled (50 mL) for RNA extraction. After optimizing the suitable RNA isolation method for nZVI spiked samples, a natural reservoir water (NRW) was collected in a spade from a local reservoir on 18 November 2018, filtered through 0.2 µm Whatman membrane filters, and served as the media in next experiment that followed the same conditions as described above.

2.2.2. *R. subcapitata*

Raphidocelis subcapitata ATCC 22662, was obtained from Culture Collection of Autotrophic Organisms (CCALA, Czech Republic). The culture was cultivated under a 130 µmol photons·m^{-2} s^{-1} of constant white light illumination and gently bubbled by 1% CO_2 mixed with air at room temperature (24 °C). The cultivations were conducted in a 500 mL flask containing Sueoka's high salt medium (HSM) [5]. Three different experimental conditions were set up, namely the: i) unexposed *R. subcapitata* (control), ii) *R. subcapitata* with 100 mg L^{-1} of nFe_3O_4 and iii) *R. subcapitata* with 100 mg L^{-1} of nZVI. A 35 mL culture was sampled immediately after nanoparticle mixture with cells in HSM for RNA extraction.

2.3. RNA isolation

2.3.1. *P. putida*

Eight RNA extraction protocols from several manufacturers including TRI reagent, RNAzol (Molecular Research Center, United Kingdom), TRIzol (Invitrogen, USA), DirectZol, Quick DNA/RNA microprep (Zymo Research, USA), NucleoSpin RNA Plus, NucleoSpin miRNA (Macherey Nagel, Germany) and ISOLATE II RNA Mini (Bioline, Canada) were used for the comparison. Based on our preliminary experiments, the magnetic nZVI particles had to be removed by a strong nickel-plated block magnet (70 mm x 70 mm x 25 mm) with a magnetic force approximately at 180 kg to minimize interference with RNA. The cell lysis and extractions were done according to the manufacturer's protocols. Complete elimination of contaminating residual DNA was further done with TURBO DNA-*free*™ kit (Invitrogen, USA). The integrity of the total RNA was determined by 2200 TapeStation system (Agilent Technologies, Germany) and the concentration using Qubit™ (Life Technologies, USA). All electropherograms of ribosomal RNA (rRNA) peaks were computed and analysed by TapeStation software version A.02.02 SR1 (Agilent Technologies, Germany).

2.3.2. *R. subcapitata*

RNA isolation of microalgae *R. subcapitata* involved two major steps: the cell lysis and then the RNA extraction procedure. Several cell lysis methods were first compared using cell ribolization on a ribolyzer, liquid nitrogen grinding, and overnight cell lyophilisation at -30 °C to effectively lyse the cell walls while releasing the cellular components. To compare different cell lysis method used, the disintegration of the microalgae cell membranes were then imaged under optical microscopy (Motic BA310, Motic, China). The efficiencies of three on-column RNA extraction protocols including ISOLATE II RNA Plant mini (Bioline, Canada), Quick-RNA™ Miniprep kit (Zymo Research, U.S.A), RNeasy Plant Mini kit (Qiagen, Germany), and phenol-chloroform extraction [6] were compared to extract the RNA following the manufacturer's instructions. Untreated cell pellets and cells exposed to nFe_3O_4 and nZVI were obtained through centrifugation at 10000 *x g* for 3 min at 4 °C and were subjected to different cell lysing methods mentioned above. The nanoparticles were not removed by the magnet for the studies of microalgae. The cell pellets including the retained nanoparticles were then immediately transferred into ZR BashingBeads™ Lysis Tubes (Zymo Research, USA) and added the RNA lysis buffer or aqua phenol was added. The tubes were put to liquid nitrogen and cell beating was performed in a ribolyzer (Precellys, France) at 6500 rpm for a total of two beating cycles with 45 s per cycle and 15 s break in between cycles. The subsequent RNA washing steps and recovery of both small and large RNA fractions were followed as instructed in the RNA purification protocol (Zymo Research, U.S.A) or isopropanol/ethanol washing using the phenol-chloroform extraction. Complete DNA removal was performed using on-column treatment and clean RNA extracts were eluted in diethylpyrocarbonate (DEPC) treated water. The integrity and concentration of the RNA extracts were determined respectively with an Agilent 2100 Bioanalyzer system (Agilent Technologies, Germany) and Nanodrop (Thermo Scientific, USA). All electropherograms of rRNA peaks were computed and analysed by 2100 Expert software (Agilent Technologies, Germany).

3. RESULTS AND DISCUSSION

3.1. Evaluation of efficient RNA extraction method from nanoparticle spiked medium

We tested and evaluated different RNA extraction protocols on the bacterium *P. putida* and green alga *R. subcapitata* in the presence of reactive nZVI. Based on our preliminary *P. putida*-nanopaticle study, the nZVI particles were removed using a strong magnet from the culture before the RNA extraction. This step prevented clogging of the columns later during the RNA washing step and, importantly enabled to yield a higher quality of RNA. A strong magnet of magnetizing force of 180 kg was capable to remove most of the nZVI particles. On the contrary, the nanoparticles were not removed in the case of *R. subcapitata* exposure and the RNA extraction was performed with the nanoparticles present in the culture. The two different sampling methods, although yielded desirable RNA quality, need further care because with nZVI, also part of the cells could be retained or, on the other hand, nZVI could react with lysis buffer when left in the culture.

3.1.1. RNA extraction from *P. putida*

Eight different extraction protocols have been compared including on-column and phenol-chloroform extractions. RNA extraction by the phenol-chloroform method was able to recover both small and large fractions of RNA (**Figures 1A-D**) while RNA extraction using most of the commercial column kits were often unable to elute both the RNA types in a single elution (**Figures 1E-H**). Phenol extraction using RNAzol and on-column extraction using Bioline ISOLATE II RNA mini kit exhibited the highest extraction efficiency with the RNA integrity number (RIN^e) and RNA concentrations shown in **Figure 1.** Each of these extraction methods (RNAzol and Bioline RNA mini) in general yield a similar RIN^e value in comparison to the untreated control and nZVI spiked samples which can be seen in their RIN^e from RNAzol extraction ($RIN_{control}$: 7.7; RIN_{nZVI}: 7.9), (**Figure 1C**) and RIN^e from Bioline ISOLATE II RNA mini kit ($RIN_{control}$: 9.0; RIN_{nZVI}: 8.9), **Figure 1G.** In general, Bioline ISOLATE II RNA mini kit has been chosen for our following analysis of the *P. putida*-nZVI spiked samples, as the extraction outcome yielded the highest RIN^e.

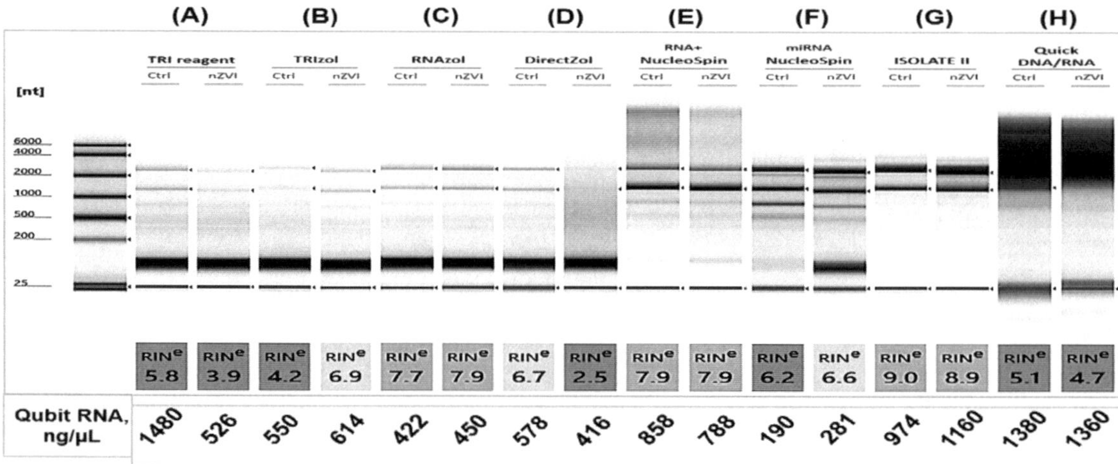

Figure 1 Comparison of RNA extraction methods performed on *P. putida*-nZVI samples in carbonate buffer (pH 8.0) on a TapeStation system based on RNA integrity number (RINe) and RNA concentrations are shown in the bottom line. Ctrl: condition without nZVI, nZVI: with nZVI. Different RNA extraction methods used were: (A) TRI reagent, (B) TRIzol, (C) RNAzol, (D) DirectZol, (E) RNA Plus NucleoSpin, (F) miRNA NucleoSPin, (G) ISOLATE II, (H) Quick DNA/RNA

The RNA extraction efficiency by Bioline ISOLATE II RNA mini kit isolated from control, nZVI Fe ions and nZVI spiked samples is shown in **Figure 2A**. The representative electropherogram peaks of the control, nZVI Fe ions and nZVI clearly showed the intact 16S and 23S peaks (**Figures 2C-E)**. Based on our experience, optimizing a suitable RNA extraction method for such difficult samples could be a daunting process at the beginning, especially when the information on the sample/organisms are still scarce. The consistency of the RINe obtained is important when selecting a suitable extraction assay fitting to the biological properties of the samples, especially when working with many treatment conditions in parallel and a huge number of samples.

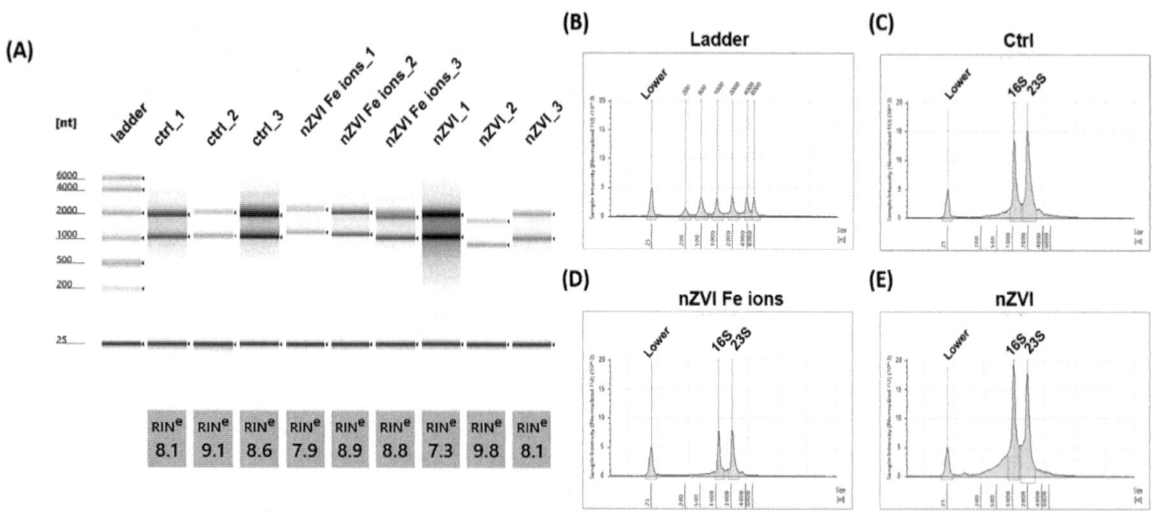

Figure 2 RNA integrity numbers of all isolated RNA from *P. putida* samples exposed to nZVI Fe ions and nZVI compared on a TapeStation system (A), and electropherograms of rRNA peaks of RNA ladder (B), control (C), nZVI Fe ions (D), nZVI (E) using Bioline ISOLATE II RNA mini kit

3.1.2. RNA extraction of *R. subcapitata*

The cell lysis efficiency by liquid nitrogen grinding, cell ribolization, and cell lyophilization was evaluated using *R. subcapitata* when in contact with 100 mg L^{-1} nFe_3O_4 or nZVI. Prior to that, the integrity of the cells were screened using a light microscope **(Figure 3)** by comparing the efficiencies of different cell lysis method used. The cells after the liquid nitrogen grinding looked very similar to those in control samples, where only a small amount of cells were lysed (**Figures 3A,B**). A previous genome study of *R. subcapitata* [7] described successful isolation of RNA from a 100 mL culture using the same liquid nitrogen grinding method, however, it should be noted that the isolation of RNA from a 100 mL culture, by theory should yield higher RNA compared to our culture volume of 35 mL. *R. subcapitata* belongs to the family *Selenastraceae*, is a robust microalgae containing very rigid polysaccharide-based cell wall recalcitrance to breakage [7,8]. These polysaccharides, upon cell disruption, co-precipitates the RNA [9] which then complicated the RNA extraction procedure and resulted low yield/quality of RNA. In our study, the RNA extraction protocol has been tailored to *R. subcapitata* using cell lysis procedure combining the overnight lyophilization of cells followed by ribolization of the cells resuspended in RNA lysis buffer resulted in the highest lysis efficiency (**Figure 3C**).

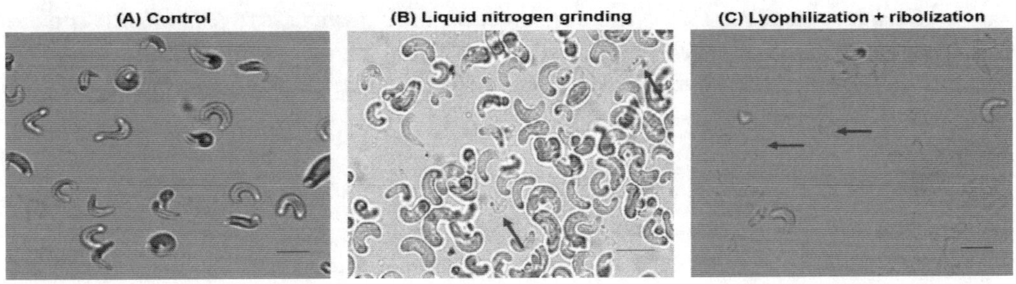

Figure 3 Light microscopic images of *R. subcapitata* cell lysis before RNA extraction: A - control cells before lysis, B - cells after liquid nitrogen grinding, C - overnight lyophilisation of wet biomass prior to ribolization. Red arrows indicate the lysed empty cells. Scale bar = 15 µm

The efficiency of different RNA extraction methods were then compared. Among the tested methods, phenol-chloroform extraction yielded the highest RIN working with the *R. subcapitata*-nanoparticles spiked samples and is shown in **Figure 4**. The representative electropherogram peaks of the experimental condition in respective to control, nFe_3O_4 and nZVI show the 18S and 28S peaks (**Figures 4B-D**).

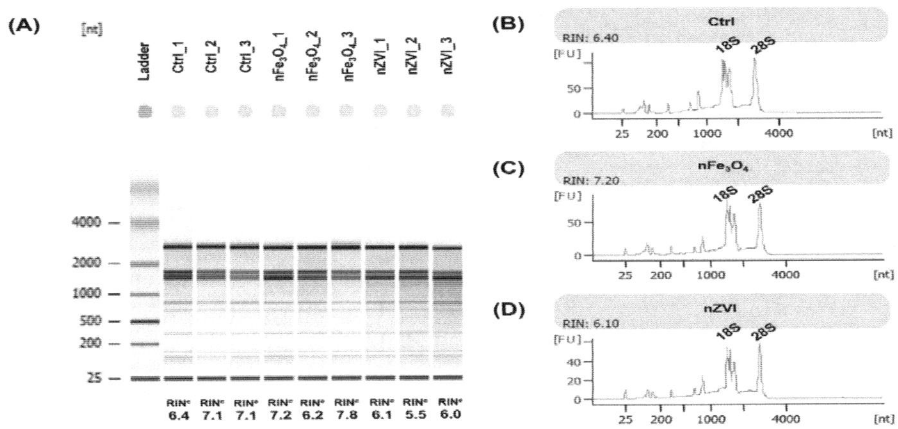

Figure 4 RNA integrity numbers of all isolated *R. subcapitata* samples compared on a bioanalyzer system (A), and electropherogram of rRNA peaks of untreated control (B), nFe_3O_4 (C), nZVI (D) using phenol-chloroform extraction method

4. CONCLUSION

Based on our data, extraction of the RNA from *P. putida*-nZVI samples was straightforward using the column-based extraction kit (Bioline ISOLATE II RNA Mini) while isolation of the RNA from freshwater microalgae *R. subcapitata* in nZVI or nFe_3O_4 spiked samples required an initial step including thorough cell lysis by combining overnight lyophilization of wet biomass, followed by ribolization of the dried biomass suspended in phenol and finally RNA isolation through phenol-based extraction. Presence of nZVI in the sample during cell lysis and RNA extraction did not considerably harmed the RNA isolated from *R. subcapitata*. In general, the column-based RNA extraction methods are recommended, except when isolation is compromised by polysaccharides or compounds which can bind to and/or co-precipitate with RNA. In such cases, phenol-based extraction methods may offer higher quality RNA obtained.

ACKNOWLEDGEMENTS

This project was financially supported by the Technical University of Liberec through project No. PURE-2019800 (Environmental fate, behaviour and biological effects of engineered nanomaterials) and partly by German Academic Exchange Service short term grants, 2019 (57440917). The authors acknowledge the assistance provided by the Research Infrastructures NanoEnviCz (Project No. LM2018124) supported by the MŠMT of the Czech Republic

REFERENCES

[1] TRATNYEK, P. G. and JOHNSON, R. L. Nanotechnologies for environmental cleanup. *Nano Today*. [online]. 2006, vol. 1, no. 2, pp. 44-48. Available from: https://doi.org/10.1016/S1748-0132(06)70048-2.

[2] SCHMID, D., MICIĆ, V., LAUMANN, S., HOFMANN, T. Measuring the reactivity of commercially available zero-valent iron nanoparticles used for environmental remediation with iopromide. *J. Contam. Hydrol.* [online]. 2014, vol. 181, pp. 36-45. Available from: https://doi.org/10.1016/j.jconhyd.2015.01.006.

[3] *Guidance document on aquatic and sediment toxicological testing of nanomaterials*. [Online]. Paris, Jul. 2020. [Accessed: Sep. 15, 2020]. Available from: www.oecd.org/chemicalsafety/.

[4] NANOFER STAR | NANOIRON. [accessed Sep. 14, 2020]. Avalaible from: https://nanoiron.cz/getattachment/7aa3e8c5-5701-4a47-b05c-b91f87279aae/NANOFER-STAR-processing-activation-manual.aspx.

[5] SUEOKA, N. Mitotic replication of deoxyribonucleic acid in chlamydomonas reinhardi. *Proc. Natl. Acad. Sci.* [online]., 1960, vol. 46, no. 1, pp. 83-91. Available from: https://doi.org/10.1073/pnas.46.1.83.

[6] CHOMCZYNSKI, P. and SACCHI, N. The single-step method of RNA isolation by acid guanidinium thiocyanate-phenol-chloroform extraction: twenty-something years on. *Nat. Protoc.* [online]. 2006, vol. 1, no. 2, pp. 581-585. Available from: https://doi.org/10.1038/nprot.2006.83.

[7] SUZUKI, S., YAMAGUCHI, H., NAKAJIMA, N., and KAWACHI, M. Raphidocelis subcapitata (=Pseudokirchneriella subcapitata) provides an insight into genome evolution and environmental adaptations in the Sphaeropleales. *Sci. Rep.* [online]. 2018, vol. 8, no. 1, pp. 1-13. Available from: https://doi.org/10.1038/s41598-018-26331-6.

[8] BURCZYK, J. and DWORZANSKI, J. Comparison of sporopollenin-like algal resistant polymer from cell wall of Botryococcus, scenedesmus and lycopodium clavatum by GC-pyrolysis. *Phytochemistry*. [online]. 1988, vol. 27, no. 7, pp. 2151-2153. Available from: https://doi.org/10.1016/0031-9422(88)80115-8.

[9] DOS REIS FALCÃO, V., PEDROSO TONON, A., CABRAL OLIVEIRA, M. and COLEPICOLO, P. RNA isolation method for polysaccharide rich algae: Agar producing Gracilaria tenuistipitata (Rhodophyta). *J. Appl. Phycol.* [online]. 2008, vol. 20, no. 1, pp. 9-12. Available from: https://doi.org/10.1007/s10811-007-9174-7.

SENSITIVE LATERAL FLOW IMMUNOASSAY OF UNDECLARED CHICKEN INGREDIENT IN MEAT PRODUCTS

Olga D. HENDRICKSON, Elena A. ZVEREVA, Anatoly V. ZHERDEV, Boris B. DZANTIEV

A.N. Bach Institute of Biochemistry, Research Center of Biotechnology of the Russian Academy of Sciences, Moscow, Russia, odhendrick@gmail.com

https://doi.org/10.37904/nanocon.2020.3761

Abstract

This study presents the development of the lateral flow assay (LFIA) for the determination of undeclared chicken additives in meat products. In the test system, immunoglobulins were proposed as biomarkers for species identification. A sandwich format of the LFIA based on gold nanoparticles (AuNPs) as nano-dispersed labels and colorimetric detection (both visual and instrumental) is used to determine immunoglobulins and, consequently, a source of meat. To achieve the highest analytical parameters, the LFIA was optimized by varying the assay conditions. A simple method of sample preparation was proposed. The developed LFIA allows distinguishing poultry (chicken, turkey) meat sources from mammalian sources within 20 min. The developed LFIA was applied to analyze meat foodstuffs and allowed revealing an adulteration with up to 0.063% (w/w) sensitivity. The proposed test system can be recommended for rapid on-site screening control of the composition and quality of meat products.

Keywords: Immunoglobulins, lateral flow immunoassay, meat adulteration, chicken additives

1. INTRODUCTION

Currently, counterfeiting food products is a relevant problem [1]. The presence of undeclared components in meat products carries risks to human health causing digestive disorders, allergic reactions, etc. [2,3]. Therefore, the task of meat quality control arises, including obtaining reliable information about raw meat sources as well as determining composition of semi-finished and finished meat products. The high efficiency of this control is ensured by application of reliable and efficient analytical methods and effective molecular markers.

Methods for identifying meat sources include traditional approaches such as microstructural, molecular genetic methods, electrophoresis, and chromatography [4]. These complicated and time-consuming techniques should be complemented by rapid and cost-effective tests to carry out mass monitoring of meat products. Immunoanalytical methods having high specificity and sensitivity can be proposed for this purpose. One of the immunoassay formats is immunochromatographic analysis (lateral flow immunoassay, LFIA) based on the movement of reagents with a liquid flow along the porous membrane followed by formation of colored bands on the test strip [5-7]. The advantages of LFIA include short time (10-20 min), easy application, and no need for complex equipment and skilled personnel.

In this study, chicken immunoglobulins Y (IgY) were selected as a molecular identifier, which satisfies the basic requirements for molecular biomarkers. They are present in muscle tissues in high concentrations, can be easily extracted from them and allow the identification based on the differences in antigenic determinants for different animal species. In addition, immunoglobulin receptor molecules (anti-species antibodies) are commercially available and cheap. The LFIA to reveal pork adulteration in beef based on IgG biomarker was developed in [8] and allowed a detection limit of 0.1% (w/w).

In this study, the LFIA is for the first time developed for IgY determination in raw meat and processed meat products. A sandwich-format LFIA is based on anti-species antibodies and their labeled conjugates. As a nano-dispersed label, gold nanoparticles (AuNPs) were selected. The main advantages of AuNPs are simple procedure of their synthesis, long-lasting stability, high analytical signal, and chemical inertness [9]. A simple and rapid technique of sample preparation was implemented that does not require heating the analyzed sample, which accelerate the entire assay.

2. EXPERIMENTAL

2.1. Materials

Sodium citrate, 3,3',5,5'-tetramethylbenzidine (TMB), chloroauric acid ($HAuCl_4$), sodium azide, Triton X-100, bovine serum albumin (BSA), Tween-20, and sucrose were obtained from Sigma Chemicals (St. Louis, MO, USA). Chicken polyclonal immunoglobulins (IgY) and rabbit anti-chicken polyclonal IgG (RACI) were purchased from Imtek (Moscow, Russia). Goat monoclonal antibodies against rabbit IgG (GARI) were obtained from Arista Biologicals (Allentown, PA, USA). All other compounds were characterized by chemical or analytical purity. Milli-Q deionized water (Millipore, Burlington, VT, USA) was used for preparation of solutions.

2.2. Synthesis of AuNPs

AuNPs were synthesized as described in [10]. Briefly, a 1% $HAuCl_4$ solution (0.5 mL) was mixed with deionized water (48.75 mL). The resulting mixture was heated to boiling followed by addition of 1% sodium citrate solution (0.75 mL). Then, the mixture was boiled while stirring for 25 min. The prepared AuNPs were cooled and stored at 4 °C.

2.3. Conjugation of RACI with AuNPs

RACI-AuNPs conjugate was prepared as described in [11]. RACI (10 µg/mL) in 10 mM Tris-HCl buffer, pH 8.5, were added to AuNPs (OD_{520} = 1) and stirred for 45 min at room temperature. After that, 10% BSA solution was added (1:40, vol./vol.) and incubated for 15 min. The conjugate was centrifuged at 8,500 g for 20 min. The pellet containing RACI-AuNPs was resuspended in 10 mM Tris buffer, pH 8.5, with 0.1% sodium azide, 1% sucrose, and 1% BSA.

2.4. Production of test strips

To obtain the test strips, MdiEasypack membrane sets (Advanced Microdevices, India) were used including a GFB-R4 separation membrane, a working CNPC membrane having pore size of 15 µm, and an AP045 adsorption membrane. GARI (0.5 mg/mL in PBS) and RACI (1 mg/mL in PBS) were applied to form a control zone and an analytical zone, respectively, with an Iso-Flow automatic dispenser (Imagene Technology, Hanover, NH, USA). The membranes were dried overnight at room temperature and assembled to the composite. Test strips of a 3.2 mm width was obtained using an automatic guillotine cutter (KinBio, Shanghai, China).

2.5. Preparation of meat samples

Raw meat (beef, pork, chicken, and turkey) as well as dumplings were purchased at local supermarkets. Beef and pork-based cooked sausages with a confirmed composition were produced at the factory for manufacturing of meat products of the V.M. Gorbatov Federal Research Center for Food Systems of the Russian Academy of Sciences. For sample preparation, all raw meat and meat products were minced. A number of raw meat mixtures were obtained from beef and pork containing 10%, 5%, 1%, 0.5%, 0.25%, 0.125%, 0.063%, and 0.031% (w/w) of chicken meat.

For extraction, 5 mL of the extraction buffer (PBS containing 0.5 M KCl and 0.1% Triton X-100) was added to 250 mg of a homogenized meat sample. The samples were mixed intensively for 15 min, sonicated in an ultrasound bath for 10 min, and then centrifuged for 10 min at 5,000 g and room temperature. Supernatants were used for the LFIA.

2.6. LFIA of IgY

Solutions of IgY in PBST (a total volume of 100 µL), in concentration ranges of 10,000-0.01 ng/mL, were added to Eppendorf tubes. Then, 2.5 µL of RACl-AuNPs conjugate (OD_{520} = 12) was added to each tube and incubated for 5 min. The test strip was inserted into the tube and incubated for 15 min. For IgY determination in meat products, the corresponding extracts were added to the tubes. All other steps of the LFIA were the same as described above.

2.7. Processing of the LFIA data

Origin 7.5 software (Origin Lab, Northampton, MA, USA) was used to approximate the dependence of the color intensity on IgY concentration. The concentration of IgY leading to 90% inhibition of the signal was taken as an instrumental limit of detection (LOD) [12]. The upper and lower limits of the working range were considered as the immunoglobulins' concentrations corresponding to 20% and 80% inhibition of the coloration, respectively. The minimum IgY concentration that would cause an appearance of the colored band in the analytical zone was interpreted as the cutoff value of the LFIA.

3. RESULTS AND DISCUSSION

3.1. Synthesis and characterization of AuNPs

To label RACl, AuNPs as a nano-dispersed marker were used. The reduction of $HAuCl_4$ by sodium citrate was used to prepare AuNPs [10]. Both the reaction time and ratio of reagents were selected to obtain AuNPs with a diameter of 30 nm. A nano-dispersed carrier of this size is considered to be optimal in immunochromatography because it provides a high analytical signal and good sorption capacity [9]. Transmission electron microscopy (TEM) on a JEM-100C microscope (JEOL, Japan) was used to analyze AuNPs. The TEM study of their dimensional characteristics and homogeneity revealed that the obtained AuNPs are o-shaped non-aggregated particles of a 33.7 ± 9.0 nm diameter. A microphotograph of nanoparticles and a histogram of their diameter distribution is presented in **Figure 1**.

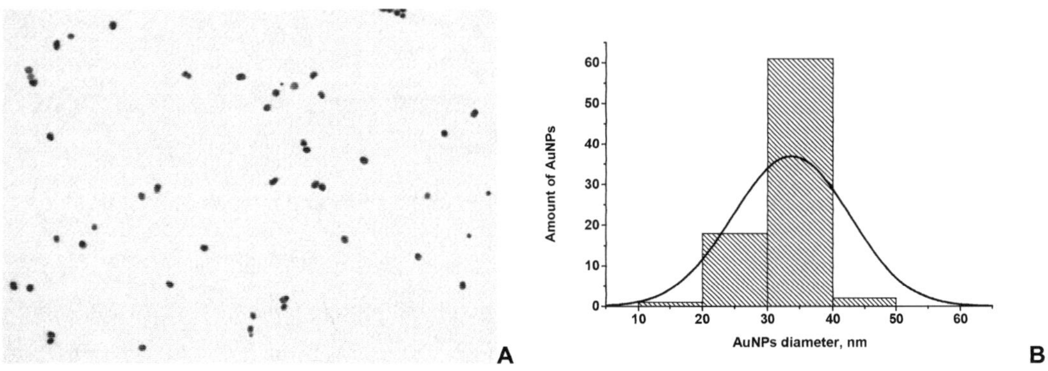

Figure 1 Image of AuNPs obtained by TEM (A) and histogram of their diameter distribution (B)

RACl were conjugated to AuNPs by a noncovalent absorption. Before conjugation, the optimal concentration of IgG was determined. For that purpose, a flocculation curve demonstrating the dependencies of AuNPs' optical density on the concentration of the immobilized IgG was studied. It was demonstrated that particles' stabilization ensured by the adsorption of protein molecules was reached at a concentration of 10 µg/mL. Therefore, we used this concentration to conjugate RACI with AuNPs.

3.2. Development of the LFIA of IgY

In this investigation, a sandwich LFIA, which is the most common format for the determination of compounds with high molecular weight was realized [13]. Here, we applied GARI and RACI on the control and analytical zones of the test strip, respectively. On the first step, the analyzed sample was preincubated with anti-species (RACI) antibodies labeled with AuNPs. Then, the test strips were dipped into the mixture and after incubation the coloration of zones was estimated. If chicken IgY present in the analyzed sample, their complexes with RACI-AuNPs conjugate are formed, followed by the interaction of these complexes with RACI adsorbed in the analytical zone and, accordingly, the formation of the first colored band. Excess of the complexes binds in the control zone and forms a second colored band. In the absence of the tested immunoglobulins, only one red-colored band is formed in the control zone.

To ensure low LOD and high intensity of coloration, different concentrations of immunoreagents, duration of steps, compositions of the reaction medium, and other parameters were tested. As a result, we selected RACI and GARI concentrations of 1 mg/mL and 0.5 mg/mL, respectively, as optimal (we varied both concentrations in the range of 0.25-1 mg/mL). RACI-AuNPs conjugate was added to the solution with chicken IgY in a volume of 2.5 µL at a dilution corresponding to OD_{520} = 12 (we tested the amounts of 0.5-3 µL). As for the duration of the assay steps, the best analytical parameters of the LFIA were reached at 5-min reaction of IgY with RACI-AuNPs followed by 15-min incubation of the strip with this mixture.

Chicken IgY calibration curve in the sandwich LFIA obtained after optimization and images of the corresponding test strips are presented in **Figure 2**. The instrumental LOD of chicken IgY in the biffer was 20 ng/mL, and the working range of the detected concentrations was 40-275 ng/mL. The cutoff was 4.6 ng/mL.

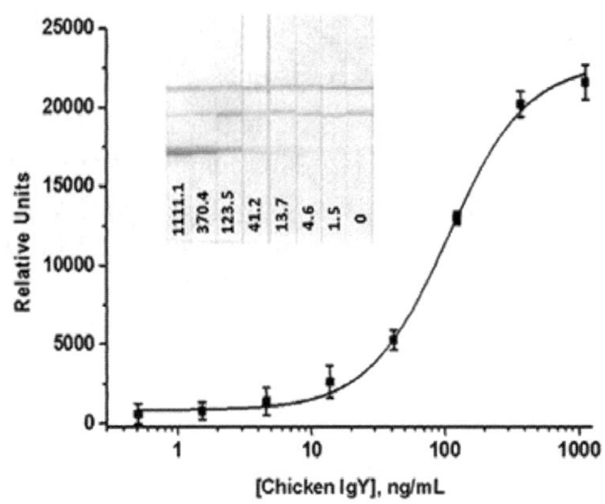

Figure 2 Calibration curve for chicken immunoglobulins in the LFIA and images of the test strips

3.3. LFIA of food samples

The obtained data allowed for the approbation of the developed test system for controlling chicken content in meat products. Since raw meat and meat products are complex matrices, which components may affect test results, it was necessary to implement sample preparation aimed at effective extracting IgY before analysis. For this, a fast and simple procedure was proposed, consisting of samples' homogenization, protein extraction with a phosphate buffer, sonication of extracts, and centrifugation. Obtained supernatants were used for the LFIA. As tested samples, raw meat, dumplings purchased in local supermarkets and beef and pork-based cooked sausages with a confirmed composition were used.

The specificity of the developed test system was determined by analyzing extracts of chicken, beef, pork, and turkey meat. It was shown that the colored bands formed only for chicken and turkey extracts (**Figure 3A**). Therefore, there was no cross-reactivity with immunoglobulins of mammalian species. High specificity of the test system excludes false positive results and contributes to their reliability.

The sensitivity of the assay was studied by analyzing extracts of beef and pork with the addition of a known amount of chicken. Based on the data obtained, the test system allowed for the detection of 0.063 to 0.125% (w/w) chicken additives in beef and pork, respectively, that is about 1 g of chicken per 1 kg of other meat.

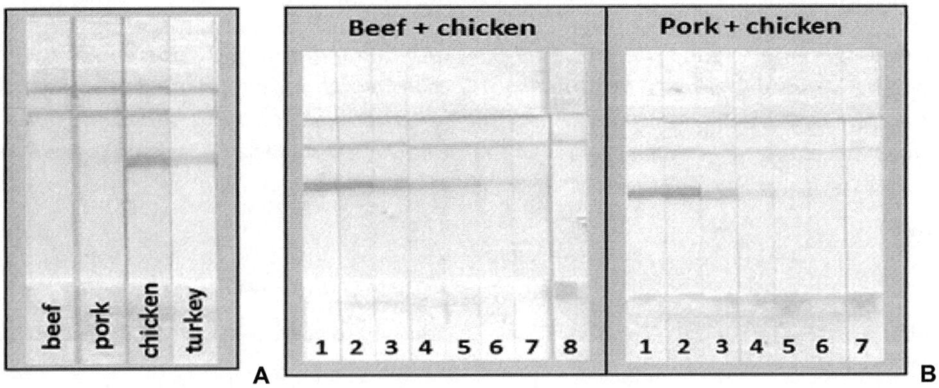

Figure 3 The results of the LFIA performed on minced meat extracts (A), and minced meat mixtures (B). The numbers in (B) indicate the chicken meat content (w/w): 10% (1); 5% (2); 1% (3); 0.5% (4); 0.25% (5); 0.125% (6); 0.063% (7); and 0.031% (8)

At the next step, two kinds of dumplings (chicken and venison/pork) were tested. Minced meat contained in dumplings was separated from the dough and processed according to the developed method of sample preparation. The images of test strips obtained after the assay are presented in **Figure 4A**. It was shown that chicken IgY were detected only in dumplings, which contained chicken according to the product labeling (sample a). Three samples of sausages (cooked, smoked/cooked/smoked, and cooked/smoked) all containing pork or bacon in addition to beef were tested. The results demonstrated the absence of chicken additives in all samples, which is evidenced by appearing no coloration of the analytical zone of the strip (**Figure 4B**).

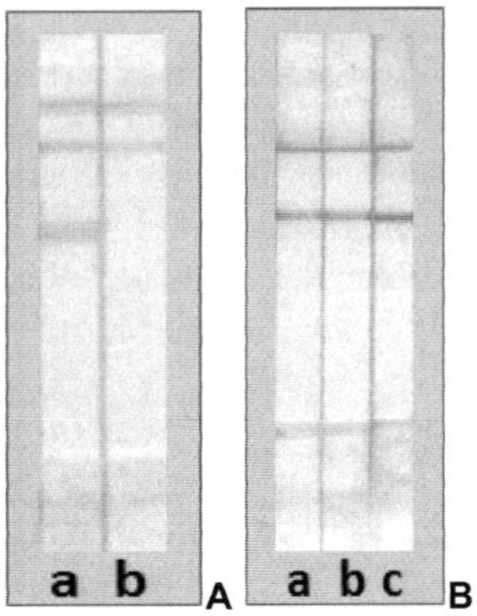

Figure 4 Images of test strips after the LFIA of the processed dumplings (A): (a) chicken dumplings, (b) venison/pork dumplings and sausages (B): cooked (a), smoked/cooked/smoked (b), cooked/smoked (c)

4. CONCLUSION

Overall, an immunochromatographic analysis was developed, which allows for the detection of chicken immunoglobulins with a cutoff of 4.6 ng/mL. A simple technique was proposed for sample preparation of raw meat and meat products before the LFIA. The test system is characterized by high specificity and allows detecting 0.063-0.125% of chicken impurities in beef and pork within 20 min. The applicability of the test system for the analysis of chicken content in dumplings and sausages was confirmed. The developed analysis can be recommended for rapid out-of-laboratory screening of meat products.

ACKNOWLEDGMENTS

This work was supported by the Russian Science Foundation (grant 19-16-00108). The authors are grateful to S.M. Pridvorova (Research Center of Biotechnology) for supplying and processing TEM microphotographs and to N.S. Vostrikova (V.M. Gorbatov Federal Research Center for Food Systems of the Russian Academy of Sciences) for manufacturing sausages of controlled composition.

REFERENCES

[1] BANSAL, S., SINGH, A., MANGAL, M., MANGAL, A.K., KUMAR, S. Food adulteration: Sources, health risks, and detection methods. *Critical Reviews in Food Science and Nutrition.* 2017, vol. 7, no. 6, pp.1174-1189.

[2] De SMET, S. VOSSEN, E. Meat: The balance between nutrition and health. A review. *Meat Science.* 2016, vol. 120, pp. 145-156.

[3] JOHNSON, I.T. The cancer risk related to meat and meat products. *British Medical Bulletin.* 2017, vol. 121, pp. 73-81.

[4] VLACHOS, A., ARVANITOYANNIS, I.S., TSERKEZOU, P. An updated review of meat authenticity methods and applications. *Critical Reviews in Food Science and Nutrition.* 2016, vol. 56, no. 7, pp. 1061-1096.

[5] HUANG, X., AGUILAR, Z.P., XU, H., LAI, W., XIONG, Y. Membrane-based lateral flow immunochromatographic strip with nanoparticles as reporters for detection: A review. *Biosensors & Bioelectronics.* 2016, vol. 75, pp. 166-180.

[6] HSIEH, Y.H. & GAJEWSKI, K. Rapid detection of bovine adipose tissue using lateral flow strip assay. *Food Science & Nutrition.* 2016, vol. 4, no. 4, pp. 588-594.

[7] MASIRI, J., BENOIT, L., BARRIOS-LOPEZ, B., THIENES, C., MESHGI, M., AGAPOV, A., DOBRITSA, A., NADALA, C., SAMADPOUR, M. Development and validation of a rapid test system for detection of pork meat and collagen residues. *Meat Science.* 2016, vol. 121, pp. 397-402.

[8] KUSWANDI, B., GANI, A., Musa, A. Immuno strip test for detection of pork adulteration in cooked meatballs. *Food Bioscience.* 2017, vol. 19.

[9] DYKMAN, L.A. KHLEBTSOV, N.G. Biomedical applications of multifunctional gold-based nanocomposites. *Biochemistry Biokhimiia.* 2016, vol. 81, no. 13, pp. 1771-1789.

[10] FRENS, G. Controlled nucleation for the regulation of the particle size in monodisperse gold suspensions. *Nature Physical Science.* 1973, vol. 241, no. 105, pp. 20-22.

[11] HENDRICKSON, O.D., ZVEREVA, E.A., SHANIN, I.A., ZHERDEV, A.V., TARANNUM, N., DZANTIEV, B.B. Highly sensitive immunochromatographic detection of antibiotic ciprofloxacin in milk. *Applied Biochemistry and Microbiology.* 2018, vol. 54, pp. 670-676.

[12] UHROVCIK, J. Strategy for determination of LOD and LOQ values--some basic aspects. *Talanta.* 2014, vol. 119, pp. 178-180.

[13] PEI, X., ZHANG, B., TANG, J., LIU, B., LAI, W., TANG, D. Sandwich-type immunosensors and immunoassays exploiting nanostructure labels: A review. *Analytica Chimica Acta.* 2013, vol. 758, pp. 1-18.

INFLUENCE OF THE APPLICATION OF LIGNITE ON THE DISTRIBUTION OF ORGANIC CARBON IN SOIL

David ŠIRŮČEK, Michal KALINA, Martina KLUČÁKOVÁ

Brno University of Technology, Faculty of Chemistry, Brno, Czech Republic, EU

https://doi.org/10.37904/nanocon.2020.3765

Abstract

This contribution is focused on utilization of a sequential chemical fractionation method for determination of organic matter content and its distribution in soil. Subsequently, this fractionation procedure was used to characterize the possible use of lignite as a soil conditioner in agriculture. For these purposes the optimized chemical fractionation procedure was used to describe the effect of lignite application on content and distribution of organic matter in a model soil. For these purposes, there were three source matrices of organic matter (lignite, soil and annual soil extraction after lignite application) fractionated by sequential chemical analysis. In parallel, these samples were also fractionated by classic alkaline extraction to obtain the so-called extractable fraction of organic matter (NOM). Individual fractions from sequential chemical fractionation as well as NOM samples were characterized by methods of elemental analysis (determination of organic elements content), thermogravimetry (contents of ash, organic matter and moisture) and FTIR spectrometry (structural analysis). The results showed that the method of sequential chemical fractionation gives higher yields of organic matter compared to classical alkaline extraction. Moreover, the obtained fractions divided according to solubility and strength of binding to soil inorganics can be better characterized by physical-chemical methods, which provides more detailed information about soil organic matter. The results of the work also indicated that the effect of lignite on soil organic matter must be considered in a larger time scale to be able to get more complex description of such a complex system.

Keywords: Soil, lignite, organic matter, chemical fractionation, elemental analysis, thermogravimetric analysis, FTIR spectrometry

1. INTRODUCTION

Soils are composed of mineral and organic particles of various sizes, that are organized in a soil matrix. This organization means that about 50% of the total volume is occupied by these particles and the remaining 50% of the volume is a porous space that contains water and air and serves as a system of channels for the transport of these substances. Soil organic matter (SOM) is one of the soil components consisting of three basic types - living organisms (worms, insects, microorganisms), dead microorganisms and finally matter formed from organic residues of plants, animals and humus. The decomposition of the first two types creates nutrients for plants (nitrogen, potassium, phosphorus) [1-3]. The main reactive part of SOM are humic substances - omnipresent natural substances arising from the chemical and biological degradation of plants and animal remains. They are crucial in ecosystems because they regulate global carbon and nitrogen cycles, the growth of plants and microorganisms, the transport of anthropogenic compounds and heavy metals, and the stabilization of soil structure. To date, however, no technologies have been developed to control the activity of humic substances due to their high molecular complexity. There is a broad variety of analytical techniques for their characterization, however, none of these techniques alone is sufficient to elucidate the structural complexity of particles of humic molecules [4,5].

In general, humic substances are supramolecular associations of heterogeneous, relatively small molecules that are held together by weak non-covalent interactions, such as hydrogen bonds and hydrophobic forces.

The complexity of the humic molecule can be reduced by the gradual destruction of intramolecular interactions that stabilize these complex suprastructures (composed of nanoparticles of organic matter) and thus individual fractions of colloidal size of humic substances (organic matter) can be isolated. These individual fractions of organic matter obtained from sequential fractionation are called humeomics. It is a gradual separation of molecules from humic suprastructures by controlled cleavage of intermolecular bonds. In terms of particle size, these particles obtained by sequential fractionation are colloidal in size which significantly improve the resolution of various analytical methods often used for characterization [6,7].

In recent years, increasing demands have been placed on crop yields which also brings with it increased demands on soil fertility. For these reasons, various substances are often used to increase fertility, which are added artificially. They are most often fertilizers. Recently, however, research has also focused on the application of alternative additives to soils in order not only to increase fertility but also to improve the physicochemical properties of the soil and to increase the content and stabilization of soil organic matter. These additives are often included in a group called - soil supportive substances (SSS). Substances that are widely used for application include, for example, lignite fly ash, biochar and a mixture of humic acids. It is also very important to apply a suitable form with a given particle size, internal structure and morphology (porous structure) [8,9].

2. EXPERIMENTAL

2.1. Materials and Methods

Three source matrices of organic matter were used.

- Soil (arid sandy soil obtained from the locality Hodonin-Panov, GPS: 48.877184°N, 17.132040°E)
- Lignite (South Moravian lignite, mine Mir near Mikulcice, GPS: 48.820864°N, 17.045283°E)
- Soil sample after one year from lignite application (the same locality as original soil)

Each of these organic matrix samples served as a starting material for studying the effect of lignite application on the distribution of organic matter in the soil. For these purposes, the method of sequential chemical fractionation was used in the work. The initial samples of lignite and soil were used mainly as comparative samples, on the basis of which the differences in the distribution of organic matter in the soil before and after the application of lignite as a model soil support substance will be assessed. Three replicates of sequential chemical fractionation were performed for each of these three samples.

2.2. Sequential Chemical Fractionation

The procedure of sequential chemical fractionation was adopted from the publications of Nebbioso and Drossos [6,7]. The details of the optimization of this chemical extraction procedure of organic matter for the samples of soil and lignite are summarized in chapters 2.2.1 - 2.3.

2.2.1. Water soluble fraction 1 (AQU1)

First step was to dry used organic material in an oven at 45 °C to evaporate all the water. Then 50 g of dried material was transferred to Erlenmeyer flask and 150 ml of 0,1 M HCl was added. Flasks were covered with a double layer of parafilm and left on a shaker overnight. The next day samples were filtered under reduced pressure. Filtrate was frozen and all the water was evaporated in a freeze drier.

2.2.2. Organic soluble fraction 1 (ORG1)

Dried solid material after AQU1 was mixed with 100 ml DCM and 50 ml MeOH in Erlenmeyer flask and covered with a double layer of aluminium foil and left on a shaker overnight. The next day samples were filtered under reduced pressure. All the solvent was evaporated on a rotary evaporator at 50 °C. The residue after evaporation was transferred to vials left to evaporate the solvent.

2.2.3. Water and organic soluble fractions 2 (AQU2 and ORG2)

Dried solid material after ORG1 separation was transferred to high-pressure sealable teflon vials and 50 ml of a 12% solution of boron trifluoride in methanol was added. Vials were tightly sealed, clamped in a metal rack and placed in an oven at 85 °C for 8 hours. Then vials were removed from the oven, let to cool down and additional 50 ml of the solution was added. Vials were sealed and clamped again and placed in the oven for another 8 hours under same conditions. Then after cooling down the solution was filtered under normal pressure and the solid material was dried. The filtrates were L/L extracted (liquid to liquid). The obtained AQU2 and ORG2 fractions were purified and dried in the same way as was described for AQU1 and ORG1.

2.2.4. Water and organic soluble fractions 3 (AQU3 and ORG3)

Dried solid material after the previous step was covered with 50 ml of 1 M solution of KOH in MeOH (for the lignite sample a 100 ml of the solution was used). A magnetic stirrer was added, the sample flask was attached to a direct condenser and heater was set to 75 °C. The mixture was refluxed under nitrogen atmosphere for 2 hours. Then all the content in the flask was filtrated under reduced pressure and the solid material was dried. The filtrates were extracted using L/L extraction. The obtained AQU3 and ORG3 fractions were purified and dried in the same way as was described for AQU1 and ORG1.

2.2.5. Water soluble fraction 4 (AQU4)

Dried solid material after the previous step was covered with 50 ml of a 47% solution of HI in water (for the lignite sample a 100 ml of the solution was used). A magnetic stirrer was added, the sample flask was attached to a direct condenser and heater was set to 75 °C. The mixture was refluxed under nitrogen atmosphere for 2 days. Then all the content in the flask was filtrated under reduced pressure and the solid material was dried. The filtrates were neutralized with $NaHCO_3$ to pH 7 and the iodine contained was reduced with $Na_2S_2O_3$. Then the filtrates were dialyzed against distilled water and freeze-dried.

2.2.6. Residual extractable organic matter fraction (ResOM)

To isolate the residual organic matter, 5 g of dried solid material after AQU4 fractionation and 45 ml of extractant (0,5 M NaOH and 0,1 M $Na_4P_2O_7$) were mixed. Samples were left on a shaker overnight. The samples were filtered and the filtrates were dialyzed against distilled water and freeze-dried.

2.3. Natural organic matter fraction isolation (NOM)

In parallel, a conventional alkaline extraction was performed. Thus 5 g of the prime material was covered with 45 ml of extractant (0,5 M NaOH and 0,1 M $Na_4P_2O_7$). After overnight shaking, the samples were filtered under reducer pressure and the filtrates were dialyzed against distilled water and freeze-dried.

3. RESULTS AND DISCUSSION

3.1. Optimization of sequential chemical fractionation procedure

The first part of experimental work was focused on the optimization of sequential chemical fractionation for analysis of soil and lignite samples to be able to provide more narrow distribution of particles. A comparison shown in **Figure 1** shows that only about a half on the organic matter can be extracted using NOM extraction (conventional alkaline extraction). But as shown in **Figure 1a**, only a very small amount of organic matter (about 10 %) was possible to obtain using sequential chemical fractionation. Comparing each fraction shown in **Figure 1b**, we may notice that most of the organic matter is contained within AQU1 and ORG1 fractions.

That is because these two fractions are only very weakly bounded to the lignite matrix. These results are indicating that significant part of lignite organic matter is strongly bound to residual non-extractable matter. This is a positive finding concerning the presumed long-term effect of lignite on the organic matter of the soil.

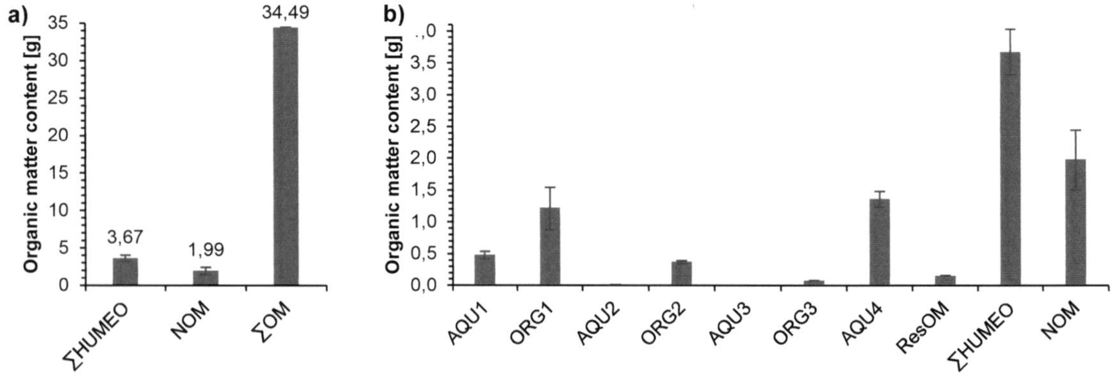

Figure 1 a) Comparison of total organic matter from lignite using alkaline extraction and sequential chemical fractionation where "∑HUMEO" means the total sum of the particle fractions obtained by sequentional fractionation and "∑OM" shows the total contain of organic matter contained in the soil matrix. This applies to all the graphs. **b)** Distribution of organic matter in the fractions of a lignite sample.

3.2. Effect of lignite application on soil

The main task of this part of the work was to use the methodology of sequential chemical fractionation to assess the effect of the addition of lignite to the soil on the composition and distribution of organic matter. In general, the organic matter content in lignite is much higher than in the soil matrix, however, across the fractions of humeomics, the difference in organic matter content between the matrices varies.

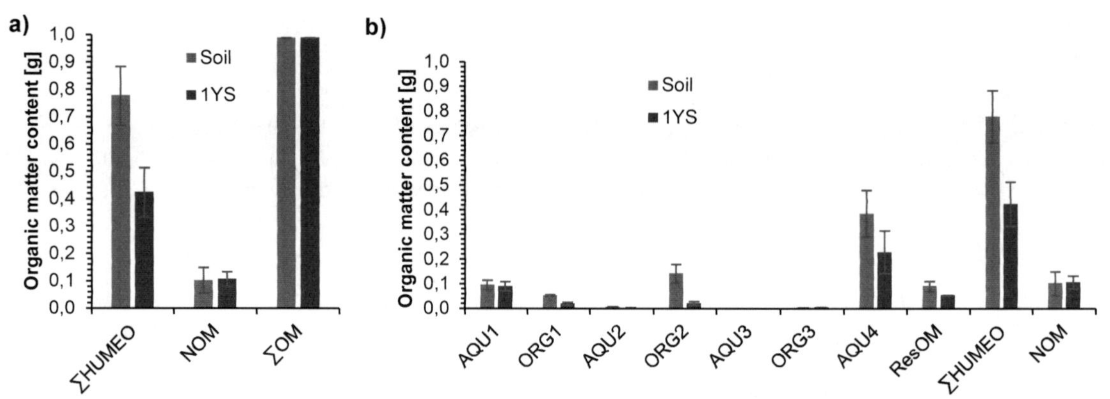

Figure 2 a) Comparison of both (conventional alkaline extraction and sequential chemical fractionation) methods with the total amount of organic matter in soil and 1YS (one year sample). **b)** Comparison of organic matter content in all fractions obtained from the soil and 1YS (one year sample) matrices

After closer examination of the individual fractions, it is visible that the contents of organic matter in the original soil matrix are higher than in the annual soil sampling. However, this contradicts the theoretical assumption that the proportion of organic matter should increase over time after application of the adjuvant. However, if we compare obtained content of organic matter by classical alkaline extraction NOM, the original sample and annual sampling are practically comparable. The decrease observed above in total yield of organic matter obtained on the soil sample after one year compared to the yield from the fractionation of the original soil sample before lignite application is probably due to the heterogeneity of the soil sample and the relatively high content of sand fractions.

However, if we compare extractable NOM and a sum of organic matter obtained from sequential chemical fractionation, it is clearly visible that with sequential chemical fractionation we can extract several times higher amount of organic matter than the NOM method. However, the difference in the content of extracted organic matter by both methods is more noticeable in soil matrices than in lignite matrices, which may be related to the total content of organic matter in the matrices.

3.3. FTIR structure of fractions

FTIR was used as a simple method for assessment of structural motifs in all the obtained fraction of relatively similar particles organic matter. The FTIR spectra of the ORG1 fractions in **Figure 3a** contain a peak in the region of 3,650-3,000 cm^{-1}, which lies in the area where N-H bonds, phenols and alcohols should occur. Furthermore, from 3,000-2,800 cm^{-1}, a significant peak appears marking the saturated C-H bonds of alkanes. In the area of 2,200-1,950 cm^{-1} we find overtones. This is followed by a pair of peaks in the range of 1,900-1,550 cm^{-1}, which indicates carbonyl bonds, and between 1,550-1,450 cm^{-1}, are present aromatic compounds. A peak with a maximum at about 1,050 cm^{-1} refers to aliphatic O-H bonds of alcohols, and the last peak with a maximum of about 800 cm^{-1} indicates the deformation transition in aromatics. For more details see [6,7].

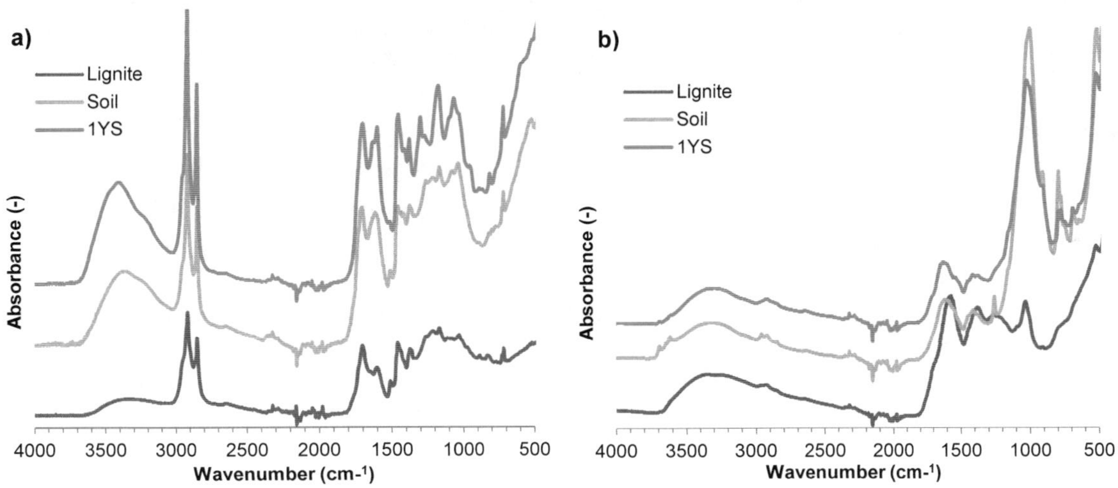

Figure 3 a) FTIR spectra of ORG1 fractions for all the source matrices. **b)** FTIR spectra of NOM fractions for all the source matrices

From the FTIR spectrum of the NOM fractions (**Figure 3b**) is obvious that when we try to characterize the total isolated organics, heterogeneity and the number of different molecules are a huge problem. Sequential chemical fractionation makes it possible to obtain smaller fractions with relatively narrow distribution of molecules, which makes the subsequent characterization easier. This resulted in the possibility to use FTIR for identification of several different types of substances present in the fractions.

4. CONCLUSION

This contribution was focused on optimization of a sequential chemical fractionation for purposes of a study on the effect of lignite (and possibly also other agriculturally attractive SSS) application on SOM, its total content and distribution in the soil. The procedure provided set of organic matter fractions with different strength of the interaction to the remaining inorganic skeleton and also with different polarity of molecules.

The obtained fractions of organic matter were characterized by elemental (mainly content of carbon and nitrogen essential for plant growth) and thermogravimetric analysis (ash, organic matter and moisture content). The results showed that a shift in the distribution carbon and nitrogen, which are essential for plant nutrition and proper soil function, was observed only in the first isolated fractions (AQU1 and ORG1), which are not firmly bound to the matrix structure (composed of nanoparticles of organic matter) and therefore are the most accessible to plants. In other fractions, no changes were observed, suggesting that the time horizon of one year is very short to monitor the changes induced by the application of lignite to the soil and is not sufficient to induce large changes deeper in the matrix structure. The FTIR spectrometry used subsequently was confirmed to be usable for monitoring of the structural changes in the individual fractions and to approximately define groups of substances that were obtained in individual fractions.

The results of the work confirmed that in order to properly assess the effect of soil support application on the content and distribution of organic matter in soil, it is necessary to study samples obtained over a longer period of time from soil supporting substance application. Also this paper assesses the effect of application of lignite on soil organic matter but of course the application form and therefore the particle size or internal structure (texture) is essential and it will be the subject of further follow-up research.

ACKNOWLEDGEMENTS

This work has been supported by project GJ20-28208Y from Czech Science Foundation and by project "Materials Research Centre at FCH BUT - Sustainability and Development" No. LO1211 of the Ministry of Education, Youth and Sports of the Czech Republic.

REFERENCES

[1] *Agronomy Fact Sheet no. 41: Soil organic matter.* Cornell University Publications, 2008. [cit. 2014-01-21].

[2] PAUL, E. A., CLARK, F. E. *Soil Microbiology and Biochemistry.* San Diego: Academic Press, 1996. p. 340.

[3] TAN, K.H. *Humic Matter in Soil and the Environment. Principles and Controversies.* New York: Marcel Dekker, Inc., 2003, p. 386.

[4] GUSTAFSON, A. F. *Soils and soil management (McGraw-Hill publications in the agricultural sciences).* London: McGraw-Hill Book Company, 1941.

[5] BOHLEN, P. J.; EDWARDS, C. A. Earthworm effects on N dynamics and soil respiration in microcosms receiving organic and inorganic nutrients. *Soil Biology and 50 Biochemistry.* 1995, vol. 27, pp. 341-348. [cit. 2017-02-26].

[6] NEBBIOSO, A., PICCOLO, A. Basis of a Humeomics Science: Chemical Fractionation and Molecular Characterization of Humic Biosuprastructures. *Biomacromolecules.* 2011, vol. 12, no. 4, pp. 1187-1199. [cit. 2019-03-31].

[7] DROSOS, M., NEBBIOSO, A., MAZZEI, P., VINCI, G., SPACCINI, R., PICCOLO, A. A molecular zoom into soil Humeome by a direct sequential chemical fractionation of soil. *Science of The Total Environment.* 2017, vol. 586, pp. 807-816.

[8] MASTO, R. ebhin, Md. a. ANSARI, J. GEORGE, V.a. SELVI a L.c. RAM. Co-application of biochar and lignite fly ash on soil nutrients and biological parameters at 77 different crop growth stages of Zea mays. *Ecological Engineering.* Elsevier B.V. 2013, vol. 58, pp. 314-322. [cit. 2019-04-05].

[9] RAM, L., SRIVASTAVA, N., JHA, S., SINHA, A., MASTO, R., SELVI, V. Management of Lignite Fly Ash for Improving Soil Fertility and Crop Productivity. *Environmental Management.* New York: Springer-Verlag, 2007, vol. 40, no. 3, pp. 438-452. [cit. 2019-04-07].

THE RELATION OF BIOCHAR TEXTURE TO ITS PHYSICOCHEMICAL AND MORPHOLOGICAL CHARACTERISTICS

Michal KALINA, Šárka SOVOVÁ, Monika TRUDIČOVÁ, Jan HAJZLER, Jiří SMILEK, Vojtěch ENEV, Ludmila MRAVCOVÁ

Brno University of Technology, Faculty of Chemistry, Brno, Czech Republic, EU,
kalina-m@fch.vut.cz

https://doi.org/10.37904/nanocon.2020.3760

Abstract

Biochar represents ubiquitous material produced by pyrolysis of various organic materials. Mainly the biochar originating from waste organic biomass residues represents highly attractive material with the possible utilization as a soil conditioner in agriculture. For these purposes, the knowledge of biochar chemical composition, its potential stability in soils, the knowledge of the elements and molecules, which can be released from biochar to surroundings and the relation of these properties to the actual texture of used material, seems to be highly important to predict the potential effect on soil and environment. This area represents the topic of present work, where we focused mainly on the effect of biochar texture to internal microstructure obtained by SEM and BET analysis and the content of organic matter. The results have shown, that the more developed internal structure of biochar with the larger specific surface area can be correlated with the higher content of aromatic regions formed by the organic structures with the high contents of the organic carbon. The high content of organic matter and organic carbon is assumed to be beneficial for agricultural application of biochar.

Keywords: Biochar, particle size, specific surface area, organic matter

1. INTRODUCTION

7.8 billion people are living on our planet right now and this number is constantly increasing. Therefore, more and more food will be necessary for the consumption of humanity. The soil is the most important for agricultural production, but it is already depleted and today's way of cultivating the land does not help it much either. It is not only erosion but also lack of organic matter, aridity and salinity is the problem. One of the possible solutions could be the use of soil conditioners such as lignite, lignohumate, alginate or biochar to improve soil fertility, water retention], enhance plant growth [1,2]. Biochar is a carbon-rich solid product of the thermochemical conversion of biomass under anaerobic conditions (pyrolysis). The attractive chemical properties of biochar are mainly in reducing greenhouse gasses, reducing nutrient (P, N, Mg) leaching, enhancing plant growth [3,4]. Physical (e.g. particle size distribution, density, porosity and surface area) and chemical (pH, electric conductivity, zeta potential, organic carbon and PAH, nutrient content and elemental composition) characteristics of biochar depend on thermochemical (pyrolysis) operating conditions and intrinsic nature of the source biomass [4]. There is a disadvantage in this because biochar is not a standardized product, and its properties are highly variable. In principle, pyrolysis is a process of converting solid biomass into bio-oil, gaseous products, and biochar under oxygen-limited or anoxic environment [5]. Various products serve as a feedstock used for biochar production, ranging from wood-based products (e.g., sawdust, woodchips and wood pellets, tree bark), organic wastes (e.g., manure and sludges,) and plant-based materials (e.g., wheat straw, leaves, husks, seeds and cobs) [6].

Generally, the effect of biochar on soil or plant growth has been widely investigated by many researchers [4,5,6] but only a few studies were focused on biochar characteristics itself. Biochar particle size affects soil physico-chemical properties and nutrient contents. The soil treated with biochar of various particle size (<3, 3-6 and 6-9 mm) shows generally decrease in the bulk density, increase in porosity, saturation percentage and the soil organic matter in comparison with the soil without biochar treatment. Biochar amendment also showed improvement in the soil mineral N, AB-DTPA (ammonium bicarbonate diethylenetriaminepentaacetic acid, multiextractant) extractable P and K over biochar control. In more detail, biochar of the smallest particle size (<3 mm) shows the maximum improvement of previously mentioned soil properties and to the plant growth parameters (tomato crop) [1]. Alkaline biochar (pH 10) can be used in acidic soil (e.g. neutralizing the acidity of peat). Different particle fractions of biochar (<3.3, 3.3-6 and 6-10 mm) were tested for the peat acid neutralizing capacity and the finest fraction has the highest neutralizing power. Although, in comparison with 2.5 g of calcium carbonate (the most used liming material), it is necessary to use 43 g of biochar to reach the same liming effect per litre of peat. Nevertheless, biochar shows additional peat-based growing media improvement, such as an increase in air content and higher physical stability during cropping [23]. Biochar nutrient extraction performed by [8] shows that the recovery of P, K and Mg was greater for smaller particle size fractions. Important to note, the size fractions after sieving was much smaller (0.15-0.60 mm, 0.60-1.18 mm, 1.18-4.00 mm and >4.00 mm) than previously mentioned researches. Here we can see that particle size fractions of the biochar vary with each other significantly. Another study [9] confirmed that particle size fractions of the same biochar have a different amount of total extractable nutrients and pH level (higher for finer fraction < 1 mm). From the other point of view, the quality and quantity of humic substances released from biochar can be affected by grain size as well. Particle size fraction >1 mm released humic substances with increasing humification degree, increasing molecular weight and aromaticity. However, there was no effect of pH on the quantity and quality of humic substances released from biochar. Also, the adsorption energy was the lowest for the finest particles and increased with the size of biochar particles. By contrast, carbon mobility between solid and liquid phases was greatest for the finest fraction (<1 mm).

Therefore, the experimental part of this work was focused on the description of the relation of the texture of biochar and its the corresponding physicochemical characteristics, morphology and the content of organic matter and organic elements. The provided set of basic characteristics will help to determine the optimal application conditions in agriculture, where we believe could serve biochar as a promising soil supplement.

2. EXPERIMENTAL

2.1. Materials

The Biochar 1 used in the work was purchased from company Biouhel.cz, s.r.o (Czech Republic). This sample, originating from solid digestate from biogas plants, was produced by pyrolysis at 450 °C as a sample specifically for the use in agriculture. Biochar 2 and 3 were selected from the declared list the official European producers of biochar having the official EBC certificate (https://www.european-biochar.org/en/home) [10]. The sample of Biochar 2 (Sonnenerde, Austria) originated from crop biomass residues pyrolyzed at 600 °C using PYREG technology. The source biomass of Biochar 3 (Novocarbo, Germany) was originating from wood chip and softwood residues, which were pyrolyzed at 600 °C using PYREG technology.

2.2. Sample pre-treatment and fractionation

The individual biochar samples were air-dried in the oven at 45 °C for 48 hours. The pre-treated samples were subsequently fractionated using laboratory sieve shaker (AS-200, Retsch GmbH) on the following fractions:

- fraction A - grain size under 0.5 mm
- fraction B - grain size from 0.5 to 2 mm

- fraction C - grain size from 2 to 4 mm
- fraction D - grain size above 4 mm

2.3. Scanning electron microscopy

The visualization of internal structure and porosity was realized using the scanning electron microscopy (SEM) imaging. For purposes of this analysis, small parts of the biochar specimen were selected. These specimens were subsequently gold-coated in a sputtering device and investigated using a scanning electron microscope ZEISS EVO LS 10 in the mode of secondary electrons (SE). The accelerating voltage was set to 5 kV.

2.4. BET analysis

The specific surface area of individual biochar samples was characterized using a NOVA 2200 analyser (Quantechrome Instruments) by BET (Brunauer-Emmett-Teller) analysis. Before the analysis, the dried sample was weighted directly into the measuring cell. The sample cell was degassed at increased temperature for 12 hours. The measurement was performed using N_2 as an absorption gas.

2.5. Elemental analysis and thermogravimetry

The elemental composition of studied biochar samples was determined using a CHNS analyser Euro Vector EA 3000. Samples (~5 mg) were packed in tin capsules and burned in an oven at 980 °C using pure oxygen as the combustion gas and pure helium as the carrier gas. The content of organic elements C, H, N, S was calculated by a calibration curve determined using a reference standard sample of sulphanilamide. The percentage of oxygen content was calculated by difference and the values obtained were corrected for ash and moisture content.

Thermogravimetric analysis was performed by TGA Q5000 (TA Instruments) with an airflow of 60 $mL \cdot min^{-1}$. Approximately 5 mg of the sample was sealed in an aluminium crucible and was heated from 25 °C to 700 °C with a heating rate of 10 $°C \cdot min^{-1}$.

3. RESULTS AND DISCUSSION

The insights from the published literature are indicating that the properties of biochar are closely linked to the conditions of pyrolysis [5], the origin of the source biomass [4,5] but also by biochar texture [7,8,9]. To be able to provide a complex view on the relation of biochar texture to its possible effect on soil, the representative samples of EBC certified biochar for the use in agriculture were selected and studied in present work. The properties of biochar samples discussed in chapter 3.2 were assessed in respect to obtained view into its internal microstructure as was obtained by SEM and BET analysis discussed in chapter 3.1.

3.1. Characterization of biochar internal microstructure

The first method used for a visual illustration of the internal structure of studied biochar samples and its relation to the sample texture was SEM imaging (**Figure 1**). For purposes of this analysis, the samples of original biochar were pre-treated as was described in chapter 2.2 by simple laboratory sieve shaker.

Figure 2 is showing the visual comparison of the same fractions (Fraction C) of Biochar 1 and Biochar 2 present work. The results of SEM imaging are indicating, that both the samples possessing the EBC certification (Biochar 2 and 3) have similar internal microstructure with a broad variety of pore distribution indicating their high potential for their possible utilization in agriculture as a soil conditioner enhancing soils properties (mainly its sorption and water holding capacity). On the other hand, the SEM image of Biochar 1 indicates fine internal structure with low content of internal pores or even more solid particle-like structures instead of porous as would be expected for biochar with the possible agricultural application.

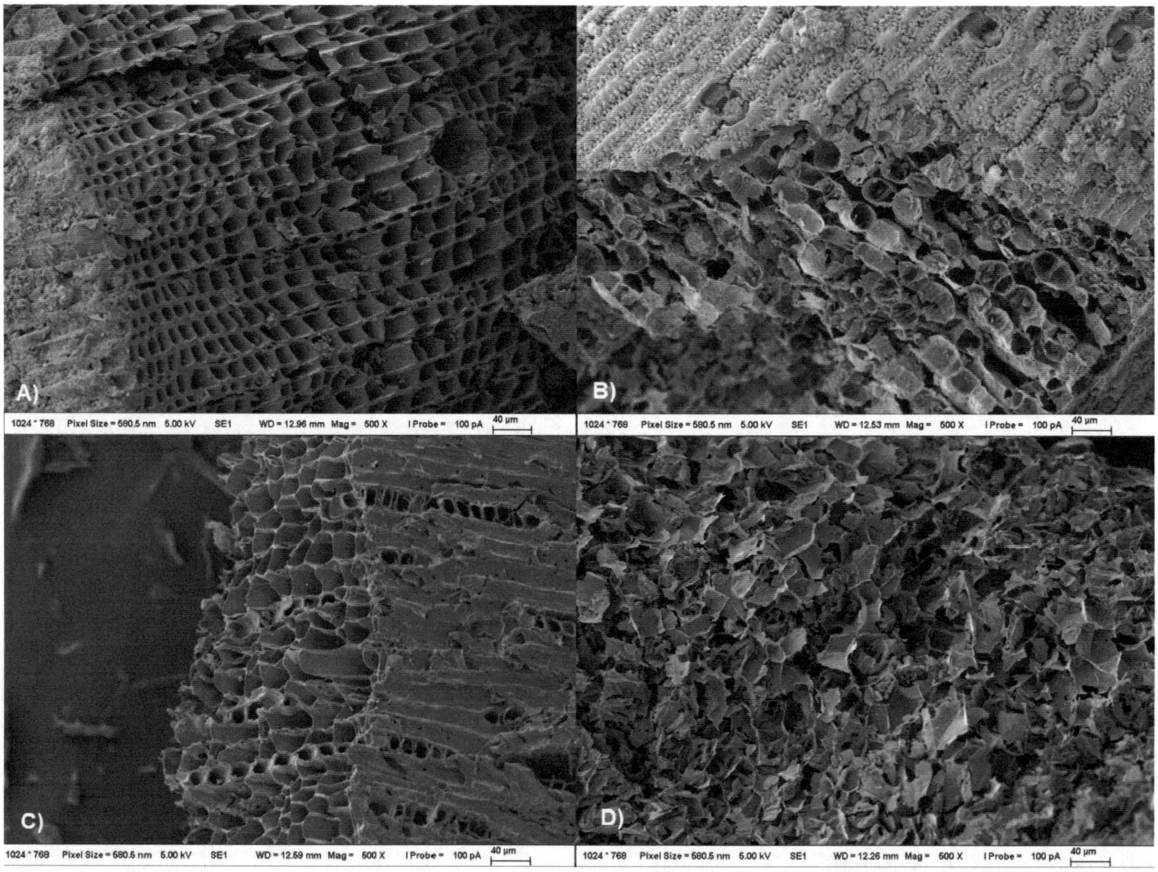

Figure 1 SEM images of the internal structure of Biochar 3 (magnification 500x) for A) fraction A, B) Fraction B, C) Fraction C and D) Fraction D as were obtained by sieve fractionation

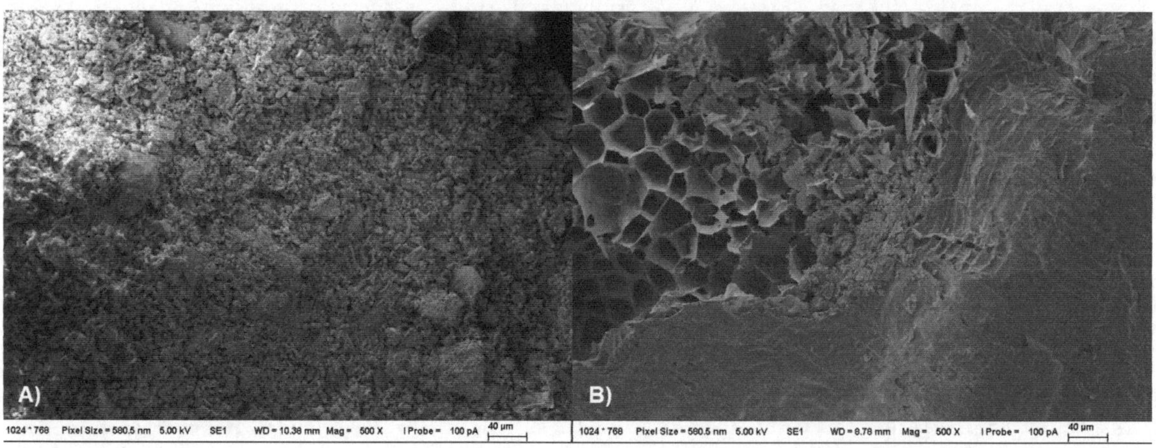

Figure 2 SEM images of the internal structure of A) Biochar 1 and B) Biochar 2 (data for fraction C)

The relation of biochar internal structure to its texture was studied also from the view of BET analysis providing information about the sample-specific surface area. The comparison of the results obtained for all the studied samples concerning the fraction of sieved material is shown in **Figure 3**.

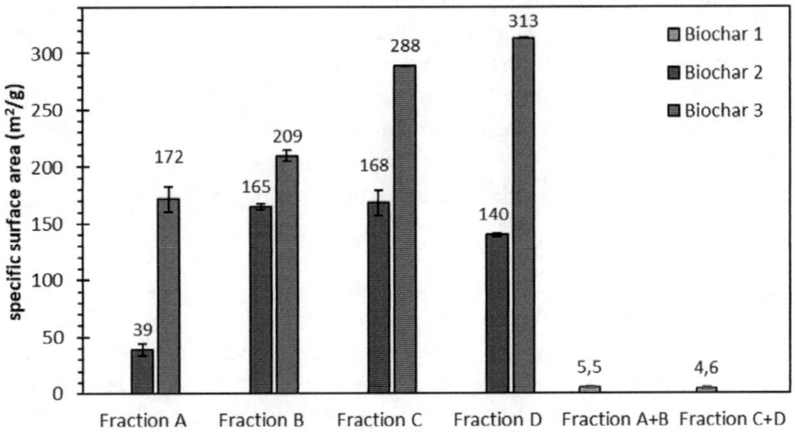

Figure 3 The relation of biochar specific surface area to its texture as was determined by BET analysis

The results from BET analysis are in good correlation with SEM imaging. The highest surface area determined by BET analysis were obtained for the most coarse fractions (B, C, D). The biochar produced with the grain sizes above 0.5 mm has a more developed porous internal structure. Such a coarse material with developed internal structure has higher sorption and water retention potential, which is desirable for the use in agriculture. The surface area analysis also confirmed that the sample of Biochar 1 has significantly less developed internal microporous structure in comparison with certified EBC Biochar samples 2 and 3.

3.2. Relation of biochar texture to its organic matter content

The biochar samples were studied regarding their potential utilization in agriculture as soil conditioners. Their role in soils could be found mainly in the improvement of physicochemical properties, the content of organic matter, the sorption ability of nutrients and the water holding capacity. The last three characteristics of soils are connected with the content of organic matter and organic carbon [5]. By these reasons, the studied biochar samples were characterized also by thermogravimetric and elemental analysis (**Table 1**).

Table 1 Total organic (w_{org}) and inorganic (w_{inorg}) content) and elemental composition of biochar samples in respect to the sample texture (recalculated on a dry sample)

sample	texture	w_{org} (wt.%)	w_{inorg} (wt.%)	Elemental composition (wt.%)			
				C	H	O	N
Biochar 1	Below 2 mm	70.35	29.65	45.39	7.54	15.06	2.36
	Above 2 mm	78.98	22.84	56.40	2.38	15.29	3.10
Biochar 2	Below 0.5mm	67.86	32.14	59.97	0.81	5.39	1.70
	0.5-2.0 mm	72.93	27.07	67.66	0.94	2.33	2.00
	2.0-4 mm	78.96	21.04	71.72	2.00	2.93	2.31
	Above 4 mm	77.42	22.58	65.66	1.61	7.05	3.09
Biochar 3	Below 0.5mm	71.44	28.56	63.40	1.57	4.69	1.78
	0.5-2.0 mm	82.56	17.44	74.48	1.63	4.54	1.92
	2.0-4 mm	91.08	8.92	84.34	2.62	2.39	1.73
	Above 4 mm	81.23	18.77	73.27	2.64	3.97	1.34

The obtained results are indicating that total organic matter is increasing in all studied biochar samples with the increasing coarseness of the fraction as was obtained by sieve fractionation. The increase in the total content of organic matter correlates with an increase in the total content of organic carbon, indicating the higher potential of fractions containing more coarse fractions of particles for the use in agriculture. EA and TGA analysis confirmed also similar content of organic matter and organic carbon of EBC certified samples of Biochar 2 and 3. On the other hand, a sample of Biochar 1 possessed a higher content of hydrogen and oxygen indicating less aromatic and more aliphatic structure with a higher content of O-bearing functional groups.

4. CONCLUSION

The results of the work are indicating that the development of the internal structure of biochar can be correlated to the specific internal area and the coarseness of biochar. These parameters together represent important characteristic with respect to the possible utilization of biochar in agriculture. More developed internal structure means higher sorption potential of a sample and higher water holding capacity. Moreover, the more developed porous internal structure can be correlated also to the total content of organic matter and organic carbon, which is again important parameter in respect to the use of biochar as a potential soil conditioner.

ACKNOWLEDGEMENTS

This work has been supported by project GJ20-28208Y from Czech Science Foundation.

REFERENCES

[1] ZEESHAN, M., AHMAD, W., HUSSAIN, F., AHAMD, W., NUMAN, M., SHAH, M. and AHMAD, I. Phytostabalization of the heavy metals in the soil with biochar applications, the impact on chlorophyll, carotene, soil fertility and tomato crop yield. *Journal of Cleaner Production*. 2020, vol. 255.

[2] YANG, C.D. and S.G. LU, S. Effects of five different biochars on aggregation, water retention and mechanical properties of paddy soil: A field experiment of three-season crops. *Soil and Tillage Research*. 2021, vol. 205.

[3] YANG, W., FENG, G., MILES, D., GAO, L., JIA, Y., LI, C. and QU, Z. Impact of biochar on greenhouse gas emissions and soil carbon sequestration in corn grown under drip irrigation with mulching. *Science of The Total Environment*. 2020, vol. 729.

[4] SIEDT, M., SCHÄFFER, A., E.C. SMITH, K., NABEL, M., ROSS-NICKOLL, M. and T. VAN DONGEN, J. Comparing straw, compost, and biochar regarding their suitability as agricultural soil amendments to affect soil structure, nutrient leaching, microbial communities, and the fate of pesticides. *Science of The Total Environment*. 2021, vol. 751.

[5] ZHU, X., LI, Y. and WANG, X. Machine learning prediction of biochar yield and carbon contents in biochar based on biomass characteristics and pyrolysis conditions. *Bioresource Technology*. 2019.

[6] RAZZAGHI, F., OBOUR, P.B. and ARTHUR, E. Does biochar improve soil water retention? A systematic review and meta-analysis. *Geoderma*. 2020, vol. 361.

[7] ZACCHEO, P., CRIPPA, L. and C. CATTIVELLO, C. Liming power of different particle fractions of biochar. *Acta Horticulturae*. 2014, vol. 1034, pp. 363-368.

[8] NEMATI, M., SIMARD, F., FORTIN, J. and BEAUDOIN, J. Potential Use of Biochar in Growing Media. *Vadose Zone Journal*. 2015, vol. 14, no. 6, pp. 1-8.

[9] PRASAD, M., CHRYSARGYRIS, A., MCDANIEL, N., KAVANAGH, A., GRUDA, N. and TZORTZAKIS, N. Plant Nutrient Availability and pH of Biochars and Their Fractions, with the Possible Use as a Component in a Growing Media. *Agronomy*. 2020, vol. 10, no. 1.

[10] The European Biochar Certificate (EBC). [online]. Arbaz, Switzerland: Ithaca institute of carbon strategies. [viewed 2020-10-15]. Available from: https://www.european-biochar.org/en/home.

SESSION E
ADVANCED METHODS OF PREPARATION AND CHARACTERIZATION OF NANOMATERIALS

Chairmen

Assoc. Prof. Dr. Pavel JELINEK	Institute of Physics of the CAS, Prague, Czech Republic, EU
Dr. Petr KLAPETEK	Czech Metrology Institute, Brno, Czech Republic, EU

INTRODUCING FORCE TRACEABILITY TO NANOINDENTATION MEASUREMENTS

[1]Radek ŠLESINGER, [2]Anna CHARVÁTOVÁ CAMPBELL, [3]Vilma BURŠÍKOVÁ

[1]*Czech Metrology Institute, Brno, Czech Republic, EU, rslesinger@cmi.cz*
[2]*Czech Metrology Institute, Brno, Czech Republic, EU, acharvatovacampbell@cmi.cz*
[3]*Masaryk University, Faculty of Science, Brno, Czech Republic, EU, vilmab@physics.muni.cz*

https://doi.org/10.37904/nanocon.2020.3774

Abstract

We present a simple and portable setup for basic characterization of force sensors in nanoindentation instruments. The device can provide traceability to mass standards in the milli- and centinewton range. We present its use with a real nanoindentation instrument. Motivated by the result, we conduct a small computational study to demonstrate the effect of sensor measurement error on material properties quantified from nanoindentation measurements.

Keywords: Nanoindentation, traceability, force calibration, indentation modulus, hardness

1. INTRODUCTION

Various local mechanical properties, notably the indentation modulus E and hardness H of materials can be determined using nanoindentation [1]. Nanoindentation is a form of so-called instrumented indentation technique (IIT), where data evaluation is based on depth and load values as measured by the respective sensors in the instrument. Proper expression of the mechanical quantities then assumes using a calibrated instrument, e.g. as described in ISO 14577-2 standard [2]. However, most instruments are delivered and further operated without any traceable calibration. Although at least basic verification of instrument performance can be performed using reference samples with certified values of hardness or elastic modulus, this is not sufficient for proper processing of load-depth data. As far as is known to the authors, sensor calibration is not actively supported by instrument manufacturers, and users interested in calibrating their instrument have to rely on their own solutions. The possibilities are, however, limited by instrument design and space available for mounting the calibration equipment. When sensor calibration is not available, attention should be paid to the values calculated in measurement evaluation.

2. FORCE CALIBRATION

In case of vertical load application, force measurement can be viewed as equivalent to weighing. As maximum loads that can be applied by nanoindentation heads of different instruments vary from units up to hundreds of millinewtons, this renders to measuring in the sub-gram up to decagram range. Given that the gravity of Earth in the instrument location is known, metrological traceability of force can be introduced by means of calibrated weights.

A key component in most special setups for very fine force measurements is a microbalance based on the electromagnetic force compensation principle, see e.g. [3]. Such balances are capable of resolving weights as low as 0.1 µg (which roughly corresponds to the load difference of 1 nN), but their dimensions and weights are often inappropriate for mounting in the indentation instrument.

Our goal was therefore to construct a device which is compact enough to fit in most instruments. It is built on a commercially available load cell (based on the usual tensometric bridge construction) with a 10-gram range, and a precise A/D converter for voltage readouts, namely:

- a GSO-10 load cell, manufactured by Transducer Techniques, USA, equipped with an extension stem for weight stacking (see **Figure 1**); the height of the sensor including the extension stem is less than 25 mm;
- a 24-bit A/D converter AD24USB, manufactured by JanasCard, Czech Republic, providing and measuring the excitation voltage for bridge input and measuring the bridge output voltage;
- a set of F1-class calibration weights (nickel-silver lamina weights, stainless steel cylindrical weights allowing easier stacking).

The sensor is mounted on a metal plate for better stability. To achieve better portability and ability to run standalone for extended periods of time, the A/D converter was connected to a single-board computer. A custom software tool was used for reading the digitalized values from the converter, expressed in the usual way in as the ratio of the output and excitation voltage in μV/V.

Figure 1 GSO-10 sensor with a stack of calibration weights, mounted in the nanoindentation instrument

Two measurement runs were carried out in the experiment:

1) using the set of calibration weights,
2) using a series of pre-defined loads in the indentation instrument software, calculated from the corresponding weights and the gravity of Earth of 9.80940003 m/s^2 as provided by the Czech Office for Surveying, Mapping and Cadastre for the location Brno, Czech Republic.

Maximum load applied by the instrument was 800 mg due to measurement head limitations. To eliminate the effect of sensor drift during continuous measurement, load applications were interleaved with zero-load periods, so that each load could be evaluated as separate measurement. Although comparisons were carried out using loads as low as 10 mg, according to general recommendations, measurements within the lower 1 % of the sensor range should not be taken into account. Unfortunately, no sensor that has a finer range and allows stacking calibration weights is known to the authors, which limits applicability of the current setup to loads of 100 mg and above.

Results of the comparison are presented in **Figure 2**. They suggest that the instrument in our experiment might systematically overstate its force measurements by approx. 1 %.

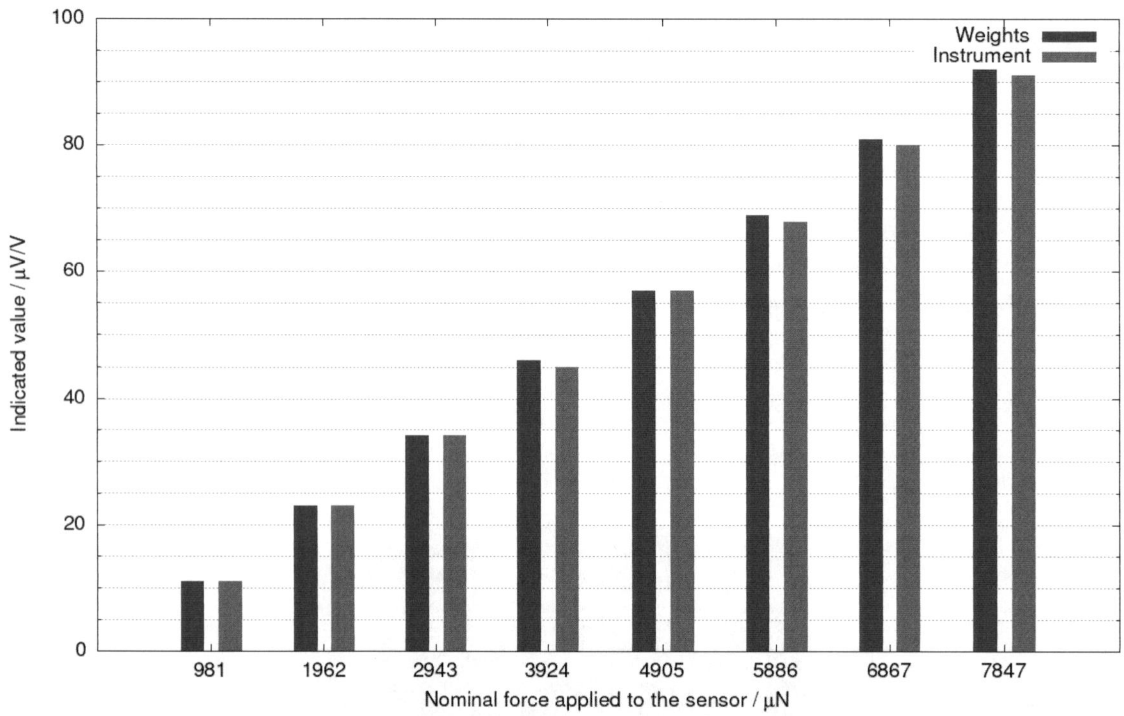

Figure 2 Comparison of indicated values between the loads generated by weights and by the nanoindentation instrument

3. DATA CORRECTION ACCORDING TO CALIBRATION RESULTS

Proper analysis of instrumented indentation data involving sensor calibration and related uncertainties remains a major endeavor. Instead, let us demonstrate on a simple example how an inaccurate measurement by the sensors of a nanoindentation instrument can affect the mechanical quantities of main interest as determined by the commonly used method due to Oliver and Pharr [2,4,5].

Based on a small set of measurement data and the elastic modulus of a fused silica reference sample, we determine the contact area function of an indentation tip in the form $A(h) = x^2 + ax + bx^{1/2} + cx^{1/4} + dx^{1/8}$ using an orthogonal least squares fit. Based on this area function, we evaluate measurements on three different samples: sapphire (Al_2O_3, load 5 mN), copper (Cu, 5 mN), and polycarbonate (PC, 1 mN).

Motivated by the results from the previous section, we simulate two basic scenarios of inaccurate sensor measurement:

3) The load sensor overstates the values, and load values have to be reduced by 1 %.

4) The depth sensor overstates the values, and depth values have to be reduced by 1 %.

The original procedure is then repeated after reducing all load or depth values by 1 %, to correct for the measurement error of the respective sensor. Results of this comparison are presented in **Table 1**. The original (i.e., based on the inaccurate measurement) values of indentation modulus and hardness are denoted E_{100} and H_{100}. The "true" values, calculated from the corrected data, are denoted E_{99L} and H_{99L} (load correction) or E_{99D} and H_{99D} (depth correction). The values in parentheses express the relative difference to the uncorrected figures.

Table 1 Influence of inaccurate measurements of the load or the depth sensor on calculated values of indentation modulus and hardness

	Al_2O_3	Cu	PC
E_{100} / GPa	286.97	132.70	2.70
H_{100} / MPa	17351.1	1312.1	132.7
E_{99L} / GPa	287.36 (+0.14 %)	132.76 (+0.05 %)	2.70 (+0.00 %)
H_{99L} / MPa	17564.4 (+1.23 %)	1326.5 (+1.10 %)	133.8 (+0.83 %)
E_{99D} / GPa	288.33 (+0.47 %)	133.55 (+0.64 %)	2.72 (+0.74 %)
H_{99D} / MPa	17137.3 (-1.23 %)	1300.9 (-0.85 %)	132.1 (-0.45 %)

While the effect of load measurement error on the indentation modulus is mostly negligible, it directly translates to hardness values (force sensor providing higher than true values results in underestimating the hardness). On the other hand, error of the depth sensor noticeably affects both indentation modulus and hardness (depth sensor providing higher than true values results in underestimating the modulus and overestimating the hardness).

In case that sensor calibration and subsequent proper uncertainty evaluation is not available, we suggest including an uncertainty term due to measurement error in the aggregate budget since such relatively small measurement errors can easily be expected. All the calculations in this section were performed using a free software tool for nanoindentation data processing Niget [6].

4. CONCLUSION

A custom setup for measuring forces in the milligram range showed that the force sensor of the evaluated nanoindentation instrument provided slightly, but noticeably inaccurate load values. This should raise attention of users of instrumented indentation technique to the possibility of calibrating their instruments. A computational study demonstrated an apparent influence of sensor measurement errors on the calculated mechanical quantities. In case of uncalibrated instruments, this suggests to expand the uncertainty budget with respective terms to account for assumed errors.

ACKNOWLEDGEMENTS

This work has been supported by the Czech Science Foundation project GA19-15240S "Multifunctional Nanocomposite Polymer Thin Films with Controlled Surface and Mechanical Properties Deposited in RF Dusty Plasma".

REFERENCES

[1] FISCHER-CRIPPS, A. C. *Nanoindentation*. New York: Springer-Verlag, 2004.

[2] ISO/IEC, 14577-2:2015. *Metallic materials - Instrumented indentation test for hardness and materials parameters - Part 2: Verification and calibration of testing machines*. Geneva: ISO/IEC, International Organization for Standardization, 2015.

[3] SCHLEGEL, C., SLANINA, O., HAUCKE, G., KUMME, R. Construction of a standard force machine for the range of 100 µN-200 mN. *Measurement*. 2012, vol. 45, pp. 2388-2392.

[4] ISO/IEC, 14577-1:2015. *Metallic materials - Instrumented indentation test for hardness and materials parameters - Part 1: Test method*. Geneva: ISO/IEC, International Organization for Standardization, 2015.

[5] OLIVER, W. C., PHARR, G. M. An improved technique for determining hardness and elastic modulus using load and displacement sensing indentation experiments. *Journal of Materials Research*. 1992, vol. 7, pp. 1564-1583.

[6] CHARVÁTOVÁ CAMPBELL, A., GROLICH, P., ŠLESINGER, R. Niget: Nanoindentation general evaluation tool. *SoftwareX*. 2019, vol. 9, pp. 248-254.

AFM CHARACTERIZATION OF NANOCOMPOSITE SAMPLES

[1]Anna CHARVÁTOVÁ CAMPBELL, [1,2]Marek HAVLÍČEK, [1,2]Petr KLAPETEK, [3]Vilma BURŠÍKOVÁ

[1]Czech Metrology Institute, Brno, Czech Republic, EU, acharvatovacampbell@cmi.cz

[2]Central European Institute of Technology, Brno, Czech Republic, EU

[3]Faculty of Science, Masaryk University, Brno, Czech Republic, EU

https://doi.org/10.37904/nanocon.2020.3775

Abstract

Nanocomposite polymer coatings combine attractive functionalities from the combination of organic matrix coatings and inorganic nanoparticles which allows to acquire unique properties. They can be tailored for specific needs by modifying optical, mechanical, electronic, magnetic and other properties, which may differ significantly from the properties of the bulk form.

In order to study the role of the incorporated nanoparticles, topography is of fundamental importance. Its relation to the deposition parameters, however, is far from trivial. Suitable statistical parameters, which capture the essential traits of the sample but are not oversensitive to local variations are needed. Roughness e.g. is a well-established, popular statistical parameter but is not sufficient to describe the topography. Parameters which describe lateral distances should be included as well. In order to ensure the same processing for multiple samples the data processing should also require as little user input as possible. As a wide range of samples must be characterized, time demands for the characterization of a single sample should also be considered.

We present a systematic atomic force microscopy study of a series of nanocomposite polymer coatings with topographies including spherical particles and snake-like structures of different length scales. Different statistical parameters, their dependence on measurement settings and related uncertainties are addressed.

Keywords: AFM, nanocomposites

1. INTRODUCTION

Nanocomposite polymer coatings combine attractive functionalities from the combination of organic matrix coatings and inorganic nanoparticles which allows to acquire unique properties. They can be tailored for specific needs by modifying optical, mechanical, electronic, magnetic and other properties, which may differ significantly from the properties of the bulk form.

Deposition under dusty plasma condition can be used for depositing nanocomposite thin films, with many successful technological applications. Varying the deposition conditions allows to obtain films with different properties, such as elasticity or hydrophobicity [1-6].

The topography is one of the key features of a film which must be characterized. Atomic force microscopy (AFM) is very well suited for this task. However, it is necessary to keep in mind several issues. Firstly, AFM measurements can be time demanding, especially if large numbers of samples should be characterized. It is thus necessary to carefully choose parameters for the measurement such as resolution, image size, scanning rate, etc. as these may affect the validity of the data. Secondly, AFM measurements need further data processing, such as levelling, row alignment, removal of scars or other artifacts. These procedures can significantly affect the results [7]. Therefore, procedures should be exactly defined with as little user choices as possible in order to ensure that all samples will be processed in the same way. Automated procedures can help to achieve this as well as reduce the time necessary to accomplish this.

A large number of statistical parameters and functions can be evaluated, for an overview see e.g. [8]. The most popular ones include the root mean square, skew, kurtosis, surface area, power spectral density function, autocorrelation function, and Euler characteristics. Further analysis is possible by marking grains and evaluating their size parameters. However, for the comparison of different samples the focus should be on reproducibility more than on the theoretical interpretation of the chosen parameter.

In this work we present the analysis of AFM measurements on a series of samples obtained by PECVD depositions in dusty plasma and suggest optimal parameters for their statistical description, with focus on their robustness.

2. METHODS

In this work we analyzed a set of 65 samples. The samples were produced using plasma enhanced chemical vapor deposition from hexamethyldisiloxane (HMDSO) and oxygen. The details of the deposition process are described in [6]. A capacitive radio frequency discharge at 13.56 MHz was generated in a parallel plate reactor. The HMDSO and oxygen flow rates varied from 1 to 10 sccm and 2 to 10 sccm, respectively. Single crystal silicon wafers were used as substrates. The applied power ranged from 25 to 75 W and the DC negative self-bias voltage between -10 to -400 V. The deposition conditions led to the creation of dusty plasma.

AFM measurements were performed using a Dimension Icon instrument from Bruker. Measurements were performed in tapping and Bruker's PeakForce tapping mode. Images of different sizes were measured ranging from 2 μm x 2 μm to 40 μm x 40 μm with resolution usually 512 x 512 or 1024 x 1024.

Data were leveled by subtracting a fitted polynomial of second degree. Lines were aligned with respect to the line median. Standard statistics were extracted, such as average, rms, skew, kurtosis, surface area, as well as the radial power spectral density function and autocorrelation. All data processing was performed within the open source software Gwyddion (www.gwyddion.net).

3. RESULTS

Several types of topography have been encountered in this study: the most common were different types of spherical nanoparticles, either individually placed on a flat surface or forming large clusters, snake-like structures and caterpillar-like structures formed by spherical particles aligning themselves into snakes. The vertical size of objects ranged between 30 nm and 730 nm. The lateral size of the objects ranged from 200 nm to 2 μm. The thickness varied between 500 nm and 3 μm.

The root mean square roughness and the ratio of surface area and projected area have been found to be particularly useful and are shown in **Figure 1**, together with some examples of topographies. As can be seen, the root mean square value of an image is only very weakly correlated with the type of the surface. The ratio of surface and projected area is more significant, notably large values have been found to correspond always to snake-like structures. A similar study of skew and excess kurtosis didn't show any significant trends, though particles tended to have positive skew whereas snakes and caterpillars had both positive and negative skews. Especially for larger structures we should check the effect of the image size on the evaluated value. Some recommendations are given in standards [9-11] but their use in this case is unclear. Instead, we performed studies on selected samples which were measured with larger scan size.

From a 40 μm x 40 μm image details of different size were extracted and processed. The variance of the different statistical parameters was estimated with respect to the location of the detail using a Monte Carlo method. In **Figure 2** we show the dependence of the roughness and excess kurtosis on the size of the detail, and the dependence of the relative uncertainty of the parameters on the size. From **Figure 2B** we can see that for this sample the roughness could be estimated with an uncertainty around 1 nm already at 10 μm. This corresponds to an uncertainty of the excess kurtosis of 0.2 which is acceptable. From **Figure 2C** it is obvious that the sensitivity of the parameter grows with growing order of the moment involved. Results for other samples are similar.

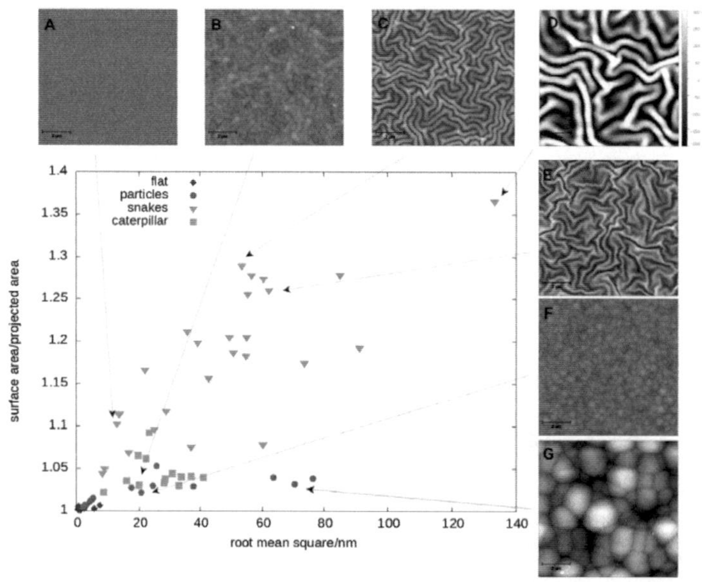

Figure 1 The root mean square value and the ratio of the surface area and projected area for the samples involved in this study. Some typical examples of topographies encountered are shown. The vertical ranges have been chosen the same for all images for better comparison.

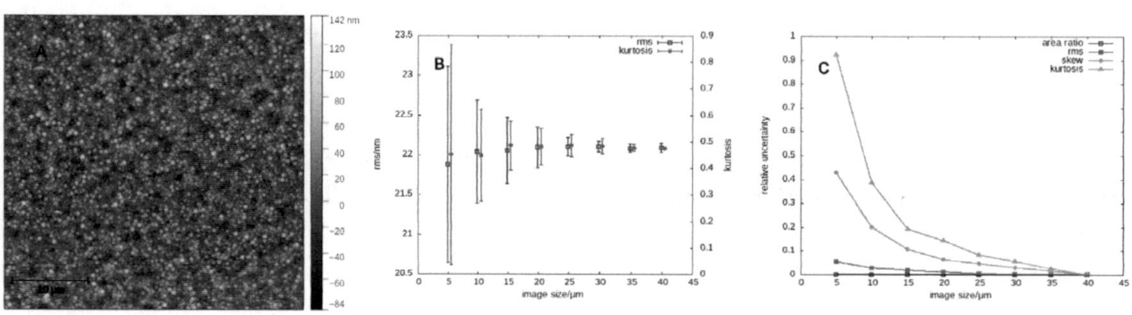

Figure 2 AFM image used for studying the dependence of statistical parameters on scan size (A), the dependence of the roughness and excess kurtosis on the scan size (B) and the dependence of relative uncertainty of statistical parameters on the size (C). Data have been shifted in the image B for better clarity.

As shown in [12], the root mean square roughness as well as skew and kurtosis are very sensitive to levelling and scan line corrections. On the other side, the surface area is largely unaffected. We found that the samples in this study had to be levelled using polynomials of at least second degree. The recommendations of the authors hold for random rough surfaces, but using them we find that the scan length should be approx. 20 times longer than the characteristic length scale in order to keep the bias from the true value below roughly 10 %. This would correspond to image sizes ranging between 4 - 40 μm. This is in reasonable agreement with the requirements based on the (in)homogeneity.

One common method for the analysis of AFM images of nanoparticles is to mark them using some of the well-established algorithms, see e.g. [13,14] and then perform a statistical analysis of these. However, in most cases this requires the choice of certain thresholds which must be made by the user. The resulting statistics may be very sensitive to this choice and there is no simple way to define the thresholds universally for all samples. Therefore, the results are not comparable between samples. Last but not least, this method is time consuming and cannot be easily automated.

However, some insight can be gained by using the mean curvature. The mean curvature is given as the average of the principal curvatures. For concave ellipsoids both principal curvatures are positive, for concave cylinders one is positive and the other zero. Thus, we expect a positive mean curvature to correspond mainly to concave areas, which can be either ellipsoidal (nanoparticles) or cylindrical (snakes), and assume other cases are less common and can be omitted. Since the mean curvature is calculated based on numerical derivatives, it is very sensitive to noise and some kind of smoothing may be necessary. We also encountered voids in the marked grains which require further processing for a rigorous, automated statistical evaluation.

Surfaces formed by nanostructures such as particles or snakes should be characterized also from the viewpoint of lateral length scales. Notably, the radius of the particles and snakes is of crucial interest. Obviously, this could be measured manually directly from the image. This is a lengthy procedure and can be biased by the user's choice.

For rough surfaces models one of the common parameters to characterize its lateral scale is the correlation length where the autocorrelation function (ACF) decays to 1/e of its maximum [8]. This corresponds to Gaussian and exponential models of roughness and does not have a simple interpretation for geometries encountered in this study. Nevertheless, the correlation length can be easily determined unambiguously. Alternatively, the Fourier transform of the autocorrelation function, the power spectral density function (PSDF), can also be used for the identification of characteristic length scales. The fitting procedures using PSDF may be favorable for numerical reasons.

For individual particles models of the ACF have been found in [15] from which the shape parameters can then be extracted. However, this model assumes a fairly low coverage and notably the existence of a reference plane on which the particles are placed. In our case the shapes found in the samples are too irregular for this model but we can still use the peaks of the ACF and PSDF as characteristic length scales. As there is a big variability in the angular directions, we use the angular average for both for ACF and PSDF, the radial autocorrelation function (RACF) and radial power spectral density function (RPSDF) in all cases.

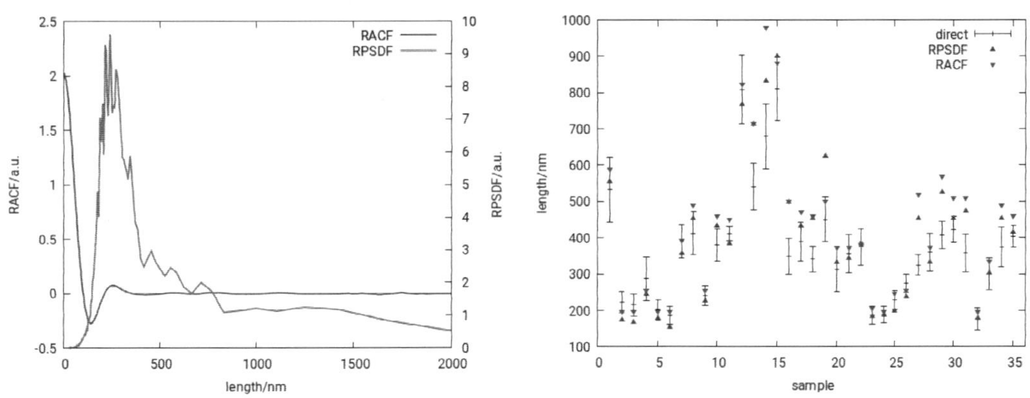

Figure 3 Example of typical RACF and RPSDF (left), characteristic length scale of particles for different samples obtained by identification of peaks in RPSDF, identification of peaks in RACF and by direct measurement from image

An example of the RACF and RPSDF and the corresponding length scales are shown in **Figure 3**. The correspondence with the direct measurement is reasonable, mainly due to the large uncertainty of the latter.

This reflects that the image size was too small. The difference between RACF and RPSDF is on the order of tens of nanometers, which is acceptable for a pixel size of 9 nm. The methods failed on samples formed by particles or snakes placed on top of each other forming hills and valleys, such as e.g. image G in **Figure 1**. The RACF method failed more often than the RPSDF method (14 and 8 out of 51 cases).

In contrast the length scale based on the decay of the RACF is simple to obtain and can be easily automated. However, this value does not offer any direct physical interpretation. No trend for the ratio of the decay rate and the length scale measured directly has been found. For the data shown in **Figure 4** the ratio varies between 0.2 and 0.65.

We illustrate the algorithms described so far for a study of the effect of deposition time with other deposition conditions kept constant. The AFM images of such samples are shown in **Figure 4** where the mean curvature is positive.

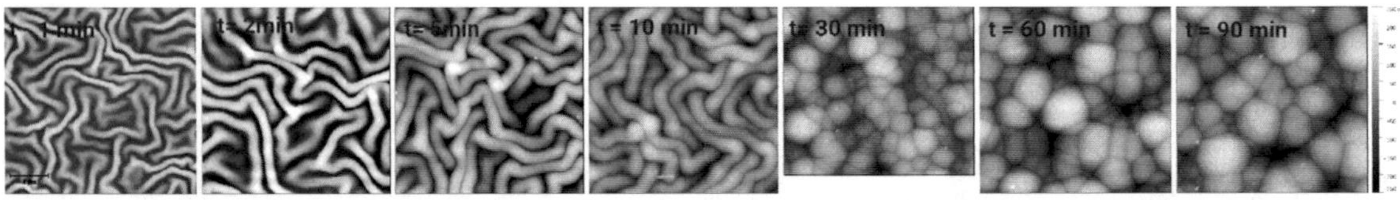

Figure 4 AFM images of a series of samples corresponding to different deposition times with otherwise identical deposition conditions

The dependence of the roughness, area ratio, number of grains marked by the mean curvature, the correlation length defined by the decay of the RACF and the size measured directly from the image on the deposition time is shown in **Figure 5**. The length scale could not be determined from the RACF and RPSDF, due to the nonplanarity of the surface, as explained above. The samples had been measured at the fixed scan size of 10 µm. This is not sufficient for samples with particles as large as the ones in this series but offers a good first estimate.

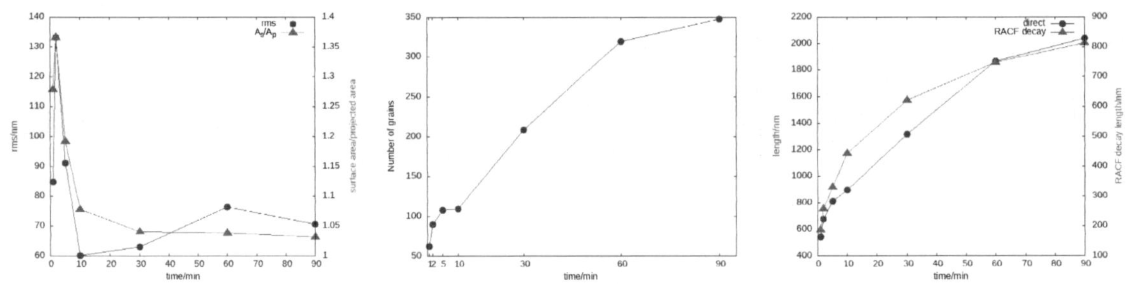

Figure 5 The time dependence of roughness and surface ratio (left), of the number of grains (middle), and of lateral scale (right). The particle size determined directly from image and RACF decay rate were used.

Care is needed for the AFM measurement itself. The scan size must be sufficiently large so as to capture inhomogeneities and offer sufficient quality of RACF and RPSDF. Artifacts such as line mismatch or contamination can significantly affect the analysis and should be corrected for. However, the correction process must be done manually which increases time demands and may introduce unintended bias due to the user choices. Large images are more prone to artifacts as the scan rate cannot be kept as low as for small images, thermal drift being one of the major issues. As a first estimate, the image size should be at least 20 times larger than characteristic length, which can be estimated as the diameter of particles or snakes

4. CONCLUSION

As it was found that the deposition process leads to a range of very different surface topographies, our goal was to find suitable statistical parameters for describing the surface topography in such a wide set. We have shown that a high ratio of surface area and projected area is related to snake like structures. Masks based on the mean curvature were shown to be capable of grain identification. Different methods of identifying length scales were compared to direct measurements. The determination of length scales from peaks in RPSDF and RACF is preferable since it produces physically meaningful results.

The usefulness of these parameters has been manifested on a series of samples which were prepared under identical deposition conditions with only the deposition time varying. The interpretation of the results from the perspective of the deposition process shall be presented elsewhere.

ACKNOWLEDGEMENTS

This work was supported by the Czech Science Foundation project GACR 19-15240S "Multifunctional Nanocomposite Polymer Thin Films with Controlled Surface and Mechanical Properties Deposited in RF Dusty Plasma.

REFERENCES

[1] FACIO, D. S. MOSQUERA, M. J. Simple Strategy for Producing Superhydrophobic Nanocomposite Coatings in situ on a Building Substrate. *ACS Appl. Mater. Interfaces.* 2013, vol. 5, pp. 7517-7526.

[2] BOUFENDI, L. BOUCHOULE, A. Particle nucleation and growth in a low-pressure argon-silane discharge. *Plasma Sources Sci. Technol.* 1994, vol. 3, p. 262.

[3] CAVARROC, M. et al. Self-excited instability ocurring during the nanoparticle formation in an Ar-SiH4 low pressure radio frequency plasma. *J. App. Phys.* 2006, vol. 99, p. 064301.

[4] CABARROCAS, P. R. et al. Synthesis of silicon nanocrystals in silane plasmas for nanoelectronics and large area electronic devices. *J. Phys. D: Appl. Phys.* 2007, vol. 40, p. 2258.

[5] BEHLER, K. et al. Nanodiamond-Polymer Composite Fibers and Coatings. *ACS Nano.* 2009, vol. 3, pp. 363-369.

[6] CHARVÁTOVÁ CAMPBELL, A., KLAPETEK, P., VALTR, M., BURŠÍKOVÁ, V. Development of reference materials for the investigation of local mechanical properties at the nanoscale. *Surf. Interface Anal.* 2012, vol. 44, p. 1151.

[7] KLAPETEK, P. NEČAS, D. Study of user influence in routine SPM data processing. *Meas. Sci. Technol.* 2017, vol 28, pp. 034014-034024

[8] ANDERSON, T. W. *The Statistical Analysis of Time Series.* New York: Wiley, 1971.

[9] ASME B46.1. Surface texture (surface roughness, waviness, lay). *Am. Soc. Mech. Eng.* 2009.

[10] ISO 19606. *Fine ceramics (advanced ceramics, advanced technical ceramics) - Test method for surface roughness of fine ceramic films by atomic force microscopy.* 2017.

[11] ISO 4288. *Geometrical product specifications (GPS)-surface texture: Profile method-rules and procedures for the assessment of surface texture.* 1996.

[12] NEČAS, D. et al. How levelling and scan line corrections ruin roughness measurement and how to prevent it. *Sci.Rep.* 2020, vol. 10, p. 15294

[13] VINCENT, L. SOUILLE, P. Watersheds in digital spaces: an efficient algorithm based on immersion simulations. *IEEE Trans. Pattern Anal. Mach. Intell.* 1991, vol. 13, pp. 586-598.

[14] OTSU, N. A Threshold Selection Method from Gray-Level Histograms. *IEEE Trans. Syst. Man Cybern. Syst.* 1979, vol. 9, pp. 62-66.

[15] MAREK, J. DEMJEN, E. Is autocorrelation image analysis the proper method in nanoparticle sizing? *J. Nanopart. Res.* 2017, vol. 19, p. 208.

PLASMA HYDROGENATION OF HYDROTHERMALLY GROWN ZnO MICROPODS

[1]Zdeněk REMEŠ, [1]Kateřina AUBRECHTOVÁ DRAGOUNOVÁ, [2]Julia MIČOVÁ

[1]*FZÚ- Institute of Physics, Czech Academy of Sciences, Prague, Czech Republic, EU,*
remes@fzu.cz, dragounova@fzu.cz

[2]*Institute of Chemistry, Slovak Academy of Sciences, Bratislava, Slovakia, EU, chemjumi@savba.sk*

https://doi.org/10.37904/nanocon.2020.3777

Abstract

The hydrothermally grown ZnO micropods have been placed on grounded stainless-steel holder and exposed to an inductively coupled plasma (ICP) monitored in-situ by optical emission spectroscopy (OES). OES shows the immediate release of oxygen during Ar ion bombardment. The prolonged exposure to hydrogen plasma leads to deterioration of the optical properties as well. The exposure, rf power and hydrogen pressure have been optimized to enhance UV-photoluminescence peak at the wavelength 384 nm related to surface bounded excitons and reduce the defect-related photoluminescence in red spectral range. The strong UV photoluminescence appears just after 1 minute of plasma hydrogenation in a radio frequency plasma discharge with power density 40 W/dm^3 and hydrogen pressure 17 Pa.

Keywords: ZnO, micropods, inductively coupled plasma, optical emission spectroscopy, photoluminescence spectroscopy, Raman spectroscopy, infrared absorption spectroscopy

1. INTRODUCTION

The zinc oxide (ZnO) crystallite powder is a low cost, environmentally friendly, wide band gap semiconducting material with unique optical properties and variety of nanoparticle (NPs) morphologies [1]. Due to the high surface-to-volume ratio and related size effects, ZnO NPs are used in many applications for energy conversion, photocatalytic wastewater treatment, electrochemical energy storage or sensing. Recently, we have applied a hydrothermal chemical synthesis as a low-cost technology for mass-production of ZnO hedgehog-like crystallite powder [2], studied their crystal quality [3] and shown that the age of precursors plays a significant role in defect formation [4]. The photoluminescence spectra (PLS) show a strong near UV emission peak related to bound exciton complexes assigned to surface states [5]. The strong correlation between surface defects and the exciton emission has been also observed in hydrothermally synthetized ZnO micropods [6].

Particularly important are electrically conductive ZnO NPs with the interstitial hydrogen acting as a donor [7]. Two-step annealing in air at around 1000 °C followed by annealing in hydrogen atmosphere at 800 °C has been demonstrated to significantly enhance UV-photoluminescence of ZnO NPs for highly efficient sub-nanosecond fast scintillators [8,9]. The inductively coupled plasma (ICP) offers an alternative way of cold hydrogenation [10]. We have already shown that the cold hydrogenation in low pressure hydrogen plasma is an effective way to significantly enhance the electrical conductivity and exciton-related emission in ZnO thin films prepared by reactive magnetron sputtering on fused silica glass substrates [11]. In this paper we optimize the plasma hydrogenation of ZnO micropods placed on grounded stainless-steel sample holder.

2. EXPERIMENTAL

2.1. Hydrothermal growth

ZnO micropods were the hydrothermally synthesized in aqueous solution containing equimolar (25 mM) amount of zinc nitrate hexahydrate p.a. ($Zn(NO_3)_2 \cdot 6H_2O$) and hexamethylenetetramine (HMTA) ($C_6H_{12}N_4$) p.a.

Both chemicals were purchased from Slavus and used without further purification. Deionized water was purified with a system So~Safe Water Technologies, having a conductivity 0.20 μS·cm^{-1} (25 °C). The reaction mixture was heated at 90 °C for 3 h. The precursor salt residues were removed from the sample by washing 5-times with deionized water followed by centrifugation at 10 000 rpm (RCF: 11 510g) for 15 min. Finally, the ZnO powder was dried by lyophilization. Scanning electron microscopy (SEM) images show ZnO micropods with hexagonal shape, the length up to 10 μm and the diameter about 0.5 μm, see **Figure 1**.

Figure 1 SEM images of hydrothermally grown ZnO micropods taken by MAIA3 (TESCAN) using the electron beam energy 5 keV (A) and 20 keV (B)

2.2. Plasma treatment

The plasma hydrogenation has been done in a prototype inductively coupled plasma (ICP) reactor currently being developed in a cooperation with the Czech company SVCS Process Innovation, s. r. o. (Valašské Meziříčí, Czech Republic). The quartz reactor of the active volume 5 liters operates at radio frequency (rf) 13.56 MHz with maximum discharge power up to 300 W corresponding to the power density 60 W/dm^3. The setup is evacuated with the Agilent Triscroll 300 dry vacuum pump protected with the ISO Flange Vacuum Filter (CSL-843-NW25). A 5 mg powder sample mechanically pressed into a round pellet with the diameter 3 mm was placed in the middle of the chamber on a grounded stainless-steel holder. The holder grounding is a recent improvement over the previously used ungrounded quartz holder. Prior the plasma treatment, the chamber, valves, flowmeters, gauges and all gas inlet and outlet tubes were evacuated to residual pressure below 0.1 Pa and flushed 5 min by 20 sccm flow of process gases to reduce residual gas contamination. The pellets were exposed for 30 s to Ar plasma (Ar purity 99.998%, rf power 100 W, Ar flow 5 sccm, pressure 16 Pa) followed by up to 20 min of hydrogen plasma exposure (H_2 purity 99.999%, rf power 200 W, H_2 flow 20 sccm, pressure 17 Pa). The originally white ZnO pellets became darker after prolonged plasma hydrogenation, see **Figure 2**.

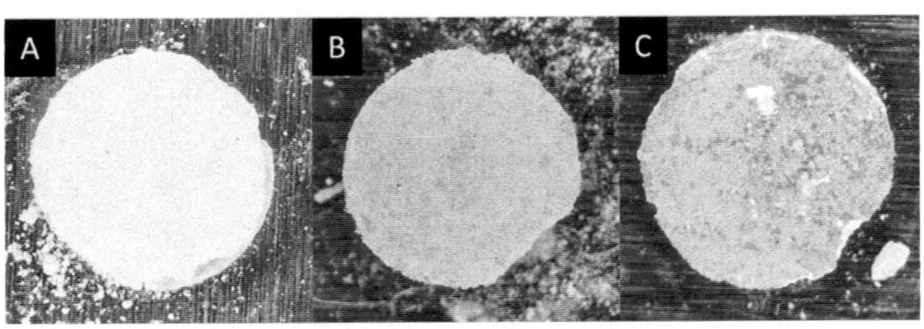

Figure 2 Optical images of ZnO pellets (diameter 3 mm) after 2 min (A), 10 min (B) and 20 min (C) plasma hydrogenation taken with a macro objective (Lumix G Macro 30 mm, F2.8 ASPH).

2.3. Characterization

Optical emission spectra (OES) were measured in 400-1000 nm spectral range with 1 nm spectral resolution by spectrally calibrated fiber coupled CCD spectrometer (B&W Tek BTC112E) focused in the middle of the quartz chamber. Dark spectra were subtracted. The integration time varied from 5 ms for Ar plasma to 200 ms for H_2 plasma. Each spectrum was averaged 10 times.

Raman spectra were recorded in backscatter geometry using a micro-spectroscopic Renishaw InVia Reflex Raman setup with integrated optical microscope and a charge-coupled device (CCD) camera. For excitation, a 442- nm-line of HeCd excitation laser. Other parameters were 100× Olympus objective, 65 µm slits, and a grating of 2400 grooves/mm.

The attenuated total reflectance (ATR) infrared absorption spectra were detected in 590-5000 cm^{-1} spectral range and 4 cm^{-1} resolution using Nicolet™ iS50 FTIR Spectrometer (Thermo Fisher Scientific) with build-in diamond ATR prism, KBr beam splitter and cooled DTGS detector. The ATR spectra were first normalized to zero at 5000 cm^{-1} and then recalculated with the build-in advanced ATR correction for diamond prism.

PLS were measured at room temperature in the 360-780 nm spectral range with 2 nm spectral resolution using the 100 mW/cm^2 UV photo-excitation provided by a focused 340 nm LED equipped with a narrow band-pass filter and operating in square pulse regime at frequency 307 Hz. The emitted and scattered light was collected and focused onto the 1 mm wide input slit of double gratings SPEX 1672 monochromator equipped with Peltier cooled multi-dynode multi-alkali red sensitive photomultiplier (PMT) to be measured at each wavelength independently by a lock-in amplifier synchronized with excitation frequency. The spectra above 600 nm were measured with a long pass filter placed in front of the monochromator. The whole setup was spectrally calibrated with Oriel #63358 Quartz Tungsten halogen lamp and converted from wavelength to energy scale for quantitative analysis [12].

3. RESULTS AND DISCUSSION

The OES spectra clearly show the presence of atomic oxygen in Ar plasma as demonstrated by the presence of oxygen-related emission peaks at 777 and 845 nm [13], see **Figure 3**. Since no nitrogen related peaks are observed, oxygen cannot originate from ambient atmosphere leak, but from ZnO powder. In pure Ar plasma the intensity of O-peaks is low and may be explained by contamination from previously processed ZnO. The intensity of O-peaks increases by an order of magnitude when a pellet is placed into the chamber while the plasma visually change color from brownish to white. Thus, OES proves the heavy ion bombardment of the sample placed on grounded holder. Since only the Balmer series lines were observed in hydrogen plasma at 656, 486 and 434 nm and no O-peaks, we conclude that ZnO was scattered by heavy Ar ions but not by light H ions.

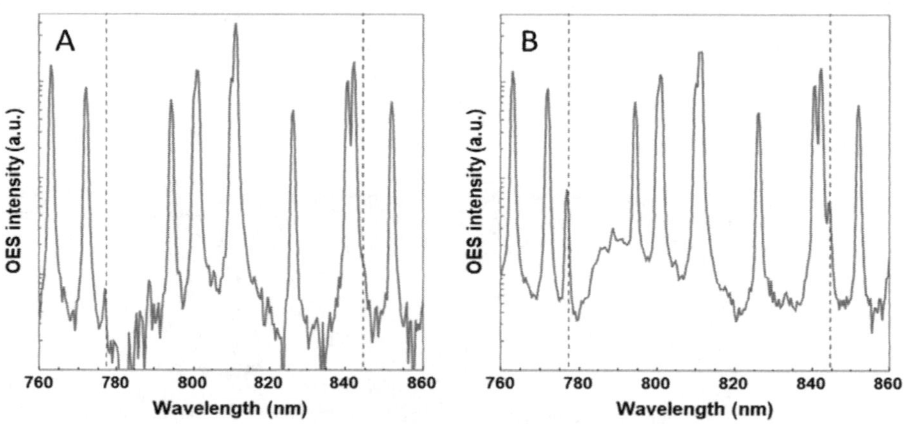

Figure 3 The semilogarithmic optical emission spectra of Ar plasma without (A) and with (B) ZnO pellet placed onto grounded stainless steel holder in the ICP reactor. The position of oxygen emission lines at 777 and 845 nm is indicated by dashed red lines.

Figure 4 (A) shows Raman spectra of plasma hydrogenated ZnO micropods, where origin of peaks is also depicted. Nonpolar phonon mode E_2(Low) expected at 100 cm^{-1} is associated with Zn sublattice, but it was out of the measured spectral range. Nonpolar phonon mode E_2(High) associated with oxygen sublattice is observed at 440 cm^{-1} [14]. The sharp, strong and dominant Raman peak is significantly amplified after hydrogen plasma, but for 10-minutes hydrogenation and longer its intensity decreases again. Same as increasing intensity of the dominant peak, broad sideband at low-frequency side also increases. This broad band with maximum about 420 cm^{-1} is attributed to E_1(TO) mode commonly seen in nano- and micro-structures. The peaks at 336 and 540 cm^{-1} correspond to the sum and differential wavenumbers E_2(High) $\pm E_2$(Low) and A_1(LO), respectively [15]. The peak at 581 cm^{-1} has been assigned to the ZnO mode E_1(LO) [16]. This mode should be inactive but it may appear as a local mode due to the disturbance of the crystal symmetry resulting from the presence of oxygen vacancies and zinc interstitials. Thus, the presence of this mode suggests that the plasma treatment increases the concentration of point defects. Moreover, from spectra normalized on the value of E_2(High) peak, see **Figure 4(B)**, could be seen that for hydrogenation time up to 5 minutes, the spectra are very similar. After longer hydrogenation, the height of the E_1(LO) peak decreases. In spectra, small band near 660 cm^{-1} and 1150 cm^{-1} correspond to multiphonon processes and peak near 1100 cm^{-1} to combination of acoustic modes with symmetry A_1 and E_2.

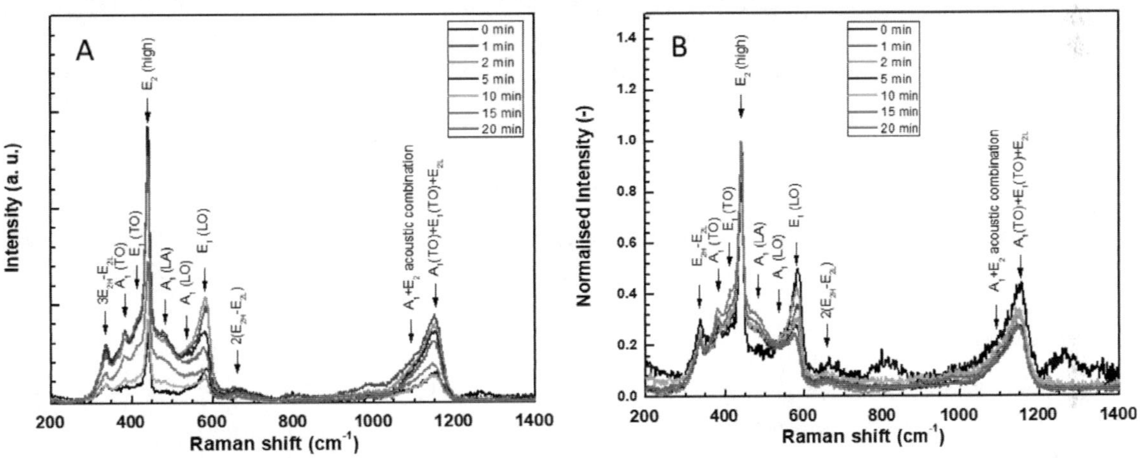

Figure 4 Raman spectra (A) and normalized Raman spectra (B) of plasma hydrogenated ZnO micropods depending on the expose to hydrogen plasma. The excitation wavelength was 442 nm (blue laser)

ATR-FTIR is a sensitive probe of free carriers in ZnO. It has been shown that the room-temperature exposure of polycrystalline ZnO films to H_2 plasma rapidly increases carrier density [17]. **Figure 5** shows the infrared absorbance spectra of plasma hydrogenated ZnO micropods depending on the expose to hydrogen plasma. Free carrier absorption dominates infrared absorbance spectra already in the unhydrogenated sample with further increase after plasma hydrogenation. The room temperature plasma hydrogenation had been sufficient to induce significant surface conductivity

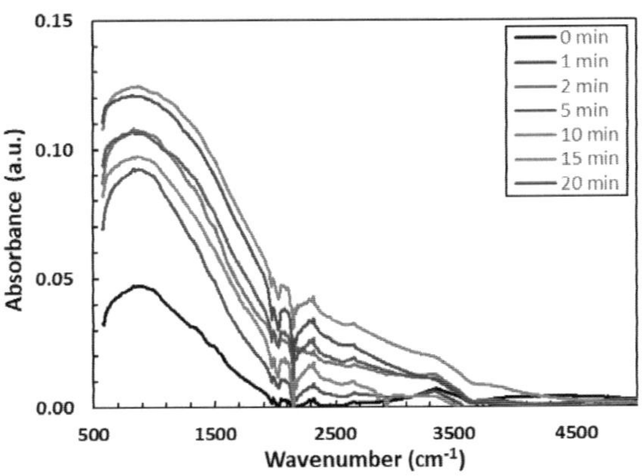

Figure 5 Infrared absorbance spectra of plasma hydrogenated ZnO micropods depending on the expose to hydrogen plasma measured by ATR FTIR and normalized to zero at 5000 cm^{-1}.

changes after 1 minute expose. It should be noted that the absorbance has been somewhat arbitrary normalized to zero at 5000 cm^{-1} and that the signal-to-noise ratio is poor in the spectral range 2000-2300 cm^{-1} where diamond ATR prism heavily absorbs.

The PLS in **Figure 6** shows that the strong exciton photoluminescence at 3.23 eV (384 nm) appears already after 1 min plasma hydrogenation at 200 W. This suggest that the bound exciton complexes are assigned to surface states. Furthermore, the hydrogen plasma suppresses the defect related broad PLS band centered in red spectra range around 2 eV. It takes about 10 min to suppress this band by an order of magnitude. Therefore, we suggest 5 min plasma hydrogenation as an optimal process time. This is significantly shorter time then 30 min previously used in plasma hydrogenation with ungrounded quartz holder.

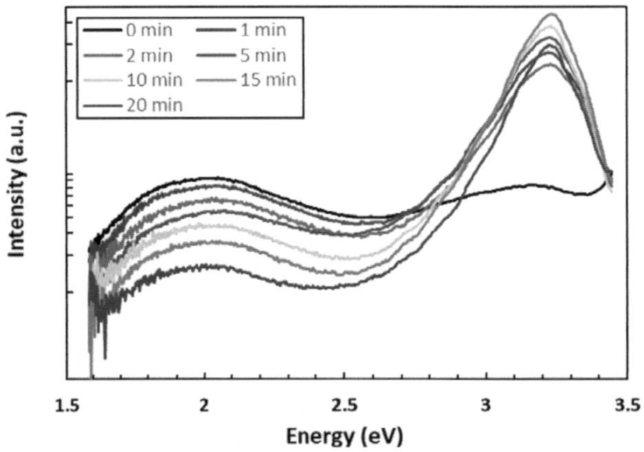

Figure 6 The room temperature PLS of plasma hydrogenated ZnO micropods in semilogarithmic intensity scale depending on the expose to hydrogen plasma. The excitation energy was 3.65 eV.

4. CONCLUSION

Ar plasma sputters ZnO placed on a grounded stainless-steel holder in an ICP reactor. Therefore, the Ar cleaning process needs to be taken only for a short time with a relatively low rf power. The strong UV photoluminescence appears just after a minute of plasma hydrogenation of ZnO micropods which is a strong evidence that the bound exciton complexes are assigned to surface states. On the other hand, the reduction of red photoluminescence needs prolonged time suggesting that the red photoluminescence is related to bulk defect states. The optimal time for plasma hydrogenation at the rf power density 40 W/dm^3 and hydrogen pressure 17 Pa seems to be just a few minutes.

ACKNOWLEDGEMENTS

This work was supported by the Czech Science Foundation project 19-02858J, by the Operational Programme Research, Development and Education project SOLID21 - CZ.02.1.01/0.0/0.0/16_019/0000760 and by the Scientific Grant Agency of Ministry of Education, Science, Research and Sport of Slovak Republic and Slovak Academy of Sciences (VEGA 2/0157/20). Special thanks to Ing. Rayisa Yatskiv from the Institute of Physics of the Czech Academy of Sciences for SEM.

REFERENCES

[1] KLINGSHIRN, C. F. (ed.). *Zinc Oxide: from fundamental properties towards novel applications.* Heidelberg ; London : Springer, 2010. Springer series in materials science, 120. ISBN 978-3-642-10576-0. QD181.Z6 Z56 2010.

[2] CHANG, Yu-Ying, REMES, Zdenek, MICOVA, Julia. Mass production of hydrogenated ZnO nanorods. **In:** *NANOCON 2019 - Conference Proceedings* [online]. Hotel Voronez I, Brno, Czech Republic:Tanger Ltd., 2020. pp. 221-225. [Accessed 11 May 2020]. ISBN 978-80-87294-95-6. Available from: https://www.confer.cz/nanocon2019-8680-chang-mass-production-of-hydrogenated-zno-nanorods.pdf

[3] MIČOVÁ, Júlia, BURYI, Maksym, ŠIMEK, Daniel, DRAHOKOUPIL, Jan, NEYKOVA, Neda, CHANG, Yu-Ying, REMEŠ, Zdeněk, POP-GEORGIEVSKI, Ognen, SVOBODA, Jan, IM, Chan. Synthesis of zinc oxide nanostructures and comparison of their crystal quality. *Applied Surface Science*. [online]. December 2018, vol. 461, pp. 190-195. Available from: https://doi.org/10.1016/j.apsusc.2018.05.176.

[4] BURYI, M., BABIN, V., CHANG, Y.-Y., REMEŠ, Z., MIČOVÁ, J., ŠIMEK, D. Influence of precursor age on defect states in ZnO nanorods. *Applied Surface Science*. [online]. September 2020, vol. 525, p. 146448. Available from: https://doi.org/10.1016/j.apsusc.2020.146448.

[5] FALLERT, Johannes, HAUSCHILD, Robert, STELZL, Felix, URBAN, Alex, WISSINGER, Markus, ZHOU, Huijuan, KLINGSHIRN, Claus, KALT, Heinz. Surface-state related luminescence in ZnO nanocrystals. *Journal of Applied Physics*. [online]. April 2007, vol. 101, no. 7, p. 073506. Available from: https://doi.org/10.1063/1.2718290.

[6] GOKARNA, Anisha, AAD, Roy, ZHOU, Junze, NOMENYO, Komla, LUSSON, Alain, MISKA, Patrice, LERONDEL, Gilles. On the origin of the enhancement of defect related visible emission in annealed ZnO micropods. *Journal of Applied Physics*. [online]. 14 October 2019, vol. 126, no. 14, p. 145104. Available from: https://doi.org/10.1063/1.5111184.

[7] VAN DE WALLE, Chris G., NEUGEBAUER, J. Universal alignment of hydrogen levels in semiconductors, insulators and solutions. *Nature*. [online]. June 2003, vol. 423, no. 6940, pp. 626-628. Available from: https://doi.org/10.1038/nature01665.

[8] BOURRET-COURCHESNE, E.D., DERENZO, S.E., WEBER, M.J. Development of ZnO:Ga as an ultra-fast scintillator. *Nuclear Instruments and Methods in Physics Research Section A: Accelerators, Spectrometers, Detectors and Associated Equipment*. [online]. April 2009, vol. 601, no. 3, pp. 358-363. Available from: https://doi.org/10.1016/j.nima.2008.12.206.

[9] PROCHÁZKOVÁ, Lenka, GBUR, Tomáš, ČUBA, Václav, JARÝ, Vítězslav, NIKL, Martin. Fabrication of highly efficient ZnO nanoscintillators. *Optical Materials*. [online]. September 2015, vol. 47, pp. 67-71. Available from: https://doi.org/10.1016/j.optmat.2015.07.001.

[10] GRILL, Alfred. *Cold plasma in material fabrication: from fundamentals to applications*. New York: The Institute of Electrical and Electronics Engineers, Inc., 1994. ISBN 0-7803-4714-5.

[11] CHANG, Y.-Y., NEYKOVA, N., STUCHLIK, J., PURKRT, A., REMES, Z. Hydrogen plasma treatment of ZnO thin films. **In**: *NANOCON 2016 - Conference Proceedings*. Ostrava, Czech Republic: TANGER Ltd., 2016. pp. 161-165. ISBN 978-80-87294-71-0.

[12] MOONEY, Jonathan, KAMBHAMPATI, Patanjali. Get the Basics Right: Jacobian Conversion of Wavelength and Energy Scales for Quantitative Analysis of Emission Spectra. *The Journal of Physical Chemistry Letters*. [online]. 3 October 2013, vol. 4, no. 19, pp. 3316-3318. Available from: https://doi.org/10.1021/jz401508t.

[13] KRAMIDA, Alexander, RALCHENKO, Yuri. NIST *Atomic Spectra Database, NIST Standard Reference Database 78* [online]. 1999. National Institute of Standards and Technology. [Accessed 25 August 2020]. Available from: http://www.nist.gov/pml/data/asd.cfm.

[14] YANG, J. H., ZHENG, J. H., ZHAI, H. J., YANG, L. L. Low temperature hydrothermal growth and optical properties of ZnO nanorods. *Crystal Research and Technology*. [online]. January 2009, vol. 44, no. 1, pp. 87-91. Available from: https://doi.org/10.1002/crat.200800294.

[15] CALLEJA, J. M., CARDONA, Manuel. Resonant Raman scattering in ZnO. *Physical Review B*. [online]. 15 October 1977, vol. 16, no. 8, pp. 3753-3761. Available from: https://doi.org/10.1103/PhysRevB.16.3753.

[16] DECREMPS, Fredéric, PELLICER-PORRES, Julio, SAITTA, A. Marco, CHERVIN, Jean-Claude, POLIAN, Alain. High-pressure Raman spectroscopy study of wurtzite ZnO. *Physical Review B* [online]. 6 February 2002, vol. 65, no. 9. [Accessed 29 February 2020]. Available from: https://doi.org/10.1103/PhysRevB.65.092101.

[17] WOLDEN, C.A., BARNES, T.M., BAXTER, J.B., AYDIL, E.S. Infrared detection of hydrogen-generated free carriers in polycrystalline ZnO thin films. *Journal of Applied Physics* [online]. 2005, vol. 97, no. 4. Available from: https://doi.org/10.1063/1.1851599.

THERMAL STABILITY OF Ti/Ni MULTILAYER THIN FILMS

[1]Richard VÁCLAVIK, [1]Lukáš ZÁBRANSKÝ, [1]Pavel SOUČEK, [1]Pavel SŤAHEL, [2]Jiří BURŠÍK, [3]Tomáš FOŘT, [1]Vilma BURŠÍKOVÁ

[1]*Department of Physical Electronics, Faculty of Science, Masaryk University, Brno, Czech Republic, EU,* richard.vaclavik@mail.muni.cz

[2]*Institute of Physics of Materials, Czech Academy of Sciences, Brno, Czech Republic, EU,* bursik@ipm.cz

[3]*Institute of Scientific Instruments, Czech Academy of Sciences, Brno, Czech Republic, EU,* fortt@isibrno.cz

https://doi.org/10.37904/nanocon.2020.3776

Abstract

In this work, thermal stability and mechanical properties of Ti/Ni multilayer thin films were studied. The multilayer thin films were synthesised by alternately depositing Ti and Ni layers using magnetron sputtering. The thickness of constituent layers of Ti and Ni varied from 1.7 nm to 10 nm, and one coating was deposited by simultaneous sputtering of both targets. Single crystalline silicon was used as a substrate. The effects of thermal treatment on the mechanical properties were studied using nanoindentation and discussed in relation to microstructure evaluated by X-ray diffraction. Annealing was carried out under low-pressure conditions for 2 hours in the range of 100-800 °C.

Keywords: Ti/Ni, multilayers, magnetron sputtering, nanoindentation, annealing

1. INTRODUCTION

By continually increasing demands and needs of humankind, science and research have reached a state where standard monolithic materials are no longer sufficient. Thanks to this, materials with a complex and advanced structure are currently being studied intensively.

One of the new trends in the thin films synthesised by plasma deposition is controlling the properties of coatings, for example, by alternating layers of various materials at the nanoscale and achieve functions that none of the original components has. In this way, it is possible to create a multilayered thin film with the option to choose the thickness of constituent layers, the ratio of layers thicknesses, the number of constituent layers, etc [1,2].

Ti/Ni multilayered thin films are one of the complex structures with superior functional properties (e.g. electric, magnetic and optical). These multilayered systems can be used to form TiNi shape memory alloys (SMA) which exhibit two closely related properties: shape memory effect (SME) and superelasticity (SE). These effects are caused by the martensitic transformation from a simple cubic structure (austenitic, phase B2) to a monoclinic crystalline structure (martensite, phase B19'), whereas this phase transformation is reversible and instantaneous. The transformation can be achieved by annealing or by applying stress [3,4]. Thanks to the remarkable SE and SME effects, TiNi SMA can be found in a wide range of fields such as medical, aeronautic, electric, telecommunication or as sensors and actuators in MEMS [4-8].

In this work, annealing was chosen to ensure the transformation. In the case of this approach, the uniformity of layers thicknesses on the nanoscale is crucial [9]. Moreover, for applications in MEMS, it is necessary to produce TiNi thin films with a thickness of several μm. For these reasons, magnetron sputtering is one of the most common deposition techniques to synthesise multilayer thin films with low total thicknesses and adequate uniformity. For the fabrication of Ti/Ni multilayer films, a dual-head sputtering system with Ti and Ni targets can be utilised and periodically turned the power on and off ensures alternating nanolayers of pure Ti and Ni. Afterwards, this multilayered system can be converted into the TiNi alloy thin film through solid state amorphisation by using a heat treatment. A significant advantage of magnetron sputtering over other deposition techniques used for multilayer thin films as e-beam evaporation, pulsed laser deposition or accumulative roll bonding, is an option of easily scalable resulting structure of multilayer by choosing deposition properties [10].

In this work, we have been mainly focused on thermal stability and development of mechanical properties with annealing of Ti/Ni multilayers prepared by dual-head magnetron sputtering of Ti and Ni targets. Annealed thin films composed of nanolayers with different thicknesses underwent nanoindentation tests, and results were discussed in relation to microstructure obtained by X-ray diffraction.

2. EXPERIMENTAL

Ti/Ni multilayers were synthesised by dual-head magnetron sputtering in an argon atmosphere. To ensure multilayer structure, the power on titanium and nickel targets was periodically turned on and off depending on which layer was currently depositing. Single crystalline silicon was used as substrates and before the deposition they were etched by ion bombardment for 5 minutes. During the deposition, the negative floating potential was applied on a substrate holder and to achieve sufficient spatial homogeneity, the substrate was rotating. By deposition of one-layered coatings of Ti and Ni, their deposition rates were found to be 0.75 nm/s and 1.52 nm/s, respectively. The desired thickness of an individual layer h was programmed by the variation of deposition time. The deposition conditions as applied power on targets, deposition pressure and substrate rotation speed for each multilayer design are listed in **Table 1**. The first presented coating $h = 0$ nm is prepared by simultaneous sputtering of both targets and therefore does not exhibits multilayered microstructure.

Table 1 Summary of deposition conditions of all Ti/Ni multilayered coatings

h (nm)	Overall thickness (nm)	Power on Ti target (W)	Power on Ni target (W)	Deposition pressure (Pa)	Rotation (rpm)
0	500	350	350	0.30	3.0
1.7	1190	300	300	0.16	4.8
2.5	1000	300	300	0.16	4.8
5.0	1000	300	200	0.16	4.8
10	500	350	350	0.30	3.0

After the deposition, one sample from each layering underwent a series of annealing in thermal desorption spectroscopy chamber from 50 to 800 °C. For each annealing, the constant temperature was kept for 2 hours.

One of the analytical methods utilised to study the effect of annealing was the depth-sensing nanoindentation performed on Hysitron TI950 Triboindenter equipped with a Berkovich tip. To determine the indentation hardness H and the reduced elastic modulus E_r, nanoscale measuring head was used. This head allows measure in the load range from 50 nN up to 11 mN with a resolution of 1 nN. Several quasistatic tests with 20 segments of partial unloading were performed in load control regime. As it is shown in **Figure 1a)**, each segment consists of three parts: loading, hold and unloading, and each part lasted 2 seconds. The result of such a loading function can be load-displacement curve plotted in **Figure 1b)**, where every partial load segment can be evaluated according to the standard procedure proposed by Oliver and Pharr [11]. Thanks to that, the depth profile of hardness and modulus can be obtained by this approach. Example of such depth profiles are plotted in **Figure 1c)**. In this work, single measurement consists of 16 load-displacement curves whose depth profiles were averaged and standard deviations were calculated. Values of the hardness and the reduced elastic modulus in the smallest common depth (negligible substrate influence) were used to compare samples and annealing temperatures.

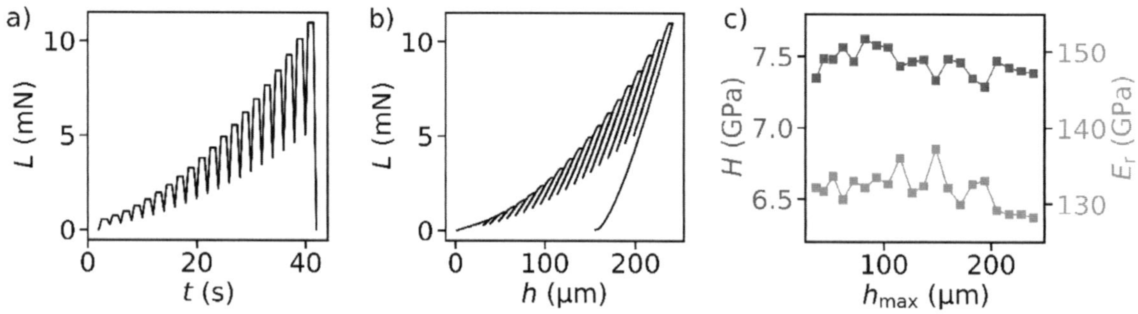

Figure 1 Quasistatic partial unload test: a) load function, b) load-displacement curve, c) hardness and reduced elastic modulus as a function of maximum depth per segment

In order to correlate the hardness and elastic modulus evolution with microstructural information, X-ray diffraction (XRD) was utilised for the phase identification. XRD experiments were performed in Rigaku Smartlab X-ray diffractometer using Cu Kα radiation with a wavelength of 0.15418 nm with a grazing angle of incidence configuration.

3. RESULTS AND DISCUSSION

The evolution of the hardness as a function of annealing temperature is plotted in **Figure 2** for each studied multilayer. The increase of hardness of as-deposited multilayers with the increasing layer thickness in the used range was already reported in our previous study [12] and interpreted as an interface crossing of single dislocations [13,14]. After the first set of annealing at 100 °C, differences between hardness values of coatings get smaller even almost equalised at 200 °C, what can be caused by alloying. With further increasing temperature, differences become more significant.

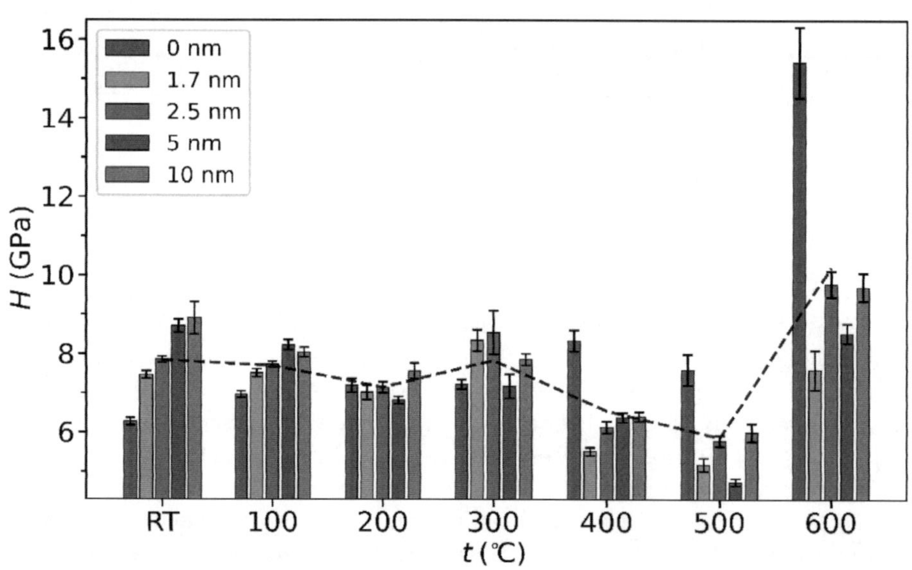

Figure 2 Development of hardness as a function of temperature for synthetised multilayers and one non-multilayer coating labelled as h = 0 nm

The average hardness for all coating and a specific temperature, marked by the dashed line, is continuously decreasing until 500 °C, except for annealing temperature 300 °C. At 600 °C hardness of multilayers significantly increased, and even more, a rapid increase occurred for non-multilayered coating (h = 0 nm) up to 15 GPa, which is more than twice as high as for the as-deposited coating. After annealing with even higher temperature, the coating has delaminated from the substrate or the coating has entirely desorbed. Substantial raise of hardness in the case of non-multilayer was not caused by higher substrate hardness, because the desorption was not observed even after annealing at 800 °C.

Reduced elastic modulus as a function of temperature was plotted in **Figure 3** in the same way as for hardness evaluation. From room temperature (RT) to annealing temperature 200 °C, order of reduced elastic modulus of multilayers was kept the same - maximum E_r for h = 5 nm and minimum E_r for h = 1.7 nm. Dashed line indicating reduced elastic modulus for all coating and the specific temperature has a very similar development as in the same graph plotted for hardness. The reduced elastic modulus is gradually decreasing until 500 °C, except for annealing temperature 300 °C, where the obtained value is slightly higher. After annealing at 600 °C, the reduced elastic modulus of multilayers increased but only a little. More significant influence of annealing temperature on the reduced elastic modulus was found in the case of multilayer with h = 1.7 nm. In this case the reduced elastic modulus decreased ~1.4 times at 500 °C in comparison with as-deposited multilayer. The significant influence of annealing was found for non-multilayer coating as well. In contrast to the as-deposited coating, after annealing to 600 °C, reduced elastic modulus increased ~1.3 times and was much higher than for multilayers.

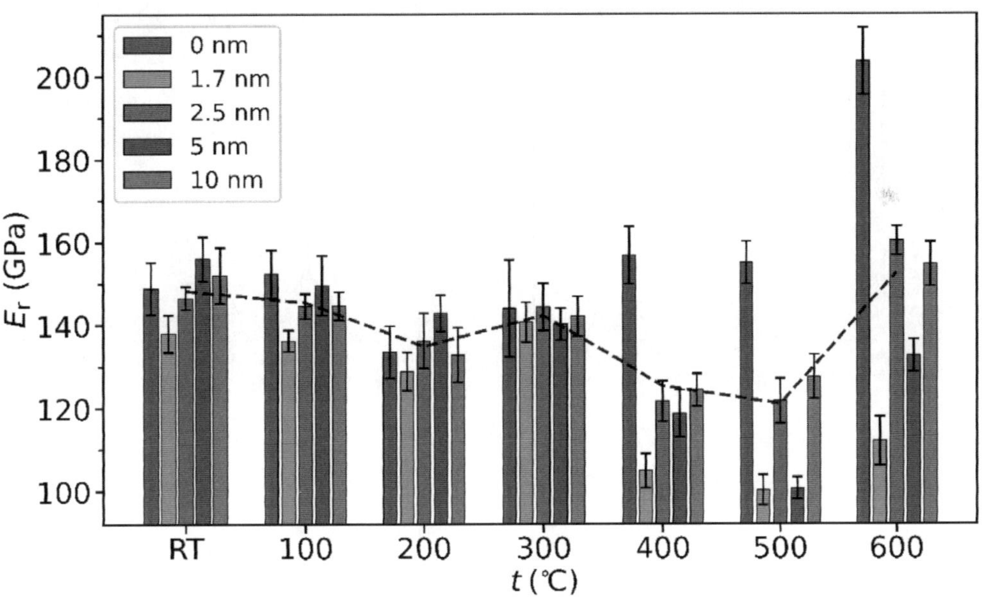

Figure 3 Development of reduced elastic modulus as a function of temperature for synthetised multilayers and one non-multilayer coating labelled as h = 0 nm

For both coatings where significant influence of annealing was found, XRD measurements were performed in the range RT-500 °C. The XRD diffractograms presented in **Figure 4a)** for h = 1.7 nm and in **Figure 4b)** for h = 0 nm exhibiting polycrystalline microstructure. The microstructure is composed of hexagonal (hcp) Ti, cubic (fcc) Ni grains and Ti-Ni intermetallic grains which emerged at higher annealing temperatures.

In the multilayer with h = 1.7 nm, Ni (111) stays as the strongest peak with increasing annealing temperature from room temperature until 300 °C. In this temperature range, the intensity of Ti (002) peak is decreasing, and this peak completely disappeared at 400 °C. Other notably lower peaks Ti (110), Ti (004) and Ni (222) disappeared as well. At this temperature, two new peaks corresponding to Ti-Ni intermetallic phase were detected, what is corroborated by previous works [15-17]. Shifted Ni (111) peak could contribute to the intensity of peak labelled as $TiNi_3$ (004). The disappearance of individual Ti and Ni peaks indicates possible disintegration of the layers and the formation of fully intermixed and alloyed structure. These phenomena can be the cause of a drop in hardness and reduced elastic modulus development. In the coating with non-multilayer structure, new intermetallic peaks did not emerge after higher annealing temperature, but they could contribute to the intensity of Ni (111) peak. This is highly probable due to a much easier way to form the alloyed structure from the non-multilayer structure. In this coating, noticeable shifting of the dominant peak is observed what can be caused by induced residual stress or by diffusion of atoms of one layer into another layer. Emerging and disappearing of Ti (010) and Ti (100) peaks is not clear yet, but more detailed investigations on this topic will be executed.

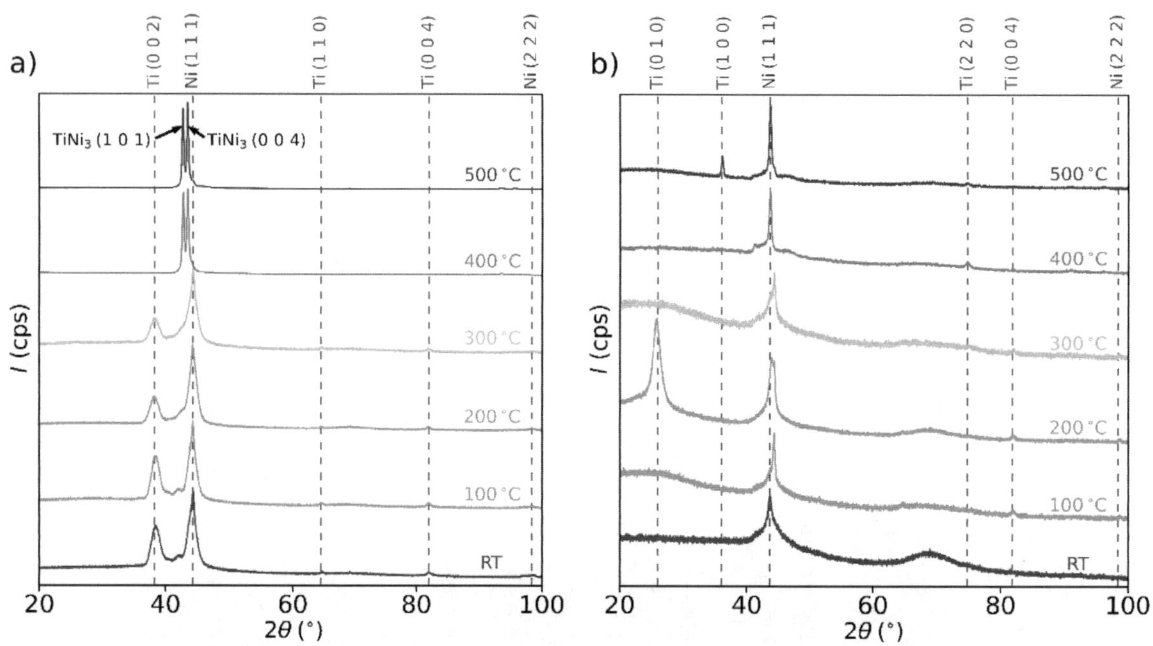

Figure 4 Diffraction patterns for Ti/Ni a) multilayer with individual layer thickness h = 1.7 nm, b) non-multilayer coating labelled as h = 0 nm

4. CONCLUSION

Several Ti/Ni multilayers synthesised by magnetron sputtering with different individual thicknesses of Ti and Ni layers were annealed. The main aim was to study the temperature dependence of their mechanical properties and to find a correlation with microstructural information. Based on the nanoindentation results, it was found out that hardness and reduced elastic modulus is decreasing with increasing annealing temperature until 500 °C. After annealing to 600 °C, both hardness and reduced elastic modulus increased especially in the non-multilayer coating (hardness of annealed at 600 °C is ~2.5x higher than for as-deposited). After annealing at even higher temperature, coating has delaminated from the substrate or entirely desorbed. From the XRD results, it was concluded that all synthesised coatings have polycrystalline microstructure, which is becoming intermix and alloy after annealing at ~400 °C. The XRD patterns were described, and different phenomena were explained, and correlation with mechanical properties was proposed.

ACKNOWLEDGEMENTS

The present work was supported by the Czech Science Foundation under project GACR 20-11321S, by the Ministry of Education, Youth and Sports of the Czech Republic under project NPU (LO1411).

REFERENCES

[1] VERESCHAKA, A.A., GRIGORIEV, S.N., SITNIKOV, N.N., OGANYAN, G.V., BATAKO, A. Working efficiency of cutting tools with multilayer nano-structured Ti-TiCN-(Ti,Al)CN and Ti-TiCN-(Ti,Al,Cr)CN coatings: Analysis of cutting properties, wear mechanism and diffusion processes. *Surface & Coatings Technology*. 2017, vol. 332, pp. 198-213.

[2] ANTONOV, M., HUSSAINOVA, I., SERGEJEV, F., KULU, P., GREGOR, A. Assessment of gradient and nanogradient PVD coatings behaviour under erosive, abrasive and impact wear conditions. *Wear*. 2009, vol. 267, pp. 898-906.

[3] MIYAZAKI, S., FU, Y.Q., HUANG, W.M. *Thin film shape memory alloys: fundamentals and device applications*. New York: Cambridge University Press, 2009.

[4] PAN, G., CAO, Z., WEI, M., XU, L., SHI, J., MENG, X. Superelasticity of TiNi thin films induced by cyclic nanoindentation deformation at nanoscale. *Materials Science and Engineering: A*. 2014, vol. 600, pp. 8-11.

[5] YAMAUCHI, K., OHKATA, I., TSUCHIYA, K., MIYAZAKI S. *Shape memory and superelastic alloys: technologies and applications*. Philadelphia, PA: Woodhead Publishing, 2011.

[6] CHOUDHARY, N., KAUR, D. Shape memory alloy thin films and heterostructures for MEMS applications: A review. *Sensors and Actuators A: Physical*. 2016, vol. 242, pp. 162-181.

[7] YONEYAMA, T., MIYAZAKI, S. *Shape memory alloys for biomedical applications*. Cambridge, England: Woodhead Publishing, 2009.

[8] JANI, J.M., LEARY, M., SUBIC, A., GIBSON, M.A. A review of shape memory alloy research, applications and opportunities. *Materials & Design*. 2014, vol. 56, pp. 1078-1113.

[9] FU, Y., DU, H., HUANG, W., ZHANG, S., HU, M. TiNi-based thin films in MEMS applications: a review. *Sensors and Actuators A: Physical*. 2004, vol. 112, pp. 395-408.

[10] CHO, H., KIM, H.Y., MIYAZAKI, S. Fabrication and characterization of Ti-Ni shape memory thin film using Ti/Ni multilayer technique. *Science and Technology of Advanced Materials*. 2005, vol. 6, pp. 678-683

[11] OLIVER, W.C., PHARR, G.M. Measurement of hardness and elastic modulus by instrumented indentation: Advances in understanding and refinements to methodology. *Journal of Materials Research*. 2004, vol. 19, pp. 3-20.

[12] ZÁBRANSKÝ, L., VÁCLAVIK, R., PŘIBYL, R., ŽENÍŠEK, J., SOUČEK, P., BURŠÍK. J., FOŘT, T., BURŠÍKOVÁ, V. Study of mechanical properties of nanolayered Ti/Ni coatings. **In**: *NANOCON 2017: 9th International Conference on Nanomaterials - Research & Application*. Ostrava: TANGER, 2017, pp. 836-841.

[13] YANG, Z., WANG, J. Temperature and Thickness Dependent Mechanical Properties of Ti/Ni Multilayer Thin Films. *Micro and Nanomechanics*. 2016, vol. 5, pp. 41-49.

[14] YANG, Z., WANG, J. Coupled annealing temperature and layer thickness effect on strengthening mechanisms of Ti/Ni multilayer thin films. *Journal of the Mechanics and Physics of Solids*. 2016, vol. 88, pp. 72-82.

[15] CAVALEIRO, A. J., SANTOS, R.J., RAMOS, A.S., VIEIRA, M.T. In-situ thermal evolution of Ni/Ti multilayer thin films. *Intermetallics*. 2014, vol. 51, pp. 11-17.

[16] GUPTA, R., GUPTA, M., KULKARNI, S.K., KHARRAZI, S., GUPTA, A., CHAUDHARI, S.M. Thermal stability of nanometer range Ti/Ni multilayers. *Thin Solid Films*. 2006, vol. 515, pp. 2213-2219

[17] LEHNERT, T., GRIMMER, L., BONI, P., HORISBERGER, M., GOTTHARDT, R. Characterization of shape-memory alloy thin films made up from sputter-deposited Ti/Ti multilayers. *Acta Materialia*. 2000, vol. 48, pp. 4065-4071.

NANOSPRAY PROCESSING OF SILVER NANOPARTICLES FOR FORMATION OF DRIED DEPOSITS

[1]Anna TYCOVA, [1]Vladimir JONAS, [1]Jan PRIKRYL, [2]Adela KOTZIANOVA, [2]Vladimir VELEBNY, [1]Frantisek FORET

[1]*Institute of Analytical Chemistry of the CAS, v. v. i., Brno, EU, Czech Republic,* tycova@iach.cz

[2]*Contipro a.s., R&D Department, Dolni Dobrouc, EU, Czech Republic,* adela.kotzianova@contipro.com

https://doi.org/10.37904/nanocon.2020.3768

Abstract

Nanospray transfers liquid into an aerosol via electrostatic forces created between an emitter and a counter electrode. Herein, we present compact laboratory-made instrumentation for nanospray-processing of silver colloid. The instrumentation is based on the pressurized polysulfone chamber fixing a disposable vial with an immersed platinum electrode and a long fused silica capillary supplying the sprayed liquid to the emitter. The combination of low flow rates (70 nL/min) with a sharp emitter, fabricated on a 3D printed grinding station, resulted in a fine aerosol. The low volume of released droplets allowed full evaporation of water during their flight towards the counter electrode without any need for drying gas or the addition of volatile solvents. The constructed device was successfully used for the deposition of water-free silver colloid without any requirement of its pretreatment. The deposition of completely dried nanoparticles on planar substrates eliminated undesirable coffee ring effect and deposits of increased homogeneity could be obtained. Electron microscopy confirmed no significant changes in the character of nanospray-processed nanoparticles. Finally, we also investigated several approaches for the improvement of the surface density of nanoparticles on the substrate at preserved time scale.

Keywords: Colloid, deposition, nanoparticles, nanospray, silver

1. INTRODUCTION

The deposition of nanostructures on the surface of a bulk material can significantly modify its properties and adjust it for target applications. The change in wettability or biological compatibility belongs to classical examples. Additionally, the localized nanoparticle deposits can act also as microelectrodes, substrates for surface-enhanced Raman spectrometry, or be part of sensing devices [1]. Most of these applications claim structures of uniform properties across the treated area. The full control of the deposition process is therefore an important prerequisite for its implementation into routine practice.

Commonly, the technology of inkjet printing or electrohydrodynamic printing is used for the highly-controlled depositions of colloids. In both cases, the experimental conditions do not allow evaporation of dispersing medium and the nanoparticles are deposited with a certain level of wetness (**Figure 1**). The amount of residual liquid highly influences the surface characteristics of the obtained structure (e.g. porosity). Moreover, significant differences in evaporation rates across the wet deposit give origin to an inhomogeneous distribution of the nanoparticles. This phenomenon is known as the coffee ring effect and challenges many procedures and protocols [2-4].

Electrospray has been proven as a potent competing tool for depositions of nanoparticles [1]. However, in many cases electrospray struggles with the residual presence of water too, which is typically addressed by long emitter-substrate distances, drying gases, or the addition of volatile solvents into a sprayed mixture. In this work, we used nano(electro)spray operated at a flow rate of 70 nL/min only. Thus, the produced aerosol became extremely fine and the colloid reached the counter electrode completely dry without the necessity of any modification of colloid composition. The water-free deposition eliminates the risk of the coffee ring effect as well as the sintering of the deposited structures. Moreover, the nanospray-generated plume is considerably narrower in comparison to classical electrospray plume and allows precise positioning of the deposit at very low consumption of processed material.

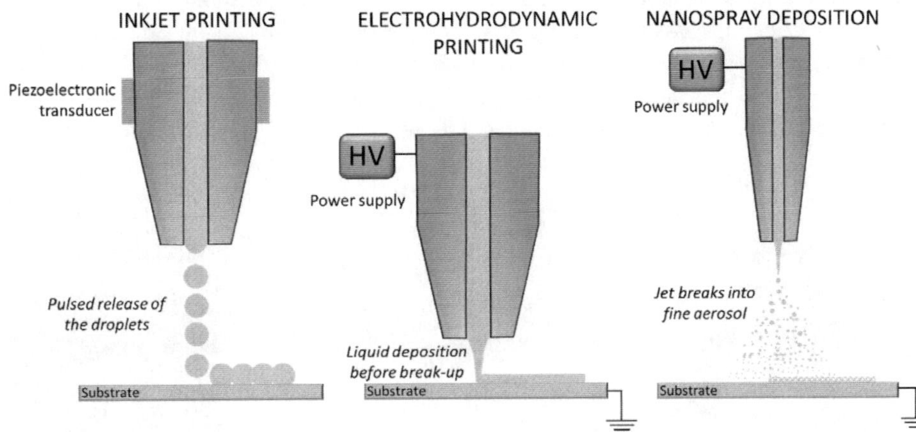

Figure 1 Schematic comparison of inkjet printing, electrohydrodynamic printing, and nanospray deposition of nanoparticles

Notably, the nanospray-assisted depositions sustain their remarkable simplicity of the instrumentation and no auxiliary drying components are needed. Thus, the operation of nanospray requires only a source of *high voltage* and continuous *supply* of sprayed mixture (typically a pump or pressurized gas) into an *emitter*. Due to this simplicity, such a set-up is barely commercially available and lab-made constructions have to be designed and constructed. Herein, we present a simple and compact yet very reliable set-up for nanospray production and we use it for the deposition of silver colloid on the substrate in a completely dried state.

2. EXPERIMENTAL

2.1. Chemicals and methods

The silver colloid synthesized by a Lee-Meisel protocol was used for nanospray-assisted depositions [5]. Its production is based on the reduction of silver nitrate (Sigma Aldrich) by sodium citrate (Lachema). In the standard protocol, the ratio of both reagents was approximately 1:2 (w/w). The obtained dispersion was characterized via absorption spectrometry (UV-1800, Shimadzu) and scanning electron microscopy (Mira3, Tescan) both giving evidence of an average nanoparticle diameter in the range of 60-70 nm.

We also used a modified protocol for silver nanoparticles synthesis. Therein, we reduced nanoparticles from silver nitrate using ten times excess of citrate (w/w). Such a colloid provided comparable characteristics as the colloid prepared according to the standard protocol.

2.2. Instrumentation

For a stable generation of nanospray aerosol, a special device was designed and fabricated. Two polysulfone parts mutually attachable via threading represent its key components. While one of the parts fixed a disposable vial with a colloid, the second part held an emitter and platinum electrode. Thus, only after the connection of both parts, the emitter and electrode immersed into a spray mixture and electrical connection was achieved. The threading sealed up the system tightly for the establishment of increased pressure via supplied nitrogen, which regulated a flow rate of the colloid through the immersed emitter. No significant pressure leakages were observed up to 6 Atm. However, for the generation of 70 nL/min, pressure of 0.35 Atm was required only.

The emitter was fabricated from fused silica capillary (Polymicro Technologies) of an inner diameter of 25 µm. Its length of 28 cm allowed user-friendly manipulation. While one end of the emitter was immersed into a sprayed colloid, the opposite end was ground into a sharp tip on a lab-designed grinding device [6] and positioned in front of a grounded planar counter electrode with an attached substrate. Since the treated area is relatively small, a plastic mask was used for its easy localization. The emitter-substrate distance was 5 mm, which provided reliably complete removal of water from aerosol during its flight towards the counter electrode. The optical camera (V160, Shenzhen Andonstar Tech Co.) monitored the behavior of the nanospray plume using the scattering of a green laser on the droplets of the aerosol. The described instrumentation is depicted in **Figure 2**.

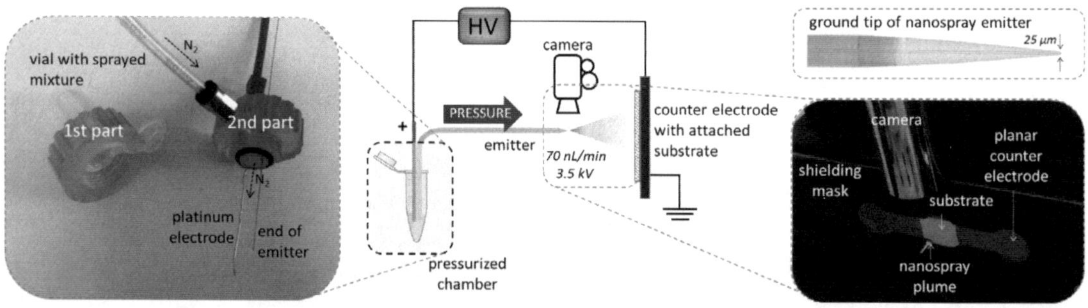

Figure 2 Schematic illustration and photographs of the developed set-up for nanospray-assisted deposition of nanoparticles on a planar substrate

3. RESULTS AND DISCUSSION

Deposits of nanostructures have got into the center of attention due to their unique properties useful in many cutting-edge devices [7-9]. The material of the processed colloid reflects the target application. Silver nanostructures belong to very popular dispersions due to their wide-range applicability and simplicity of their synthesis. In this work, we deposited via nanospray the silver colloid stabilized by molecules of citrate. The formation of a stable nanospray plume did not claim any colloid pretreatment and it could be reliably sprayed in its crude form. We determined a voltage of 3.5 kV at a flow rate of 70 nL/min as optimal conditions for long term performance. Within an hour of systematic monitoring, we did not observe any significant instabilities or changes in the plume character (**Figure 3A**).

The used low flow rate generated aerosol of very fine droplets. Their small volumes allowed fast evaporation of the dispersing medium at ambient conditions even at a short distance of 5 mm. Thus, no components supporting the water evaporation were required and the instrumentation sustained its extraordinary simplicity and the drying was achieved only by the sufficient emitter-substrate distance. It should be also stressed, that the process of nanospraying did not change the overall character of the nanoparticles and that their shape and size were comparable with their state in the unprocessed colloid (**Figure 3B**). The absence of water in the deposited structures eliminated completely the coffee ring effect, which makes nanospray a very potent tool for the formation of evenly distributed deposits.

With respect to the uniform character of the deposit, one should consider a certain level of the size distribution of synthesized nanoparticles too. The effect of electrical field on the trajectory of nanoparticles is related with its size (i.e. mass), which might result preferential deposition of heavier entities in the central part of the target [10]. However, our microscopic observations did not reveal any significant central maximum in the surface density of nanoparticles.

Further, the substrate-emitter distance influences also the treated area. At the emitter-substrate distance of 5 mm we treated round area with the estimated diameter of ~8 mm. While the increased gap would result in the larger spot and could be used for coating of extended area, at reduced distances the deposition of the nanoparticles becomes more precise. Additionally, very detailed patterns can be achieved using a fine stencil mask [11].

Although nanospray depositions bring a lot of benefits, the time of deposition procedure can significantly prolong due to the low volume flow rate. Therefore, we investigated possibilities of the reduction of deposition time via processing a colloid with five times increased concentration of nanoparticles.

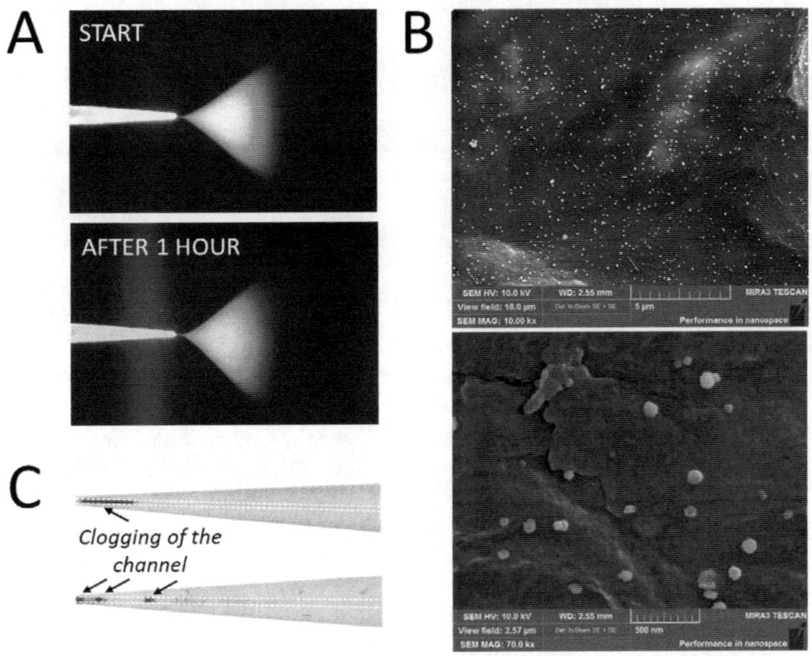

Figure 3 A - The comparison of nanospray plumes generated from silver colloid at the beginning of an experiment and after an hour. B - SEM figures of silver nanoparticles deposited on common office paper via nanospray. C - Two examples of emitters clogged by extensive structures created during the processing of silver colloid, which was concentrated five times by centrifugation.

Since the synthesis of such a colloid from its five times concentrated reagents (i.e., from solutions of silver nitrate and sodium citrate) would end up by the immediate formation of silver microstructures, we used for initial experiments a colloid synthesized by the standard protocol and concentrated it by centrifugation. Unfortunately, nanospraying of this dispersion resulted in a clogging of the emitter channel by extended structures created within several minutes (**Figure 3C**). To improve the stability of silver nanoparticles, we used for their reduction from silver nitrate approximately ten times excess (w/w) of citrate in the reaction mixture. This approach led to an excellent system providing a very stable performance of nanospray even in its centrifuge-concentrated form. Therefore, it represents a powerful possibility of the significant reduction of procedure time.

4. CONCLUSION

We proved that nanospray-assisted depositions of nanoparticles have great potential for the formation of evenly distributed structures. This can be achieved particularly due to low flow rates, which allow complete evaporation of water without the need for any complicated instrumentation. The increase of the concentration of stabilization agent in the silver colloid supports its stability and allows robust processing of concentrated dispersions and reduce the deposition time.

ACKNOWLEDGEMENTS

The authors gratefully acknowledge Czech Science Foundation for financial support (Grant No. 20-14069Y). Additional support was provided by Contripro a.s. company (Dolni Dobrouc, Czech Republic) and by Institutional support RVO 68081715 of Institute of Analytical Chemistry, Czech Academy of Sciences in Brno, Czech Republic.

REFERENCES

[1] JAWOREK, A., SOBCZYK, A.T., KRUPA, A. Electrospray application to powder production and surface coating. *Journal of Aerosol Science*. 2019, vol. 125, pp. 57-92.

[2] TANG, J., GOMEZ, A. Controlled mesoporous film formation from the deposition of electrosprayed nanoparticles. *Aerosol Science and Technology*. 2017, vol. 51, no. 6, pp. 755-765.

[3] CASTILLO, J. L., MARTIN, S., RODRIGUEZ-PEREZ, D., HIGUERA, F. J., GARCIA-YBARRA, P. L. Nanostructured porous coatings via electrospray atomization and deposition of nanoparticle suspensions. *Journal of Aerosol Science*. 2018, vol. 125, pp. 148-163.

[4] NOVAK, S., JOHNSTON, D. E., LI, C., DENG, W. Deposition of Ge23Sb7S70 chalcogenide glass films by electrospray. *Thin Solid Films*. 2015, vol. 588, pp. 56-60.

[5] LEE, P. C., MEISEL, D. Adsorption and surface-enhanced Raman of dyes on silver and gold sols. *Journal of Physical Chemistry*. 1982. vol. 86, no. 17, pp. 3391-3395.

[6] TYCOVA, A., PRIKRYL, J., FORET, F. Reproducible preparation of nanospray tips for capillary electrophoresis coupled to mass spectrometry using 3D printed grinding device. *Electrophoresis*. 2016, vol. 37, no. 7-8, pp. 924-930.

[7] CUI, Z., HAN, Y., HUANG, Q., DONG, J., ZHU, YONG. Electrohydrodynamic printing of silver nanowires for flexible and stretchable electronics. *Nanoscale*. 2018, vol. 10, no. 15, pp. 6806-6811.

[8] AN, B. W., KIM, K., LEE, H., KIM, S. Y., SHIM, Y., LEE, D. Y., SONG, J. Y., PARK, J. U. High-resolution printing of 3D structures using an electrohydrodynamic inkjet with multiple functional inks. *Advanced Materials*. 2015, vol. 27, no. 29, pp. 4322-4328.

[9] HWANG, G. B., HEO, K. J., YUN, J. H., LEE, J. E., LEE, H. J., NHO, C. W., BAE, G. N., JUNG, J. H. Antimicrobial air filters using natural Euscaphis japonica nanoparticles. *Plos One*. 2015, vol. 10, no. 5.

[10] BROWN, N. A., ZHU, Y., GERMAN, G. K., YONG, X., CHIAROT, P.R. Electrospray deposit structure of nanoparticle suspensions. *Journal of Electrostatics*. 2017, vol. 90, pp. 67-73.

[11] KIM, J. W., YAMAGATA, Y., KIM, B. J., HIGUCHI, T. Direct and dry micro-patterning of nano-particles by electrospray deposition through a micro-stencil mask. *Journal of Micromechanics and Microengineering*. 2009, vol. 19, no. 2.

CHARACTERIZATION OF EDGE STRUCTURE AND MISORIENTATION BETWEEN LAYERS OF MICROWAVE PLASMA SYNTHESIZED FEW-LAYER GRAPHENE NANOSHEETS

[1]Jana JURMANOVÁ, [1]Ondřej JAŠEK, [1]Jozef TOMAN, [1]Dalibor VŠIANSKÝ, [1]Pavel SŤAHEL

[1]Faculty of Science - Masaryk University Brno, Brno, Czech Republic, EU,
janar@physics.muni.cz

https://doi.org/10.37904/nanocon.2020.3766

Abstract

Topological and edge defects and misalignment of graphene layers in few-layer graphene strongly influence its chemical reactivity and thermal stability. Scanning and transmission electron microscopy and image analysis was used to determine alignment, degree of rotation, between layers in few-layer graphene prepared by decomposition of ethanol in microwave plasma torch at atmospheric pressure. The prepared nanosheets consisted of 1 to 20 layers, with interlayer distance of 0.34 nm, and the main structure was formed by successive growth of individual layers on top of each other. Using FFT, the edges and wrinkles were separated from the graphene layers themselves. The layers were spread out on each one separately and the angles of rotation between them were measured. The rotation angle between layer was from 20 to 30 degrees and the high quality graphene nanosheets, Raman bands 2D/G ratio of 1.6 and D/G ratio of 0.5, exhibited predominantly closed edges and opened edges were mostly found in the layers forming islands on the main structure. Graphene nanosheets remain fully stable in vacuum up to 1000 °C and thermogravimetric analysis showed complete burnout of the sample in synthetic air at 770 °C with more defective sample exhibiting higher weight loss between 400 and 700 °C.

Keywords: Graphene, edge structure, layer orientation, microwave plasma

1. INTRODUCTION

In-plane and edge defects, as well as misalignment of graphene layers have significant impact on many practical applications of few-layer graphene. Freestanding graphene nanosheets can be used as composite filler, anti-corrosive coatings, gas and chemical sensors or light weight and transparent conductors in flexible electronics and displays [1]. High temperature stability under inert or oxidation atmosphere plays a key role in these future key enabling technologies such as batteries for electric transport, flexible electronics and smart building and textile materials. It was also shown recently that twisted graphene with small rotation between layers exhibits superconductivity [2] opening further possible applications in quantum computing and spintronics. Due to the limited size of microwave plasma synthesized graphene nanosheets, from tens to hundreds of nanometers, the structure needs to be stabilized by elimination of free dangling bonds and various types of defects. Formation of curved and closed edges is one of the mechanisms responsible for the stabilization of the structure by minimizing the energy of nanosheet structure [3]. Another way to limit a chemical reactivity is the formation of carbon-hydrogen bonds during the synthesis process either by addition of -CH groups or by reactions with atomic hydrogen. Therefore, the elimination of zero dimensional defects in the graphene structure by optimization of growth conditions further increases the importance of corrugations and edges in the chemical reactivity of freestanding graphene nanosheets. In this work, we investigate structure of edges and misorientation of individual layers in microwave plasma synthesized few-layer graphene nanosheets and their effect on nanosheet's high temperature oxidation.

2. EXPERIMENTAL

Graphene nanosheets were synthesized by decomposition of ethanol in argon carrier gas using dual-channel microwave plasma torch (MPT) at atmospheric pressure. Depending on the deposition conditions two kinds of samples were prepared. High quality graphene (hqG) nanosheets were prepared with central channel flow Qc 500 sccm and 350 W delivered microwave power in laminar flow regime. Defective graphene (dG) nanosheets with high number of defects were synthesized using central channel flow of 920 sccm and 350 W delivered microwave power in unstable gas flow dynamics. In all cases the liquid mass flow rate of ethanol was 45 mg per minute carried by secondary argon gas channel Qs (700 sccm) into reaction chamber. The detailed description of the experimental procedure can be found in our previous publications [4], [5]. Samples were imaged with TESCAN scanning electron microscope (SEM) MIRA3 with Schottky field emission electron gun equipped with Oxford Instruments EDX analyzer. Transmission electron microscopy (TEM) was carried out using JEOL JEM-2100F and FEI Tecai F20 microscope. ImageJ Fiji software was used for determination of nanosheet size and Fast fourier transform (FFT) image analysis. Raman spectroscopy was carried out using HORIBA LabRAM HR Evolution system with 532 nm laser, using 100x objective, and 5% ND filter (500 mW maximum power), 600 grating and 30 s acquisition time in the range from 1000 to 3200 cm^{-1}. Thermogravimetric analysis (TGA) was carried out using a Setaram Setsys Evoluton 1750 instrument. The analyses were conducted in a dynamic air atmosphere (20 $sccm^{-1}$) with a constant heating rate of 5 $°C.min^{-1}$ in the temperature range from 40 to 1000 °C. The obtained data were processed using the Setaram Processing software. The thermal stability of the carbon nanomaterial was investigated as a function of thermal annealing under UHV conditions using thermal desorption spectroscopy (TDS). The samples, graphene powder on Si/SiO_2 substrate were annealed at pressure of 10^{-5} Pa up to 1000 °C with constant heating rate of 10 $°C.min^{-1}$. The mass spectrometer Pfeiffer Vacuum Prisma 80 was set in order to follow the evolution of hydrogen and hydrocarbon species in time.

3. SEM AND TEM ANALYSIS OF GRAPHENE NANOSHEETS

Two samples were analyzed: high quality (hqG) and defective (dG) graphene. Both types of samples are prepared in the form of foam formed from nanosheets and individual nanosheets are oriented in various directions (**Figure 1**).

Figure 1 SEM image of hqG and dG nanosheet samples (from left to right). The good sheets are in green circles, the damaged in red.

The individual nanosheets are rectangular in shape with size of several hundreds of nm and it was difficult to distinguish between high-quality and low-quality graphene for the untrained eye. Therefore, it was necessary to evaluate orientation of multilayer structure of nanosheets and whether the sheets have torn edges or not i.e. high number of defects on the structure boundary which would be a sign of poor-quality graphene. The more defective sheets exhibit small changes of contrast in the crystal plane and breaks around the edges. In **Figure 1**, the nanosheets with closed edges are circled in green and the ones with broken ones are circled in red. Detailed images of graphene nanosheets were obtained by high resolution TEM. As can be seen in **Figure 2**, the hqG sample consisted of overlapping graphene layers with closed edges, clean straight lines in the image. dG sample consisted of a main graphene layer covered with small islands of graphene and closed carbon networks. The edges of the small nanosheets were mostly opened and the main structure edge consisted of opened and closed sections.

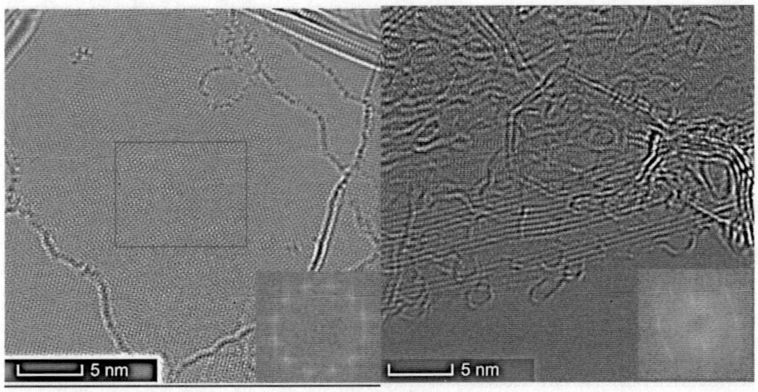

Figure 2 HRTEM image of hqG (left) and dG (right) nanosheet samples. Inset - FFT analysis of multilayer structure

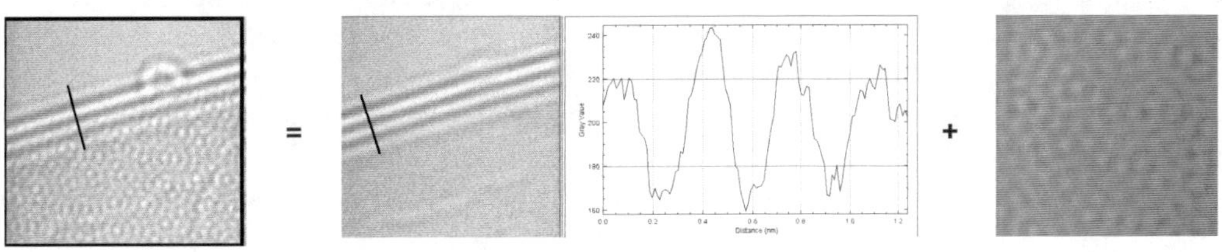

Figure 3 Separation of the edges and wrinkles from the graphene layer itself and determination of distance between graphene layers (0.3 - 0.4 nm)

The FFT (Fast Fourier Transformation) of graphene [6] is a very powerful tool that allows us determination of orientation of individual layers, inset of **Figure 2**, and the separation of an edge from the surface of a layer [7] as shown in **Figure 3**. The FFT of graphene exhibits six-fold symmetry, so the number of dots indicates the number of graphene layers on top of each other. By measuring the angle between the lines connecting the points, that represent different layers, and the center of the shape, it is possible to determine how much these layers are rotated towards each other [8], see **Figure 4**.

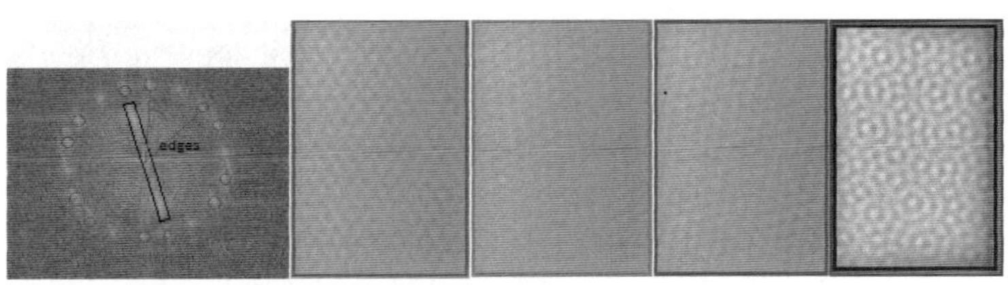

Figure 4 FFT analysis of three-layer graphene (on the Figure 3) and the modeling of the whole layer. The angles between layers are approximately 20 degrees.

The intact edge gives the FFT pattern with the preferred direction (**Figure 5** FFT B, C, D on the left), which indicates the orientation of the edge in space. The defect edge creates a random arrangement in the FFT pattern (bright area inside the circle on FFT A on the left). On the regular edges with a local defect, the FFT pattern is a combination of the above (FFT A,B,C,D on the right) [9]. Such analysis of our nanosheets showed substantially higher number of defects on the edges of dG sample than in case of hqG sample.

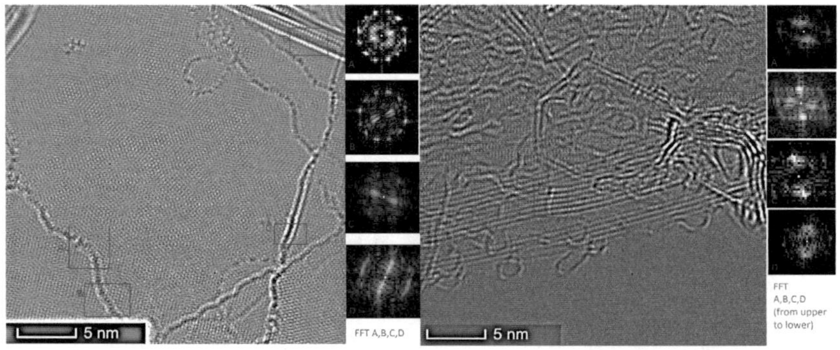

Figure 5 FFT analysis of the edges of hqG (left) and dG (right) graphene nanosheets

4. RAMAN SPECTROSCOPY OF GRAPHENE NANOSHEETS

To investigate the degree of disorder in the studied samples we compared Raman spectra of synthesized graphene nanosheets (**Figure 6**). Raman spectra of both types of samples consisted of D, G and 2D bands [10] at 1350, 1580 and 2690 cm^{-1}, respectively. The G band is related to the in-plane bond stretching of carbon atoms in crystal structure with sp^2 hybridization and D band is activated in the presence of defects in the hexagonal structure. In our case it was also found in the Raman spectra due to the bending and folding of nanosheets edges, which play an important role in the stabilization of the whole structure. 2D band is highly enhanced in the single layer graphene and with increasing number of layers its intensity decreases and full width half maximum (FWHM) of the 2D peak is increasing, from 30 to 60 cm^{-1}. In our high-quality sample, the 2D/G ratio was 1.6 and FWHM of 2D band was 50 cm^{-1}. In case of more defective sample, the 2D/G ratio decreased to 1.1 and D/G ratio increased from 0.5 to 0.8.

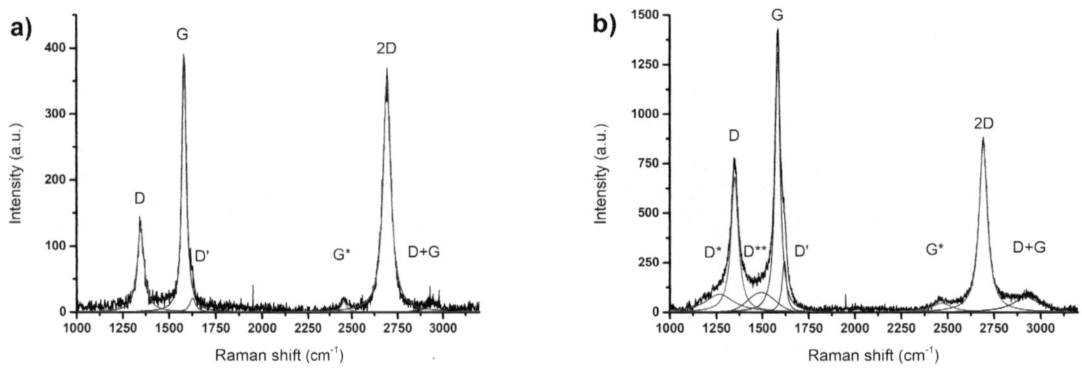

Figure 6 Raman spectra of a) hqG and b) dG nanosheet samples

Substantial difference was found in the intensity of disorder related bands D* - 1260 cm^{-1}, D** - 1495 cm^{-1} and D´ - 1618 cm^{-1}. These bands are activated in the presence of amorphous phase and opened edges in the nanosheets structure. The intensity of these bands was negligible in the case of hqG sample but in the spectra of dG sample, the (D*+D**+D')/G ratio was 0.8. Except first order Raman bands, second order bands G* at ~2450 cm^{-1} and D+G band at ~2950 cm^{-1} were observed in the measured spectra as well.

5. THERMAL DESORPTION SPECTROSCOPY ANALYSIS

At first, thermal stability of graphene nanosheets was investigated by thermal annealing and mass spectrometry in high vacuum. Measured mass spectra were consistent with expected thermal decomposition of carbon nanostructures. CO and CO_2 molecules and C_2H_xO precursor fragments were observed at temperatures of 960 °C and 640 °C, respectively. CO and CO_2 were formed by the reaction of carbon and oxygen incorporated into graphene nanosheets structure and residual oxygen in the apparatus. The observed intensity of these compounds was in agreement with the thermodynamic calculations of standard Gibbs energy for reactions of carbon and oxygen [11] where the formation of CO is favored over CO_2 with increasing system temperature. No visible change of the nanomaterial was observed at the whole temperature range and Raman spectroscopy analysis of annealed sample showed no significant variation of either intensity or FWHM of Raman peaks showing good thermal stability of graphene nanosheets in vacuum. Due to the small amount of oxygen, several atomic percent, even more disordered graphene structure did not exhibit any substantial structural changes.

6. THERMOGRAVIMETRY ANALYSIS OF GRAPHENE NANOSHEETS

We further investigated the influence of the amount of disorder on thermal stability of prepared nanosheets in synthetic air at temperature range between 40 and 1000 °C (**Figure 7**). Size of nanosheets and amount of in-plain defects and structure of edge play the main role in the oxidation resistance of carbon nanomaterial. Morgan et al. [12] developed the so-called "shrinking core model", where the particles with smaller diameter exhibit lower temperature of oxidation. Similarly, nanostructures with lower level of graphitization and higher amount of defects will exhibit lower temperature of combustion, because the point and linear defects in the crystal structure are more susceptible to thermal decomposition by oxidation reaction [13].

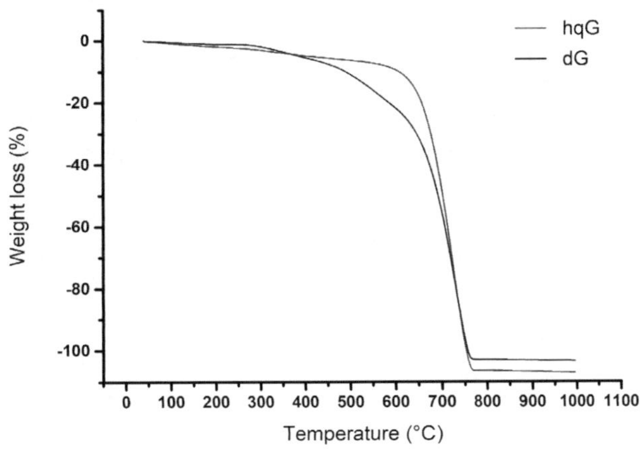

Figure 7 Thermogravimetry analysis of prepared few-layer graphene nanosheets

Overall TGA curve of carbon based materials exhibited several regions. The initial mass loss was occurring around 100 °C and corresponds to the release of water vapors from the carbon particle surface. At higher temperatures between 200 and 300 °C, the thermal decomposition of unstable oxygen-containing functional groups as well as intercalated water release can occur, but this region was negligible in our samples. The graphene based nanomaterial itself begins to combust above 300 °C, where decomposition of light amorphous poly-carbons to carbon dioxide occurs which are easily vaporized as can be seen on the TGA curve of dG sample. At last, gradual decomposition of graphene nanosheets structure itself followed above 600 °C due to the breaking of C-C bond and exothermic reaction between carbon and oxygen formed CO and CO_2. Due to small number of defects and stable nanosheets edges, hqG sample exhibited only the last described region above 650 °C and complete loss of material was observed at 770 °C. Abrupt loss of material at this temperature was consistent with first-order reaction kinetics of simple oxidation reaction. dG sample with higher amount of disorder exhibited loss of material above 300 °C and between 450 and 650 °C, but reached the same temperature of complete weight loss (100 %) at 765 °C.

7. CONCLUSIONS

Orientation and edge structure of individual layers of few-layer graphene prepared by microwave plasma decomposition of ethanol was studied by high resolution electron microscopy. Misorientation of layers was 20° or more and it was independent of the degree of disorder determined by Raman spectroscopy. Detailed image and FFT analysis of individual nanosheets determined large contributions of opened edges to sample disorder in nanosheets prepared in an unstable gas flow regime. Such nanosheets exhibited higher oxidation rate in air during thermogravimetric analysis with two additional regions related to amorphous and highly disordered carbon.

ACKNOWLEDGEMENTS

This work was supported by The Czech Science Foundation under project 18-08520S and in part by project LM2018097 funded by the Ministry of Education, Youth and Sports of the Czech Republic. We acknowledge CEITEC Nano Research Infrastructure supported by MEYS CR (LM2018110). We would like to thank Jiri Bursik for TEM analysis.

REFERENCES

[1] FERRARI, A. C. et al. Science and technology roadmap for graphene, related two-dimensional crystals, and hybrid systems. *Nanoscale.* 2015, vol. 7, no. 11, pp. 4598-4810.

[2] CAO, Y. et al. Unconventional superconductivity in magic-angle graphene superlattices. *Nature.* 2018, vol. 556, no. 7699, pp. 43-50.

[3] YANG, G., LI, L., LEE, W. B., NG, M. C. Structure of graphene and its disorders: a review. *Sci. Technol. Adv. Mater.* 2018, vol. 19, no. 1, pp. 613-648.

[4] TOMAN, J., JASEK O., SNÍRER M., KUDRLE V., JURMANOVA, J. On the interplay between plasma discharge instability and formation of free-standing graphene nanosheets in a dual-channel microwave plasma torch at atmospheric pressure. *Journal of Physics D: Applied Physics.* 2019, vol. 52, no. 26. p. 265205.

[5] JASEK, O., TOMAN, J., JURMANOVÁ, J. et al. Study of graphene layer growth on dielectric substrate in microwave plasma torch at atmospheric pressure. *Diamond and Related Materials.* 2020, vol. 105. p. 107798.

[6] YEHLIU, K., VANDER WAL, R. L., BOEHMAN, A. L. Development of an HRTEM image analysis method to quantify carbon nanostructure. *Combustion and Flame.* 2011, vol. 158, no. 9. pp. 1837-1851.

[7] SHEN, Z. et al. Preparation of graphene by jet cavitation. *Nanotechnology.* 2011, vol. 22, no. 36, p. 365306.

[8] ROBERTSON, A. W., WARNER, J. H. Atomic resolution imaging of graphene by transmission electron microscopy. *Nanoscale.* 2013, vol. 5, no. 10, pp. 4079-4093.

[9] WARNER, J. H. et al. Structural transformations in graphene studied with high spatial and temporal resolution. *Nat. Nanotechnol.* 2009, vol. 4, no. 8, pp. 500-504.

[10] DRESSELHAUS, M. S., JORIO, A., SOUZA FILHO, A. G. et al. Defect characterization in graphene and carbon nanotubes using Raman spectroscopy. *Philos. Trans. A Math. Phys. Eng. Sci.* 2010, vol. 368, no. 1932, pp. 5355-5377.

[11] DEMIDOV, A. I. MAKRELOV, I. A. Thermodynamics of Reaction of Carbon with Oxygen. *Russian Journal of Applied Chemistry.* 2005, vol. 78, no. 5. pp. 707-710.

[12] MORGAN, P. A., ROBERTSON, S. D., UNSWORTH, J.F. Combustion studies by thermogravimetric analysis. *Fuel.* 1986, vol. 65, no. 11. pp. 1546-1551.

[13] BOM, D. et al. Thermogravimetric Analysis of the Oxidation of Multiwalled Carbon Nanotubes: Evidence for the Role of Defect Sites in Carbon Nanotube Chemistry. *Nano Letters.* 2002, vol. 2, no. 6. pp. 615-619.

ORGANOSILICON PLASMA POLYMERS DEPOSITED IN TRIMETHYLSILYL ACETATE/CH_4 PLASMA OF CAPACITIVELY COUPLED RF GLOW DISCHARGE

[1]Štěpánka KELAROVÁ, [1]Monika STUPAVSKÁ, [1]Roman PŘIBYL, [1]Vilma BURŠÍKOVÁ

[1]*Masaryk University, Faculty of Science, Brno, Czech Republic, EU,* kelarova.s@mail.muni.cz

https://doi.org/10.37904/nanocon.2020.3773

Abstract

Thin solid films based on organosilicon monomers are perspective in many branches of industry as well as for bioapplications. In the present study, plasma of RF capacitively coupled glow discharge in gaseous mixture of trimethylsilyl acetate (TMSA) monomer and methane was used to create $SiO_xC_yH_z$ coatings. This study monitors properties of resulting thin films (surface chemistry, wettability, surface structure and mechanical properties) in dependency on deposition parameters. The main subject of the presented research is the investigation of the relationship between the above-mentioned properties of prepared organosilicon coatings and the flow rate ratio of TMSA monomer and CH_4 carrier gas applied during deposition process.

Keywords: Trimethylsilyl acetate, PECVD, XPS, microindentation, confocal microscopy

1. INTRODUCTION

Thin solid films based on organosilicon monomers have a wide application range in many industrial fields. Organosilicon materials prepared using plasma techniques can be successfully used as anti-scratch layers on plastic substrates, corrosion protection coatings, barrier films, super-hydrophobic coatings, anti-reflection coatings for solar cells etc. [1]. The PECVD process leads to wide variation of organosilicon-based coatings from inorganic SiO_2-like materials [1-4], through soft organic $SiO_xC_yH_z$ plasma polymers [1-4] to DLC films doped by silicon and oxygen atoms [5-7]. Desired properties of organosilicon material are achieved by optimization of deposition process, including the choice of proper precursor, carrier gas (Ar, O_2, CH_4 etc.) and other factors of used discharge like gas pressure, supplied power, bias voltage etc. [1-8]. Tetraethoxysilane (TEOS) [2], hexamethyldisiloxane (HMDSO) [3-7] and trimethylsilane (TMS) [8] and are among the most widely used monomers for preparation of organosilicon coatings.

The present work is focused on preparation and characterization of $SiO_xC_yH_z$ films prepared from gaseous mixture of trimethylsilyl acetate (TMSA) monomer and methane using plasma of RF capacitively coupled discharge. Unlike commonly used precursors mentioned above, TMSA monomer described by linear formula $CH_3CO_2Si(CH_3)_3$ includes C=O group in its structure [1], which makes it very perspective not only for industrial applications, but also for preparation of carbonyl-functionalized organosilicon coatings suitable for bioapplications. The main aim of this study is to find the relationship between properties (chemical composition, mechanical properties, surface structure and degree of hydrophobicity) of prepared TMSA-based materials and the flow rate ratio R of methane in the used gaseous mixture.

2. EXPERIMENTAL

Organosilicon thin films were prepared in capacitively coupled RF glow discharges at low pressures of ~40 Pa from mixture of TMSA and methane in the parallel plate reactor. The bottom electrode served as the silicon substrate holder. This electrode was coupled to RF generator (13.56 MHz) via a blocking capacitor. The supplied power was kept constant at 75 W for all depositions. The flow rates of used monomer and CH_4 carrier gas were varied. Changes of the flow rates are represented by the ratio R of methane in gaseous mixture given by an equation (1), where Q_{CG} means the flow rate of CH_4 carrier gas and Q_M means the flow rate of TMSA monomer in sccm. Flow rates of used gases varied in range from 0.5 sccm to 6.5 sccm. A total flow rate of gaseous mixture was kept at 7 sccm for all depositions. The bias voltage varied from -60 V to -300 V.

$$R = \frac{Q_{CG}}{Q_{CG} + Q_M} \qquad (1)$$

Properties of the prepared films were studied by several characterization methods. Chemical composition of TMSA-based surfaces was determined by X-ray photoelectron spectroscopy (XPS). XPS spectra of studied films were measured using Escalab 250Xi device (ThermoFisher Scientific) using an X-ray source AlKα. All spectra were measured with the energy step of 0.01 eV with a pass energy of 20 eV. Atomic concentrations of individual elements (silicon, carbon, oxygen) presented on the studied surfaces were calculated from measured data using the Avantage software. Concentrations of different chemical bonds were determined by fitting Si 2p and C 1s signals.

The degree of surface hydrophobicity of each coating was determined by water contact angle measurements using Krüss DSA 30 device. Surface topography was observed by confocal laser microscope LEXT OLS4000 using high magnification (400x-800x).

Mechanical properties (Indentation hardness H_{IT} and effective elastic modulus E) were measured using Hysitron TI 950 (Bruker) nanoindentation device. The standard Berkovich diamond indenter with tip radius of approx. 70 nm was used for nanoindentation tests. Quasistatic nanoindentation tests with 20 partial unloading segments were used to study the depth profile of the hardness H_{IT} and the effective elastic modulus E. Each indentation test was repeated at least 10 times. The maximum indentation load was in the range from 0.1 to 11 mN. The mechanical parameters were determined at indentation depths less than 1/10 of film thickness to avoid any substrate effect.

3. RESULTS AND DISCUSSION

3.1. Surface chemistry

The surface chemistry of prepared TMSA-based coatings was determined using XPS analysis. **Figure 1a** shows an evolution of concentration of carbon atoms presented at studied surfaces in dependency on the methane ratio R defined by the equation 1. The carbon concentration varied between 45 at. % and 48 at. % if the ratio R in range of 0.07 - 0.50 was used during PECVD process. TMSA-based coatings prepared using high ratios of methane in gaseous mixture showed significantly higher incorporation of carbon atoms into the resulting surface structure. Increasing ratio R from 0.50 to 0.86 led to the increase in carbon concentration from 45 at. % to 68 at. % (**Figure 1a**). Further increase of the methane content in gaseous mixture to the R=0.93 caused decrease of concentration of carbon atoms at the resulting organosilicon thin film to 59 at. %.

Concentrations of carbon bonds presented at prepared surfaces were determined by fitting of C 1s signals. TMSA-based coatings included significant content of $\underline{C}$-C/$\underline{C}H_x$ bonds (binding energy BE=284.8 eV) and $\underline{C}$-Si bonds (BE=284.2 eV). Carbon bonded to oxygen atoms was presented mainly in $\underline{C}$-O links (BE=286.1 eV). Carbonyl groups (BE=287.6 eV) and carboxyl groups (BE=289.4 eV) were detected at studied surfaces as well, however concentrations of these bonds varied from 1.6 % to 3 % of carbon atoms at all prepared surfaces. The only one exception was the thin film prepared using ratio R=0.5 where concentration of $\underline{C}$=O bonds reached up to the 5 % of carbon atoms. **Figure 1** shows trends of concentrations of previously mentioned significant carbon bonds: $\underline{C}$-C/$\underline{C}H_x$, $\underline{C}$-Si and $\underline{C}$-O.

Based on the experimental results, concentration of $\underline{C}$-C/$\underline{C}H_x$ bonds at studied TMSA-based surfaces varies between 73-87 % of carbon atoms (**Figure 1b**). The minimum concentration of $\underline{C}$-C/$\underline{C}H_x$ chains was determined at TMSA-based coating prepared using the methane ratio of R=0.50 (**Figure 1b**).

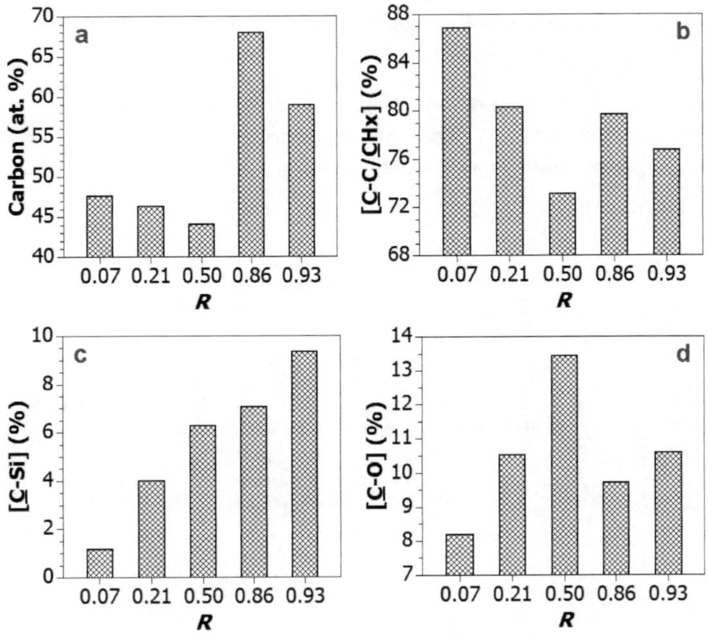

Figure 1 An atomic concentration of the surface carbon atoms and percentage content of the significant carbon bonds in dependency on the ratio *R*

The evolution of C-Si concentration shown in **Figure 1c** is gradually increasing from 1 % to 9 % of carbon with an increasing methane ratio *R* in range of 0.07-0.93, although the number of silicon atoms presented at studied TMSA coatings is rather decreasing (see **Figure 2b**).

The percentage concentration of C-O bonds presented at the prepared TMSA coatings shows nonlinear trend (**Figure 1d**) complementary to the evolution of C-C/CH_x bonds (**Figure 1b**). The lowest concentration of these links was detected at TMSA-based surface prepared using *R*=0.07 and the highest concentration of C-O groups was observed at thin film prepared using the ratio *R*=0.50.

For TMSA coating including the highest ratio of C-O links is also characteristic the most significant integration of oxygen atoms into the surface structure (see **Figure 2a**). This coating prepared using *R*=0.50 shows 32 at. % of oxygen at the surface. The increase of the methane ratio *R* from 0.50 to 0.86 led to significant drop in the oxygen concentration: the resulting coating included only 21 atomic % of oxygen in its structure. The atomic concentration at the rest of prepared TMSA coatings was ~27 at. %.

The atomic concentration of silicon can be considered stable at 26 at. % in range of applied CH_4 ratios *R* in range from 0.07 to 0.50 (see **Figure 2b**). The next increase of the ratio *R* caused rapid decrease in silicon concentration. The content of silicon atoms at TMSA coatings prepared using ratios 0.86 and 0.93 varies between 11 at. % and 14 at. %.

Silicon atoms present at the surface of prepared TMSA coatings were bonded in the highly oxidized SiO_4 links (BE=103.7eV) or in X_nSiO_m bonds where X represents carbon or hydrogen atom. The concentration of SiO_4, which varies from 17 % to 24 % of silicon atoms (**Figure 2c**), is low compared to the $XSiO_3$ structures that shows values of concentrations between 40-53 % (**Figure 2d**). Increased values of $XSiO_3$ are probably a result of integration of carbon atoms from the carrier gas into resulting TMSA-based coatings. However, based on the XPS analysis we are not able to discuss the influence of hydrogen integration on the trend of X_nSiO_m structures (**Figures 2d-f**).

Another significant silicon structures are $X_2\underline{Si}O_2$ links that show a decreasing trend from 37 % to 20 % with the increasing ratio *R* from 0.07 to 0.93 (**Figure 2e**). Concentration of $X_2\underline{Si}O_2$ bonds can be considered stable at 25 % of Si in range of methane ratios from 0.21 to 0.86.

Concentration of $X_3\underline{Si}O$ structures are very low in comparison with other silicon components (see **Figure 2f**). The most of studied coatings shows concentrations of these bonds in range of 1-4 %. The only one exception is TMSA-based surface prepared using ratio *R*=0.86 where concentration of $X_3\underline{Si}O$ structures reaches the value of 14 %.

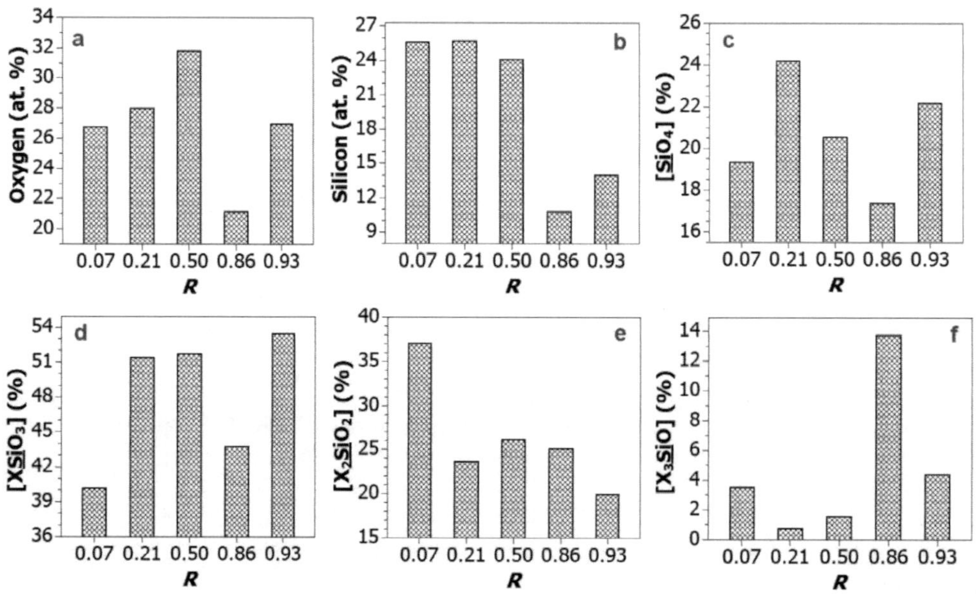

Figure 2 An atomic concentration of the surface oxygen and silicon in dependency on the ratio *R*. Figure includes evolution of percentage content of the identified silicon bonds as well.

3.2 Mechanical properties

Indentation hardness H_{IT} and effective elastic modulus *E* were determined using microindentation technique (Section 2) for all studied TMSA-based coatings. Values of these parameters were relatively low in case of thin films prepared using ratios R≤0.50 (**Figure 3**). Values of indentation hardness varied from 0.7 GPa to 2.3 GPa in this range of *R* and effective elastic modulus was below 20 GPa. TMSA-based coatings prepared using *R* in range from 0.07 to 0.50 can be considered as a soft polymeric materials [1]. An increase of methane ratio *R* to 0.86 and 0.93 led to the rapid increase of H_{IT} and *E* (**Figure 3**). Thin films prepared using high ratios of CH_4 were characteristic by indentation hardness equal to 11 GPa and by elastic modulus ~95 GPa. These TMSA-based materials showed mechanical properties of highly cross-linked DLC coatings [6,7].

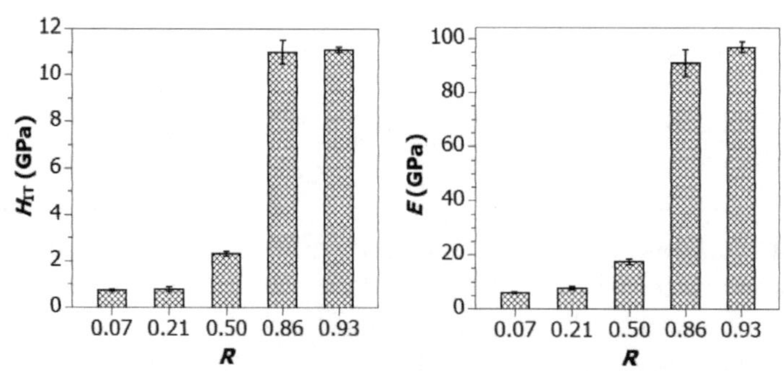

Figure 3 An evolution of the indentation hardness H_{IT} (left) and effective elastic modulus *E* (right) in dependency on the methane ratio *R*

3.3. Surface structure and wettability

Figure 4 shows an example of surface structures of three chosen TMSA-based coatings which were determined using confocal microscopy (Section 2). Based on the results, structure of deposited thin films gradually changes from the surface covered with protrusions to the surfaces including defects in the form of holes (**Figure 4**). Observed changes may be related with the degree of crosslinking of prepared materials.

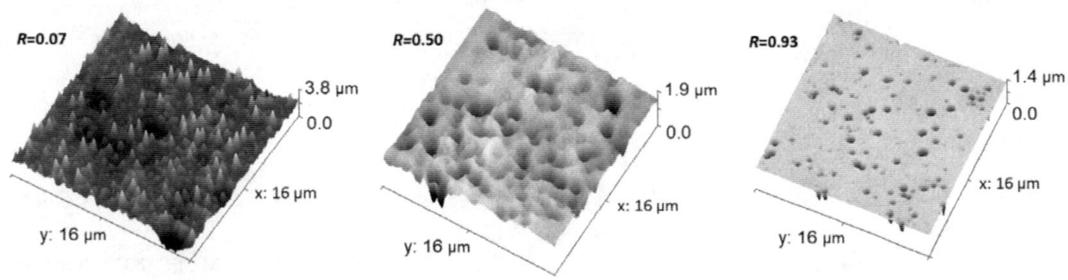

Figure 4 Examples of surface structures of three chosen coatings prepared using different ratios *R*

Degree of surface hydrophobicity was determined by water contact angle measurements. Values of water contact angle gradually decreased from 93° to 81° with an increasing ratio *R* from 0.07 to 0.93. Decrease of hydrophobicity of prepared coatings is connected with concentrations of different chemical structures presented at studied surfaces (**Figures 1, 2**). The most hydrophilic TMSA-based coatings with water contact angle equal to 81° were prepared using high ratios *R* equal to 0.86 and 0.93. Since these coatings showed at the same time high values of indentation hardness (Section 3.2), the degree of hydrophobicity is probably connected with a degree of crosslinking as well.

4. CONCLUSION

In the present work, organosilicon coatings were prepared using TMSA/CH_4 plasma of capacitively coupled RF glow discharge using different ratios of methane *R* in the gaseous mixture. The variation of the ratio *R* had a significant impact on the chemical composition of resulting surfaces as well as on the surface structure and wettability. The increase of the methane ratio *R* caused increased integration of carbon atoms into the resulting organosilicon structures at the expense of oxygen and silicon atoms presented in TMSA monomer. TMSA-based coatings had rather hydrophobic character: determined values of water contact angle varied between 81-93°.

This study proves that it is possible to prepare hydrophobic soft polymeric materials as well as hard DLC coating doped by silicon and oxygen atoms using different ratios of methane. The hard coatings characteristic by indentation hardness equal to 11 GPa and effective elastic modulus of ~95 GPa were achieved by using high ratios of methane in gaseous mixture $R \geq 0.86$.

ACKNOWLEDGEMENTS

The present work was supported by Czech Science Foundation under project GACR 19-15240S and by the project LM2018097 funded by Ministry of Education Youth and Sports of the Czech Republic. Štěpánka Kelarová is Brno Ph.D. Talent Scholarship Holder-Funded by the Brno City Municipality.

REFERENCES

[1] KELAROVÁ, Š., HOMOLA, V., STUPAVSKÁ, M., ČERMÁK, M., VOHÁNKA, J., PŘIBYL, R., ZÁBRANSKÝ, L., BURŠÍKOVÁ, Deposition of organosilicon coatings from trimethylsilyl acetate oand oxygen gases in capacitively coupled RF glow discharge. *Progress in Organic Coatings.* 2020, vol. 149, pp. 105927.

[2] GOULLET, A., VALLÉE, C., GRANIER, A. and TURBAN, G. Optical spectroscopic analyses of OH incorporation into SiO_2 films deposited from O_2/tetraethoxysilane plasmas. *Journal of Vacuum Science & Technology A: Vacuum Surfaces and Films.* 2000, vol. 18, no. 5.

[3] BOUSQUET, A., BURSIKOVA, V., GOULLET, A., DJOUADI, A., ZAJICKOVA, L., GRANIER, A. Comparison of structure and mechanical properties of SiO_2-ike films deposited in O_2/HMDSO pulsed and continuous plasmas. *Surface and Coatings Technology*. 2006, vol. 200, no. 22-23, pp. 6517-6521.

[4] BORVON, G., GOULLET, A., MELLHAOUI, X., CHARROUF, N., GRANIER, A. Electrical properties of low-dielectric-constant films prepared by PECVD in O_2/CH_4/HMDSO. *Materials Science in Semiconductor Processing.* 2003, vol 5, no. 2-3, pp. 279-284.

[5] BURŠÍKOVÁ, V., SLÁDEK, P., SŤAHEL, P., ZAJÍČKOVÁ, L. Improvement of the efficiency of the silicon solar cells by silicon incorporated diamond-like carbon antireflective coatings. *Journal of Non-Crystalline Solids.* 2002, vol. 299-302, no. 12, pp. 1147-1151.

[6] CHEN, L.-Y., CHAU-NAN HONG, F. Effects of SiO_x-incorporation hydrocarbons on the tribological properties of DLC films. *Diamond and Related Materials.* 2001, vol. 10, pp. 1058-1062.

[7] BATORY, D., JEDRZEJCZAK, A., SZYMANSKI, W., NIEDZIELSKI, P., FIJALKOWSKI, M., LOUDA, P., KOTELA, I., HROMADKA, M., MUSIL, J. Mechanical characterization of a-C:H:SiO_x coatings synthesized using radio-frequency plasma-assisted chemical vapor deposition method. *Thin Solid Films.* 2015, vol. 590, pp. 299-305.

[8] COCLITE, A. M., MILELLA, A., PALUMBO, F., PEN, C.L., d' Agnostino, R. Plasma deposited organosilicon multistacks for high-performance low-carbon steel protection. *Plasma Processes and Polymers*. 2010, vol. 7, no. 9-10, pp. 788-796.

COMPARISON OF HMDSO AND HMDSZ THIN FILMS GROWTH UNDER DUSTY PLASMA CONDITIONS

[1]Roman PŘIBYL, [1]Štěpánka KELAROVÁ, [1]Lukáš ZÁBRANSKÝ, [1]Vilma BURŠÍKOVÁ

[1]Faculty of Science, Department of Physical Electronics, R&D Center for Plasma and Nanotechnology Surface Modifications, CEPLANT, Brno, Czech Republic, EU, romanpribyl@mail.muni.cz

https://doi.org/10.37904/nanocon.2020.3778

Abstract

The present study is focused on the preparation of thin films by plasma enhanced chemical vapor deposition (PEDCV) in capacitively coupled plasma (CCP). Thin films were deposited from a mixture of oxygen and hexamethyldisiloxane (HMDSO) or hexamethyldisilazane (HMDSZ). Both monomers are well known and enable to prepare films with excellent properties such as high hardness, good abrasion resistance, hydrophobicity, and antibacterial properties. Also, these monomers are known for the creation of complex structures in plasma. This phenomenon is so-called dusty plasma. The main aim of the present work was to prepare a comparative study on the dust formation in both monomers. Complex study of surface and mechanical properties and chemical composition was done by a wide range of analytical instruments such as atomic force microscopy (AFM), nanoindentation technique, confocal microscopy, infrared spectroscopy with Fourier transformation (FTIR), stylus profilometer, and surface energy evaluation system (SEE system).

Keywords: Thin films, PECVD, dusty plasma, surface properties

1. INTRODUCTION

The organosilicons andorganosilazanes are widely studied precursors for plasma depositions. They are studied due to the chemical bond between silicon and carbon, this bond is weaker than the bond between two carbons in the organic chain [1]. This weaker bond can be used for the deposition of SiO_x and SiN_x materials, which are crucial insulators in the semiconductor industry. HMDSO and HMDSZ are frequently used for their suitable properties for plasma depositions and high vapor pressure [2,3]. The chemical structure of both precursors is displayed in **Figure 1**.

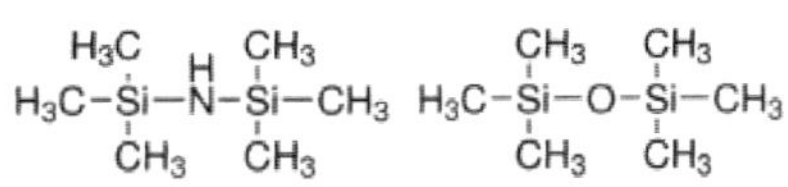

Figure 1 Structural formulas of HMDSZ and HMDSO

Properties of deposited thin films are controlled by process conditions (bias voltage, pressure, power input, etc.), but mainly are guided by the combination of precursor and carrier gas [4,5]. There are a large number of studies that are focused on the study of these two precursors, but they are all made in different reactors. It is a well-known fact, that the geometry of the reactor influences the self-bias voltage on the capacitively coupled electrode and that self-bias is one of the most important process parameter of PECVD. Due to this verity, we made the study of the deposition of thin films using the combination of oxygen (carrier gas) and HMDSO or HMDSZ (precursors) in the same reactor [6].

The combination of oxygen and HMDSO was previously studied due to formation of dust in plasma during the deposition process [7]. Dusty plasma was firstly observed in the universe, where the formation of dust was caused by part of comets [8]. In the laboratory environment was dusty plasma observed during plasma processes for microelectronic devices in silane (SiH_4) and hydrogen-carbon plasmas (C_2H_2, etc.) [8-10]. After that, there were several studies which were mainly focused on the dusty plasma of organosilicones containing methyl groups (CH_3) which can in plasma react similarly to hydrogen-carbon plasmas and after binding layout of methyl groups there may occur similar reactions like in silane plasmas. The formation of dust is a complex problem because the formation of dust contributes to heterogeneous and homogenous reactions in plasma. The formation of dust can be an unwanted process during microelectronic processes. Contrariwise dusty plasma has a high growth rate and by dusty plasma can be grown micro and nanocomposite thin film, which has high hydrophobicity and report viscoelastic properties.

In this study, we prepared thin films using mixtures of oxygen and HMDSO or HMDSO. We studied the chemical composition, surface, and mechanical properties of deposited thin films. For the formation of dusty plasma three different values of power supply were used. The main focus was on analysis of thin films surface with AFM because the surface appearance can lead to the quantification of the formation of dusty particles and their size.

2. EXPERIMENTAL

Thin films were deposited in previously developed plasma reactor [6]. All thin films were deposited from a mixture of 5.0 sccm oxygen and 2.0 sccm precursor under deposition pressure around 15 Pa. The deposition times were carried out between 30 s to 600 s to achieve a different thicknesses of thin films. The power input was held on 25 W, 50 W, and 75 W to determine the different formation of dust. During all deposition were collected data (bias, reflected power, etc.) through the digital output of the generator. Thin films were deposited on silicon (Boron doped, (100), 0.008-0.013 Ω·cm, 625±15 μm) double-polished silicon (Phosphorus doped, (100), 0.1954-0.2034 Ω·cm, 381±25 μm) and glass. For determination of chemical composition a double-polished silicon wafer was used. Glass substrates were used for the determination of water contact angle and for other analyzes only one side-polished silicon wafers were used.

The thickness of thin films was measured by stylus profilometer Bruker DektakXT with stylus radius of 2.5 μm. The thickness was measured from the interface thin film - substrate, which was obtained by the removal of a small part of the thin film on the silicon substrate. The growth rate was calculated from thickness and deposition time.

For the measurement of surface properties three different devices were used. First one - the confocal microscope was used for imaging of the film surface after deposition. Confocal microscope Olympus OSL4100 was used to display the presence of dust immediately after deposition. For determination of water contact angle (WCA) SEE system was used WCA of water drops with volume of 1.0 μm placed on films deposited on glass substrates were measured after removal of physisorbed dust. The measurement of surface roughness was conducted on AFM - Ntegra Prima NT-MDT in semi-contact mode. The roughness of the samples was calculated from scans with a resolution of 512X512 dpi and scanning rate from 0.5 Hz to 0.7 Hz (the scanning rate was chosen with respect to dust particles sizes).

Chemical composition of thin films was measured by FTIR. The measurement was conducted in wavenumber range from 3700cm^{-1} to 7500 cm^{-1} with 500 scans and resolution of 8 cm^{-1}. The measurements were performed using Bruker vertex 80v device.

Mechanical properties of thin films were determined by Hysitron TI950 Triboindenter. We used a load function with 20 a partial unloading segments in order to determine the mechanical properties in different indentation depths. The maximum load was 1.000 mN. To illustrate the viscoelastic behaviour of thin films, we also used quasi-static load function with a maximal load of 1.000 mN.

3. RESULTS AND DISCUSSION

From literature [4,5] it is well known, that in processes with longer deposition times grow thicker films (unless there is an etching process involved), also it is known, that deposition rate decreases during the deposition process. A decrease in the deposition process during the deposition of non-conductive thin films can be caused by the evolution of self- bias voltage on the substrate holder electrode. Self-bias voltage evolution during the deposition with HMDSZ precursor with different power input is shown in **Figure 2**.

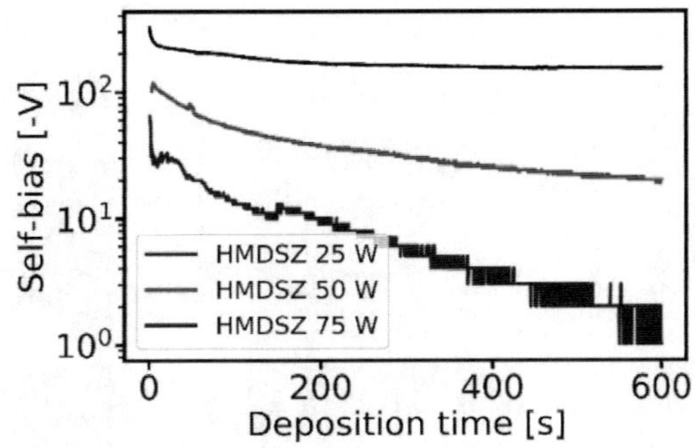

Figure 2 Evolution of self-bias during deposition for different power inputs

The dependence of the measured film thickness on the deposition time is plotted in **Figure 3**. From the thickness and deposition time it is possible to calculate the deposition rate. The time dependence of the deposition rate is also shown in **Figure 3**. From the graph it is clearly visible, that for thin films from HMDSZ precursor the deposition rate is less stable and after short deposition time the deposition rate dramatically decreases. This could be affected by physisorbed dust previously showed by confocal microscopy [6]. From graphs in **Figure 3** it is also clear, that during depositions with higher power input than 25 W films are growing faster, but there is a minor difference between higher power inputs (75 W and 50 W) than between lower inputs (50 and 25 W). This is probably caused by fragmentation of molecules. This means that there is an ideal value of power input for deposition in which is a combination of homogeneous and heterogeneous reactions.

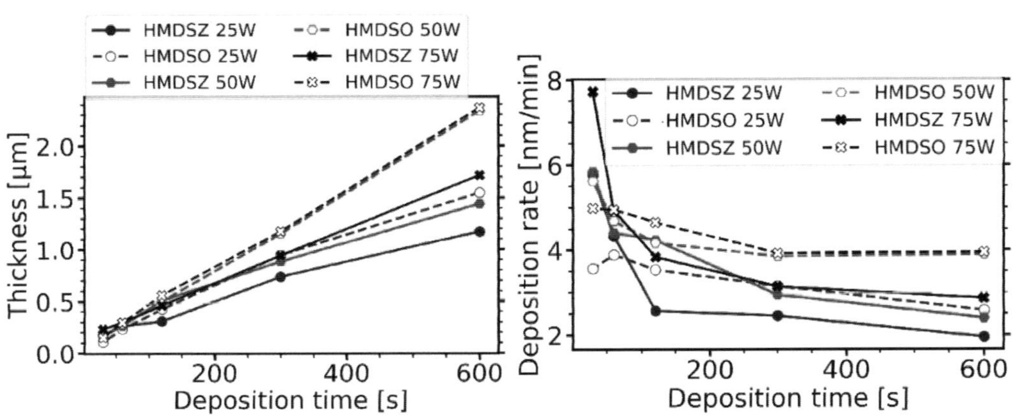

Figure 3 Left: Influence of deposition time on increasing a thin film thickness. Right: Graph showing decreasing deposition rate with deposition time.

Fragmentation of molecules causes the qualitative origin of dust in plasma. Formation of dust in plasma can be observed with diagnostic devices such as ICCD camera, but there is nontrivial behavior of dust in plasma.

That means that the prediction of properties of thin films deposited in dusty plasma is nearly impossible with plasma diagnostic devices. Due to this fact, we are using AFM for the determination of dust quality and quantity on sample surfaces. **Figure 4** shows surfaces of thin films deposited with different power inputs with deposition time 300 s. From scans it is clearly visible, that HMDSZ makes bigger particles of dust in plasma. This verity corresponds with previously showed physisorbed macroscopic dust on samples [6]. This causes, that HMDSO thin films have better homogeneity. Moreover HMDSO thin films have surface roughness (RMS) in order of tenths of nanometers, whereas HMDSZ thin films have surface roughness between 5 to 50 nm.

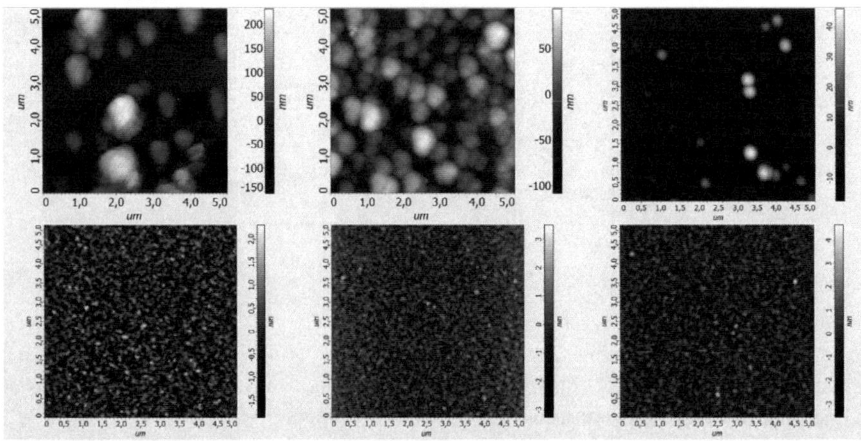

Figure 4 AFM scans of deposited films. First/second row shows films deposited from HMDSZ/HMDSO

Chemical composition was measured by FTIR and peaks were determined on the basis of these publications [11,12]. Thin films with deposition time of 60 s were chosen for this study. The results of the measurements are shown on **Figure 5**. From graphs it is visible that with increasing input power the larger fragmentation of CH_x containing bonds occurs. For HMDSZ is this verity more noticeable because HMDSZ contains nitrogen in its chain [1,2].

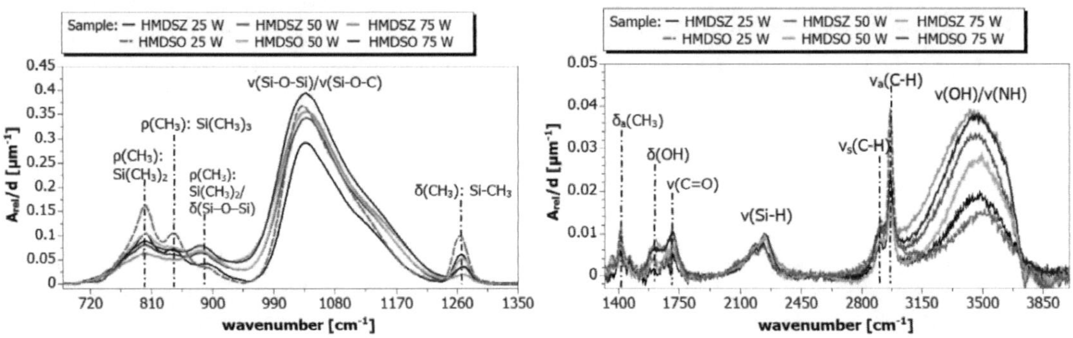

Figure 5 Measured FTIR spectra on samples with deposition time 60 s

WCA was measured on glass substrates. Glass reference's WCA was (62±2)°. Measured WCAs for deposited films are showed in the graph in **Figure 6**. From the graph is clearly visible, that all deposited films are more hydrophobic than the used substrate. The WCA is nearly stable and slightly decreases with increasing power input, whereas the highest value of WCA is probably caused by insufficient removal of macroscopic dust from the sample's surface. The hydrophobicity of deposited films is caused by CH_x groups [13].

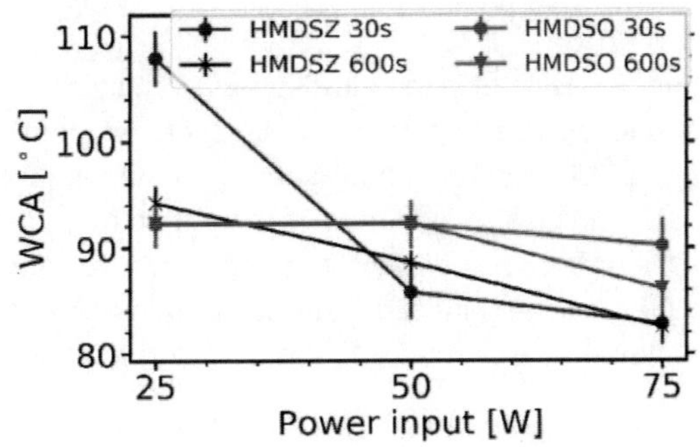

Figure 6 WCA for selected thin films

Indentation hardness (HIT) and reduced elastic modulus (E_r) was measured by nanoindentation technique with partial unload function. In graphs in **Figure 7** values of HIT and E_r obtained in 100 nm depth are plotted. From graphs is visible, that with HIT and E_r are increasing with increasing power input.

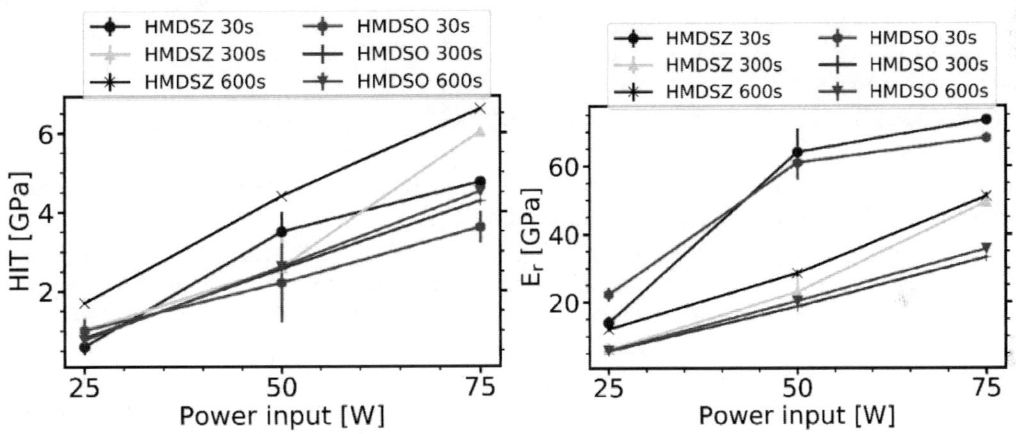

Figure 7 Values of HIT and E_r in approximately 100 nm indentor depth

On the graph in **Figure 7** there are shown results obtained for three deposition times, but values of HIT and E_r are meaningful only for depositions with higher deposition time. This verity is shown in **Figure 8**, where the influence of silicon substrate for thin film from HMDSO precursor with deposition time 30 s is visible. Also from **Figure 8** is nicely visible that all deposited thin films are viscoelastic.

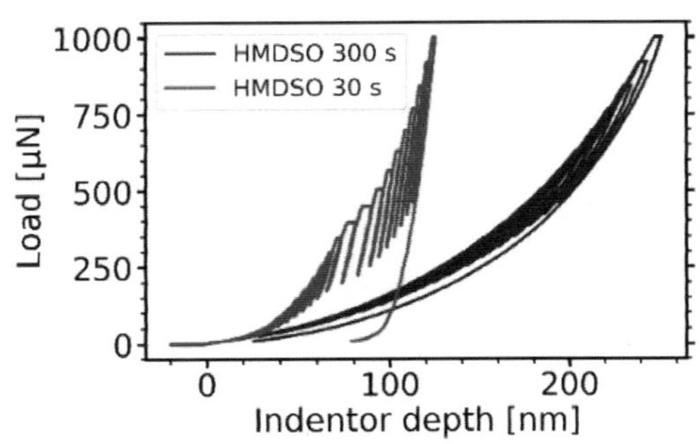

Figure 8 Quasistatic measurement of two films with input power 25 W

4. CONCLUSION

The paper summarizes results from depositions in the atmosphere containing oxygen and HMDSO or HMDSZ precursor. The main reason for this study was to compare these types of thin film because of the wide usage of these precursors in a wide range of different reactors. For both precursors, there is an evolution of self-bias during the deposition process which causes the evolution of deposition rate. Despite the fact that the mixture of HMDSZ with oxygen creates bigger particles of dust, the deposition rate for HMDSO precursor is higher. Also due to bigger dust particles, the homogeneity of the surface is lower for thin films deposited from HMDSZ precursor. All deposited thin films have WCA around 90° and all deposited thin films were viscoelastic.

ACKNOWLEDGEMENTS

The present work was supported by the Czech Science Foundation under project GACR 19-15240S, by the Ministry of Education, Youth and Sports of the Czech Republic under project NPU (LO1411).

REFERENCES

[1] PAVLENKO, S. *Organosilicon chemistry*. Berlin 1896.

[2] Hexamethyldisilazane. Merck [online]. Available from: https://www.sigmaaldrich.com/catalog/product/sigma/h4875?lang=en&region=CZ

[3] Hexamethydisiloxane. Merck [online]. Available from: https://www.sigmaaldrich.com/catalog/product/aldrich/326739?lang=en&region=CZ

[4] FRIDMAN, A. A. *Plasma chemistry*. Cambridge: Cambridge University Press, 2012. ISBN 978-1107684935.

[5] LIEBERMAN, M.A., LICHTENBERG, A. J. *Principles of plasma discharges and materials processing*. 2nd ed. Hoboken, N.J.: Wiley-Interscience, 2005. ISBN 0471720011.

[6] PŘIBYL, R., KELAROVÁ, Š., HOMOLA, V., BURČÍKOVÁ, V. Development of Plasma Enhanced Chemical Vapor Deposition Reactor for Preparation of Oxygen Containing Organosilazane Polymer Thin Films [online]. **In**: *International Conference on Nanomaterials NANOCON 2019*. Brno: Tanger, 2020, pp. 637-641. Available from: https://doi.org/10.37904/nanocon.2019.8749

[7] HOMOLA, V., PŘIBYL, R., KELAROVÁ, Š., et al. Study of Nanostructured Plasma-Polymer Thin Films Growthunder Dusty Plasma Conditions [online]. **In**: *International Conference on Nanomaterials NANOCON 2019*. Brno: Tanger, 2020, pp. 642-647. Available from: https://doi.org/10.37904/nanocon.2019.8699.

[8] BOUCHOULE, A. (ed). *Dusty Plasmas: Physics, Chemistry and Technical Impacts in Plasma Processing*. New York: Wiley, 1999. pp. 77-180.

[9] SHUKLA, S., PADMA, K., MAMUN, A. A. *Introduction to Dusty Plasma Physics*. Bristol: Institute of Physics Pub., 2002

[10] BOUCHOULE, A., BOUFENDI, L. Particulate formation and dusty plasma behaviour in argon-silane RF discharge. *Plasma Sources Science and Technology* [online]. 1993, vol. 2, no. 3, pp. 204-213. DOI: 10.1088/0963-0252/2/3/011. ISSN 0963-0252. Available from: http://stacks.iop.org/09630252/2/i=3/a=011?key=crossref.8c4b30177541661a90505553151cb5b41

[11] GEGENBACH, T. R., GRIESSER, H. J. Post-deposition ageing reaction figger markedly between plasma polymers deposited from siloxane and silazane monomers. *Polymer*. 1999, vol. 40, p. 50795094.

[12] CASSERLY, T. B., GLEASON K. K. Chemical Vapor Deposition of Organosilicon Thin films from Methylmethoxysilanes. *Plas. Proc. Polym.* [online]. 2005, vol. 2, pp. 679-687, Available from: https://doi.org/10.1002/ppap.200500055.

[13] PARK, S. Y., KIM., N., KIM, U. Y., HONG, S., SASABE, H. Plazma polymerization of hexamethyldisiloxane. *Polymer Journal*. 1990, vol. 3, pp. 242-249.

[14] BONNAR, M. P., BURNSIDE, B. M., CHRISTIE, J., SCEAL, E. J., TROUPE, C. E., WILSON, J. I. B. Hydrophobic Coatings from Plasma Polymerized Vinyltrimethylsilane. *Chemical Vapor Deposition*. [online]. 1999, vol. 5, no. 3, pp. 117-125. Available from: https://doi.org/10.1002/(SICI)1521-3862(199906)5:3<117::AID-CVDE117>3.0.CO;2-4.

CONTROLLING THE INTERNAL MICROSTRUCTURE AND PROPERTIES OF PHYSICALLY CROSS-LINKED PVA HYDROGELS BY THE RATE OF FREEZING

[1]Monika TRUDICOVA, [1]Jan ZAHRADKA, [1]Petr SEDLACEK, [1]Miloslav PEKAR

[1]*Brno university of technology, FCH, Brno, Czech Republic,* xctrudicova@fch.vut.cz

https://doi.org/10.37904/nanocon.2020.3769

Abstract

PVA hydrogels can be formed via physical crosslinking (e.g. by cyclic freezing/thawing of aqueous polyvinyl alcohol solutions) or with a chemical cross-linker. Physical crosslinking is more useful for biomedical applications since it contains no harmful cross-linker residues. This work, therefore, focused on studying properties of physically crosslinked hydrogels with different concentrations of polyvinyl alcohol (2.5 to 15 wt%) prepared via cyclic freezing/thawing under different cryogenic conditions: in the liquid nitrogen (-196 °C), in two different laboratory freezers (-80 °C and -18 °C) and the ice bath. Furthermore, the effects of the addition of several cryoprotectants were evaluated. The optical and mechanical properties of the prepared samples were studied, and the microstructure of the hydrogels was observed by scanning electron microscopy after freeze-drying.

Keywords: Hydrogel, polyvinyl alcohol, rheology, scanning electron microscopy

1. INTRODUCTION

Hydrogels are defined as systems consisting of a three-dimensional network of polymer chains and water filling the space between these macromolecules. They can be used in a wide range of medical applications, such as wound dressings, controlled drug release, or as scaffolds in tissue engineering [1]. Optical, mechanical, and transport properties of hydrogels are crucial for their potential applications; therefore, the possibility of modifying their properties and relevant material parameters according to the specific needs of a particular application is still being researched [2,3]. One of the basic tools for modifying the material properties of hydrogels is a manipulation of the internal chemical and morphological architecture [4].

This work focuses on the possibilities of modifying optical and mechanical properties of polyvinyl alcohol hydrogels via adjustment of their preparation procedure. It aims to understand the way how these properties can be controlled by manipulating the internal structure in physically crosslinked polyvinyl alcohol hydrogels.

2. EXPERIMENTAL PART

2.1. Preparation of polyvinyl alcohol hydrogels

Polyvinyl alcohol (PVA) is one of the synthetic polymers most widely used for the preparation of hydrogels for biomedical applications. It is a linear polymer, which is produced by radical polymerization of vinyl acetate and subsequent hydrolysis of acetate groups to hydroxyl groups, the degree of this hydrolysis (usually 85 - 100%) determining the properties of the polymer such as solubility in aqueous solutions, etc. [5]. The PVA hydrogel can be formed either by physical crosslinking by repeated freezing cycles or by chemical crosslinking with crosslinkers [6]. In this work, all hydrogels were prepared via cyclic freezing/thawing. The polyvinyl alcohol used in this work was purchased from Sigma Aldrich, average Mw 130,000, 99+% hydrolyzed; CAS number 9002-89-5. To monitor the effect of PVA content in the gel, hydrogels were prepared from aqueous solutions with different concentrations of polyvinyl alcohol (2.5, 5.0, 7.5, 10.0, 12.5 and 15.0 wt%) by cyclic freezing/thawing in the freezer (-18 °C).

Furthermore, for the gels prepared from PVA solution with a concentration of 10.0 wt% of polyvinyl alcohol, additives in the form of cryoprotectants were added in concentrations of 10.0 wt% to prevent damage to the three-dimensional polymer network during freezing due to the restriction of ice crystal growth. Trehalose, sucrose, urea, and glycerol were used as cryoprotectants. These samples were also prepared in the freezer (-18 °C).

According to the literature, the properties of a polyvinyl alcohol hydrogel can be influenced both by the concentration of PVA and by the temperature of freezing that defines the freezing rate [7]. Therefore, in another set of experiments four different cryogenic conditions were tested: the liquid nitrogen (-196 °C), two different laboratory freezers (-80 °C and -18 °C), and the ice bath. For these experiments were prepared hydrogels with 10.0 wt% of polyvinyl alcohol. A series of hydrogels with different concentrations of polyvinyl alcohol (2.5, 5.0, 7.5, 10.0, 12.5, and 15 wt%) were prepared in the ice bath for comparison with the reference samples prepared previously in the freezer (-18 °C).

2.2. Study of optical properties

The first proposed method for evaluating the optical properties of hydrogels was an objective photometric analysis of samples using a spectrophotometer. However, most of the samples did not have sufficient transmittance, therefore the optical properties were evaluated visually. The samples were placed on the pad with an auxiliary cross, which formed a reference point for comparing the transparency (**Figure 1**).

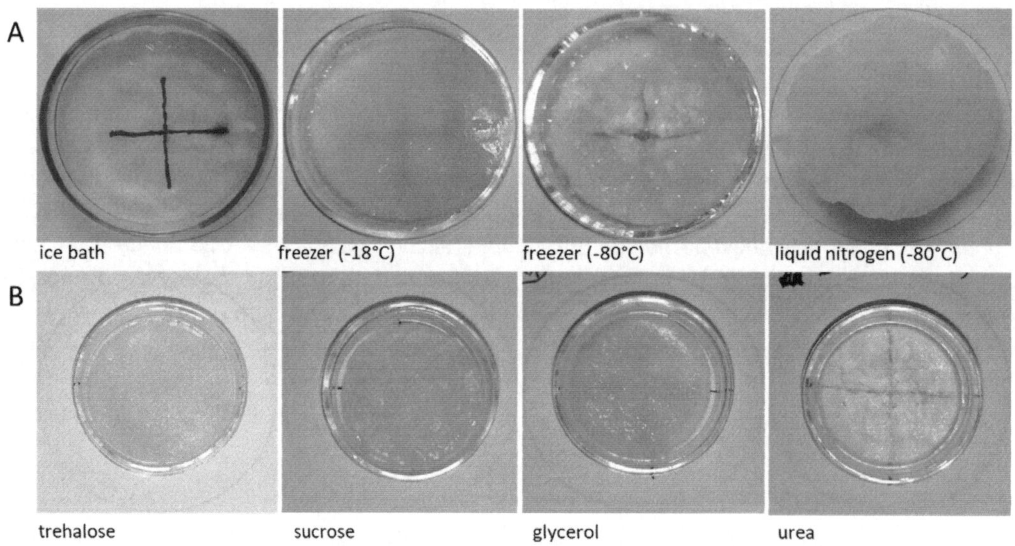

Figure 1 Visual evaluation of samples with concentration 10.0 wt% of PVA prepared under different cryogenic conditions (A) and with the addition of cryoprotectants prepared in the freezer (-18 °C) (B)

It was clear that the freezing rate (**Figure 1a**) had a significant effect on the transparency of the hydrogels prepared by crosslinking the same solution. The samples frozen in the ice bath appear to be the most transparent. According to the results, highly transparent PVA hydrogels can be created thanks to slow freezing and the associated slow growth of ice crystals. The samples with different concentrations of polyvinyl alcohol prepared in the ice bath and in the freezer (-18 °C) were investigated as well. The results showed that the polymer concentration did not have a significant effect on the final optical properties.

As mentioned, the kinetics of the ice crystal formation during freezing have a key influence on the optical properties of the resulting PVA hydrogels. Suitable gelation conditions can be therefore ensured by slow gelation at a temperature close to the freezing point of water. However, this procedure is time-consuming and also difficult to automate. Therefore, the effect of the cryoprotectants on the transparency of PVA hydrogels at higher (freezer, -18 °C) than optimal freezing rates was proposed and tested as an alternative approach. Cryoprotectants are substances used to protect biological tissue from freezing damage (i.e. that due to ice formation). The results show (**Figure 1b**) that the selected cryoprotectants did not significantly affect the optical properties except for urea, which alone affected the optical properties and thus appears to be a potentially interesting component allowing further manipulation of the internal structure of PVA hydrogels.

2.3. Study of mechanical properties

Rheology was applied to test the mechanical properties. Various series of PVA hydrogels were prepared for rheological measurements, these samples were measured on the MCR 72 rheometer from Anton Paar. Strain sweep test was chosen as suitable for the description of mechanical properties, this test provides information about the linear viscoelastic region (LVR, it tells us where the moduli are independent on the amplitude of deformation). The data obtained during the measurement were evaluated and processed in the MS Excel software in the form of the dependence of elastic (G') and viscous (G") moduli on the changing amplitude of deformation (**Figure 2** shows an example for different cryogenic conditions). The values of phase angles were calculated from viscoelastic moduli. These values provide information about a relative contribution of elastic and viscous types of deformation. Furthermore, the values of the complex modulus as a parameter characterizing the total rigidity of the samples were determined.

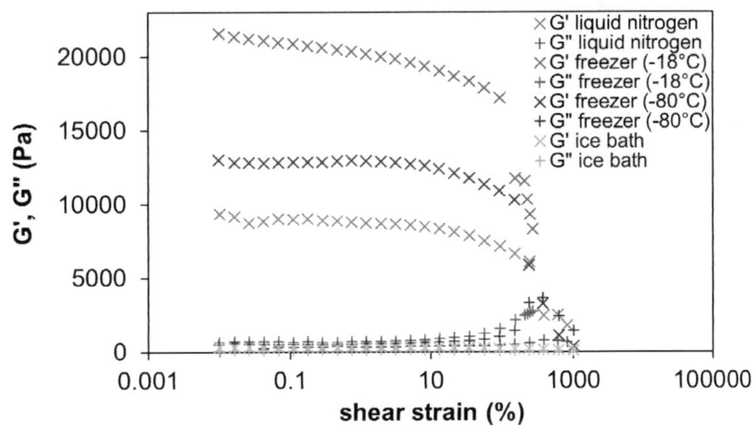

Figure 2 Dependence of elastic and viscous moduli on the changing amplitude of deformation for samples with concentration 10.0 wt% of polyvinyl alcohol prepared under the different temperature of freezing

The samples prepared in the ice bath were different from the others. The difference in the phase angles (**Figure 3a**) can be considered as a sign of a difference in the character of the junctions of the hydrogel network. As is known, the rate of freezing of water (depending on the cryogenic conditions) affects the rate of growth of ice crystals, which push the polymer chains at the phase interface. For this reason, in the freezers and the liquid nitrogen bath, contact of multiple chains is achieved in a short time, which creates conditions for multiple physical connections. In the ice bath, due to the relatively high temperature, there is a slow growth of small crystals, which approaches a smaller number of chains and forms fewer junctions, less resistant to deformation. The values of complex modulus (**Figure 3b**) support the conclusions obtained from the comparison of phase angles, which provide information mainly on the quality of the junctions of the hydrogel network and supplement it with information on the density of crosslinking.

The effect of the addition of cryoprotectants on the mechanical properties was also monitored, but there were no obvious differences between the samples with and without cryoprotectants, respectively.

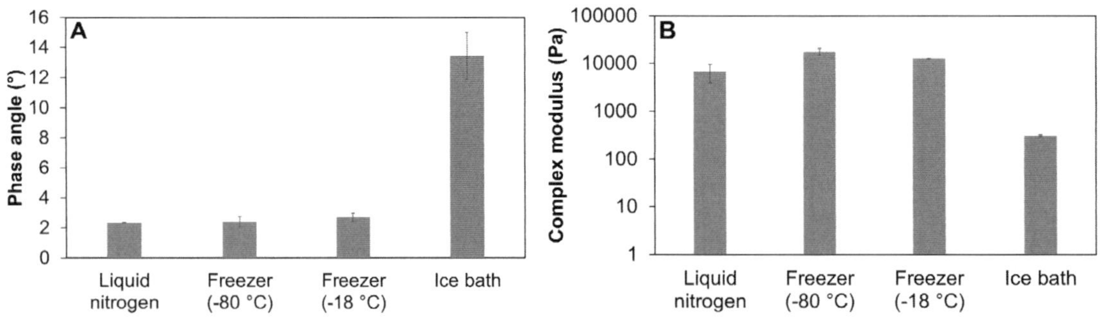

Figure 3 Phase angles (A) and complex moduli (B) for the samples with concentration 10.0 wt% of polyvinyl alcohol prepared under the different cryogenic conditions

The series of samples with different concentrations of PVA prepared in the freezer (-18 °C°) and in the ice bath, respectively, were also compared. The sample with the concentration of 7.5 wt% prepared in the ice bath behaved viscously. This can be caused by incomplete gelation of the sample, which could be due to the insufficient gelation time. For the other samples, the values of the phase angle in LVR are below the limit of 45 ° and these samples therefore already show an elastic character. As the PVA content in the samples increases, the phase angle decreases (**Figure 4a**). Comparing the values of complex modulus (**Figure 4b**) again supports the information obtained from the comparison of phase angles. Samples prepared in the freezer have high values of complex modulus. This indicates their high rigidity, which does not differ with increasing PVA concentration. Conversely, the samples prepared in the ice bath show a trend that the rigidity increases with increasing concentration. Thus, as the values of the phase angles decrease the stiffness of the samples increases, which is most likely a sign of an increasing concentration of junctions in the gel network.

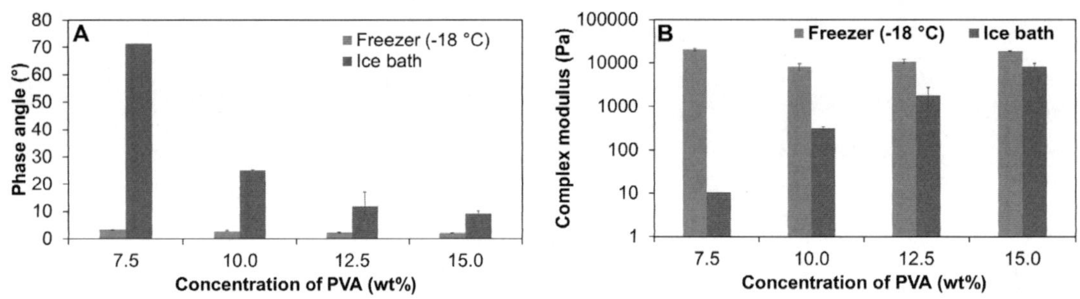

Figure 4 Phase angles (A) and complex moduli (B) for samples with different concentrations of polyvinyl alcohol prepared in the freezer (-18 °C) and in the ice bath

2.4. Study of microstructure

Selected hydrogels were analyzed by direct visualization method in their dried form. Scanning electron microscopy was chosen as a suitable method. The purpose was to obtain information about the internal structure of selected hydrogels to support the hypothesis associated with their properties. For this purpose, the selected samples were freeze-dried (after shock-freezing in liquid nitrogen - to preserve the internal structure of the hydrogels without artifacts [8]). Then small parts of the specimens were taken. These specimens were gold coated in a sputtering device and investigated using a scanning electron microscope ZEISS EVO LS 10 with detection of secondary electrons (SE). Hydrogels selected for this analysis were with different concentrations of PVA (-18°C) and samples with 10.0 wt% of PVA prepared under different temperatures, thus with different freezing rates. A significant part of the samples had a collapsed structure on most of their surface due to the partial recrystallization of water.

A set of samples prepared at different freezing rates was observed first (**Figure 5**). These samples have a clearly visible porous structure with different pore sizes, which depended on the temperature of freezing and ranged from hundreds of nanometers to several micrometers. For the samples with different concentrations of PVA prepared in the freezer (**Figure 6**), there is a visible trend in the change of pore size despite the collapsed structure. With increasing concentration of polymer content, the pore sizes decrease. This is due to the higher content of polymer (gelling component), which provides a higher crosslinking density. Hydrogels in the concentration range of 2.5 to 7.5 wt% of PVA have almost identical porous structure with pore sizes from tens of micrometers (hydrogels with 2.5 wt.% PVA) to hundreds of nanometers (hydrogels with 7.5 wt.% PVA). The sample with 10.0 wt% of PVA appears as a disordered tangle of fibers, slowly merging into a smooth surface. The remaining two samples with 12.5 and 15.0 wt% of PVA look completely smooth. It is possible that for these two samples, spots with preparation artifacts were selected for the analysis. Nevertheless, with a higher content of the polymer, it is less likely that the sample will retain its original structure after freeze-drying.

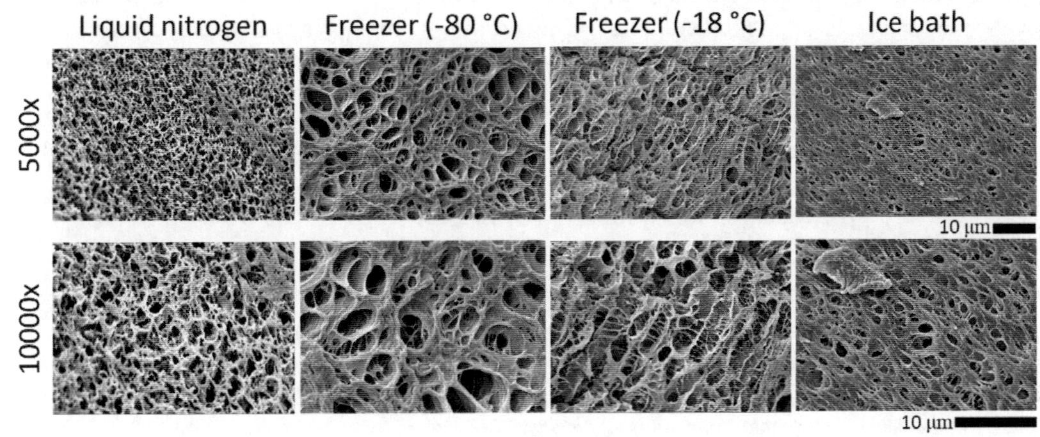

Figure 5 Micrographs of samples with concentration 10.0 wt% of polyvinyl alcohol prepared under different temperatures of freezing with magnification 5000× and 10000× (SEM ZEISS EVO LS 10)

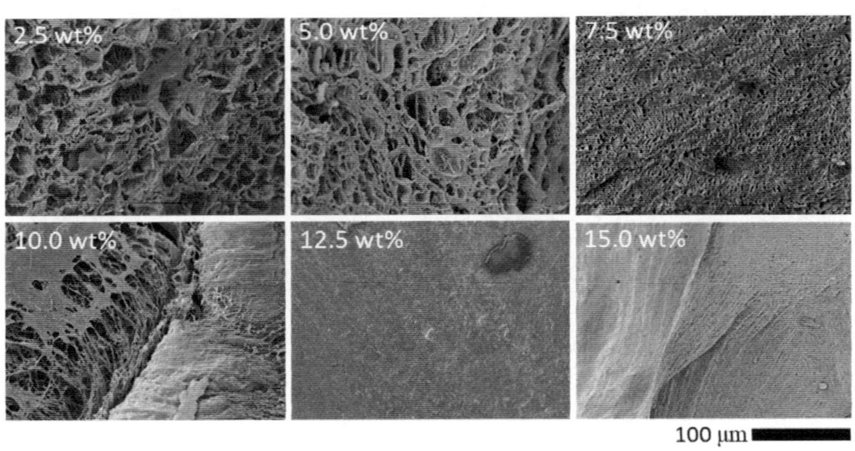

Figure 6 Micrographs of samples prepared in the freezer (-18 °C) with different concentrations of polyvinyl alcohol with magnification 1000× (SEM ZEISS EVO LS 10)

3. CONCLUSION

This work focused on studying properties of physically crosslinked hydrogels with different concentrations of polyvinyl alcohol (2.5 to 15.0 wt%) prepared via cyclic freezing/thawing under different cryogenic conditions: in the liquid nitrogen (-196 °C), in two different laboratory freezers (-80 °C and -18 °C) and in the ice bath. Furthermore, the effects of the addition of several cryoprotectants were evaluated. The optical and mechanical properties of the prepared samples were studied, and the microstructure of the hydrogels was observed by scanning electron microscopy after shock-freezing followed by freeze-drying.

The above results show that the properties of polyvinyl alcohol hydrogels can be varied in many ways. One way to effectively change the structure and properties of hydrogels prepared from polyvinyl alcohol by cyclic freezing/thawing is controlling the freezing rate, which can be affected by adjusting the freezing temperature. By changing the freezing rate, all monitored properties were altered. The cryoprotectants we chose did not sufficiently affect the resulting hydrogels. Therefore, these cryoprotectants are not suitable as additives to alter the properties of polyvinyl alcohol-based hydrogels. The concentration of polyvinyl alcohol in the hydrogel partially changes the properties of the resulting hydrogel. In this case, however, it is necessary to focus on the freezing rate. Because when the sample is frozen in a regular freezer, it is achieved the contact of more chains in a short time independent of the concentration of PVA. However, for slower freezing (the ice bath), due to the relatively low temperature gradient, there is a slow growth of small crystals, which approach a smaller number of chain contacts and form fewer junctions than for rapid freezing and this is the reason why the impact of changing the concentration will be greater for these samples.

ACKNOWLEDGEMENTS

The research was supported by project COST LD15047.

REFERENCES

[1] PEPPAS, N. Hydrogels in pharmaceutical formulations. *European Journal of Pharmaceutics and Biopharmaceutics*. 2000, vol. 50, no. 1, pp. 27-46.

[2] LI, X., SUN, Q., KAWAZOE, N. CHEN, G. Functional Hydrogels With Tunable Structures and Properties for Tissue Engineering Applications. *Frontiers in Chemistry*. 2018, vol. 6.

[3] CURVELLO, R., RAGHUWANSHI V.S., GARNIER, G. Engineering nanocellulose hydrogels for biomedical applications. *Advances in Colloid and Interface Science*. 2019, vol. 267, pp. 47-61.

[4] MEANS, A.K., GRUNLAN, M.A. Modern Strategies To Achieve Tissue-Mimetic, Mechanically Robust Hydrogels. *ACS Macro Letters*. 2019, vol. 8, no. 6, pp. 705-713.

[5] BUWALDA, S.J., BOERE, K.W.M., DIJKSTRA, P.J., FEIJEN, J., VERMONDEN, T., HENNINK W.E. Hydrogels in a historical perspective: From simple networks to smart materials. *Journal of Controlled Release*. 2014, vol. 190, pp. 254-273.

[6] BARUI, Ananya. Synthetic polymeric gel. In: *Polymeric Gels*. Woodhead Publishing, 2018, p. 55-90.

[7] HOLLOWAY, J. L., LOWMAN, A.M., PALMESE, G.R. The role of crystallization and phase separation in the formation of physically cross-linked PVA hydrogels. *Soft Matter*. 2013, vol. 9, no. 3, pp. 826-833.

[8] RAGHUWANSHI, V.S., GARNIER, G. Characterisation of hydrogels: Linking the nano to the microscale. *Advances in Colloid and Interface Science*. 2019, vol. 274.

RADICAL-BASED TUNING THE SURFACE FUNCTIONALITY OF MXENE

[1,2]Anastasiia OLSHTREM, [3]Sergii CHERTOPALOV, [1,2]Olga GUSELNIKOVA, [1]Vaclav SVORCÍK, [1,2]Oleksiy LYUTAKOV

[1]VŠCHT - University of Chemistry and Technology, Prague, Czech Republic, EU, lyutakoo@vscht.cz

[2]Tomsk Polytechnic University, Research School of Chemistry and Applied Biomedical Sciences, Tomsk, Russian Federation

[3]Institute of Physics of the Czech Academy of Sciences, Prague, Czech Republic, EU

https://doi.org/10.37904/nanocon.2020.3770

Abstract

The family of MAX phases and their derivative MXenes are continuously growing in terms of both crystalline and composition varieties. MXenes are a new family of two-dimensional (2D) transition metal carbides, carbonitrides and nitrides, with a general formula Mn+1AXn, where n = 1-3, M denotes a transition metal, A is an element such as aluminum or silicon, and X is either carbon or nitrogen. Considering the various elemental composition possibilities, surface functional tunability, various magnetic orders, and large spin-orbit coupling, MXene can truly be considered as multifunctional materials that can be used to realize highly correlated phenomena. However, a change in surface chemical groups can significantly alter the properties and functionality of MXene flakes and may even damage the flakes. In this paper, we propose the possibility of using soft, chemical transformation to tune the MXene surface chemistry and termination. We used fluorinated and brominated substituents for MXenes grafting and subsequent analysis of the surface composition of the MXene flakes indicated a decrease in oxygen and a simultaneous increase in fluorine and bromine surface concentrations. The ability to graft organic groups with various substituents to the surface of the flakes opens up new possibilities for their application. The presence of fluorinated groups on the surface makes it hydrophobic, which allows the creation of water-repellent flakes, and prevents rapid oxidation by atmospheric oxygen and related formation of titanium oxide on the surface.

Keywords: Chemical transformation, MXene, surface grafting, tuned functionalization

1. INTRODUCTION

Creation and study of two-dimensional (2D) materials is a young and very promising area of modern materials science [1-4]. These materials are very thin (often less than one nm), so they can be used to create layered heterostructures that are used in modern electronics, from transistors to sensors, solar cells and LEDs [5-10]. The most famous two-dimensional material is graphene, its discovery in 2010 was awarded the Nobel Prize in physics [11]. Graphene possesses high values of electrical and thermal conductivity and is sufficiently strong in tensile strength [12-15]. At the same time, it forms folds and is unstable as a separate free-hanging film [16,17]. Discovered in 2011, the MXene have surpassed graphene in both electrical characteristics and manufacturability [18,19]. MXene exhibits conductivity superior to graphene coating. In addition, MXene combines many characteristics, including high shielding efficiency, low density, low thickness, high flexibility and ease of processing [20-22]. So, it is a great candidate for numerous applications, such as transparent conductive coatings, protective layers, and electrochemically-active supports [23,24].

It has been proven that the surface chemistry of Mxene affects its conductive properties, which can be controlled and even rearranged. However, methods of modifying the surface chemistry of MXene flakes often damage the MXene structure.

In this contribution, we propose a new approach for modifying a new and interesting class of 2D materials - Mxenes with formula Ti3AlC2. Our approach is based on the surface modification under attack by higly reactive radicals.

2. EXPERIMENTAL

2.1. Materials

3,5-Bis(trifluoromethyl)phenyl-boronic acid (≥95 %), 1-iodo-3,5-bis(trifluoromethyl)benzene (98%), boron trifluoride diethyl etherate (99%), 3-Chloroperbenzoic acid (≤77%), methanol and were purchased from Sigma-Aldrich. Powder of titanium (99%), aluminum (99.5%) and graphite (99%) were purchased from Alfa Aesar. All reagents were used without further purification. Throughout the all experiments deionized water was used. Ti3AlC2 MAX phase and Mxene flakes were prepared according to [25,26, 27].

2.2. Preparation of Ti3AlC2 MAX phase

Ti3AlC2 MAX phase was performed by the procedure described in [25]. Powders of titanium, aluminum and graphite were mixed in molar ratio 3.00:1.10:1.88 with zirconia balls (diameter 3 mm) by ball milling at 60 rpm during 3 hours in a plastic jar. The mixed powders were putted into alumina boat and transferred to a tube furnace (4016T, Clasic CZ). Before synthesis, vacuum pumping was carried out twice to a pressure of 2 mbar, followed by a purge with argon. The MAX phase synthesis was accomplished by heating the mixture at 10°C/min to 1550°C in argon atmosphere followed by 2 hours holding period at 1550°C and cooling down to room temperature at 10°C/min.

Preparation of MXenes flakes

Ti3C2 MXene was synthesized using the MILD method described in [26]. Before selective etching of aluminum from Ti3AlC2 MAX phase, the MAX phase ceramics were crushed by mortar and pestle and sieved to separate the particles of size below 45 µm. The etchant was prepared by dissolving 300 mg of LiF (99.98 % metals basis, Alfa Aesar) in 6 mL of 6M HCl in the plastic centrifuge tube. Then, the 300 mg of sieved MAX phase powder (particle size below 45 µm) was added to prepared etchant and stirred at 22°C for 24 hours. After etching, the MXene were washed several times until the pH of the supernatant reached 5.5. Delamination of MXene flakes was carried out by hand shaking of the sample (15 mL DI water in 50 mL plastic test tube) for 5 min followed by 15 min of centrifugation at 3500 rpm to precipitate and separate the non-delaminated MXene.

Surface grafting and MXene thin film preparation

The colloidal suspension of MXene flakes (2 mL, 5 g/L) was mixed with a 1 mL of a radical source (1 mM solution) in a 9:1 water/methanol mixture and activated under the continuous mixing for different time intervals. After the modification, the MXene flakes were collected by centrifugation (15 min, 5000 rpm) and 3x subsequently washed by water and a methanol. For coating preparation, the purified MXene flakes were dispersed (1 g/L) in water/methanol mixture (1:1 ratio) and sprayed on previously cleaned glass or silicon surfaces using home-made equipment.

2.3. Measurement techniques

For the characterization of the solutions, the UV/Vis/NIR spectroscopy technique was used in the spectral range 300-1000 nm, scanning rate 480 nm min^{-1}, data collection interval 1 nm. The solutions were measured in 1 cm quartz cells.

TEM images were obtained on a JEOL JEM-1010 transmission electron microscope with a SIS MegaView III digital camera.

Fourier transform infrared (FTIR)–attenuated total reflection (ATR) spectra were recorded using a Nicolet 6700 spectrometer (Thermo Scientific, France) with a Smart ATR accessory device (1000 scans and 4 cm-1 resolution).

The crystal structure of Ti3AlC2 MAX phase and Ti3C2 MXene phase were characterized by X-ray diffractometer (Empyrean, Malvern Panalytical) using Cu K<α> radiation (photon energy - 8.04 keV, wavelength λ = 1.54151 Å, U = 45 kV, I = 30 mA) in grazing incidence X-ray diffraction mode and in 2θ-θ mode. The incident angle was 0.85 corresponding to ~10 mm of sample irradiation.

X-ray photoelectron spectroscopy (XPS) was performed using an Omicron Nanotechnology ESCAProbeP spectrometer fitted with a monochromated Al K alpha X-ray source at 1486.7 eV. MXene flake samples were deposited on Si wafers, the analyzed area had dimensions of 2×3 mm2.

3. RESULTS AND DISCUSSION

The schematic representation of main experimental concept is given in **Figure 1**. The MXene flakes were dispersed in an aqueous methanol solution containing radical source and then activated by external triggering. Excitation of the surface MXene increases the energy of electrons on the surface, which in turn leads to homolytic of radical source and the appearance of reactive radicals. The created radicals were then grafted to the MXene surface. Moreover, simultaneous triggering and radical grafting can result in substitution of terminated groups on flake surface, leading to pronounced modification of MXene surface composition.

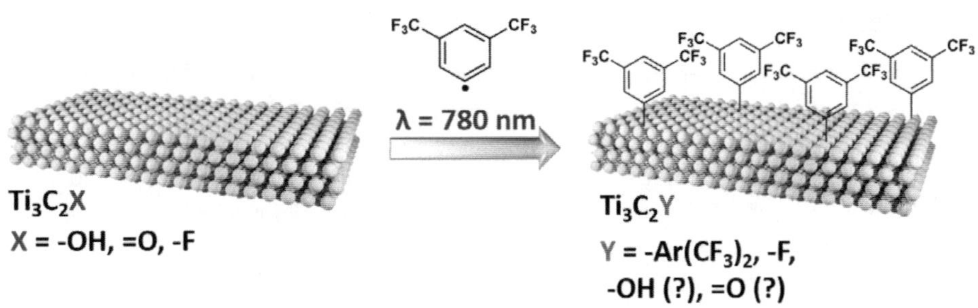

Figure 1 Schematic representation of proposed experimental concept

UV/Vis spectra of pristine MXenes in the water/methanol solution (**Figure 2A** - insert) were measured to determine the wavelength position of MXene absorption band. Next, the UV spectra were measured after different modification times (**Figure 2A**). We can observe that the absorption peak gradually shifts to the blue region with increasing modification time. After 3 hours of modification, the peak shift no longer occurred. The grafting of MXene flakes surface was further confirmed by IR measurements. IR spectra are presented in the **Figure 2B**. Pristine MXene contains peaks at 1740 (C=O), 1408 (O-H), and 595 (Ti-O) cm^{-1} related to terminated oxidized groups. After radical grafting the appearance of new, well pronounced absorption bands on modified flakes indicate the presence of grafted chemical moieties.

The intensity of characteristic band, located at 1275 cm^{-1} (C-F stretch in $-CF_3$), is plotted against the time of radicals grafting in **Figure 2B** insert. Given dependency corresponds well with UV/Vis results - apparent increase of band intensity during the first 30 min of triggering and it's saturation after 3 hours of reaction. So, results of UV/Vis and IR spectroscopy indicate that radicals grafting of MXene flakes mainly occurs at the initial stages of triggering and is further enhanced under the prolongation of triggering time up to 3 hours.

In addition, the structure and crystallinity of MXene flakes were evaluated by TEM and XRD, XPS measurements before and after radicals grafting. TEM analysis confirm the preservation of flake structure during the grafting. Results of XPS and XRD analysis are in a good agreement and approve the successful grafting of organic radicals to the surface of MXene.

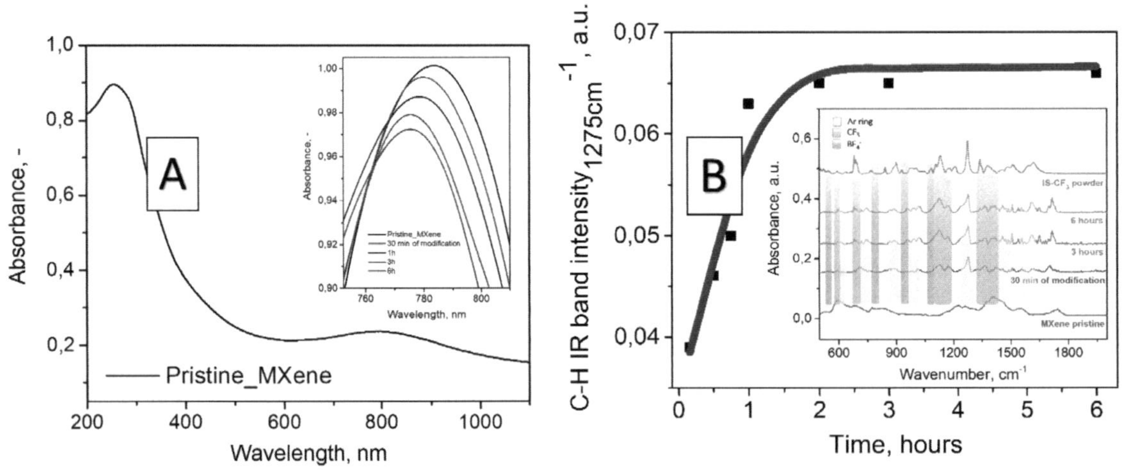

Figure 2 (A) UV/Vis absorption spectrum of MXene after different time of grafting (insert shows the full UV/Vis absorption spectrum of pristine flakes suspension); (B) IR spectra, measured on MXene flakes after the different time of radicals grafting (insert show the time dependent changes of characteristic (1275cm-1) IR band intensity)

4. CONCLUSION

A surface modification of MXene flakes under radical attack has been proposed. The mixture of flakes with the radical source was activated for different times. As a result of chemical bond homolysis the active radicals appear, attack the MXene surface and change the chemical composition of the surface terminated groups. Due to the high MXene catalytic potential the proposed experimental route is very simple and does not require high-energy cleaning of the flake surface. As a model example the fluor-substituted radicals were used, resulting in hydrophobization of MXene flakes surface. The proposed method provides the creation of conductive, superhydrophobic and water-repellent coatings with improved resistance of MXene to oxidation.

ACKNOWLEDGEMENTS

This work was financially supported by the Internal Grant Agency UCT № 126 88 2010.

REFERENCES

[1] MIRO, P., AUDIFFRED, M., HEINE, T. An atlas of two-dimensional materials. *Chem. Soc. Rev.* 2014, vol. 43, pp. 6537-6554.

[2] SINGH, A. K., MATHEW, K., ZHUANG, H. L., HENNIG, R.G. Computational Screening of 2D Materials for Photocatalysis. *J. Phys. Chem. Lett.* 2015, vol. 6, pp. 1087-1098.

[3] SCHULMAN, D. S., ARNOLD, A. J., DAS, S. Contact engineering for 2D materials and devices. *Chem. Soc. Rev.* 2018, vol. 47, pp. 3037-3058.

[4] MAS-BALLESTE, R., GOMEZ-NAVARRO, C., GOMEZ-HERRERO, J., ZAMORA, F. 2D materials: to graphene and beyond. *Nanoscale*. 2011, vol. 3, pp. 20-30.

[5] CAI, Z., LIU, B., ZOU, X., CHENG, H-M. Chemical Vapor Deposition Growth and Applications of Two-Dimensional Materials and Their Heterostructures. *Chem. Rev.* 2018, vol. 118, pp. 6091-6133.

[6] KUMAR, K. S., CHOUDHARY, N., JUNG, Y., THOMAS, J. Recent Advances in Two-Dimensional Nanomaterials for Supercapacitor Electrode Applications. *CS Energy Lett.* 2018, vol. 3, pp. 482-495.

[7] ZHAO, H., CHEN, X., WANG, G., QIU, Y., GUO, L. Two-dimensional amorphous nanomaterials: synthesis and applications. *2D Mater.* 2019, vol. 6, p. 032002.

[8] POMERANTSEVA, E., GOGOTSI, Y. Two-dimensional heterostructures for energy storage. *Nat. Energy*. 2017, vol. 2, p. 17089.

[9] WANG, H., LIU, F., FU, W., FANG, Z., ZHOU, W., LIU, Z. Two-dimensional heterostructures: fabrication, characterization, and application. *Nanoscale*. 2014, vol. 6, pp. 12250-12272.

[10] CHIMENE, D., ALGE, D. L., GAHARWAR, A. K. Two-Dimensional Nanomaterials for Biomedical Applications: Emerging Trends and Future Prospects. *Adv. Mater.* 2015, vol. 27, pp. 7261-7284.

[11] GERSTNER E. Nobel Prize 2010: Andre Geim & Konstantin Novoselov. *Nature Physics*. 2010, vol. 6, p. 836.

[12] SUN, Z., CHANG, H. Graphene and Graphene-like Two-Dimensional Materials in Photodetection: Mechanisms and Methodology. *ACS Nano*. 2014, vol. 8, pp. 4133-4156.

[13] GRIGORENKO, A. N., POLINI, M., NOVOSELOV, K. S. Graphene plasmonics. *Nat. Photonics*. 2012, vol. 6, pp. 749-758.

[14] PAPAGEORGIOU, D. G., KINLOCH, I. A., YOUNG, R. J. Mechanical properties of graphene and graphene-based nanocomposites. *Prog. Mater. Sci.* 2017, vol. 90, pp. 75-127.

[15] CUI, S., MAO, S., JU, G., CHEN, J. Graphene Coupled with Nanocrystals: Opportunities and Challenges for Energy and Sensing Applications. *J. Phys. Chem. Lett.* 2013, vol. 4, pp. 2441-2454.

[16] LEE, S-M., KIM, J-H., AHN, J-H. Graphene as a flexible electronic material: mechanical limitations by defect formation and efforts to overcome. *Mater. Today*. 2015, vol. 18, pp. 336-344.

[17] MOUCHEL, P., KEMEL, M., SEMAAN, G., SALHI, M., FLOHIC, M. L., SANCHEZ, F. Limitations of graphene nanocoated optical tapers for high-power nonlinear applications. *Opt. Mater. X*. 2019, vol. 1, p. 100003.

[18] NAGUIB, M., KURTOGLU, M., PRESSER, V., LU, J., NIU, J., HEON, M., HULTMAN, L., GOGOTSI, Y., BARSOUM, M. W. Two-Dimensional Nanocrystals: Two-Dimensional Nanocrystals Produced by Exfoliation of Ti3AlC2. *Adv. Mater.* 2011, vol. 23, pp. 4248-4253.

[19] NAGUIB, M., COME, J., DYATKIN, B., PRESSER, V., TABERNA, P-L., SIMON, P., BARSOUM, M. W., GOGOTSI, Y. MXene: a promising transition metal carbide anode for lithium-ion batteries. *Electrochem. commun.* 2012, vol. 16, pp. 61-64.

[20] CHERTOPALOV, S., MOCHALIN, V. N. Environment-Sensitive Photoresponse of Spontaneously Partially Oxidized Ti3C2 MXene Thin Films. *ACS Nano*. 2018, vol. 12, pp. 6109-6116.

[21] LIU, J., ZHANG, H-B., SUN, R., LIU, Y., LIU, Z., ZHOU, A., YU, Z-Z. Hydrophobic, Flexible, and Lightweight MXene Foams for High-Performance Electromagnetic-Interference Shielding. *Adv. Mater.* 2017, vol. 29, p. 1702367.

[22] LIU, R., MIAO, M., LI, Y., ZHANG, J., CAO, S., FENG, X. Ultrathin Biomimetic Polymeric Ti3C2Tx MXene Composite Films for Electromagnetic Interference Shielding. *ACS Appl. Mater. Interfaces*. 2018, vol. 10, pp. 44787-44795.

[23] XIONG, D., LI, X., BAI, Z., LU, S. Recent Advances in Layered Ti3C2Tx MXene for Electrochemical Energy Storage. *Small*. 2018, vol. 14, p. 1703419.

[24] GUSELNIKOVA, O., TRELIN, A., MILIUTINA, E., ELASHNIKOV, R., SAJDL, P., POSTNIKOV, P., KOLSKA, Z., SVORCIK, V., LYUTAKOV, O. Plasmon-Induced Water Splitting-through Flexible Hybrid 2D Architecture up to Hydrogen from Seawater under NIR Light. *ACS Appl. Mater. Interfaces*. 2020, vol. 12, pp. 28110-28119.

[25] ALHABEB, M., MALESKI, K., ANASORI, B., LELYUKH, P., CLARK, L., SIN, S., GOGOTSKI, Y. Guidelines for Synthesis and Processing of Two-Dimensional Titanium Carbide (Ti3C2Tx MXene). *Chem. Mater.* 2017, vol. 29, pp. 7633−7644.

[26] DONG, Y., CHERTOPALOV, S., MALESKI, K., ANASORI, B., HU, L., BHATTACHARYA, S., RAO, A. M., GOGOTSKI, Y., MOCHALIN, V. N., PODILA, R. Saturable absorption in 2D Ti3C2 MXene thin films for passive photonic diodes. *Adv. Mater.* 2018, vol. 30, p. 1705714.

[27] OLSHTREM, A., GUSELNIKOVA, O., POSTNIKOV, P., TRELIN, A., YUSUBOV, M., KALACHYOVA, E., LAPCAK, L., CIESLAR, M., ULBRICH, P., SVORCIK, V., LYUTAKOV, A. Plasmon-assisted grafting of anisotropic nanoparticles - spatially selective surface modification and the creation of amphiphilic SERS nanoprobes. *Nanoscale*. 2020, vol. 12, pp. 14581-14588.

ZnO NANOPARTICLES: SYNTHESIS AND EVOLUTION

[1,2]Vojtěch PŘIKRYL, [1,2]Zuzana BYTEŠNÍKOVÁ, [1,2]Pavel ŠVEC, [1,2]Lukáš RICHTERA, [1,2]Vojtěch ADAM

[1]Department of Chemistry and Biochemistry, Mendel University in Brno, Brno, Czech Republic, EU

[2]Central European Institute of Technology, Brno University of Technology, Brno, Czech Republic, EU

https://doi.org/10.37904/nanocon.2020.3771

Abstract

ZnO is a material that is biocompatible, biodegradable, and has low toxicity. Recently it has emerged as an interesting material for use in biomedicine, cosmetics and agriculture. Chemical synthesis of ZnO nanoparticles was investigated due to its potential ease of preparation and upscalability. Ethanol was used as a solvent that promotes the continued growth of the as-prepared nanoparticles. This work presents facile methods of ZnO nanoparticle preparation and a potential method for ZnO nanowire growth at room temperature.

Keywords: Zinc oxide, nanoparticles, nanowires, chemical synthesis

1. INTRODUCTION

ZnO is a material with promising potential for use in various fields including biomedicine, cosmetics and agriculture [1-4] due to its biocompatibility, biodegradability, and low toxicity [5]. Nanoparticles are used in the same fields for their high surface to volume ratio, and antibacterial properties [6,7]. Studies show that nanoparticles exhibit different properties depending on their shape and size [8, 9]. As such new methods for synthesis of nanoparticles of various dimensions are needed. Chemical synthesis offers a way to synthesize nanoparticles in an inexpensive and easy way without the use of specialized equipment [10,11]. In this case, it also allows for use of environmentally friendly materials which is crucial in the above mentioned fields. Due to the increased use of nanoparticles in highly industrialized fields such as agriculture, there is a need for methods that allow for the synthesis of large volumes of nanoparticles. At such scales storage and transportation form a massive obstacle due to their prohibitive expensiveness. One method that allows to reduce the volume of nanoparticles is lyophilization. However, lyophilization can alter the parameters of nanoparticles [12] and so a method that synthesizes nanoparticles that are stable even after lyophilization is needed. This study proposes multiple methods for synthesis of ZnO nanoplates, spherical nanoparticles, and nanowires of various shapes and dimensions that are inexpensive, simple, upscalable, and stable after lyophilization.

2. MATERIALS AND METHODS

2.1. Materials and equipment

All chemicals in this study, unless otherwise stated, were purchased from Sigma-Aldrich (St. Louis, MO, USA). The demineralized water was produced using reverse osmosis apparatus Aqual 25 (Aqua Osmotic, Tišnov, Czech Republic). The demineralized water was further treated by the Milli-Q Direct QUV equipment furnished with a UV lamp (Aqua Osmotic, Tisnov, Czech Republic). The resistance value was 18.20 MΩ·cm (at 25 °C). The drying oven used for drying (if applicable) was Memmert UM 400 (Memmert, Schwabach, Germany). The oven used for calcination was L laboratory chamber furnace (LAC, Rajhrad, Czech Republic). Each calcination process included a 30 min ramping time prior to calcination at 400 °C for 3 h and cooling to room temperature overnight. Lyophilization was performed by FreeZone 2.5 Liter Benchtop Freeze Dryer at 0.014 mBar, −55 °C overnight (Labconco, Kansas City, MO, USA).

2.2. Preparation of ZnO nanoplates

ZnO nanoplates preparation was based on a method reported elsewhere [13]. The method consists of dropwise addition of 33.5 ml, 0.1 M NaOH (Mikrochem, Olomouc, Czech Republic) into 30 ml of 0.1 M $ZnSO_4 \cdot 7H_2O$. The resulting mixture was stirred at 820 rpm for 15 min at room temperature and then washed several times with Milli-Q water. A scaled up version of the preparation was performed by using 10x the amount of the above-mentioned chemicals with unchanged concentrations. The samples were lyophilized to test their resistance to damage caused by lyophilization.

2.3. Preparation of spherical ZnO nanoparticles

Spherical ZnO nanoparticles were prepared via method reported by Chung et al. [14]. A sol-gel was formed by dropwise addition of 0.1 M oxalic acid dihydrate (Lach-Ner, Neratovice, Czech Republic) in 60 ml 99.8 % ethanol (Lach-Ner) into 0.1 M zinc acetate dihydrate in 40 ml of 99,8 % ethanol (Lach-Ner) heated to 60 °C. The resulting mixture was stirred at 820 rpm for 90 min and then dried overnight at 60 °C. The dried powder was calcinated and redispersed in 50 ml of Milli-Q water. A scaled up synthesis was performed by using 10x the amount of the used chemicals with unchanged concentrations. Experiment using the original procedure with double concentration of oxalic acid was also performed.

2.4. Preparation of ZnO nanowires

ZnO nanowires were prepared by modification of the method outlined in 2.3. The nanowire seed solution was made from 0.1 M oxalic acid dihydrate (Lach-Ner) in 60 ml 99.8 % ethanol (Lach-Ner) which was added dropwise into 0.1 M zinc acetate dihydrate in 40 ml of 99.8 % ethanol (Lach-Ner) heated to 60 °C and stirred at 500 rpm. The resulting mixture was left to age. After 1 month of aging at room temperature the solution was topped to 100 ml with 99.8 % ethanol to compensate for ethanol evaporation. Then the solution was washed several times with Milli-Q water. This procedure was scaled up using 10× the amount of the necessary chemicals with unchanged concentrations. The scaled up product was split into three aliquots. The first aliquot was simply washed with Milli-Q water. The second was washed with Milli-Q water, redispersed in water, dried at 60 °C overnight and calcinated. The third aliquot was dried overnight at 60 °C without washing and calcinated.

2.5. Scanning electron microscopy

The samples were examined by SEM on a Tescan MAIA 3 equipped with a FEG (Tescan Ltd., Brno, Czech Republic). The best pictures were obtained using the In-lens SE detector at working distance between 2.91 - 3.06 mm and at 5 kV acceleration voltage. 768×858 pixel images were obtained at 1,500 - 100,000 fold magnification covering sample area of 2.08 - 138.00 µm. Full frame capture was performed in UH resolution mode and accumulation of image with image shift correction was enabled, and it took about 0.5 minutes with the ~0.32 µs/pixel dwell time. Spot size was set at 2.4 nm.

2.6. Image analysis

The nanoparticle parameters stated in this study were determined via image analysis using the ImageJ software (ver. 1.53c). The dimensions of ZnO nanoplates were determined by fitting an ellipse to the hexagonal nanoparticles in order to get an estimate of their length and width from the major and minor ellipse axes. Spherical nanoparticle diameters were determined using the Analyze Particles function with a suitable threshold. The length and width of ZnO nanowires were determined by fitting a rectangle to the nanowire outline.

3. RESULTS

3.1. ZnO nanoplates

SEM micrograph of ZnO nanoplates by the method outlined in 2.1. is shown in **Figure 1**.

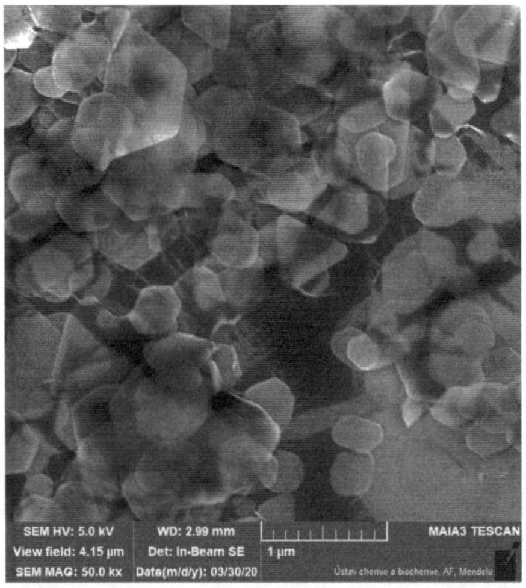

Figure 1 SEM micrograph of ZnO nanoplates

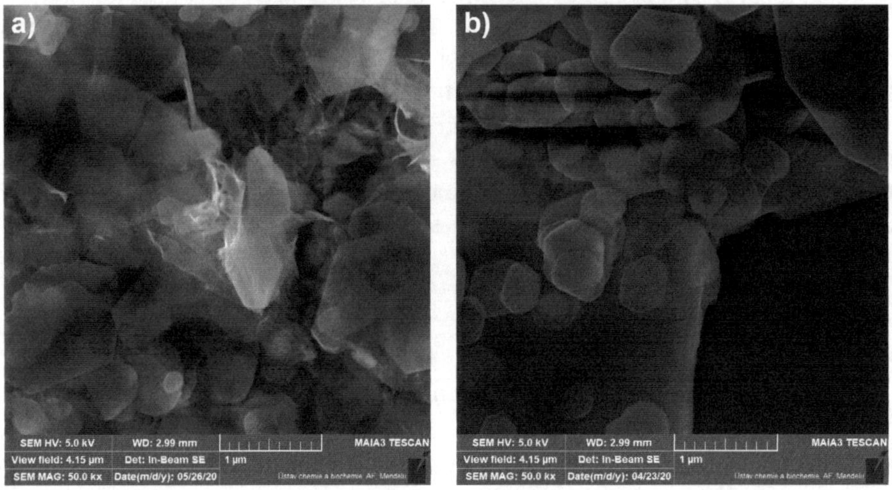

Figure 2 SEM micrograph of nanoplates: a) 10x upscaled synthesis, b) ZnO nanoplates after lyophilization

From the **Figure 1** we can see that nanoplates with a wide range of sizes were synthesized, with the smallest having a length of around 0.5 μm and the largest having over 3 μm. The structure of the nanoplates is mostly of hexagonal crystals which is in agreement with theoretical structure of ZnO which is hexagonal wurtzite [15, 16]. This synthesis proved to be easily upscalable by simple multiplication of the amount of used chemicals and shown only small structural modification when lyophilized as evidenced by **Figure 2**. From the figure it is clear that while the structure in **Figure 2a)** of the nanoplates is nearly identical to that of **Figure 1** the structure of **Figure 2b)** shows nanoplates with visibly larger length and width but otherwise seemingly unchanged. The simple preparation, ease of upscalability and relatively small structural modification of the sample by lyophilization suggest the synthesis is interesting in regards to industrialization and mass production.

3.2. Spherical ZnO nanoparticles and ZnO nanowires

Spherical ZnO nanoparticles were synthesized as described in section 2.3. SEM micrograph of these particles is shown in **Figure 3a)**. The figure shows that spherical nanoparticles with diameter ranging from 30 to 80 nm were formed with the average nanoparticle size being around 50 nm. Further experiments with increasing concentration of oxalic acid were made. When the concentration of used oxalic acid was doubled an interesting phenomena occurred. As shown in **Figure 3b)** the nanoparticles had a tendency to aggregate and in some cases they formed chainlike structures.

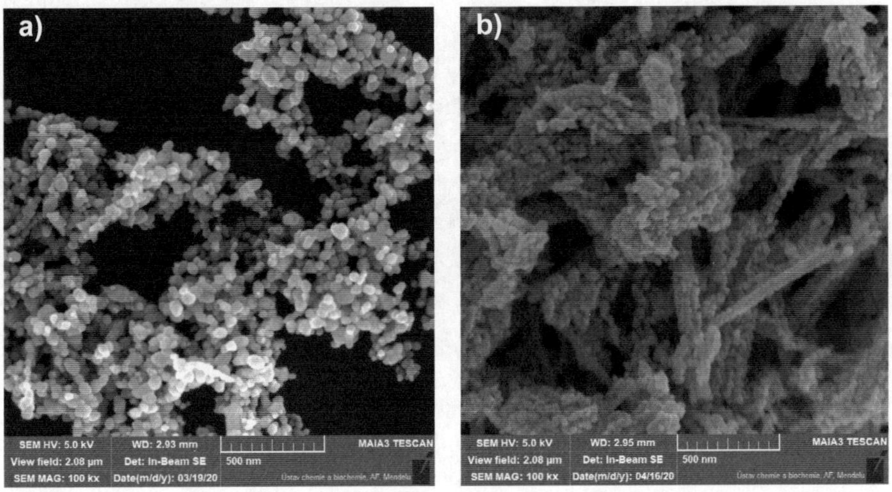

Figure 3 SEM micrograph: a) spherical ZnO nanoparticles, b) nanoparticles made with 2× concentration of oxalic acid

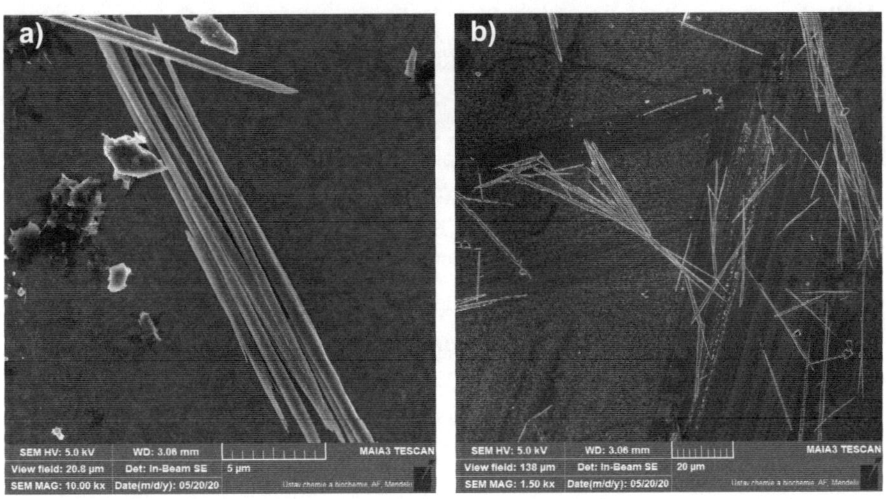

Figure 4 SEM micrograph of ZnO nanowires: a) close-up, b) wide view

This result suggested that by modification of the procedure 1D nanostructures could be created. Consequently, a modified synthesis was performed as described in section 2.4. Ethanol was used as aging dispersant because it was previously shown to facilitate 1D nanostructure growth at room temperature [17]. **Figure 4** shows the SEM micrographs of the ZnO nanowires created using this method. The figure shows nanowires with length of over 10 μm with some up to 50 μm long. The thickness of the wires ranges between 0.2 μm to

0.6 µm. The wires are not uniform in thickness with the central parts being noticeably wider than the ends which are narrowed into sharp tips. Further studies are necessary to determine the dimensions of the wires in different stages of the growth process. **Figure 5** shows the comparison of the three aliquots made from the upscaled preparation of ZnO nanowires (2.4.).

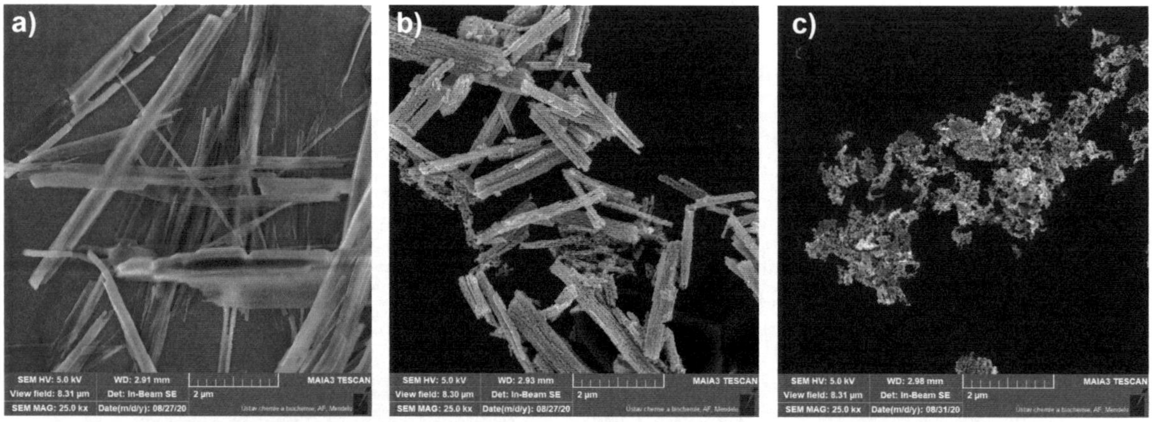

Figure 5 SEM micrographs of upscaled solution: a) only washed, b) washed and calcinated, c) only calcinated

Figure 5a) shows nanowires that are similar to the original synthesis result. **Figure 5b)** shows a structure that is similar to nanowires composed from the smaller spherical nanoparticles. **Figure 5c)** shows that simple calcination caused the structure to revert to the spherical nanoparticles that were formed with no aging in ethanol involved.

4. CONCLUSION

This study shows multiple methods for facile and inexpensive synthesis of ZnO nanoplates and nanowires. The nanoplates can be prepared quickly, are simple to upscale and can be lyophilized with only little alteration of their structure. This study also shows a method for evolution of spherical nanoparticles into nanowires using only ethanol at room temperature. Both methods show promise regarding mass production of Zn based nanoparticles. The need for further research of the growth process and optimization of the methods is clearly indicated.

ACKNOWLEDGEMENTS

This work was supported by ERDF "Multidisciplinary research to increase application potential of nanomaterials in agricultural practice" (No. CZ.02.1.01/0.0/0.0/16_025/0007314) and by the Ministry of Education, Youth and Sports of the Czech Republic under the CEITEC 2020 project (LQ1601).

REFERENCES

[1] BOGUTSKA, K., SKLYAROV, Y.P., PRYLUTSKYY, Y.I. Zinc and zinc nanoparticles: biological role and application in biomedicine. *Ukrainica bioorganica acta*. 2013, vol. 1, pp. 9-16.

[2] RACCA, L., CANTA, M., DUMONTEL, B., et al. Zinc oxide nanostructures in biomedicine. *Smart nanoparticles for biomedicine*. 2018, pp. 171-187.

[3] SABIR, S., ARSHAD, M., CHAUDHARI, S.K. Zinc oxide nanoparticles for revolutionizing agriculture: synthesis and applications. *The Scientific World Journal*. 2014, vol. 2014.

[4] TAHERI, M., QARACHE, H.A., QARACHE, A.A., et al. The effects of zinc-oxide nanoparticles on growth parameters of corn (SC704). *STEM Fellowship Journal*. 2016, vol. 1, no. 2, pp. 17-20.

[5] REDDY, K.M., FERIS, K., BELL, J., et al. Selective toxicity of zinc oxide nanoparticles to prokaryotic and eukaryotic systems. *Applied physics letters*. 2007, vol. 90, no. 21, pp. 213902.

[6] SIRELKHATIM, A., MAHMUD, S., SEENI, A., et al. Review on Zinc Oxide Nanoparticles: Antibacterial Activity and Toxicity Mechanism. *Nanomicro Lett*. 2015, vol. 7, no. 3, pp. 219-242.

[7] ZHANG, L., JIANG, Y., DING, Y., et al. Investigation into the antibacterial behaviour of suspensions of ZnO nanoparticles (ZnO nanofluids). *Journal of Nanoparticle Research*. 2006, vol. 9, no. 3, pp. 479-489.

[8] CHEN, H., KOU, X., YANG, Z., et al. Shape-and size-dependent refractive index sensitivity of gold nanoparticles. *Langmuir*. 2008, vol. 24, no. 10, pp. 5233-5237.

[9] XIA, T., KOVOCHICH, M., LIONG, M., et al. Comparison of the mechanism of toxicity of zinc oxide and cerium oxide nanoparticles based on dissolution and oxidative stress properties. *ACS nano*. 2008, vol. 2, no. 10, pp. 2121-2134.

[10] BARUI, S., GERBALDO, R., GARINO, N., et al. Facile Chemical Synthesis of Doped ZnO Nanocrystals Exploiting Oleic Acid. *Nanomaterials*. 2020, vol. 10, no. 6, pp. 1150.

[11] WANG, Q., GENG, B., WANG, S. ZnO/Au hybrid nanoarchitectures: wet-chemical synthesis and structurally enhanced photocatalytic performance. *Environmental science & technology*. 2009, vol. 43, no. 23, pp. 8968-8973.

[12] FONTE, P., REIS, S., SARMENTO, B. Facts and evidences on the lyophilization of polymeric nanoparticles for drug delivery. *Journal of controlled release*. 2016, vol. 225, pp. 75-86.

[13] MOEZZI, A., CORTIE, M., MCDONAGH, A. Aqueous pathways for the formation of zinc oxide nanoparticles. *Dalton Trans*. 2011, vol. 40, no. 18, pp. 4871-4878.

[14] CHUNG, Y.T., BA-ABBAD, M.M., MOHAMMAD, A.W., et al. Synthesis of minimal-size ZnO nanoparticles through sol-gel method: Taguchi design optimisation. *Materials & Design*. 2015, vol. 87, pp. 780-787.

[15] ABRAHAMS, S., BERNSTEIN, J. Remeasurement of the structure of hexagonal ZnO. *Acta Crystallographica Section B: Structural Crystallography and Crystal Chemistry*. 1969, vol. 25, no. 7, pp. 1233-1236.

[16] XING, Y.J., XI, Z.H., ZHANG, X.D., et al. Nanotubular structures of zinc oxide. *Solid State Communications*. 2004, vol. 129, no. 10, pp. 671-675.

[17] CAO, H.L., QIAN, X.F., GONG, Q., et al. Shape- and size-controlled synthesis of nanometre ZnO from a simple solution route at room temperature. *Nanotechnology*. 2006, vol. 17, no. 15, pp. 3632-3636.

MOLECULAR MODELING OF INTERACTIONS BETWEEN CATALYTIC NANOPARTICLES AND POLYMER CARRIERS

[1,2]Adam VERNER, [1,3,4]Jonáš TOKARSKÝ

[1]*Nanotechnology Centre, VŠB - Technical University of Ostrava, Ostrava, Czech Republic, EU,* adam.verner@vsb.cz, jonas.tokarsky@vsb.cz

[2]*ENET Centre, VŠB - Technical University of Ostrava, Ostrava, Czech Republic, EU,* adam.verner@vsb.cz

[3]*IT4Innovations, VŠB - Technical University of Ostrava, Ostrava, Czech Republic, EU,* jonas.tokarsky@vsb.cz

[4]*Institute of Environmental Technology, VŠB - Technical University of Ostrava, Ostrava, Czech Republic, EU,* jonas.tokarsky@vsb.cz

https://doi.org/10.37904/nanocon.2020.3772

Abstract

Nowadays, the scientific and technological field is at a very high level, which is related, among other things, to the large production of various products, and this unfortunately brings a high degree of environmental threat. For example, highly hazardous gases might be released into the environment accidentally, therefore a solution to these dangerous situations needs to be found. A research is conducted into cerium(IV) oxide, platinum, and palladium nanoparticles (NPs), which have been found to have hazardous gases degrading properties. This work complements this field by studying the interactions between NPs and their potential polymer nanofiber carriers, polyamide 6 (PA) and β-polyvinylidene fluoride (PVDF). In order to determine the suitability of these carriers, molecular modeling (geometry optimization using COMPASS forcefield) was involved. Interaction energies (E_{int}) between the most occupied (hkl) planes of NPs ((100), (110), (111), and (311)) and different (hkl) planes of PA and PVDF surfaces ((001), (100) and (010), (001), (00-1), respectively) were determined. Although all types of NPs showed attractive interactions with all types of surfaces, preferred orientations are clearly identifiable. Attention was focused on the possible influence of the NPs interlayer distance d_{hkl} on the resulting E_{int}.

Keywords: Nanofiber, nanoparticle, molecular modeling, interaction energy, COMPASS

1. INTRODUCTION

Today, the scientific and technical field is at a very high level, which is associated not only with new advanced knowledge of the biological, chemical and physical nature of environment or large number of high quality products, but also with enormous environmental impact [1]. In this regard, attention should be focused, among other things, on the development of systems and methods that eliminate pollutants from the gas and liquid phases. The use of nanoparticles and nanofibers has proven to be effective due to their interactivity based on their specific properties. In the case of nanofibers, primarily small pore sizes are used and the principle of filtration thus consists in the impermeability of undesirable particles. Nanoparticles work on the principle of chemical interaction with pollutants, which either capture or degrade [2]. Nowadays, cerium(IV) oxide, palladium and platinum nanoparticles are frequently studied due to its catalytic and antioxidant properties with the potential to degrade hazardous gases in the air [3,4]. Interactions between nanofiber layers formed of polyamide 6 (PA) or poly(vinylidene fluoride) (PVDF) and incorporated CeO_2 (CeO_2), palladium (Pd) and platinum (Pt) nanoparticles (NP) are investigated using molecular modeling.

2. MATERIALS AND METHODS

2.1. Preparation of models

In this study, Biovia Materials Studio 7.0 (MS) modeling environment was used [5]. Unit cells of CeO_2 (lattice parameter a = b = c = 5.411 Å, α = β = γ = 90°), Pt (a = b = c = 3.924 Å, α = β = γ = 90°), Pd (a = b = c = 3.891 Å, α = β = γ = 90°) were taken from the MS structures database.

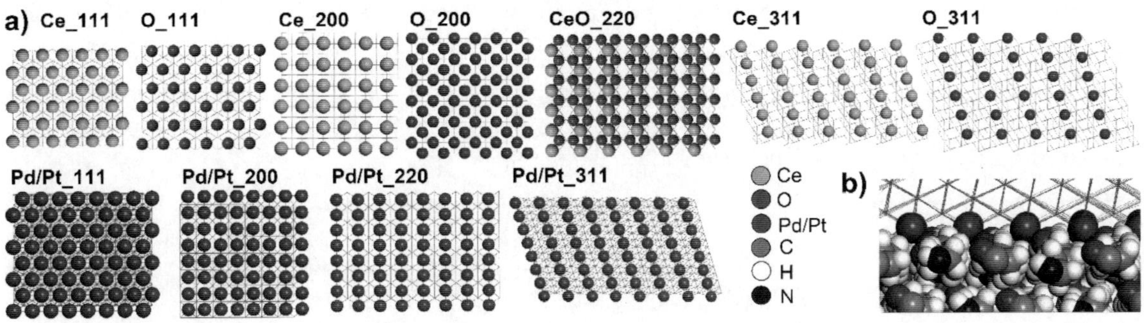

Figure 1 a) View of CeO_2 and Pd/Pt NP bases made by cleaving unit cells along different (h k l) planes. b) The model of Pd/Pt_311_0 lying on PA_001 with the polymer chains penetrating gaps between the lines of Ce atoms

CeO_2, Pd, and Pt NP models were created by cleaving the periodic structures along (h k l) planes with the highest atom occupation (according to XRD analysis in MS) - these are (h k l) planes (2 0 0), (2 2 0), (1 1 1), and (3 1 1), for NP bases see **Figure 1**. Each of these planes forms the base of the respective NP with the size given by the number of surface atoms (6 × 6 Ce atoms in the case of CeO_2 NPs). The height of the NP was determined so that the total number of atoms in NP was 594. CeO_2 NPs had Ce, O atoms or both atom types forming bases. CeO_2 NPs were denoted as Ce_200 (NP base cleaved along (2 0 0) plane and formed with Ce atoms), O_200, Ce_111, O_111, Ce_311, O_311, and NPs containing both Ce and O atoms in their base were denoted as CeO_220. Pd and Pt NPs were denoted as Pd_200, Pd_220, Pd_111, Pd_311, and Pt_200, Pt_220, Pt_111, Pt_311, respectively.

Monoclinic unit cell of β-polyamide 6 (PA) [6], having parameters a = 16.88 Å, b = 4.78 Å, c = 9.33 Å, α = 90°, β = 67.5°, γ = 90°, was obtained from the Cambridge structural database [7]. 2D models of PA surfaces were prepared by cleaving the cell along (0 0 1) plane (22 H + 2 O atoms per unit cell perpendicular to the plane; **Figure 2**) and (1 0 0) plane (20 H atoms per unit cell perpendicular to the plane; **Figure 2**).

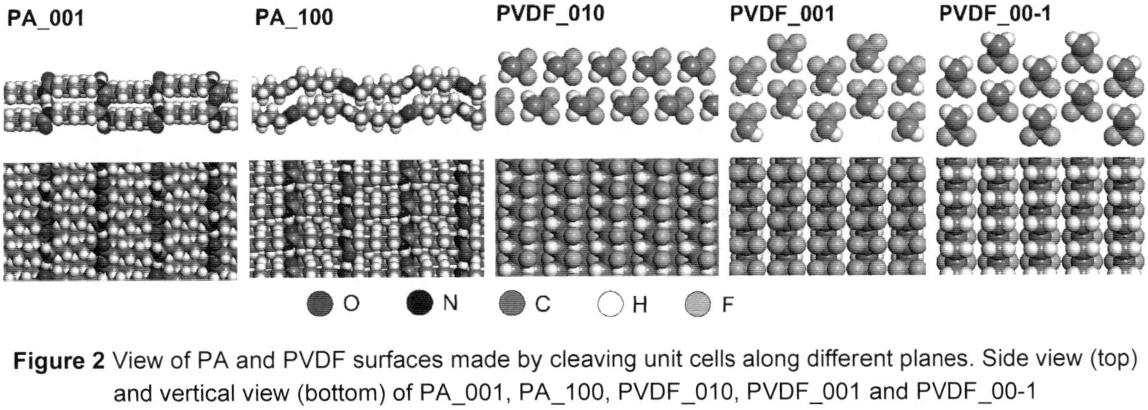

Figure 2 View of PA and PVDF surfaces made by cleaving unit cells along different planes. Side view (top) and vertical view (bottom) of PA_001, PA_100, PVDF_010, PVDF_001 and PVDF_00-1

Orthorhombic unit cell of γ-poly(vinylidene fluoride) (PVDF), having parameters a = 2.56 Å, b = 4.91 Å, c = 8.58 Å, α = β = γ = 90°, was prepared according to the research by Hasegawa et al. [8]. 2D models of PVDF surfaces were prepared by cleaving the cell along (0 1 0) plane (H and F atoms perpendicular to the plane; **Figure 2**), (0 0 1) plane (F atoms perpendicular to the plane; **Figure 2**) and (0 0 -1) plane (H atoms perpendicular to the plane; **Figure 2**).

Area of (0 0 1), (1 0 0) PA surface and (0 1 0), (0 0 1), (0 0 -1) PVDF surface was enlarged to a size of 102.63 × 101.28 Å, 101.28 × 100.38 Å and 98.2 × 99.84 Å, 99.84 × 102.96 Å, 102.96 × 99.84 Å, respectively. Vacuum slab of height 400 Å was added perpendicular to each surface. Models of periodic cells containing PA and PVDF surfaces were denoted as PA_001, PA_100 and PVDF_010, PVDF_001, PVDF_00-1, respectively.

Models were prepared by placing single NP in the center of PA or PVDF surfaces oriented with the base parallel to the polymer surfaces and different rotations to polymer chains of the surfaces. 9 models were prepared for each NP type on each polymer surface type.

2.2. Modeling conditions

Geometry optimization of each model was performed in MS/Forcite module. Atoms in models were parameterized and their charges were assigned by COMPASS force field [9].

Smart algorithm as implemented in MS with $5 \cdot 10^5$ steps was used. Convergence thresholds for the maximum energy and maximum force changes were $1 \cdot 10^{-4}$ kcal/mol and $5 \cdot 10^{-3}$ kcal/mol/Å, respectively [10]. For the Coulombic and the van der Waals forces, atom based summation method as implemented in MS was used. The cell parameters were not optimized. For each model, interaction energy (E_{int}) was calculated from potential energies (E_p) using the following equation (all energies are in kcal/mol):

$$E_{int} = E_{p1} - E_{p2} - E_{p3} \quad (1)$$

where:

E_{p1} - E_p of whole model

E_{p2} - E_p of PA or PVDF surface without the NP

E_{p3} - E_p of the NP without the PA or PVDF surface

3. RESULTS AND DISCUSSION

Interaction energies between the NPs and PA and PVDF surfaces of nanofibers do not depend on the rotation of the NP bases on the polymer surfaces (except of Pd_311 and Pt_311, see below). The main factor determining average interaction energies of models (E_{int}) was the size of the NP base (S) adjacent to the polymer surfaces. The larger the S, the higher the number of interatomic interactions between the NPs and the surfaces, resulting in lower E_{int}. Among models with PA and PVDF surfaces, the lowest E_{int} was obtained for Ce_311 lying on PA_001 (E_{int} = -13 240 kcal/mol) and PVDF_001 (E_{int} = -18 924 kcal/mol), respectively. In order to determine interaction energies of models irrespective of the size of the NP base S, E_{int} of the models were divided by S and interaction energies ($E_{int/S}$) were thus related to one square nanometer (kcal/mol/nm^2) (**Figures 3a** and **3b**).

$E_{int/S}$ is related to the distance between atomic layers (d_{hkl}) of the NPs. The larger the d_{hkl}, the lower $E_{int/S}$ it shows with PA or PVDF surfaces (**Figures 3a** and **3b**). The largest d_{hkl} (Ce_111, O_111, Pd_111 and Pt_111) provides the greatest specificity of each atomic layer charge, which also refers to the longest, and therefore weakest, atomic bonds between the atomic layers thanks to which the NPs are able to make stronger non-covalent intermolecular attractive interactions with the polymer surfaces.

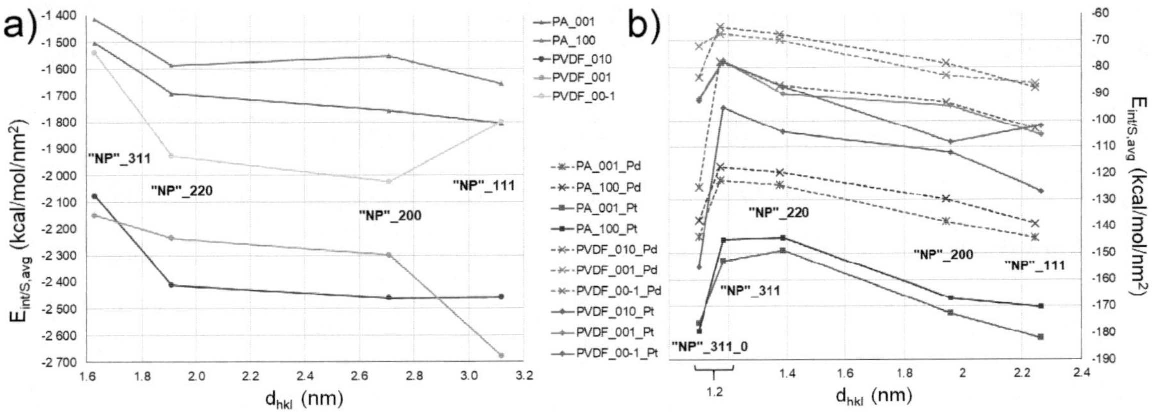

Figure 3 The interaction energy $E_{int/S}$ dependence on the distance d_{hkl} of a) CeO_2 NPs and b) Pd and Pt NPs lying on PA and PVDF surfaces. "NP" refers to the NP denotations according to the contact atoms in the base, i.e., a) Ce, O or CeO, b) Pd or Pt.

Interactions of CeO_2 NPs lying on PVDF surfaces are 34 % stronger than on PA surfaces, however Pd and Pt NPs interact more strongly by 60 % with PA surfaces than with PVDF surfaces (**Figures 3a** and **3b**, **Tables 1 and 2**). Since CeO_2 is a binary compound (**Figure 1**), partial charges and thus polarity are shown on atoms, which provides stronger interactions with polar chains of the surface. Pd and Pt are elements (**Figure 1**), so there is no polarity. PA chains are characterized by polar (peptide bonds -COHN-) and nonpolar (aliphatic) parts alternation (**Figure 2**), while the polarity direction of PVDF chains is perpendicular to the chain axis (one side of the chain forms bonds with F atoms, the other one with H atoms; **Figure 2**). Therefore, stronger polar interactions with PVDF surfaces occur in the case of CeO_2, while Pd and Pt NPs interact more strongly with PA surfaces due to the presence of nonpolar aliphatic parts of PA chains (**Table1**).

Table 1 Average interaction energies $E_{int/S,avg}$ of all models with PA or PVDF surfaces containing every NP type with information of NP base compositions (* - structures with the lowest $E_{int/S,avg}$)

CeO_2 NP	NP base composition per nm²	PA $E_{int/S,avg}$ (kcal/ mol/nm²)	PVDF $E_{int/S,avg}$ (kcal/ mol/nm²)	Pd/Pt NP	NP base composition per nm²	PA $E_{int/S,avg}$ (kcal/ mol/nm²)	PVDF $E_{int/S,avg}$ (kcal/ mol/nm²)
Ce_111	7.9 Ce	-1 842 ± 72 *	-2 846 ± 94 *	Pd_111	17.5 Pd	-142 ± 3	-92 ± 6
O_111	7.9 O	-1619 ± 67	-2 291 ± 79	Pd_200	14.8 Pd	-134 ± 3	-85 ± 7
Ce_200	6.8 Ce	-1 659 ± 74	-2 673 ± 77	Pd_220	10.5 Pd	-122 ± 6	-75 ± 7
O_200	13.7 O	-1 651 ± 72	-2 086 ± 149	Pd_311	8.9 Pd	-120 ± 10	-70 ± 13
CeO_220	4.8 Ce + 9.7 O	-1 639 ± 61	-2 323 ± 139	Pd_311_0	8.9 Pd	-144 ± 3 *	-94 ± 2 *
Ce_311	4.1 Ce	-1 467 ± 45	-2 167 ± 72	Pt_111	17.2 Pt	-176 ± 5	-111 ± 6
O_111	3.4 O	-1 452 ± 62	-2 057 ± 61	Pt_200	14.6 Pt	-173 ± 5	-105 ± 9
				Pt_220	10.4 Pt	-147 ± 7	-94 ± 10
				Pt_311	8.7 Pt	-149 ± 14	-84 ± 16
				Pt_311_0	8.7 Pt	-178 ± 2 *	-113 ± 4 *

CeO_2 NPs exhibits lower $E_{int/S}$ on PA_001 in comparison with PA_100 (**Figure 3a**). In the case of CeO_2 NPs on PA_001, average interaction energy of all NP types ($E_{int/S,avg}$) is 8 % lower than on PA_100. This is because PA_001 contains 15.9 H and 1.4 O atoms per nm² in the upper layer of the surface, while PA_100 has there only 12.1 H atoms (**Table 2**), which means different interacting atoms number resulting in different $E_{int/S,avg}$. Among PA surfaces, model with the lowest $E_{int/S}$ (-1 904 kcal/mol/nm^2) contains Ce_111 lying on PA_001.

Table 2 Average interaction energies $E_{int/S,avg}$ of all models with CeO_2, Pd or Pt NPs lying on PA_001, PA_100, PVDF_010 or PVDF_001 surfaces with contact atoms of PA and PVDF surfaces (* - structures with the lowest $E_{int/S,avg}$)

polymer surface	contact atoms per nm^2	CeO_2 $E_{int/S,avg}$ (kcal/ mol/nm^2)	Pd $E_{int/S,avg}$ (kcal/ mol/nm^2)	Pt $E_{int/S,avg}$ (kcal/ mol/nm^2)
PA_001	15.9 H + 1.4 O	-1 628 ± 200	-134 ± 31 *	-166 ± 38 *
PA_100	12.1 O	-1 495 ± 181	-128 ± 30	-159 ± 39
PVDF_010	8 F + 8 H	-2 213 ± 353	-94 ± 27	-115 ± 35
PVDF_001	9.1 F	-2 244 ± 474 *	-77 ± 15	-93 ± 20
PVDF_00-1	9.1 H	-1 744 ± 291	-76 ± 18	-95 ± 20

In the case of CeO_2 on PVDF surfaces, $E_{int/S}$ trends are different for each surface type (**Figure 3a**). Models with CeO_2 NP on PVDF_010 and PVDF_001 have comparable $E_{int/S,avg}$ (**Table 2**), which is 22 % lower than on PVDF_00-1. This is due to the fact, that the upper layer of PVDF_010 and PVDF_001 contains F atoms providing strong hydrogen bonds with Ce atoms of the NP, because of the highest difference in electronegativities (Ce - F = 2.86 [11]) within the possible interacting atomic pairs. For comparison according to atomic pair denotation "NP - polymer surface": Ce - H = 1.08, O - F = 0.54 and O - H = 1.24. All chains in the upper layer of PVDF_010 interact with the NP, but only a half of the interacting atoms are F (**Figure 2**), which results in more interacting atoms but less F atoms per nm^2. In the case of PVDF_001, all atoms in the upper layer are F, but only a half of the chains are available for interactions with NP (**Figure 2**), which is less interacting atoms but more F atoms per nm^2. In the case of PVDF surfaces, the model containing Ce_111 lying on PVDF_001 exhibits the lowest $E_{int/S}$ (-3 073 kcal/mol/nm^2) due to strong interactions between positive Ce atoms (of Ce_111) and negative F atoms (of PVDF_001). Models containing CeO_2 NP lying on PVDF_00-1 exhibits different $E_{int/S}$ trends (**Figure 3a**) due to the H atoms forming upper surface layer (**Figure 2**). O_200 lying on PVDF_00-1 shows the lowest $E_{int/S}$. Regarding to PVDF_00-1 having formed the upper layer from H atoms (**Figure 2**), previous result corresponds to making stronger interactions with O atoms of the NP instead of Ce atoms according to influence of electronegativity difference (O:H = 1.24 > Ce:H = 1.08). O atoms number of the NP base has another impact on $E_{int/S}$ besides atomic layer distance d_{hkl}. O_200 has the second highest d_{hkl} (O_111 has the first) and the base contains 13.7 O atoms, while O_111 base contains 7.9 O atoms per nm^2 (**Table 2**), which provides more attractive polar interactions and consequently lower $E_{int/S}$. Model with the lowest $E_{int/S}$ (-2 467 kcal/mol/nm^2) contains O_200 lying on PVDF_00-1.

$E_{int/S}$ of models containing Pd and Pt NP lying on the PA and PVDF surfaces is on average 16× higher (i.e. weaker) than in the case of CeO_2 NP (**Figures 3a** and **3b**). Pt NPs exhibit 23 % lower $E_{int/S,avg}$ than Pd NP on all PA and PVDF surfaces, which corresponds to the difference in atomic layer distances d_{hkl} based on the lattice parameters (3.891 Å for Pd, 3.924 Å for Pt). The lower lattice parameter indicates shorter and thus stronger bonds between atoms and consequently lower tendency to interact with other molecules. $E_{int/S}$ trends of models containing Pd and Pt NPs are dependent on d_{hkl}, as in cases of models with CeO_2 NPs. The higher the d_{hkl}, the lower the $E_{int/S}$ (**Figures 3a and 3b**). Exceptions are models containing Pd_311 and Pt_311 (denoted as Pd_311_0 and Pt_311_0, respectively) on PA or PVDF surfaces, where the gaps between the lines of Ce atoms (of NP bases; **Figure 1a**) are parallel to the PA or PVDF polymer chains. This position allows the polymer chains of the surfaces to penetrate the NP bases gaps (**Figure 1b**), leading to increased attractive interactions between the NPs and PA and PVDF surfaces and consequently lower $E_{int/S}$. While models containing Pd_311 and Pt_311 NPs show the highest $E_{int/S}$, models with Pd_311_0 and Pt_311_0 show the lowest $E_{int/S}$ (**Table 1**).

4. CONCLUSION

The modeling focused on CeO_2, Pd and Pt NPs on the polymer surfaces of PA and PVDF. The strongest interactions are shown by CeO_2 NP with the highest d_{hkl} Ce_111 on PVDF_001, in the case of Pd and Pt NPs it is Pd_311_0 on PA_001 and Pt_311_0 on PA_100, respectively. CeO_2 NPs interact more strongly with PVDF surfaces than with PA surfaces due to the polar interactions, while Pd and Pt NPs interact more strongly with aliphatic parts of PA chains in PA_001 and PA_100 surfaces. The lowest average $E_{int/S,avg}$ of all NPs having bases cleaved along (111) plane corresponded to the lowest atomic layers distance d_{hkl} and the highest number of atoms per nm^2. Within the types of surfaces, it showed on average the strongest interactions PA_001, PVDF_010 and PVDF_100 (comparable), in the case of NP types, it was Ce_111, Pd_111 and Pd_311_0 (comparable), Pt_111 and Pt_311_0 (comparable). Further research will clarify degrading effects against hazardous gases of NPs incorporated on the carriers.

ACKNOWLEDGEMENTS

This work was supported by The Ministry of Education, Youth and Sports of the Czech Republic (projects SP2020/24 and LQ1602).

REFERENCES

[1] MADUNA, K., TOMAŠIĆ, V. Air pollution engineering. *Physical Sciences Reviews*. 2017, vol. 2, no. 12, article no. 20160122.

[2] CHO, D., NAYDICH, A., FREY M.W., JOO, Y.L. Further improvement of air filtration efficiency of cellulose filters coated with nanofibers via inclusion of electrostatically active nanoparticles. *Polymer*. 2013, vol. 54, no. 9, pp. 2364-2372.

[3] JANOŠ, P., HENYCH, J., PELANT, O., PILAŘOVÁ, V., VRTOCH, V., KORMUNDA, M., MAZANEC, K. ŠTENGL, V. Cerium oxide for the destruction of chemical warfare agents: A comparison of synthetic routes. *Journal of Hazardous Materials*. 2016, vol. 304, pp. 259-268.

[4] CHEN, X., WANG, H., HE, J., CAO, Y., CUI, Z., LIANG, M. Preparation, Structure and Catalytic Activity of Pt-Pd Bimetallic Nanoparticles on Multi-Walled Carbon Nanotubes. *Journal of Nanoscience and Nanotechnology*. 2010, vol. 10, no.5, pp. 3138-3144.

[5] Dassault Systèmes BIOVIA, Materials Studio [software], Version 7.0, San Diego: Dassault Systèmes, 2020

[6] ČAPKOVÁ, P., ČAJKA, A., KOLSKÁ, Z., KORMUNDA, M., PAVLÍK, J., MUNZAROVÁ, M., DOPITA, M., RAFAJA, D. Phase composition and surface properties of nylon-6 nanofibers prepared by nanospider technology at various electrode distances. *Journal of Polymer Research*. 2015, vol. 22, no. 6, article no. 101..

[7] GROOM, C.R., BRUNO, I.J., LIGHTFOOT, M.P., C. WARD, S.C. The Cambridge Structural Database. *Acta Crystallographica Section B Structural Science, Crystal Engineering and Materials*. 2016, vol. 72, no. 2, pp. 171-179.

[8] HASEGAWA, R., TAKAHASHI, Y., CHATANI, Y., TADOKORO, H. Crystal Structures of Three Crystalline Forms of Poly(vinylidene fluoride). *Polymer Journal*. 1972, vol. 3, no. 5, pp. 600-610.

[9] SUN, H. COMPASS: An ab Initio Force-Field Optimized for Condensed-Phase Applications Overview with Details on Alkane and Benzene Compounds. *The Journal of Physical Chemistry B*. 1998, vol. 102, no. 38, pp. 7338-7364.

[10] VERNER, A., TOKARSKÝ, J. Molecular modeling study of antibacterial molecules on nylon 6,6 surfaces. *Materials Today: Proceedings*. 2020. https://doi.org/10.1016/j.matpr.2019.12.221

[11] PAULING, L. *The Nature of the Chemical Bond and the Structure of Molecules and Crystals: An Introduction to Modern Structural Chemistry*. Ithaca: Cornell University Press, 1960.